THE
NUCLEAR PROPERTIES
OF THE
HEAVY ELEMENTS

II

DETAILED

RADIOACTIVITY PROPERTIES

Earl K. Hyde

Senior Chemist
Lawrence Radiation Laboratory
University of California, Berkeley

Isadore Perlman

Associate Director
Lawrence Radiation Laboratory
Professor of Chemistry
University of California, Berkeley

Glenn T. Seaborg

Chairman, U.S. Atomic Energy Commission
Professor of Chemistry
University of California, Berkeley

PRENTICE-HALL, INC., ENGLEWOOD CLIFFS, NEW JERSEY

PRENTICE-HALL INTERNATIONAL, INC., *London*
PRENTICE-HALL OF AUSTRALIA, PTY., LTD., *Sydney*
PRENTICE-HALL OF CANADA, LTD., *Toronto*
PRENTICE-HALL OF INDIA (PRIVATE) LTD., *New Delhi*
PRENTICE-HALL OF JAPAN, INC., *Tokyo*
PRENTICE-HALL DE MEXICO, S. A., *Mexico City*

© 1964 by
PRENTICE-HALL, INC.
Englewood Cliffs, New Jersey

Library of Congress Catalog Card Number:
64—23184

PHYSICS

PRINTED IN THE UNITED STATES OF AMERICA
62561—C

PREFACE

Heavy element radioactivity has played a central role in the development of nuclear science ever since the penetrating radiations of uranium were discovered by Becquerel at the end of the last century. During the decades when the only radioactive materials consisted of the natural radioelements, an enormous literature on their properties was published. In this period, the concept of the nuclear atom evolved, and the first reaction of nuclear transmutation was accomplished. From time to time it seemed desirable to codify and summarize the essential features of this knowledge, and several books appeared which have become classics. Among the most important were the ones written by Rutherford* in the years 1905, 1912, and 1930. Other publications which had great influence and importance were the French texts of Madame Curie† and the German text of Meyer and Schweidler.‡

The discovery of artificial radioactivity, the discovery of the neutron, the preparation of radioactive isotopes by neutron-induced reactions, the invention of machinery for the acceleration of charged particles, and the discovery of fission—events which occurred in about a ten year span from 1930 to 1940—led to great qualitative changes in our knowledge of the structure of nuclei and the nature of radioactivity. In one sense these developments switched emphasis away from the heavy elements as the interest of experimentalists and theorists was drawn to the study of artificial radioactivities of

---

* E. Rutherford, *Radioactivity* (London: Cambridge University Press, 1905); E. Rutherford, *Radioactive Substances and Their Radiations* (London: Cambridge University Press, 1912); E. Rutherford, J. Chadwick, and C. D. Ellis, *Radiations from Radioactive Substances* (London: Cambridge University Press, 1930).

† Mme. P. Curie, *Traité de radioactivité* (Paris: Gauthier-Villars, 1910).

‡ S. Meyer and E. V. Schweidler, *Radioaktivität* (Berlin: Teubner, 1916; 2nd ed., 1927).

v

nearly every element in the periodic system.   But the heavy elements were of unique importance for the phenomenon of nuclear fission and of almost unique importance for the phenomenon of alpha radioactivity.   Furthermore, the techniques for the preparation of artificial radioactivity were just as applicable to the heavy as to the light elements and were applied to them by many workers.   It was a particularly interesting matter to explore the possibility of synthesizing elements above uranium.   It is a well-known story how fruitful these studies were.   Whereas there exist about 40 distinct nuclear species in the natural radioactive elements, the number of nuclides prepared by reactions of artificial transmutation is now well over 200 for the same group of elements.   The periodic system of the elements has been extended by 11 synthetic elements, for which we have information on nearly 100 nuclear species.

The present literature on the nuclear properties of the heavy elements is enormous and is expanding at a rapid rate.   Scientists in a variety of areas of fundamental and applied research deal in some way with the nuclear properties of the heavy elements, so it seemed desirable to codify and summarize this information.   In recent years certain publications have done this in limited areas.   The research results of the American scientists on the Manhattan District Project of World War II have been set down in a series of volumes with the general title of the National Nuclear Energy Series.   The volumes in this series which are most important for the heavy elements are the following: *The Transuranium Elements; Research Papers*, edited by G. T. Seaborg, J. J. Katz, and W. M. Manning, Volume 14B, Plutonium Project Record, National Nuclear Energy Series (New York: McGraw Hill, 1949), and *The Actinide Elements* edited by G. T. Seaborg and J. J. Katz, Volume 14A, same series.   One of us has also set down in book form a summary of properties of the transuranium elements.*   Nuclear data tabulations of several groups have provided from time to time up-to-date summaries of important properties of radioactive decay.   Among these are the Tables of Isotopes published at about four year intervals in *The Reviews of Modern Physics* and the compilation of The Nuclear Data Project formerly of the National Academy of Sciences–National Research Council, Washington, D.C., and presently of the Oak Ridge National Laboratory.   From time to time excellent review articles covering certain parts of our knowledge of the heavy elements have appeared.

None of these publications has attempted the comprehensive analysis of all published information on the nuclear properties of the heavy elements which we have set as the purpose of our publication. We have been stimulated to

---

* G. T. Seaborg, *The Transuranium Elements* (New Haven, Conn.: Yale University Press, 1958); E. K. Hyde and G. T. Seaborg, "The Transuranium Elements," *Handbuch der Physik*, Vol. 42, S. Flugge, ed. (Berlin: Springer-Verlag, 1957); G. T. Seaborg, *Man-made Transuranium Elements* (Englewood Cliffs, N.J.: Prentice Hall, Inc., 1963).

do this partly because of our great personal interest in this subject.   Each of us has devoted the major portion of his scientific career to the study of the nuclear properties of the heavy elements.   We also have had the great advantage and stimulation of many years' association with a large group of nuclear chemists and physicists located at the Lawrence Radiation Laboratory of the University of California.   These associates have supplied many of the data recorded here and have been of unceasing help in the evaluation and checking of the facts.   The personal association of all three of us with many research workers at the University of Chicago on the Plutonium Project during the war years has also been of value to us in this task.   We have also had splendid assistance from our close personal friends and colleagues at other Atomic Energy Commission laboratories and in many universities.   We make detailed acknowledgement of our great debt to our colleagues in a special section following this preface.

We have also been stimulated to undertake this task by our belief in the continuing importance of the heavy elements not only to nuclear chemists and physicists but to a wide variety of professional people.   The scientists, engineers, and managers associated with the growing nuclear power industry constitute an obvious example.   Those concerned with industrial uses of radioactive isotopes also need to be familiar with these elements.   Workers in environmental studies of radioactivity, ecological studies, geophysics, health physics, and health chemistry need a complete source book of information on heavy nuclei and fission produced activities.   Astronomers and cosmologists have found a knowledge of heavy nuclei—their lifetimes, their fission characteristics, and so forth—to be of great importance for the proper formulation of models of stellar reactions and evolution.   The special properties of the synthetic elements make them attractive for special scientific and industrial uses which will become more widely exploited in the future.   Examples of these are the use of Pu^{238} and Cm^{242} as heat sources in compact heat-to-electricity conversion devices used as lightweight, long-lived, and dependable power sources in space vehicles and other specialized terrestrial applications.   Another example is the potential use of such isotopes as Cf^{252}, which has a high rate of spontaneous fission, as a simple and compact source of neutrons.

We have had to examine and digest an enormous amount of published and unpublished literature in the course of our work.   In order to achieve the comprehensive coverage which we set as our goal, our final publication must be divided into three volumes.   In the following remarks we shall set down the plan and purpose of each of the three volumes.   This compilation will perhaps most often be consulted for specific types or items of information.   Hence, we believe that some description of the organization will be helpful.   We hope that our tables of contents and indices are also detailed enough for efficient location of desired information.

PLAN OF VOLUME I:

SYSTEMATICS OF NUCLEAR STRUCTURE AND RADIOACTIVITY

The first two chapters of this volume present a general survey of alpha and beta radioactivity of the heavy elements, including a comprehensive summary of decay-energy data and decay-rate data. The related subject of atomic masses of heavy nuclides is also covered. Chapter 1 introduces the subject with general comments on nuclear instability of the heavy elements and the relationship of these to the termination of the natural elements. It reviews semi-empirical mass equations and discusses several which are of special importance to the heavy elements. It discusses beta and alpha decay trends, and relates these to the general mass surface. Chapter 2 is a detailed summary of alpha and beta decay data for ground-state-to-ground-state transitions. It covers the extension of data to unmeasured or unmeasurable cases by extrapolation of systematic trends and by the use of decay-energy cycles. The decay-energy cycles are the basis for the preparation of a comprehensive table of atomic masses for all heavy nuclides. Tables of neutron and proton separation energies are given.

The third chapter is a moderately detailed analysis of theoretical models of nuclear structure and their application to the heavy elements. The first half of this chapter is a review of the two most important models: the "independent particle (shell) model" and the extension of that model to non-spherical nuclei known as the "unified (or Bohr-Mottelson) model." This is written not as a theoretical treatise but as a concise summary of those features of these important recent theoretical developments which an experimentalist or general reader will find helpful if he wishes to realize and understand the depth and detail of our present-day knowledge of the radioactivity properties and nuclear structure of the nuclides of the heavy elements. The second half of Chapter 3 is a systematic and comprehensive summary of data on heavy nuclei which can be correlated with the aid of the theories of nuclear structure. Experimental data on nuclides close to Pb^{208} have played an important role in the testing of the independent particle model (in several modifications) for spherical nuclei. Similarly, data from the region of thorium upward have been extremely important in testing and in stimulating new developments of the unified model description of non-spherical nuclei.

Chapter 4 covers the subject of alpha radioactivity in considerable detail. Our principal goal was to tabulate with accuracy and completeness the great amount of data on alpha decay energies and rates including all alpha particle groups. General features of alpha decay for emitters of different nuclear type are emphasized. The theory of alpha decay is discussed. This is not presented in the form of a theoretical treatise but as a summary of the important features which an experimentalist can use to correlate or interpret his data. The agreement of the simple theory with the available data relating to even-even emitters is emphasized. Hindrance in alpha decay due to spin change and to alpha-preformation factors is reviewed. Modern developments, which indicate that a satisfactory explanation of preformation factors can be achieved by computing alpha particle wave functions in the nuclear surface region from overlap of wave function of independent neutron and proton orbitals, are reviewed briefly. Other matters of importance to alpha decay are discussed, such as the exchange of angular momentum between the nucleus and the escaping alpha particle.

Chapter 5 presents a discussion of the methods now available to the experimentalist for the synthesis of any nuclide in the group of elements considered in these volumes. A wide variety of methods, including reactions with light and heavy charged particles and neutrons, is discussed. A great deal of pertinent experimental data on reaction cross sections is tabulated. Complete references to the original literature are given throughout.

In addition, we have collected in a series of appendixes to Volume I, several kinds of nuclear and atomic data for the heavy elements. These include the electron binding energies, the K and L x-rays, the Auger electron energies, and the K and L fluorescent yields.

PLAN OF VOLUME II:

DETAILED RADIOACTIVITY PROPERTIES

This volume summarizes nuclear information on each one of the known nuclear species of atomic number 82 or greater. The discussion is organized in five main groups. Chapter 6 treats the natural radioactivities. After an introductory section on the early history of the subject, there is a section on each of the three main series. Following this, there is a section on the application of the heavy elements to problems of geochronology. The chapter concludes with a section on the natural occurrence of transuranium elements in trace quantities owing to natural nuclear synthesis. Chapter 7 covers a number of families of radioactive isotopes which are produced by nuclear synthesis in accelerators or reactors; this includes the $4n + 1$ family, missing in nature, and a number of "collateral" radioactive series. Chapter 8 considers individually and systematically the isotopes of thorium, protactinium, and uranium. Chapter 9 covers all the isotopes of each of the synthetic transuranium elements. Chapter 10 discusses the isotopes of lead, bismuth, polonium, astatine, emanation, francium, and radium which lie below 126 in neutron number.

Throughout Volume II we have attempted to give a complete account of each nuclide including the following types of information:

1. Early history including name of discoverer and date of discovery and (in the case of an artificial species) the first method of preparation.
2. Alternate or best methods of production.

3. Tables or summaries of types, abundances, and energies of radiation.
4. Half-life, ratios for branching decay, and other pertinent information.
5. Decay schemes.
6. Interpretation of the radiations and decay schemes in terms of the shell model or unified model. In this we make repeated detailed use of the material covered in Chapter 3 of the first volume.
7. Special uses where remarks on these seem important.

Fission properties are *not* discussed in this volume but in Volume III.

To summarize, we present a rather complete account of the experimental data available on the nuclear properties of these nuclides, and, in addition, we show the extent to which these data can be correlated and explained by modern theories of nuclear structure and decay. Our discussion gives detailed citation of the original research papers throughout.

PLAN OF VOLUME III:
FISSION PHENOMENA

In this volume, we have summarized as thoroughly as we could the enormous literature on the phenomena of nuclear fission. We have divided the volume into two parts: a part devoted to low energy fission, by which we mean spontaneous fission or fission induced by thermal neutrons, and a part devoted to moderate and high energy fission. In Part One, we include chapters on fission theory, fission probability, mass division, charge division, the kinetic energy of the fragments, prompt neutrons, delayed neutrons, and gamma rays. Part Two contains chapters on fission phenomena at moderate excitation energy (referring to an upper energy limit of roughly 50 MeV) and a high bombardment energy (ranging up to many GeV). There are also sections on fission induced by mesons and on photofission. In every section of this volume, detailed tables of data are presented, and complete references to the original data are included.

EARL K. HYDE
ISADORE PERLMAN
GLENN T. SEABORG

Lawrence Radiation Laboratory
University of California
Berkeley, California

ACKNOWLEDGEMENTS

VOLUME II

The authors wish to express appreciation to the editors of several journals for permission to quote figures and tables. We wish also to acknowledge the kindness of many individuals who granted us permission to quote their work, supplied us with figures or tables, and, in many cases, discussed their work personally with us. These individuals include Drs. D. E. Alburger, E. Arbman, G. Bastin-Scoffier, S. Bjørnholm, P. Day, B. J. Dropesky, D. W. Engelkemeir, T. R. Gerholm, C. J. Herrlander, J. M. Hollander, J. R. Huizenga, L. S. Kisslinger, J. D. Knight, T. P. Kohman, R. M. Lessler, C. Mayer-Böricke, N. Newby, O. B. Nielsen, Elizabeth Rona, C. Ruiz, K. Siegbahn, P. Stelson, R. Stockendal, S. G. Thompson, W. W. True, R. Vandenbosch, S. Vandenbosch, S. Wahlborn, and R. S. Walen. We wish also to thank the Technical Information Division and Graphic Arts Department of the Lawrence Radiation Laboratory for much help with drawings originating in this laboratory.

Some parts of this volume were prepared with extensive help of our immediate colleagues and for this assistance we wish to give special thanks to Drs. Frank Asaro, Royal G. Albridge, Jack M. Hollander, Frank S. Stephens, Jr., T. Darrah Thomas, Stanley G. Thompson, and Albert Ghiorso.

Professors John H. Reynolds and Garniss H. Curtiss gave us counsel on the section on geochronology. Drs. S. Bjørnholm and O. B. Nielsen were most generous in their help on matters concerning their published and unpublished work.

Professor W. W. True allowed us to quote extensively from his work and assisted us in the interpretation of the material covered in Chapter 10. Our thanks are also due to Professor J. O. Rasmussen, R. Griffioen, and R. M.

Macfarlane for calling our attention to recent work which we have quoted in Chapter 10. We thank Professor L. S. Kisslinger for permission to quote extensively from an important paper by himself and Professor R. A. Sorensen.

In the preparation of early versions of these chapters we received much technical assistance from Mrs. Suzanne Vandenbosch for which we are pleased to declare our appreciation. In the later stages we had the expert assistance of Miss Eileen Carson to whom we owe an enormous debt for a variety of tasks including preparation of tables and figures, checking of facts and references, proofreading at all stages, etc.

The typing of technical material of this nature is a matter of considerable difficulty, and we are grateful for the expert work of Mrs. Libbi Huffman, Mrs. Gloria Carrillo, Miss Yoshi Uchida, Mrs. Nancy Schorn, Mrs. Lillian Lee, Mrs. Patricia Howard, Miss Connie Louvau, and Mrs. Mary Lou Hasey. We thank Mrs. Elinor G. Potter for the preparation of the author index.

Finally, we thank the staff of Prentice-Hall, Inc. for their help, particularly, our production editor, Mr. Don Earnest, and his associates for expert handling of a difficult production job.

CONTENTS

VOLUME II

6

NATURAL RADIOACTIVITY
OF THE HEAVY ELEMENTS, 409

7

ARTIFICIALLY PREPARED
FAMILIES OF RADIOACTIVE NUCLIDES, 577

8

THE ISOTOPES OF
THORIUM, PROTACTINIUM, AND URANIUM, 623

9

THE TRANSURANIUM ELEMENTS, 745

IO

NUCLEI NEAR LEAD-208, 991

DETAILED
RADIOACTIVITY PROPERTIES

6

NATURAL RADIOACTIVITY
OF THE HEAVY ELEMENTS

This chapter describes the three heavy-element families of radioelements which occur in nature. It begins with an account of the early history of radioactivity. This was one of the most fascinating periods in the whole history of science and in our account we attempt to show how the experiments, designed to explore this strange new phenomenon of radioactivity and to unravel the confusing genetic relationships of the radioelements, stimulated the formulation of bold new ideas on the nature of radioactivity and on the fundamental composition of the atom.

6.1 EARLY HISTORY OF RADIOACTIVITY*

Becquerel's Discovery of the Radioactivity of Uranium. The discovery of radioactivity followed within a few months the announcement of Röntgen's mysterious x-rays and was the direct but unexpected result of experiments designed to clarify certain phenomena described by Röntgen. It had been observed that x-rays were emitted from those parts of the glass wall of the discharge tube which were bombarded with cathode rays. It had also been noted that the bombarded parts of the glass wall emitted a greenish or bluish fluorescence. Professor HENRI BECQUEREL immediately interested himself in the question whether materials rendered fluorescent or phosphorescent by absorption of light would at the same time be induced to emit x-rays.

BECQUEREL had been interested in fluorescence for some years in keeping

---

* Throughout Section 6.1 names of investigators are given without references to published literature.

with a family tradition extending back to his grandfather.   In particular, he had on hand a compound of uranium—a double sulfate of uranium and potassium—which he had prepared fifteen years before and had observed to fluoresce brilliantly under ultraviolet light.   He placed two samples of this double salt upon a photographic plate wrapped in black paper.   Between the black paper and one of the salt samples he placed a coin.   Knowing that sunlight could excite fluorescence and believing that such excitation would be required for any other radiations, he exposed the combinations of wrapped photographic plate and uranium compounds to the sun.   After an exposure of several hours, he developed the plate and observed a light image of the uranium samples and a shadow where the metal coin was interposed.   Apparently a penetrating radiation akin to x-rays had been induced in the uranium salt!

BECQUEREL then proceeded to a study of the penetration of the new radiations through various thicknesses of absorber, always placing his uranium salts in the sun as part of the experiment.   On February 26, 1896, he had prepared such a set of experiments but was prevented from completing them by poor weather which obscured the sun.   The assembly consisting of the photographic plates, the absorbers, and the double salts of uranium and potassium were placed in a desk drawer for a period of several days.   On March 1 the sun reappeared and BECQUEREL prepared to resume his experiments.   He was somewhat uneasy that the interrupted exposure to sunlight would introduce unknown effects and decided to replace the stored plates with new ones, thus keeping one aspect of the experiments constant.   Nevertheless, he dropped the withdrawn plates into a developer bath expecting to see very light impressions or none at all.   To his astonishment the silhouettes of the uranium salts were of much greater intensity than in any of his previous experiments!   Exposure to sunlight evidently was not essential to the emission of the penetrating radiation.   The date of this observation, March 1, 1896, may be taken as the birthdate of radioactivity.*

Further experiments revealed that the effect on the photographic plate was not related to the ability of uranium compounds to fluoresce and in fact that any uranium salt would produce the effect.   Furthermore the strength of the photographic images under identical conditions of exposure was directly proportional to the atomic content of uranium in the preparation.   HENRI BECQUEREL concluded correctly that the new property was to be associated with the uranium atom and did not depend upon its state of chemical combination.

So it came about that the penetrating radiations emitted by radioactive bodies were first noticed and called to the attention of the scientific world.

---

* Henri Becquerel himself used the term "activité radiante."   The word radioactivity, adopted later, was proposed by Marie Curie.

Discovery of Radioactivity of Thorium. Immediately after the discovery of the radioactivity of uranium, a large number of elements were tested for radioactivity using an electroscope as the detector. In this survey only thorium was found to be radioactive, a discovery reported independently by G. C. SCHMIDT and by MADAME CURIE in 1898.

Discovery of Polonium and Radium. The experiments of BECQUEREL and others had established that the amount of radioactivity in any uranium compound was directly proportional to the uranium content. Hence it came as a considerable surprise when measurement of the radioactivity of certain pitchblende ores gave values about 4 times greater than that expected from the uranium content. (MME. CURIE, 1898). MME. AND P. CURIE deduced correctly that this could be so only if pitchblende contained small quantities of an element or elements of greater specific activity than uranium or thorium. Working on this hypothesis the CURIES carried through a systematic fractionation of the ore, using the radioactivity of the various fractions as a guide. This type of methodology was to become known as *radiochemistry*.

Polonium was the first of the active substances to be concentrated from pitchblende. A bismuth fraction isolated by precipitation of bismuth sulfide removed the new element from the bulk of the pitchblende ore. Further purification was carried out by partial precipitation of the subnitrate of bismuth, the polonium concentrating in the precipitate. No completely satisfactory method for the preparation of chemically pure polonium was developed in these early years. MARCKWALD removed polonium from a bismuth chloride solution obtained from uranium residues by dipping a rod of bismuth metal into the active solution. Polonium (and considerable inert tellurium impurity) electrodeposited on the bismuth metal surface. MARCKWALD believed his activity was different from MME. CURIE'S polonium and for some time referred to his substance as radio-tellurium.

Even though the polonium preparations were manifestly impure, certain properties could be ascertained which differed from those of uranium and thorium preparations. In the first place, the specific activity was so great that in strong preparations there was not enough polonium to observe spectral lines. Polonium also showed a complete absence of penetrating radiations (β and γ-rays) and therefore provided a demonstration that pure alpha emitters could exist. Finally, polonium activity was found to diminish with time. An explanation for this phenomenon which enjoyed a certain vogue for a time was that polonium was not a new radioactive substance, but merely bismuth in which radioactivity had somehow been induced by admixture with radioactive substances. In retrospect it seems fortuitous that the first new radioactive substance concentrated did indeed turn out to be a new element rather than a radioactive isotope of a known element such as thorium, bismuth or lead.

Shortly after the discovery of polonium a second extraordinarily active body was isolated from pitchblende by the CURIES (1898). This substance was radium. Radium, the next highest homologue of barium, resembles it closely in chemical properties. Considerable barium is present in pitchblende and when it is isolated from the other elements found in the ore, the radium is separated with it. To separate radium from barium the CURIES employed the method of fractional crystallization making use of the circumstance that radium chloride is more insoluble than barium chloride. A short time later GIESEL found that fractional crystallization of the bromides was more effective. In all of these experiments the progress of the radium was followed by measuring the radioactivity and when nearly pure the specific activity reached a value more than one millionfold greater than that of uranium. The amount of radium in pitchblende is such that several tons of the ore must be worked up to obtain a few hundred milligrams of radium. Despite the extraordinary labor involved, several rather pure preparations of radium were made and the same process was employed for many years, even when radium became an article of commerce.

A number of experiments were performed to determine beyond question that radium was a distinct chemical element. The emission spectrum of radium was measured by DEMARCAY and shown to consist of characteristic lines similar to those of the alkaline earths. In its chemical properties it was found that radium forms a series of compounds similar to barium. Radium metal was prepared by MME. CURIE and DEBIERNE in 1910.

The atomic weight of radium was determined by MME. CURIE in 1902 by weighing a 90-milligram sample of radium chloride and determining the chloride content by precipitation and weighing of silver chloride. The purity of the radium, with particular emphasis on barium content, was determined spectroscopically. The value of the atomic weight was 225.2. MME. CURIE repeated her work in 1907 with 400-milligram samples of radium chloride and obtained the value of 226.45. A very careful series of determinations was carried out by HÖNIGSCHMID in 1911 using samples of radium chloride as large as 680 milligrams. HÖNIGSCHMID's value of the atomic weight was 225.95 based on the value 107.88 for silver and 35.457 for chlorine. These may be compared with the more accurate value 226.035 based upon mass spectroscopy and obtained many years later.

The determination of the atomic weight and of the distinctive physical and chemical properties of radium fixed its location in the periodic chart in the eka-barium position. This knowledge served as a valuable reference point in the assignment of other members of the uranium-radium decay chain as they were discovered later. For many years, except for uranium and thorium, the atomic weight of no other radioactive element was known. The placement of actinium and of its decay products in the periodic system, for example, was uncertain for decades because it was not isolated in sufficient purity to permit an exact determination of its atomic weight.

Discovery of Actinium. DEBIERNE assisted the CURIES in their early studies of the radioactive substances present in pitchblende by supervising the large scale crude fractionation of pitchblende residues. In 1899 while engaged in this work, he discovered a new activity which followed the iron group of metals in the fractionation. He called this substance actinium and stated that it was very similar to thorium in its chemical properties. In 1900–1902 GIESEL reported the discovery of another active substance from pitchblende which he called "emanium" because it emitted a short-lived emanation. GIESEL showed that his substance was similar in chemical properties to the rare earths. It was later concluded that GIESEL's "emanium" was identical with DEBIERNE's actinium and the name "emanium" was dropped.

Radiolead. HOFFMAN AND STRAUSS in 1901 concluded that the radioactivity observed in a lead fraction removed from pitchblende was due to a new substance which they called radiolead. The identification of this activity with radium D came some years later.

The Radioactive Emanations. Before 1900 it was observed that radium, thorium, and actinium continuously emit into the surrounding space a material emanation with the properties of a radioactive gas. This emanation diffused in a current of air, and diffused through paper, plugs of glass wool and other porous materials. It could be pumped away and condensed at a low temperature. The first emanation to be discovered was the 54-second *thoron* produced in samples of thorium. It was at first presumed that thoron was a direct result of the disintegration of thorium, but RUTHERFORD AND SODDY in 1902 showed that thoron was in fact a decay product of ThX, an intermediate product.

The first report of the existence of *radon* is credited to DORN. He found that a small amount of radioactive gas was released by radium preparations at ordinary temperatures but that much more was released if the radium was heated or dissolved. The first attempt to measure the rate of decay of radon was carried out in 1902 by P. CURIE who obtained a half-life of 3.71 days. RUTHERFORD AND SODDY reported a value of 3.99 days the following year. Careful measurements by MME. CURIE in 1910 and by RUTHERFORD in 1911 gave 3.85 days.

GIESEL in 1903 found that actinium gives out an emanation which has a much more rapid rate of decay than thoron or radon. The emanation later received the name *actinon.*

Because the short half-lives of thoron and actinon made them difficult to study, radon received the greatest attention. Radon was subjected to severe chemical treatments to see whether it could be made to undergo chemical change. It was found that it showed a truly remarkable inertness and retained its gaseous nature throughout. The only known elements possessing these properties were the then recently discovered members of the argon family of rare gases. (RAMSAY). However, it was found that radon (and thoron) could be condensed at low temperatures. Some detailed experiments of RUTHERFORD AND SODDY in 1903 placed the condensation temperature at $-150°$C. The first measurement of the atomic weight of radon was carried out by GRAY AND RAMSAY in 1911. Using a remarkably sensitive quartz microbalance these experimenters measured gas samples weighing less than one microgram and determined a value of 223 for the mass number. The emission spectrum of radon was observed by a number of investigators in the period 1908–1909.

The emanations from the three radioactive series were to play central roles in disentangling the complex genetic relationships of the many radioactive species. As gases they could readily be pumped away isolating clearly the lower members of each decay series.

Nature of the Radiations. Radioactivity was detected and measured by three methods in this early period; the photographic method, the "electric" method, and the excitation of fluorescence in fluorescent materials. Photographic plate detection was particularly useful for β and γ detection. The "electric method" was based on the ionization caused in a gas volume by passage of the radiations and was particularly useful for alpha particles. A number of sensitive electrometers and electroscopes were developed for this purpose. Fluorescent materials such as barium platinocyanide and zinc sulfide were found to be useful chiefly for alpha radiation, and the spinthariscope, consisting of a low power magnifier focused on a screen of zinc sulfide, was developed to count individual alpha particles. In 1911 C. T. R. WILSON introduced the expansion cloud chamber for observing the tracks of individual ionizing rays.

RUTHERFORD in 1899 distinguished two kinds of rays from uranium which differed greatly in penetrating power; he called these the α and β rays. Alpha rays are readily absorbed by the absorber foils, but are heavily ionizing throughout their range. Beta rays are far more penetrating than α rays but have much less ionizing power. Later a third type of ray even more penetrating than the β rays was discovered by VILLARD and these were named γ rays. An important advance in the understanding of the nature of the radiations came in 1899 when several laboratories independently observed the deflection of the β rays in a magnetic field. Quantitative measurements of the deflection in magnetic and electric fields showed that beta-rays were negatively charged particles with the same e/m as cathode rays and were soon identified as electrons moving with velocities approaching the speed of light. The inhomogeneity in energy of the beta rays was also well established by 1900, but many years were to pass before a clear distinction between beta rays and conversion electrons would be made.

The identity between β rays and electrons led STRUTT in 1901 to suggest that α rays are the same as canal rays, that is, heavy positively charged particles. Similar suggestions were made by CROOKES, MME. CURIE, AND RUTHERFORD on the basis of this analogy and because of peculiarities in the absorption behavior. However, magnetic fields capable of bending a beam of β rays were not sufficient to produce an observable deflection of α rays and several years elapsed before RUTHERFORD refined magnetic deflection techniques sufficiently to prove that α particles are indeed heavy charged particles. Further measurements with magnetic and electric fields showed that the e/m value was similar to that of hydrogen.

During this period it had become well established that helium occurred in radioactive minerals, but not in others. RUTHERFORD AND SODDY (1902) suggested that helium might be a disintegration product and RAMSAY AND SODDY (1903) did a key experiment in showing that helium accumulates in α emitters at a rate corresponding to the α-emission process. Another important development was reported in 1908 when RUTHERFORD AND GEIGER perfected counting techniques to permit determination of the numbers of α rays emitted from a source. Information so obtained, when combined with the measurement of the total charge carried off by the α rays, established the charge number as 2. This fact fixed the mass of the α-particle close to that of the helium atom. RUTHERFORD AND ROYDS soon extended these findings in an important way by placing radon in a thin-walled glass vessel such that α rays could penetrate and showing that helium could be recovered outside of the vessel. This experiment clearly proved that α rays are rapidly moving ions of helium.

In distinction from the alpha and beta radiations the gamma radiation could not be deflected by electric or magnetic fields. It was shown to be similar to the x radiation produced in vacuum tubes but of considerably shorter wave length.

A great deal of attention was devoted to the study of the absorption and scattering of the α, β, and γ rays. We shall not review these studies in this historical account except to discuss some properties of alpha rays which had a very marked influence on the developing knowledge of radioactivity.

Concept of Alpha Particle Range. Let us first discuss the development of the concept of alpha range. MME. CURIE made measurements on thin samples of polonium shortly after her discovery of this element which showed that the ionization caused by the alpha rays ceased suddenly after traversing a definite thickness of air or other absorber. This was a markedly different behavior from gamma radiation or x radiation which was attenuated exponentially.

When it began to be clear that alpha rays were positively charged atoms moving with very high velocities, BRAGG put forth the view that each alpha particle traveled in nearly a straight line, expending energy in ionization until its velocity was reduced below a certain value.   According to his view each alpha particle should have a definite range of travel.   Experiment showed that each alpha emitter emitted particles with a characteristic range, usually expressed in centimeters of air at atmospheric pressure and 15°C.   From this time forth the range (or the related energy) of the alpha particles emitted by a new radioelement became an important characteristic in deciding whether it was actually different from previously known radioelements.

As α-range data began to accumulate RUTHERFORD (1907) noted that long ranges are associated with short half-lives.   It remained for GEIGER AND NUTTALL (1911–1912) to examine this relationship more systematically and to formulate a "law" which bears their names.   They showed that in a particular radioactive family the logarithm of the decay constant changed linearly with the logarithm of the range.   This relationship is partly fortuitous in that it depends on the data available at the time.   However, the Geiger-Nuttall law had the important function of providing a focus for attempts at a theory for α decay.   It also had an important empirical function in making it possible to estimate the half-lives of α emitters whose α ranges could be measured but whose decay could not be measured for one reason or another.   The half-life of uranium II (U^{234}), for example, was estimated to be about 10^6 years from the observed range of the alpha particles. This was the only way in which the half-life of this isotope could be estimated until A. O. NIER in 1939 measured the isotopic composition of natural uranium.

The Rutherford Nuclear Model of the Atom.   Another outcome of the study of the detailed properties of alpha particles which had the utmost importance for the development of radioactivity and of all nuclear physics was the formulation of the RUTHERFORD model of the atom.   GEIGER AND MARSDEN observed in 1909 that when a beam of alpha particles impinged on a thin sheet of matter, most of the particles were scattered only a few degrees or less from their incident direction.   Some, however, changed their direction sharply, in some cases to the extent that they were scattered backwards from the foil.   The number which were scattered through large angles, while small, was too large to be explained by multiple scattering or by single scattering by the most intense electrical potential (of the order of 100,000 electron volts) supposed to exist within the atom according to the THOMSON model of the atom in favor at that time.

To explain the anomalous scattering RUTHERFORD proposed (1911) his brilliant theory of the nuclear atom.   In order to explain an intense electrical field within the atom RUTHERFORD proposed that the positive charge was concentrated into a very small central region which he termed the nucleus and that the compensating negative charge is distributed over a sphere whose radius is identifiable with the radius of an atom.   Using this atomic model RUTHERFORD calculated quantitatively the expected distribution of scattered alpha particles. This distribution in all its particulars was verified later (1913) by the meticulous experiments of GEIGER AND MARSDEN.

A few years later in a series of papers published during the period 1913–1915 NIELS BOHR used the Rutherford nuclear atom and the quantum theory of radiation as developed by PLANCK and EINSTEIN to develop the quantum theory of atomic structure which came to be known as the Bohr-Rutherford atom. This model of the atom had its most sweeping success in the explanation of atomic spectra and atomic phenomena but it was also of very great importance in making understandable many of the main features of radioactive decay.

An important element of the Rutherford nuclear atom was the charge number Z to be associated with the nucleus. The identification of this number with *atomic number* was not clear until the work of MOSELEY appeared during 1913–1914. MOSELEY made a systematic study of the wave lengths of the K series and L series of x-rays which were emitted by the elements when bombarded with cathode rays. He noted that there was a regular change in the wave length of each series when the elements were arranged in the order of their position in the periodic table. The extreme regularities which he noted could be explained only if there was a very regular change in some quantity within the atom in going from one element to the next heaviest element; he concluded that this quantity was the positive charge on the nucleus. MOSELEY concluded that the number of unit positive charges on the nucleus is the same as the number of the place occupied by the element in the periodic system; this number he called the atomic number. The atomic number immediately replaced the atomic mass number as the fundamental quantity to be associated with any element.

In the region of the radioactive elements it was recognized that the atomic number of uranium was 92, of thorium 90, etc. When the atomic number concept of MOSELEY and the Rutherford Nuclear Atom were used in connection with the SODDY isotope concept and the displacement laws of radioactivity it was possible at once to write down in simple and understandable form nearly the entire sequence of radioactive decay for the three naturally-occurring series. It is necessary to recognize, however, that during the first decade and a half of intensive investigation of the radioelements initiated by BECQUEREL'S discovery these theories were unknown. The nature of each new radioelement had to be deduced from its chemical and physical behavior and its genetic relationship to other radioelements. By 1913, 32 separate radioactive species had been discovered and studied.

Energy Release and the Nature of Radioactivity. Soon after the first studies of radioactivity, it was pointed out that the total energy represented by these energetic radiations was enormously greater than for any known chemical process. Furthermore the rate of energy emission was totally uninfluenced by variation in temperature, pressure, by chemical form, or by any other physical or chemical factor which causes changes in ordinary chemical reactions. The first direct measurements of the heat emitted by radium, carried out by P. CURIE AND LABORDE in 1903, showed that one gram of radium emits about 100 gram calories of heat per hour and that this large heat emission apparently had continued for centuries.

The many suggestions put forward to explain this large store of energy could be divided into two broad groups. According to one set of views the radioactive elements possessed some peculiar property enabling them to extract heat from their surroundings or from unknown radiations impinging on all matter and to convert the energy so abstracted into the form of α, β and γ rays. The second view was that radioactivity in some ways involved the breakup of the atom and the ejection of part of the atomic system and that this process released large amounts of potential energy residing in the atom. The material nature of the α and β rays supported this view. It was

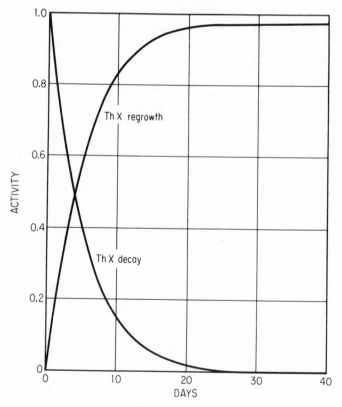

FIG. 6.1. Decay of beta-activity in ThX (3.64 day Ra^{224}) freshly separated from thorium and the regrowth of activity into the thorium.

impossible to formulate any detailed theory since at that time nothing was known about the structure of the atom or of a distinction between the atomic nucleus and the extra-nuclear electrons. The picture of the atom current at that time followed the ideas of J. J. THOMSON, (and of LARMOR AND LORENTZ and of KELVIN) who conceived of the atom as a sphere containing positive and negative particles distributed in some regular fashion throughout and held in equilibrium by electrical forces.

   The Rutherford-Soddy Theory of Radioactivity. The discovery of the radioactive emanations and the isolation of other short-lived radioactive elements provided valuable clues to the true nature of the radioactive transformations. These clues led to the theory of radioactivity put forward by RUTHERFORD AND SODDY in 1902. The observations which were particularly illuminating were those connected with the discovery of the substances given the names of uranium X (UX) and thorium X (ThX).

   In 1900 SIR WILLIAM CROOKES showed that the source of the beta radiation associated with uranium could be isolated from uranium in a single chemical operation. If uranium were precipitated as the carbonate and then dissolved in an excess of ammonium carbonate, a residue of impurity elements remained behind and with this residue remained all the beta activity. This activity was called uranium X. The alpha radiation as measured by the electrical method remained entirely with the uranium. BECQUEREL showed that this uranium X activity could be removed from uranium solution by precipitation of barium sulfate. The inactive uranium and the active barium were laid aside. They were re-examined a year later and the surprising fact was found that *the uranium had regained its activity while the barium sulfate had become completely inactive.*

   Similarly in the case of thorium, RUTHERFORD AND SODDY found that an active constituent, named by them thorium X (ThX), could be found in solution when thorium was precipitated with ammonia. The specific activity of the ThX was at least several thousandfold greater than that of the thorium. Within a period of a month the thorium regained its activity while the ThX became quite inactive. The rate of decay and recovery of activity was studied and curves such as that shown in Fig. 6.1 were obtained.

   Consideration of these phenomena led RUTHERFORD AND SODDY to formulate their famous theory of radioactive decay. According to this theory (1) there is a constant production of fresh radioactive matter by the decay of another radioactive body and (2) the activity of the matter so formed decreases according to an exponential law from the moment of its formation. The daughter radioactive matter has chemical properties distinctly different from its parent and can be isolated chemically from it. When such a separation is made the daughter activity decays in an exponential fashion with a decay constant characteristic of that particular radioactive element; the rate of this decay is uninfluenced by any external condition. The regrowth of the daughter activity into the separated parent also occurs at a characteristic rate uninfluenced by external conditions. In an undisturbed sample the amount of daughter activity reaches an equilibrium amount when the rate of distintegration of the matter already in the sample is just balanced by the rate of production of new matter.

To explain the differing chemical properties of the parent and descendant radioactivities it was postulated by RUTHERFORD AND SODDY in 1903 that radioactive decay was an atomic phenomenon. Atoms of some elements possess a fundamental instability and on the average a constant small percentage of them break up every second by expelling one or more material particles—α or β rays—with great velocity. The part of the atom left behind has different chemical properties. These new atoms may in turn be unstable and, if so, a certain percentage of them will break up each second.

It is inherent in the RUTHERFORD AND SODDY theory that each pure radioactive substance has a characteristic disintegration constant, λ, or some quantity related to it such as the half-life ($T_{1/2} = 0.693/\lambda$). In the case of uranium X the half-life was easily determined to be 24.6 days corresponding to a disintegration constant $\lambda = 0.0288$ days^{-1}. In the case of thorium X the half-life was determined to be 3.65 days corresponding to a disintegration constant $\lambda = 0.190$ days^{-1}.

The disintegration theory was applicable to any series of genetically related radioelements. The logarithmic law of radioactivity is very simple when a single activity is considered. However, when a series of several genetically related radioelements is considered the changes in the amount of an individual product or of the gross activity following a chemical separation can be quite complex. RUTHERFORD deduced the general mathematical expressions applicable to the major types of decay chains observed in practice. This mathematical development was a very powerful tool in unraveling the chain of radioactive transformations in the active deposits left by the radioactive emanations. It was used constantly in deciding on the relationship of any newly discovered radioactive element to those already known.

The Active Deposits. P. AND MME. CURIE in 1899 noted that any substance placed in the neighborhood of a radium preparation behaved as if its surface were covered with an invisible deposit of intensely radioactive matter. This activity became known as "induced" or "excited" radioactivity. RUTHERFORD independently noted the same phenomenon for thorium preparations. It soon became established that this activity was intimately related to the emanations of radium and thorium and that it consisted of non-gaseous radioactive products resulting from the disintegration of the gaseous emanations. The term "induced activity" was dropped in favor of the more suitable "active deposit."

It was found that the active deposit could be highly concentrated on negatively charged metal wires or surfaces placed in closed vessels containing the emanation. Such wires or foils gave convenient sources for study of the radiations because the activity was highly concentrated and essentially weightless. It was found that treatment of the surface with acids would remove the radioactive deposit from the wire and the chemical properties of its components could be studied.

The Active Deposit from Thoron. The active deposit left by the decay of thoron, radon, or actinon is not a simple activity but a mixture of activities. In the case of the thoron active deposit it was ultimately determined that the sequence of products was the following:

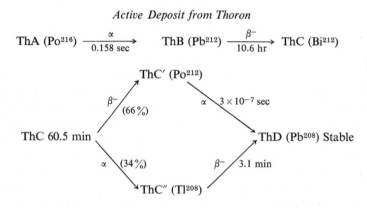

Active Deposit from Thoron

The first product, ThA, is so short-lived that special methods are required to measure it. MOSELEY AND FAJANS first determined (1911) the half-life of ThA by collecting it on a rapidly rotating, negatively charged metal disc as it was formed from the decay of the thoron. The activity of the matter so deposited was examined at different angular distances from the point of deposit. They determined in this way a half-life of 0.14 seconds, which is quite close to the value presently accepted. MOSELEY AND FAJANS applied this same method to the first product in the active deposit of actinon and found a half-life of 0.002 seconds for AcA. This was the shortest half-life known for any radioactive element at that time.

The controlling activity in the active deposit of thoron is ThB which decays with a half-life of 10.6 hours. Further details on the active deposit of thoron will be presented later when the various members of the naturally occurring decay chain are discussed separately.

The Active Deposit from Radon. The active deposit left on surfaces exposed to radon shows a complex decay. The transformation sequence can be divided into a preliminary sequence of rapid change involving the activities with the designation RaA, RaB, RaC, RaC', and RaC" and a final sequence of very slow change composed of the activities RaD, RaE, and RaF. These products will be discussed systematically in the next section.

It would take us too far afield to discuss in detail the interesting detective work involved in unravelling the course of this decay sequence but a few points may be mentioned. One approach to the problem was to follow the decay of the active deposit starting immediately after removal of the emanation and to deduce the half-lives of the successive products by the shape

Main Decay Sequence of the Active Deposit of Radon

$$\text{Po}^{218} \text{ (RaA)} \xrightarrow[3.05 \text{ min}]{\alpha} \text{Pb}^{214} \text{ (RaB)} \xrightarrow[26.8 \text{ min}]{\beta^-} \text{Bi}^{214} \text{ (RaC)} \xrightarrow[19.7 \text{ min}]{\beta^-}$$

$$\text{Po}^{214} \text{ (RaC')} \xrightarrow[1.5 \times 10^{-4} \text{ sec}]{\alpha} \text{Pb}^{210} \text{ (RaD)} \xrightarrow[19.4 \text{ yr}]{\beta^-} \text{Bi}^{210} \text{ (RaE)} \xrightarrow[5.0 \text{ day}]{\beta^-}$$

$$\text{Pb}^{210} \text{ (RaF)} \xrightarrow[138 \text{ day}]{\alpha} \text{Pb}^{206} \text{ (RaG) Stable}$$

of the observed curves using the mathematical relations derived by RUTHERFORD. The analysis was difficult because the shape of the decay curve was dependent on the length of time of exposure to emanation and because the alpha emitting products were detected so much more efficiently than the beta emitting products. Nevertheless it was concluded that the first three changes consisted of radium A, decaying by alpha particle emission with a half-life of 3 minutes, radium B, a rayless product decaying with a half-life of 27 minutes and radium C, decaying with a half-life of 20 minutes and emitting α, β and γ rays. The separation of radium B from radium C was carried out by BRONSON (1905) by volatilizing the radium B (a lead isotope) from radium C (a bismuth isotope). VON LERCH (1906) showed that radium C could be obtained in a pure state by contacting a foil of nickel with a solution of the active deposit.

The Recoil Collection Method. Somewhat later (1909) the recoil collection method for the separation of radioactive daughter products was introduced by HAHN and by RUSS AND MAKOWER. The general method consists of placing a negatively charged collector plate quite near to a plate covered with active material. During radioactive decay the daughter atom is given enough momentum to balance the momentum of the ejected α or β ray. This may be sufficient to eject it from the surface as a positively-charged ion which is then accelerated toward the collector plate. This process can be quite effective for the daughter products of energetic alpha emitting parents. It is much less prominent for daughter atoms of beta-emitting parents because of the much smaller recoil momentum. RUTHERFORD had previously calculated the recoil momenta to be expected from alpha and beta processes.

Pure samples of 26.8-minute RaB could be obtained in high yield by this method using the 3-minute alpha emitter RaA as the source activity. Pure samples of RaC could be obtained from the beta emitter RaB, but the collection efficiency was only about 1/6000.

The recoil method is of general applicability and was an important aid in determining the course of the decay chains. It helped to determine the direct parent-daughter relationship of two activities in several instances. It also aided in the discovery of quite short-lived products which had been missed. For example the recoil method was instrumental in showing that radium C was a complex activity decaying by two paths. The work of HAHN AND MEITNER (1909) and FAJANS (1911) showed that a product which they called radium C_2 (later relabeled RaC″) was produced in a very small percentage of the disintegrations. This product showed a half-life of 1.38 minutes. The main decay resulted in the direct production of radium D (actually years later it was found that the short-lived alpha emitter RaC′ occurred between RaC and RaD). The discovery of radium C_2 was important because it was the first instance in which definite evidence was presented for branching decay. Later several instances of branching decay were verified.

The active deposit observed on bodies which have been exposed to radon gas decreases to a very low level within a day's time after removal of the radon but does not decrease to zero. The residual activity, known as the active-deposit-of-slow-transformation, consists of radium D, radium E, and radium F. Radium D, a slowly decaying substance emitting soft β rays, was found to be identical with the "radiolead" separated earlier by HOFFMANN AND STRAUSS from uranium minerals. The half-life of RaD was too long to determine by direct counting methods and was determined indirectly by an application of the RUTHERFORD AND SODDY disintegration hypothesis. RUTHERFORD in 1904 estimated a value of 40 years; ST. MEYER AND SCHWEIDLER in 1907 estimated 37.5 years. ANTONOFF in 1910 determined a value of 16.5 years which in view of the difficulties is rather close to the presently accepted value of 19.4 years.

Radium E is a 5-day activity emitting high energy beta rays. It can be separated from radium D or radium F by deposition on a nickel plate.

Radium F was shown to be an alpha emitter identical with the element polonium which MME. CURIE had isolated from pitchblende. Radium F has the important property that its transformation product shows no radioactivity. Hence it was deduced that the chain of radioactive changes initiated by radium comes to an end at this stage.

The Active Deposit from Actinon. The active deposit from actinon is now known to go through the sequence shown here. We have mentioned how MOSELEY AND FAJANS (1911) used the method based on recoil collection of AcA on a rapidly revolving disc to measure the very short half-life of actinium A. They reported a value of 0.002 seconds. The course of the transformation of AcB through a series of products to the stable end-product actinium D was determined through the contributions of many investigators. Analysis of the decay curves of the mixture, and separation of individual products by volatilization, by electrodeposition, or by recoil collection aided in the assignments.

Decay Sequence of the Active Deposit of Actinon

$$\text{AcA (Po}^{215})\ \xrightarrow[1.83 \times 10^{-3}\ \text{sec}]{\alpha}\ \text{AcB (Pb}^{211})\ \xrightarrow[36\ \text{min}]{\beta^-}\ \text{AcC (Bi}^{211})\ 2.16\ \text{min}$$

Ionium. The discovery of ionium had an interesting history. It was an outcome of a search for a radioactive parent of the element radium. Consideration of the relatively short half-life of radium and of the RUTHERFORD-SODDY transformation theory led to the conclusion that radium must be continuously replenished in radioactive minerals by some longer-lived precursor. The constancy of the ratio between radium and uranium in minerals suggested that uranium was the parent of radium. However, if this were the case, radium should grow back at a readily detectable rate into purified uranium samples, and experimental checks showed that the regrowth of radium was more than one thousandfold less rapid than would be predicted. It was necessary to postulate a relatively long-lived intermediate between uranium and radium.

BOLTWOOD (1906) proceeded to search for this missing intermediate and during some experiments with the mineral carnotite isolated a preparation which he at first believed to be actinium. BOLTWOOD kept his "actinium" preparation in a sealed bulb and periodically tested it for radium content by measuring the radon gas content. He observed that radium was growing into his sample and concluded that actinium was the parent of radium. To confuse the situation further RUTHERFORD obtained a sample of actinium from GIESEL, who had discovered actinium in 1902 almost simultaneously with DEBIERNE, and found that radium rapidly grew into this preparation too. This was caused by a considerable ionium impurity in GIESEL's actinium sample. BOLTWOOD (1907) re-examined his original preparation and found it was not actinium but a new substance which he called ionium. By separating ionium from a number of minerals, he found that the rate of production of radium was directly proportional to the amount of ionium. The experiments of BOLTWOOD, of KEETMAN, and of AUER V. WELSBACH showed that ionium was identical in its chemical properties to thorium and could not be separated from thorium.   This made it difficult to measure the half-life of ionium by specific activity measurements but various lines of evidence served to bracket the half-life in the range of 100,000 years.

Uranium 2 (Uranium II).   With the discovery of ionium it was possible about 1910 to write the uranium decay chain as follows:

$$\text{Uranium} \xrightarrow{\alpha} \text{Uranium X} \xrightarrow{\beta^-} \text{Ionium} \xrightarrow{\alpha} \text{Radium} \xrightarrow{\alpha}$$

$$\longrightarrow \text{Radium Emanation} \xrightarrow{\alpha} \text{Active Deposit.}$$

The fact that uranium itself is not simple but must contain two alpha emitting substances was deduced from a very simple experimental fact.   In the decay chain of uranium as understood at the time were six products which emitted alpha particles.   According to this the number of alpha particles emitted by a thin deposit of a uranium ore in equilibrium with its descendants should be just seven times that of an equivalent amount of pure uranium.   Instead, it was found that the mineral samples emitted just four times the number of alpha particles released by uranium.   It was concluded that (1) uranium emits two alpha particles per disintegration, or (2) uranium consists of two distinct substances in equilibrium.   The first possibility was eliminated by experiments of MARSDEN AND BARRATT who showed that the alpha particles of uranium did not occur as doubles.   Range measurements did show the existence of two distinct alpha groups of range 2.5 cm and 2.9 cm of air.   From the Geiger-Nuttall relationship a half-life of approximately 10^6 years was calculated for this second component of uranium.   (The presently accepted value of the half-life of U^{234} is 2.5×10^5 years.)   Attempts to separate the two radioactive components of uranium chemically were, of course, unsuccessful.   Following these discoveries the early part of the uranium decay chain was written (incorrectly) in this way for some period of time:

$$\text{Uranium I} \xrightarrow{\alpha} \text{Uranium II} \xrightarrow{\alpha} \text{Uranium X} \xrightarrow{\beta^-} \text{Ionium}$$

We shall mention a little further on how this error came to be corrected.

Discovery of Radiothorium.   Radiothorium was discovered by HAHN in 1905 shortly after he had joined Sir William Ramsay as a laboratory assistant.   RAMSAY had given HAHN a sample of barium containing alpha activity believed to be radium and asked him to purify the radium according to the methods of MME. CURIE and of GIESEL.   This "radium" sample had been isolated not from an ordinary uranium ore but from thorianite, containing a high percentage of thorium, obtained from Ceylon.   HAHN soon found that this preparation did not behave as did normal radium and in his experiments succeeded in isolating a new and very active substance which he called

radiothorium. This substance gave rise to thorium X and thorium emanation. This made it necessary to revise previous views of the relationship
of thorium X to thorium, as it had been thought that thorium X was the
direct descendent of thorium.

Radiothorium is an isotope of thorium and it is clear in the light of later
knowledge that its presence in Hahn's radium sample is to be explained by the
isolation of mesothorium, an isotope of radium, with the barium carrier and
by the subsequent growth of radiothorium into the sample.

Discovery of mesothorium. The discovery of mesothorium, the radium
isotope which is the direct descendant of thorium, was the result of a slight
controversy between HAHN AND BOLTWOOD. HAHN had determined a value
of about two years for the half-life of his newly-discovered radiothorium.
BOLTWOOD had estimated a considerably longer half-life by an indirect
method. BOLTWOOD had found that the activity of thorium oxide samples
prepared from commercial sources was in some cases only about half the
activity of thorium in minerals. This difference was attributed to the removal of radiothorium during chemical purification. If this were true, the
rate of growth of activity back into the thorium should give the half-life
of radiothorium, since radiothorium was then believed to be the direct
descendant of thorium. The growth of activity, however, indicated a half-
life of about six years, much longer than HAHN's value.

HAHN deduced that the difference could be resolved if an unknown
product intervened between thorium and radiothorium. To test this hypothesis he obtained a series of thorium samples, whose dates of purification
were known, from the firm of Knöfler and Company. HAHN found (1907)
that the activity of thorium preparations was normal immediately after
separation but gradually decreased with age to a minimum at about 4.6
years. After this, however, the activity then rose slowly toward the initial
normal value. (This variation in thorium activity is shown exactly in Fig.
6.21). Using his previously determined value of two years for the half-life
of radiothorium, HAHN deduced from the activity measurements that the
intermediate substance did not emit alpha rays and was converted to radiothorium with a half-life of about 5.5 years. This new substance was called
mesothorium.

$$\text{Thorium} \xrightarrow{\alpha} \text{Mesothorium} \xrightarrow[5.5\ \text{yr}]{\beta^-} \text{Radiothorium} \xrightarrow[2\ \text{yr}]{\alpha}$$

BOLTWOOD later found that mesothorium was easily removed from tho-
rium by precipitation of the thorium with ammonia. The original radiothorium remained with the thorium but new radiothorium at once com-
menced to grow into the mesothorium fraction. BOLTWOOD, SODDY, AND
MARCKWALD in separate investigations found that mesothorium was identical in chemical properties with radium.

Mesothorium 2. About one year after the discovery of mesothorium, HAHN reported that an activity with a half-life of 6.2 hours rapidly grew into freshly isolated samples of mesothorium. The 6.2 hour activity could be removed from mesothorium by precipitating a little zirconium or thorium with ammonia. The radiations from this new activity were interesting because of a prominence of several groups of monoenergetic electrons in contrast to the continuous spectrum of electron energies seen in the case of most beta emitters. This new activity was named mesothorium 2 and mesothorium itself was relabeled mesothorium 1.

Mesothorium was isolated in considerable quantity for commercial sale as a radium substitute. The 5.5 year half-life of mesothorium 1 (now known to be 6.7 years) was short enough to provide high specific activity material but still long enough to give a convenient working life for the samples. The mesothorium 2 which quickly grew into equilibrium and was maintained by the longer-lived parent emitted strong beta and gamma radiations which could be used for medical or other purposes. These commercial sources of mesothorium or "German radium" were usually not pure because the monazite sands from which they were prepared contained some uranium as well as thorium. Hence radium was isolated with the mesothorium.

Actinium X and Radioactinium. Independent work by GODLEWSKI AND GIESEL (1905) showed that if actinium is precipitated with ammonia a new substance called actinium X remains in the solution. GODLEWSKI determined a half-life of 10.2 days for this substance. It was found to be the parent of the actinium emanation. Actinium X has properties similar to thorium X and to radium. HAHN (1906) found that the actinium X was not produced directly from the decay of actinium but that an intermediate alpha ray product, radioactinium, came between actinium and actinium X. The half-life of radio-actinium was found to be 19.5 days.

When the series of radioactive changes in the active deposit of the actinium emanation was worked out the decay chain for actinium could be written (1912) as follows:

$$\text{Actinium} \xrightarrow{\beta^-} \text{Radioactinium} \xrightarrow{\alpha} \text{Actinium X} \xrightarrow{\alpha} \text{Actinon} \xrightarrow{\alpha}$$

$$\text{Actinium A} \xrightarrow{\alpha} \text{Actinium B} \xrightarrow{\beta^-} \text{Actinium C} \xrightarrow{\alpha} \text{Actinium D}$$

Except for some later information on the actinium C branch products and a small alpha branching of actinium itself this sequence is complete and correct. However, at this time there was great uncertainty as to the origin of actinium itself.

Discovery of Uranium Y. The first crude estimate of the half-life of actinium reported by MME. CURIE in 1911 gave a value of about 30 years and a later measurement by HAHN AND MEITNER gave about 20 years indicating that some other radioactive product in pitchblende must be continuously replenishing the actinium. The search for this parent was unavailing for many years. It was not possible to separate actinium completely enough from the rare earths with which it was always mixed so that an atomic weight determination could be made. Nor could this be done for any disintegration product of actinium. The one fact that seemed to provide a clue was that the actinium content of any uranium mineral always bore a constant small ratio, in terms of disintegrations per unit time, to the amount of uranium. This led to the belief that actinium stood in some genetic relationship to the uranium decay chain and that it might arise from a small branching of uranium or one of its main-line decay products. In 1911 ANTONOFF reported his results on a new product, designated uranium Y, which could be isolated together with uranium X from uranium solutions by precipitation of ferric hydroxide. The amount of the 1.5-day uranium Y was small compared to uranium X. It did not appear to be genetically related to uranium X and its presence was most logically explained as being due to a branching decay of uranium, most probably at uranium 2. The possibility that uranium Y was related to actinium and might even be its immediate parent was considered. It became clear that uranium Y could not be the immediate parent of actinium for otherwise actinium would be observed to grow into pure uranium at a detectable rate.

Discovery of Protactinium and the Origin of Actinium. Some years later a new search was made for the parent of actinium using the SODDY-FAJANS displacement rules of alpha and beta decay which we shall discuss presently. From its chemical properties actinium clearly belongs in Group III of the periodic chart. If the parent of actinium were an alpha emitter it should be placed in Group V in the eka-tantalum position. This parent must be long-lived to explain the past difficulties in observing the growth of actinium into purified uranium. Following these considerations HAHN AND MEITNER searched for a long-lived alpha emitter with chemical properties of eka-tantalum in suitable residues from pitchblende processing. They succeeded (1918) in isolating a new alpha emitting activity and demonstrated the growth of actinium into their samples. At this time they were unable to isolate a quantity in sufficient purity to determine the specific activity; however, they were able to estimate a half-life in the range 1200 to 180,000 years using the GEIGER-NUTTALL relationship. The new isotope was named protactinium. This was not the first isotope of the element to be discovered for FAJANS and GÖHRING had previously identified the isotope UX_2.

At about the same time as the work of HAHN AND MEITNER independent work by SODDY AND CRANSTON had also shown the existence of protactinium which they called eka-tantalum. Their chemical separation technique was based on the known volatility of tantalum chloride at high temperatures. They heated pitchblende in a stream of carbon tetrachloride and found that the material which sublimed gave rise to actinium.

The discovery of protactinium made it possible to write the early part of the actinium chain as follows:

$$\text{Uranium II} \xrightarrow[\text{branch}]{?} \text{Uranium Y} \xrightarrow{\beta^-} \text{Protactinium} \xrightarrow{\alpha} \text{Actinium.}$$

The correct assignment of the origin of uranium Y and a final settlement of the relationship of the actinium series to the other three series were not made for many years, but were finally achieved by the following developments.

1. In 1929 ASTON found a small amount of Pb^{207} by examining the isotopic composition of lead obtained from a uranium mineral. From the high ratio of Pb^{207} to Pb^{208} in the sample it was clear that Pb^{207} could not be present simply because of contamination with ordinary lead. RUTHERFORD concluded from ASTON's experiment that Pb^{207} must be in part due to actinium-lead, the end product of the actinium series. Assuming this to be correct, one could conclude that the atomic weight of protactinium must be 231 since six alpha particles are emitted in converting protactinium into actinium lead. This in turn meant that the uranium isotope from which protactinium is derived cannot be uranium II but must be an unknown isotope of mass 235, termed actinouranium. A. PICARD had hypothesized the isotope U^{235} as early as 1917.

2. Definite evidence for a uranium isotope of mass 235 was obtained by the mass-spectrographic analysis of DEMPSTER in 1935. The first accurate measurement on the isotopic composition of uranium was reported by NIER in 1939. NIER reported a value of 0.72% for U^{235} and also for the first time observed U^{234}, the uranium II of the uranium-radium decay chain.

3. The atomic weight of protactinium was determined by A. V. GROSSE in 1935 by preparing, weighing, and analyzing a pure compound of the element. He reported a value of 230.6 ± 0.5.

The Concept of Isotopes and the Displacement Laws. During the first decade and a half of radioactivity when a large number of radioelements were being discovered two important perplexing facts were forced on the attention of most of the principal investigators in the field. The first was that the number of radioelements was much larger than the number of places available in the periodic chart on any reasonable extension of the periodic system of the elements as it was then known; the number of different radioelements was in the neighborhood of thirty and these somehow had to be fitted into the chart in the elements between lead and uranium.   Secondly, a number of the radioelements showed a truly remarkable chemical similarity to each other or to one of the previously known inactive elements. For example, it had been found impossible to separate ionium from thorium, radiolead from ordinary lead, mesothorium-1 from radium, uranium II from uranium I, etc.   These perplexities were removed in 1913 by the introduction of the concept of the isotope and of the so-called displacement laws.   The clearest statement of the new concepts was made by SODDY and independently by FAJANS although many persons such as FLECK AND RUSSELL shared in this important discovery.   The term "isotope" or "isotopic element" was suggested by SODDY for a group of two or more substances of different atomic weight occupying the same place in the periodic table and being in consequence chemically non-separable and identical.   Under this concept radiolead and ordinary lead are not elements with remarkable chemical similarity but merely different forms of the same element.   The element thorium thus had at least six different forms of differing atomic weight, these being thorium, ionium, radioactinium, radiothorium, uranium Y, and uranium X.   The displacement laws were formulated by SODDY as follows:

1. The product resulting from an alpha transition is shifted two places in the periodic chart in the direction of diminishing mass from the place of the original substance.

2. The product resulting from a beta transition is shifted one place in the direction of the higher elements from that of the original substance.

These rules and the isotope concept assisted enormously in the placement of the radioactive products of the three series and in making understandable the chemical behavior of the elements.   Shortly after the formulation of the displacement laws the MOSELEY concept of atomic number became a cornerstone of nuclear science and made even more explicit the meaning of the transformation laws.   These new concepts assisted the search for new products and the correction of errors.   An interesting example of this is the placement of uranium II in the early part of the uranium decay chain.   We have reported previously how from radioactivity evidence the chain had been written:

$$\text{Uranium I} \xrightarrow{\alpha} \text{Uranium II} \xrightarrow{\alpha} \text{Uranium X} \xrightarrow{\beta^-} \text{Ionium} \xrightarrow{\alpha} \text{Radium.}$$

Application of the displacement laws immediately showed that this could not be correct because uranium II should then be an isotope of thorium and easily separable from uranium I (mass number 238).   Uranium II was in fact inseparable from uranium I.   Hence the chain was rewritten as follows:

$$\text{Uranium I} \xrightarrow{\alpha} \text{Uranium X} \xrightarrow{\beta^-} \text{Uranium II} \xrightarrow{\alpha} \text{Ionium} \xrightarrow{\alpha} \text{Radium.}$$

This scheme still had one serious flaw. In view of the diplacement laws, uranium X, an isotope of thorium, could not be expected to transform itself in a single beta transition to uranium II, an isotope of uranium. To correct this, RUSSELL AND FAJANS presented the hypothesis that an unknown beta emitter must exist between uranium X and uranium II and that this substance should have properties similar to tantalum. FAJANS AND GÖHRING (1913) used tantalum as a carrier to isolate a new radioactive element with a half-life of 1.15 minutes. This activity was given the name UX_2. This was the first isotope to be discovered of the element which we now call protactinium. At the time of their discovery of UX_2 FAJANS AND GÖHRING suggested the name brevium because of the short half-life. Later when the isotope, protactinium, was found by HAHN AND MEITNER the name brevium was abandoned, with Fajan's consent, in favor of protactinium as the name of the new element.

Discovery of UZ—The First Isomer. We shall close this account of the early years of radioactivity with a mention of one radioactive isotope whose chief importance lies in the fact that it was the first instance of isomerism to be discovered. As we have previously mentioned FAJANS AND GÖHRING found that UX_2, a 1.15-minute isotope of element 91, was produced by the disintegration of UX, a 24.1 day isotope of thorium. Somewhat later (1921) HAHN showed that UX_1 gave rise not only to UX_2 but in a very small proportion of its disintegrations to a new substance named uranium Z. Uranium Z has a half-life of 6.7 hours and emits beta rays. From its origin and from its chemical properties it had to be regarded as an isotope of protactinium and, what was more significant, as an isotope identical in mass number with UX_2. This was the first instance of a phenomenon later to be termed "isomerism." (STEFAN MEYER had already indicated the possibility of the existence of such nuclear species which he had termed "isotopes of higher order.") It was not until the occurrence of nuclear isomers among artificially radioactive isotopes was shown to be a general phenomenon that the nature of UZ was completely understood.

Conclusion. This account of the early period of radioactivity brings us approximately to the year 1920 at which time the majority of products of the naturally occurring radioactive series had been identified. Some more branch products were discovered later and, as we have mentioned, the important isotope U^{235} was found in the late nineteen thirties. The main emphasis of the next decade before the discovery of artificial radioactivity was placed on a detailed study of the radiations of the individual isotopes. Hence at this point we shall conclude this review of the early period and turn to a systematic review of the properties of the naturally occurring isotopes.

The reader who is interested in more detailed information on the early history of radioactivity can turn to the following publications.

References on Early History of Natural Radioactivity.

"*Natural Radioactivity,*" *Encyclopaedia Britannica.*

Mme. P. Curie, *Traité de Radioactivité,* Gauthier-Villars, Paris, 1910.

E. Rutherford, *Radioactivity* (Cambridge University Press, 1905).

Oeuvres de Marie Sklodowska Curie, collected by Irene Joliot Curie, Polish Academy of Sciences, Warsaw 1954.

E. Rutherford, *Radioactive Substances and their Radiations* (Cambridge University Press, 1912).

S. Meyer and E. V. Schweidler, *Radioaktivität* (Teubner, Berlin, 1916; Second Edition, 1927).

Gmelin, *Handbuch der Anorganischen Chemie,* 8th Edition, 1928, Verlag Chemie, G. M. bH., Berlin. See especially SL System nummer 31, "Radium und isotope"; System nummer 40, "Actinium und isotope"; System nummer 44, "Thorium und isotope," and System nummer 51, "Protactinium und isotope."

K. W. F. Kohlrausch, "Radioaktivität," Volume XV, *Handbuch der Experimental Physik,* Wien-Harnes, Leipzig, 1928.

A. F. Kovarik and L. McKeehan, "Radioactivity," *Bulletin of the National Research Council of the National Academy of Sciences,* Washington, revised edition, 1929.

F. Soddy, *The Chemistry of the Radio-Elements,* 1911.

K. Fajans, "*Radioaktivität und die Neuste Entwicklung der Lehre von den Chemischen Elementen,*" F. Vieweg u. Sohn, Braunschweig, 1921.

G. E. M. Jancey, "The Early Years of Radioactivity," *Am. J. Phys.* **14,** 226–241 (1946).

6.2 THE URANIUM-RADIUM SERIES (THE $4n + 2$ SERIES)

We now proceed to a more systematic discussion of the naturally-occurring radioactivities starting first with the uranium-radium series. Fig. 6.2 shows this decay chain and Table 6.1 lists essential data for each isotope. The modes of decay are listed for each isotope but the radiations are not given in detail at this point. Each isotope is listed according to the standard isotopic designation and also by its classical generic name. Although these classical symbols were chosen, as we have seen, before the isotopic identities were known, the older nomenclature still retains some attractive features. For example, all of the A-products are the immediate alpha-decay descendants of the noble gas isotopes in the three series so that radium A(RaA) immediately suggests the polonium daughter of the emanation whereas the symbol Po^{218} may require some reflection to associate it with radium preparations. Similarly the B-products in all three series are lead isotopes which decay to the C-products which are all bismuth isotopes. The C-products in turn undergo branched decay to the C'-products (polonium isotopes) and the C" products (thallium isotopes).

TABLE 6.1. The uranium-radium series

Radioelement	Symbol	Radiation	Half-life
Uranium I	U^{238}	α	4.507×10^9 yr
$\quad\downarrow \alpha$			
Uranium X$_1$	Th^{234}	β	24.1 day
$\quad\downarrow \beta$			
Uranium X$_2$	Pa^{234}	β	1.175 min
93.87% I.T. 0.13%			
$\beta\downarrow$ Uranium Z	Pa^{234}	β	6.7 hr
Uranium II	U^{234}	α	2.48×10^5 yr
$\quad\downarrow \alpha$			
Ionium	Th^{230}	α	7.52×10^4 yr
$\quad\downarrow \alpha$			
Radium	Ra^{226}	α	1622 yr
$\quad\downarrow \alpha$			
Radon	Em^{222}	α	3.825 day
$\quad\downarrow \alpha$			
Radium A	Po^{218}	α and β	3.05 min
99.98% 0.02%			
$\alpha\downarrow$			
Radium B	Pb^{214}	β	26.8 min
Astatine^{218}	At^{218}	α	2 sec
$\beta\downarrow$ α			
Radium C	Bi^{214}	β and α	19.7 min
99.96% 0.04%			
$\beta\downarrow$ α			
Radium C′	Po^{214}	α	1.58×10^{-4} sec
α Radium C″	Tl^{210}	β	1.32 min
$\quad\beta$			
Radium D	Pb^{210}	β	19.4 yr
$\quad\downarrow \beta$			
Radium E	Bi^{210}	β and α	5.02 day
$\quad\alpha$			
~100% ~10^{-5}% 1.8 $\times$ 10^{-6}%			
$\beta\downarrow$ α Mercury^{206}	Hg^{206}	β	8.6 min
Radium F	Po^{210}	α	138.4 day
$\quad\beta^-$			
α Thallium^{206}	Tl^{206}	β	4.19 min
$\quad\beta$			
Radium G	Pb^{206}	stable	

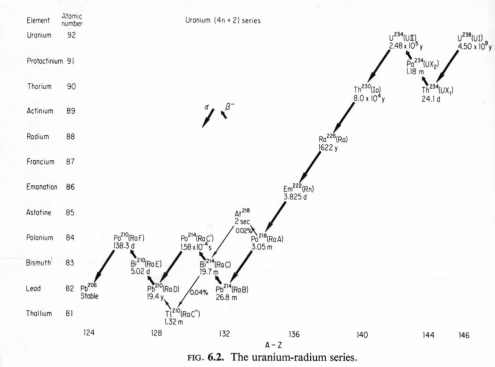

Element	Atomic number							
Uranium	92					U^{234}(UII) 2.48 x 10^5 y		U^{238}(UI) 4.50 x 10^9 y
Protactinium	91					Pa^{234}(UX$_2$) 1.18 m		
Thorium	90				Th^{230}(Io) 8.0 x 10^4 y		Th^{234}(UX$_1$) 24.1 d	
Actinium	89		α β^-					
Radium	88				Ra^{226}(Ra) 1622 y			
Francium	87							
Emanation	86			Em^{222}(Rn) 3.825 d				
Astatine	85		At^{218} 2 sec 0.02%					
Polonium	84	Po^{210}(RaF) 138.3 d	Po^{214}(RaC') 1.58 x 10^{-4} s	Po^{218}(RaA) 3.05 m				
Bismuth	83	Bi^{210}(RaE) 5.02 d	Bi^{214}(RaC) 19.7 m					
Lead	82	Pb^{206} Stable	Pb^{210}(RaD) 19.4 y 0.04%	Pb^{214}(RaB) 26.8 m				
Thallium	81		Tl^{210}(RaC") 1.32 m					
		124	128	132	136	140	144	146

A – Z

FIG. 6.2. The uranium-radium series.

A point of nomenclature which demands clarification is the family name for the isotopes of element 86, the noble gas. This element is perhaps most often termed *radon* which is also the isotopic designation for radium emanation. However, we prefer to adopt the family name *emanation* (symbol Em) which has also been used. (See for example K. Fajans, *Radioaktivität und die Neueste Entwicklung der Lehre von den Chemischen Elementen*, F. Vieweg u. Sohn, Braunschweig, 1919, p. 94.)

We shall also frequently refer to the uranium-radium series as the $4n + 2$ series, the thorium series as the $4n$ series, etc., in recognition of the fact that the mass number of all members of a single series are divisible by four with a common remainder. This results from the fact that alpha decay always causes a change of 4 in mass number while beta decay proceeds without any change in mass number.

The Uranium Isotopes in Natural Uranium. Natural uranium consists of three alpha-emitting isotopes: U^{238} (uranium I) present in 99.27 per cent abundance, U^{234} (uranium II), and U^{235} (actinouranium). U^{238} is the primary source material from which all the other (secondary) members of the uranium-radium series are derived since only U^{238} is sufficiently long-lived to have existed since the formation of the elements. A small amount of U^{234} must be found in every uranium sample in which radioactive equilibrium has been established. The ratio of atoms of U^{234} to U^{238} is simply the ratio of the half-lives or 5.5×10^{-5}. The equilibrium under discussion is given by the chain.

$$\text{UI} \xrightarrow[4.5 \times 10^9 \text{ yr}]{\alpha} \text{UX}_\text{I} \xrightarrow[24.1 \text{ day}]{\beta^-} \text{UX}_\text{II} \xrightarrow[1.17 \text{ min}]{\beta^-} \text{U II} \xrightarrow[2.5 \times 10^5 \text{ yr}]{\alpha}$$

The U^{235} present in natural uranium is unrelated to the $4n + 2$ series and is the long-lived primary isotope from which all secondary members of the actinouranium series are derived.

The isotopic composition of natural uranium and the half-lives of the uranium isotopes are of fundamental importance for such diverse matters as the derivation of radioactive constants for other members of the decay chain, the preparation of counting standards, the age of minerals and the heat balance of the earth. Hence, we shall summarize the best values for these quantities.

DEMPSTER[1] first detected U^{235} in natural uranium and reported an isotopic abundance of less than one per cent. The first accurate mass-spectrographic analyses were made by NIER[2] who also detected U^{234} for the first time. The results obtained in NIER'S work and in several more recent studies are given in Table 6.2. Among the best recent measurements of the abundance of U^{238} and U^{235} are those of LOUNSBURY.[3] The half-lives of U^{238} and U^{234} may be calculated from measurements of the specific activity and isotopic composition of natural uranium together with a correction for the contribution of U^{235}. This correction requires a knowledge of the half-life of U^{235} which must be determined by some independent method. However, the contribution of U^{235} to the total alpha activity of normal uranium is less than 5 per cent, so large errors in the U^{235} half-life are not reflected in similar errors in the calculation of the half-lives of U^{234} and U^{238}.

Since the introduction of large-scale plants for the gaseous diffusion and electromagnetic separation of uranium isotopes it has been possible to make direct determinations of the half-lives of the uranium isotopes by specific activity measurements on samples highly enriched in U^{234} and U^{235}. FLEMING, GHIORSO, AND CUNNINGHAM[4] have measured the half-lives of U^{234} and U^{235} on such enriched samples and have given a detailed and critical evaluation of the errors involved. Table 6.2 contains a summary of the principal half-life determinations. We adopt as "best values" those selected by FLEMING.[4] The table also lists various determinations of the isotopic composition of natural uranium. In Part III of Table 6.2 we

---

[1] A. J. Dempster, *Nature* **136**, 180 (1935).

[2] A. Nier, *Phys. Rev.* **55**, 150 (1939).

[3] M. Lounsbury, *Can. J. Chem.* **34**, 259 (1956).

[4] E. H. Fleming, Jr., A. Ghiorso, and B. B. Cunningham, *Phys. Rev.* **88**, 642 (1952).

TABLE **6.2.** Values of radioactivity constants for the
uranium isotopes occurring in nature.

PART I

Isotope	Half-life (years)	Specific activity (disint/min mg)	Decay constant λ in yr^{-1}	Ref.
U^{234}	$(2.7 \pm 0.27) \times 10^5$	$(1.3 \pm 0.13) \times 10^7$		a
	$(2.29 \pm 0.14) \times 10^5$	$(1.48 \pm 0.09) \times 10^7$		b
	$(2.35 \pm 0.14) \times 10^5$	$(1.44 \pm 0.09) \times 10^7$		b
	$(2.522 \pm 0.008) \times 10^5$	$(1.345 \pm 0.004) \times 10^7$		c
	$(2.67 \pm 0.04) \times 10^5$	$(1.27 \pm 0.02) \times 10^7$		d
	$(2.475 \pm 0.016) \times 10^5$	$(1.370 \pm 0.009) \times 10^7$		e
	$(2.48 \pm 0.02) \times 10^5$	$(1.37 \pm 0.01) \times 10^7$	$2.79 \times 10^{-6} yr^{-1}$ "Best Value" j
U^{235}	$(7.06 \pm 0.21) \times 10^8$	$(4.78 \pm 0.14) \times 10^3$		a
	$(8.8 \pm 1.1) \times 10^8$	$(3.82 \pm 0.49) \times 10^3$		c
	$(7.13 \pm 0.16) \times 10^8$	$(4.74 \pm 0.10) \times 10^3$		e
	8.91×10^8			f
	$(7.53 \pm 0.23) \times 10^8$	$(4.48 \pm 0.14) \times 10^3$		g
	$(7.13 \pm 0.14) \times 10^8$	$(4.74 \pm 0.09) \times 10^3$	$9.72 \times 10^{-10} yr^{-1}$ "Best Value" j
U^{238}	$(4.49 \pm 0.01) \times 10^9$	742.7 ± 1.6		c
	$(4.51 \pm 0.01) \times 10^9$	738.6 ± 1.6	$1.537 \times 10^{-10} yr^{-1}$ "Best Value" j
Natural Uranium		1501 ± 6		h
		1501 ± 3		i
		1502 ± 1.5		c
		1501 ± 3		"Best Value" j

PART II

Composition of natural uranium (literature values).

Atom ratio U^{238}/U^{235}	Abundance U^{234} (atom per cent)	Ref.
138.9 ± 1.4	0.0059 ± 0.00059	a
137.0 ± 0.7	0.00555 ± 0.00017	k
138.0 ± 0.3	—	k
139	$0.00504 \pm .00030$	b
137.8	—	l
138.24 ± 0.05	—	o
137.8 ± 0.14	—	m
	0.00557 ± 0.00006	c
138.0 ± 1.4	0.00545 ± 0.00004	n

PART III

Composition of natural uranium (best values).

Isotope	Abundance (atom per cent)	Abundance (weight per cent)
234	0.0055 ± 0.0002	0.0054 ± 0.0002
235	0.7204 ± 0.0007	0.7114 ± 0.0007
238	99.2741 ± 0.0007	99.2830 ± 0.0007

Atom Ratio U^{238}/U^{234}	= 18,180 ± 550
Atom Ratio U^{238}/U^{235}	= 137.80 ± 0.14
Specific Activity	= 1501 ± 3 dis/min mg total uranium
Contribution of U^{235}	= 33.7 ± 0.7 dis/min mg total uranium
Contribution of U^{238}	= 733.6 ± 1.6 dis/min mg total uranium
Contribution of U^{234}	= 733.6 ± 1.6 dis/min mg total uranium

a. A. O. Nier, *Phys. Rev.* **55**, 150, 153 (1939); U^{235} half-life recalculated in accordance with the work of KOVARIK AND ADAMS.
b. O. Chamberlain, D. Williams, and P. Yuster, *Phys. Rev.* **70**, 580 (1946).
c. C. A. Kienberger, *Phys. Rev.* **76**, 1561 (1949); *Phys. Rev.* **98**, 46 (1955).
d. A. S. Goldin, G. B. Knight, P. A. Macklin, and R. L. Macklin, *Phys. Rev.* **76**, 336 (1949).
e. E. H. Fleming, A. Ghiorso, and B. B. Cunningham, *Phys. Rev.* **88**, 642 (1952).
f. Clark, Spencer-Palmer, and Woodward, Imperial Chemical Industries, Ltd. Research Department, *Declassified Report BR-522*, unpublished (October 1944).
g. G. B. Knight, *Oak Ridge National Laboratory Report K-663*, unpublished (August 1950).
h. A. F. Kovarik and N. I. Adams, *J. Appl. Phys.* **12**, 296 (1941).
i. Curtiss, Stockman and Brown, *National Bureau of Standards Report A-80*, unpublished (December 1941).
j. "Best values" taken from Fleming, *et al.* Ref. e.
k. M. Fox and B. Rustad, *Carbide and Carbon Chemicals Corp. Report, Bd-R-88*, unpublished (1946).
l. M. G. Inghram, *National Nuclear Energy Series*, Div. II, Vol. 14, Chapter V, p. 35 (1946).
m. M. Lounsbury, *Can. J. Chem.* **34**, 259 (1956).
n. Calculated as described by Fleming *et al.*, Ref. e using "best values" of specific activities of U^{234}, U^{235} and natural uranium and the U^{238}/U^{235} atom ratio. These values constitute a self-consistent set.
o. B. R. Grundy and A. N. Hamer, *J. Inorg. Nucl. Chem.* **23**, 178 (1961).

quote "best values" for the isotopic composition. To construct this table we accepted LOUNSBURY's U^{238}/U^{235} atomic ratio of 137.8 ± 0.14 and FLEMING's "best values" for the half-lives of the isotopes and for the specific activity of natural uranium.

Recent studies have shown that the weight per cent of U^{235} in natural uranium may vary by as much as 0.1% depending on the source of the sample. In 1963 an official announcement of the U.S. Atomic Energy Commission declared that no single value carried to four places can be established as truly representing the U^{235} content of natural uranium. The official value for purposes of that agency was set at 0.711 weight per cent U^{235}.

The "best value" given in part III, Table 6.2 for the U^{234} content of natural uranium is the equilibrium value calculated from the ratio of the U^{238} and U^{234} half-lives. The U^{234} content of natural uranium shows wide variations from this equilibrium value depending on the geological origin and past history of the sample. The specific activity of natural uranium is not significantly changed by these slight variations in U^{234}.

One milligram of pure natural uranium emits exactly 1501 alpha particles per minute. Of these 733.6 are emitted by U^{238}, an equal number by U^{234}, and 33.7 are emitted by U^{235}. Pure uranium grows daughter alpha-activity only at a very slow rate because of the long half-life of ionium; it would take several hundred years before the alpha activity of pure natural uranium increased by one per cent. (The growth curve for ionium appears in Fig. 6.4.) The energy of the main group of alpha particles of U^{238} and U^{234} have been measured as 4.195 ± 0.005 MeV and 4.768 ± 0.003 MeV, respectively, by the gridded ion-chamber technique.[5] In addition, each isotope has a group of alpha particles in about 25 per cent abundance approximately 50 keV smaller in energy and a third group approximately 160 keV lower in energy in a few tenths of one per cent abundance.[6] The alpha spectrum of U^{235} is complex as described in Chapter 8 (see Section 8.5.9).

Pure uranium emits no beta particles and essentially the only gamma radiation associated with U^{238} and U^{234} is 45 keV and 52 keV γ radiation, respectively, which is very low in abundance. These transitions have been studied chiefly through their conversion electrons.[7,8] The growth of UX_1 and UX_2 soon introduces hard beta and gamma radiation into uranium. This beta activity reaches equilibrium in undisturbed samples several months after the last purification of the uranium as shown in Fig. 6.3.

[5] B. G. Harvey, H. G. Jackson, T. A. Eastwood, and G. C. Hanna, *Can. J. Phys.* **35**, 258 (1957).

[6] G. E. Kocharov, A. P. Komar, and G. A. Korolev, *Zhur. Eksp. Teor. Fiz.* **36**, 68 (1959) report abundances of 23 ± 4 per cent and 0.23 ± 0.07 per cent for alpha groups leading to levels in the Th234 daughter of 48 ± 5 keV and 160 ± 5 keV, respectively.

[7] The conversion electrons of the 48 keV transition in U238 decay were studied by the following workers: G. Albouy, *Ann. Phys.* **1**, 99 (1956); G. Albouy and J. Teillac, *Compt. Rend.* **234**, 829 (1952); B. Zajac, *Phil. Mag.* **43**, 264 (1952); and D. C. Dunlavey and G. T. Seaborg, *Phys. Rev.* **87**, 165 (1952).

[8] The photons and conversion electrons of the 52 keV transition in U234 decay were studied by the following authors: G. Scharff-Goldhaber in *Report BNL-103*, June 1951; P. R. Bell and co-workers in *ORNL-1164*, April 1952; A. A. Vorob'ev, *et al.*, *Sov. Phys. JETP* **5**, 516 (1957); and Teillac, *Compt. Rend.* **230**, 1056 (1950).

Uranium X_1 *(Th^{234}) and Uranium* X_2 *(Pa^{234}).*   The growth of UX_1 into pure uranium is shown in Fig. 6.3.   Because UX_2 has a half-life of only 1.17 minutes it comes to equilibrium with UX_1 within a few minutes.   Hence, Fig. 6.3 can also be used to evaluate the growth of UX_2 into pure uranium. When equilibrium is reached, the number of disintegrations per minute of U^{238} is precisely equal to the number of disintegrations per minute of UX_1 and UX_2.   Because of this equilibrium uranium is often employed as a

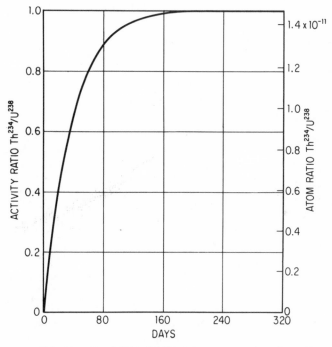

FIG. **6.3.** Growth of UX_1 (Th^{234}) into pure uranium ($t_{1/2}$ of $UX_1 = 24.1$ days).

standard of radioactive intensity for calibrating the counting efficiency of radiation detection equipment.   A sample of pure uranium is analyzed by igniting a suitable compound to the oxide, U_3O_8, and weighing the oxide, or by some other standard analytical method.   The disintegration rate is calculated by use of the value 733.6 disintegrations per minute per milligram of normal uranium.   The sample is usually covered with a foil of sufficient thickness (about 30 mg/cm^2 aluminum) to filter out the soft beta particles of UX (end point energy = 193 keV) so that only the energetic beta rays of

UX_2 are counted (end point energy $= 2.32$ MeV). This is done so that uncertain corrections due to absorption of soft electrons in the sample and in the counter window can be eliminated.

UX_1 is a convenient tracer for the element thorium. It can be readily isolated in carrier-free form from uranium by any of a number of chemical methods.

In the historical section we have shown how the discovery of the regrowth of $UX_1 + UX_2$ beta activity into purified uranium and the decay of the 24.1 day UX_1 activity, which had been separated from uranium by coprecipitation on barium sulfate, was of considerable importance in calling

TABLE 6.3. Amount of individual nuclides present in unaltered natural uranium ore bodies containing one metric ton of uranium.

Nuclide	Half-life	Amount	
U²³⁸	4.507×10^9 yr	992.9	kilograms
U²³⁵	7.13×10^8 yr	7.11	kilograms
U²³⁴	2.48×10^5 yr	54	grams
Pa²³¹	3.43×10^4 yr	334	milligrams
Th²³⁰ (Ionium)	7.52×10^4 yr	16	grams
Ac²²⁷	22.0 yr	0.21	milligrams
Ra²²⁶	1622 yr	340	milligrams
Pb²¹⁰ (RaD)	19.4 yr	3.77	milligrams
Po²¹⁰ (RaF)	138.4 day	7.4	micrograms

attention of early workers to the continuous production of radioactive matter from the decay of a parent element. UX_2 is of historical importance also because its discovery by FAJANS AND GÖHRING in 1913 constituted the first discovery of an isotope of element 91. They called the element brevium from the short half-life of UX_2 but when Pa²³¹ was discovered in 1918 this name was dropped.

In the beta decay of Th²³⁴ the principal daughter product is the 1.17-minute UX_2. However, in 0.14 percent of its disintegrations an isomeric form of Pa²³⁴ with a 6.66-hour half-life is produced. This activity has the special name of uranium Z. It was discovered by HAHN in 1921 and constituted the first example of nuclear isomerism.

The $UX_1 — UX_2 — UZ$ mixture emits a complex mixture of beta particles, gamma rays, and conversion electrons. Present knowledge of these radiations and of the decay schemes of these nuclides is summarized in Chapter 8. (Section 8.2.12)

Ionium. Ionium was discovered by the American radiochemist BOLTWOOD in 1907. It is an isotope of thorium which decays by alpha emission with the relatively long half-life of 7.52×10^4 years.[9]   In Table 6.3 we note that 16 grams of ionium are to be found in a uranium ore sample containing one metric ton of uranium.   Figure 6.4 shows the growth of ionium into pure uranium starting with an equilibrium mixture of uranium I and uranium II.   The rate of growth is linear for many years and amounts to 0.147

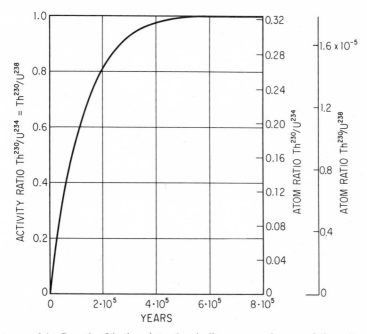

FIG. **6.4.** Growth of ionium into chemically pure uranium consisting of the natural mixture of uranium isotopes.   The ionium is expressed in units of mass and also in units of activity.   The half-life value of 8.0×10^{-4} years for ionium was used in the preparation of this figure.

micrograms per kilogram of uranium per year.   The growth of radium into pure ionium is shown in Figure 6.5.   The initial rate of growth, which is linear for many years, is 9.05 micrograms per year for one gram of ionium.   This is 1.98×10^7 disintegrations per minute of Ra^{226}.

It is important to realize that ionium isolated from uranium ores is not isotopically pure, because of the presence of Th^{232} in all uranium ores. The amount of thorium is quite variable and in the purest uranium ores may

[9] E. K. Hyde, *National Nuclear Energy Series, Plutonium Project Record* **14B**, "The Transuranium Elements," Paper 19.16, p. 1435 (New York: McGraw-Hill, Inc., 1949) reports $(8.0 \pm 0.3) \times 10^4$ years based on a specific activity measurement; Attree, Cabell, Cushing, and Pieroni, *Can. J. Phys.* **40**, 194 (1962) report $(7.52 \pm 0.16) \times 10^4$ years based on a calorimetric measurement.

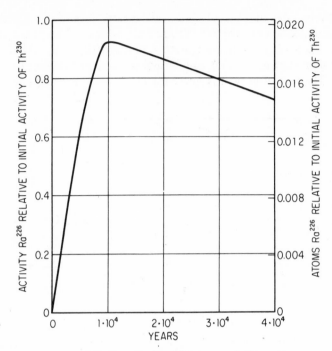

FIG. 6.5. Growth of Ra[226] into pure ionium.

be quite low expressed as a ratio of thorium to uranium. However, the weight ratio of ionium to uranium is only 0.000017 so that a mere trace of thorium in the ore will cause a considerable isotopic dilution of the ionium isolated therefrom. ELIZABETH RONA[10] has studied the isotopic composition of thorium fractions isolated from a variety of uranium ores with the results shown in Table 6.4. Since the specific activity in disintegrations per minute per microgram is 45,700 for ionium and only 0.246 for thorium the activity due to thorium is negligible in all of these preparations.

Ionium is an excellent radiochemical tracer for thorium.

Ionium and its daughter product, radium, are found in ocean sediments in amounts much greater than would be accounted for by the uranium content of the sediments. This is a consequence of the selective removal of ionium from sea water by ferric and manganic hydroxide. The ionium and radium content of ocean sediments can be used to measure the age of sediments and to fix the dates of various geological eras. This subject is reviewed by RANKAMA[11] and by PETTERSSON.[12]

---

[10] E. Rona, *Transactions American Geophysical Union* **38**, 754 (October 1957).

[11] K. Rankama, *Isotope Geology*, (New York: McGraw-Hill, Inc., 1954) pp. 405–408.

[12] H. Pettersson, "Radium and the Deep Sea," *American Scientist* **41**, 245 (1953).

Ionium is a useful target material in many cyclotron bombardment studies, neutron irradiation studies, etc. For these purposes, the presence of Th^{232} contamination is troublesome as it results in the production of extraneous activities. For example, gram amounts of ionium, isolated by PEPPARD and his associates[13] at the Argonne National Laboratory have been

TABLE **6.4.** Th^{232}/Th^{230} ratio in uranium minerals (E. RONA)

Sample	Mineral	Source	$\dfrac{Th^{232}}{Th^{230}}$	Uranium content (per cent)	$\dfrac{Th^{232}}{U^{238}} \times 10^6$
1	Pitchblende	Joachimsthal Czechoslovakia	0.00 ± 0.001	45.7	0
2	Pitchblende	Cinch Lake, Uraninite Mine, Lake Athabaska, Sask. Canada	0.77 ± 0.01	—	14.1
3	Pitchblende	Eldorado Mines, Great Bear Lake N.W.T., Canada	1.55, 1.66 1.35, 1.37	52.0	29.3 24.9
4	Pitchblende	Katanga	9.9, 9.50, 9.72	75	177.5
5	Pitchblende	Katanga	9.27, 9.40	75	170.7
6	Pitchblende	Katanga	7.60	75	139.0
7	Presumably Pitchblende	Unknown, Probably Great Bear Lake Region	2.86, 2.88 3.0	—	51.4
8	Pitchblende	Kirk Mine, Gilpin County, Colorado	27.9, 26.2	39.0	47.4
9	Uraninite	Wilberforce, Canada	53	60.0	969.4
10	Carnotite	Colo-Utah region	28.0	—	512.0
11	Samarskite	Mosambique, East Africa	1300	6.2	23,790

irradiated in high flux reactors in order to produce the valuable isotope Pa^{231} according to the following sequences of reactions.

$$Io^{230} \ (n, \gamma) \ Th^{231} \ (UY) \ \xrightarrow[24 \text{ days}]{\beta^-} \ Pa^{231}$$

The capture cross section is 26 barns. This is a valuable procedure for the preparation of protactinium because the isolation of protactinium in quantity from uranium ores has proved to be rather difficult. However, a difficulty with this artificial synthesis of Pa^{231} arises from the presence of Th^{232} in the ionium. The particular samples irradiated by PEPPARD had the isotopic

---

[13] Peppard, et al., "Isolation of Gram Quantities of Ionium from a Pitchblende Residue," *J. Am. Chem. Soc.* **75**, 4576 (1953).

composition 12% ionium and 88% Th^{232} so that large amounts of the 27.4-day beta-emitter Pa^{233} were produced according to the sequence.

$$Th^{232}\ (n, \gamma)\ Th^{233}\ \xrightarrow[\text{23.5 min}]{\beta^-}\ Pa^{233}$$

$$\sigma = 7.55 \text{ barns}$$

The beta and gamma activity of this Pa^{233} is so huge that it necessitates the use of considerable shielding in the isolation of the protactinium. Furthermore, even when it is isolated the protactinium has an undesirable specific activity for beta and gamma radiation. Consequently, the protactinium must be stored for a few years to permit the decay of the Pa^{233}. Difficulties of this type can be reduced by the use of isotopically enriched ionium. Some ionium has been separated at Oak Ridge by the electromagnetic process to produce ionium enriched to greater than 90% isotopic abundance.[14]

Thorium ores usually contain some uranium and therefore purified thorium will contain ionium. The amount is always negligible in terms of weight percentage but, depending on the original uranium content of the ore, may not be negligible in terms of specific activity.

The alpha spectrum and the details of the decay scheme of ionium are discussed in Chapter 8. (See Section 8.2.8.)

Radium—General Comments. Radium was discovered by PIERRE CURIE, MARIE CURIE, AND G. BEMONT in 1898 at the Sorbonne in Paris. In 1902 MME. CURIE prepared the first pure salt of radium after a tedious process of isolation in which several tons of pitchblende residues were treated. Radium is the heaviest member of the alkaline earth group of elements and has chemical properties similar to barium. Barium is frequently used as a carrier element in the isolation of radium. The name "radium" was originally applied only to the 1622 year radium occurring in the uranium decay series but later was adopted as the general name for element 88. Ra^{226} is the longest-lived of all the radium isotopes and all studies of the physical and chemical properties of the element with weighable quantities of material are carried out with it.

Ra^{226} is the immediate daughter of ionium in the uranium decay chain. The growth of radium into pure ionium is displayed in Fig. 6.5. The growth of radium into an equilibrium mixture of U^{238} and U^{234} containing no ionium or radium at zero time is shown in Fig. 6.6. Radium is present in natural minerals only because of its constant replenishment from ionium and from its ultimate parent, U^{238}, and hence is found primarily in uranium ores. Radium salts are quite soluble in water, however, and any uranium minerals subject to leaching may be deficient in radium content; secondary

---

[14] B. Harmatz, H. C. McCurdy, and F. N. Case, *Oak Ridge National Laboratory Report*, *ORNL-1724* (Jan. 3, 1954).

minerals with a non-equilibrium excess amount of radium may form at a new site. Because of the leaching of radium from uranium ore bodies, small amounts of radium are found in springs, rivers, and sea water. Ocean sediments contain non-equilibrium amounts of radium because of the adsorption of the ionium parent on basic materials on the ocean floor. References to the literature on such studies can be found in RANKAMA.[11]

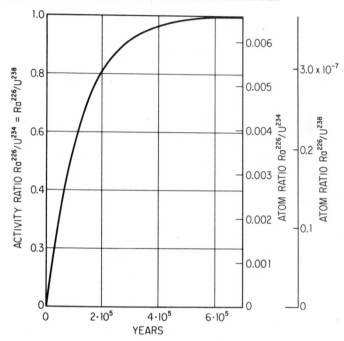

FIG. **6.6.** Growth of radium into natural uranium after purification from ionium and radium. The uranium is assumed to consist initially of an equilibrium amount of U[238] and U[234].

Radium and its daughter products played a prominent role in the early history of radioactivity as we have seen. For many years radium was of great commercial importance as a source of penetrating radiations for medicinal and radiographical purposes. For these applications it is the radiations of the daughter products which are chiefly effective since Ra^{226} itself emits only alpha particles and a 188-keV gamma ray. The immediate daughter of radium is radon (Rn^{222}) which has a half-life of 3.825 days, and also emits only alpha particles. The next series of products RaA, RaB, RaC, RaC', and RaC'' are quite short-lived and rapidly come to transient equilibrium with the radon. A radium preparation in solid form from which the radon does not escape, or a sealed radium preparation, comes to equilibrium with these daughter products within a couple of weeks. The growth of radon into pure radium is shown in Fig. 6.7.   The shapes of the growth curves for RaA, RaB, RaC, RaC', and RaC" growing into pure radium are nearly identical because their half-lives are short compared to that of radon.

The mixture of radium and its daughter products emits a very potent complex of gamma rays especially those contributed by RaC (Bi^{214}); see Table 6.12 later in this chapter.

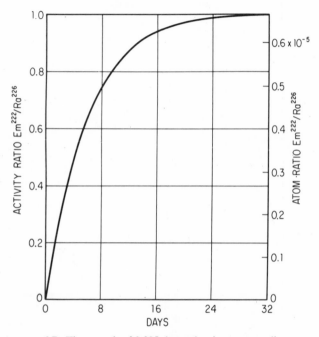

FIG. 6.7. The growth of 3.825 day radon into pure radium.

For medical purposes a radium compound (usually radium sulfate) is sealed in a platinum capsule which can be placed near the tissue to be irradiated.   The walls of the capsule absorb the alpha rays completely but the penetrating gamma radiation is absorbed only slightly.   Alternatively, the radium source can be used simply as a source of radon which is periodically removed and compressed into a small glass capillary.   This radon sample (plus products) is then used for application to the tissue.   Radium is used primarily for treatment of cancer.   In some applications (in particular, cancer of the cervix uteri) the use of radium therapy is routine and is successful in a high percentage of cases.   In a good many other applications the success of radium therapy is limited.   The availability of radioactive isotopes from nuclear reactors or accelerators, or the use of high voltage x-ray machines, betatrons, etc. has lessened the need for radium for medical radiology.

This is also true for industrial radiography and other commercial applications of radium.

Radium has been used widely to prepare laboratory neutron sources. An intimate mixture of a radium salt and some light element such as beryllium will emit neutrons because of (α, n) reactions which occur in the mixture. This is discussed in Section 5.5.4 of Chapter 5.

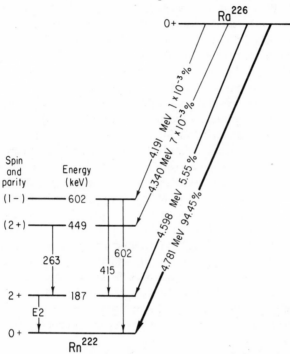

FIG. **6.8.** Decay scheme of Ra²²⁶. Alpha energies are relative to Po²¹⁸ $E_\alpha = 6.002$ MeV.

Decay Scheme of Radium. The alpha decay of radium is summarized in Fig. 6.8. Several measurements have been made of the energy of the main group in magnetic spectrometers.[15-17] For several years the accepted value was 4.777 MeV but a more recent and careful determination[18] resulted in the value 4.781. This shift in energy was caused chiefly by a shift in the

---

[15] G. Bastin-Scoffier, *Compt. Rend.* **233**, 945 (1951).

[16] G. Bastin-Scoffier and J. Sant'ana-Dionisio, *Compt. Rend.* **236**, 1016 (1953).

[17] S. Rosenblum, M. Perey, M. Valadares, and M. Guillot, private communication (Oct. 1952) quoted by Hollander, Perlman, and Seaborg, *Revs. Mod. Phys.* **25**, 469 (1953).

[18] R. J. Walen and G. Bastin-Scoffier, *Compt. Rend. du Congrès Int. de Physique Nucléaire,* Paris: Dunod, 1958, p. 910. R. J. Walen, C. F. Leang, and G. Bastin-Scoffier, unpublished results, 1963.

accepted value of the alpha energy of the alpha particles of Po^{218} which was used as an energy standard. A second alpha group in 6 per cent intensity was reported from two laboratories.[19,20] Two additional groups of much lower intensity were discovered by WALEN AND BASTIN-SCOFFIER[18] in some experiments which exploited new techniques for reducing background effects in alpha spectroscopy. The results of this study are quoted in Table 6.5.

The most prominent gamma radiation is the 186 keV transition which de-excites the first excited state. HAHN AND MEITNER[21] reported this transition in 1924. CORK[22] measured the conversion electrons. ROY AND GOES[23] characterized the radiation as $E2$ by measurement of the K-conversion coefficient and the subshell conversion ratios. These results were confirmed by JURIC AND STANOJEVIC.[24] The $E2$ assignment was strengthened by the α-γ coincidence experiments of MILTON AND FRAZER.[25]

Very careful experimental technique is required to detect other gamma transitions because of their low intensity. STEPHENS[26] reported a 260 keV gamma ray with an intensity only 1/400 of the 187 keV gamma ray and found it to be in coincidence with the 187 keV gamma ray. HARBOTTLE, MCKEOWN, AND SCHARFF-GOLDHABER[27] also reported these results. In order to study a gamma ray of this low intensity in Ra^{226} decay it is necessary to remove radon continuously; otherwise it is obscured by the intense gamma radiation of the radon decay products. STEPHENS[26] further reports a very low intensity 420 keV gamma ray, in coincidence with the 187 keV transitions, and a gamma ray of ~ 610 keV. The intensities of the known gamma rays per disintegration of Ra^{226} are the following: 187 keV (0.057); 260 keV (7×10^{-5}); 420 keV (2×10^{-6}); 610 keV (2×10^{-6}). There is a strong possibility that the 610 keV gamma ray originates at the level labeled 599 keV in the figure; the discrepancy in energy may be ascribed to experimental error.

The energy level system of Rn^{222} observed in the decay of Ra^{226} is of some theoretical interest. The two $2+$ states are believed to be quantum states of collective excitation of a nucleus which is spherical in its ground state but soft toward harmonic oscillations around the favored spherical shape. This matter is discussed more fully in Section 3.2 of Chapter 3.

---

[19] Rosenblum, Guillot, and Bastin-Scoffier, *Compt. Rend.* **229**, 191 (1949); S. Rosenblum, *Compt. Rend.* **195**, 317 (1932).

[20] F. Asaro and I. Perlman, *Phys. Rev.* **88**, 129 (1952).

[21] O. Hahn and L. Meitner, *Z. Physik* **26**, 161 (1924).

[22] J. M. Cork, *et al.*, *Phys. Rev.* **83**, 681 (1951).

[23] R. R. Roy and M. L. Goes, *Compt. Rend.* **238**, 469, 581 (1954).

[24] M. K. Juric and D. M. Stanojevic, *Bull. Inst. Nucl. Sci., Boris Kidrich*, **5**, (1955).

[25] J. C. D. Milton and J. S. Fraser, *Phys. Rev.* **95**, 628A (1954).

[26] F. S. Stephens, F. Asaro, and I. Perlman, *Phys. Rev.* **119**, 796 (1960).

[27] G. Harbottle, M. McKeown, and G. Scharff-Goldhaber, *Phys. Rev.* **103**, 1776 (1956).

The $1-$ state at 610 (or 599) keV is also believed to be a state of collective excitation related to general occurrence of negative parity states in even-even nuclei of the heavy elements. This class of nuclear excitation is discussed in Section 3.5.3 of Chapter 3, Volume I.

TABLE **6.5**. Alpha particles of Ra^{226}.

α-Particle energy (MeV)	ΔE_α (keV)	Energy of excited state (keV)	Intensity (per cent)
4.781 ± .001	0	0	94.45
4.598 ± .001	183	187	5.55
4.340 ± .001	441	449	$(6.5 \pm 0.3) \times 10^{-3}$
4.191 ± .002	590	602	$(1.0 \pm 0.1) \times 10^{-3}$
4.160 ± .002	621	633	$(2.7 \pm 0.5) \times 10^{-7}$

R. J. Walen and G. Bastin-Scoffier, *Compt. Rend. du Congrès Int. de Physique*, Paris: Dunod, 1958. R. J. Walen, G. Bastin-Scoffier, and C. F. Leang, unpublished results, 1963. Energies were measured relative to Po^{218} $E_\alpha = 6.002$ MeV.

Measurements of the Half-life of Radium. The practical unit of radioactivity, known as the curie, was originally based upon the specific activity of radium and was defined as the number of disintegrations per second occurring in a gram of radium exclusive of its decay products. Hence it was of considerable importance to determine a precise value for the specific activity of radium. This turned out to be a problem of considerable difficulty because of the complications of daughter activity. A variety of methods gave values clustering around 3.7×10^{10} disintegrations per second per gram for the specific activity corresponding to 1600 years for the half-life. Table 6.6 summarizes the principal determinations which have been made. In 1931 an international committee of distinguished workers in the field of radioactivity[28] reviewed the experimental determinations up to that time and chose 1590 years as the best value. KOHMAN, AMES, AND SEDLET[29] devoted considerable attention to this problem in 1945 and reported the value 1622 ± 13 years which value will be adopted in this book. A redetermination by a calorimetric method reported in 1958 gave a value of $(3.71 \pm 0.02) \times 10^{10}$ disintegrations sec^{-1} $gram^{-1}$ corresponding to a half-life of 1577 ± 9 years.[30] MARTIN AND TUCK[31] in 1959 critically evaluated all published

[28] M. Curie, A. Debierne, A. S. Eve, H. Geiger, O. Hahn, S. C. Lind, St. Meyer, E. Rutherford, and E. Schweidler, *Revs. Mod. Phys.* **3**, 427 (1931).

[29] T. P. Kohman, D. P. Ames, and J. Sedlet, Paper 22.60, "The Specific Activity of Radium", *NNES* Vol. **14B**, "The Transuranium Elements," Seaborg, Katz, and Manning, Editors, McGraw Hill Book Co., 1949.

[30] G. V. Gorshkov, *et al.*, *Zur. Eksp. Teor. Fiz.* **34**, 756 (1958).

[31] G. R. Martin and D. G. Tuck, *Int. J. Appl. Rad. Isotopes* **5**, 141 (1959).

TABLE 6.6. Summary of experimental determinations of the specific alpha activity of radium up to the year 1949.

Method	Experimenters and reference	Value[a]
Visual counting of galvanometer deflections from RaC α particles in proportional counter	E. Rutherford and H. Geiger, *Proc. Roy. Soc.* London, A81 : 141 (1908)	3.4 3.57[b]
Growth rate of Ra in Io	B. B. Boltwood, *Am. J. Sci.* 4 25: 493 (1908)	2.98[c]
Rate of He evolution by Ra	J. Dewar, *Proc. Roy. Soc.* London, A81: 280 (1908)	2.9[d] 3.88[d,e]
Rate of He evolution by Ra	J. Dewar, *Proc. Roy. Soc.* London, A83: 404 (1910)	3.70[d]
Rate of He evolution by Ra	B. B. Boltwood and E. Rutherford, *Phil. Mag.* 6 22: 586 (1911)	3.33
Heat generation by Ra α particles	V. F. Hess, *Wien. Ber.* IIa 121: 1419 (1912)	3.75[f]
Electric charge of α particles from Rn and descendants	J. Danysz and W. Duane, *Am. J. Sci.* 4, 35: 295 (1913)	3.22 3.15[g]
Growth rate of Ra in Io	E. Gleditsch, *Am. J. Sci.* 4 41:112 (1916)	3.53[a]
Growth rate of Ra in Io	S. Meyer and R. W. Lawson, *Wien. Ber.* IIa 125: 723 (1916)	3.4
Visual counting of galvanometer deflections from RaC α particles in proportional counter	V. F. Hess and R. W. Lawson, *Wien. Ber.* IIa 127: 405 (1918)	3.72
Photographic oscillographic counting of RaC α particles in proportional counter	R. W. Lawson and V. F. Hess, *Wien. Ber* IIa 127: 461 (1918)	3.7
Visual counting of scintillations from Rn and descendants by two observers	H. Geiger and A. Werner, *Z. Physik* 21, 187 (1924)	3.40
Pressure and volume measurements of Rn	L. Wertenstein, *Phil. Mag.* 7 6:17 (1928)	3.62 3.60[h]
Electric charge of α particles from RaB + C deposit	H. Jedrzejowski, *Compt. Rend.* 184: 1551 (1927); *Ann. phys.* 10 9:128 (1928)	3.50 3.48[g]
Heat generation by α particles from Rn + RaA + B + C, RaB + C, and RaC	S. W. Watson and M. C. Henderson, *Proc. Roy. Soc.* London, A118: 318 (1928)	3.72 3.63[i]
Comparison of ionization of single RaC α particles with gross ionization from RaC deposit	H. Ziegert, *Z. Physik* 46: 668 (1928)	3.71
Electric charge of α particles from RaB + C deposit	H. J. J. Braddick and H. M. Cave, *Proc. Roy. Soc.* London, A121: 367 (1928)	3.68 3.69[j] 3.67[g]
Photographic oscillographic counting of RaB + C α particles in ionization chamber	F. A. B. Ward, C. E. Wynn-Williams, and H. M. Cave, *Proc. Roy. Soc.* London, A125: 713 (1929)	3.66
Heat generation by Po standardized against Ra by ionization measurements	L. Meitner and W. Orthmann, *Z. Physik* 60: 143 (1930)	3.68

TABLE 6.6 (*cont.*). Summary of experimental determinations of the specific alpha activity of radium up to the year 1949.

Method	Experimenters and reference	Value[a]
Growth rate of Ra in Io	E. Gleditsch and E. Foyn, *Am. J. Sci.* **5** 24:387 (1932)	3.47[c]
Electric charge of α particles from Po standardized against Ra by ionization measurements	R. Grégoire, *Ann. phys.* **11** 2: 161 (1934)	3.68 3.65[g,i]
Growth rate of Ra in Io	E. Gleditsch and E. Foyn, *Am. J. Sci.* **5** 29: 253 (1935)	3.47[c]
Rate of He evolution by Ra	P. Guenther, *Z. physik. Chem.* **A185**: 367 (1939)	3.67
Electrical counting of α particles from weighed and purified Ra in ionization chamber	T. P. Kohman, D. P. Ames, and J. Sedlet, Ref. 29	3.61

This table prepared by Kohman, Ames, and Sedlet, 1949.

[a] In units 10^{10} α particles per second per gram.

[b] Corrected to International Radium Standard (E. Rutherford, J. Chadwick, and C. D. Ellis "Radiations from Radioactive Substances," p. 60, Cambridge University Press, London, 1930).

[c] Calculated from disintegration constant given using currently accepted value of Avogadro number.

[d] Calculated from rate of helium evolution given using currently accepted value of Loschmidt number.

[e] Corrected according to paper 22.70 by D. P. Ames *et al.* in Vol. **14B**, Ref. 29.

[f] Calculated from heat generation rate given using currently accepted value of α disintegration energy.

[g] Recalculated using currently accepted value of electronic charge.

[h] Recalculated using currently accepted value of Loschmidt number.

[i] Recalculated using currently accepted values of α disintegration energies.

[j] Corrected by authors elsewhere.

information on disintegration energies in the radium series and combined them with the calorimetric measurements of MANN[32] for the heating effects of several national primary standards to derive a specific activity for radium of 3.655×10^{10} disintegrations per second per gram corresponding to a half-life of 1602 years.

It can be seen from these values, even the most recent ones, that the disintegration rate of radium is still uncertain to a few per cent. In recent years the attempt to identify the curie unit of activity with the specific activity of radium was abandoned. The curie has been redefined as 3.700×10^{10} disintegrations per second. Nonetheless, it would be desirable and is within the reach of present techniques to reduce the uncertainty in the radium half-life to less than one per cent.

---

[32] W. B. Mann, *J. Res. Nat. Bur. Stand.* **53**, 277 (1954).

Assay Methods for Radium. The accurate measurement of quantities of radium is important in experimental research, in radium therapy, and in commercial applications and can be done by several essential different methods. These methods are outlined below. More detailed information can be found in the references listed in Table 6.7.

TABLE 6.7. Bibliography on techniques for estimation of radium content.

1. S. C. Brown, L. G. Elliott, and R. D. Evans, "Detection of Radon by Means of a Proportional Counter," *Rev. Sci. Inst.* **13**, 147 (1942).
2. J. H. J. Poole, *Sci. Proc. Roy. Dublin Soc.* **21**, 595, 609 (1938).
3. L. F. Curtiss and F. J. Davis, *J. Res. Nat. Bur. Stand.* **31**, 181 (1943); Davis, *Ibid.* **39**, 545 (1947), "A Counting Method for the Determination of Small Amounts of Radium and of Radon."
4. P. Fineman, *et al.*, "An Emanation Method for Radium Analysis," Paper 16.7, Vol. 14B, *The Transuranium Elements*, National Nuclear Energy Series, (New York: McGraw-Hill Book Co., 1949).
5. E. Rutherford, J. Chadwick, and C. D. Ellis, *Radiations from Radioactive Substances*, Cambridge University Press, 1930.
6. T. H. Oddie, "The Gamma Ray Measurement of Radium," *Proc. Phys. Soc. London* **51**, 58 (1939).
7. T. P. Loftus, *et al.* "Comparison of National Radium Standards," *J. Res. Nat. Bur. Stand.* **58**, 169 (1957).
8. R. D. Evans, "Apparatus for the Determination of Minute Quantities of Radium, Radon and Thoron in Solids, Liquids and Gases," *Rev. Sci. Inst.* **6**, 99 (1935).
9. G. V. Gorshkov and N. S. Shimanskaya, "Calorimetric Measurements on Preparations of Naturally Radioactive Families of Elements," *Sov. J. Atom. Energ.* (in English translation) No. 5, p. 761 (1956). See also *Atomnaya Energ.* **6**, 474 (1959) in Russian.
10. K. W. F. Kohlrausch, "Radioaktivität," Vol. XV of *Handbuch der Experimental Physik*, Wien-Harms Leipzig, 1928. See pp. 684–728.

1. *Radium Analysis by Measurement of Radium Alpha Particles.* For small samples the disintegration rate can be determined by direct counting of the alpha particles. The contribution of radon and other daughter products to the counting rate cannot be calculated because of the variable retention of radon in the sample, but can be determined by alpha spectrum analysis. In this measurement, a sample of radioactivity (thin compared to the range of the alpha particles) is placed in an ionization chamber of sufficient size that the alpha particles expend their entire range in the chamber. The pulse developed from the charge collected on the positive electrode is subjected to pulse height analysis. From the pulse height spectrum and the known energies and abundances of the alpha particle groups from radium and its daughters the disintegration rate of the Ra^{226} in the sample can be determined. This method is accurate to a few per cent. It is used chiefly for small samples in research studies. Solid state counters may be substituted for the ionization chamber.

2. *The Gamma-ray Method of Radium Analysis.* A radium salt sealed in

a tube so that no radon can escape will equilibrate with radon and its short-lived descendants (see Fig. 6.7). The intensity of the gamma radiation from the equilibrium mixture is compared with that of a standard sample containing a known quantity of radium. The gamma radiation is measured with some sort of electroscope, ionization chamber, or other radiation detector. The contribution from beta activity is removed by absorbers or by using sufficiently thick-walled detecting instruments. When properly used, this method is accurate to about one-half of one per cent but the accuracy which is ordinarily achieved may be only 1–5 per cent. The accuracy can be improved by using the detection instrument as a null instrument. For example, RUTHERFORD AND CHADWICK[33] devised a balance method in which the ionization current produced in a lead ionization chamber was balanced against an equal and opposite ionization current supplied by some constant source of radiation such as uranium oxide in another ionization chamber. The balance distances were determined for the unknown sample and for the standard radium sample with which it was compared. The accuracy of this method approaches a quarter of one per cent.

The gamma ray method has the advantage that the radium itself is undisturbed within its sealed tube. It is well suited for quantities ranging from 10 micrograms to one gram. It is not applicable to radium samples containing appreciable amounts (by activity) of mesothorium because of the hard gamma radiation of mesothorium decay products.

The Radioactivity Section of the National Bureau of Standards, Washington, D.C. offers for sale a series of radium gamma ray standards consisting of 5 ml of radium solution sealed in glass ampoules. These have a radium content varying from 0.1 to 100 micrograms.

3. *The Emanation Method of Radium Assay.* An extremely sensitive method for the measurement of low intensity samples is the emanation method. In this method the gaseous radon in equilibrium with a radium sample is removed and introduced into an ionization chamber together with the filling gas.

The slightly acidic radium solution to be assayed is boiled for several minutes to expel radon and is then sealed for one month to allow radon to come to equilibrium. The solution is then boiled to expel radon; the radon is collected and passed into the ion chamber or electroscope. The rate of leakage of the electroscope is compared with that caused by the radon from a standard solution of radium. This standard solution can be made by taking a very small aliquot of a solution of a radium salt originally standardized by the gamma ray method. Another type of standard which can be used is a sample of pitchblende with an accurately known content of uranium. The alpha particles of radon and of its short-lived alpha emitting

---

[33] E. Rutherford and J. Chadwick, *Proc. Phys. Soc.* **24**, 141 (1912).

daughters, RaA and RaC', are heavily ionizing and a small number of disintegrations per minute give a readily detectable signal. The radon from 10^{-9} grams of radium can be measured with ease; with care the method can be extended to 10^{-11} grams. If the individual alpha particles are counted, as little as 10^{-14} grams of radium can be detected.

The emanation method can also be used to assay samples for ThX or RdTh content. In this case the thoron daughter is removed and counted. The method must be modified suitably because of the 51 second half-life of the thoron.

4. *The Calorimetric Method of Radium Assay.* The amount of radium in a sample may be determined by measuring the heat output with a suitable calorimeter. This is an absolute method and has several advantages over the gamma ray comparison method. The α, β, and γ radiations of radium

TABLE **6.8.** Average radiation energies emitted in single disintegrations by equilibrium preparations of radium, mesothorium, radiothorium and actinium and the heat effects, q, of the corresponding sources with activities of one curie.

Preparation	$E_{\alpha+\beta}$*	$E_{\alpha+\beta+\gamma}$	$q_{\alpha+\beta}$	$q_{\alpha+\beta+\gamma}$
	keV/disintegration		cal/hr curie	
Ra†	25,350	27,140	129.3	138.4
MsTh	33,920	36,510	173.0	186.2
RdTh	33,390	35,060	170.3	178.8
Ac	33,690	34,210	172.0	174.4

From G. V. Gorshkov and N. S. Shimanskaya, *Sov. J. Atom. Energ.*, 1956. These authors later revised the radium figures slightly to 138.9 ± 0.7 cal/hr. See *Atomnaya Energ.* **6**, 474 (1959) or *Sov. J. Atom. Energy.* **6**, 339 (1960).
  * The value $E_{\alpha+\beta}$ includes the energy of the recoil atoms, the conversion electrons and the x-radiation.
  † No allowance is made for RaDEF which would be present in aged radium samples.

and its daughters are sufficiently well known that this heat release can be calculated to better than 0.5 per cent. Most of the heat is produced by the alpha emitters and for these the energies are precisely known and are dissipated completely within the calorimeter. The beta particles and conversion electrons are absorbed nearly completely in the calorimeter. The absorption of gamma-radiation is not easy to compute with accuracy but since the gamma rays account for only about 9 per cent of the total energy an error of a few per cent in estimating its heat contribution does not strongly affect the measurement. The uncertainty in the gamma-contribution can be reduced by using a so-called β-calorimeter i.e., a thin-walled calorimeter in which γ-absorption is slight. Table 6.8 taken from a paper by GORSHKOV AND SHIMANSKAYA[34] lists the total energy release from an average

---

[34] See Ref. 9 in Table 6.7.

disintegration of Ra^{226} in equilibrium with its decay products through RaC, RaC' and RaC". A radium sample which is old enough to have appreciable amounts of 19.2 year RaD (plus RaE and RaF) will have an additional heat contribution from these nuclides. The calorimetric assay method is also useful for mesothorium, radiothorium and actinium, the data for which are included in Table 6.8.

International Radium Standards. In 1910 the Congress of Radiology and Electricity appointed a committee to make arrangements for the preparation of an International Radium Standard. MME. CURIE prepared a sample of 21.99 milligrams of pure radium chloride (August 1911) which was accepted as this standard and arranged that it be located in the Bureau International des Poids et Mesures at S̀evre, near Paris. This sample was carefully compared by the gamma-ray balance methods with similar standards prepared by HÖNIGSCHMID for his atomic weight determinations. One of HÖNIGSCHMID'S preparations, containing at that time 31.7 milligrams of radium chloride, was selected by the Vienna Academy of Sciences as a secondary standard. Duplicate standards have been prepared by comparison with the Vienna and Paris standards using the gamma-ray method. In the use of such standards it is necessary to allow for the decay of the radium which occurs at the rate of 0.043 per cent per year.

Radon. Radium emanation was discovered by E. DORN in 1900. The name radon, first suggested by C. SCHMIDT, was originally applied only to the emanation of the radium decay chain. Later the name radon came to be used for element 86 and all of its isotopes. An alternate name for the element is emanation, symbol Em.

The growth of radon into an initially pure sample of radium is shown above in Fig. 6.7.

Some recent determinations of the half-life of radon are the following:

J. ROBERT[35]	3.825 $\pm$ 0.004 days
J. TOBAILEM[36]	3.825 $\pm$ 0.005 days
P. C. MARIN[37]	3.8229 $\pm$ 0.0027 days

The energy of the principal alpha particle group of radon was reported as 5.486 MeV by BRIGGS[38] in 1936. In 1953 BASTIN-SCOFFIER AND SANT'ANA-DIONISIO[16] reported the slightly lower value of 5.482 MeV based on a value of 7.685 MeV for the alpha particle of Po^{214}. WALEN AND BASTIN-SCOFFIER[18] recomputed this result using WHITE'S[39] value of 5.3054 MeV for Po^{210} and using slightly different corrections for absorption in the source.[18] They report a corrected result of 5.490 MeV.

[35] J. Robert, *J. Phys. Rad.* **17**, 605 (1956).
[36] J. Tobailem, *Compt. Rend.* **233**, 1360 (1951); *Ann. Phys.* **10**, 783 (1955).
[37] P. C. Marin, *Brit. J. Appl. Phys.* **7**, 188 (1956).
[38] G. H. Briggs, *Proc. Roy. Soc.* (London) **157A**, 183 (1936).
[39] F. A. White, *et al.*, *Phys. Rev.* **109**, 437 (1958).

WALEN AND BASTIN-SCOFFIER applied advanced techniques of low background alpha spectroscopy to detect complex structure in the spectrum of radon. Their results are summarized in the table. The second of these groups had been predicted by the gamma ray measurements of MADANSKY AND RASETTI[40] who had found a 510 keV gamma ray in 0.07 percent intensity.

Alpha Groups of Radon

Particle energy (MeV)	Energy of excited state (keV)	Intensity (per cent)
5.486 ± 0.001	0	~100
4.983 ± .002	512	~8 × 10⁻²

From Walen, Leang, and Bastin-Scoffier, unpublished results, 1963. Based on standards determined by Rytz, *Helv. Phys. Acta* **34**, 240 (1962).

General Comments on the Active Deposit of Rapid Change. Any surface exposed to radon gas becomes coated with an invisible deposit of radioactive matter known as the active deposit. It is convenient to discuss separately the *active-deposit-of-rapid-change* consisting of the products RaA, RaB, RaC, RaC' and RaC", of which the longest-lived is 26.8 minute RaB, and the *active-deposit-of-slow-change* consisting of 22-year RaD and its descendants RaE and RaF. The active-deposit-of-rapid-change is diagrammed in Fig. 6.9.

To prepare a sample of the active deposit it is necessary only to expose a disc or wire to radon in a suitable vessel. Exposures of a few seconds or minutes duration yield relatively pure Radium A while exposures of 4.5 hours or longer give the equilibrium mixture of products. When the radon gas is pumped away small traces of radon may still be occluded on the surface. The active disc can be washed in alcohol and heated lightly to remove this occluded radon. The RaA daughter product is positively charged at the instant of disintegration of the parent radon atom and can be attracted preferentially to a negatively charged wire or surface. This technique allows the preparation of highly concentrated and localized sources of the active deposit. It is also possible to freeze radon on a cooled surface upon which it is desired to locate the active deposit. The active deposit may also be prepared by compressing radon into a tube of small volume; later when the radon has been pumped away the deposited activity can be removed from the walls of the tube by rinsing them with hydrochloric acid.

The rate of growth and decay of the various components of the active deposit for different times of exposure to radon is of some importance.

---

[40] L. Madansky and F. Rasetti, *Phys. Rev.* **102**, 464 (1956).

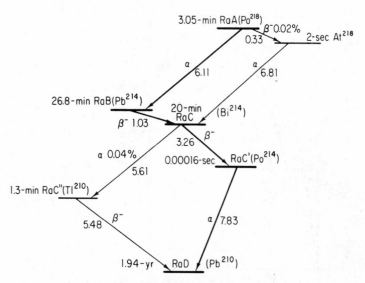

FIG. **6.9.** Decay scheme of the active deposit of rapid change. Details of the complex radiations are not shown. The total disintegration energy of each mode of decay is given in MeV.

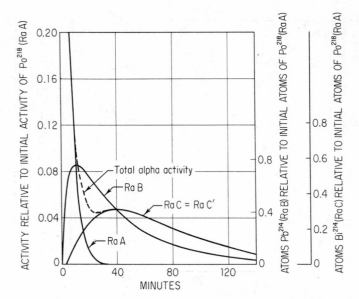

FIG. **6.10.** Activity changes in RaA sample prepared by briefly exposing a surface to radon and quickly removing radon; i.e., initial sample is essentially pure RaA. Growth and decay of RaA (Po[218]), RaB (Pb[214]), RaC (Bi[214]), and RaC' (Po[214]).

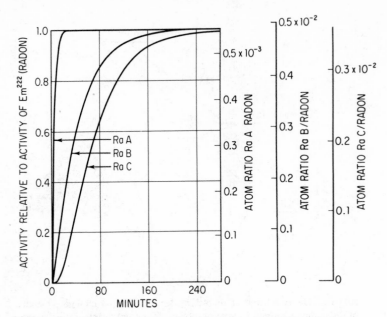

FIG. 6.11. Growth of RaA, RaB, and RaC into an initially pure sample of radon. Radon not removed.

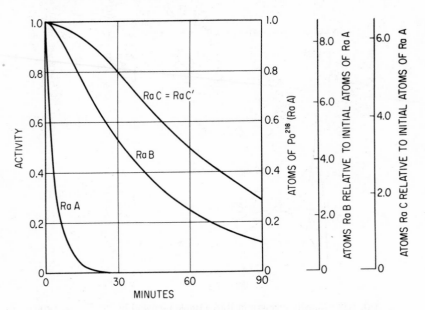

FIG. 6.12. Activity changes in active deposit prepared by exposing a surface to radon for a sufficient time (∼4.5 hours or longer) to achieve equilibrium and then removing radon.

Quantitative information is presented in Figs. 6.10, 6.11, and 6.12. Detailed information on the radiations of the individual members of the active deposit is summarized in the discussion below. References to research papers published before 1958 containing more detailed data can be found in the data compilation of STROMINGER, HOLLANDER, AND SEABORG.[41]

The active deposit can be chemically fractionated so that the individual activities can be separately studied. Separation of RaB and RaC and examination of the radiations and decay characteristics of the separated samples played a prominent role in the original determination of the course of the decay chain. Pure samples of 26.8-minute RaB (Pb^{214}) may readily be prepared by recoil from RaA. A negatively charged plate is placed above a sample of RaA, preferably in a vacuum. A considerable fraction of the RaB atoms are ejected from the source plate during the energetic alpha decay of RaA and are collected. RaC grows into such samples but the radiations of RaB predominate for some minutes and can be clearly distinguished.

Pure samples of RaC (Bi^{214}) can be prepared by the recoil technique using as a source the RaB present in the active deposit from radon after the RaA has completely decayed. The yield is quite low because RaB is a beta emitter and the recoil energy is small. However, by various chemical techniques RaC can be separated cleanly and in good yield from RaB. Samples of RaC do not remain pure because the principal decay product, RaC′ (Po^{214}), grows into equilibrium virtually instantaneously; also the branch product RaC″ (Tl^{210}) grows into equilibrium within 10 minutes.

The half-life of RaC″ (Tl^{210}) is very short but by fast operations with intense sources of active deposit it is possible to isolate pure samples for study of the radiations. It is possible to isolate RaC″ by alpha recoil from samples of RaC. In spite of the small alpha branching of RaC (0.04%) it is possible to prepare pure samples because the main-line decay product, RaC′, is collected with very low efficiency and furthermore decays completely within one second. HAHN AND MEITNER (1909) and FAJANS (1911) first studied samples of RaC″ prepared by the recoil method and established the existence of the branching decay of RaC. This was the first case of branching decay to be established clearly.

Radium A and Its Rare Branch Product, At^{218}. Radium A decays more than 99% by the emission of 6.000 MeV alpha particles.[42,43] In 10^{-3} per cent of the alpha disintegrations a lower energy group with energy 5.182 MeV

[41] D. Strominger, J. M. Hollander, and G. T. Seaborg, "Table of Isotopes," *Revs. Mod. Phys.* **30**, 2, Pt. 2, 585–904 (1958).

[42] G. H. Briggs, *Proc. Roy. Soc.* (London) **157A**, 183 (1936); M. G. Halloway and M. S. Livingston, *Phys. Rev.* **54**, 18 (1938). The alpha particle energy quoted in these earlier references is 5.998 MeV.

[43] R. J. Walen and G. Bastin-Scoffier, *Compt. Rend. du Congrès Int. de Physique Nucléaire*, Paris: Dunod, 1959, p. 910; and private communication, Oct. (1963).

is emitted.[43]   In addition, radium A should be heavier than At^{218} by about 0.4 MeV so that some branching decay by beta emission might be expected. With this decay energy and the most favorable beta transition (allowed, log ft = 5) the beta branching could be as large as one per cent.

KARLIK AND BERNERT[44] proved the existence of this branching decay. By examining the alpha particle groups emitted from freshly-deposited radium active deposit, they were able to observe alpha particles of 6.72 MeV energy.

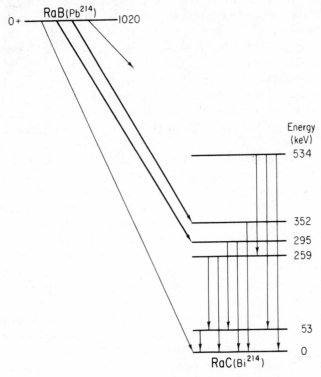

FIG. **6.13.** Partial decay scheme of radium B (Pb²¹⁴).

These were observed to grow into the RaA sample with a half-life of a few seconds. From the later work of WALEN[45] and of HIESSBERGER AND KARLIK[46] the best value for the half-life of At^{218} is about 2 seconds and the branching ratio of RaA is 2.1×10^{-4}.   In all cases the alpha energy measurements were made with an ionization chamber. These results have been confirmed very satisfactorily by the beautiful alpha spectra obtained by WALEN

[44] B. Karlik and T. Bernert, *Naturwiss* **31**, 298 (1943); *Zeit. f. Phys.* **123**, 51 (1944).
[45] R. J. Walen, *J. Phys. Rad.* VII/X, 95 (1949); *Compt. Rend.* **227**, 1090 (1948).
[46] F. Hiessberger and B. Karlik, *Sit. Öst. Akad. der Wiss.* **161**, 51 (1952).

AND BASTIN.[43]   These workers remeasured the alpha spectra of radium and its alpha-emitting daughters by new techniques of low-background alpha spectroscopy in a magnetic spectrometer of high precision.   In their spectra they were able to resolve three alpha groups of At^{218} for which they determined the following energies: 6.757 (3.6%), 6.694 (90%), and 6.654 (6.4%). The branching of RaA to produce At^{218} was set at 1.85×10^{-4} in excellent agreement with the previous work.   The decay scheme of At^{218} is further discussed by WALEN AND BASTIN-SCOFFIER.[47]

   The Decay of Radium B.   This nuclide decays 100 per cent by β emission. The β and γ spectra are complex and the decay scheme is not completely fixed or interpreted.   A partial decay scheme is shown in Fig. 6.13 based largely on the work of NIELSEN, NIELSEN, AND WAGGONER[48] and of KAGEYAMA.[49]   WALEN AND BASTIN-SCOFFIER[47] also comment on the decay scheme of Pb^{214}.   Table 6.9 lists several determinations of the gamma rays

TABLE 6.9. Gamma rays of radium B (Pb^{214})
(energy in keV)

Ref. a	Ref. b	Ref. c
52.23	53	53.2
	196 (weak)	
	206	
241.92 (20)	242 (6.7)	241.9 Ml
	259	258.9
	272 (weak)	
	275	
	279 (weak)	
295.22 (55)	295 (15.9)	295.2 Ml
352.0 (100)	352 (31.6)	352.0 Ml
	481	
	534	
	549 (weak)	
	777	

Relative intensities are given in parentheses.
  a. Muller, Hoyt, Klein, and DuMond, *Phys. Rev.* **88**, 775 (1952). These precise values
     were measured in a crystal spectrometer.
  b. Nielsen, Nielsen, and Waggoner, *Nucl. Phys.* **2**, 476 (1957).
  c. M. Mladjenovic and H. Slätis, *Arkiv Fysik* **8**, 65 (1954).
  In the classical literature a special nomenclature was used for the γ-transitions of the
active deposit.   In Ellis' notation (*Proc. Roy. Soc.* **143A**, 350 (1933)) the 242, 295 and 352
keV transitions were called *F*, *G* and *H*.

[47] R. J. Walen and G. Bastin-Scoffier, *Nucl. Phys.* **16**, 246 (1960).
[48] K. O. Nielsen, O. B. Nielsen, and M. A. Waggoner, *Nucl. Phys.* **2**, 476 (1957).
[49] S. Kageyama, *J. Phys. Soc.* (Japan) **8**, 689 (1953).

of radium B. The beta spectrum has been resolved into several components. BERLOVICH[50] reports a main group with 0.73 MeV end-point energy and a second at 0.67 MeV with relative intensities 100 to 33. KAGEYAMA[49] resolves out one component at 0.59 MeV and a second at 0.65 MeV with 56 and 44 relative intensities. DANIEL[51] resolves a ground state beta transition with energy 1.03 MeV in 6 per cent intensity.

Long Range Alpha Particles of Radium C'. A source of the 20-min β-emitter RaC (Bi^{214}) is almost immediately in equilibrium with its short-lived daughter RaC' (Po^{214}). Two modern measurements of the half-life of RaC' by the delayed coincidence technique gave 1.64×10^{-4} and 1.58×10^{-4} sec, respectively.[52,53] Radium C' is a pure α-emitter and decays almost entirely directly to the ground state of RaD with an energy given as 7.680 MeV in the classical work of BRIGGS[42] and as 7.683, 7.685, or 7.687 MeV in more recent determinations[43,54,55]. A second group of 6.905 MeV in $10^{-2}\%$ intensity has also been reported.[43]

A RaC source also has with it other alpha groups. Some of these come from the small alpha branching of RaC itself and these are dealt with in the following section. There are also seen in low intensity a number of very high energy alpha groups (known as "long-range alpha particles") which arise in the following way. Radium C has a β-decay energy of 3.26 MeV and therefore can populate a number of excited states of RaC'. The long-range alpha groups represent decay from these excited states; because of their high energies they can compete with the γ-ray de-excitation. There are a number of cases known in which alpha decay is observable from isomeric states, but only in a case such as this where alpha energies can be very high is alpha emission seen from states which are not particularly metastable. The other instance in which this phenomenon has been well investigated is that of ThC'.

Table 6.10 lists twelve long-range alpha groups assignable to RaC'. A large number of gamma-rays are observed in the decay of RaC and many of these correspond to transitions between the energy levels from which alpha decay is occurring. See later discussion.

Decay of Radium C. The 0.021 per cent alpha branching of radium C will be mentioned first as our knowledge of this decay can be more quickly summarized. The most complete study of the alpha spectrum was made by WALEN AND BASTIN-SCOFFIER[55a] with the results summarized in Table 6.11.

[50] E. E. Berlovich, *Izvest. Akad. Nauk SSSR, Ser. Fiz* 16, 314 (1952).

[51] H. Daniel, *Z. Naturforsch* 11A, 759 (1956).

[52] G. von Dardell, *Phys. Rev.* 79, 734 (1950); see also T. Dobrowski and J. Young, *Proc. Phys. Soc.* (London) 77, 1219 (1961).

[53] R. Ballini, *Ann. Phys.* 8, 441 (1953).

[54] W. J. Sturm and V. Johnson, *Phys. Rev.* 83, 542 (1951).

[55] A. Rytz, *Helv. Phys. Acta* 34, 240 (1961).

[55a] R. J. Walen and G. Bastin-Scoffier, *Nucl. Phys.* 16, 246 (1960).

TABLE 6.10. Long range alpha groups from RaC' (W. B. Lewis and B. V. Bowden, *Proc. Roy. Soc.* (London) 145A, 235 (1934); G. H. Briggs, *Revs. Mod. Phys.* 26, 1 (1954).)

Energy of alpha particle (MeV)	Energy of disintegration (MeV)	Difference of energy of disintegration from main group (MeV)	Relative number of alpha-particles
*Main Group**			
7.680	7.829	0	10^6
Long Range Groups			
8.277	8.437	0.608	0.43
8.938	9.112	1.283	0.45
9.065	9.241	1.412	22
9.313	9.493	1.663	0.38
9.489	9.673	1.844	1.35
9.657	9.844	2.015	0.35
9.779	9.968	2.138	1.06
9.905	10.097	2.268	0.36
10.074	10.269	2.439	1.67
10.146	10.342	2.513	0.38
10.326	10.526	2.697	1.12
10.506	10.709	2.880	0.23

* The energy of the main group has been redetermined as 7.687 by RYTZ[55] and as 7.683 by STURM AND JOHNSON.[54]

TABLE 6.11. Alpha spectrum of radium C (Bi^{214})

Walen and Bastin-Scoffier, *Nucl. Phys.* 16, 246 (1960).

Energy* (MeV)	Relative intensity	Energy of excited state of daughter
5.512	39.2	0
5.448	53.9	65
5.268	5.8	249
5.184	0.6	336
5.023	0.2	498
4.941	0.25	581

* Measured relative to E_α (Po^{210}) = 5.304 MeV.

The beta decay energy of Radium C is 3.26 MeV[56] and the number of energetic beta and gamma rays emitted in the course of the decay is quite large. Sixty gamma rays have been reported and more than forty of these are above 1 MeV in energy. About ten per cent of the beta transitions lead

---

[56] H. Daniel and R. Nierhaus, *Z. Naturforsch* 11A, 212 (1956).

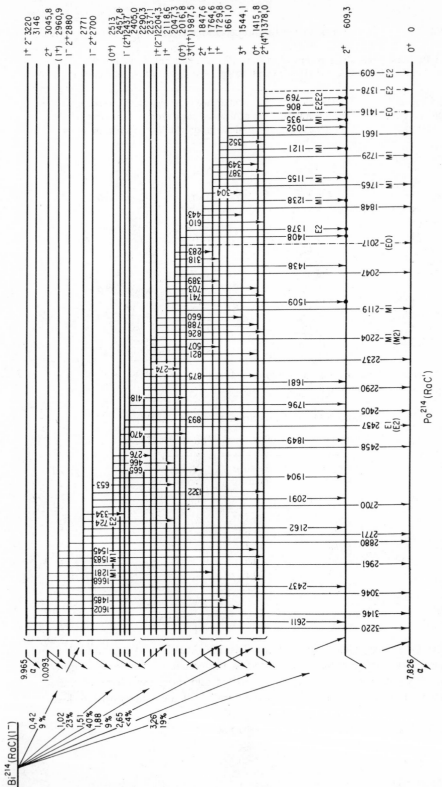

FIG. **6.14.** Decay scheme of radium C as drawn by LÜHRS AND MAYER-BÖRICKE.[57a]   Energies of β groups are given in MeV, the γ-energies in keV.   The long range alpha groups originating from the excited levels of radium C′ are shown as slanting arrows at the left end of the levels.   γγ coincidence measurements are indicated by dots at the tips of the arrows which indicate the γ-transito levels in Po^{214} lying 2.4 MeV or higher in energy so that the intensity of many of the high energy gamma rays is high. Most of the penetrating radiation associated with radium and radium preparations is attributable to the radium C present.

These radiations have been studied by a variety of experimental techniques, but it would require too much space to summarize the numerous published works in any detail. MAYER-BÖRICKE[57] has published a very extensive paper which summarizes his own findings and those of most other authors in publication by 1959. We reproduce here a long table (see Table 6.12) from this article which summarizes published information on the gamma transition energies and intensities. Over the years many authors[57-69] have constructed partial decay schemes showing the placement of the most intense radiations. Some of the older versions of the decay scheme have had to be discarded because of incompatibility with later measurements of $\gamma\gamma^{62,64,65}$ or $\beta\gamma$ cascades.[63,67] We reproduce here as Fig. 6.14 the decay scheme published by LÜHRS AND BÖRICKE.[57a] Without going through the detailed justification of this scheme we wish to call attention to a few important considerations in its construction.

Firstly, the numerous long-range alpha particles of Radium C' (summarized in Table 6.10 above) are extremely helpful in constructing a level skeleton. Under the assumption that each of these long-range groups goes to the ground state of Pb^{210} one deduces a set of levels in Bi^{214} which are identical with those listed in the third column of Table 6.10. This assumption turns out to be correct for all but three of the long-range alphas; in the case of alpha particles with 9.313, 9.779, and 9.905 MeV energy HAUSER[69] has presented arguments proving that these events must terminate in excited levels in Pb^{210} at 0.778 or 1.077 MeV.

The fact that most of the long-range alpha transitions do terminate in the

[57] C. Mayer-Böricke, Z. Naturforsch, 14A, 609 (1959); for an extension of this study see Ref. 57a and 57b.

[57a] G. Lührs and C. Mayer-Böricke, Z. Naturforsch 15a, 939 (1960).

[57b] C. Mayer-Böricke and G. Lührs, Z. Naturforsch 15a, 103 (1960).

[58] Rutherford, Lewis, Bowden, Proc. Roy. Soc. (London) A142, 347 (1933).

[59] C. D. Ellis and N. F. Mott, Proc. Roy. Soc. (London) A141, 502 (1933).

[60] C. D. Ellis, Int. Conf. Phys. London (1934).

[61] J. Surugue, J. Phys. Rad. 7, 145 (1946).

[62] F. Demichelis, R. Malvano, Nuovo Cim. 12, 358 (1954).

[63] R. A. Ricci and G. Trivero, Nuovo Cim. 2, 745 (1955).

[64] S. A. E. Johansson, Arkiv. Fys. 9, 561 (1955).

[65] R. E. Rowland, Phys. Rev. 99, 757 (1955).

[66] N. Feather in Siegbahn "β and γ Spectroscopy," North Holland Pub. Co., Amsterdam (1955).

[67] Nierhaus and Daniel, Z. Naturforsch 12a, 1 (1957).

[68] G. R. Bishop, Nucl. Phys. 5, 358 (1958).

[69] U. Hauser, Dissertation, Hiedelberg 1957; Z. Physik 150, 593, 599 (1958).

TABLE 6.12. Gamma transitions in the decay of radium $C(Bi^{214})$ reproduced from C. Mayer-Böricke, Z. f. Naturforsch. 14a, 609 (1959).

Ref.	No. 1 E(MeV) 0.426	2 0.450	3 0.498	4 0.609	5 0.652	6 0.661	7 0.703	8 0.769	9 0.787	10 0.806	11 0.821	12 0.935	13 1.120	14 1.155	15 1.207	Method
a	0.426		0.498	0.607				0.766				0.933	1.120			ce^- $s\pi$ (ph)
b				0.606				0.766				0.933	1.120			$ce^-ce^\pm$ $s\pi$ (gm)
													2.41			Cpt-Lin
c				0.606				0.766				0.933	1.120			ce^- $s\pi$ (gm)
d				0.609				0.769				0.935	1.122			ce^- s
e				0.6093				0.7687				0.9348	1.1204	1.1554		ce^-pe^- $s\pi$ (ph)
f								(0.769)		0.807		(0.935)	(1.120)	(1.155)		ce^- sl
g				0.612 / 8.9				0.773 / 0.88				0.941	1.130			pe^-ce^- $s\pi$
h	0.426 / 0.36	0.450 / 0.16	0.496 / 0.56	0.607 / 2.96				0.781 / 0.52				0.91	2.78			pe^- sl
i		0.452	0.500										1.12 / 0.36?			sl
j				0.607				0.783				0.932	1.123			pe^- sl
k											0.860					pe^- $sl.$
l																pe^- scin
m				0.61 / 5.5								0.94 / 0.67	1.12 / 1.75			Dyp Cpt e^- $s\pi$
n																Cpt e^- sl
o													1.100 / 1.76			Cpt-Lin $s\pi$ (gm)
p				(0.606) / 9				(0.766) / 1.3				(0.933) / 1.1	(1.120) / 2.6			Cpt-Lin $s\pi$ (gm)
q				0.605			0.699	0.770				0.907	(1.12)			Cpt-Lin $s\pi\sqrt{2}$ (gm)
r				(0.609) / 5.10				(0.769) / 1.10				(0.935) / 0.54	(1.120) / 3.9			Cpt-Lin $s\pi\sqrt{2}$ (gm)
s				(0.6093) / 4.64	0.6524*	0.6609*	0.7032* / 0.19	(0.7687) / 0.70	0.7871* / 0.17	0.8063* / 0.17	0.8213* / 0.13	(0.9348) / 0.52	(1.1204) / 2.06	(1.1553) / 0.40	1.2071* / 0.19	Cpt-Lin $s\pi$ (gm)
t																Cpt-Lin $s\pi$ (gm)
u				0.61				0.76				0.95	1.11	1.151 / 0.4	1.205 / 0.19	scin pr scin

(For ref s, the values 0.6524* and 0.6609* in columns 5 and 6 are joined by a brace with the combined value 0.38.)

Ref.	No. 16	17	18	19	20	21	22	23	24	25	26	27	28	29	30	Method
E(MeV)	1.238	1.281	1.324	1.378	1.385	1.391	1.396	1.402	1.408	1.416	1.438	1.483	1.509	1.583	1.620	
a	1.238			1.379						1.414						ce⁻ sπ (ph)
b	1.234 / 0.56	1.290 / 0.44		1.370 / 1.19						1.414			1.520 / 0.71		1.620 / 0.54	ce⁻ce± sπ (gm)
c	1.238			1.379												Cpt-Lin sπ (gm)
d	1.241									1.414						ce⁻ s
e	1.2383	1.2813		1.3782						1.419			1.5093			ce⁻pe⁻ s
f	(1.238)									1.4159						ce⁻ sl
g	1.248 / 0.85															pe⁻ce⁻ sπ
h	1.22 / 0.96					1.390 / 0.87		1.40 / 0.92								pe⁻ sl
i																pe⁻ sl
j	1.236							1.400								pe⁻ sl
k													1.525			pe⁻ scin
l																Dγp
m	1.20 / 1.42					1.39 / 1.5							1.55 / 0.58			Cpt e⁻ sπ
n	1.210															Cpt e⁻ sl
o		1.290 / 0.41				1.390							1.520 / 0.56		1.620	Cpt-Lin sπ (gm)
p	(1.238) / 1.0			1.32 (1.379) / 0.9									1.520 / 0.7			Cpt-Lin sπ (gm)
q	1.247			1.379 (1.378) / 1.66									1.504 (1.509) / 0.56		1.627	Cpt-Lin sπ√2 (gm)
r	(1.238) / 1.42															Cpt-Lin sπ√2 (gm)
s	(1.2383) / 0.88	(1.2813) / 0.26		(1.3782) / 0.72	1.3853*	1.3911*	1.3965*	1.4017*	1.4080*		1.4380*		(1.5093) / 0.43	1.5829* / 0.21	1.6052* / 0.07	Cpt-Lin sπ (gm)
t							1.394?		1.407 / 0.56		1.436? / ≤0.08	1.483 / ~0.12				scin pr
u	(1.238) / 0.84	1.282 / 0.23	1.324 / ≤0.10	1.379 / 1.02									1.521 / 0.36	1.578 / 0.25	1.633 / 0.18	Cpt-Lin sπ (gm); scin

(For reference s the intensity value 0.73 is bracketed across the 1.4017–1.4080 MeV lines.)

Note: Energies are given in MeV. If the intensity of the gamma ray was reported in the cited article it is given directly underneath the energy value; the numbers in parentheses were taken over from other authors. Energy values are relative to the 2.204 MeV line.

Ref.	31 / 1.680	32 / 1.728	33 / 1.764	34 / 1.784	35 / 1.793	36 / 1.848	37 / 1.862	38 / 1.905	39 / 1.970	40 / 2.017	41 / 2.051	42 / 2.085	43 / 2.117	44 / 2.160	45 / 2.204	Method
a	1.690 0.40		1.761												2.198	ce^- $s\pi$ (ph)
b			1.761			1.820 0.41									2.200	$ce^-ce^\pm$ $s\pi$ (gm)
			2.42									2.090 0.37			1.00	Cpt-Lin
c			1.761												2.200	ce^- $s\pi$ (gm)
d		1.7283	1.766													ce^-pe^- s
e			1.7644			1.8485				2.0167			2,1170		2.2042	ce^- $s\pi$ (ph)
f			1.778 3.49												2.219	ce^- sl
g			1.77 4.0												1.00	pe^-ce^- $s\pi$
h															2.21	pe^- sl
															1.00	
i															2.208	pe^- sl
															1.00	
j			1.750 1.76 3.22		1.800										2.192 2.20	pe^- sl
k															1.00	pe^- $scin$
l			1.77 2.66												2.22	Dyp
m															~1.00	Cpt e^- $s\pi$
n															2.20	Cpt e^- sl
															1.00	
o	1.690		1.750 2.51††			1.820 0.32						2.090		1.00	2.200	Cpt-Lin $s\pi$ (gm)
p	1.679		(1.761) 3.2			1.820 0.22						2.090			(2.200)	Cpt-Lin $s\pi$ (gm)
q		1.727	(1.76)			1.832									1.00	Cpt-Lin $s\pi\sqrt{2}$ (gm)
r			(1.764) 3.14			(1.848) 0.33				(2.016)			2.116 (2.117)		(2.19) (2.204)	Cpt-Lin $s\pi\sqrt{2}$ (gm)
															1.00	
s		(1.7283) 0.29	(1.7644) 2.52	1.7838* 0.44	1.7907* 0.14	(1.8485) 0.28	1.8623* 0.22	1.900 0.19		(2.0167) 0.06		2.085 0.09	(2.1170) 0.23		(2.2042) 1.00	Cpt-Lin $s\pi$ (gm)
t		1.728 0.29	(1.764) 2.84		1.793 <0.17	1.852 0.50		1.905 0.07	1.970? ≤0.05	2.010 ≤0.06	2.051 0.04	2.082 0.06	2.115 ≤0.21	2.160 0.21	(2.204) 1.00	Cpt-Lin $s\pi$ pr
u	1.688 0.10														1.00	scin

No.	46	47	48	49	50	51	52	53	54	55	56	57	58	Method
Ref. / E(MeV)	2.234	2.292	2.335	2.400	2.435	2.620	2.700	2.772	2.877	2.959	3.045	3.142	3.221	
a														ce^- $s\pi$ (ph)
b					2.420 0.50									$ce^-ce^\pm$ $s\pi$ (gm) Cpt-Lin
c														ce^- $s\pi$ (gm)
d														ce^-pe^- s
e														ce^- $s\pi$ (ph)
f														ce^- sl
g					2.40									pe^-ce^- $s\pi$
h														pe^- sl
i					2.452 0.4–0.35	2.60?								pe^- sl
j					2.42 0.48									pe^- sl
k					2.438 (0.41)									pe^- scin
l					2.45 ~0.58	2.6 ≤0.0075	2.700 0.0242	2.775 0.013	2.886 0.0093		3.0463 0.012			Dyp
m					2.45 0.41									Cpt e^- $s\pi$
n					2.420 0.34		2.72 0.026		2.89 0.005		3.03 0.013			Cpt e^- sl
o					2.420 0.5									Cpt-Lin $s\pi$ (gm)
p					2.420 (2.432) 0.36									Cpt-Lin $s\pi$ (gm)
q					(2.432) 0.41									Cpt-Lin $s\pi\sqrt{2}$ (gm)
r														Cpt-Lin $s\pi\sqrt{2}$ (gm)
s		2.290 0.07	2.340 0.04		2.450 (0.41)		2.468 0.0096	2.768 0.0082	2.893 0.009	2.992 0.0082	3.070 0.0078			Cpt-Lin $s\pi$ (gm)
t		2.292? ≤0.03	2.335 0.04		2.435 0.34		2.703 0.0165	2.772 0.0161	2.877 0.0143	2.959 0.012	3.045 0.008			Cpt-Lin $s\pi$ (gm)
u	2.234 0.15			2.400 0.13		2.620 0.0077						3.142 ≤0.00193	3.221 0.0025	scin pr scin

Note: Energies are given in MeV. If the intensity of the gamma ray was reported in the cited article it is given directly underneath the energy value; the numbers are relative to the 2.204 MeV line. Energy values in parentheses were taken over from other authors. See original reference.

*These values depend upon certain assumptions in the interpretation of conversion electrons.

Key to Methods Used:

s	Magnetic spectrometer	scin	single crystal scintillation spectrometer
$s\pi$	magnetic 180° spectrometer	Dyp	measurement through photoprotons from deuterium
$s\pi\sqrt{2}$	magnetic double focusing spectrometer	pe^-	photoelectrons (external conversion)
sl	magnetic	ce^-	conversion electrons
ph	photographic recording	$ce^\pm$	conversion electron pairs
gm	Geiger-Müller counter recording	Cpt-Lin	Compton Line spectrometer
scin pr	scintillation pair spectrometer	Cpt e^-	measurement based on Compton electrons

The chief methods employed in the cited publications were the following: conversion electrons (a–f); external conversion (g–k), photoproton energy in deuterium-filled counter (l), Compton distributions (m–n), Compton line method (o–t) and scintillation pair spectrometer (u).

Publications Cited in Table 6.12

a C. D. Ellis, *Proc. Roy. Soc.*, London, **143A**, 350 (1934).

b G. D. Latyshev, *Revs. Mod. Phys.* **19**, 132 (1947).

c M. Miwa and S. Kageyama, *J. Phys. Soc. Japan*, **5**, 416 (1950).

d J. M. Cork, *et al.*, *Phys. Rev.* **83**, 681 (1951).

e M. Mladjenovic and H. Slätis, *Arkiv. Fysik* **8**, 65 (1954).

f K. O. Nielsen, O. B. Nielsen, and M. A. Waggoner, *Nucl. Phys.* **2**, 476 (1957).

g C. D. Ellis and G. H. Aston, *Proc. Roy. Soc.* London, **129A**, 180 (1930).

h K. C. Mann and M. J. Ozeroff, *Can. J. Res.* **A27**, 164 (1949).

i J. L. Wolfson, *Phys. Rev.* **78**, 176 (1950).

j R. M. Pearce and K. C. Mann, *Can. J. Phys.* **31**, 592 (1943).

k G. Backenstoss and K. Wohlleben, *Z. Naturforsch* **10A**, 384 (1955).

l U. Hauser, *Dissertation*, Heidelberg, 1957 and *Z. Physik* **150**, 593, 599 (1958).

m J. Itoh and Y. Watase, *Proc. Phys. Math. Soc. Japan* **23**, 142 (1941).

n H. Daniel, *Z. Naturforsch* **12a**, 194 (1957).

o G. D. Latyshev, A. F. Kompaneetz, N. P. Borisov, and J. H. Gucak, *J. Phys.*, USSR, **3**, 251 (1940).

p S. Kageyama, *J. Phys. Soc. Japan* **7**, 93 (1952).

q M. Mladjenovic and A. Hedgran, *Physica* **18**, 1242 (1952).

r M. Mladjenovic and A. Hedgran, *Arkiv Fysik* **8**, 49 (1954).

s B. S. Dzelepov and S. A. Sestopalova, *Nuovo Cim.* **3**, Supple. 1, 54 (1956).

t B. S. Dzelepov, S. Sestopalova, and I. Uchevatkin, *Nucl. Phys.* **5**, 413 (1958).

u C. Mayer-Böricke, *Z. Naturforsch* **14A**, 609 (1959).

0+ ground state of Pb^{210} helps to fix the spin and parity of the RaC′ levels. Since alpha transitions can remove only even units of angular momentum in combination with positive parity or odd units of angular momentum in combination with odd parity, the radium C′ levels are restricted to 0+,1−, 2+, 3−, 4+. ... From the γ-transition data and from the alpha decay probabilities the range of possible assignments can be further reduced to 0+, 1− or 2+.

Multipolarity assignments of $M1$ or $E2$ have been made to several of the prominent transitions chiefly by measurement of conversion electron ratios. See particularly the work of NIELSEN, NIELSEN, AND WAGGONER[70] and of LÜHRS AND MAYER-BÖRICKE.[57a] These assignments help in fixing the spin and parity assignments of several levels. One important transition with 1.416 MeV energy is identified with certainty as an $E0$ transition by the prominence of its conversion electrons and absence of photons; this fixes the spin of the 1.416 level as 0+. TUTTER[71] has measured the half-life of this level as 2.3×10^{-10} seconds. There is evidence[57] for an additional $E0$ transition in the decay of the level at 2.510 MeV to ground so this level also is designated 0+. All the other levels from which long-range alpha particles are emitted are de-excited to the ground state of RaC′ by the emission of gamma rays; this fact eliminates 0+ as a possible assignment and fixes the assignments as either 1− or 2+.

A number of the prominent levels below 2.5 MeV are placed with the help of $\gamma\gamma$ and $\beta\gamma$ coincidence results of several workers;[62–65,67] some of these measurements are summarized in the decay scheme by the dots, as explained in the figure caption. Above 2.5 MeV the level scheme is based chiefly on two types of evidence. The first is an analysis by HAUSER[69] of the pattern of alpha emission of the longest-range alpha particles. The second is the measurement[57] of many new energetic gamma rays lying above 2.6 MeV. Since the total decay energy is 3.26 MeV and the first excited state is 0.609 MeV the most energetic gamma rays cannot be in coincidence with any of the gamma rays of lower energy and hence must represent direct transitions to ground. This fixes the positions of a number of the highest-lying levels.

Many authors have published analyses of the complex beta spectrum but these reports are discordant.[49,56,63,65,67,72–76] The analysis by DANIEL AND NIEHRAUS[56] was used by MAYER-BÖRICKE[57] in the construction

[70] K. O. Nielsen, O. B. Nielsen, and M. A. Waggoner, *Nucl. Phys.* **2**, 476 (1957).
[70a] B. S. Dzelepov and S. A. Sestopalova, *Nuovo Cim.* **3**, Supple. 54 (1956).
[71] M. Tutter, *Z. Physik.* **155**, 368 (1959).
[72] G. R. Bishop and F. Demichelis, *Nuovo Cim.* **4**, 1599 (1956).
[73] W. Bothe and H. Maier-Leibnitz, *Z. Physik* **104**, 604 (1937).
[74] B. W. Sargent, *Proc. Roy. Soc.* (London) **A139**, 659 (1933).
[75] A. A. Constantinov and G. D. Latyshev, *J. Phys.* USSR **5**, 239 (1941).
[76] A. H. Wapstra, *Physica* **18**, 1247 (1952).

of Fig. 6.14. The possibility that the beta ray groups are still incompletely resolved is recognized and is represented in the figure by brackets which group the levels which may be fed by each partially resolved beta group.

There exists no theoretical interpretation of the complex level scheme of Po²¹⁴. MAYER-BÖRICKE[57,57b] discusses the possibility that the lowest levels of excitation may represent collective quadrupole vibrations of the entire even-even Po²¹⁴ nucleus about its spherical equilibrium shape. The pattern of the gamma ray de-excitation characteristics follows closely the pattern for such collective vibrations first pointed out by SCHARFF-GOLDHABER AND WENESER.[77] These vibrations are discussed in Chapter 3. The characteristic features are a first excited 2+ state de-excited by an E2 transition with greatly enhanced transition probability and a second excited state lying at ~ 2.2 times the energy of the first; this second excited state has 2+ character (although according to some theories it may have 0+, 2+, 4+ triplet character), an enhanced E2 transition probability for a transition to the first excited state, and negligible probability for a direct transition to ground. In the case of Po²¹⁴ the 2+ level at 609 keV and the 2+ level at 1.378 MeV seem to fit these characteristics. LÜHRS AND MAYER-BÖRICKE[57b] measured the K/L ratios of the 609 and 769 keV radiations and characterized them as pure E2 radiations. They discussed the level system of Po²¹⁴ in terms of the theoretical model of WILETS AND JEAN.[77a]

Decay of Radium C″ (Thallium-210). This rare branch product has a half-life of 1.3 minutes for beta decay. From a closed decay-energy cycle the decay energy of Tl²¹⁰ is estimated to be 5.47 ± 0.04 MeV. The end point energy of the beta particles is 1.96 MeV showing that the beta decay selects a very high-lying level (~3.5 MeV) in the Pb²¹⁰ daughter nucleus. Good agreement on the beta energy has been obtained by several authors using different techniques: LECOIN[78] reports 1.95 MeV based on a cloud chamber method; DEVONS AND NEARY[79] find 1.95 ± 0.15 MeV by an absorption technique; MAYER-KUCKUK[80] obtains 1.96 ± 0.1 MeV and STETTER[80a] obtains 1.97 ± 0.05 MeV by scintillation spectrometer measurements.

The most detailed study of the radiations of radium C″ was made by STETTER.[80a] The short half-life and, in particular, the slight alpha branching of radium C make it almost impossible to prepare intense sources. Hence, the radiations had to be studied with scintillation counters of high efficiency but low resolution. By pushing scintillation techniques to the

[77] G. Scharff-Goldhaber and J. Weneser, *Phys. Rev.* **98**, 212 (1955).
[77a] L. Wilets and M. Jean, *Phys. Rev.* **102**, 788 (1956).
[78] M. Lecoin, *J. Phys. Rad.* (7) **9**, 81 (1938).
[79] S. Devons and G. J. Neary, *Proc. Camb. Phil. Soc.* **33**, 154 (1937).
[80] T. Mayer-Kuckuk, *Z. Naturforsch* **11a**, 627 (1956).
[80a] G. Stetter, unpublished report of work at Physical Institute of the University of Vienna, TID-14880 (1961). Final report published by P. Weinzierl *et al.*, *Phys. Rev.* **134**, B257 (1964).

limit and overcoming many experimental difficulties in sample preparation STETTER succeeded in resolving the many gamma rays listed in the accompanying table. $\beta\gamma$ and $\gamma\gamma$ coincidence results helped him to formulate the decay scheme shown in the figure.

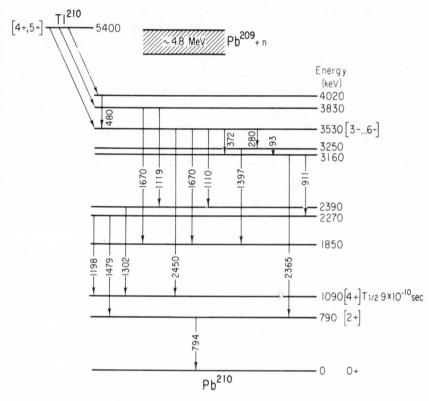

Decay scheme of radium C'' as formulated by Stetter.   For more complete scheme see P. Weinzierl *et al.*, *Phys. Rev.* **134,** B257 (1964).

It is seen that nearly all beta transitions populate a few levels above 3.5 MeV which are de-excited through a series of parallel γ-ray cascades, all of which funnel through a 2+ level lying at 790 keV.   The total decay energy is 5.5 MeV.

It is of interest to compare the experimental level scheme of Pb^{210} seen in the decay of Tl^{210} with the predictions of shell model theories.   Lead-210 has just 2 neutrons more than the closed shell nucleus Pb^{208} so that it is a very favorable case for a shell model calculation of the level system.   In principle one starts with the neutron wave functions predicted by theory for $N > 126$ and the energies of neutrons in these states as observed in the

Pb^{209} nucleus.   One considers all possible combinations of 2 neutrons in the available states and computes the energy of these combinations from the sum of the energies of the individual orbitals reduced by the energy of the residual interaction between the two neutrons.   PRYCE,[81] MAYER-KUCKUK[80] and STETTER[80a] have outlined how such a calculation is carried out and have shown what form the theoretical spectrum might take.   The weak point in these tentative calculations is the uncertainty of the shell model assignment of the neutron levels of Pb^{209}, particularly in view of the later work of MUKHÉRJEE AND COHEN.[81a]

The shell model interpretation of the Tl^{210} nucleus is an $s_{1/2}$ proton hole state combined with 3 neutrons in $g_{9/2}$ states—all coupled to 4+ or 5+.

The decay of RaC″ has the interesting feature that the total beta-decay

Gamma rays emitted in the decay of radium C″ (Thallium-210).

Gamma ray	MAYER- KUCKUK	P. WEINZIERL		STETTER	
	Energy (keV)	Energy (keV)	Intensity (per cent)	Energy (keV)	Intensity (per cent)
1				93·	4
2	297	298	71	286	80
3				372	4
4				425	3
5				480	2
6	783	800	100	794	100
7				911	8
8	1070	1100	10	1054	12
9	1100			1119	7
10				1198	17
11	1300	1340	9	1302	21
12				1398	5
13				1479	2
14				1550	2
15				1590	2
16				1670	2
17		2000⎫	12	1995	7
18		2090⎭		2101	5
19				2285	3
20	2360	2350⎫	18	2365	8
21		2460⎭		2450	9

Th. Mayer-Kuckuk, Z. Naturforsch 11a, 627 (1956).
P. Weinzierl, Sit. Öst. Akad. der Wiss. IIa, 166, 139 (1957).
G. Stetter, TID-14880 (1961).

[81] M. L. H. Pryce, Proc. Phys. Soc. (London), A65, 773 (1952).
[81a] P. Mukhérjee and B. L. Cohen, Phys. Rev. 127, 1284 (1962).

energy (5.4 MeV) to produce Pb^{210} is greater than the neutron binding energy (4.81 MeV) of Pb^{210}. KINSEY, BARTHOLOMEW, AND WALKER[82] pointed out that this suggests the possibility that neutrons may be emitted in the disintegration of RaC″ provided some of the beta transitions lead to excited states above the neutron binding energy. These authors looked for such neutrons from commercial sources of radium in equilibrium with their products and were unable to detect any neutrons other than those to be expected from (α, n) reactions on light element impurities in the container or the sample. On the other hand KOGAN AND RUSINOV[83,84] have obtained neutron counting data on the active deposit of radium emanation which indicates rather clearly that neutrons are indeed emitted in the decay of radium C″. They estimate the number as 2×10^{-4} per disintegration. STETTER[80a] confirms this by direct measurement of neutrons from a radium C″ sample.

General Comments on the Active Deposit of Slow Change. When radon samples or high-intensity samples of the active deposit are permitted to decay there always remains a residual long-lived activity after the radon and the active-deposit-of-rapid-change has decreased below the detectable limit. This residual activity is the radium D-E-F complex, at one time referred to as the active-deposit-of-slow-change.

$$RaD(Pb^{210}) \quad \xrightarrow[19.4\ yr]{\beta^-} \quad RaE(Bi^{210}) \quad \xrightarrow[5.0\ d]{\beta^-}$$

$$RaF(Po^{210}) \quad \xrightarrow[138\ d]{\alpha} \quad RaG(Pb^{206})\ \text{STABLE}$$

Radium D is identical with the radiolead first reported by HOFFMANN AND STRAUSS in 1901. Radium F is identical with the radioelement, polonium, found by the CURIES in 1898. We summarize recent determinations of the properties of these important nuclides in the following paragraphs. Numerous references to older measurements of these radiations are cited in the compilation of STROMINGER, HOLLANDER, AND SEABORG.[85] Some important growth curves are given in Figs. 6.15, 6.16, and 6.17.

Radium D (Pb^{210}). Modern determinations of the radium D half-life include those of TOBAILEM[86] (measurement of decay over 4 month period by dual ion-chamber technique leading to the result 19.4 ± 0.35 years), of HARBOTTLE[87] (measurement of decay over 280 day period by dual ion-chamber technique leading to the result 20.4 ± 0.3 years) and of ECKELMANN,

---

[82] B. B. Kinsey, G. A. Bartholomew and W. H. Walker, *Phys. Rev.* **82**, 386 (1951).
[83] A. V. Kogan, *Sov. Phys. Doklady* **1**, 372 (1957).
[84] A. V. Kogan and L. I. Rusinov, *Sov. Phys. JETP* **5**, 365 (1957).
[85] D. Strominger, J. M. Hollander, and G. T. Seaborg, *Revs. Mod. Phys.* **30**, 585 (1958).
[86] J. Tobailem. *J. Phys. Rad.* **16**, 235 (1955).
[87] G. Harbottle, *J. Inorg. Nucl. Chem.* **12**, 6 (1959).

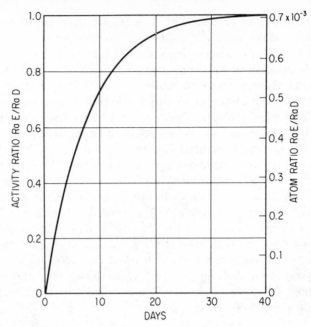

FIG. **6.15.** Growth of RaE (5-day Bi[210]) into pure RaD (19.4 year Pb[210]).

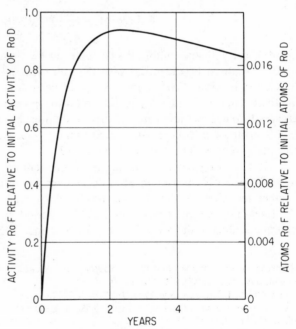

FIG. **6.16.** Growth of RaF (138-day Po[210]) into pure RaD (19.4 year Pb[210]).

BROECKER, AND KULP[88] (a geological method consisting of the isolation of lead from an undisturbed uranium mineral and the determination of the Pb^{210} content from Po^{210} in equilibrium with it, leading to a Pb^{210} half-life of 21.4 ± 0.5 years).

The beta particles of radium D are very soft and consist of two groups.[89,90] The weaker group is in 15 per cent intensity and has an end

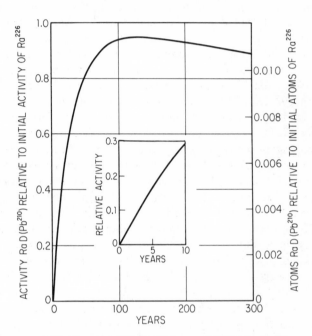

FIG. **6.17.** Growth of RaD (19.4 year Pb²¹⁰) into Ra²²⁶.

point energy of 64 keV; it represents the ground state transition. The stronger group is in 85 per cent intensity and has an end point energy of only 17 keV. Careful techniques of sample preparation and counting are required to detect these low-energy beta particles. This beta group is followed by an $M1$ gamma transition of 46.7 keV energy which is almost completely converted. No other gamma rays are present.[91]

For many years it was suspected that radium D must emit alpha particles in a small fraction of its disintegrations. Because of the slight magnitude of this branching and the unknown properties of the Hg^{206} daughter it was

[88] W. R. Eckelmann, W. S. Broecker, and J. L. Kulp, *Phys. Rev.* **118**, 698 (1960).

[89] W. Stanners and M. A. S. Ross, *Proc. Phys. Soc.* (London) **69A**, 837 (1956).

[90] J. Tousset and A. Moussa, *Comp. Rend.* **245**, 1617 (1957).

[91] A discussion of all measurements of the gamma radiations in the decay of radium D and radium E is given by Fink, Warren, Edwards, and Danon, *Phys. Rev.* **103**, 651 (1956).

difficult to obtain evidence for this mode of decay.   This evidence was eventually obtained by the Finnish scientists, NURMIA AND CO-WORKERS[91a] who measured alpha particles of approximately 3.7 MeV and isolated and identified the Hg^{206} daughter, which proved to be an 8.6 minute beta-emitter. The alpha branching is only 1.8×10^{-8} corresponding to a partial alpha half-life of 10^9 years.   The element mercury, in the form of its isotope Hg^{206}, must now be included among the natural radioactivities.

Radium E (Bi^{210}).   A recent careful redetermination of the half-life of radium E yielded the value 5.013 ± 0.005 days.[92]   Among the most careful work on the beta spectrum is that of PLASSMANN AND LANGER[93] who report the value 1.155 MeV for the maximum energy.   The beta decay goes directly to the ground state of radium F and no gamma radiation is detected.   Radium E also decays to Tl^{206} by alpha emission[94] but the alpha branching is only 1.3×10^{-4} per cent.[91a,104]   This alpha branching is discussed in detail below in connection with the discussion of the isomeric forms of Bi^{210}.

The shape of the beta spectrum of RaE has been of great interest to beta decay theorists for many years and so has been studied and restudied carefully by many experimentalists.   It was the first beta spectrum definitely proved to have a shape differing markedly from the shape characteristic of allowed beta transitions.   The spectral shape appeared to correspond to that expected for a twice-forbidden ($\Delta I = 2$, no change of parity) beta transition.   Since RaE decays into the ground state of an even-even nucleus which must have spin $0+$, the spin of RaE was assigned the value $2+$. When the shell model of the nucleus was developed it became clear that RaE could not have even parity.   (The odd, 83rd, proton in Bi^{210} has available to it only the negative parity states $h_{9/2}, f_{7/2}$, and $p_{3/2}$; the odd 127th neutron can only be in the positive parity states $i_{11/2}$, $g_{9/2}$, or $d_{5/2}$.   Hence RaE must have odd parity.)   At a later date the spin of RaE was definitely determined to be 1 by the atomic beam experiments of K. SMITH[95].   Hence, the theoretical problem became how to account for the striking deviation from the allowed spectrum shape for a transition of the type, $1- \rightarrow 0+$. A satisfactory but not completely convincing fit was obtained by invoking different mixtures of the five fundamental beta coupling components: S, V, T, A and P.   The status of the theoretical interpretations of the RaE beta spectrum shortly before the parity conservation law for weak interactions was shown to be invalid is well reviewed by PLASSMANN and LANGER[96]

[91a] M. Nurmia, P. Kauranen, *et al.*, *Nature* **190**, 427 (1961); P. Kauranen, *Ann. Acad. Sci. Fenn.*, Series A VI, *Physica* No. 96 Helsinki (1962).

[92] J. Robert and J. Tobailem, *J. Phys. Rad.* **17**, 440 (1956).

[93] E. A. Plassmann and L. M. Langer, *Phys. Rev.* **96**, 1593 (1954).

[94] E. Broda and N. Feather, *Proc. Roy. Soc.* (London) **190A**, 20 (1947).

[95] K. F. Smith, as quoted by C. S. Wu in Ref. 97.

[96] E. A. Plassmann and L. M. Langer, *Phys. Rev.* **96**, 1593 (1954).

and by C. S. Wu.[97] The theoretical interpretation of the RaE spectrum underwent further changes as ideas on beta decay interactions were reviewed subsequent to the discovery of the non-conservation of parity. We shall not review this matter here.*

The β spectrum of RaE is also of importance in a practical sense in connection with the so-called FEATHER analytical method[98] for determining the ranges of beta emitters. Frequently, it is desired to determine the maximum range (hence energy) of an unknown beta emitter or mixture of beta-emitters by noting the reduction in counting rate in a Geiger counter or similar detector when various thicknesses of absorber are placed between the sample and the detector. The "visual end-point" is easily determined for a simple beta emitter uncomplicated by gamma radiation, but is hard to estimate with confidence when a mixture of beta emitters or considerable gamma radiation is present. In such cases, a comparison of the shape of the absorption curve of the unknown sample with that of the standard substance according to the FEATHER method will reveal the beta range or ranges with more certainty. RaE has frequently been used as the standard substance because it has only a single beta group and no gamma radiation. Details on the application of the Feather method, which has been much used in the past, may be found elsewhere.[99]

Isomerism in Bi^{210}. Studies of bismuth isotopes produced artificially have shown the existence of a form of Bi^{210} isomeric with RaE. It will be convenient to discuss this isomerism here.

NEUMANN, HOWLAND, AND PERLMAN[100] found that neutron irradiation of bismuth in a high neutron flux produced a new bismuth alpha-emitter of low activity which could best be assigned to Bi^{210}. This work was extended by LEVY AND PERLMAN.[100] The evidence for the mass assignment is very strong and consists of the following.

1. The new radioactivity is provided by irradiation of Bi^{209} with neutrons.

2. The alpha particle energy, $4.935 \pm .020$ MeV (total minimum disintegration energy 5.031 MeV) corresponds to that expected for Bi^{210} and *not* to that for Bi^{208} or Bi^{211}, the only other bismuth isotopes which conceivably could be formed.

---

[97] C. S. Wu in Chapter XI of "Beta and Gamma Ray Spectroscopy", by K. Siegbahn, ed., (New York: Interscience Publishers, 1955).

[98] N. Feather, *Proc. Cambridge Phil. Soc.* 34, 599 (1938).

[99] L. E. Glendenin, *Nucleonics* 2, 1, 12 (1948); G. B. Cook and J. F. Duncan, *Modern Radiochemical Practice*, Oxford Univ. Press, 1952, pp. 98–107.

[100] H. M. Neumann, J. J. Howland, Jr., and I. Perlman, *Phys. Rev.* 77, 720 (1950); H. B. Levy and I. Perlman, *Phys. Rev.* 94, 152 (1954).

* Interested readers may consult J. Fujita, *Phys. Rev.* 126, 202 (1962), R. M. Spector, *Nucl. Phys.* 40, 338 (1963), and the references cited therein. See also the remarks of KIM AND RASMUSSEN, *Nucl. Phys.* 47, 201–3 (1963).

3. Daughter activity agreeing in properties with the 4.2 ± 0.5 min beta emitter, Tl^{206}, could be isolated in about the correct amount.

4. When a sample of bismuth containing the new alpha emitter was subjected to calutron isotope separation the alpha activity was found to concentrate in the mass 210 fraction.

5. The neutron absorption cross-section[101,102] of Bi^{209} as determined by activation of RaE is 19 ± 2 millibarns whereas the total absorption cross section is 33 ± 2 millibarns.   The difference of 14 ± 3 millibarns is attributed to the formation of the long-lived isomer of Bi^{210}.

6. Po^{210} alpha activity has been observed to grow into bismuth samples containing Bi^{210} (long-lived) long after the RaE had completely decayed.[100]

The half-life of Bi^{210} (long-lived) was calculated by HUGHES AND PALEVSKY[101] to be (2.6 ± 0.8) × 10^6 years assuming 14 millibarns for the neutron activation cross section of Bi^{209} to produce Bi^{210} (long) and using data of NEUMANN, HOWLAND, AND PERLMAN[100] on the specific alpha activity of the purified bismuth. The integrated flux was determined from the amount of Po^{210} produced and the 19 millibarns activation cross section for RaE from which the Po^{210} was derived.   This half-life is calculated in an indirect fashion and may be considered an upper limit.

From the information available in 1954 LEVY AND PERLMAN[100] constructed a decay scheme for the isomers which was consistent with all the then known properties. This decay scheme indicated that the energy difference between the two isomers was only a few kilovolts and that radium E probably was slightly higher in energy than Bi^{210} (long). This decay scheme assumed that the observed alpha group of 4.935 MeV energy represented the ground state transition and was crucially dependent on an 0− shell model assignment for radium E.   When the spin of radium E was determined to be 1 by the atomic beam method,[95] and when further information was obtained on the alpha particles of both isomers this decay scheme had to be abandoned.   We turn now to a discussion of later data on the alpha spectra.

BRODA AND FEATHER[94] established the existence of a slight branching decay of radium E by alpha emission.   They did this by isolating the daughter product Tl^{206} and established a branch decay of (1.2 to 10) × 10^{-7}. FINK et al.[103] confirmed this. WALEN and BASTIN[104] carried this work further and measured the energies of the alpha particle groups.   The results of this study are given in Table 6.13.

---

[101] D. Hughes and H. Palevsky, Phys. Rev. 92, 1206 (1953).
[102] D. J. Littler and E. E. Lockett, Proc. Phys. Soc. (London) A66, 700 (1953).
[103] R. Fink, et al., Bull. Amer. Phys. Soc. II, 171 (1956).
[104] R. J. Walen and G. Bastin, J. Phys. Rad. 20, 589 (1959).

GOLENETSKII, RUSINOV, AND FILIMONOV[105] procured a sample of the long-lived isomer with the higher specific activity of 14,000 alpha disintegrations per minute per milligram. With this sample they were able to measure the complex spectrum reported in Table 6.14 by an ionization chamber technique. These workers in collaboration with ANDREEV AND KISLOV[106] studied the gamma rays and conversion electrons emitted by the sample. They found photons of 262 ± 10, 301 ± 10, 340 ± 15 and 620 ± 20 keV and conversion electrons of 262 ± 5 and 301 ± 5 keV transitions. Some crucial information for construction of the decay scheme was obtained by alpha-electron and alpha-gamma coincidence experiments.

TABLE 6.13. Alpha groups of radium E

E_α (MeV)	Intensity per Disintegration
4.686	0.5×10^{-6}
4.649	0.75×10^{-6}

Walen and Bastin, *J. Phys. Rad.* **20**, 589 (1959). On the energy scale used by these authors the energy of the Po^{210} alpha particles is 5.305 MeV.

Particularly important was the finding that the most energetic alpha group was in coincidence with 262 keV photons. These new results are incorporated into the decay scheme shown here as Figs. 6.18 and 6.19. The half-lives of the Tl^{206} levels at 262 and 301 keV were determined to be 1.2 $\times 10^{-9}$ seconds and 3.2×10^{-9} seconds, respectively. A small amount of Po^{210} alpha activity, which did not decay with the Po^{210} half-life, was found in the alpha spectrum which suggests the existence of a slight γ-decay of Bi^{210m} to form RaE. Based on a 2.6×10^6 years half-life for Bi^{210m} the partial half-life of the isomeric transition is $\sim 5 \times 10^{10}$ years.

This work clearly establishes that the long-lived isomer of Bi^{210} lies approximately 250 keV above radium E. A reasonable spin assignment for the isomer is $9-$ based on a $g_{9/2}$ neutron and an $h_{9/2}$ proton with spins aligned in the same direction. The large spin difference of 8 then accounts for the long half-life for the isomeric transition.

It would be desirable to have a redetermination of the alpha half-life of Bi^{210} (long) by a more direct method. To secure agreement with the expected decay rate estimated from decay rates of nearby nuclei one would

[105] S. V. Golenetskii, L. T. Rusinov, and I. I. Filimonov, *Sov. Phys. JETP* **8**, 917 (1959) and **10**, 395 (1960).

[106] L. I. Rusinov, Yu. N. Andreev, S. V. Golenetskii, M. I. Kislov, and Yu. I. Filimonov, *Sov. Phys. JETP* **13**, 707 (1961).

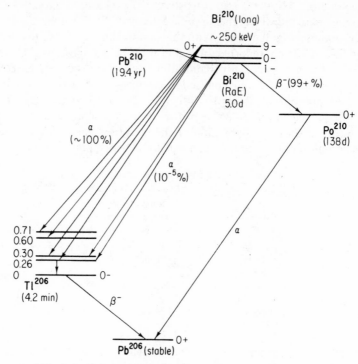

FIG. **6.18.** Overall decay scheme of radium DEF complex and of the Bi²¹⁰ isomers.   See also Fig. 6.19.

TABLE **6.14.** Alpha groups of Bi²¹⁰ (long).

Alpha groups	E_α (MeV)	Relative intensity	Energy of excited states (keV)
α_0	not detected		0
α_{260}	4.93 ± 0.01	60	262
α_{300}	4.89 ± 0.01	34	300
α_{610}	4.59 ± 0.01	5	610
α_{720}	4.48 ± 0.015	~0.5	720

Golenetskii, Rusinov and Filimonov, *Sov. Phys. JETP*, **10**, 395 (1960) and Rusinov, Andreev, Golenetskii, Kislov and Filimonov, *Sov. Phys. JETP* **13**, 707 (1961).   Energies are relative to Th²³⁰ ($E_\alpha = 4.682$ MeV), U²³³ ($E_\alpha = 4.816$ MeV), Pu²³⁹ ($E_\alpha = 5.147$ MeV) and Am²⁴¹ ($E_\alpha = 5.480$ MeV). See also the results of G. A. Korolev and G. E. Kocharov, *Bull. Acad. Sciences, USSR Phys. Series* **26**, No. 2, 233 (1962) Columbia Technical Translations.

need a half-life of about 5×10^5 years. ZEH AND MANG[107] have made calculations of the alpha spectrum of radium E by a method in which the alpha particle wave function is projected out of the shell model wave functions of individual particles. This calculation is a sensitive test of the shell model wave functions contributing to parent and daughter levels.

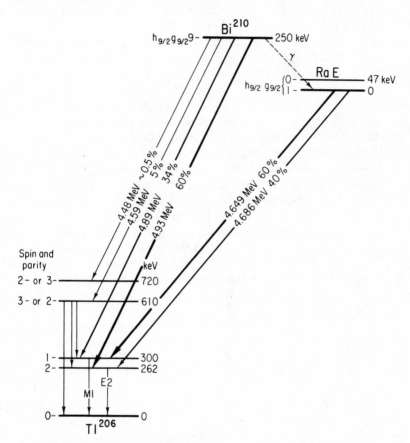

FIG. 6.19. Detailed decay scheme of Bi²¹⁰ isomers. The shell model assignments give the proton assignment first.

*Theoretical Analysis of Bi*²¹⁰ *Level System.* The low-lying energy-level spectrum of Bi²¹⁰ has been of considerable interest to theorists because Bi²¹⁰ contains a single neutron and a single proton beyond the double-closed-shell nucleus Pb²⁰⁸. The lowest proton orbital is $h_{9/2}$ and the lowest neutron orbital is $g_{9/2}$. The residual interaction between these two particles gives rise to a low-lying multiplet of 10 levels with spins from zero to nine. It is

107 H. D. Zeh and H. J. Mang, *Nucl. Phys.* 29, 529 (1962).

of interest to learn what prescription for the interaction of these unlike particles yields results in good agreement with experimental data. It is also important to know in what way the residual np interaction differs from the residual nn interaction which successfully accounts for the level system in such nuclei as Pb^{206} (see Chapter 10). The experimental facts which must be accounted for are the following.

1. The beta decay properties of radium E.

2. The spin sequence 1, 0, 9 for the ground state and first two excited levels. The spin 0 state falls at 47 keV as is known from the decay scheme of Pb^{210}. The spin 9 state is the long-lived isomeric form of Bi^{210}.

3. The numerous energy levels of Bi^{210} observed in high resolution studies[108] of protons resulting from the reaction Bi^{209}(d, p) Bi^{210}. The properties of these protons (relative intensities, angular distributions) also are important for identification of the nature of the levels.

Many authors[109] have made calculations of the Bi^{210} level system. In some cases the calculations were made before all the experimental information cited above was published and some of the conclusions are incorrect. It is beyond the scope of the discussion here to discuss these calculations except to make two general remarks about them.

The first is that all calculations which use for the np interaction a central force of the type used successfully for the nn interaction in such nuclei as Pb^{206} do *not* succeed in reproducing the correct order of the ground state multiplet in Bi^{210}. This is true even when a wide range of parameters is tested. In particular no reasonable central force residual attraction will place the spin 1 level below the spin 0 level. The second remark is that it has been shown by MELLO AND FLORES[109] and by KIM AND RASMUSSEN[109] that the addition of a short-range tensor force of reasonable strength *does* account for the 1− state of the $h_{9/2} g_{9/2}$ multiplet being the ground state of Bi^{210} instead of the 0− predicted by central forces. The experimental order of the 10 levels of the multiplet can be adequately reproduced.

Radium F (Po^{210}). Two modern determinations of the radium F half-life are those of CURTIS[110] and of EICHELBERGER, JORDAN, ORR AND PARKS[111] who reported 138.37 ± 0.03 days and 138.4005 ± 0.0058 days, respectively.

---

[108] P. Mukhérjee and B. L. Cohen, *Phys. Rev.* **127**, 1284 (1962); P. Mukhérjee, *Phys. Rev.* **131**, 2162 (1963); J. R. Erskine, W. W. Buechner, and H. A. Enge, *Phys. Rev.* **128**, 720 (1962); and G. B. Holm, J. R. Burwell, and D. W. Miller, *Phys. Rev.* **118**, 1247 (1960).

[109] N. Newby and E. J. Konopinski, *Phys. Rev.* **115**, 434 (1959); L. A. Sliv, G. A. Sogomonova, and Yu. I. Kharitonov, *Sov. Phys. JETP* **13**, 661 (1961) and *Nucl. Phys.* **28**, 210 (1961); P. A. Mello and J. Flores, *Nucl. Phys.* **47**, 177 (1963); and Y. E. Kim and J. O. Rasmussen, *Nucl. Phys.* **47**, 184 (1963).

[110] M. L. Curtis, *Phys. Rev.* **92**, 1489 (1953).

[111] J. F. Eichelberger, K. C. Jordan, S. R. Orr, and J. R. Parks, *Phys. Rev.* **96**, 719 (1954).

Recent absolute measurements of the polonium 210 alpha particle energy.
(Table prepared by F. Asaro*)

Value	Author
5.3048 ± 0.0006	Rytz, *Compt. Rend.* **250**, 3156 (1960) and *Helv. Phys. Acta* **34**, 240 (1961).
5.3054 ± 0.0010	White, *et al.*, *Phys. Rev.* **109**, 437 (1958).
5.3043 ± 0.0029	Collins, McKenzie, and Ramm, *Proc. Roy. Soc.* (London), **216A**, 219 (1953).
5.3086 ± 0.003	Browne, Galey, Erskine, and Warsh, *Phys. Rev.* **120**, 905 (1960).
5.3028 ± 0.0010	Wapstra*
5.3025 ± 0.0015	Beckner, Bramblett, Phillips, and Eastwood, *Phys. Rev.* **123**, 2100 (1961).

* *Proceedings of the International Conference on Nuclidic Masses*, McMaster University, Canada, September (1960).

Polonium 210 is beta stable and its decay is characterized by a single alpha group which populates directly the ground state of Pb^{206}.   This statement must be qualified because 803 keV gamma radiation does occur in an intensity of (1.06 ± 0.02) per 10^5 disintegrations.[112]   This observation indicates a very slight alpha branching to a state at 803 keV in Pb^{206} which decays by emission of electric quadrupole radiation.

Computation of energy of Po^{210} alpha particle from experimental measurement of ratio of Po^{210} and RaC′ alpha energies and from Brigg's value of 7.6804 MeV for the main RaC′ alpha particle.

Energy (MeV)	Author
5.3003	Rytz, *Compt. Rend.* **250**, 3156 (1960).
5.2995	Collins, McKenzie, and Ramm, *Proc. Roy. Soc.* (London), **216A**, 219 (1953).
5.2988	Lewis and Bowden, *Proc. Roy. Soc.* (London), **145A**, 235 (1934).
5.2978	Agapkin and Gol'din, *Izvest. Akad. Nauk.*, USSR. *Ser. Fiz.*, **21**, 909 (1957).
5.2985	C. P. Browne, *Phys. Rev.*, **126**, 1139 (1962).

FENYES[113] and BASTIN-SCOFFIER AND WALEN[112] have made a direct measurement of the weak alpha group: the latter authors report an energy 802 keV less than the main group and an intensity of 1.07×10^{-5}.

Polonium 210 is widely used for a variety of purposes for which a long-lived alpha emitter, unaccompanied by gamma radiation, is needed.   It

---

[112] Rojo, *et al.*, *Phys. Rev.* **99**, 1629A (1955); Hayward, *et al.*, *J. Research Nat. Bur. Stand.* **54**, 47 (1955); Shimanskaya, *et al.*, *Sov. Phys. JETP* **4**, 165 (1957); Ascoli, *et al.*, *Nuovo Cim.* **4**, 946 (1956); G. Bastin-Scoffier **and** R. J. Walen, *Compt. Rend.* **247**, 2333 (1958).

[113] T. Fenyes, *Nucl. Phys.* **16**, 529 (1960).

is also widely used as a standard in alpha particle spectroscopy so that the value of its alpha particle energy is a matter of considerable importance. The energy of the Po^{210} alpha particle has often been measured relative to the main alpha group of RaC' for which BRIGGS[114] has measured an absolute value with great accuracy. LEWIS and BOWDEN[113a] calculate an absolute value of 5.299 MeV for Po^{210} from a consideration of several measurements of the RaF to RaC' energy ratio. Many published alpha particle energies in the translead region are based directly or indirectly on this value of the Po^{210} alpha particle as a standard. Some recent direct determinations of the Po^{210} alpha particle energy have given values a few kilovolts higher. These newer determinations are summarized in the table. On the other hand, if recent determinations of the ratio of the Po^{210} alpha particle energy to the RaC' alpha particle energy are combined with the accepted Brigg's value for the RaC' alpha particle one obtains the alternate set of values summarized in the second table. These values cluster strongly around the old value 5.299 MeV. This strongly suggests that the energy of the RaC' alpha particle as well as the Po^{210} alpha particle needs to be raised a few kilovolts from its formerly-accepted value. An excellent discussion of remaining difficulties in the selection of an absolute energy standard is given by G. C. HANNA.[114a]

Radium D-E-F Radioactivity Standards. A sample of radium D-E-F makes a convenient beta-ray standard. The alpha disintegration rate of radium F can easily be determined in a suitable alpha counter to an accuracy of 1 per cent or better, and, at equilibrium, the alpha-disintegration rate of radium F is equivalent to the beta disintegration rate of radium E. If the radium D-E-F standard is covered with approximately 11 milligrams per square centimeter of aluminum absorber the activity detected in a Geiger tube, proportional counter, or other beta-ray detector is due solely to RaE; the alpha particles of RaF and the soft beta-particles from RaD are completely absorbed by the aluminum. The counting rate of such a standard decreases with the 19.40-year half-life of RaD. Such a standard has the advantage of a relatively long half-life and an energetic β-spectrum uncomplicated by conversion electrons and γ-rays.

Radium G (Uranium lead). The stable end-product of the uranium-radium decay chain is Pb^{206} known as RaG or uranium-lead. The isotopic abundance of Pb^{206} compared to the other uranium isotopes had considerable importance historically in the understanding of natural radioactivity and continues to have great significance for dating of minerals, etc. These matters are discussed in Sec. 6.5 of this chapter.

[113a] W. B. Lewis and B. V. Bowden, *Proc. Roy. Soc.* (London) **145A**, 235 (1934) Summary.

[114] G. H. Briggs, *Proc. Roy. Soc.* (London) **157A**, 183 (1936).

[114a] G. C. Hanna in *Experimental Nuclear Physics*, Vol. III, E. Segrè, ed. (New York: John Wiley & Sons, Inc., 1959), pp. 219–25.

6.3 THE THORIUM (4n) SERIES

The second of the three naturally-occurring series of radioactive elements which we discuss in this chapter is the thorium series. This series originates with Th^{232} which is the primary activity and terminates with the stable nuclide, Pb^{208}. The course of the decay chain is shown in Fig. 6.20 and Table 6.15.

The thorium series could be extended indefinitely to elements above thorium as follows:

$$Cm^{244} \xrightarrow[\text{17.9 yr}]{\alpha} Pu^{240} \xrightarrow[\text{6580 yr}]{\alpha} U^{236} \xrightarrow[\text{2.39} \times 10^7 \text{ yr}]{\alpha} Th^{232}$$

It is quite possible that several of these higher members of the series were present at the time the elements were formed, but in the long period which has elapsed (more than 4.5 billion years) these precursors of thorium have completely decayed to the much longer-lived thorium.

Thorium. BERZELIUS discovered thorium in 1828 in a Norwegian mineral, but the fact that thorium was radioactive was not discovered until the independent experiments of MME. CURIE and G. C. SCHMIDT in 1898. Before the discovery of nuclear fission, the principal interest in thorium, aside from its radioactive properties, resided in the fact that thorium was an excellent material for the preparation of incandescent gas mantles. This discovery of AUER VON WELSBACH gave rise to a thriving industry until the more efficient

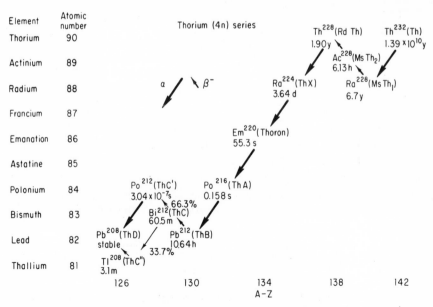

FIG. **6.20.** The thorium (4n) decay series.

TABLE 6.15. Principal decay characteristics of the thorium decay series.

Radioelement	Symbol	Radiation	Half-life
Thorium	Th^{232}	$\alpha(\beta$ stable)	1.39×10^{10} yr
Mesothorium 1	Ra^{228}	$\beta-$	6.7 yr
Mesothorium 2	Ac^{228}	$\beta-$	6.13 hr
Radiothorium	Th^{228}	$\alpha(\beta$ stable)	1.91 yr
Thorium X	Ra^{224}	$\alpha(\beta$ stable)	3.64 day
Thoron	Em^{220}	$\alpha(\beta$ stable)	55.3 sec
Thorium A	Po^{216}	$\alpha(\beta$ stable)	0.158 sec
Thorium B	Pb^{212}	$\beta-$	10.64 hr
Thorium C	Bi^{212}	$\beta-$	60.5 min
66.3% 33.7%		α	
Thorium C'	Po^{212}	$\alpha(\beta$ stable)	3.04×10^{-7} sec
Thorium C"	Tl^{208}	$\beta-$	3.1 min
Thorium D	Pb^{208}	stable	

electric incandescent lamp industry was well-established. Thereafter, interest in thorium chemistry, mineralogy, and metallurgy declined until the discovery of nuclear fission and the successful release of nuclear energy. Thorium itself does not undergo fission upon capture of slow neutrons, but it can be converted into the fissile nuclide U^{233} by neutron irradiation, as was first demonstrated by SEABORG, GOFMAN, AND STOUGHTON.[115]

$$Th^{232}(n,\gamma)Th^{233} \xrightarrow[\text{23.3 min}]{\beta-} Pa^{233} \xrightarrow[\text{27.4 day}]{\beta-} U^{233}$$

$$\sigma = 7.5 \text{ barns}$$

[115] G. T. Seaborg, J. W. Gofman, and R. W. Stoughton, *Phys. Rev.* **71**, 378 (1947) (Submitted April 13, 1942).

This reaction provides a means by which the world's total supply of nuclear fuel can be increased substantially. To do this it would be necessary to build "breeder" or "converter" reactors in which excess fission neutrons were absorbed in thorium to produce U^{233}.

Thorium is widely distributed in the earth's crust. It is estimated that total thorium reserves in deposits which may ultimately be usable for nuclear fuel are approximately equal to those of uranium. The most important commercial source of thorium is monazite, which is a rare-earth orthophosphate in which thorium occurs as a minor constituent. Large deposits are found in Brazil, India, Ceylon, and Australia. Thorium exists in a great variety of minerals as a minor constituent and only in a very few as a major component; none of these latter have the commercial importance of monazite.

The half-life of thorium was reported to be 1.31×10^{10} years by GEIGER AND RUTHERFORD[116] in the year 1910. This value was based upon the determination of the number of alpha particles emitted per gram of thorium in equilibrium with all its daughters and the knowledge that 6 alpha particles were emitted during the total transformation sequence. The early half-life determination is very close to the more recent redeterminations cited in Table 6.16. In this book we accept the value of 1.39×10^{10} found by

TABLE 6.16. Determinations of the half-life of thorium.

Kovarik and Adams, *Phys. Rev.* **54**, 413 (1938)	1.39×10^{10} yr
Picciotto and Wilgain, *Nuovo Cim.* **4**, 1525 (1956)	1.39×10^{10} yr $\pm 2\%$
Macklin and Pomerance, *J. Nucl. Energy* **2**, 243 (1956)	1.45×10^{10} yr
Senftle, Farley, and Lazar, *Phys. Rev.* **104**, 1629 (1956)	1.42×10^{10} yr* $\pm 5\%$
T. A. Farley, *Can. J. Phys.* **38**, 1059 (1960)	1.41×10^{10} yr $\pm 1\%$
Adopted "best" value	1.39×10^{10} yr
Decay Constant $\lambda =$	4.98×10^{-9} yr^{-1}
Specific activity $=$	246 dis/min^{-1} mg^{-1}

* This value was obtained by determining an absolute gamma-disintegration rate for Tl^{208} (RaC″) in equilibrium with aged thorium salts.

KOVARIK AND ADAMS in 1938. The total specific alpha activity of pure thorium may vary considerably depending upon the amount of radiothorium present in the sample; this in turn depends upon the history of the sample. The reasons for this may be visualized by consulting Fig. 6.20. When thorium is purified the equilibrium amount of radiothorium will remain with the thorium since radiothorium is an isotope of thorium. In a matter of days (consult Fig. 6.26) the remainder of the series below radiothorium

---

[116] H. Geiger and E. Rutherford, *Phil. Mag.* **20**, 691 (1910).

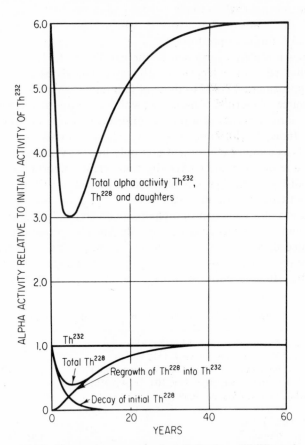

FIG. **6.21.** Change in amount of radiothorium (Th^{228}) and change in the total alpha activity to be found in Th^{232} starting with pure thorium freshly isolated from an undisturbed ore sample. The decay of RdTh initially present and the regrowth of RdTh into the sample via the decay sequence below are shown separately:

$$Th^{232} \xrightarrow[1.39 \times 10^{10} \text{ yrs}]{\alpha} MsTh_1 \xrightarrow[6.7 \text{ yrs}]{\beta^-} MsTh_2$$
$$\xrightarrow[6.13 \text{ yrs}]{\beta^-} RdTh \xrightarrow[1.90 \text{ yrs}]{\alpha}$$

The uppermost curve is the total specific alpha activity of the thorium; this consists of a constant activity equal to 1 contributed by Th^{232} and the variable contribution of RdTh plus the 4 short lived alpha-emitting descendants of RdTh. The relative value 1 on the ordinate scale is equivalent on an absolute scale to 246 disintegrations per minute for one milligram of thorium.

will grow back into equilibrium with the radiothorium. The total alpha activity will then be six times the activity of Th^{232} alone. However, the radiothorium and its decay products will begin to decay with the 1.9 year half-life of radiothorium because the 6.7 year radium isotope, mesothorium-1, was removed during the chemical purification. Over a period of years the mesothorium will grow back into the thorium provided the thorium is not subjected to further chemical purification. The net result is that the amount of radiothorium and the total alpha activity declines to a minimum at 5 years and then slowly rises again until complete equilibrium with Th^{232} is once more established. These specific activity changes in thorium are quite appreciable over normal periods of use and storage. In this respect pure thorium is quite unlike pure natural uranium which would have to be stored for 2000 years before the specific alpha activity increased by as much as one per cent. The specific activity changes in thorium are shown quantitatively in Fig. 6.21. Another effect which can contribute to the specific alpha activity of thorium is ionium contamination. If thorium is isolated from an ore containing appreciable amounts of uranium, the ionium will add appreciably to the specific activity even though the contamination on an atom basis is miniscule.

The long half-life of thorium makes it somewhat difficult to measure the specific activity or to measure the alpha particle energy because of self-absorption effects. Some careful measurements in a gridded ionization chamber have shown the alpha particle energy of the main alpha particle group to be 4.007 MeV.[117] A smaller peak appears in the pulse spectrum from the ion chamber corresponding to an alpha particle group of about 55 keV less energy.[117,118] Several investigators[119-121] have confirmed the presence of this lower energy group by impregnating nuclear emulsions with thorium salts and observing electron tracks from the conversion of a 55–60 keV gamma transition emanating from the same point as many of the alpha tracks.

The intensities of the main alpha particle group and the lower energy group are 76 per cent and 24 per cent, respectively, A third alpha group has been observed[118] in 0.2 per cent intensity at an energy 185 keV below the main group. It is likely that other alpha particle groups and gamma rays are present in the decay of thorium but in very low abundance.

Normal thorium is essentially monoisotopic on an atom per cent basis

[117] B. G. Harvey, H. G. Jackson, T. A. Eastwood, and G. C. Hanna, *Can. J. Phys.* **35**, 258 (1957).

[118] G. E. Kocharov, A. P. Komar and G. A. Korolev, *Zhur. Eksp. Teor. Fiz.* **36**, 68 (1959).

[119] S. W. Peat and M. A. S. Ross, *Proc. Phys. Soc.* (London), **68A**, 923 (1955).

[120] G. Albouy, *J. Phys. Radium* **13**, 309 (1952). *Ann. Phys.* **1**, 99 (1956).

[121] D. C. Dunlavey and G. T. Seaborg, *Phys. Rev.* **87**, 165 (1952).

because the only other thorium isotope in the decay series, RdTh^{228}, is present only to the extent of 5 parts in 10^{10}. This made it possible to determine the atomic mass number of thorium rather early in the history of radioactivity. This was important as it made it possible to assign correct mass numbers to all radioelements which could be related to thorium by a series of α and β transformations. Very precise measurements of the atomic weight of thorium were published by HÖNIGSCHMID in 1916, his preferred value being 232.12. Since that time the mass spectrometric method has replaced chemical weighing methods for atomic weight determination. STANFORD, DUCKWORTH, HOGG, AND GEIGER[122] in 1952 reported a value of 232.1093 $\pm$ 0.0010 atomic mass units. Other redeterminations are listed in Table 2.4 in Chapter 2.

Thorium in equilibrium with all its radioactive descendants contains on a weight basis the very small amounts of the products listed in Table 6.17.

TABLE 6.17. Amount of individual thorium decay products in ore
relative to the amount of thorium.

Isotope	Half-life	Relative Amount by Weight
Th^{232}	1.39×10^{10} yr	1.0
Ra^{228} (MsTh$_1$)	6.7 yr	4.74×10^{-10}
Th^{228} (RdTh)	1.91 yr	1.34×10^{-10}
Ra^{224} (ThX)	3.64 day	7×10^{-13}

Mesothorium 1 (Ra^{228}) *and Mesothorium 2* (Ac^{228}). The immediate product of Th^{232} decay is the 6.7 year beta-emitter MsTh$_1$, an isotope of radium. Since the total decay energy is only 55 keV the radiations of MsTh$_1$ are extremely weak and are difficult to detect and measure accurately because of self-absorption and window absorption effects. Literature reports on its radiations are not in complete agreement. Among recent reports, careful study by GOETZE[123] revealed a single ground-state-to-ground-state beta transition with 55 $\pm$ 3 keV energy (log ft = 5.6). He found no conversion electrons, x-rays or gamma rays. On the other hand TOUSSET[123a] saw low energy electrons interpreted as the conversion electrons of a 10.5 keV transition occurring in 25 per cent of the disintegrations. One of the great difficulties in a study of this nuclide is that after MsTh$_1$ is purified, daughter

---

[122] G. S. Stanford, H. E. Duckworth, B. G. Hogg, and J. S. Geiger, *Phys. Rev.* **85**, 1039 (1952).

[123] G. Goetze, *Z. Physik* **158**, 347 (1960).

[123a] J. Tousset, *J. Phys. Rad.* **21**, 461 (1960); J. Tousset and A. Moussa, *J. Phys. Rad.*, **22**, 683 (1961).

activity of the 6.13 hour MsTh$_2$, an isotope of actinium, quickly grows in. This isotope has a total beta decay energy of 2.18 MeV and decays with the emission of a complex mixture of electrons and gamma rays. Six groups of beta rays have been identified ranging in energy from 450 keV to 2.18 MeV. A number of gamma rays ranging in energy from 58 keV to 1640 keV have been reported. The radiations of MsTh$_2$ are discussed in some detail in the next subsection.

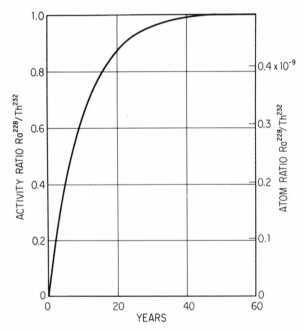

FIG. **6.22.** Growth of MsTh$_1$ (6.7 yr Ra^{228}) into pure Th^{232}.

Mesothorium, a term applied to MsTh$_1$ and MsTh$_2$ in equilibrium, received considerable use in medical and industrial applications for which intense sources of gamma radiation were required. In recent years mesothorium has been replaced for most purposes by radioactive isotopes prepared in nuclear reactors.

The gamma activity of a mesothorium sample does not decay with a simple 6.7 year half-life because of the growth of radiothorium (plus its short-lived daughters) into the mesothorium. This growth function is shown in Fig. 6.23. Some of the shorter-lived descendants of radiothorium, particularly ThC″, have hard and intense gamma radiation. Hence, a mesothorium preparation will have variable total hard gamma radiation rising to a maximum in about five years.

Mesothorium isolated from purified thorium is free of extraneous activities (after ThX has decayed) but the amounts which can be prepared after a reasonable period of growth are somewhat limited as can be seen from Figure 6.22. Larger amounts are readily prepared by isolating a radium fraction from thorium ores. Such samples contain a variable amount of

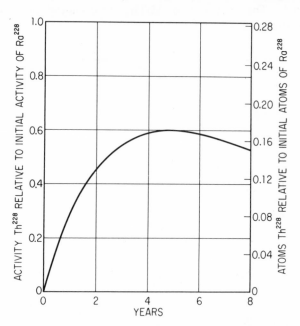

FIG. **6.23.** Growth of radiothorium (1.9 yr Th228) into pure MsTh₁ (6.7 yr Ra228). Since the half-lives of all the radioactive descendants of RdTh are short-lived compared to RdTh this curve can be taken to represent the growth of all these products into pure MsTh₁.

Ra^{226} depending on the ratio of thorium to uranium in the ore. Similarly, Ra^{226} samples isolated from uranium ores may contain some mesothorium contamination because of thorium present in the uranium ore. A convenient way to analyze for the amounts of these two radium isotopes in an aged radium preparation is to remove the gaseous emanation fraction and to measure the amount of 55.3 second thoron and 3.825 day radon.

Mesothorium is used in the preparation of photoneutron sources. (See Section 5.5.4 and Table 5.21 in Chapter 5.) The usefulness of mesothorium depends upon the growth of ThC″ which emits high energy gamma rays in high intensity. The 2.62 MeV gamma ray in the decay of ThC″ is particularly effective.

The Radiations of MsTh₂ (Ac^{228}). Several sets of measurements of the numerous conversion electrons and photons emitted in the decay of meso-thorium-2 are summarized in the accompanying tables.[124-129] The most comprehensive study is that of BJØRNHOLM, NATHAN, NIELSEN, AND SHELINE[129] from which we chiefly quote here in discussing the decay scheme. The precise values for transition energies and the multipolarity assignments of the most prominent gamma rays form the most important basis for the construction of a decay scheme, but very important contributory evidence comes from coincidence experiments of the electron-electron, electron-gamma, beta-gamma, and gamma-gamma types.

The daughter product is the even-even nucleus Th^{228}. The observed levels of excitation resemble those known to occur systematically throughout the heavy element group of nuclides; namely levels of collective rotation and vibration of a deformed nucleus. Thorium 228 is also the product of the alpha decay of U^{232} and the electron capture decay of Pa^{228}, both of which have been studied, so that many features of the level schemes of Th^{228} are firmly fixed by a consideration of three independent decay schemes. The most extensive information comes from a study[130] of the electron capture decay of Pa^{228} and consequently a more comprehensive discussion of the Th^{228} level scheme is given in Chapter 8 where the decay of Pa^{228} is discussed (Section 8.3.4).

The low-lying levels of Th^{228} seen in the decay of Ac^{228} are shown in Fig. 6.24. The $0+$, $2+$, $4+$ levels at 0, 58, and 157 keV, respectively, constitute the familiar rotational band of levels for an axially-symmetric but non-spherical nuclear ground state. The 58 keV transition is definitely characterized as $E2$ by its L-subshell conversion ratios. This transition is almost completely converted ($\alpha_L = 144$) and the lifetime of the 58 keV level was found to be $(4.0 \pm 0.3) \times 10^{-10}$ seconds.*[135] The corresponding

[124] D. H. Black, Proc. Roy. Soc. (London) A106, 632 (1924).
[125] J. Thibaud, Ann. Phys. 5, 73 (1926).
[126] J. Kyles, C. G. Campbell and W. G. Henderson, Proc. Phys. Soc. (London), A66, 519 (1953).
[127] W. D. Brodie, Proc. Phys. Soc. (London), A67, 265 (1954).
[128] H. C. Box and G. S. Klaiber, Phys. Rev. 95, 1247 (1954).
[129] S. Bjørnholm, O. Nathan, O. B. Nielsen, and R. K. Sheline, Nucl. Phys. 4, 313 (1957).
[130] E. Arbman, S. Bjørnholm, and O. B. Nielsen, Nucl. Phys. 21, 406 (1960).
[131] M. Lecoin, M. Perey, and J. Teillac. J. Phys. Rad. 10, 33 (1949).
[132] F. Suzor and G. Charpak, J. Phys. Rad. 15, 682 (1954).
[133] F. Asaro and I. Perlman, Phys. Rev. 99, 37 (1955).
[134] G. Scharff-Goldhaber, et al., Phys. Rev. 99, 180 (1955).
[135] R. E. Bell, S. Bjørnholm, and J. C. Severiens, Dan. Mat.-fys. Medd. 32, No. 12 (1960).

* In earlier literature reports surprisingly long half-lives of >0.01 seconds,[126,131] and >0.5 seconds[132] were reported for this transition. These reports were not confirmed by later studies[133,134] made specifically to check them, nor by the study quoted here.[129]

$E2$ transition probability is more than 200 times the single particle transition value which confirms the collective nature of the state. The 127.5 keV transition connecting the 4+ and 2+ levels is also an electric quadrupole transition as deduced from the K/L conversion ratio and the prominent conversion in the L_{II} and L_{III} subshells. These two radiations are also prominent[133] in the alpha decay of U^{232}.

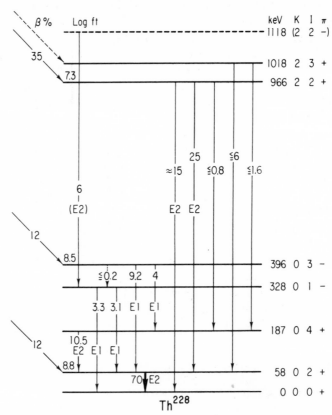

FIG. **6.24.** Low-lying levels of Th^{228} seen in the decay of Ac^{228}. From Bjørnholm et al.[129] The numbers associated with the vertical arrows are transition intensities.

A prominent 184-keV transition seen in the decay of Ac^{228} has the K/L ratio and the high $L_I/(L_{II} + L_{III})$ subshell conversion ratio expected of an $M1$ transition. Kyles and co-workers[126] and Box and Klaiber[128] regarded this gamma ray as a crossover transition from a 184-keV 1+ level in parallel with a 127.5—57 keV cascade. This view is not consistent with what is known about the low-lying levels of even-even nuclei.[133] Bjørnholm and co-workers[129] found that the 184-keV transition is coincident with gamma rays de-exciting a level at 966 keV and interpret it as a transition connecting levels at 1150 and 966 keV.

BJØRNHOLM, NATHAN, NIELSEN, AND SHELINE[129] found an end-point energy of 2100 keV for the most energetic beta group and further found that this beta group was strongly coincident with low energy electrons but with no gamma rays. It is thus confirmed that this beta group excites the 58 keV level. The beta intensity is 12%.

TABLE 6.18. Gamma transitions from Ac²²⁸ decay.

Gamma energies from conversion electron measurements (Energy in keV)				NaI crystal measurements
Black[124]	Thibaud[125]	Kyles, Campbell and Henderson[126]	Brodie[127]	Box and Klaiber[128]
Energy	*Energy*	*Energy*	*Energy* (keV)	
58	—	56.75	57.0	—
80	—	78.05	78.1	—
—	—	97.77	97.4	98
—	—	113.0	—	—
129	—	127.5	127.5	127
—	—	179.0	—	155
184	—	184.2	183.7	—
—	—	—	—	220
250	—	232.2	—	278
338	333	336.0	—	336
—	—	410.1	—	410
462	462	457.6	—	458
—	—	—	—	790
914	913	907.1	—	—
969	968	964.5	—	935 (complex)
—	—	1035	—	—
—	—	1095	—	—
—	—	1587	—	1587
—	—	1640	—	—

In Fig. 6.24 occur a pair of levels at 328 keV and 396 keV which are given assignments of 1− and 3−, respectively. This pair of levels is interpreted as the beginning of a rotational band based on a 1− state which represents the excitation of an octupole (pear-shaped) deformation of the nucleus. Collective levels of this type are seen systematically in the heavy element group of nuclides. The pattern of gamma ray de-excitation seen in the Th²²⁸ is similar to that observed before and predicted by theory. The 1− level de-excites by a pair of E1 transitions to the 0+ and 2+ members of the ground state rotational band. The 3− level de-excites by a pair of E1 transitions to the 2+ and 4+ members of that band. According to theory the relative transition probabilities of the γ-transitions in these two pairs of $E1$ transitions after the energy dependence has been factored out (i.e., the

TABLE **6.19.** Gamma transitions of Th^{228} from conversion electron studies of BJØRNHOLM AND CO-WORKERS.[129, 130]

E_γ (keV)	Transition intensity
57.5	70
99.4	
129.1	10.5
137.8	
178.0	
184.5	
209.0	4
270.0	3.1
282.2	
327.5	3.3
338.5	9.5
409.7	
443	
463.3	
473	
484	
510	
555	
573	
619	
749	
756.2	
769	
773.5	(0.8)
782.6	
795.8	(4.5)
836.4	(1.6)
912.2	25
924	
970.0	
966.0	19
1464	
1593	

Energies from ARBMAN, BJØRNHOLM, AND NIELSEN.[130] Intensities from BJØRNHOLM, NATHAN, NIELSEN, AND SHELINE.[129]

ratios of the reduced transition probabilities) should be given by Clebsch-Gordan coefficient ratios. The observed ratios in the two cases are in agreement[133,134,129] with theory for the K and I quantum number assignments given to the levels in Fig. 6.24.

Above the negative parity rotational band there is a gap until a pair of levels at 966 and 1018 keV is reached. The 966 keV level is de-excited by electric quadrupole transitions to the 0+ and 2+ levels of the ground state rotational band. This fixes the spin of the 966 keV level as 2+. It is suggested that this level represents the first quantum state of a quadrupole vibration around the equilibrium spheroidal shape of the nucleus. Further,

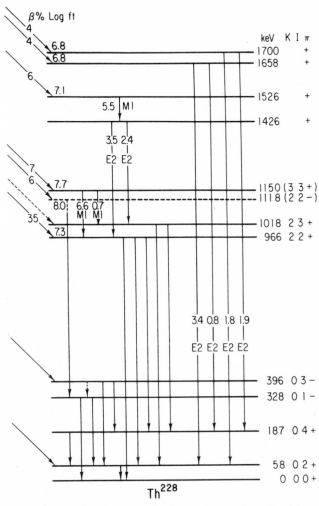

FIG. 6.25. Decay scheme of Ac[228] (MsTh₂) as formulated by BJØRNHOLM ET AL.[129] Compare with decay scheme of Pa[228] which appears in Section 8.3.4. The numbers associated with the vertical arrows are transition intensities.

this vibrational excitation is believed to be of the γ-vibrational type discussed in Chapter 3.   The quantum numbers K, I, and π for this state are 2, 2 and $+$, respectively.   The level at 1018 has the spacing above the 966 keV level and the gamma ray de-excitation pattern expected for the first $(3+)$ rotational level based on the $2+$ vibrational state.   Its position is also well-established by coincidence experiments.

A number of other higher-lying levels have been identified as shown in Fig. 6.25.   The existence of these levels is confirmed by the study of the orbital electron decay of Pa[228].   In addition, a number of other levels are observed by the study of the Th[228] radiations which may also occur in the beta decay of Ac[228].   Further remarks concerning the interpretation of these upper levels is made in Section 8.3.4 of Chapter 8.   Figure 6.25 does not include many of the lower intensity gamma transitions listed in the tables.

TABLE **6.20(a)**. Beta groups of Ac[228] (MsTh₂).
KYLES, CAMPBELL, AND HENDERSON[126]

Energy (MeV)	Abundance (per cent)	Log ft
2.18	10.1	8.9
1.85	9.6	8.7
1.70	6.7	8.6
1.11	53	7.1
0.64	7.6	7.2
0.45	13.0	6.4

The continuous beta spectrum of Ac[228] was resolved into the six groups shown in Table 6.20(a) by KYLES, CAMPBELL, AND HENDERSON. It was suggested by them that the most energetic component excites the 58 keV level in Th[228]. This was confirmed by BJØRNHOLM, ET AL.[129] who found a strong coincidence of the most energetic beta particles with low energy electrons but with no γ-rays. These authors deduced the values of beta group intensities and log ft values summarized in Table 6.20(b), basing their calculations chiefly on gamma transition intensity balances.

The levels most heavily populated by the beta decay of Ac[228] have spin 2 and 3 which suggests a spin value $I = K = 2$ or 3 for Ac[228] with 3 the more probable. The low intensity for the β-decay to the two lowest rotational bands relative to the transitions to high energy levels is thus probably caused by K-forbiddeness. This effect may also explain the fact that an excited β-vibrational band with $K = 0$ and $I = 0+, 2+, 4+...$ has not been observed. The $I = 0+$ level of such a band might be expected at about 650 keV in Th[228].

Radiothorium (Th[228]). We have already seen in Figs. 6.21 and 6.23 how the amount of the alpha-emitter, radiothorium, varies with time in an initially pure sample of thorium or mesothorium. It is clear that in order to obtain pure radiothorium, mesothorium must first be isolated.

A process similar to this sometimes occurs in nature. Water-leaching of a thorium ore may cause the selective removal of the more soluble radium isotope $MsTh_1$ to some location removed from the thorium ore and the

TABLE **6.20(b)**. Beta groups of Ac^{228} (MsTh₂)
BJØRNHOLM AND CO-WORKERS.[129,130]

Energy of daughter level (keV)	K, I, π for level	β-intensity	log ft
0	0, 0, +		>8.8
57.5*	0, 2 +	12	8.8
327.5	0, 1 −		>9.5
395.8	0, 3 −	12	8.5
969.5	2, 2 +	35	7.3
1023.2	2, 3 +		≥8.0
1123.4	2, 2 −	6	8.0
1154.0	3, 3 +	7	7.7
1432.8	?, 4 +		>8.0
1451.0	?, 3 +		≥8.3
1532.2	?, 4 +	6	7.1
1650.0	2, 3 +	4	6.8

* The energy of the beta group populating this level was reported as 2100 keV.

subsequent formation of the radiothorium in the new location. Hence, it is possible to isolate from nature small samples of radiothorium with a smaller Th^{232} dilution than that corresponding to the equilibrium value.

Radiothorium can be made artificially by irradiating radium or actinium in a high flux reactor, as has been discussed by KIRBY, GROVE, AND TIMMA.[136]

$$Ra^{226}(n, \gamma)Ra^{227} \qquad Ra^{227} \xrightarrow[41 \text{ min}]{\beta^-} Ac^{227}$$
$$\sigma = 18 \text{ barns}$$

$$Ac^{227}(n, \gamma)Ac^{228} \qquad Ac^{228} \xrightarrow[6.13 \text{ hr}]{\beta^-} Th^{228}$$
$$\sigma = 495 \text{ barns}$$

The radiothorium isolated from neutron-irradiated radium or actinium is contaminated with 18 day Th^{227} (Radioactinium) which comes from the beta decay of Ac^{227}. The amount of this contamination depends on the integrated flux and on the time elapsed since the actinium-thorium separation was made.

---

[136] H. W. Kirby, G. R. Grove, and D. L. Timma, *Phys. Rev.* **102**, 1140 (1956).

Radiothorium may also be isolated as the decay product of U^{232}. If the U^{232} is mixed with U^{233} there will be some contamination with the 7340 year Th^{229} daughter product of U^{233}.

The alpha spectrum of radiothorium has been investigated by ASARO, STEPHENS, AND PERLMAN[137] who reported the following groups:

5.421 MeV	71 per cent
5.338 MeV	28 per cent
5.208 MeV	0.4 per cent
5.173 MeV	0.2 per cent
5.137 MeV	0.03 per cent

All energies relative to E_{α_0} Ra^{224} = 5.681 MeV

The alpha particles reveal excited states at 84 keV (2+), at 253 keV (4+), at 217 keV (1−) and at 289 keV (3−); these levels are de-excited by gamma rays of 84 keV, 169 keV, 137 keV and 212 keV. Further details on the characterization of these radiations and on the construction and interpretation of the decay scheme of the Th^{228} are given in Section 8.2.6 of Chapter 8.

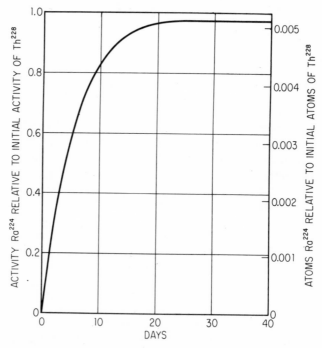

FIG. 6.26. Growth of 3.64 day ThX (Ra²²⁴) from RdTh (Th²²⁸).

[137] F. Asaro, F. Stephens, Jr., and I. Perlman, *Phys. Rev.* **92**, 1495 (1953).

L. MEITNER[138] in 1918 reported the half-life of RaTh to be 1.907 years with an uncertainty of one per cent. KIRBY, GROVE, AND TIMMA[136] found 1.910 ± 0.002 years in their 1955 redetermination.

Thorium X (Ra^{224}). Pure samples of 3.64 day ThX may be isolated from thorium. To do this, it is necessary first to separate the thorium ($Th^{232} + Th^{228}$) cleanly from MsTh, and then allow a period of two weeks for the ThX to grow into the sample. A radium fraction which is then removed from the thorium consists of pure thorium X. If a pure radiothorium source is available the ThX may be separated directly (see Fig. 6.26).

Thorium X is an alpha emitter with two prominent alpha particle groups. ROSENBLUM AND CO-WORKERS[139] report a main group with energy 5.681 MeV in 95 per cent abundance and a second group at 5.448 MeV in 4.6 per cent abundance. ASARO, STEPHENS, AND PERLMAN[137] obtained closely-similar values (5.681 MeV, 95 per cent and 5.445 MeV, 4.9 per cent). They were unable to detect (upper limit 0.1 per cent) a third group at 5.194 MeV which ROSENBLUM[139] had reported to be in 0.4 per cent abundance. WALEN AND BASTIN[140] restandardized the energy of the main group at the slightly higher value of 5.686 MeV. Gamma ray studies and gamma-gamma coincidence measurements of STEPHENS, ASARO, AND PERLMAN[141] indicate that 5.15 MeV and 5.04 MeV alpha groups must be present in about 0.009 and 0.012 per cent abundance, respectively. WALEN AND BASTIN-SCOFFIER[141a] confirmed these alpha groups in a careful redetermination of the spectrum; their results include the following groups: 5.684 MeV (94 per cent), 5.447_3 (5.5 per cent), 5.159 MeV (7.3×10^{-3} per cent), 5.049 MeV (7.2×10^{-3} per cent), and 5.032 MeV (3.1×10^{-3} per cent).

The decay scheme of Ra^{224} is shown in Fig. 6.27. The most prominent gamma radiation is the 241.1 keV transition which ROSENBLUM, VALADARES, AND GUILLOT[142] have characterized in detail. The photon intensity is 3.7 per cent, the K conversion coefficient is 0.13 and the $K/L_{II}/L_{III}$ conversion ratio is 0.46/0.3/0.28. The multipolarity of the radiation is electric quadrupole ($E2$). MULLER AND CO-WORKERS[143] used a crystal spectrometer to determine a very precise value of 240.98 keV for the energy of the photon. STEPHENS, ASARO, AND PERLMAN[141] used a scintillation spectrometer to

[138] L. Meitner, Z. Physik 19, 257 (1918).

[139] S. Rosenblum, M. Valadares, M. Perey, and J. Vial, Compt. Rend. 229, 1009 (1949).

[140] R. J. Walen and G. Bastin, Compt. Rend. Congres International de Physique, Paris, 1958.

[141] F. Stephens, Jr., F. Asaro, and I. Perlman, Phys. Rev. 119, 796 (1960).

[141a] R. J. Walen, Compt. Rend. 255, 1604 (1962); G. Bastin-Scoffier, Compt. Rend. 254, 3854 (1962).

[142] S. Rosenblum, M. Valadares, and M. Guillot, J. Phys. Rad. 15, 129 (1954).

[143] D. E. Muller, H. C. Hoyt, D. J. Klein, and J. W. M. DuMond, Phys. Rev. 88, 775 (1952).

find additional gamma rays with the following energies and abundances: 290 keV ($\sim 8 \times 10^{-3}$ per cent), 410 keV ($\sim 4 \times 10^{-3}$ per cent), 650 keV ($\sim 9 \times 10^{-3}$ per cent). The 241 keV gamma ray was observed to be in coincidence with the 290 and 410 keV transitions. These authors have interpreted the level scheme of Fig. 6.27 in the following way. The thoron nucleus is below the mass region where nuclei are stabilized in a non-spherical shape (see Chapter 3), but it lies well beyond the closed shell region and

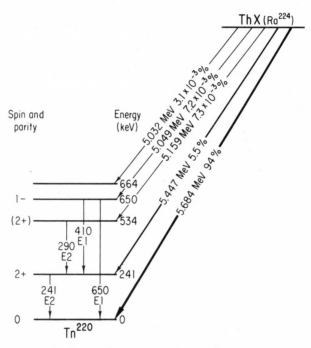

FIG. 6.27. Decay scheme of thorium X (Ra²²⁴). The alpha data are taken from WALEN AND BASTIN-SCOFFIER.[141a]

among a group of nuclei which can be deformed rather easily from the spherical ground state. The excited states in Fig. 6.27 are not single particle quantum states representing different intrinsic particle excitation; rather they are quantum states arising from collective motions. The levels at 241 and at 530 keV, respectively, are simple collective vibrations about the spherical equilibrium state. The absence of a crossover gamma ray from the 530 keV (2+) level to the ground state is strong evidence for this interpretation. (See Section 3.3 of Chapter 3.) The level at 650 keV is de-excited by E1 transitions to the ground state and to the first 2+ state. This identifies the 650 keV level as a 1−state. Negative parity states in heavy element even-even nuclei are believed to be the result of collective octupole vibrational motions. This phenomenon is discussed in Chapter 3 (see Sections 3.4.4. and 3.5.3).

Thoron (Em^{220}) *and ThA* (Po^{216}). Thoron has a half-life of 55.3 seconds* and hence comes to equilibrium with its parent, thorium X, within a few minutes. Thorium A, the daughter of thoron, has a half-life of only 0.158 seconds so that ThA alpha activity and thoron alpha activity are virtually inseparable. Thoron emits alpha particles of 6.296 MeV ($\sim$ 100 per cent abundance) and 5.761 ($\sim$0.3 per cent abundance) and ThA emits alpha particles with an energy of 6.777 MeV;[141a] ThA emits a small-intensity group of 5.984 MeV particles in 2.1×10^{-3} per cent intensity.[141a] A gamma ray of 542 keV energy appears in $\sim$0.03 per cent abundance in thoron decay, corresponding to the difference in energy of the alpha particle groups.

Analysis for thoron is a very sensitive test for the presence of any of the members of the thorium series which lie above it in the decay sequence. The substance to be analyzed can be put into solution and the thoron removed by bubbling a carrier gas through the solution and into an ionization chamber or electrometer. The energetic alpha particles of thoron and ThA are readily detected and a half-life determination identifies the activity conclusively.

For special studies it is possible to collect ThA activity by the recoil collection method on a rapidly-revolving electrically-charged disc. MOSELY AND FAJANS (1911) introduced this method of separation of ThA from thoron and used it to determine the half-life of ThA. Their value was 0.14 seconds. A more precise value of 0.158 seconds was measured in 1942 by A. G. WARD.

A word should be said concerning the beta branching of ThA which has been reported by KARLIK AND BERNERT.[144] These workers observed 7.57 MeV alpha particles in a fresh sample of thoron and these decayed with the 55 second half-life of thoron. They ascribed this alpha group to At^{216} arising from a 1.35×10^{-2} per cent beta branching of ThA. Because of the short half-life of ThA there was no chance to observe the growth of these new alpha particles into the fresh thoron sample. This interpretation is open to serious question upon grounds unrelated to the particular experiment as was recognized by the authors themselves, by FEATHER,[145] by FLÜGGE AND KREBS,[146] and by PERLMAN, ET AL.[147]. The difficulty is readily understood when the following closed decay-energy cycle is considered.

---

[144] B. Karlik and T. Bernert, *Naturwiss* **31**, 492 (1943); *Z. Physik* **123**, 51 (1944).
[145] N. Feather, *Nucleonics* **5**, 22 (1949).
[146] Flügge and Krebs, *Naturwiss* **32**, 71 (1944).
[147] I. Perlman, A. Ghiorso, and G. T. Seaborg, *Phys. Rev.* **77**, 26 (1950).
* This value is taken from J. E. Gindler and D. W. Engelkemeir, *Radiochim. Acta* **2**, 58 (1963). All previous half-life determinations are reviewed in this article.

$$\text{ThC (Bi}^{212}) \xleftarrow[\;7.94 \text{ MeV}\;]{\alpha} \text{At}^{216}$$

$$\beta^- \uparrow 0.58 \text{ MeV} \qquad\qquad \text{E.C.} \downarrow 0.45 \text{ MeV (calculated)}$$

$$\text{ThB (Pb}^{212}) \xleftarrow[\;6.91 \text{ MeV}\;]{} \text{ThA (Po}^{216})$$

The total decay energy of ThA and of ThB are known from experimental measurements. The decay energy of At^{216} is known from measurements of At^{216} present in the decay chain of the artificially-produced isotope, Pa^{228}. Since the energy summation around the closed cycle must be zero, At^{216} is actually unstable with respect to ThA by 0.45 MeV and β^- decay of ThA is impossible. For beta decay of ThA to proceed to the extent reported it would be necessary for ThA to be unstable with respect to At^{216} by > 1.0 MeV.

KARLIK AND BERNERT[144] suggested an explanation which retained their assignment of the 7.57 MeV alpha groups to At^{216} by assuming that ThB decays only to a 1.15 MeV excited state of Bi^{212}, this isomer having the properties associated with ThC, while the alpha decay of At^{216} proceeds to the ground state. This explanation seems untenable for a number of reasons. If ThC represents the postulated isomeric state of Bi^{212} then the alpha decay energy from the ground state of Bi^{212} would be 1.15 MeV lower than the measured value of ThC (6.2 MeV), that is, about 5.0 MeV. But from the regularities of alpha decay energies we know that the ground state alpha decay energy of Bi^{212} must fall between the values for Bi^{211} and Bi^{213}. The value 6.2 MeV fits this requirement whereas 5.0 MeV is completely out of line. In addition, the explanation is in conflict with the known properties of the collateral decay series starting with 22 hour Pa^{228} because in this series At^{216}, arising from the alpha decay of Fr^{220}, decays to Bi^{212} identical in properties with ThC. (See discussion of Pa^{228} series in Chapter 7.) All in all, it appears to be highly unlikely that ThA is β^- unstable and therefore the 7.57 MeV low-intensity alpha groups found by KARLIK AND BERNERT must arise from some isotope other than At^{216}. Confirmatory evidence for this point of view comes from the work of BASTIN-SCOFFIER AND WALEN[141a] who reinvestigated the alpha spectrum of ThA and found no alpha particles in the energy range 6.800–8.600 MeV above an intensity limit of 5×10^{-4} per cent.

The Thoron Active Deposit—General Comments. The active deposit left after the decay of thoron consists of Thorium B, C, C' and C". Thorium A decays so rapidly that in no practical sense is it useful to regard it as a real member of the thorium active deposit even though it is the direct descendent of thoron. Samples of Thorium B can be collected by letting a sample of thoron decay in a capillary tube or in some suitable vessel. All surfaces exposed to the gas will be coated with an invisible deposit of ThB.

Alternatively, the non-gaseous products of thoron decay can be collected on a charged wire or metal surface. The electrical collection method makes it possible to localize the active deposit, an asset in the preparation of beta ray spectrometer sources.

The initial activity of the active deposit consists of nearly-pure 10.6 hour ThB because the growth of the remainder of the decay chain is slowed down by the comparatively long half-life of the 60.5 minute ThC. Pure samples

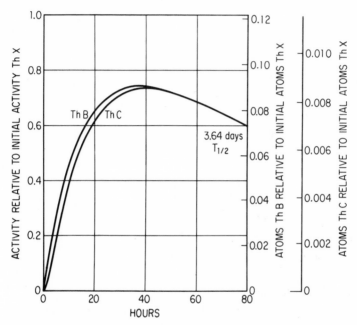

FIG. **6.28.** The growth of ThB (10.6 hr Pb^{212}) and ThC (60.5 min Bi^{212}) into ThX (3.64 day Ra^{224}).

of thorium B can also be isolated chemically from a solution of the active deposit or from a solution of ThX or of radiothorium. The growth of ThB into radiothorium is very nearly the same (on an activity basis) as the growth of ThX shown in Fig. 6.26. The growth of ThB and ThC into ThX is shown by Fig. 6.28. The growth of ThC into ThB is shown in Fig. 6.29.

The electron spectrum of ThB in equilibrium with ThC and ThC″ is characterized by a large number of conversion lines. Since the energies of many of these conversion electrons have been very carefully measured, Th(B—C—C″) sources are valuable for calibration of electron spectrometers. An excellent detailed summary of these electrons and examples of the spectrum observed on high resolution permanent magnet spectrographs and semi-circular beta spectrometer is given by K. SIEGBAHN.[148] Energies of some of the principal lines are summarized in Table 6.21.

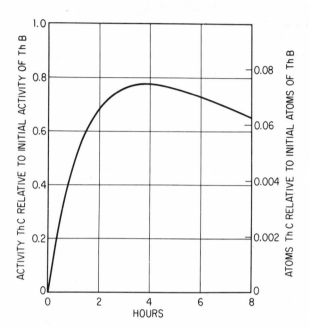

FIG. **6.29.** The growth of ThC (Bi²¹²) into pure ThB (Pb²¹²);

$$ThB \xrightarrow[10.6 \ hr]{\beta^-} ThC \xrightarrow[60.5 \ min]{\alpha, \beta}$$

The growth curve for ThC′ is identical in shape but rises only to 64% of the activity of ThC because of the branching decay of ThC.

An overall view of the complex nature of the thorium B active deposit can be obtained from Fig. 6.30. Attention is called to the complexity of the β^- decay of ThB, ThC and ThC″; note the long-range alpha particles originating from the excited levels of ThC′; note the prominent gamma ray with the high energy of 2.62 MeV which occurs in 100 per cent of the disintegrations of ThC″; and note the branching decay of ThC.

We wish to discuss this decay sequence in more detail in the following pages, but we shall limit our remarks to those features which are definitely established and not try to review all the extensive literature on these nuclides. Not all the radiations are definitely assigned and there are conflicting reports

---

[148] K. Siegbahn, ed., *Alpha, Beta, Gamma Spectroscopy*, 2nd ed. (Amsterdam: North Holland Publishing Co., 1964).

concerning the existence or abundance of certain low intensity gamma rays
and beta ray groups. Reference to a large number of research papers

TABLE **6.21.** Energies of prominent conversion electrons
in Th(B + C + C″) spectrum.

Line	Electron energy keV	Conversion shell	Origin	Relative intensity
A	24.507	LI	ThC——→ThC″	6
B	36.152	MI	ThC——→ThC″	4
Bb	39.012	NI	ThC——→ThC″	1.0
C	58.0		ThB——→ThC	1.4
D	61.0		ThB——→ThC	1.4
E	98.778			3.4
F	148.083	K	ThB——→ThC	200
G	189.35	K	ThC″——→ThD	4.0
H	209.59	K	ThB——→ThC	6.0
I	222.217	LI	ThB——→ThC	22
Ia	222.895	LII	ThB——→ThC	1.4
J	234.60	MI	ThB——→ThC	6.0
Ja	237.76	NI	ThB——→ThC	1.8
L	422.71	K	ThC″——→ThD	1.4
M	495.09	K	ThC″——→ThD	1.4
X	2526.30	K	ThC″——→ThD	0.1

This is a selection from a longer table prepared by K. Siegbahn for the volume *Alpha,
Beta, Gamma Spectroscopy*, 2nd ed., K. Siegbahn, ed. (Amsterdam: North-Holland
Publishing Co., 1964).

published before 1958 can be found in the data compilation of STROMINGER,
HOLLANDER, AND SEABORG[149] or in the LANDOLT-BÖRNSTEIN tables,[149a] or
in the Nuclear Data Sheets published by the National Research Council.

[149] See Table of Isotopes by D. Strominger, J. M. Hollander, and G. T. Seaborg,
Rev. Mod. Phys. **30,** 794 (1958).
[149a] Landolt-Börnstein Tables, New Series, Group I, Vol. I, "Energy Levels of Nuclei:
$A = 5$ to $A = 257$," Springer-Verlag, Berlin (1961).

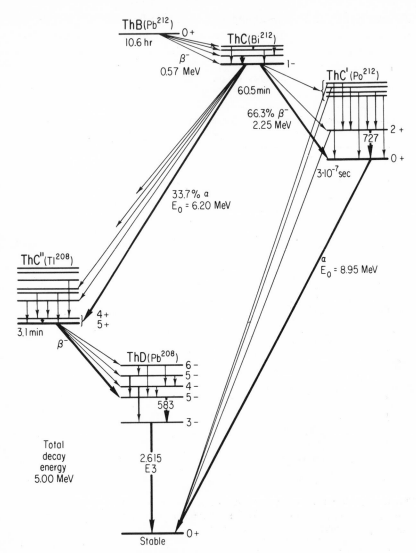

FIG. 6.30. Decay schemes for the principal transitions in the thorium active deposit; ThB $\xrightarrow{\beta}$ ThC $\xrightarrow{\alpha\beta}$ .... . Notice that the short-range α rays of the ThC are α transitions *to* excited levels, whereas the long-range α rays of ThC′ are α transitions *from* excited levels. Notice the origin of the very important and useful 2.62-MeV γ ray, which is in cascade with a preceding 0.58-MeV γ ray and the β transition. When all α, β, and γ-ray energies are summed, the total disintegration energy is the same (11.19 MeV) in the two competing branches ThC $\xrightarrow{\beta}$ ThC′ $\xrightarrow{\alpha}$ ThD and ThC $\xrightarrow{\alpha}$ ThC″ $\xrightarrow{\beta}$ ThD. The angular momentum and parity assignments in ThD are as determined by Elliott and coworkers.

Since 1956 a series of papers[150-157] by Russian authors has given much valuable new information on the electron spectra of the thorium active deposit and has cleared up many of the discrepancies in the older literature. This work was supplemented by a careful study of external conversion lines made by EMERY AND KANE[158] and by a series of photon measurements and α-γ coincidence measurements by SCHUPP, ET AL.[158a] and by U. HAUSER AND W. KERLER.[158b]

The Decay of Thorium B (Pb^{212}). The rather simple decay scheme of Thorium B is shown in Fig. 6.31. This scheme, which follows closely that given by ELLIS in 1934, is taken from the work of KRISYUK, SERGEYEV, LATYSHEV, AND VOROBYOV[154] except for the spin assignment of the upper two levels for which the $\gamma\gamma$ angular correlation experiments of ROETLING, GANLEY, AND KLAIBER[158c] specify spins at variance with those given by KRISYUK, ET AL. This scheme includes all the gamma rays known with certainty to occur in the decay of Pb^{212}. The level at 415.3 keV decays by a direct gamma transition to ground and also by two gamma ray cascades; the energy sums of the cascades are equal to the energy of the ground state transition to well within the small experimental error.

The assignment of 1− for the ground state of Bi^{212} comes from the work of HORTON[159] who measured the $\alpha\gamma$ angular correlation in Bi^{212} α-decay and analyzed the log ft data in Bi^{212} β-decay. The spin assignments of the upper states come from the multipolarity determinations of the

[150] E. M. Krisyuk, et al., Izvest. Akad. Nauk. SSSR, Ser. Fiz. **20**, 363 (1956); [translation: Bull. Acad. Sci. USSR **20**, 322 (1956)] E. M. Krisyuk, et al., Izvest. Akad. Nauk., SSSR, Ser. Fiz. **20**, 883 (1956); [translation: Bull. Acad. Sci., USSR **20**, 803 (1956)].

[151] E. M. Krisyuk, G. D. Latyshev, and A. G. Sergeev, Izvest. Akad. Nauk. SSSR, Ser. Fiz. **20**, 367 (1956); [translation: Bull. Acad Sci., USSR **20**, 335 (1956)].

[152] E. M. Krisyuk, et al., Izvest. Akad. Nauk. SSSR, Ser. Fiz. **20**, 877 (1956); [translation: Bull. Acad. Sci. USSR **20**, 797 (1956)]; V. D. Vorobev, et al., Izvest. Akad. Nauk. SSSR, Ser. Fiz. **21**, 954 (1957); [translation Bull. Acad. Sci. USSR **21**, 956 (1957)].

[153] A. I. Zhernovoi, et al., Zhur. Eksp. Teor. Fiz. **32**, 682 (1957); [translation: Sov. Phys. JETP **5**, 563 (1958)].

[154] E. M. Krisyuk, et al., Nucl. Phys. **4**, 579 (1957).

[155] E. M. Krisyuk, et al., Zhur. Eksp. Teor. Fiz. **33**, 1144 (1957); [translation: Sov. Phys. JETP **6**, (33), 880 (1958)].

[156] A. G. Sergeev, et al., Zhur. Eksp. Teor. Fiz. **33**, 1140 (1957); [translation: Sov. Phys. JETP **6**, (33) 878 (1958)].

[157] A. G. Sergeev, et al., Izvest. Akad. Nauk. SSSR, Ser. Fiz. **22**, 785 (1958); [translation: Bull. Acad. Sci. USSR **22**, 779 (1958)].

[158] G. T. Emery and W. R. Kane, Phys. Rev. **118**, 775 (1960); see also G. T. Emery, Atomic Energy Commission document, AECU-4169 (1958).

[158a] G. Schupp, H. Daniel, G. W. Eakins, and E. N. Jensen, Phys. Rev. **120**, 189 (1960).

[158b] U. Hauser and W. Kerler, Z. Physik **158**, 405 (1960).

[158c] P. G. Roetling, W. P. Ganley, and G. S. Klaiber, Nucl. Phys. **20**, 347 (1960).

[159] J. W. Horton, Phys. Rev. **101**, 717 (1956).

gamma rays and from arguments based on log ft values and $\gamma\gamma$ angular correlations.

KRISYUK AND CO-WORKERS[154] and WALEN AND BASTIN-SCOFFIER[160] speculate on the shell model interpretation of Bi^{212} but arrive at somewhat different conclusions. A proper shell model calculation of the level scheme

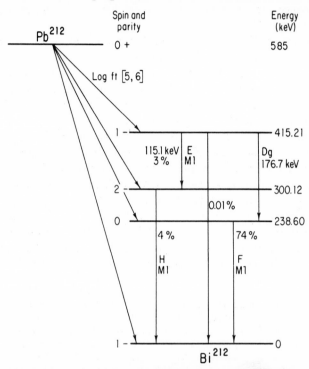

FIG. 6.31. Decay scheme of thorium B (Pb^{212}) as formulated by KRISYUK ET AL.[154] The gamma transitions are labeled by the classical nomenclature of Ellis. The spins of the upper two levels are those suggested by ROETLING ET AL.[158c]

of Bi^{212} is not simple because the interaction of 3 neutrons beyond the closed shell and 1 proton hole must be computed. Furthermore, recent calculations of the simpler case of Bi^{210} have shown that tensor force contributions to the neutron-proton interaction are quite important. A successful shell model calculation should explain not only the levels observed in the decay of thorium B but the numerous levels observed in the study of the $Bi^{209}(d, t)Bi^{208}$ reaction and the occurrence of a 2.7 millisecond isomeric state of Bi^{208}. (See Section 10.2.2.)

[160] R. J. Walen and G. Bastin-Scoffier, *Nucl. Phys.* **16**, 246 (1960).

Direct measurement and resolution of the beta spectrum of Pb^{212} was carried out by Martin and Richardson[161], who reported groups at 331 and 569 keV, and by Feather, Kyles, and Pringle[162], who reported the values 355 and 589 keV. The gamma ray studies indicate that lower-energy beta groups must be present in lower intensity as is indicated in the figure.

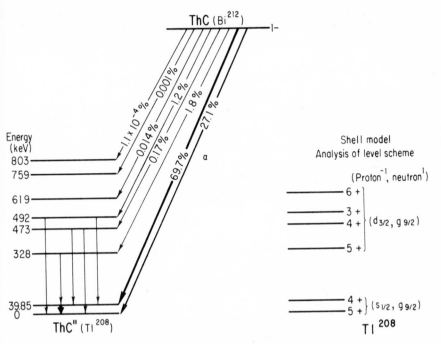

FIG. 6.32. Alpha branch decay scheme of ThC (Bi^{212}). ThC decays 33.7 per cent by alpha emission. The alpha intensity figures are taken from Walen and Bastin and Leang Chin-Fan.

The α-Decay of Thorium C (Bi^{212}). Thorium C resembles radium C of the uranium series and actinium C of the actinouranium series by decaying partially by alpha emission and partially by beta emission. In the case of thorium C the alpha branching is 33.7 per cent. Data on alpha particles taken by Rytz,[163] Walen and Bastin-Scoffier,[160] and of Leang[163a] are summarized in the accompanying table. Figure 6.32 summarizes much of the known information on the α-decay scheme of Bi^{212}. Measurements of

[161] D. G. E. Martin and H. O. W. Richardson, *Proc. Roy. Soc.* (London) **195A**, 287 (1948).

[162] N. Feather, J. Kyles, and R. W. Pringle, *Proc. Phys. Soc.* (London) **61**, 466 (1948).

[163] A. Rytz, *Compt. rend.* **233**, 790 (1951); *Helv. Phys. Acta* **34**, 240 (1961).

[163a] Leang Chin-Fan, Thesis, Paris, 1962, as reported to the authors by R. J. Walen.

the gamma radiations have been contributed* by many authors.[150-157, 164, 166, 166a]   The most prominent gamma transition is the one of 40 keV originating at the first excited state of Tl^{208}; it has an abundance of 70 per cent. Its energy has been precisely measured[151, 153, 165] as 39.85 keV.   From the L_I, L_{II}, L_{III} conversion ratios it is clear that this transition is magnetic dipole radiation ($M1$).   NIELSEN's measurements on the conversion electrons of transitions with energies of 287, 327, 431, 452, and 471 keV prove that they also are $M1$ in nature.   HORTON[159] assigned the values $5+$ to the Tl^{208} ground state and $4+$ to the 40 keV state on the basis of his study of the

Table of Bi^{212} Alpha Particles.

α-particle energy (MeV)	Abundance (%)	Energy of excited state in Tl^{208}
6.090	27.1	0
6.051	69.7	38.95
5.768	1.8	328
5.626	0.17	473
5.606	1.2	492
5.483	0.014	619
5.341	0.001	759
5.298	1.1×10^{-4}	803

The energies of the two most intense groups were determined by A. RYTZ[163].   The other energies and abundances were measured relative to these by WALEN AND BASTIN-SCOFFIER[160] and by LEANG CHIN-FAN.[163a]

asymmetry of the angular correlation of the 6.05 MeV α-ray with the 40 keV gamma ray.   WEALE's[166b] work also contributed to this conclusion.   These assignments are also consistent with the beta decay of Tl^{208} as discussed later in this chapter.

The experimental levels at 328, 473, 492, and 619 keV have spins and parities $5+$, $4+$, $3+$, and $6+$, respectively.   These assignments are consistent with the conversion electron measurements of NIELSEN,[166] and of EMERY AND KANE,[158] and with the α-γ angular correlations studied by COBB.[167]

[164] J. Surugue, Ann. Phys. 8, 484 (1937); J. Phys et radium 7, 145 (1946).

[165] D. I. Meyer and F. H. Schmidt, Phys. Rev. 94, 927 (1959).

[166] O. B. Nielsen, Kgl. Danske Videnskab. Selskab Mat. Fys. Medd. 30, No. 11 (1955).

[166a] G. Bertolini, et al., Nuclear Physics 30, 599 (1962).

[166b] J. W. Weale, Proc. Phys. Soc. (London), 68A, 35 (1955).

[167] W. C. Cobb, Phys. Rev. 132, 1693 (1963).

* See the summary of conversion electron data on the thorium active deposit compiled by K. Siegbahn in Alpha, Beta, Gamma Spectroscopy, 2nd ed., K. Siegbahn, ed. (Amsterdam: North Holland Publishing Company, 1964).

Thallium-208 differs from the closed shell nucleus Pb[208] by only one neutron and one proton and thus is a logical candidate for detailed shell model calculations. PRYCE's[168] exploratory analysis of this nucleus was based on a central delta-function force to represent the residual neutron-proton interaction and harmonic oscillator wave functions with energies taken from experimental data on nearby nuclei. These calculations indicated that the two lowest states were a 5+, 4+ doublet resulting from the $(s_{1/2}, g_{9/2})$ configuration. Similarly, the next four levels were attributed to a quartet arising from the $(d_{3/2}, g_{9/2})$ configuration. These conclusions are probably correct, but the calculations do not reproduce the correct order of the spin states for the upper quartet. The later work of KIM AND RASMUSSEN[168a] indicates that this is due to the inadequacy of the central force approximation. They obtained a superior agreement of theory and experiment by addition of a tensor force component of short range to the shell model residual interaction.

β-*Decay of Thorium C* (Bi[212]). We now turn to a consideration of the beta branching decay of thorium C. The complex gamma spectrum accompanying this decay has been studied by many authors,[151–158,166a,169–75, 176a,b,c,d] but unfortunately the published reports contain many contradictory data. It seems clear that in some cases gamma rays belonging to other members of the thorium active deposit or to members of the radium decay chain, present as an impurity in the samples under study, were falsely assigned to thorium C. In the summary presented here the conclusions of EMERY AND KANE[158] and of SERGEEV AND CO-WORKERS[156] are followed. These are re-enforced, except for one spin assignment, by the work of

[168] M. H. L. Pryce, *Proc. Roy. Soc.* (London) **A65**, 773, 962 (1952).
[168a] Y. E. Kim and J. O. Rasmussen, "Energy Levels of Tl[208] and Bi[208]," *Phys. Rev.* (1964).
[169] G. D. Latsyshev, *Revs. Mod. Phys.* **19**, 132 (1947).
[170] A. Johansson, *Arkiv F. Mat. Astr. Fysik* **A34**, 9 (1947).
[171] D. G. E. Martin and H. O. W. Richardson, *Proc. Phys. Soc.* **63A**, 223 (1950).
[172] D. G. E. Martin and G. Parry, *Proc. Phys. Soc.* **68A**, 1177 (1955).
[173] B. Chinaglia and F. Demichelis, *Nuovo Cim.* **4**, 1160 (1956).
[174] A. I. Alichanian and V. P. Dzelepov, *Compt. Rend.* (USSR) **20**, 115 (1938).
[175] S. C. Currano, P. I. Dee, and J. E. Strothers, *Proc. Roy. Soc.* (London) **A174**, 546 (1940).
[176] J. Itoh and Y. Watase, *Proc. Phys. Math. Soc.* (Japan) **23**, 142 (1941).
[176a] M. Giannini, D. Prosperi, and S. Sciuti, *Nucl. Phys.* **19**, 380 (1960); *Nuovo Cim.* (10) **22**, 31 (1961).
[176b] Yu. P. Gangrskii, G. M. Gusinskii, and I. Kh. Lemberg, *Bull. Acad. Sci., Phys. Ser.* (USSR) **24**, 1443 (1960) Columbia Technical Translation.
[176c] F. C. Flack and J. E. Johnson, *Proc. Phys. Soc.* (London) **79**, 10 (1962).
[176d] Schupp, Daniel, Eakins, and Jensen, *Phys. Rev.* **120**, 189 (1960).

SCHUPP, ET AL.,[158a] of HAUSER AND KERLER[158b], of GIANNINI, PROSPERI, AND SCIUTI[176a] and of GANGRSKII, GUSINSKII, AND LEMBERG.[176b] The electromagnetic transitions occurring between levels of the Po^{212} nucleus are summarized in Table 6.22. In order to place these transitions in a decay scheme one can first construct a skeleton level system from the data

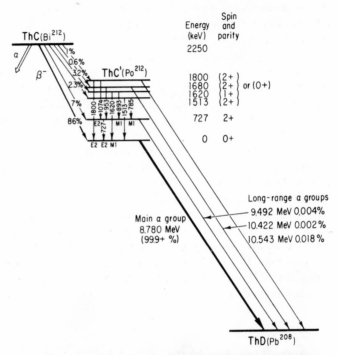

FIG. 6.33. Beta branch decay scheme of ThC (Bi²¹²). The ThC decays 66.3 per cent by beta emission. The level scheme of Po²¹² is that published by Russian authors. The beta group intensities are those deduced by Emery and Kane from their γ-intensity figures. The data on long range alphas come from the work of Lewis and Bowden and of Rytz. According to Schupp, Daniel, Eakins, and Jensen, the 1800 keV level is 2+ and the 1800 keV transition is E2. Additional gamma rays are reported by Giannini, Prosperi, and Sciuti.

on the long-range alpha particles of thorium C′. Our knowledge of these comes from the careful work of LEWIS AND BOWDEN[177] and of RYTZ[163] as reviewed by BRIGGS.[178] The three long-range α-groups define levels at 727, 1680, 1800 keV in Po^{212}. It is possible to fit six of the observed gamma

---

177 W. B. Lewis and B. V. Bowden, *Proc. Roy. Soc.* (London) **A145**, 235 (1935).

178 G. H. Briggs, *Revs. Mod. Phys.* **26**, 1 (1954).

rays into the decay scheme as transitions between these levels or between one of those levels and the ground state. The other γ-transitions indicate a need to postulate levels at 1620 and 1513 keV.[156] The decay scheme constructed in this way is shown in Fig. 6.33. The beta intensity figures given

TABLE **6.22.**

Part I. Electromagnetic transitions in Po^{212}.
Table reproduced from Emery and Kane, *Phys. Rev.* **118**, 755 (1960).

Gamma[a]	E (keV)	$I_k(\%)$[b]	$I_\gamma(\%)$	ε_k	Multi-polarity
O	727	0.106	10.1 ± 0.6	0.0105 ± 0.008	$E2$
Oa	785	0.051	1.5 ± 0.3	0.034 ± 0.008	$M1$
Pa	893	0.014	0.6 ± 0.3	0.023 ± 0.012	$M1$
Pa2a	953	0.010	$\leqslant 0.8$	$\geqslant 0.009$	$(M1 + E2)$
R	1074	0.006 ⎫	1.0 ± 0.2	—	$(E2)$
Ra	1078	0.014 ⎭	—	—	—
—	1350	—	$\leqslant 0.33$	—	—
S	1513	0.008	$\leqslant 0.7$	$\geqslant 0.008$	?
Sa	1620	0.013	2.6 ± 0.4	0.0050 ± 0.0015	$M1$
—	1680	—	$\leqslant 0.4$	—	—
Sb	1800	0.007	$\leqslant 0.4$	$\geqslant 0.012$	EO^c
—	2200	—	$\leqslant 0.27$	—	—

Intensities are given in per cent of the decays of Bi^{212} to Po^{212}.
ε_k is the K-conversion coefficient.
[a] The letter designations follow the classical nomenclature.
[b] These figures come from the Russian literature.[156]
[c] Schupp, Daniel, Eakins and Jensen (*Phys. Rev.* **120**, 189 (1960)) present a table with values in rather good agreement with Emery and Kane, but there is a major discrepancy in the multipolarity assignment of the 1800 keV gamma. In an $\alpha\gamma$ coincidence experiment Schupp, et al., saw photons of 1800 keV energy and assigned a multipolarity of $E2$ to the transition. Their result is confirmed by Hauser and Kerler, *Z. Physik* **158**, 405 (1960) and others.

Part II. Beta transitions from Bi^{212} to Po^{212}.

Energy of excited state (MeV)	Maximum energy of betas (MeV)	Intensity in per cent	log ft
0	2.25	86	7.3
0.727	1.52	7	7.7
1.513	0.74	~ 2	~ 7.1
1.620	0.63	~ 3.2	~ 6.6
1.680	0.57	< 1.2	> 7.0
1.800	0.45	~ 1.2	~ 6.7

The branch intensities are derived from the gamma-ray intensities.
From G. T. Emery and W. R. Kane, *Phys. Rev.* **118**, 755 (1960); for another slightly different set of intensities and ft values see Gangrskii, Gusinskii and Lemberg.[176b]

in this figure are those estimated by EMERY AND KANE from a consideration of the gamma ray intensities. The beta groups and the corresponding log ft values are summarized in Table 6.22. The log ft are all consistent with first forbidden transitions, as they must be if the spin assignments are correct.

EMERY AND KANE[158] call attention to the fact that the level scheme of Po^{212} bears a close similarity to the lower levels of Po^{214} as displayed in Fig. 6.14. In the discussion of the decay scheme of radium C' (Bi^{214}) appearing earlier in this chapter it is mentioned that the first excited 2+ level and a second 2+ level lying at little more than twice the energy of the first 2+ state may constitute a one phonon and two phonon excitation of a collective quadrupole vibrational motion about an equilibrium spherical shape. One important characteristic of such a series of levels is that the second 2+ state de-excites by a cascade of two $E2$ transitions and does not de-excite by a direct $E2$ transition to the ground state. Such a pattern of decay appears here in the Po^{212} level system.

A more general interpretation of the low-lying levels of Po^{212} may be the one provided by the calculations of BAND, KHARITONOV, AND SLIV[178a] and of GLENDENNING.[178b] These authors consider the possible shell model wave functions for the two protons and the two neutrons which are added to the Pb^{208} closed shell core to construct the Po^{212} nucleus. The residual forces working between nn, pp, and pn pairs strongly influence the properties of the levels. The interaction of the four external particles with surface oscillations also influence the results somewhat but these collective oscillations are not a dominant feature of the lowest levels. The theoretical spectrum can account for the spin and parity assignments of the chief levels seen in the decay of ThC and for the characteristics of the γ-rays de-exciting these levels.

The most prominent gamma ray in the beta decay of thorium C is the 727 keV transition from the first excited state at 2+ to the ground state. This is thoroughly characterized as electric quadrupole by its K/L conversion ratio and its total conversion coefficient. The ten-fold increase of the reduced transition probability $B(E2)$ over the "single proton" value has been cited[158] as evidence of the collective nature of this transition, but the wave functions of BAND, KHARITONOV, AND SLIV[178a] also account for the enhancement in rate while assigning a completely different nature to the 727 keV 2+ level.

The Decay of Thorium C' (Po^{212}). ThC' (Po^{212}) decays with the emission of 8.780 MeV alpha particles. The half-life of 3.04×10^{-7} seconds has been measured by delayed coincidence methods. The alpha particles of ThC' are the most energetic among the naturally occurring isotopes (except

[178a] I. M. Band, Yu. I. Kharitonov, and L. A. Sliv, *Nucl. Phys.* **35**, 136 (1962).

[178b] N. K. Glendenning, *Phys. Rev.* **127**, 923 (1962); see also H. D. Zeh, *Zeit. f. Physik* **175**, 490 (1963).

for low intensity long-range alphas of ThC' and RaC') and the alpha particle energy has been measured with great accuracy.[178,178c]   It is currently used as one of the absolute alpha standards in the calibration of magnetic spectrometers.

The decay scheme of ThC' is characterized by the appearance of long-range alpha groups whose origin is best understood by reference to Fig. 6.33. Excited levels in ThC' de-excite by alpha emission to the ground state of ThD. Alpha emission from an excited state is a very rare occurrence and among all the naturally occurring radioelements the only other isotope in which it is observed is RaC'.   Usually gamma emission to the ground state occurs so much more readily that alpha emission, a relatively slow process, cannot compete.   In ThC' and RaC', however, the alpha disintegration energy is so large that the alpha decay half-life becomes short enough to compete with gamma emission and the excited states show branching decay by alpha emission to a significant degree.   For every 10^6 alpha particles representing decay from the ground state of ThC' there are 230 long-range alpha particles representing decay from excited states.

Isomeric form of Po^{212}.   By reactions of artificial transmutation PERLMAN, ASARO, GHIORSO, LARSH, AND LATIMER[178d] have prepared and identified an isomeric form of ThC' with exceedingly interesting properties.   This isomer does not occur in natural radioactivity, but we find it convenient to discuss it here.

The isomer is most conveniently prepared by helium ion bombardments of bismuth but it was first discovered in irradiations of bismuth and lead targets with more complex particles such as accelerated ions of C^{12}, B^{10}, and O^{16}.   The most prominent radiation emitted by the isomer is an alpha particle group with the large energy of 11.65 $\pm$ 0.02 MeV and a half-life of 45 seconds.   Two other α-groups were identified: 9.08 $\pm$ 0.015 MeV (1% intensity) and 8.52 $\pm$ 0.015 MeV (2.05 $\pm$ 0.09% intensity).   These energies are all relative to At^{211} and Po^{212} standards taken as 5.862 MeV and 8.780 MeV, respectively.   By alpha-gamma coincidence measurements the presence of a 0.57 MeV gamma ray in $\sim$ 2 per cent intensity and a 2.61 MeV gamma ray in 2.6 per cent intensity was established.   These results led to the decay scheme shown in the figure.   It is seen that excited levels of Pb^{208} are populated at 2.61 and 3.19 MeV.   These levels are known to exist from previous work on the decay of ThC'' (Tl^{208}); see Fig. 6.34.   No radiations indicating an isomeric transition of Po^{212m} to the ground state were observed.

[178c] Unfortunately more recent determinations have been about 5.5 keV higher in energy so that there remains some doubt about the correct energy of this important standard; Collins, et al., *Proc. Roy. Soc.* (London) **A216**, 219 (1953) give 8.7857 $\pm$ 0.004 and Rytz, *Helv. Phys. Acta* **34**, 240 (1961) gives 8.7854 $\pm$ 0.008.

[178d] I. Perlman, F. Asaro, A. Ghiorso, A. Larsh, and R. M. Latimer, "An Isomeric State of Po^{212}," *Phys. Rev.* **127**, 917 (1962).

This is an extraordinary instance of alpha decay because a half-life of 45 seconds for an 11.65 MeV alpha groups implies a hindrance in the alpha emission process by a factor of 10^{13}. This implies an unusual structure and high angular momentum for Po^{212m} and a severe restriction on the possible excited states of Po^{212} which lie between Po^{212m} and the ground state.

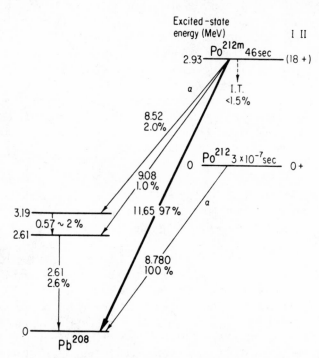

FIGURE showing decay scheme of Po[212] isomers.

Po^{212} is an even-even nucleus with 2 protons and 2 neutrons beyond Pb^{208}, which has a particularly stable configuration. In the Po^{212} ground state the 2 neutrons and 2 protons are paired off to a net spin of zero. In its excited states, however, these four nucleons, which individually have high intrinsic spin, can recouple in various ways to give very high resultant spin. In order to predict the spectrum of levels expected from this recoupling one must assume some definite form for the residual interaction between the nucleons and carry through a detailed calculation. This has been done by GLENDENNING[178b] who concluded that the most important particle configuration is $(h_{9/2}^2 i_{11/2}^2)$ and that the sequence of levels in order of energy is 0+, 2+, 4+, 6+, 8+, 10+, 18+, 16+, etc. The isomerism is identified with the 18+ state which has a "spin gap" of 8 between itself and the state of highest spin lying beneath it.

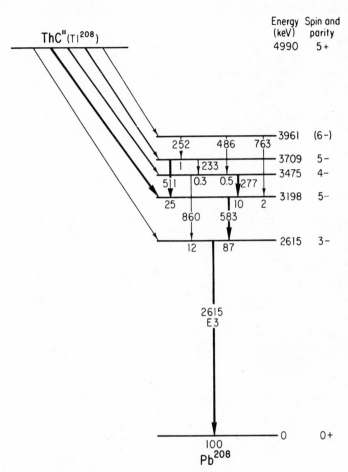

FIG. **6.34.** Decay scheme of thorium C″ (Tl²⁰⁸). All energies are given in keV. Gamma intensities in per cent are given beneath the arrow tips. See also Tables 6.23 and 6.24.

ThC″ (Tl²⁰⁸). The decay of 3.1 minute ThC″ is shown in Fig. 6.34. One of the features of principal interest is the very high energy gamma ray of 2.615 MeV which occurs in 100 per cent abundance. This is the most energetic gamma ray to be found among the natural radioactivities. It is commonly used as a standard to calibrate gamma ray or electron spectrometers. The photons can be used to calibrate a scintillation spectrometer, and since the *K* conversion coefficient is 0.0018, an appreciable number of mono-energetic electrons of 2.526 MeV energy are available for calibration of electron spectrometers. For this purpose one prepares an intense source of the thorium active deposit.

Several investigations which led to the decay scheme shown in Fig. 6.34 may be mentioned. MARTIN AND RICHARDSON,[179,180] made an analysis of the energies and intensities of the gamma ray and beta particles and established the existence of excited levels at 2.62, 3.20, 3.48 and 3.71 MeV. There was considerable uncertainty about the spin and parity assignments of these levels until definite choices were made by ELLIOTT, GRAHAM, WALKER,

TABLE 6.23. Electromagnetic transitions in Pb^{208} from decay of Tl^{208}.

Gamma	E (keV)	Electron Intensity I_k (%)[a]	Photon Intensity I_γ (%)[b]	ε_k	Multi-polarity
E_c	211	0.15	—	—	($M1$)
E_d	233	0.13	—	—	($M1$)
F_b	252	0.37	1.5 ± 0.7	0.25 ± 0.15	($M1$)
G	277	2.4	6.9 ± 1.2	0.35 ± 0.06	$M1$
J_c7	486	0.01	—	—	($E2$)
L	511	1.7	23.0 ± 2.0	0.074 ± 0.007	$M1 + E2$[e]
M	583	—	86.4 ± 5.6	0.0156[c]	$E2$
$O2$	763	0.058	1.9 ± 0.5	0.031 ± 0.008	$M1$
P	860	0.27	11.4 ± 1.2	0.024 ± 0.003	$M1$
X	2614	0.17	(100)	(0.0017)[a, c, d]	$E3$

Intensities are given in per cent of Tl^{208} decays. The classical letter designations are given in the first column. ε_k is the K-conversion coefficient.

[a] Krisyuk[155], et al.

[b] Emery and Kane[158].

[c] Elliott, et al.[181].

[d] Alichanian and Nikitin, Phys. Rev. 53, 767 (1938).

[e] Various authors have given differing values of the multipole mixing of the 511 keV transition: Elliott, et al., reported the intensity ratio of $E2$ to $M1$ as 1.7 ± 0.3 and later as 1.0 ± 0.4; Wood and Jastram (Nucl. Phys. 32, 411 (1962)) reported a ratio 0.18 ± 0.03 and Emery and Kane[158] give 0.18 ± 0.15.

AND WOLFSON[181] on the basis of gamma-gamma angular correlation experiments and conversion coefficients. The unique shape of the correlation between the prominent 583 keV and 2.615 MeV gamma rays is quite strong evidence for the 5—3—0 sequence; in particular, the 4—2—0 sequence which one might have expected is definitely ruled out. Additional gamma rays reported by ELLIOTT, ET AL.[181] and confirmed by KRISYUK, ET AL.[155] establish the existence of a further level at 3.961 which most probably has the spin 6. EMERY AND KANE[158] measured the intensity of the photons emitted in the decay of thorium C'' by an external conversion technique and

[179] H. O. W. Richardson, Nature 161, 516 (1948).

[180] D. G. E. Martin and H. O. W. Richardson, Proc. Phys. Soc. 60, 466 (1948).

[181] L. G. Elliott, R. L. Graham, J. Walker, and J. L. Wolfson, Phys. Rev. 93, 356 (1954) prelim. note; Proc. Roy. Soc. Canada 48, 12A (1954).

combined their results with the internal conversion measurements of KRISYUK, ET AL.[155] to arrive at the intensity figures summarized in Table 6.23. They used these gamma ray intensity figures to compute the beta ray spectrum and log ft values summarized in Table 6.24. SCHUPP, DANIEL, EAKINS, AND

TABLE 6.24. Beta transitions from thallium-208 to lead-208.

Energy of excited state (MeV)	Maximum energy of betas (MeV)	Emery and Kane[158] intensity in per cent	log ft	Schupp, et al.[158b] Intensity in per cent	log ft
2.62	2.38	~0.03*	9.3	<0.5	>8.1
3.20	1.80	51.3	5.6	48.8	5.7
3.48	1.52	20.6	5.7	22.7	5.7
3.71	1.28	24.3	5.4	23.9	5.3
3.96	1.03	3.6	5.8	4.6	5.8

* This figure comes from unpublished work of ELLIOTT AND CO-WORKERS.

JENSEN[158b] have made a similar analysis based on their β-γ coincidence and γ-intensity data. WOOD AND JASTRAM[181a] reinvestigated the spin and parity assignments of the levels by means of a combination of polarization-correlation and directional-correlation measurements.

Several authors[155,159,167] have chosen 5 as the most likely spin for the ground state of thorium C″.

The level scheme of Pb^{208} is anomalous for an even-even nucleus and has excited the interest of the theorists of nuclear structure. A discussion of the possible interpretations is given in Section 10.2.2 of Chapter 10.

6.4 THE ACTINIUM $(4n + 3)$ SERIES

We have discussed the uranium-radium and the thorium series in the preceding sections of this chapter and now turn to a consideration of the third family of heavy element radioactive elements, the series known as the actinium series or, alternatively, as the actinouranium series.

The actinium decay chain is summarized in Fig. 6.35 and in Table 6.25.

Uranium-235. The primary activity from which all the other (secondary) activities in the actinium series are derived is U^{235}. It is likely that higher-mass nuclides in the 4n + 3 family—nuclides such as Pu^{239}, Cm^{243}, Am^{243}, Bk^{247}, etc.—were also present when the elements were first formed, but of all the nuclides of the 4n + 3 mass type above the element lead, only U^{235} is sufficiently long-lived to have persisted throughout geologic time. The half-life of U^{235} is 7.13 × 10⁸ years. Any sample of natural uranium no

[181a] G. T. Wood and P. S. Jastram, *Nuclear Physics* 32, 411 (1962).

TABLE 6.25. The actinium series.

Radioelement	Symbol	Radiation	Half-life
Actinouranium	U^{235}	α	7.13×10^8 yr
Uranium Y	Th^{231}	β	25.64 hr
Protactinium	Pa^{231}	α	3.48×10^4 yr
Actinium	Ac^{227}	β and α	22.0 yr
98.8% 1.2%			
Radioactinium	Th^{227}	α	18.17 day
*Actinium K	Fr^{223}	β	21 min
Actinium X	Ra^{223}	α	11.68 day
Actinon	Em^{219}	α	3.92 sec
Actinium A	Po^{215}	α	1.83×10^{-3} sec
Actinium B	Pb^{211}	β	36.1 min
Actinium C	Bi^{211}	β and α	2.16 min
0.32% 99.68%			
Actinium C'	Po^{211}	α	0.52 sec
Actinium C"	Tl^{207}	β	4.79 min
Actinium D	Pb^{207}	stable	

* 0.004% α-branching of AcK not shown; see Fig. 6.35.

matter what its source contains U^{235} in a constant amount, namely 0.720 atom per cent or 0.711 weight per cent.* We have discussed natural uranium and the determination of the specific activity of uranium isotopes in Section 6.2. See particularly Table 6.2.

Because of the constant amount of U^{235} in natural uranium the amount of protactinium, actinium, etc. found in uranium minerals bears a constant ratio to the total uranium content and to the members of the uranium-radium

* Slight variations of about 0.1 per cent are found in natural uranium from various sources so that the average U^{235} content cannot be specified closer than 0.711 weight per cent.

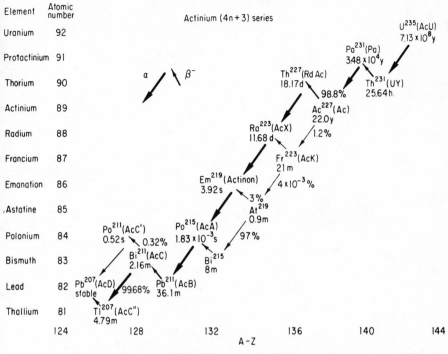

FIG. **6.35.** The actinium (4n + 3) series.

decay chain as we have seen in Table 6.3. This fact was noted early in the study of the natural radioactivities and led to some confusion. For many years it was believed that actinium must be a member of the uranium-radium decay series as a result of a branching decay somewhere near the beginning of the series, perhaps at uranium I or uranium II. This confusion was understandable because U^{235} was not discovered until the mass-spectrographic work of DEMPSTER in 1935 and because no member of the actinium series could be isolated in sufficient amount and isotopic purity for an accurate atomic weight determination. It was not until 1935 that A. V. GROSSE measured the atomic weight of protactinium by weighing a pure compound of known composition.

Uranium-235 is an alpha emitter with a complex alpha spectrum and a complex gamma spectrum. These radiations and the decay scheme are thoroughly discussed in Section 8.4.8 of Chapter 8.

The fissionability of U^{235} and the characteristics of the fission process are described in detail in Volume III, Part 1.

Uranium-Y (Th^{231}). The immediate decay product of U^{235} is 25.6 hour uranium-Y, an isotope of thorium. Uranium-Y is a beta emitter with a complex decay scheme which is thoroughly discussed in Section 8.2.10

of Chapter 8. The most energetic beta group has an energy of 300 keV and the total decay energy is 383 keV.

Uranium-Y can be isolated from isotopically-pure U^{235} after a few days growth period. If it is necessary to prepare UY samples from natural uranium, the samples will be contaminated with UX_1 and UX_2 since in each milligram of natural uranium there are 733.6 disintegrations per minute of UX_1 and UX_2 and 33.7 disintegrations per minute of UY. This ratio can be improved somewhat in favor of UY by purifying the uranium from thorium, waiting a few hours or a day, and then isolating a UY fraction before much UX has had a chance to grow in. To prepare samples for beta spectrometric studies a better approach is to prepare Th^{231} artificially by neutron bombardment of ionium[182] or of thorium.[183]

$$Io^{230}(n, \gamma)Th^{231}$$

$$\sigma = 26 \text{ barns}$$

$$Th^{232}(n, 2n)Th^{231}$$

Protactinium. Protactinium was discovered by HAHN AND MEITNER in 1918 and almost simultaneously by SODDY AND CRANSTON. A. V. GROSSE, who made many early contributions to the chemistry of this element, prepared the first pure compound in 1927.

Protactinium is an alpha emitter with a half-life of 34,800 years as determined by specific activity measurements on a weighed sample of pure ignited protactinium oxide. The value of 34,300 ± 300 years quoted by VAN WINKLE, LARSON, AND KATZIN[184] is based on the formula Pa_2O_5. Using later information that the ignited oxide corresponds more closely to $PaO_{2.25}$ ELSON[185] recalculated the value 34,800 ± 300 years. Protactinium-231 is the longest-lived of the isotopes of element 91 and the only isotope suitable for the isolation of the element in weighable quantities. The name protactinium was given to Pa^{231} by HAHN AND MEITNER because it was the long-sought-for progenitor of actinium. The name has since been taken over as the name of the element and all its isotopes. An earlier spelling, *protoactinium*, has been shortened to *protactinium*.

Because of its origin as a decay product of U^{235}, protactinium is found only in uranium ores where its equilibrium concentration is only 343 milligrams per metric ton of natural uranium or almost exactly the same concentration as that of the rare element, radium. If one starts with a pure

182 A. H. Jaffey and E. K. Hyde, report *ANL-4249* (1949) unpublished.

183 Nishina, Yasaki, Kimura, and Ikawa, *Nature* 142, 874 (1938).

184 Q. Van Winkle, R. G. Larson, and L. I. Katzin, *J. Am. Chem. Soc.* 71, 2585 (1949).

185 R. Elson, Chapter 5. "The Actinide Elements," J. J. Katz and G. T. Seaborg, eds. *National Nuclear Energy Series*, Vol. 14A (New York: McGraw-Hill Book Co., 1954).

sample of U^{235}, protactinium will grow in at the rate shown in Fig. 6.36. Samples of protactinium ranging in size from milligrams to grams have been isolated from uranium ores but the chemical properties of protactinium are such that its isolation is a matter of considerable difficulty.   In 1961 it was

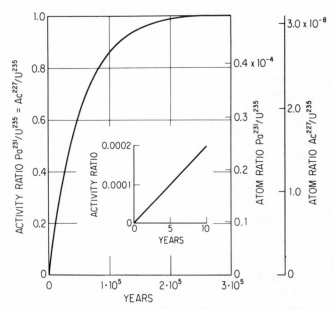

FIG. **6.36.** Growth of Pa²³¹ and Ac²²⁷ into pure U²³⁵.   Half-life values used are those listed in Table 6.25.

revealed by English government authorities that English scientists and engineers had succeeded in isolating the large quantity of 150 grams of protactinium from 60 tons of raffinate wastes of a uranium solvent extraction process.[185a]   It is also possible to synthesize protactinium by the neutron irradiation of ionium as is described earlier in this chapter in the ionium part of Section 6.2.

The alpha and gamma spectra of protactinium, in common with that of most of the alpha emitters in the actinium series, are quite complex.   These spectra and the decay scheme of Pa^{231} are thoroughly discussed in Section 8.3.7. of Chapter 8.

Early Difficulties in the Study of Actinium.   From the historical standpoint actinium is the most important member of the $4n + 3$ series.   The discovery and the early study of actinium were greatly hampered by difficulties arising from the following unfavorable circumstances.

[185a] *Chem. and Eng. News* (August 7, 1961), p. 48; D. A. Collins, J. J. Hillary, J. S. Nairn, and G. M. Phillips, *J. Inorg. Nucl. Chem.* **24**, 441 (1962).

1. The equilibrium amount of actinium in uranium ores is very small; the ratio of Ac^{227} to normal uranium is 0.21×10^{-9}; the amount of Ac^{227} in pitchblende is only 0.625×10^{-3} of the amount of Ra^{226} present.

2. Actinium resembles the rare-earth elements closely in its chemical properties and is separated with difficulty from them. Uranium ores almost invariably contain considerable quantities of rare-earth impurities which are concentrated with the actinium.

3. Actinium itself has very weak radiations and, in fact, for some years it was thought that actinium was "rayless". After 1911 it was recognized from the "displacement laws" that actinium must be a beta emitter, but it was not until 1935 that HULL, LIBBY, and LATIMER[186] detected electrons emitted by actinium. Even then, in view of knowledge obtained later on the alpha branching of actinium to AcK and on the energy of the Ac^{227} beta rays, it seems probable that these investigators had observed the beta particles of AcK. The end point energy of the Ac^{227} beta particles is only 45 keV. The most energetic beta rays are stopped completely in an absorber of three milligrams per cm^2 and the majority of the electrons in the spectrum are stopped by less matter than that. When actinium is mixed with rare earth or other carrier material, the beta particles are almost completely absorbed within the sample itself.

The difficulties (1), (2) and (3) listed above still apply today and have hindered the detailed study of the properties of this interesting element. During the first years in which actinium was studied, the confusion was naturally greater because the daughter products were not known. The direct decay products, radioactinium and actinium-X, were first discovered with certainty 6 and 7 years, respectively, after the discovery of actinium. Furthermore, ionium was not discovered until 1907 and it was frequently a contaminant of actinium preparations because of the similar behavior of actinium and ionium in many chemical separations. This contamination had a curious result in the period 1905–1907 when actinium received consideration as the possible missing parent of the element radium. Proof of the formation of radium from actinium preparation was sought and was in fact found. Later, however, it became apparent that the radium formation was caused by ionium contamination in the actinium.

DEBIERNE in 1899 found that after the complete removal of uranium, polonium, and radium from pitchblende solutions it was possible to precipitate a mixed hydroxide fraction with ammonia and to find radioactivity which could not be assigned to these elements. The new activity appeared to follow thorium in many chemical steps. DEBIERNE gave the name actinium after the Greek word, Aktis, meaning ray, to this strange activity. His

---

[186] D. E. Hull, W. F. Libby, and W. M. Latimer, *J. Am. Chem. Soc.* **57**, 593, 1650 (1935).

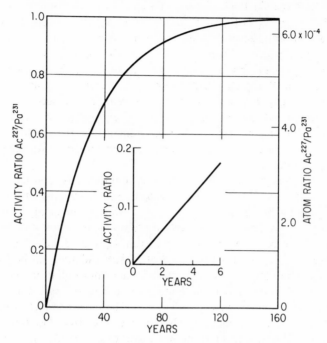

FIG. **6.37.** Growth of Ac²²⁷ into Pa²³¹.

samples of actinium were, in fact, quite impure. GIESEL contributed greatly
to the early studies of actinium. During the course of studies of pitchblende
residues GIESEL isolated rare-earth fractions which had radioactive properties
different from radium and polonium and, from what was known at the time,
from DEBIERNE's actinium. In particular, GIESEL noted that his preparations
gave rise to an active gas (actinon) similar to radium emanation or thorium
emanation but of much shorter period. Surfaces exposed to this emanation
became strongly radioactive. GIESEL gave the name "emanium" or emanation body to the substance isolated with the rare earths which appeared to be
the source of the radioactive gas. He withdrew this name when it later
became evident that his "emanium" and DEBIERNE's actinium were actually
the same substance. GIESEL's contribution was to show the close similarity
of actinium to the rare earths rather than to thorium, as DEBIERNE had
reported, and to call attention to the actinium emanation.

The rate at which actinium grows into pure U^{235} or pure Pa^{231} is
shown in Figs. 6.36 and 6.37, respectively.

The Beta Decay of Actinium. For some years the value 13.5 year was
accepted as the half-life of Ac^{227}, but CURIE and BOUISSIERES[187] reported a

---

[187] I. Curie and G. Bouissieres, *Cahiers Phys.* **26**, 1 (1944).

value of 21.7 year in 1944. Three subsequent investigations have given the values 22.0 year,[188] 21.6 year,[189] and 21.6 year,[189a] respectively, very close to CURIE AND BOUISSIERES' value. The measurement of a half-life in this range requires a precise technique because the activity changes are slight within a convenient period of measurement (i.e., a few months to a year). The double ionization chamber method in which the ion current from one chamber is nearly balanced by the ion current from a second chamber in which a long-lived radium sample of nearly equivalent activity is placed is well-suited for this purpose. A measurement by the coulometric technique[190] gave a value of 21.2 ± 0.8 years in good agreement with the balanced chamber technique.

The end point of the beta spectrum of actinium was reported to be only 40 keV in an unpublished study by FRIEDMAN AND CO-WORKERS.[191] A careful study by BECKMANN AND HUSTER[192] showed an energy of 45.5 ± 1.0 keV with no evidence of a second component. NOVIKOVA AND CO-WORKERS[193] placed the end point between 42 and 45 keV. LECOIN AND CO-AUTHORS[194] reported the presence of 37 keV radiation in the beta decay of actinium but later[195] it was shown that this radiation was actually fluorescent K x-radiation of lanthanum excited in the rare earth impurity in the sample by higher energy radiation. The most complete study of the gamma transitions was made by NOVIKOVA, VOLKOVA, GOLDIN, ZIV, AND TRETYAKOV[193] who measured the M, N and O shell conversion electrons of gamma transitions with the energies 9.3 ± 0.1, 15.2 ± 0.1 and 24.5 ± 0.2 keV. From the conversion ratios in the M subshells it was concluded that all three transitions were mixed $E2 + M1$ in multipolarity, although the more energetic two were >99 per cent $M1$. The 9.3 and 15.2 keV transitions add to 24.5 so it is believed that they represent a cascade de-exciting a level at 24.5 keV. The gamma intensities imply a composite beta spectrum.

The Alpha Branching of Ac^{227} and the Decay Properties of Actinium K. In 1914 MEYER, HESS, AND PANETH[196] observed a group of low-intensity

---

[188] J. M. Hollander and R. F. Leininger, *Phys. Rev.* **80**, 915 (1950).

[189] J. Tobailem, *J. Phys. Rad.* **16**, 48 (1955).

[189a] J. Robert, *Ann. Phys.* **4**, 89 (1959).

[190] N. S. Shimanskaya and E. A. Yashugina, *Soviet Journal of Atomic Energy* (in English translation), No. **5**, 817 (1956).

[191] M. Freedman, J. May, R. Pairs, W. Ramler, and M. Rusnak, reported in *Argonne National Laboratory Classified Report ANL-4380* (March 1950).

[192] W. Beckmann and E. Huster, *Z. Naturforsch* **10a**, 86 (1955); *Z. Physik* **142**, 585 (1955).

[193] G. I. Novikova, E. A. Volkova, L. L. Gol'din, D. M. Ziv, and E. F. Tretyakov, *Sov. Phys. JETP* **37**, 10 No. 4, 663 (1960).

[194] Lecoin, Perey, Riou, and Teillac, *J. Phys. Rad.* **11**, 227 (1950).

[195] Bouchez, Michalowicz, Riou, and Teillac, *J. Phys. Rad.* **16**, 344 (1955).

[196] S. J. Meyer, V. F. Hess, and F. Paneth, Sitzber. *Aka. Wiss. Wien., Math. Naturw. Kl. Abt.*, IIa, **123**, 1473 (1914).

alpha particles in a pure actinium preparation in addition to alpha groups ascribed to unremoved traces of AcX. These new alpha particles of 3.56 cm range in air were ascribed to branch decay in Ac^{227}. This observation was subject to considerable doubt over the next two decades since it seemed possible that the new alpha particles could be ascribed to traces of protactinium or of actinium daughters. MLLE. PEREY[197] settled the doubts conclusively in 1939 by chemically isolating from pure actinium preparation a 21 min beta emitter which had the expected properties of the ekacesium

TABLE **6.26.** Alpha spectrum of Ac^{227}.
NOVIKOVA, ET AL.[193]

Alpha group	Alpha particle energy (keV)	Energy of daughter level (keV)	Alpha transition intensity	Hindrance factor
α_0	4949 ± 2	0	48.7 ± 3	67
α_{12}	4936.5 ± 3	12.7	36.1 ± 3	8
α_{84}	4866 ± 3	84.5	6.9 ± 1	14
α_{102}	4849 ± 3	102	5.5 ± 1	14
α_{166}	4786 ± 5	166	1.0 ± 0.5	40
α_{193}	4759 ± 5	193	1.8 ± 0.5	17
α_{225}?	4728 ± 8	225	~ 0.1	—
α_{250}	4704 ± 8	250	0.4 ± 0.2	38
α_{440}	4516 ± 10	440	~ 0.2	—

isotope which the alpha decay of actinium should produce. The beta-emitting ekacesium was named Actinium K. PEREY established that the alpha branching in Ac^{227} was 1.2 per cent. Since AcK was the first isotope of element 87 ever to be established, MLLE. PEREY is credited with the discovery of this element. For the name of the element, she chose francium (symbol Fr). The isotopes of francium are reviewed in Section 10.6 of Chapter 10 where it is shown that AcK is the longest-lived form of this element.

An energy of 4.942 MeV was reported[198] for the alpha particles of Ac^{227} in 1952. These alpha particles were later given a careful restudy by NOVI-KOVA, VOLKOVA, GOL'DIN, ZIV, AND TRETYAKOV[193] who found the complex spectrum which is summarized in Table 6.26. They also studied the conversion electrons emitted during the alpha decay of Ac^{227}. This study is difficult to carry out because of the low alpha branching and because of the electron lines contributed by daughter activities which grow into the sample. Most of the difficulties were circumvented by electron-alpha coincidence

---

[197] M. Perey, *J. Phys. Rad.* (7) **10**, 435 (1939); *Compt. Rend.* **208**, 97 (1939).

[198] S. Rosenblum, M. Perey, M. Valadares, and M. Guillot, private communication, (Oct. 1952) quoted by Strominger, Hollander, and Seaborg, *Revs. Mod. Phys.* **30**, 794 (1958).

techniques.   Evidence for transitions of the following energy was found: 12.7, 70.4, 84.5, 101, 166 and 193 keV.   These gamma rays could be fitted naturally into the level scheme of Fr^{223} revealed by the alpha groups, as shown in Fig. 6.38.

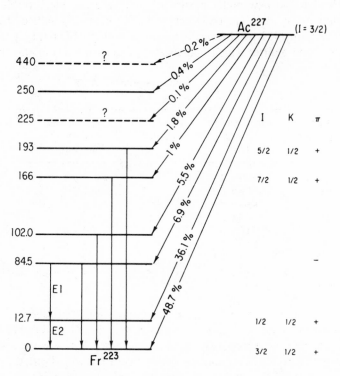

FIG. **6.38.** Decay scheme for the alpha branch decay of Ac^{227} as formulated by NOVIKOVA ET AL.[193]

These authors discuss a possible interpretation of the Fr^{223} level scheme in terms of the collective model of the nucleus.   According to this interpretation the levels at 0, 12.7, 166 and 193 keV are the $I = 3/2$, $1/2$, $7/2$ and $5/2$ members of a rotational band based on a $K = 1/2$ ground state assignment.   This is an "anomalous" rotational band in which the I-spin ordering of the levels is reversed for the $1/2$, $3/2$ and $5/2$, $7/2$ pairs.   NOVIKOVA, ET AL. call attention to the fact that a similar set of levels occur in the nucleus, Fr^{221}.   One interesting consequence of this interpretation is that it indicates that nuclei as light as 223 and 221 are deformed in the ground state, at least if the mass number is odd.

We turn now to a discussion of the decay characteristics of actinium K. The endpoint energy of the beta particles of AcK is 1.2 MeV[197].   The

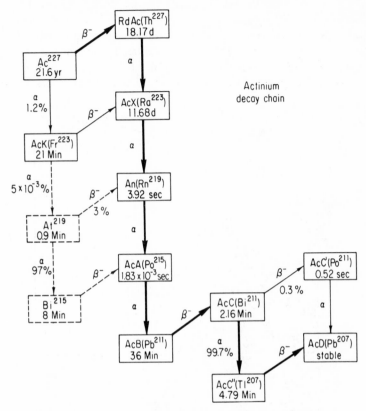

FIG. 6.39. Decay of actinium and its daughters showing branch products. The main path of the decay is shown in bold arrows. Actinium K and its rare branch products are shown at the left.

gamma rays have been studied by LECOIN, ET AL.[199] and by HYDE.[200] In the work of the latter it was found that photons of a 49.8 keV gamma ray appear in 40 per cent of the beta disintegrations and that photons of an 80 keV gamma ray appear in 24 per cent of the disintegrations. Additional low intensity gamma rays appear at 215 and 310 keV. A complete decay scheme has not been established.

From considerations of the systematics of alpha decay which are thoroughly discussed in Chapters 2 and 4, it was later deduced that AcK, which arises from a small alpha branching of Ac^{227}, must in turn show a small, but measurable, alpha branching. HYDE AND GHIORSO[201] established the

[199] M. Lecoin, M. Perey, M. Riou, and J. Teillac, *J. Phys. Rad.* **11**, 227 (1950).
[200] E. K. Hyde, *Phys. Rev.* **94**, 1221 (1954).
[201] E. K. Hyde and A. Ghiorso, *Phys. Rev.* **90**, 267 (1953).

correctness of this prediction by isolating the At^{219} daughter from a purified sample of AcK.   Figure 6.39 summarizes their findings.   The At^{219} daughter was isolated in an amount corresponding to an alpha branching of only 4×10^{-5} in AcK.   The At^{219} product has a half-life of 0.9 min and shows an observable alpha branching of about 97 per cent to produce the previously-unreported isotope, Bi^{215}.   These experiments of HYDE

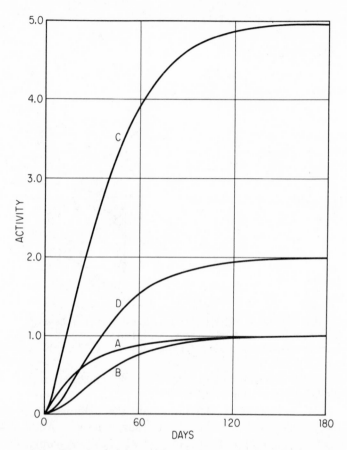

FIG. **6.40.** Growth of alpha activity of 18.17 day radioactinium (Th^{227}) (curve A) and 11.68 day actinium X (Ra^{223}) (curve B) into pure actinium. Curve C is the total alpha activity in the sample and includes contributions from the short-lived descendants actinon (3.92 sec Em^{219}), actinium A (1.83×10^{-3} sec Po^{215}), and actinium C (2.16 min Bi^{211}) which are in equilibrium with the actinium X.   Curve C is based on the assumption that no actinon is lost.   Growth of hard beta activity into actinium (curve D); this curve represents the activity of AcB (36.1 min Pb^{211}) and AcC (4.79 min Tl^{207}) whose growth into pure actinium is controlled by the growth of AcX.

AND GHIORSO[201] have the additional interest that they represent the first *chemical* isolation of astatine from a natural source. The alpha particle energy of AcK itself has been measured by photographic emulsion studies of freshly purified AcK samples by ADLOFF.[202] He found a value of 5.34 ± 0.08 for the alpha particles of AcK and an alpha branching of 0.6×10^{-4}.

PEREY[202a] has published an excellent and authoritative short review of the physical and chemical properties of Actinium K.

Analysis of Actinium. Methods for the detection and analysis of actinium may be summarized as follows:

1. *Measurement of total alpha activity.* The disintegration rate of a sample of pure actinium can be determined by measuring the total alpha activity of the daughters after these have come to equilibrium. Alternatively, one can measure the growth of the alpha activity over the first few weeks and compare this with the theoretical growth curve of Fig. 6.40. Any extraneous, alpha activity such as ionium impurity will give an erroneous result. It is therefore desirable to check the identity of the daughter alpha activity by alpha spectrum analysis using an ionization chamber or solid state detector coupled to a pulse-height analyzer.

2. *Measurement of total beta activity.* Two beta-emitters appear in the decay chain of actinium; these are AcB and AcC″. When actinium comes to equilibrium with its daughters a measurement of the beta radiation indicates the amount of actinium. This growth of hard beta radiation into purified actinium is shown by curve D of Fig. 6.40. The sample is usually covered to prevent the escape of actinon. Some absorber must be placed over the sample to filter out the alpha particles when thin window beta-counters are used. Any beta-emitting impurities in the sample will cause erroneous results. A modification of this method[203] consists of the chemical isolation of AcB (Pb^{211}) by coprecipitation with added lead carrier precipitated as lead sulfide. The radioactivity of the 36 minute AcB in equilibrium with its AcC daughter is then followed in a suitably calibrated counter. This method is very sensitive and can be applied to samples containing as little as 10^{-2} microcuries of actinium. The method can be applied to advantage when the actinium samples are diluted with rare earth elements. Also, the actinium sample can be contaminated with beta emitting nuclides provided they do not coprecipitate with lead sulfide from acid solution. It cannot be applied to actinium samples contaminated with radium or thorium.

[202] J. P. Adloff, *Compt. Rend.* **240**, 1421 (1955). See also M. Perey and M. J. Adloff, *J. Phys. Rad.* **17**, 545 (1956).

[202a] M. Perey, "Francium" in Volume III, *Nouveau traité de chimie minérale*, Masson et Cie, Paris, 1957.

[203] M. Perey and A. Hettler, *Compt. Rend.* **242**, 2552 (1956).

3. *Measurement of total gamma activity.* When the source strength is of the order of a millicurie or greater a suitable method of measurement is the determination of the gamma activity of the equilibrium mixture of activities.[204] The sample is sealed in a glass tube and lead absorbers 1 cm in thickness are used to cut out beta particles and low-energy gamma rays. The gamma activity registered in an ion chamber can be compared to a standard radium sample. This determination can be made to an accuracy of about 3 per cent and sample size can be as low as 1 microcurie. The sensitivity of this method can be raised by use of an end-window counter to measure the radiations emitted from a standard volume of solution containing actinium in equilibrium with its descendants.[205] Samples as small as 0.003 microcuries can be assayed. No chemical operations are necessary.

4. *Calorimetric measurement.* The amount of actinium in a sample can be determined by direct measurement of the heat liberated by a source in a calorimeter.[204,206,207] The principal energy is derived from absorption of the alpha particles and the alpha-recoil products. The energy of each successive alpha disintegration can be accurately calculated taking into account branching and complex structure. (See Table 6.8 in *radium* section.) The partial absorption of beta and gamma radiations contributes 10 per cent as much energy as do the alpha particles plus recoils.[207] From the inner wall thickness of the calorimeter and the absorption curve of the beta-gamma radiation, one can calculate the total heat liberated per hour by a curie of actinium. The calorimetric measurement can be made with an accuracy of 1 to 2 per cent.

5. *Separation and measurement of actinon.* A sensitive test for the presence of actinium or of radioactinium or of actinium-X in a radioactive sample is the identification of the gaseous emanation, actinon. The actinon may be swept from a solution in a stream of air and carried directly into a counter. It is also possible to collect the active deposit from the air stream on a negatively-charged plate and count it separately. The actinon method does not lend itself to an accurate analysis because of the 3.92 sec half-life of actinon but it serves as a very sensitive method of detection. In the case of recently purified actinium it is necessary to wait first until RdAc and AcX have grown into the sample before actinon is extracted.

6. *Separation of actinium-X and the measurement of its activity by subsequent separation and counting of actinium-B.* In this method,[208] actinium-X

204 M. Lecoin, M. Perey, and A. Pompei, *J. Chem. Phys.* **46**, 158 (1949).

205 M. Perey, *Compt. Rend.* **243**, 1411 (1956).

206 A. S. Sanielevici, *J. Chem. Phys.* **33**, 785 (1936).

207 G. V. Gorshkov and N. S. Shimanskaya, *Sov. J. Atom. Energ.* (in English translation), No. 5, **161**, 761 (1956).

208 M. Perey and A. Hettler, *Compt. Rend.* **243**, 1520 (1956).

is separated by coprecipitation on barium sulfate. The sulfate is converted to the carbonate and then to the soluble chloride. When the separated actinium-X is again in solution its daughter product actinium-B, the 36 minute Pb^{211} isotope, is removed by coprecipitation[203] on lead sulfide and the beta decay of AcB and its short-lived AcC daughter are followed in a suitably calibrated counter. With a slight modification this can be applied to samples contaminated with the radium or the thorium series activities. It can be applied to insoluble or partially soluble solid samples and is particularly suited to the assay of actiniferous minerals. In the case of insoluble samples such as minerals, a fusion with the bisulfate of potassium in the presence of 100 milligrams of barium chloride is carried out. The barium sulfate formed in this step removes the actinium-X, plus all other isotopes of radium, lead or bismuth in the sample. The barium sulfate is metathesized successively to the carbonate and the chloride. The chloride is put into solution and emanation isotopes are removed by boiling. A scavenger precipitate of lead sulfide removes a mixture of the lead and bismuth activities of all three natural radioactive series. The activities constituting the active deposit of the actinium series re-establish equilibrium much more quickly than the corresponding activities in the decay chains of radium and thorium. Hence a second lead sulfide precipitate removed 30 minutes later will carry down only AcB.

7. *Isolation of AcK daughter product.* Methods 1 through 6 depend upon the growth of 18.17 day RdAc and 11.68 day AcX into the actinium and hence all suffer from the serious disadvantage that many weeks must elapse before an accurate analysis is possible. There are two alternative methods which deal with actinium more directly. One of these is discussed in (8) overleaf. The other method is based on the isolation and measurement of AcK (Fr^{223}), the alpha decay branch product of Ac^{227}. As is discussed above, Ac^{227} undergoes alpha decay in 1.2 per cent of its disintegrations. The alpha-decay product is the 21 min beta emitter AcK which comes to equilibrium with Ac^{227} within two hours. PEREY,[209] who proposed this rapid method, recommended the following procedure:

Sodium carbonate is added to the actinium solution to precipitate actinium and rare earths leaving AcK in solution. Barium chromate is then precipitated to remove AcX and AcC″ and lanthanum hydroxide is precipitated to carry out any traces of actinium which may remain. The filtered solution is then evaporated rapidly to dryness and the beta activity is measured. From the decay curve of the 21 min activity the amount of AcK present at the time of removal of the carbonate precipitate is determined by back-extrapolation. From this the amount of actinium can be

[209] M. Perey, *Compt. Rend.* **214**, 797 (1942); M. Perey, *J. Chim. Phys.* **43**, 269 (1946); *Compt. Rend.* **241**, 953 (1955).

calculated after allowing for the alpha branching of 1.2 per cent. With suitable counting techniques the range of applicability of this method is 1 microcurie to 100 millicuries of actinium.

Hyde[210] has proposed a modified version of the AcK procedure based on the coprecipitation of AcK on silicotungstic acid (which is insoluble in concentrated hydrochloric acid).

8. *Measurement of alpha particles of* Ac^{227}. If a sample of Ac^{227} is thoroughly decontaminated from all daughter activity and then immediately inserted in an alpha counter the observed alpha activity corresponds to the 1.2 per cent alpha branching of Ac^{227}. To insure that the alpha particles detected are in fact due to Ac^{227} and not to unseparated daughter activity (RdAc being the most difficult to separate) it is desirable to determine the alpha-particle energies with an ionization chamber (or solid-state detector) coupled to a pulse-height analyzer. PEPPARD[211] has discussed this method of actinium assay. It has also been studied by GLOVER, BEADLE, AND ROGERS[212] who report that with proper sample preparation and proper analysis of the alpha spectrum the Ac^{227} alpha particles can be measured even in the presence of unseparated daughter activity.

Artificial Synthesis of Actinium. In modern times the availability of high neutron fluxes in nuclear reactors has made it possible to synthesize weighable quantities of Ac^{227} by means of the reactions:

$$Ra^{226}(n, \gamma)Ra^{227} \qquad Ra^{227} \xrightarrow{\quad \beta^- \quad}_{41.2 \text{ min}} Ac^{227}$$

$$\sigma = 15 \text{ barns}$$

PETERSON[213] in 1945 first demonstrated this synthesis by irradiation of 1 milligram of radium. Later HAGEMANN[214] irradiated a series of one gram samples of radium and isolated milligram quantities of actinium. This was the first isolation of chemically-pure actinium on the milligram scale; previous to this, the best preparations of actinium contained only a few per cent of actinium. The synthetic approach has two pronounced advantages: (1) the material which needs to be isolated from radioactive ores is radium, which occurs in much higher concentration and is relatively easy to

210 E. K. Hyde, *J. Am. Chem. Soc.* **74**, 4181 (1952); see also monograph *NAS-NS 3003* entitled, "Radiochemistry of Francium" by E. K. Hyde, issued by National Academy of Sciences and available from Office of Tech. Serv., Dept. of Commerce, Washington, D.C.

211 D. F. Peppard, G. W. Mason, P. R. Gray, and J. F. Mech, *J. Am. Chem. Soc.* **74**, 6081 (1952).

212 K. M. Glover, A. B. Beadle, and F. J. G. Rogers, *Atomic Energy Research Establishment Report, AERE CR 2359* (1957).

213 S. Peterson, Paper 19.9 "The Transuranium Elements," *National Nuclear Energy Series* (New York: McGraw-Hill Book Co., 1949).

214 F. Hagemann, *J. Am. Chem. Soc.* **72**, 768 (1950).

obtain in the pure state, and (2) contamination with the difficultly-separable rare earths is completely avoided.

Radioactinium (Th^{227}). The immediate decay product of the beta decay of Ac^{227} is Th^{227}, which is an alpha emitter with a half-life of 18.17 days.[215] This isotope, also called radioactinium, has been the subject of considerable interest because of the extraordinary complexity of its alpha and gamma spectra. A detailed account of these radiations is given in Section 8.2.5 of Chapter 8.

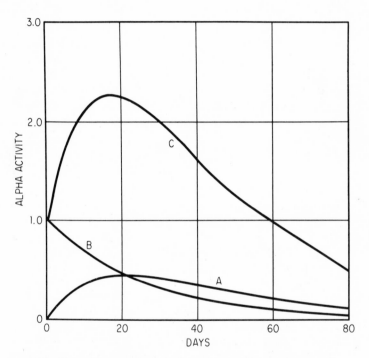

FIG. **6.41.** Curve A: regrowth of 11.68 day AcX (Ra^{223}) alpha activity into purified 18.17 day RdAc (Th^{227}). Curve B: decay of alpha activity of RdAc. Curve C: total alpha activity in initially pure RdAc sample including contributions from RdAc, AcX, actinon, AcA, and AcC.

By standard radiochemical methods radioactinium can easily be separated from its actinium parent and from its daughter products. Its immediate daughter, actinium-X, has a half-life of 11.68 days so that contaminating daughter-product activity grows in only at a moderate rate. This growth is shown quantitatively in Fig. 6.41. The growth of radioactinium into an initially pure sample of actinium is shown in Fig. 6.40.

215 G. R. Hagee, M. L. Curtis, and G. R. Grove, *Phys. Rev.* **96**, 817A (1954).

Actinium-X (Ra^{223}). The independent discovery of actinium-X by Godlewski (1905) and Giesel (1904) is mentioned in the historical introduction, Section 6.1. This nuclide is an alpha emitter whose half-life has recently been redetermined as 11.68 ± 0.06 days,[215] and as 11.22 ± 0.05 days.[216]

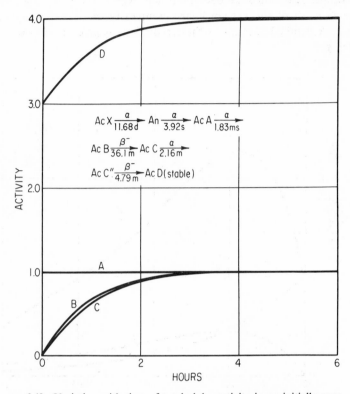

FIG. **6.42.** Variation with time of total alpha activity in an initially pure sample of 11.7 day AcX (Ra[223]). Curve *A* shows AcX itself. After a few seconds, Curve *A* also represents 3.92 sec. actinon. (Em[219]) and 0.00183 sec. AcA (Po[215]). Curve *B* shows 36.1 min. beta-emitter AcB (Pb[211]). Curve *C* represents 2.16 min. AcC (Bi[211]) which is an alpha emitter. Curve D is the total alpha activity including AcX, An, AcA, and AcC. When transient equilibrium is reached all activities decay with the controlling half-life of 11.7 days.

It can be separated from actinium or from radioactinium after a suitable growth period, which can be determined from Fig. 6.40 or 6.41. Samples of actinium-X are never pure from the radioactivity standpoint because actinon and AcA daughters re-establish their equilibrium value within a minute of the purification of actinium-X. The longest-lived daughter is AcB (Pb[211])

216 J. Robert, *Ann. Phys.* **4**, 89 (1959).

but even this product comes to equilibrium within a few hours.　Figure 6.42 shows the growth of daughters into actinium-X.

Actinium-X is an alpha emitter resembling its parent, radioactinium, in the complexity of its alpha and gamma ray spectrum.　ROSENBLUM, PEREY, VALADARES, AND GUILLOT,[217] ASARO,[218] PILGER,[219] RYTZ,[219a] and WALEN, NEDOVESSOV, AND BASTIN-SCOFFIER[219b] have studied the alpha spectrum of AcX.　The gamma and conversion electron spectra have been measured by several groups,[219-226] and partial decay schemes have been constructed by several authors.　The study of PILGER[219] was particularly thorough in its experimental analysis of the alpha spectrum, the gamma spectrum, and the conversion electron spectrum and we quote here the principal findings of his report.　He studied the alpha spectrum in a homogeneous-field magnetic spectrograph of high resolution and also in a double-focusing magnetic spectrometer of high resolution and transmission and obtained the results summarized in Table 6.27.　With a sodium iodide crystal spectrometer he was able to resolve a few of the prominent gamma rays from the complex gamma spectrum in spite of serious interference from the gamma radiation of the daughter products.　He performed some gamma-gamma coincidence studies.　More significantly, he was able to employ the double-focusing alpha spectrometer in an alpha-gamma coincidence arrangement in which the gamma spectrum in coincidence with alpha particles of a particular energy could be measured.　This coincidence technique is a very powerful method for testing the placement of gamma rays in the decay scheme of an alpha emitter.　The results are summarized in Table 6.28.　The angular correlation of the 270 keV photons with respect to the alpha particles leading to the 270 keV level in the daughter nucleus was measured and shown to agree with the spin and multipolarity assignments of the proposed decay scheme.

PILGER found some difficulty in studying the conversion electrons of

[217] Rosenblum, Perey, Valadares, and Guillot, as quoted by Hollander, Perlman and Seaborg in *Revs. Mod. Phys.*, **25**, 600 (1953).

[218] F. Asaro, Thesis, *University of California Radiation Laboratory Report UCRL-2180* (1953).

[219] R. C. Pilger, Jr., F. Asaro, and I. Perlman, unpublished results; see R. C. Pilger, Jr., Thesis, *University of California Radiation Laboratory Report UCRL-3877* (July 1957).

[219a] A. Rytz, *Helv. Phys. Acta* **34**, 240 (1961).

[219b] R. Walen, V. Nedovessov, and G. Bastin-Scoffier, *Nucl. Phys.* **35**, 232 (1962).

[220] M. Frilley, *J. Phys. Rad.* **1**, 34 (1940).

[221] O. Hahn and L. Meitner, *Z. Physik* **34**, 795 (1925).

[222] J. Surugue, *Ann. Phys.* **8**, 484 (1937).

[223] B. F. Bayman and M. A. S. Ross, *Proc. Roy. Soc.* (London) **68A**, 110 (1955).

[224] B. Karlik and T. Matitsch, *Osterr. Akad. Wiss., Math. Naturw. Kl. Sitzbe.* **10**, 164–168 (1955).

[225] C. Matiassek, *Sitsber Akad. Wiss. Wien, Abt.* **164**, 161 (1955).

[226] H. Paul and H. Warhanek, *Helv. Phys. Acta* **30**, 272 (1957).

AcX in a standard permanent-magnet electron spectrograph because the actinon diffused out of the necessarily-thin source plate, spread throughout the spectrograph chamber, and fogged the emulsion. This difficulty was not so marked in his double-focusing variable-field beta spectrometer and he was able to measure many of the conversion electrons from the numerous gamma

TABLE **6.27.** Alpha groups of Ra^{223}.

Data of WALEN, NEDOVESSOV, and BASTIN-SCOFFIER[c]				Data of PILGER[a]		
Energy (MeV)	Intensity (%)	Energy of daughter state (keV)	Log hindrance factor	Energy (MeV)	Intensity (%)	Energy of daughter state (keV)
5.8696	0.87	0	3.46	5.870	0.96	0
5.8654	<.02	(4.3)	>5.1	5.865?		(4.8)
5.8555	0.32	14.35	3.82	5.856	0.3	14.4
5.7454[b]	9.1	126.4	1.84	5.745	10.5	127.0
5.7141[b]	53.7	158.3	0.91	5.715	50.4	158.9
5.6051[b]	26	269.3	0.67	5.605	23.6	269.6
5.5376[b]	9.1	338.1	0.77	5.537	10.3	338.5
5.4996	0.8	378.9	1.63	5.500	0.86	376.5
5.4792	~8 × 10⁻³	397.5	3.51			
5.4316	2.3	446	0.80	5.432	2.4	445.6
5.3636	0.11	515	1.80	5.363	0.20	515.6
5.3367	0.10	542.6	1.64	5.337	0.07	541.8
5.2853	0.13	595	1.24	5.282	0.3	589.6
5.2808	0.095	600	1.33			
5.2568	0.043	624	1.55			
5.2343	0.042	647	1.43			
5.2096	0.0054	672	2.18			
5.1708	0.026	712	1.27			
5.1498	0.021	733	1.24			
5.1328	~1.7 × 10⁻³	748	2.24			
5.1104	~6 × 10⁻⁴	773	2.57			
5.0842	~3 × 10⁻⁴	800	2.71			
5.0540	~2 × 10⁻⁴	830	2.69			
5.0340	~4 × 10⁻⁴	851	2.25			
5.0235	~6 × 10⁻⁴	861	1.99			
5.0124	~4 × 10⁻⁴	873	2.07			

[a] Pilger's energy values were recalculated on the basis of the energy standards used by Walen, et al.[219b]

[b] Rytz gives the values 5.7455, 5.7143, 5.6053 and 5.5371 MeV, respectively, for the four main groups.

[c] These authors[219b] report an error of ±1 keV for groups in >1 per cent intensity, ±2 keV for those of 10⁻² to 1 per cent intensity, and ±3 keV for those in 10⁻⁴ to 10⁻² per cent intensity. The energy difference of neighboring groups is determined to ±0.2 keV.

TABLE 6.28. Summary of Ra^{223} α-γ coincidence study (Pilger).

Alpha group	Observed radiation (keV)	Intensity[1] photons/alpha	α_K
α_{127}	K x-ray	0.68	
	122	0.19	3.6
α_{158}	K	0.54	
	144	0.082	
	154	0.11	
α_{270}	K	0.41	
	270	0.43	0.95
α_{338}	K	0.25	
	145–155	0.05	
	180	0.05	
	270	0.017	
	338	0.49	0.33
α_{376}	K	0.31	
	376	0.45	0.71
α_{445}	K	0.34	
	445	0.48	0.71[2]

[1] K x-ray intensity in vacancies/alpha; i.e., the Auger effect correction has been made.
[2] A possible cascade was not distinguished with certainty from Compton distribution and backscatter peak.

TABLE 6.29. Internal transitions in decay of Ra^{223} (Pilger).

Energy (keV)	Intensity (%)	Multipolarity
31.2	1.4	$M1$
68.4	0.34	
122.2	11	$M1$–$E2$
143.0	~1	$(M1\ ?)$
144.1	19	$M1$ (Some $E2$?)
154.1	28	$M1$
158.3	3.2	$M1$
179.6	1.1	$M1$
269.6	21.4	$M1$
323.8	4.9	$M1$
338.0	4.2	$M1$
371.1	0.7	$M2$
440.6	0.6	$M2$
445.6	1.4	$M2$
580.4	~0.4	

transitions in the decay of AcX.   His deductions on the energies, intensities
and multipolarities of the gamma transitions are summarized in Table 6.29.
From consideration of all his data, PILGER was able to formulate the
principal features of the decay scheme of Ra^{223} with reasonable certainty

TABLE **6.30**. Alpha groups of actinon.

Group	Particle energy (MeV)	Abundance (%)	Excited state energy (keV)
Rosenblum			
α_0	6.807[a]	69	(0)
α_{270}	6.542	15	270
α_{397}	6.417	12	397
α_{622}	6.197	4	622
Pilger			
α_0	6.813 ± 0.002[b]	82	(0)
α_{271}	6.547	13	271.6
α_{401}	6.419	5	401
Rytz			
α_0	6.8176 ± 0.0010[c]		(0)
α_1	6.5509		271.6
α_2	6.4239		401
Walen, Nedovessov, and Bastin-Scoffier[d]			
α_0	6.8175	81	0
α_1	6.5513	11.5	271.2
α_2	6.5275	0.12	295
α_3	6.4232	7.5	401.6
α_4	6.3103	0.054	516.6
α_5	6.2221	2.6×10^{-3}	606.4
α_6	6.1571	1.74×10^{-2}	672.6
α_7	~6.1462	~2.6×10^{-3}	683.7
α_8	6.1005	3×10^{-3}	730.3
α_9	5.9993	4.4×10^{-3}	833.4

[a] Recalculated by BRIGGS.
[b] Relative to α_0 of Cm^{242} taken as 6.110 MeV.
[c] Relative to Po^{210} $E_\alpha = 5.3048$.
[d] These authors[219b] report an error of ±1 keV for groups in >1 per cent intensity,
±2 keV for those of 10^{-2} to 1 per cent intensity, and ±3 keV for those in 10^{-4} to 10^{-2} per
cent intensity.   The energy difference of neighboring groups is determined to ±0.2 keV.

and to draw the decay scheme shown in Fig. 6.43.   Our knowledge of the
intrinsic quantum states and of collective modes of excitation are in an
elementary and developing stage for nuclei in this range of atomic masses
so that no detailed interpretation of this decay scheme is given.

Later work by WALEN, NEDOVESSOV, AND BASTIN-SCOFFIER[219b] on the alpha spectrum showed 14 additional low-intensity groups beyond those observed by Pilger. These are listed in Table 6.27. Drawing on their own

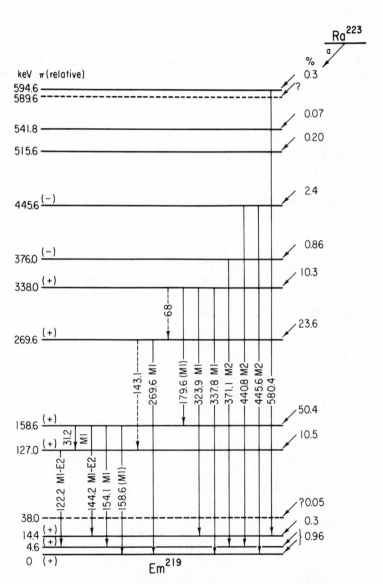

FIG. **6.43.** Decay scheme of AcX (Ra^{223}). After PILGER.[219] This figure does not show the 13 low intensity alpha transitions to An levels above 595 keV reported by WALEN ET AL.[219b]

results and on some results of BRAGANÇA-GIL[226a] and of PETIT[226a] these authors drew tentative conclusions about the intrinsic and collective nature of several of the An^{219} levels; because of the necessarily tentative nature of these conclusions we do not reproduce them here.

Actinon. The gaseous emanation in the actinium series is the 3.92 second nuclide, An^{219}. The alpha spectrum of actinon has been investigated in magnetic spectrographs by ROSENBLUM, GUILLOT, AND PEREY,[227] by PILGER,[219] by RYTZ[219a] and by WALEN, NEDOVESSOV, AND BASTIN-SCOFFIER[219b] with results shown in Table 6.30. PILGER did not observe the group at 6.197 MeV reported by ROSENBLUM, ET AL.

There is difficulty in the precise measurement of the alpha energies of Em^{219}. Because of the short half-life the spectrum has to be studied in samples of Ra^{223} with which the emanation is in equilibrium. Since the product nuclei recoil with considerable kinetic energy after alpha emission, they are expelled from the source plate or imbedded in it. Those expelled are no longer in focus in the spectrograph; the alpha spectrum obtained from those remaining in the plate shows significant line-broadening due to energy loss from the imbedded ions.

Gamma rays of 270 and 400 keV have been observed by sodium iodide crystal spectrometer examination of gaseous actinon and the conversion electrons of these same transitions of actinon were observed by PILGER[219] in his study of Ra^{223} samples. BRAGANÇA-GIL AND PETIT[227b] have also investigated the decay of An^{219} by alpha-gamma coincidence techniques.

Actinium-A (Po^{215}). AcA (Po^{215}) decays with a half-life of 0.00183 seconds. It emits alpha particles the energy of which have been given as 7.38 MeV,[227a] 7.36 MeV[219] and 7.384 MeV.[219a] Two additional alpha groups of very low intensity have been reported;[227c] 6.954 MeV ($\sim 3.4 \times 10^{-2}\%$) and 6.948 MeV ($\sim 2.2 \times 10^{-2}\%$).

Some evidence for a possible β^- branching of AcA to produce At^{215} has been presented. KARLIK AND BERNERT[228] examined the alpha activity in a weak sample of the 3.92 second actinon activity from the U^{235} series and found a small number of previously unreported 8.4 MeV alpha-particles. These were ascribed to an extremely short-lived At^{215} resulting from a $5 \times 10^{-4}\%$ β^- branching in AcA. As originally reported these results were open to objections on energetic ground as discussed by FEATHER.[229]

[226a] F. Bragança-Gil, Thèse, Paris 1961; G. Y. Petit, Thèse, Paris (1959). F. Bragança-Gil, R. Foucher, and G. Y. Petit, *J. Phys. Rad.* **22**, 289 (1961).

[227] Rosenblum, Guillot, and Perey, *Compt. Rend.* **202**, 1274 (1936).

[227a] G. H. Briggs, *Revs. Mod. Phys.* **26**, 1 (1959).

[227b] F. B. Gil and G. Y. Petit, *J. Phys. Rad.* **22**, 680 (1961).

[228] B. Karlik and T. Bernert, *Z. Physik* **123**, 51 (1944); *Naturwissenschaften* **32**, 44 (1943).

[229] N. Feather, *Nucleonics* **5**, 22 (1949).

TABLE **6.31**. The actinium series active deposit.

Nuclide	Type of radiation	Energy and abundance	Reference
AcB (Pb^{211}) 36.1 min. β^-	β^-	1.355 MeV (92.4%) 0.951 MeV (1.4%)	1
		0.525 MeV (5.5%) 0.251 MeV (0.7%)	
	γ	0.404 MeV (4.3%) 0.426 MeV (1.1%)	
		0.700 MeV (0.63%)	1
		0.830 MeV (4.17%) 1.104 MeV (0.18%)	
AcC (Bi^{211}) 2.16 min.	α	6.617 (83%) 6.273 (17%)	
β 0.32%		5.929 (3.7 × 10^{-3}%)	2–6, 11, 12
α 99.68%	β^-	Energy unknown $Q_{\beta^-} = 0.61$ calc.	
AcC' (Po^{211})	γ	0.351 $M1$ (with alpha branch)	1, 3, 13
0.52 sec.	α	7.434 (99%) 6.895 (0.50%)	7, 8, 9, 10
AcC'' (Tl^{207})	γ	0.562, 0.88	10
4.76 min.	β^-	1.47	1
β^-	γ	0.870 (~0.5%)	2
AcD (Pb^{207}) Stable			

1. S. E. Vandenbosch, C. V. K. Baba, P. R. Christensen, O. B. Nielsen, and H. Nordby, *Nucl. Phys.* **42**, 482 (1963). See this report for many details of Pb^{211} decay scheme.
2. R. Walen, V. Nedovessov, and G. Bastin-Scoffier, *Nucl. Phys.* **35**, 232 (1962).
3. R. C. Pilger, Jr., Ph.D. Thesis, *Univ. of Calif. Rad. Lab. Report UCRL-3877* (July 1957).
4. M. G. Holloway and M. S. Livingston, *Phys. Rev.* **54**, 18 (1938); Summarizes work of various investigators.
5. E. Rutherford, C. E. Wynn-Williams, and W. B. Lewis, *Proc. Roy. Soc.* (London) **133A**, 351 (1931).
6. G. Vieira and L. Salgueiro, *Compt. rend.* **234**, 1765 (1952).
7. W. B. Lewis and B. V. Bowden, *Proc. Roy. Soc.* (London) **145A**, 235 (1935); Summarizes the results of various investigators.
8. G. H. Briggs, *Rev. Mod. Phys.* **26**, 1 (1954) compilation.
9. R. W. Hoff, *Univ. of Calif. Rad. Lab. Report URCL-2325* (Sept. 1953).
10. J. W. Mihelich, A. W. Schardt, and E. Segrè, *Phys. Rev.* **95**, 1508 (1954).
11. The highly-hindered alpha decay of Bi^{211} is discussed by Perlman and Rasmussen, p. 185, "Alpha Radioactivity" in Vol. XLII, *Handbuch der Physik*, Springer-Verlag, Berlin 1957.
12. A. Rytz, *Helv. Phys. Acta* **34**, 240 (1961) reports the values of 6.622 and 6.277 for the Bi^{211} alpha groups based on Po^{210} $E_\alpha = 5.3048$; see also Walen, Nedovessov, and Bastin-Scoffier, *Nucl. Phys.* **35**, 232 (1962).
13. Detailed investigations of the 351 keV γ in the α-branch decay of AcC have been reported by G. Y. Petit, Thesis, Paris (1954); S. Gorodetzki, *et al.*, *Compt. Rend. Acad. Sci.* (Paris) **237**, 245 (1953); F. B. Gil and G. Y. Petit, *J. Phys. Rad.* **22**, 680 (1961); and S. Gorodetzki *et al.*, unpublished results, Strasbourg (1961).

The work was repeated by AVIGNON[230] in France on a considerably larger sample with substantially the same results except that the alpha-particle energy was determined to be 8.04 MeV. This revision of the alpha-energy removes one main objection to the assignment (i.e., the non-equivalence of the AcA—At[215]—AcC energy sum and the AcA—AcB—AcC energy sum) and makes it possible to identify this At[215] with the At[215] discovered by MEINKE[231] in the Pa[227] collateral series produced by cyclotron bombardments. Nevertheless, more conclusive evidence is desirable on this question.

The Active Deposit of Actinon. The gas, actinon, deposits an invisible film of radioactive daughter products upon any surface exposed to it. By collection of the charged daughter products on an electrically-charged wire

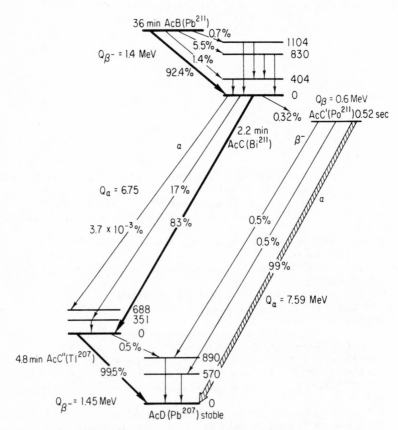

FIG. 6.44. Decay scheme of the active deposit of actinon. Energies of levels are given in keV and Q values are given in MeV.

230 P. Avignon, *J. Phys. Rad.* **11**, 521 (1950).
231 W. W. Meinke, A. Ghiorso, and G. T. Seaborg, *Phys. Rev.* **81**, 782 (1951).

or surface the deposit can be highly localized.   Since the immediate daughter product of actinon is the 0.00183 second AcA, the active deposit of actinon is normally considered to consist of AcB and its daughter products, which are listed in Table 6.31.   The decay schemes and genetic relationships of the members of the active deposit of actinon are displayed in Fig. 6.44.   The activity changes in a sample of active deposit as a function of time are plotted in Fig. 6.45.

Rather pure samples of AcC can be obtained by the simple technique of heating the plate on which the active deposit is located, since bismuth is less

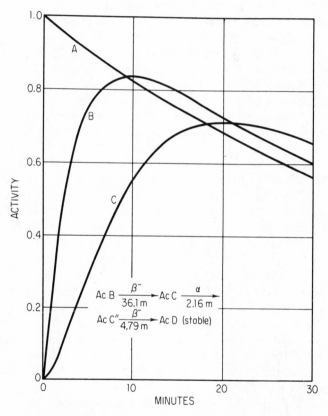

FIG. **6.45.** Activity changes in actinon active deposit.   Curve *A* shows decay of AcB beta activity or AcC alpha activity for a sample of active deposit prepared by a long exposure to actinon.   Curve *B* shows growth of AcC alpha activity into an initially pure sample of AcB prepared by a short exposure to actinon.   Curve *C* illustrates the growth of AcC″ beta activity into a sample of active deposit prepared by a short exposure to actinon.

volatile than lead or thallium.   AcB, AcC or AcC" can also be prepared in a
pure state by electrodeposition or by chemical separation methods.

AcC undergoes branching decay in 0.32 per cent of its disintegrations to
produce AcC' (Po^{211}). For many years the value of the half-life of Po^{211}
was listed as 5×10^{-3} seconds. This value had not been obtained experimentally, but by an estimate based on the Geiger-Nuttall energy-versus-half-
life relationship. LEININGER, SEGRÈ, AND SPIESS^{232,233} determined this
half-life experimentally and obtained a value of 0.52 seconds.

It has been shown by experiments of artificial transmutation that Po^{211}
exists in two isomeric forms. The ground state is the 0.52-second alpha
emitter which appears as AcC' in the active deposit of the actinium series,
as the electron capture decay product of the artificially prepared isotope
At^{211}, and as the alpha-decay product of Em^{215}, also an artificially prepared isotope. SPIESS^{233} found that helium ion bombardment of Pb^{208}
produces the 0.52-second Po^{211}, and in addition, a 25-second isomeric form
emitting 7.14 MeV alpha particles. JENTSCHKE AND CO-WORKERS^{234} and
PERLMAN AND CO-WORKERS^{234a} extended this investigation and constructed
the decay scheme shown in Fig. 6.46. This is one of the most unusual cases
of isomerism known. The failure to see any transition from the 25-second
level in Po^{211} to the 0.52-second level means that these two levels differing
in energy by 1.27 MeV must have a spin difference of 5 or more.

The shell model provides a reasonable explanation for this decay scheme.
The levels of Pb^{207} are known quite well from a study of the decay of Bi^{207}
(see Chapter 10) and the spin and parity assignments correspond to those
expected of a nucleus with one neutron less than a closed shell of 126.
These single particle (hole) assignments are given in Fig. 6.46. The ground
state of Po^{211} (the 0.52-second isomer) may be expected to have the spin
value 9/2 resulting from a configuration with two protons beyond Pb^{208}
as $(h_{9/2})^2$ paired to a resultant $J = 0$ and an odd neutron as $g_{9/2}$. The
25-second isomer of Po^{211} must have a spin $\geqslant 19/2$ according to the arguments advanced by JENTSCHKE, JUVELAND, AND KINSEY.^{234} One cannot
account for a spin value of this magnitude by the angular momentum of the
odd neutron alone. It is necessary to consider the excitation of the 2 protons
as well as the single neutron beyond the Pb^{208} core. When this possibility
is included it is possible to write down several configurations of the available
shell-model states which couple to a total angular momentum greater than
19/2.

^{232} R. F. Leininger, E. Segrè, and F. N. Spiess, *Phys. Rev.* **82**, 334A (1951); See also
Spiess^{233}.

^{233} F. N. Speiss, *Phys. Rev.* **94**, 1292 (1954).

^{234} W. Jentschke, A. C. Juveland, and G. H. Kinsey, *Phys. Rev.* **96**, 231 (1954).

^{234a} I. Perlman, F. Asaro, A. Ghiorso, A. Larsh, and R. Latimer, *Phys. Rev.* **127**,
917 (1962).

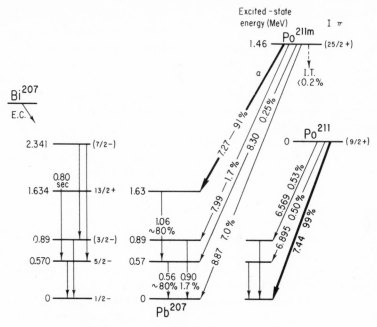

FIG. 6.46. Decay schemes of the Po²¹¹ isomers and of Bi²⁰⁷.

MANG[235] has made a highly interesting theoretical study of the alpha decay of the 0.52-second isomer of Po²¹¹. The usual one-body treatment of alpha decay contains an unrealistic assumption of a preformed alpha particle moving freely within the nuclear interior and prevented from escape only by the potential barrier at the nuclear edge. MANG[235] replaced this picture with a much more realistic model in which the particles within the nucleus are considered as individual shell model particles. Alpha emission is presumed to occur when the wave functions of 2 neutrons and 2 protons overlap at the nuclear edge within a nuclear volume corresponding to the dimensions of an alpha particle. By inserting into his theoretical equations shell model oscillator wave functions chosen to agree with experimental Po²⁰⁷ energy levels and spin assignments, MANG was able to predict a correct value for the alpha decay constant and for the relative intensities to the ground, and the first two excited states of Pb²⁰⁷. He was also able to specify the mixture of alpha waves of various angular momentum values leading to the excited states. The agreement of theoretical and experimental values for these quantities is excellent. MANG[235a] assigned to Po²¹¹ᵐ the configuration

$$[(h^2_{9/2})_8 g_{9/2}]_{I = 25/2}$$

[235] H. J. Mang, Z. Physik **148**, 582 (1957) and Phys. Rev. **119**, 1069 (1960).

[235a] H. J. Mang, Univ. of Calif. Lawrence Rad. Lab. Report UCRL-8931 (October 1959); H. D. Zeh and H. J. Mang, Nucl. Phys. **29**, 529 (1962).

552 NATURAL RADIOACTIVITY OF THE HEAVY ELEMENTS CHAP. 6

Actinium-D. The stable end-product of the actinium series is Pb^{207}, known as AcD or actinium-lead. AcD has undetectable alpha activity. Lead of mass 207 was first found by ASTON in lead isolated from a uranium mineral. RUTHERFORD concluded from the high ratio of Pb^{207} to Pb^{208} that Pb^{207} must be identical with actinium-lead. This observation helped to clear up some of the confusion surrounding the origin of the actinium series and of the mass numbers of the members of the series.

The ratio of Pb^{207} to U^{235} in a uranium mineral which contains no primary lead and which has remained unaltered since its formation is a direct measure of the age of the mineral through straightforward application of the laws of radioactive decay. Another widely used dating method is the Pb^{207}/Pb^{206} ratio method. These methods are described in the following main section of this chapter.

6.5 THE ISOTOPES OF LEAD AND THEIR IMPORTANCE IN GEOCHRONOLOGY

General Classification of Lead Samples. Any sample of terrestrial lead consists of a mixture of the four stable isotopes; Pb^{204}, Pb^{206}, Pb^{207} and Pb^{208}. Lead differs from the great majority of elements in that the proportions of the various isotopes vary markedly from sample to sample. This result can be attributed to the steady accumulation of the isotopes Pb^{206} (RaG), Pb^{207} (AcD) and Pb^{208} (ThD) from the decay of uranium and thorium widely distributed in the rocks of the earth's crust. Several types of lead mixtures have been distinguished:

Primeval (or primordial or original) lead. This is that particular mixture of lead isotopes which existed at the time of the completion of the element forming process which produced the matter of which the solar system is composed. It is not known with certainty what that isotopic mixture was. One can set upper limits to the contents of Pb^{206}, Pb^{207}, and Pb^{208} in primordial lead by analyzing many lead samples with particular attention to samples with a high content of Pb^{204}. Since Pb^{204} is *not* formed in any decay process occurring in the natural radioactivities, primeval lead must have a Pb^{204} content at *least* as great as that of any single analyzed sample. Among many hundreds of terrestrial lead samples, one taken from the Rosetta Mine, South Africa, has shown the highest content of Pb^{204}, the complete analysis being given in Table 6.32. In 1953 an important paper by PATTERSON, BROWN, TILTON, AND INGHRAM[236] reported an analysis of meteoritic lead samples in which the relative content of Pb^{204} was considerably higher than that of the Rosetta Mine sample. As an example, the troilite phase of the Cañon Diablo Meteorite had the composition given in Table 6.32.

---

[236] C. Patterson, H. Brown, G. Tilton, and M. Inghram, *Phys. Rev.* **92**, 1234 (1953).

TABLE 6.32. Relative atomic abundances of lead fraction of important terrestrial and meteoritic samples.

Sample	Relative Abundances			
Rosetta Mine, South Africa	Pb^{204}	Pb^{206}	Pb^{207}	Pb^{208}
(Collins, Russell, and Farquhar 1953)	1	12.65	14.27	32.78
Cañon Diablo Meteorite	1	9.41	10.27	29.16
Troilite Phase				
(Patterson, Brown, Tilton, and				
Inghram, 1953)				

A chemical analysis of the lead and uranium content of the troilite phase gave 18 ppm Pb and 0.009 ppm U. The significance of this is that radiogenic lead could not have formed in appreciable quantity after the separation of the troilite phase so that this meteoritic lead may be representative of the composition of primeval lead in the solar system. This conclusion depends on the assumption that meteoritic matter is a true sample of solar material and that the solidification of meteoritic material into separate phases occurred soon after element formation, at least in a time short compared to the total time which has elapsed since. Many experimental facts have been cited to substantiate these assumptions.

Radiogenic Lead. Any lead formed as the stable end product of the decay of uranium or thorium is referred to as radiogenic lead.

Common (or Ordinary) Lead. This is lead obtained from non-radioactive lead minerals or from rock-making minerals which accommodate lead in their structures. The constituents of common lead are primeval lead and varying small amounts of radiogenic lead. The mixing of primeval and radiogenic lead has occurred at various times in the past by various geologic processes about which we have incomplete information. The common leads formed by these processes in different parts of the earth's crust have widely differing isotopic composition.

Primary Lead. This is the lead present in a particular mineral at the time of its formation. If the mineral contains appreciable amounts of uranium or thorium, the isotopic composition of this lead will change with time, due to the steady addition of radiogenic lead. In dating a uranium mineral, the primary lead is a contribution to the lead content which must be subtracted.

The Chemical Lead-Uranium Method of Mineral Dating. The ultimate products of the decay of natural uranium and thorium are helium and lead as given by the equations

$$U^{238} \longrightarrow 8 \ He^4 + Pb^{206}$$
$$U^{235} \longrightarrow 7 \ He^4 + Pb^{207} \qquad (6.1)$$
$$Th^{232} \longrightarrow 6 \ He^4 + Pb^{208}$$

Because of the finite half-lives of the intermediate products, it takes some years before the uranium-lead equilibrium is established; namely $\sim 10^6$ years, $\sim 10^5$ years, and $\sim 10^2$ years, respectively, for the three series. After this length of time, the time variation in the relative amounts of parent and daughter atoms may be expressed as

$$(\text{Lead daughter})_{\text{now}} = (\text{Parent})_{\text{now}}(e^{\lambda t} - 1) \qquad (6.2)$$

where λ is the decay constant of the parent.

This relationship was first proposed as a means of calculating the ages of minerals bearing uranium or thorium by the American radiochemist, Bertram Boltwood, working in Lord Rutherford's laboratory. The first minerals were dated by this method in the first decade of this century.[237]

In an isolated chemical system such as a mineral, a determination of the amounts of parent and daughter and a knowledge of the rate of decay λ of the parent leads to a solution for the age, t, of the system. For example in a uranium (or thorium) mineral to which nothing has been added and nothing removed and in which no lead was present when the system originally formed, an age can be found by analyzing for lead and uranium (or thorium) and solving for t. The technique is usually referred to as the chemical lead-uranium (or lead-thorium) method. The word chemical, in this title, means that the amount of lead in the mineral is determined by a chemical analytical technique, that is, no isotopic analysis is performed. Many hundreds of mineral specimens have been dated by this method but a large fraction of these dates are questionable because it has been found that the premises on which the method rests are not valid for most minerals. We consider briefly some of the difficulties and possible sources of error.

1. Most minerals contain a mixture of uranium and thorium so that both elements have to be analyzed quantitatively, since the two elements produce lead at different rates. (The fact that U^{235} is always present in natural uranium does not cause trouble, since the isotopic percentage is so low and does not vary from sample to sample.)

2. Lead must be isolated quantitatively, and lead contamination from laboratory air, reagents, etc. must be rigorously excluded.

3. The method assumes that the mineral contained no lead at the time of its formation (primary lead); frequently, however, uranium and thorium minerals do contain primary lead so that the apparent age of the mineral is too high. In the evolution of the lead-uranium method, an attempt was made to correct for primary lead by determination of the atomic weight of the lead fraction; since the atomic weight of RaG is 206.04 while that of common lead is 207.2, it is possible by very accurate measurement of the

---

[237] B. B. Boltwood, *Am. J. Sci.* **23**, 77 (1907).

atomic weight to estimate the relative amounts of radiogenic and primary lead in the sample. Even with this method, however, the correction is only approximate since the composition of the primary lead is a variable quantity depending on unknown factors. A further disadvantage is that the method is limited to minerals from which enough lead can be isolated for the atomic weight determinations. The atomic weight determination has been replaced by the more accurate mass spectrometric method to be described below.

4. The method assumes no alteration of the mineral during the geologic period since its formation. Selective leaching of uranium, thorium, and lead has been noted in many samples. Later addition of lead from other sources can also give erroneous results. It is quite important that the form of the mineral and geologic setting of the specimen be known and considered. This consideration applies to other dating methods as well.

5. It is necessary to consider the possible loss by diffusion of the emanation isotope in the radioactive chain. This is not a serious problem in the U^{235} decay chain or in the thorium series since the half-life of the gaseous actinon and thoron are only 3.9 seconds and 55 seconds, respectively. But Rn^{222} has a half-life of 3.8 days; hence, if the structure of the uranium-bearing mineral is such that an appreciable amount of the gaseous product could have diffused away during a period of a few days, there might have been an appreciable reduction in the amount of Pb^{206} produced in the mineral.

Because of these difficulties, the chemical lead-uranium method has had limited success and is in disrepute. The essential simplicity of the method is appealing and some modern workers have found it to be reliable when applied to a few fairly common minerals (zircon, zenotime, and some monazites) which are resistant to chemical change and which were nearly completely free of lead content at the time of their formation.

The Mass Spectrometric Lead-Isotope and Lead-Lead Methods of Mineral Dating. Determination of the isotopic composition of the lead fraction is now considered essential for general application. This determination can be made by atomic weight measurements or by spectroscopic hyperfine structure analyses, but more usually is made with the mass spectrometer. The isotopic analysis plus a quantitative analysis for lead, thorium and uranium makes it possible in principle to calculate the age of the mineral in the four different ways summarized in the following equations:

$$N_{\text{Pb-206}} = N_{\text{U-238}}(e^{\lambda 238 t} - 1) \tag{6.3a}$$

$$N_{\text{Pb-207}} = N_{\text{U-235}}(e^{\lambda 235 t} - 1) \tag{6.3b}$$

$$N_{\text{Pb-208}} = N_{\text{Th-232}}(e^{\lambda 232 t} - 1) \tag{6.3c}$$

$$\frac{N_{\text{Pb-206}}}{N_{\text{Pb-207}}} = \frac{N_{\text{U-238}}}{N_{\text{U-235}}} \frac{(e^{\lambda 238 t} - 1)}{(e^{\lambda 235 t} - 1)} \tag{6.3d}$$

The symbol N refers to the number of *atoms* of the indicated nuclides *present at the time of analysis*. The number of atoms of the lead isotopes must be corrected for primeval lead before the calculation is made. The required decay constants λ are tabulated in Table 6.33.

TABLE 6.33. Decay constants required in age calculations.

Nuclide	Half-life	Disintegration constant, λ
U^{238}	4.51×10^9 yr	1.537×10^{-10} yr^{-1}
U^{235}	7.13×10^8 yr	9.72×10^{-10} yr^{-1}
Th^{232}	1.39×10^{10} yr	4.99×10^{-11} yr^{-1}

The first three equations represent the three lead-isotope methods, whereas the fourth constitutes the basis of the lead-lead method. The lead-lead calculation is not independent of the other three. The lead-lead method is based on the fact that U^{238} and U^{235} decay at rates differing by a factor of 6.3 so that the ratio of their stable end-products Pb^{207}/Pb^{206} varies systematically with the age of the radioactive mineral. See Fig. 6.47. In the application of Eq. 6.3d, it is not necessary to determine the ratio $N_{U\text{-}238}/N_{U\text{-}235}$, since this is simply the abundance ratio of natural uranium which is constant for all uranium samples (139 as determined by Nier in 1939, or 138 as determined by Lounsbury in 1956). Nor is it necessary to determine the quantity of lead accurately since only the ratio of the lead isotopes appears in the equation. Hence, the lead-lead method is one of extreme simplicity.

However, the lead-lead method can give erroneous results if the correction for primary lead is incorrectly made or if alterations in the amounts of daughter products have occurred in the mineral being dated. For example, appreciable loss of radon from the mineral would cause incomplete deposition of Pb^{206} and hence a high apparent age. Therefore, it is desirable to cross-check the age by an independent determination made by one or more of the other Eqs. 6.3a through 6.3c or by the Rb^{87}-Sr^{87} or K^{40}-Ar^{40} methods discussed below. If the results agree, they can be accepted with some confidence; if they do not agree, the pattern of disagreement may help to locate the cause. The use of the lead isotope methods requires quantitative analysis for lead and uranium and thorium. The chemical recovery factor for lead fractions can be determined mass spectrometrically by the isotope dilution method. For some reasons, not clearly understood, the Pb^{208}-thorium method seldom gives results in agreement with the other methods and hence cannot be relied on. There is some evidence that Pb^{208} is more readily leached from the mineral crystal sites previously occupied by the thorium parent, thus leading to ages which are too low. This mysterious behavior may be associated with the particular nature of the minerals and with selective dislocations caused by recoils from the alpha decay processes.

The recoil energies and the lifetimes and chemical identities of intermediate products are different in the different series. It should also be noted that the determination of Pb^{208} often involves a correction for primary Pb^{208} which often amounts to ten per cent of the total.

The mass spectrographic analysis of the lead fraction puts the correction for primary lead on a more secure basis because the abundance of non-radiogenic Pb^{204} can be used as a guide to the primary lead content. When the Pb^{204} content is negligible, no correction need be made to the lead isotope ratio and the calculated age is subject to error only from alteration effects. When the Pb^{204} content is appreciable, its abundance is used together with an estimate of the common lead composition for lead in igneous rocks of that particular age and in that particular part of the earth's crust.

Figure 6.47 shows the variation in the isotope ratios as a function of age for the three most used methods.

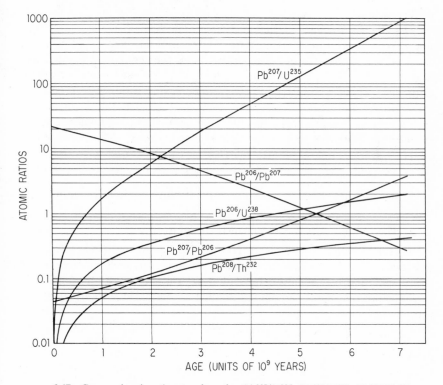

FIG. 6.47. Curves showing the atomic ratios Pb^{207}/U^{235}, Pb^{206}/U^{238}, Pb^{208}/Th^{232}, and Pb^{206}/Pb^{207} in minerals which have been undisturbed for the number of years given by the abscissa and which contained no primary lead. It is important to note that both the numerator and the denominator in all ratios refer to the species present at the time of the analysis.

The lead isotope and lead-lead methods received their first real impetus from the splendid mass spectrographic exploratory work of NIER at the end of the 1930's. The method underwent rapid development in the early 1950's when advances in chemical techniques and extension of mass spectrometer sensitivity by orders of magnitude made it possible to apply the method to a very wide range of igneous rocks. By 1960 it had become clear that one class of uranium minerals, namely the uraninites, most often gives concordant ages when determined by two or more methods. Hence, for uraninites the lead-isotope methods are of certified reliability. For a wide variety of other uranium-bearing minerals the wide distribution of age measurements achieved by two or more methods has been discouraging. However, even in these cases the direction of the discordance may give interesting hints on the geological alteration of minerals since their time of formation.

For a fuller account of these methods and their application to geophysical problems consult the references given in the bibliography at the end of this section.

The Pb-210 Method of Mineral Dating. The age of a uranium-bearing mineral can be determined by the ratio of any one of the members of the decay series to the stable lead end-product provided the series is in equilibrium. The Pb^{206}/U^{238} and Pb^{207}/U^{235} methods just discussed may be taken as examples. Equally good, theoretically, would be such ratios as Pb^{206}/Ra^{226}, Pb^{206}/Io^{230}, Pb^{206}/Po^{214} or Pb^{206}/Pb^{210}. However, the evaluation of each ratio involves practical difficulties; the half-lives may be inconveniently short or the chemical purification may be troublesome. The Pb^{206}/Pb^{210} (RaD) method, first suggested by HOUTERMANS,[238] and first tested by BEGEMANN AND CO-WORKERS,[239] is uniquely satisfactory for several reasons.

1. It is not necessary to carry out a quantitative analysis for uranium or lead.

2. The radioactivity measurement is straightforward.

3. It is unlikely that the lead fraction will be contaminated with other radioactive members of the series, since any uranium series member which is not quantitatively removed has either such a short half-life that it will decay before the sample is counted or such a long half-life that the activity will be negligible.

4. The half-life of Pb^{210} is 22 years.

5. The Pb^{206}/Pb^{210} age is not badly affected by uranium leaching late in the history of the mineral because Pb^{210} should be in equilibrium with the

    [238] F. G. Houtermans, *Sitzber. Heidelberg Akad. Wiss. Math. Naturwiss, Kl.* **123** (1951).
    [239] F. Begemann, H. V. Buttlar, F. G. Houtermans, N. Isaac, and E. Picciotto, *Bull. Con. Phys. Nucl. Univ. libre Bruxelles*, No. 37 (1952).

80,000 year ionium long after an appreciable amount of uranium has been leached out.

6. The chemical steps are not complicated and chemical handling is minimal since the spectrometer analysis and the radiation counting can be done on the same sample.

7. The Pb^{210} age is independent of radon leakage if radon loss has been constant, since the yield of Pb^{210} and Pb^{206} are reduced proportionately.

The amount of Pb^{210} is a monitor of the amount of uranium in the mineral via the equilibrium expression,

$$(N\lambda)_{Pb\text{-}210} = (N\lambda)_{U\text{-}238}$$

where N refers to the number of atoms and λ to the decay constant.

The counting of the disintegrations of Pb^{210} requires consideration of the sequence:

$$\underset{(\text{RaD})}{Pb^{210}} \xrightarrow[\text{weak }\beta^-]{22 \text{ yr}} \underset{(\text{RaE})}{Bi^{210}} \xrightarrow[1 \text{ MeV }\beta^-]{5 \text{ day}} \underset{(\text{RaF})}{Po^{210}} \xrightarrow[\alpha]{138 \text{ day}} \underset{(\text{RaG})}{Pb^{206}}$$

The weak beta particles of RaD cannot be counted, but if the sample is set aside for a few weeks until RaE is in equilibrium, the strong beta particles of RaE are easily counted. Alternatively, the alpha particles of polonium can be observed to grow in and the growth can be compared with standard growth curves. The properties of a RaDEF mixture are discussed in Section 6.2 of this chapter.

If no common lead and no appreciable amount of thorium is present in the mineral, the fraction of Pb^{206} may be estimated to a few per cent without mass analysis for comparatively young samples. In most cases, however, these uncertainties are much too large so that mass spectrometric measurement of the isotopic composition is imperative to obtain reliable results.

The Pb-210 method is a useful alternative or supplement to the lead-uranium or lead-lead methods. KOHMAN AND SAITO[240] review published applications of the method.

The lead fraction from a uranium ore also contains Pb^{211} (AcB) when first isolated and, if the ore also contains thorium, the lead fraction will also contain Pb^{212} (ThB). Hence, in principle, as HOUTERMANS[238] pointed out, one can consider a Pb^{207}/AcB and Pb^{208}/ThB ratio for age determinations. The half-life of AcB is only 36 minutes and that of ThB is only 10.6 hours which makes these methods much less attractive than the Pb^{206}/Pb^{210} method, although some application of these alternative methods may prove useful.

Holmes Computation of the Age of the Earth. In 1946 HOLMES[241] proposed

[240] T. Kohman and N. Saito, *Ann. Rev. Nucl. Sci.* **4**, 418 (1954).
[241] A. Holmes, *Nature* **157**, 680 (1946); **159**, 127 (1947); **163**, 453 (1949).

an ingenious method for the estimation of the age of the earth's crust based on the analysis of many lead minerals carried out by NIER.[242]   This method is based on the following model for the formation of lead minerals.

1. Primeval lead had a uniform composition throughout the earth up to the time the crust was formed.

2. When the crust was formed the Pb/U and Pb/Th ratios in different areas varied slightly, were frozen at a particular value for any one region, and did not subsequently vary through any geologic process from that time until the present, except for radioactive decay.

3. Each lead ore has been derived from one such area and has not been mixed with lead from any other source.   At the time of the formation of the lead mineral no uranium or thorium was deposited with the lead so that no radiogenic lead has been added since the formation of the mineral.   Hence, the isotopic analysis should serve as a record of the isotopic composition of the common lead in the magma of that region at the time of formation of the lead mineral.

4. The age of the lead mineral can be determined by stratigraphic correlations or by dating nearby uranium-bearing minerals.

We let x_m and y_m be the abundance of Pb^{206} and Pb^{207}, respectively, relative to Pb^{204} in the mineral sample today and x_o and y_o be the same quantities at the time, t_o, when the earth's crust was formed.   We define V_m as the ratio of atoms of U^{235} relative to Pb^{204} in the sample today.   This is not a universal constant for the entire crust but applies to the isolated geologic region within which a particular lead mineral was formed.   The quantity α is defined as the ratio of U^{238} to U^{235} at the present time; α is 139.   The time elapsed since formation of the earth's crust is represented as t_o and the time of deposition (dating backward from the present) of the lead ore is taken as t_m.   With these definitions and the above assumptions the laws of radioactive decay lead directly to the following equations:

$$x_m = x_o + \alpha V_m(e^{\lambda 238 t_o} - e^{\lambda 238 t_m}) \tag{6.5a}$$

$$y_m = y_o + V_m(e^{\lambda 235 t_o} - e^{\lambda 235 t_m}) \tag{6.5b}$$

Equations 6.5a and 6.5b give in an α, x_m, y_m diagram the "lines of the lead development" for constant values of V_m as a function of time.   Dividing the two equations we get:

$$\frac{x_m - x_o}{y_m - y_o} = \frac{\alpha(e^{\lambda 238 t_o} - e^{\lambda 238 t_m})}{(e^{\lambda 235 t_o} - e^{\lambda 235 t_m})} \tag{6.5c}$$

242 A. Nier, J. Am. Chem. Soc. 60, 1571 (1938); Nier, Thompson, and Murphey, Phys. Rev. 60, 112 (1941).

This equation yields a family of straight lines (isochrones) corresponding to different values of t_o. These lines intersect at the point x_o, y_o corresponding to the isotopic composition of primeval lead.

Several authors have used NIER's[242] data on the isotopic composition and age of formation of lead minerals to calculate an age of the earth and the composition of primeval lead. The calculation is made graphically or by least squares fit to Eq. (6.5c). Some results are summarized in Table 6.34.

For many years the value $(3.3 \pm 0.3) \times 10^9$ years, obtained by this method, was generally accepted as the age of the earth's crust. It was also considered an approximate measure of the time since the formation of the elements, since there was some reason to believe that the time elapsed from nucleogenesis to the formation of the earth was short compared to 3.3 billion years. However, the figure arrived at by this method has never been accepted without reservations since the assumptions upon which it is based are unproved and the extrapolations involved are extreme. Particularly disturbing is the fact that not all the mass spectrographic data on the lead minerals is included in the calculations, about one third of the data being rejected as anomalous. The values listed in Table 6.34 could be regarded as

TABLE **6.34.** Estimates of age of earth's crust (lithosphere) by HOLMES' method.

Author	t_0	$x_0 = \dfrac{Pb^{206}}{Pb^{204}}$	$y_0 = \dfrac{Pb^{207}}{Pb^{204}}$	$z_0 = \dfrac{Pb^{208}}{Pb^{204}}$
		Primeval Lead Abundances		
HOLMES 1947	3.35×10^9 yr	10.95	13.51	—
HOUTERMANS 1947	2.9×10^9 yr	11.52	14.03	31.6
BULLAR AND STANLEY 1949	3.29×10^9 yr	11.86	13.86	—
COLLINS, RUSSELL, FARQUHAR* 1953	3.5×10^9 yr	11.33	13.55	31.10

* In addition to NIER's 1940 data COLLINS, RUSSELL, AND FARQUHAR considered new data of their own on lead minerals.

meaningful as long as no lead mineral had values of x_m and y_m less than the x_o and y_o values in this table. When the meteoritic lead abundances listed in Table 6.32 were reported by PATTERSON, BROWN, TILTON, AND INGHRAM[236] in 1953 it became almost certain that the age calculated by the HOLMES method was too low.

Because of the uncertainties in the HOLMES assumptions, certain authors have preferred to use a somewhat similar calculation based on the NIER data to calculate only a maximum age of the elements. In this approach one calculates backwards in time to determine at what time the amount of *one* of the three isotopes Pb^{206}, Pb^{207}, or Pb^{208} drops to zero, since, obviously, a negative quantity (negative value of x_o or y_o) is physically inadmissible. ALPHER

AND HERMAN,[243] using NIER'S[242] data, calculate that the Pb^{206}/Pb^{204} ratio drops to zero at a time $\sim 5.3 \times 10^9$ years. COLLINS, RUSSELL, AND FARQU-HAR[244] using more extensive data calculate that the first ratio to drop to zero is Pb^{207}/Pb^{204}, and calculate a maximum age of 5.5×10^9 years.

Calculation of the Age of the Earth (From Lead Data on Meteoritic and Terrestrial Lead Samples)[245]. BROWN[246] proposed that lead isolated from meteorites might be used as a measure of the isotopic composition of lead at the time of formation of the solar system. The data of PATTERSON, ET AL.[236] on meteoritic leads probably reveals the true composition of primeval lead. See Table 6.32. We can use these data to calculate the age of the earth as follows.

Let us define x_o and y_o as the ratios Pb^{206}/Pb^{204} and Pb^{207}/Pb^{204}, respectively, in primeval lead and set them equal to the lead ratios found in the troilite phase of the Cañon Diablo Meteorite (Table 6.32). Let us further define x_m and y_m as the corresponding ratios for recent common leads isolated from the surface of the earth. The constant α is taken equal to 139 and is the ratio of U^{238} atoms to U^{235} atoms in present-day uranium. We can then write

$$\frac{x_m - x_o}{y_m - y_o} = \frac{\alpha(e^{\lambda 238 t_o} - 1)}{(e^{\lambda 235 t_o} - 1)} \tag{6.6}$$

We can solve this equation for t_o, the age of the earth, if we have a reliable value for x_m and y_m. Equation (6.6) is very similar to Eq. (6.5c) if one notes that t_m in the present case is zero so that $e^{\lambda t_m} = 1$.

Nearly all analyzed terrestrial lead samples (except those from uranium minerals) that have been isolated from their uranium environments since tertiary times (< 30 million years ago) have x_m and y_m values which fall within the ranges:

$$x_m = 18.07 - 18.95$$
$$y_m = 15.40 - 15.76 \tag{6.7}$$

Substitution of these values into Eq. (6.6) leads to a value of approximately 4.5×10^9 years for t_o.

A very useful type of lead sample is that found in deep sea sediments particularly in the sediments known as manganese nodules. These nodules grow at a very slow rate and the lead deposited in them must constitute a

[243] R. A. Alpher and R. C. Herman, Phys. Rev. 84, 1111 (1951).
[244] C. B. Collins, R. D. Russell, and R. M. Farquhar, Can. J. Phys. 31, 402 (1953).
[245] For a discussion of this topic see PATTERSON, TILTON, AND INGHRAM, Science 121, 69 (1955) and HOUTERMANS, Nuovo Cim. 10, No. 12, 1623 (1953).
[246] H. Brown, Phys. Rev. 72, 348 (1947).
[246a] C. C. Patterson, Geochim. et Cosmochim. Acta 10, 230 (1956).
[247] R. R. Marshall and D. C. Hess, J. Chem. Phys. 28, 1258 (1958).

reliable sampling of the lead eroded from enormous masses of continental rock and washed ultimately into the sea from enormous volumes of surface drainage waters.   Table 6.35 lists the composition of present day common

TABLE **6.35.** Composition of present-day common lead as determined in lead isolated from deep sea sediments (manganese nodules)*

$x_m = \dfrac{Pb^{206}}{Pb^{204}}$	$y_m = \dfrac{Pb^{207}}{Pb^{204}}$	$z_m = \dfrac{Pb^{208}}{Pb^{204}}$
18.91	15.69	38.68

* C. Patterson, E. Goldberg, and M. Inghram, *Bull. Geol. Soc. Am.* **64**, 1387 (1953). Slightly different values are reported by T. S. Chow and C. C. Patterson in *Geochim. et Cosmochim. Acta.* **26**, 263–308 (1962).

lead as determined from such deep sea samples.   These values of x_m and y_m again lead to an age of the earth of 4.5 × 10^9 years.   This calculation assumes that earth matter came from the same source as did that of the meteorites.

Another calculation based on Eq. (6.6) can be made from the lead isotope data obtained from a variety of meteorites.   If we make the assumption that all meteorites were condensed at about the same time from matter which had a uniform isotopic composition of lead, then all present-day lead-isotope ratios should fit Eq. (6.6) with a constant value for t_o.   The lead isotope ratios in different meteorites may be greatly different because of their differing content of uranium, but the ratios should differ in a systematic way. Figure 6.48 illustrates this.   This figure shows that a Pb^{206}-Pb^{207} "isochrone" with a t_o value of 4.61 × 10^9 years fits a wide variety of data from meteorites as well as terrestrial oceanic lead.

An excellent check on this age figure for meteorites has been obtained by dating meteorites by the K^{40}–Ar^{40} and the Rb^{87}–Sr^{87} methods described below.   Results in the range 4.3 to 4.8 billion years have been obtained on several meteorites.[248]

At the present time it is a widely held view that meteorites and the earth's crust (lithosphere) condensed out of the same "batch" of elementary material and that both formed condensed phases at about the same time, namely about 4.5 billion years ago.   This age is not identical with the age of the elements, since nucleogenesis may have been completed at a significantly earlier time than that of the formation of the lithosphere.   Furthermore, nucleogenesis itself may have required a quite significant period of time.   The latter is a strong function of the cosmological model of nucleogenesis which is adopted, and we shall not discuss these models here other than to call attention to the fact that some modern models suggest a period of the order of

[248] J. Geiss and D. C. Hess, *Astrophys. J.* **127**, 224 (1958).

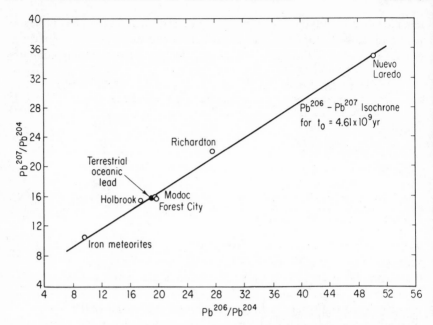

FIG. 6.48. A plot of the lead isotope ratios observed in terrestrial oceanic lead and in a variety of meteorites, showing agreement with a Pb^{206}–Pb^{207} isochrone with a t_0 value of 4.6×10^9 years. Figure prepared by J. H. Reynolds from data of PATTERSON ET AL.[236, 246a], of MARSHALL AND HESS,[247] and others. In the terminology of equation (6), the abscissa and ordinate are x_m and y_m, respectivley. The agreement of the data with the straight line suggests that all meteorites and the earth belong to a common "array" of bodies which were separated out from matter containing a common primordial lead composition about 4.6×10^9 years ago.

10^{10} years for the duration of the element-forming process. The time elapsed since the end of the element-forming process and the condensation of matter in our solar system can be estimated experimentally by an interesting method which we can discuss briefly. This method depends upon the discovery by REYNOLDS[249–251] of a great excess of Xe^{129} in the xenon fraction isolated from the chrondritic (stone) meteorite, Richardton, and, later, from the enstatite chrondrite, Indarch.[251] This excess Xe^{129} is believed to be the decay product of I^{129} originally present in the meteorite but now completely extinct because of its relatively short 1.7×10^7 year half-life. The presence of the excess Xe^{129} in itself indicates that the condensation of the meteoritic mass to a condition which could retain xenon must

[249] J. H. Reynolds, *Phys. Rev., Letters* **4**, 8 (1960); for important comments on this paper see Wasserburg, Fowler, and Hoyle, *Phys. Rev., Letters* **4**, 112 (1960).

[250] J. H. Reynolds, *Phys. Rev., Letters* **4**, 351 (1960).

[251] P. M. Jeffery and J. H. Reynolds, *J. Geophys. Res.* **66**, 3582 (1961).

have occurred in a time roughly of the order of magnitude of 10^7 years after the last element forming process had occurred. In order to measure this period more definitely the following quantitative information is required.

1. The ratio of stable Xe^{129} to stable I^{127} in the meteorite plus the assurance or assumption that no Xe^{129} has been lost during the 4.5 billion year lifetime of the meteorite. This ratio was measured by Reynolds by quantitative neutron activation analysis and mass spectrometry.

2. The ratio of radioactive I^{129} to stable I^{127} at the end of nucleogenesis. This ratio cannot be obtained directly and must be estimated by an examination of systematic trends in the isotopic abundance figures and a consideration of possible nuclear models. If nucleogenesis took a short time compared to the I^{129} half-life, the ratio $(I^{129}/I^{127})_o$ was probably about 1. If nucleogenesis took a long time compared to 10^7 years the primordial I^{129} stock would have leveled off while the I^{127} content would have continued to rise. In this case $(I^{129}/I^{127})_o$ might have attained the value equal to the mean life of I^{129} divided by the duration of nucleosynthesis. Following a suggestion of CAMERON,[252] REYNOLDS chose the effective value of 2×10^{10} years and arrived at a value for $(I^{129}/I^{127})_o = 0.00125$.

The time period whose calculation we are now discussing is given by the expression

$$\Delta t = \frac{T_{1/2}^{(I^{129})}}{0.693} [\ln(I^{127}/Xe^{129})_{\text{meteorite}} + \ln(I^{129}/I^{127})_o] \qquad (6.8)$$

We note that an error of a factor of 10 in either ratio leads to only a 16 per cent error in Δt.

Reynolds has calculated preliminary values of 120 million years for Δt from the data taken on the Richardton meteorite and 86 million years for data from the meteorite, Indarch. The exact meaning of this time interval measured by the Xe^{129} excess is given different interpretations by the different experts who have discussed it. It is beyond the scope of our interest to pursue the matter further here or to enter into the large question of the course and duration of the element formation process. Ideas about cosmology and nucleosynthesis are undergoing many changes at the present time.

Dating Methods Based on the Radioactivity of Rubidium and Potassium. In this chapter we are concerned chiefly with the heavy element series of natural radioactivities and their use in dating of minerals. No summary of dating methods for older minerals would be complete, however, without a mention of the K^{40}–Ar^{40} and Rb^{87}–Sr^{87} methods. We shall not review C^{14} dating which applies to quite recent dates, comparatively speaking, i.e., up to 30,000 years.

---

[252] A. G. W. Cameron, private communication to J. R. Reynolds.

The isotope Rb^{87} decays by beta emission to stable Sr^{87} with a half-life of 5.0×10^{10} years* (decay constant $= 1.39 \times 10^{-11}$ yr^{-1}). The isotopic content of Rb^{87} in natural rubidium is 27.8 per cent. The principle of mineral dating by the Rb^{87}–Sr^{87} method is very simple; one merely determines the total amount of rubidium and the total amount of Sr^{87} in the mineral, and applies the law of radioactive decay. For the success of the method it is necessary to establish that no selective elution of rubidium or strontium occurred since the formation of the mineral. It is also necessary that the amount of non-radiogenic strontium in the mineral be low and it is essential that the half-life of Rb^{87} be known accurately. The soft beta particle emitted by Rb^{87} seriously delayed the determination of an accurate decay constant and reduced the reliability of the method until recent years. A detailed review of this point is given by ALDRICH AND WETHERILL.[253]

HAHN, STRASSMANN, AND WALLING[254] first found radiogenic strontium in lepidolite, the mineral with the highest rubidium concentration, and HAHN AND WALLING[255] made the first age determinations by this method in 1938. The method was placed on a much firmer basis in 1953 by the introduction of the isotopic dilution mass spectrometric prodecure.[256–257] All modern Rb–Sr age determinations include isotopic analysis of the strontium and correction for non-radiogenic Sr^{87}.

The second method we are discussing is based on the decay scheme of K^{40}, which is shown in Fig. 6.49. Potassium 40 is a rare isotope of potassium which occurs in natural potassium only to the extent of 0.0119 per cent. It decays 11 per cent by electron capture to form Ar^{40}. One of the attractions of the K^{40}–Ar^{40} method is that argon can be easily studied in a mass spectrometer.

Because of the branching decay the mathematical expression which is used to compute the age of the mineral is somewhat more complicated than in the Rb^{87}–Sr^{87} case. This expression may be written as follows

$$t = \frac{1}{\lambda_{ec} + \lambda_\beta} \ln\left(1 + \frac{\lambda_{ec} + \lambda\beta}{\lambda_{ec}} \frac{Ar^{40}}{K^{40}}\right) \tag{6.9}$$

where λ_{ec} and λ_β are the respective decay constants for electron capture and beta decay, and Ar^{40}/K^{40} is the atom ratio of the nuclides in the mineral.

253 L. T. Aldrich and G. W. Wetherill, *Ann. Rev. Nucl. Sci.* **8**, 257 (1958).

254 O. Hahn, F. Strassmann, and E. Walling, *Naturwiss* **25**, 189 (1937).

255 O. Hahn and E. Walling, *Chem. Z.* **67**, 55 (1938).

256 G. L. Davis and L. T. Aldrich, *Bull. Geol. Soc. Amer.* **64**, 379 (1953).

257 R. H. Tomlinson and A. K. Das Gupta, *Can. J. Chem.* **31**, 909 (1953).

* We quote here the value chosen by ALDRICH AND WETHERILL[253] after a consideration of all determinations published up to 1958; more recent determinations include those of W. Rausch ($4.72 \pm 0.08 \times 10^{10}$ yr) published in a thesis study and of Egelkraut and Leutz ($5.82 \pm 0.1 \times 10^{10}$ yr) published in *Z. Physik* **161**, 13 (1961).

The K^{40}–Ar^{40} method developed slowly because of certain experimental difficulties and because of the great difficulties involved in an exact determination of the decay constants. These have been largely overcome and the method has recently taken its place as one of the most reliable and generally useful of the dating methods. A good review of the measurements of the K^{40} radiations is given by ALDRICH AND WETHERILL.[253] The principal remaining uncertainty is whether there is a slight unobserved electron capture decay directly to the ground state of Ar^{40}.

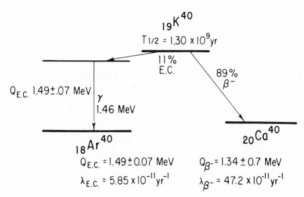

FIG. **6.49**. Decay scheme of potassium 40.

The dating method consists in determining quantitatively the potassium content and argon content of a potassium-bearing mineral. The argon content must be corrected for non-radiogenic argon. It is assumed that argon diffusion is insignificant, an assumption which has been checked by dating potassium minerals associated with other minerals which were independently dated by the lead methods. Results show that argon retention is quantitative in micas but often incomplete in feldspars. It is not surprising that argon diffusion loss is low since recoil effects are insignificant and, although argon is a large atom, it presumably occupies a site previously occupied by the large K^+ (1.33A°) and, hence, does not cause undue strain in the structure, particularly as the ratio of argon to potassium atoms is never large.

The first argon age determinations were reported by SMITS AND GENTNER[258] in 1950. The method was improved by introduction of the isotopic-dilution mass spectrometric technique by WASSERBURG AND HAYDEN.[259] The argon method appears capable of wide application for dating igneous rock. It can be applied to micas and feldspars which are ubiquitous minerals. It has been applied also to the dating of meteorites, as was mentioned

---

[258] F. Smits and W. Gentner, *Geochim. et Cosmochim. Acta* **1**, 22 (1950).

[259] G. J. Wasserburg and R. J. Hayden, *Geochim et Cosmochim. Acta* **7**, (1955).

568 NATURAL RADIOACTIVITY OF THE HEAVY ELEMENTS CHAP. 6

above. Results indicate an age of 4.3 to 4.8 billion years in excellent agreement with the lead–lead ages of meteorites.[248]

The Helium Age Methods. Helium was first identified in the sun's spectrum and was first discovered in terrestrial materials in 1895 when RAMSAY identified helium gas in uranium and thorium-bearing minerals. The constant association of helium with radioactive minerals helped later to confirm the identification of alpha particles with ionized rapidly-moving helium. RUTHERFORD suggested that the amount of helium in radioactive minerals might be a means of measuring geologic time, and LORD RAYLEIGH soon afterwards began research on the content of helium in pitchblende and thorianite.

Since those early years there has been a continuing interest in the helium content of minerals and a formidable number of samples have been analyzed in many laboratories. Unfortunately, the helium age method frequently gives low results when checked against other dating methods, mainly because of loss of helium. The causes of this helium loss are complex and a major part of the helium analysis work has been devoted to study of helium migration and loss in various types of minerals.

We shall not discuss the helium age measurements further in this book. The interested reader is referred to an extensive review by HURLEY.[260]

Bibliography in Nuclear Geology. The entire subject of nuclear geology is a fascinating subject now under very rapid development. The heavy elements play an important role in this research field. The dating of minerals by lead isotope methods and the study of ionium and radium content in ocean sediments are some examples of the applications. It is beyond the scope of this book to discuss all applications of heavy element studies to geology. The appended bibliography may serve as a guide to further reading.

1. K. Rankama, *Isotope Geology*, New York: McGraw-Hill Book Company, 1954.
2. R. D. Russell and R. M. Farquhar, *Lead Isotopes in Geology*, New York: Interscience Publishers, 1960.
3. L. H. Ahrens, K. Rankama, S. K. Runcorn, *Physics and Chemistry of the Earth*, New York: McGraw-Hill Book Company, 1956.
4. H. Faul, editor, *Nuclear Geology*, New York: John Wiley and Sons, 1954.
5. "Nuclear Processes in Geologic Settings," *Nuclear Science Series Report No. 19*, July 31, 1956, National Research Council, National Academy of Sciences.
6. T. Kohman and N. Saito, "Radioactivity in Geology and Cosmology," *Ann. Rev. Nucl. Sci.* **4**, 401 (1954).
7. C. Patterson, G. Tilton and M. Inghram, "Age of the Earth," *Science* **121**, 69 (1955).
8. H. Brown, "The Age of the Solar System," *Scientific American*, April 1957.

---

260 P. M. Hurley, "The Helium Age Method and the Distribution and Migration of Helium in Rocks," pp. 301–329 in *Nuclear Geology*, ed. by H. Faul (New York: John Wiley and Sons, 1954).

9. A. Holmes, *Nature* **157**, 680 (1946); **163**, 453 (1949).
10. L. T. Aldrich, "Measurement of Radioactive Ages of Rocks," *Science* **123**, 871 (1956).
11. F. G. Houtermans "Determination of the Age of the Earth from the Isotopic Composition of Meteoritic Lead," *Nuovo Cim.* **10**, No. 12, (1953).
12. J. P. Marble, "Reports of the Committee on the Measurement of Geologic Time," National Research Council, Washington D.C., *Publication 212* (1952); *245* (1953), and *319* (1954).
13. L. T. Aldrich and G. W. Wetherill, "Geochronology by Radioactive Decay," *Ann. Rev. Nucl. Sci.* **8**, 257 (1958).
14. J. L. Kulp "Advances in Geophysics," Vol. 2, 179 (1955), Academic Press, New York.
15. J. T. Wilson, R. D. Russell, and R. M. Farquhar, *Handbuch der Physik*, **47**, 288–363 (1956) Springer-Verlag, Berlin.
16. G. R. Tilton and G. L. Davis, *Frontiers in Geochemistry*, P. H. Abelson, editor, John Wiley and Sons, New York, 1958.
17. Knopf, Schuchert, Kovarik, Holmes, and Brown, "The Age of the Earth", National Academy of Sci. (U.S.)—National Research Council, p. 487 (1931). A review of the early period.
18. W. A. Fowler, "Rutherford and Nuclear Cosmochronology," *Proc. Rutherford Jubilee Internat. Conf.*, Manchester, England, Heywood and Co., Ltd. 1962.
19. E. Anders, "Meteorite Ages," *Rev. Mod. Phys.* **34**, 287 (1962).

6.6 THE NATURAL OCCURRENCE OF TRANSURANIUM ELEMENTS IN TRACE AMOUNT

Pu^{239} *in Nature.* Pu^{239} has a half-life of 24,400 years so that any primordial plutonium would long since have decayed to form U^{235}. However, in uranium-bearing minerals the action of natural neutrons can cause the formation of small quantities of plutonium via the sequence

$$U^{238} + n \longrightarrow U^{239}; \quad U^{239} \xrightarrow{\beta^-} Np^{239} \xrightarrow{\beta^-} Pu^{239}$$

This was first proven experimentally in 1942 by G. T. SEABORG AND M. L. PERLMAN[261] who chemically separated the plutonium from a sample of Canadian pitchblende concentrate and conservatively estimated the plutonium content of the ore to be roughly one part in 10^{14} by weight. From considerations of possible methods of formation of plutonium it was assumed that the plutonium was Pu^{239}. Similarly, GARNER, BONNER AND SEABORG[262] searched in 1942 for naturally occurring plutonium in carnotite, hatchettolite, and fergusonite. They found Pu^{239} present in carnotite to the extent of

---

[261] G. T. Seaborg and M. L. Perlman, Paper 1.3 *Nat. Nucl. Energ. Ser.* **14B**, "The Transuranium Elements," Seaborg, Katz, and Manning, editors, (New York: McGraw-Hill Book Co., 1949).

[262] C. S. Garner, N. A. Bonner, and G. T. Seaborg, Paper 1.10, same volume as Ref. 261.

about one part in 10^{14}. The sensitivity for detection in other ores was poorer and no Pu^{239} could be detected.

Later, when the chemical properties of plutonium and the instrumental techniques for alpha activity detection and analysis were better understood, LEVINE AND SEABORG[263] studied this problem more thoroughly. Plutonium was separated in known yield from the uranium minerals listed in Table 6.36 and identified by alpha spectrum analysis as Pu^{239}.

TABLE **6.36.** Plutonium occurring in radioactive minerals
LEVINE AND SEABORG[263]

Mineral	Uranium content per cent	Ratio Pu²³⁹ to ore (by weight)	Ratio Pu²³⁹ to U
Canadian pitchblende	13.5	9.1×10^{-13}	7.1×10^{-12}
Belgian Congo pitchblende	38	4.8×10^{-12}	12×10^{-12}
Belgian Congo pitchblende*	45.3	7.0×10^{-12}	15×10^{-12}
Colorado pitchblende	50	3.8×10^{-12}	7.7×10^{-12}
Brazilian monazite	0.24	2.1×10^{-14}	83×10^{-12}
N. Carolina monazite	1.64	5.9×10^{-14}	3.6×10^{-12}
Colorado fergusonite	0.25	$<1 \times 10^{-14}$	$<4 \times 10^{-12}$
Colorado carnotite	10	$<4 \times 10^{-14}$	$<0.4 \times 10^{-12}$

* Peppard, et al., Ref. 264.

PEPPARD AND CO-WORKERS[264] isolated microgram quantities of plutonium from the aqueous wastes left in the processing of ton quantities of Belgian Congo pitchblende. They found one part Pu^{239} per 1.4×10^{11} parts of the pitchblende concentrate (45.3% uranium). This plutonium was analyzed carefully by differential pulse height analysis of the alpha spectrum, by neutron irradiation studies and by mass spectrometry, and no plutonium isotope other than Pu^{239} was found.

Possible sources of neutrons to account for this natural production of plutonium include:

1. the spontaneous fission of uranium,

2. (α, n) reactions caused by the action of alpha particles from the heavy elements on the nuclei of light elements in the ore,

3. cosmic rays,

4. induced fission of U^{235}.

In the case of pitchblende ores the first two sources are of comparable

263 C. A. Levine and G. T. Seaborg, *J. Am. Chem. Soc.* **73**, 3278 (1951).

264 D. F. Peppard, M. H. Studier, M. V. Gergel, G. W. Mason, J. W. Sullivan, and J. F. Mech, *J. Am. Chem. Soc.* **73**, 2529 (1951).

importance. In thorium ores neutrons from (α, n) reactions are probably dominant. Cosmic rays appear to contribute a negligible number of neutrons by comparison.

LEVINE AND SEABORG[263] have estimated the relative importance of these neutron sources very crudely in the following way.

Assuming an average of two neutrons per fission, and a spontaneous fission decay constant of 1.1×10^{-16} per year for U^{238}, one can calculate that about 1.1 neutrons per gram of uranium are emitted per minute from spontaneous fission. A 100-g sample of ore containing 13.5 per cent uranium will emit about 15 neutrons per minute by this means.

As suggested previously[265] there is another source of neutrons to be considered. One gram of uranium and the decay products in equilibrium with it emit about 6×10^6 alpha particles per minute whose maximum energies range from 4.2 to 7.68 MeV. These alpha particles, impinging on the nuclei of the light elements present, cause reactions whereby neutrons are emitted; (α, n reactions). ROBERTS[266] has reported on the number of neutrons emitted when thick samples of the light elements are bombarded with 5.3 MeV alpha particles. STUHLINGER[267] has given the excitation functions for the neutron emitting reactions involving alpha particles on boron and beryllium with alpha particle energies up to 8.8 MeV. With these data and those of others,[268–272] the number of neutrons emitted per alpha particle (of a given energy) impinging on a target of a light element can be estimated. Using the chemical analysis of a sample of Canadian pitchblende reported by MARBLE,[273] one can calculate that in a 100-g sample of ore containing 13.5 per cent uranium, fifteen to twenty neutrons per minute will be formed from the action of alpha particles on the nuclei of the light elements in the ore; (α, n reactions). However, if, for example, as much as 1 per cent of beryllium, boron, or lithium is present in the ore in addition to the elements reported in the analysis, the additional neutron yields due to (α, n) reactions in such a 100-g sample would be about 100, 40 and 10 neutrons per minute, respectively.

---

[265] G. T. Seaborg, *Chem. Eng. News* **25**, 358 (1947).

[266] J. H. Roberts, *U.S. Atomic Energy Commission Declassified Document MDDC-371* (January, 1947).

[267] E. Stuhlinger, *Z. Physik* **114**, 185 (1938).

[268] E. Segrè and C. Wiegand, *U.S. Atomic Energy Commission Declassified Document MDDC-185* (1949).

[269] R. L. Walker, *U.S. Atomic Energy Commission Declassified Document AECD-2883* (1948).

[270] I. H. Halpern, *Phys. Rev.* **74**, 1234 (1948).

[271] L. N. Ridenour and W. J. Henderson, *Ibid.* **52**, 889 (1937).

[272] H. L. Anderson, *U.S. Atomic Energy Commission Unclassified Document NP-851* (1943).

[273] J. P. Marble, *Am. Min.* **24**, 272 (1939).

MONTGOMERY AND MONTGOMERY[274] have estimated the neutron intensity at sea level in the cosmic radiation to be about 0.1 neutron per cm^2 per minute. Although the actual cosmic ray neutron intensity in the ores may be somewhat higher than this (owing to the action of other types of cosmic rays on the ore), the neutron contribution from cosmic rays to the total neutron flux in the ores seems small.

For a typical 100-g sample of pitchblende ore containing 13.5 per cent uranium, then, somewhat more than some thirty neutrons per minute are available from the sources mentioned above.   Simple calculations show that U^{238} in this sample must capture some ten to fifteen neutrons per minute, or something less than about 30 to 50 per cent of those available, in order to account for an equilibrium concentration of one part Pu^{239} per 1.4×10^{11} parts uranium.   A consideration of the neutron absorption cross sections of the elements in the ore, together with their abundances from the above mentioned analysis, indicates that absorption of this fraction of the neutrons by the uranium is reasonable.

It should be emphasized that these estimations of the neutron flux are necessarily quite approximate.   Thus, values for the spontaneous fission decay constant of U^{238}, varying from about half to twice the value quoted and used above, have been reported.[275-277]   Similarly, the estimation of the neutron flux from the (α, n) reactions is subject to error from the uncertainty of the composition of the ores and the lack of precise knowledge for the yields of the (α, n) reactions; the estimation of the numbers of neutrons from this source could be in error by a factor of two or possibly even more. Therefore, the relative importance of these two major sources for the neutrons may differ somewhat from that suggested in this discussion.

A situation similar to the Canadian pitchblende exists in the cases of the other pitchblende ores having a greater uranium content.   More neutrons are available from spontaneous fission of the uranium and the (α, n) reactions, but the high uranium content of the ore absorbs them, so the plutonium to uranium ratio remains essentially constant.   It should be mentioned that when an appreciable fraction of the neutrons is absorbed by uranium, the additional neutrons which result from the fission of U^{235} contribute significantly to the production of Pu^{239}.

Somewhat different considerations seem to apply in the cases of the monazite ores.   In view of the smaller concentration of uranium in monazite, the ratio of Pu^{239} to uranium in monazite might be expected to be definitely smaller than the ratio in pitchblende if a major source of neutrons were still the spontaneous fission of U^{238}, since the relatively large amounts of elements other than uranium in the ore would capture neutrons, leaving a

[274] C. S. Montgomery and D. D. Montgomery, *Phys. Rev.* **56**, 10 (1939).
[275] N. A. Perfilov, *J. Physiol.* (U.S.S.R.) **11**, No. 3 (1947).
[276] H. Yagoda and N. Kaplan, *Phys. Rev.* **76**, 702 (1949).
[277] W. Maurer and H. Pose, *Z. Physik* **121**, 285 (1943).

smaller proportion of neutrons available for capture by the U^{238}. Neutrons due to the spontaneous fission of thorium would not compensate for this effect since the spontaneous fission rate of thorium is smaller than that of uranium by a factor of 10^5 or more. However, the contribution of neutrons from (α, n) reactions is relatively more important. The α particles emitted in the decay of thorium and its daughters will give rise to (α, n) reactions with nuclei of the light elements in the same manner as the α particles from the uranium decay chains. One gram of thorium and its decay products will produce 1.5×10^6 α particles per minute capable of producing neutrons in this manner. Thus, for example, a 100-g sample of a typical monazite, which contains 6.5 per cent thorium, 1.6 per cent uranium and light elements in about the same abundance as in the pitchblende used in the previous example, will emit about two neutrons per minute from spontaneous fission and about five or ten neutrons per minute from (α, n) reactions. In order to maintain the Pu^{239} to uranium ratio seen in North Carolina monazite, about 0.4 neutrons per minute must be captured by the uranium. If just the uranium and thorium competed for the neutron capture, the uranium in the ore would capture somewhat less than half of those available. Monazite ore, however, contains an appreciable amount of the rare earth elements, which capture neutrons with appreciable cross sections, so that the low fraction of the available neutrons captured by the uranium is reasonable. As the ratio of uranium to thorium in the thorium ores decreases, the number of neutrons obtained from (α, n) reactions becomes an even more important factor. Thus, the number of neutrons produced in the ore per gram of uranium is greater in the case of the monazite ores than in the cases of the pitchblende ores, this effect somewhat compensating for the number of neutrons captured by nuclei other than U^{238} in the monazite ores.

Since these explanations for the source of the plutonium in ores suggest that the presence of large amounts of neutron-absorbing impurities, together with small amounts of uranium (or thorium), should reduce the ratio of Pu^{239} to uranium, the fergusonite and carnotite ores were investigated in order to test these suggestions further. Carnotite is a potassium uranyl vanadate, while fergusonite is a niobate and tantalate of the rare earth elements with a small amount of uranium. In carnotite, the large amounts of potassium and vanadium would be expected to capture most of the available neutrons. Tantalum, having a high neutron absorption cross section, would be expected to capture most of the neutrons available in fergusonite. In the case of the carnotite ore, the ratio of Pu^{239} to uranium present was set at 0.4×10^{-12} and this should probably be considered to be an upper limit. This is a factor of ten to thirty below the ratio found in the pitchblendes and monazites. GARNER, BONNER, AND SEABORG[262] working with a five-kilogram sample of ore, reported one part Pu^{239} per 10^{14} parts carnotite ore. On the assumption of the same uranium content, this puts the value of the ratio of Pu^{239} to uranium in carnotite below the value of the ratios in pitchblende and monazite by a factor of forty to one hundred.   Thus, it can be seen that the presence in the ore of elements with high neutron absorption cross sections tends to decrease the amount of Pu^{239} present relative to the uranium content.   Of the neutrons available in the ore, a smaller fraction can be utilized for the production of Pu^{239}.   In the case of the fergusonite ore, less than 0.01 α particle per minute due to Pu^{239} was seen, this being the lower limit of detection in this experiment.   Unfortunately, this lower limit corresponds to the same order of magnitude as the Pu^{239} contents of the pitchblende and monazite ores investigated.   With larger samples of fergusonite, a better limit could be set.

This concludes our quotation from LEVINE AND SEABORG.

The 4n + 1 Series in Nature.   Except for minute traces of Np^{237} and U^{233} produced continuously by reactions of natural neutrons, the $4n + 1$ radioactive series is missing in nature and our knowledge of the properties of the isotopes making up the series is derived from studies of artificially synthesized materials, as is discussed in Chapter 7.

It was pointed out by SEABORG that uranium-bearing ores should contain trace quantities of Np^{237} formed by the U^{238} $(n, 2n)U^{237} \xrightarrow{\beta^-} Np^{237}$ reaction; and it has been suggested by GARNER, BONNER, AND SEABORG[262] that uranium-bearing ores containing an appreciable relative quantity of thorium should contain some long-lived U^{233} formed as the result of the Th^{232} $(n, \gamma)Th^{233} \xrightarrow{\beta^-} U^{233}$ reaction.

PEPPARD AND CO-WORKERS[278] have isolated minute amounts of Np^{237} from aqueous waste concentrates from the processing of many tons of Belgian Congo pitchblende.   This neptunium was identified chemically and by determination of its alpha particle energy.   These workers also established that the thorium fraction from this concentrate contained Th^{229} in minute amount.   This thorium fraction was 10.6 per cent Io^{230} and 89.4 per cent Th^{232}.   The amount of Th^{229} found in this sample relative to Th^{232} was $(4.0 \pm 0.6) \times 10^{-11}$ so that this very small amount could be detected and measured only by isolation and identification of the 10-day Ac^{225} daughter. It can be assumed that the Th^{229} present in the thorium was derived from U^{233} in the original pitchblende, the decay sequence being the following:

$$U^{233} \xrightarrow[1.6 \times 10^5 \text{ yr}]{\alpha} Th^{229} \xrightarrow[7340 \text{ yr}]{\alpha} Ac^{225} \xrightarrow[10.0 \text{ day}]{\alpha}$$

The calculated ratio of U^{233} to U^{238} in the pitchblende is $(1.3 \pm 0.2) \times 10^{-13}$. PEPPARD AND CO-WORKERS[278] believe that most of this U^{233} was contributed by the $Th^{232}(n, \gamma)Th^{233} \xrightarrow{\beta^-} U^{233}$ route and that only a small fraction is

278 D. F. Peppard, G. W. Mason, P. R. Gray, and J. F. Mech, *J. Am. Chem. Soc.* **74**, 6081 (1952).

derived from the decay of Np^{237} produced via the $U^{238}(n, 2n)U^{237} \xrightarrow{\beta^-}$ Np^{237}route. If all the U^{233} is, in fact, derived from Np^{237} decay, then one can set an upper limit of $(1.8 \pm 0.4) \times 10^{-12}$ for the Np^{237} to U^{238} mass ratio in the pitchblende deposit. The amount of Np^{237} is considerably less than the amount of Pu^{239} in the same mineral. The neutrons necessary for the production of Np^{237} or U^{233} in mineral samples are derived from the same reactions discussed above in accounting for the natural occurrence of plutonium.

PEPPARD, ET AL. examined thorium obtained from monazite for evidence of Th^{229}. They found none and could set an upper limit of 7×10^{-13} for the U^{233} to Th^{232} mass ratio in the monazite ore. It is reasonable that the U^{233} content of the monazite ore be so much less than the pitchblende since the uranium content of the former (0.1 per cent) is so much lower than the latter (45.3 per cent).

Other Induced Natural Activities. No other transuranium element isotopes have been observed in nature although it is apparent that other substances which can be formed through a neutron-induced reaction in uranium and thorium minerals can be found by sufficiently diligent search. Similarly, products of the spontaneous fission process can and have been found. The stable end products of the fission product decay chains are particularly likely candidates for detection since these have been accumulating since the ore was laid down. The identification of such spontaneous fission products in uranium minerals is discussed in Volume III, Part 1.

Unlikelihood of the Existence on Earth of Traces of a Primordial Stock of any Transuranium Element. Consideration has been given to the possibility that the half-lives of some of the transuranium nuclides might be just long enough that a diligent search in the proper minerals might reveal the present day existence of slight traces of a primordial stock of these nuclides. However, as the chart of the nuclides has been filled in and as more accurate information has been obtained on the half-lives of the border-line cases it has become clear that there is very little likelihood that any such traces will ever be found. From an examination of all the half-life measurements and nuclear stability trends which are reviewed in Chapters 1–3 we reach the conclusion that Pu^{244} and Cm^{247} are the longest-lived of the transuranium nuclides. But DIAMOND AND BARNES[279] report a value of only $(7.6 \pm 0.2) \times 10^7$ years for the half-life of Pu^{244}. If the primeval abundance of Pu^{244} was equivalent to that of Th^{232}, and if the elements were formed only 5.5 billion years ago, the present day ratio of Th^{232} to Pu^{244} in thorium ores must be 10^{22}. If more reasonable choices of the relative primeval abundances and of the date of the last element-forming process are taken, the ratio of

[279] H. Diamond and R. F. Barnes, *Phys. Rev.* **101**, 1064 (1956); see also the paper of J. P. Butler and co-workers, *Phys. Rev.* **103**, 634 (1956).

Th^{232} to Pu^{244} is orders of magnitude greater. Hence, it does not seem possible that present day amounts of Pu^{244} exceed the limits of detectability. FIELDS AND CO-WORKERS[280] report a value of $(1.64 \pm 0.24) \times 10^7$ years for the half-life of Cm^{247}. If this value is correct it is certain that any primordial stock of Cm^{247} would have decayed below the limits of detectability.

KOHMAN[281] uses the term *extinct natural radioactivity* to refer to nuclides whose half-lives are too short for the nuclides to have survived in detectable amount, but nevertheless long enough for their decay to have produced effects in nature which can be identified at the present time.   He has written an extensive review of this topic.   The nuclides, Pu^{244} and Cm^{247}, may fall into this category.

There has been some speculation in the literature[279,280,282] that the extinct activities U^{236}, Pu^{244}, and Cm^{247} have contributed importantly to the radioactive heating of the earth and other objects during the early history of the solar system.   It requires a detailed consideration of the possible element-forming processes, the time scale for element formation, the time scale for the condensation of matter into sizeable objects, and of other cosmological questions before a proper evaluation of this suggestion can be made.   We refer the reader to an article by KOHMAN[283] who concludes that it is unlikely that U^{236}, Pu^{244}, or Cm^{247} ever contributed importantly to the heating of the earth compared to U^{238}, U^{235}, Th^{232}, and K^{40}.

[280] P. R. Fields, A. M. Friedman, J. Lerner, D. Metta, and R. Sjoblom, *Phys. Rev.* 131, 1249 (1963).

[281] T. P. Kohman, "Extinct Natural Radioactivity," *New York Academy of Sciences* 62, 503 (1956).

[282] D. B. Rosenblatt, *Phys. Rev.* 91, 1474 (1953).

[283] T. P. Kohman, *J. Chem. Educ.* 38, 73 (1961).

7

ARTIFICIALLY PREPARED

FAMILIES OF RADIOACTIVE NUCLIDES

The natural radioactivities, distributed in three families of about one dozen members each, are outnumbered several fold by the artificial radio-activities in the same mass number region. These substances differ in no important respect from the natural radioactivities other than that some of them are on the neutron deficient side of stability and decay by orbital electron capture. In this chapter and in the three succeeding chapters we shall carry out a survey of the artificial radioactive isotopes of elements with atomic number greater than 81. It will be seen that these species cover a range of half-lives not unlike those of the natural radioactivities although obviously none has a half-life as long as the three nuclides which sustain the three natural series.

Any system for dividing the artificial radioactivities into groups for pur-poses of discussion is bound to have some arbitrary features. The natural series were segregated (Chapter 6) not only to pay heed to historical de-velopments, but because in many situations several members of a family are indeed encountered together. In this chapter we shall treat the artificial radioactive decay series, which parallel in a real sense the natural families. The first of these will be the "missing" $4n + 1$ series which is sometimes termed the neptunium series after Np^{237}, its longest lived member.

Also treated in this chapter are a number of decay series, collateral to the four main series, which merge with them near their termination. Again we choose to begin each series with the member lying near uranium because such members are usually the longest lived and the isolation of these members is the chief means of preparation of the series. These collateral series lie on the neutron deficient side of β-stability and they have no parallel on the

577

neutron excess side.   For example, the Pa^{228} series, which is collateral to the thorium ($4n$) series, begins a sequence of α-decay steps which joins the main series at Bi^{212} (ThC).   On the other hand Pa^{236}, which is on the neutron excess side, is a 12-minute β-emitter which decays to long-lived U^{236}. Upon the decay of U^{236} the junction is made with the thorium series at Th^{232}.   The reason that the neutron deficient species form series of alpha emitters lies in the relation between mass number and alpha energy for a series of isotopes (see Fig. 1.8 Chapter 1).

If one were to focus only upon *mass type* to delineate a decay series, then each of the natural series should be extended into the transuranium element region.   However, the reasons for discussing a family as a group lie in the historical associations and the real associations of the individual members with the parent substance.   If the uranium series, for example, is extended into the transuranium element region both of these associations are in large part missing.   Let us consider one of these branches starting with Cf^{250}:

$$Cf^{250} \xrightarrow[11y]{\alpha} Cm^{246} \xrightarrow[6600y]{\alpha} Pu^{242} \xrightarrow[3.8 \times 10^5y]{} U^{238}$$

When Pu^{242} is made artificially, the species with which it is associated are other plutonium isotopes not genetically related.   Also, because of the long half-life of U^{238}, it and lower members of the $4n + 2$ series are not inevitably present.   Similarly, the normal radioactive contaminants in Cm^{246} and Cf^{250} are other isotopes of curium and californium and *not* nuclides which are related to them as daughter products.   It is for these reasons that all transuranium nuclides are best segregated for purposes of discussion according to atomic number (Chapter 9)*.

Even more arbitrarily, the isotopes of thorium, protactinium, and uranium have been segregated in Chapter 8 for discussion of nuclear properties.   The modes of preparation and genetic relations of many of the nuclides are covered in Chapters 6 and 7 where the families to which they belong are considered. However, a number of the other isotopes of these three elements do not fit into the criteria first outlined for grouping within a decay series.   It was therefore considered best to handle these separately and to combine the discussion of their detailed nuclear properties with that for the isotopes of the series members.   Thus, in Chapter 8 will be found all of the discussion pertinent to Pa^{237}; for Pa^{231}, the discussion of its identity as a member of the actinouranium series appears in Chapter 6 and its nuclear properties in Chapter 8.   Where this formula is violated suitable cross references appear.

---

* For the final section, section 9.12, of Chapter 9 the genetic interrelationships of all known transuranium nuclides to members of the 3 naturally occurring series and to the artificial $4n + 1$ series are summarized in a set of four diagrams, Figs. 9.62 through 9.65.

7.1 THE 4n + 1 SERIES—THE NEPTUNIUM FAMILY

One of the interesting results of the research program connected with the early studies of the transuranium elements was the artificial synthesis of a heavy-element radioactive family of the $4n + 1$ mass type, similar in length and complexity to the three naturally-occurring radioactive families. The decay sequence of the entire $4n + 1$ series of nuclides has been traced from the transuranium region down to the stable end product Bi^{209}. This work was carried out during the decade 1940 to 1950. Although by normal criteria this fourth series is missing from nature, it has been established that trace amounts of Np^{237} are being formed in uranium ores and trace amounts of U^{233} are being formed in thorium ores by the action of a small flux of naturally occurring neutrons, as is discussed in Section 6.6 of Chapter 6.

Early Predictions of Decay Sequence of $4n + 1$ Series. As early as 1923 A. S. RUSSELL[1] deduced that there should be four independent disintegration series, rather than only the three then known, and he predicted for the fourth, the $4n + 1$ series, the following decay sequence, which is wrong in important particulars:*

$$_{92}U^{237} \xrightarrow{\alpha} {}_{90}Th^{233} \xrightarrow{\beta^-} {}_{91}Pa^{233} \xrightarrow{\alpha} {}_{89}Ac^{229} \xrightarrow{\beta^-}$$

$$_{90}Th^{229} \xrightarrow{\alpha} {}_{88}Ra^{225} \xrightarrow{\alpha} {}_{86}Em^{221} \xrightarrow{\alpha} {}_{84}Po^{217} \xrightarrow{\alpha}$$

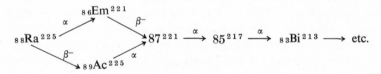

The following year W. P. WIDDOWSON and A. S. RUSSELL[2] revised this prediction to say that, beginning with Ra^{225}, the decay chain should proceed as follows:

[1] A. S. Russell, *Phil. Mag.* **46**, 642 (1923).

[2] W. P. Widdowson and A. S. Russell, *Phil. Mag.* **48**, 293 (1924).

* In the discussion which follows immediately the species which appear in these decay sequences will be assigned their proper decay properties. However, attention is called to Ac^{229}, Em^{221}, Po^{217} and Pb^{213} which do not appear in measurable amounts in the main $4n + 1$ series. This is because the alpha branchings of Pa^{233} and Ra^{225} have not been observed. The species mentioned have been prepared by other means and are discussed elsewhere.

A good many years later, in 1940, L. A. Turner[3] predicted a different beginning and other differences which have important consequences. He proposed the following decay sequence and speculated correctly on the absence of this series in nature:

$$_{92}U^{237} \xrightarrow{\beta^-} {}_{93}Np^{237} \xrightarrow{\alpha} {}_{91}Pa^{233} \xrightarrow{\beta^-} {}_{92}U^{233} \xrightarrow{\alpha} {}_{90}Th^{229} \xrightarrow{\alpha}$$

$$_{88}Ra^{225} \xrightarrow{\beta^-} {}_{89}Ac^{225} \xrightarrow{\alpha} {}_{87}221 \xrightarrow{\alpha} {}_{85}217 \xrightarrow{\alpha}$$

L. Ponisovsky[4] also was led from his considerations to predict a decay scheme which is very similar to this with the difference that Th^{229} is predicted to emit beta-particles leading to an alpha-active Pa^{229} which decays to the Ac^{225}.

Summary of $4n + 1$ *Series.* Experimental work has led to the observation of all the members of this $4n + 1$ radioactive series and to a complete elucidation of the course which this series takes in its decay. It should be noted that the longest-lived member is now known to be an isotope of a transuranium element, Np^{237}, and this justifies the suggestion that the series be known as the "neptunium family" by analogy with the uranium, thorium, and actino-uranium families whose parents are U^{238}, Th^{232}, and U^{235}.

The half-life of Np^{237} is very short compared to the age of the elements which explains the absence of the family in nature.

The neptunium series is displayed in Fig. 7.1 starting with Np^{237}, the longest-lived member. The $4n + 1$ series members are also listed in Table 7.1. The series can, of course, be extended indefinitely into the trans-uranium region although these nuclides are of shorter half-life. Several of these higher mass-number members are included in the Table 7.1. A detailed presentation of the $4n + 1$ series extended upward through the trans-uranium elements einsteinium and fermium is shown in Fig. 9.62.

The neptunium series includes U^{233}, an isotope of very great importance because of its long half-life and its high cross section for fission upon capture of thermal neutrons.

It is interesting to note that the decay chain below U^{233} contains no emanation isotope in contrast to the other three radioactive families. Instead, there are main-line representatives of astatine and francium (atomic numbers 85 and 87, respectively) which are not found in the main line of decay for the other families.

3 L. A. Turner, *Phys. Rev.* **57**, 950 (1940).
4 L. Ponisovsky, *Nature* **152**, 187 (1943).

Uranium-237 and Neptunium-237. The nuclide U^{237} is a collateral member rather than a main-line member of the neptunium series. The discovery of Np^{237}, however, was intimately connected with the discovery of U^{237} and it is convenient to discuss these two nuclides together.

Uranium^{237} was one of the first heavy-element nuclides of the $4n + 1$ mass type to be discovered but its connection with the other then-known members (Th^{233}, Pa^{233}, and Pb^{209}) could not be appreciated. NISHINA AND CO-WORKERS[5] prepared it by bombardment of uranium with fast

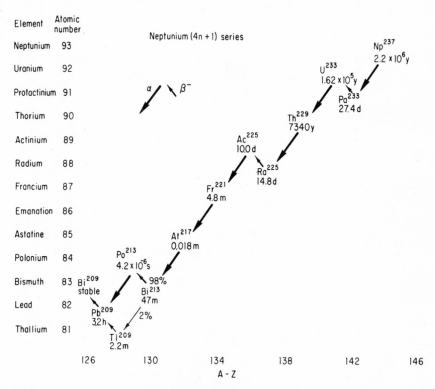

FIG. 7.1. The neptunium ($4n + 1$) series.

neutrons obtained from low energy deuterons impinging on lithium targets. MCMILLAN[6] independently prepared it using fast neutrons from a beryllium target struck by 16 MeV deuterons. Extensive chemical purification of the uranium after bombardment showed that a new 7.0 day beta activity could

[5] J. Nishina, T. Yasaki, H. Ezoe, K. Kimura, and M. Ikawa, *Phys. Rev.* **57**, 1182 (1940).

[6] E. McMillan, *Phys. Rev.* **58**, 178 (1940).

TABLE **7.1.** The neptunium series.

Radioelement	Symbol	Radiation	Half-life
Californium	Cf^{253}	β^-	18 day
↓			
Einsteinium	Es^{253}	α	20 day
↓			
Berkelium	Bk^{249}	β^-	314 day
↓			
Californium	Cf^{249}	α	360 yr
↓			
Curium	Cm^{245}	α	9300 yr
↓			
Plutonium	Pu^{241}	β	13 yr
↓			
Americium	Am^{241}	α	458 yr
↓			
Neptunium	Np^{237}	α	2.2×10^6 yr
↓			
Protactinium	Pa^{233}	β	27.4 day
↓			
Uranium	U^{233}	α	1.62×10^5 yr
↓			
Thorium	Th^{229}	α	7340 yr
↓			
Radium	Ra^{225}	β	14.8 day
↓			
Actinium	Ac^{225}	α	10.0 day
↓			
Francium	Fr^{221}	α	4.8 min
↓			
Astatine	At^{217}	α	0.018 min
↓			
Bismuth	Bi^{213}	β and α	47 min
98% β 2% α			
↓			
Polonium	Po^{213}	α	4.2×10^{-6} sec
Thallium	Tl^{209}	β	2.2 min
↓			
Lead	Pb^{209}	β	3.2 hr
↓			
Bismuth	Bi^{209}	stable	

not be separated from uranium and hence was most likely U^{237} produced by the fast neutron reaction

$$U^{238} (n, 2n) \ U^{237} \xrightarrow[\beta^-]{7.0 \text{ days}} Np^{237} \qquad (7.1)$$

This conclusion was checked by showing that the yield of U^{237} dropped when the uranium target was surrounded by paraffin and that it did not drop when the target was covered by cadmium to remove thermal neutrons. The presently accepted value of the half-life is 6.75 days.

McMILLAN[6] looked for the Np^{237} daughter by separating a neptunium fraction from an 80 microcurie sample of U^{237} after its complete decay but detected no activity because of the long half-life of Np^{237}. Somewhat later, WAHL AND SEABORG[7] prepared a larger sample of U^{237} and, by examination of the neptunium fraction after a suitable decay period, were able to detect the alpha particles of Np^{237}. Their first crude estimate of the half-life was $\sim 3 \times 10^6$ years, considered to be accurate to a factor of 2 and determined by measuring the ratio of 7 day U^{237} activity to that of its daughter Np^{237}. A more accurate measurement was made in 1944 by MAGNUSSON AND LA CHAPELLE[8] who isolated and purified several micrograms of Np^{237} from cyclotron and pile produced material. The specific alpha activity of a known weight of neptunium dioxide was measured and from this, the half-life was calculated to be 2.20×10^6 years. These experiments constituted the first isolation of weighable amounts of neptunium in pure form.

In nearly all nuclear reactors the fast neutron flux is appreciable so that considerable quantities of Np^{237} are produced by reaction 7.1. This co-production of neptunium is fortunate because it makes possible the isolation of kilogram quantities of this important isotope as a by-product in the chemical processing of the reactor fuel elements. In reactors operating on enriched U^{235} fuel considerable Np^{237} is produced via the double neutron capture sequence:

$$U^{235}(n,\gamma)\ U^{236}(n,\gamma)\ U^{237} \xrightarrow{\ \beta^-\ } Np^{237}$$

$$\sigma = 112\ b \qquad \sigma = 25b$$

(7.2)

The alpha particle spectrum of Np^{237} and the decay scheme of Np^{237} have been studied by several authors as is discussed fully in Section 9.1.10 of Chapter 9.

Thorium-233 and Protactinium-233. The daughter of Np^{237} is the 27.4-day beta emitter Pa^{233}. This isotope was first observed as a result of the neutron bombardment of thorium. FERMI AND CO-WORKERS[9] first showed that neutron bombardment of thorium leads to the production of a 23-minute isotope presumed to be Th^{233}. This was the first heavy nuclide of the 4n + 1 type to be identified. The beta-emitting daughter Pa^{233} was first

[7] A. C. Wahl and G. T. Seaborg, paper 1.5 "The Transuranium Elements" *Nat. Nucl. Energ. Ser.* **14B,** New York: McGraw-Hill Book Company, Inc., (1949); *Phys. Rev.* **73,** 940 (1948) report written April 14, 1942.

[8] L. B. Magnusson and T. J. LaChapelle, "The Transuranium Elements," *Nat. Nucl. Energ. Ser.,* Paper 1.7, **14B,** New York: McGraw-Hill Book Co., Inc., (1949).

[9] E. Fermi, E. Amaldi, O. D'Agostino, F. Rasetti, and E. Segrè, *Proc. Roy. Soc.* **A146,** 483 (1934).

reported by MEITNER, STRASSMANN, AND HAHN[10] and was the first known member of the $4n + 1$ series in the main line of decay. The equations of synthesis are:

$$Th^{232}(n, \gamma)\ Th^{233}$$

(7.3)

$$Th^{232} \xrightarrow[23\ min]{\beta^-} Pa^{233}$$

The later discovery of fission led some to suggest that this activity was a fission product but this doubt was cleared up by the work of GROSSE, BOOTH, AND DUNNING[11] and by SEABORG, GOFMAN, AND KENNEDY.[12] Protactinium-233 has no measurable α-branching and it can now be predicted that this branching should not be more than 10^{-10}. This is mentioned because one of the early predictions had Pa^{233} as an α-emitter and the main decay sequence proceeding through Ac^{229}. (See discussion of predictions above.) This nuclide has been prepared in another way: neutron irradiation of MsTh (Ra^{228}) yields short-lived Ra^{229} which decays to Ac^{229}, identified as a 66-min β^--emitter.[12a] Nothing detailed is known of its decay properties. The radiations of U^{233} and Pa^{233} are discussed in detail in Chapter 8.

Uranium-233. The isotope U^{233}, which is the daughter of the Pa^{233}, was first separated and examined by SEABORG, GOFMAN, AND STOUGHTON[13] in 1941–42. These investigators produced this isotope by the irradiation of thorium with cyclotron produced neutrons and observed that it decays by the emission of alpha-particles; from measurements on its rate of growth from known amounts of the parent isotope Pa^{233} they determined a rough value for the half-life of about 1.2×10^6 years. SEABORG, GOFMAN, AND STOUGHTON[13] also showed that U^{233} has the very important property of undergoing fission with slow neutrons with a large cross section. Its half-life has been determined by HYDE[14] to be $1.62\ (\pm 0.01) \times 10^5$ years by specific activity measurements on a sample whose isotopic composition had been determined in a mass spectrograph by RALL AND DEMPSTER.[14a]

The isotope U^{233} is a very important one in the study of other members of the neptunium series because it serves as a convenient source for the shorter-lived descendants. This isotope has been available in kilogram amounts formed as a result of the intense neutron bombardment of thorium

[10] L. Meitner, F. Strassmann, and O. Hahn, *Zeit. f. Physik* 109, 538 (1938).

[11] A. V. Grosse, E. T. Booth, and J. R. Dunning, *Phys. Rev.* 59, 322 (1941).

[12] G. T. Seaborg, J. W. Gofman, and J. W. Kennedy, *Phys. Rev.* 59, 321 (1941).

[12a] F. Depocas and B. G. Harvey, *Phys. Rev.* 85, 499 (1952).

[13] G. T. Seaborg, J. W. Gofman, and R. W. Stoughton, *Phys. Rev.* 71, 378 (1947). Also published as Paper 19.13 in "The Transuranium Elements," National Nuclear Energy Series, Div. IV, Vol. 14B, (New York: McGraw-Hill Book Co., 1949).

[14] E. K. Hyde, Paper No. 19.15, "The Transuranium Elements," National Nuclear Energy Series, Div. IV, Vol. 14B, (New York: McGraw-Hill Book Co., 1949).

[14a] W. Rall and A. J. Dempster, unpublished report CP-3530 cited by Hyde in Ref. 14.

in uranium reactors. It has been fortunate that this isotope has been available in such amounts because its immediate daughter, Th^{229}, is quite long-lived (about 7340 year half-life); since the entire series following the Th^{229} depends on the growth of this long-lived member, it is necessary to have at least milligram amounts of U^{233} in order to make feasible a study of all of its decay products. The decay products of U^{233} were thoroughly studied and completely identified during the war by two research teams, who worked independently: A. C. ENGLISH, T. E. CRANSHAW, P. DEMERS, J. A. HARVEY, E. P. HINCKS, J. V. JELLEY, AND A. N. MAY,[15] working on the Canadian atomic energy project and F. HAGEMANN, L. I. KATZIN, M. H. STUDIER, A. GHIORSO AND G. T. SEABORG,[16] working on the American project.

The complex alpha spectrum and the decay scheme of U^{233} are discussed in detail in Chapter 8, Section 8.4.6. The characteristics of the fission of U^{233} are discussed in Volume III, Part 1.

Thorium-229. Samples of Th^{229} are prepared by isolating a thorium fraction radiochemically from a pure sample of U^{233} which has been undisturbed for an appreciable length of time since its last purification. Because of the 7340 year half-life of Th^{229}, equilibrium is not reached for tens of thousands

TABLE **7.2.** Growth of Th^{229} into one gram of initially pure U^{233}.

Time	Disintegrations per minute Th^{229}	Micrograms Th^{229}
30 day	1.63×10^5	0.346
6 month	9.91×10^5	2.10
1 year	1.98×10^6	4.20
5 year	9.91×10^6	21.4
10 year	1.98×10^7	42.0

of years. Table 7.2 gives the amounts of Th^{229} growing into a gram of U^{233} after selected periods of time.

Th^{229} isolated in this fashion is frequently contaminated with 1.9 year radio-thorium, Th^{228}, arising from U^{232} present in the U^{233}. When Th^{232} is irradiated with neutrons in a reactor to produce U^{233} appreciable amounts of U^{232} are produced by side reactions;[17] for example, fast neutrons give rise to Pa^{231} via the sequence

$$Th^{232}(n, 2n) \; Th^{231}(UY) \xrightarrow[\text{25 hours}]{\beta^-} Pa^{231}.$$

---

[15] A. C. English, T. E. Cranshaw, P. Demers, J. A. Harvey, E. P. Hincks, J. V. Jelley, A. N. May, *Phys. Rev.* **72**, 253 (1947).

[16] F. Hagemann, L. I. Katzin, M. H. Studier, A. Ghiorso, and G. T. Seaborg, *Phys. Rev.* **72**, 254 (1947) preliminary note; and *Phys. Rev.* **79**, 435 (1950).

[17] D. S. St. John and E. C. Toops, *Dupont Co. Report DP-279*, "Formation of U^{232} during the Irradiation of Thorium," 1958.

The Pa^{231} has a large capture cross section for thermal neutrons and is converted into U^{232} via the sequence:

$$Pa^{231}(n, \gamma)Pa^{232} \xrightarrow[\text{2.0 days}]{\beta^-} U^{232}.$$

$$\sigma = 293 \text{ barns}$$

Because the half-life of U^{232} is short compared to U^{233} (73.6 years compared to 1.62×10^5 years) and because the half-life of radiothorium is short compared to that of Th^{229} (1.9 years compared to 7340 years) the thorium fraction which is isolated from the U^{232}–U^{233} mixture may have amounts of Th^{228} and Th^{229} of comparable activity even though the atom ratio is quite small.

The procedure for obtaining Th^{229} with high isotopic purity is tedious and technically difficult. Thorium is irradiated in a high neutron flux and the protactinium fraction is isolated after an interval in which much of the 27-day Pa^{233} is still present but 1.3-day Pa^{232} has decayed to the desired level. After a suitable interval (a few months) the uranium fraction is isolated and, since the U^{233} so obtained is free of U^{232}, the Th^{229} which it produces is pure. As already mentioned, macroscopic amounts of U^{233} are required to obtain desired amounts of Th^{229} in a reasonable period of time; therefore macroscopic amounts of intensely radioactive Pa^{233} must be handled. Small amounts of pure Th^{229} can be obtained by suitably short irradiations of thorium, thus minimizing the production of U^{232} since it arises from a second order process. In principle, pure Th^{229} can also be made by irradiating thorium in such a way that no appreciable numbers of high energy neutrons are produced in the sample or enter from external sources.

The half-life of Th^{229} was determined by measurement of the disintegration rates of samples isolated in known yield from a known amount of purified U^{233} which had stood a known period of time since its last separation from thorium.[16] A detailed review of the radiations of Th^{229} is given in Chapter 8, Section 8.2.7.

Radium-225. This isotope may be isolated directly by radiochemical methods from a U^{233} source. It is not practicable to measure the half-life by following the weak beta particles (320 keV)[18] because of the growth of daughter activity for nuclides further down the decay chain. The half-life of 14.8 days was determined by observing the shape of the growth and decay of the 10-day Ac^{225} daughter activity. Fig. 7.2 shows the shape of this curve. (This curve will not be reproduced precisely by a sample containing appreciable amounts of ThX arising from U^{232} impurity in the U^{233} source.)

---

    [18] M. Freedman, J. May, M. Rusnak, and F. Wagner, Jr., *Argonne National Laboratory Report ANL-4717* (April 1952).

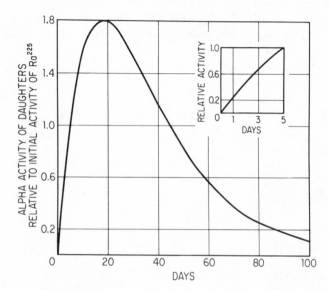

FIG. 7.2. Growth of alpha activity into initially pure 14.8 day Ra[225]. There are four alpha-emitting daughters, Ac[225], Fr[221], At[217], and Po[213]. The limiting half-life is that of 10-day Ac[225].

STEPHENS[19] has studied the gamma radiations of Ra[225]. He found only a 40 keV gamma ray which he characterized definitely as an $E1$ transition. It is in coincidence with the 320 keV beta particles. The half-life of this transition was measured to be $< 2 \times 10^{-9}$ seconds by RASMUSSEN AND STROMINGER.[20] The simple decay scheme of Ra[225] is shown in Fig. 7.3.

It should be mentioned that Ra[225] samples isolated from U[233] are contaminated with 3.64 day Ra[224](ThX) if U[232] is present in the U[233]. If this contamination is large enough to be troublesome, some relief may be achieved by repurifying the sample after a few weeks decay period.

In each of the three naturally occurring decay chains an emanation isotope arises from the alpha decay of a radium isotope. This is not true in the 4n + 1 chain and this fact is one of its principal differences from the other series. From consideration of systematics of decay energies and kinetics, it can be predicted that Ra[225] should show a small but appreciable alpha branching to produce Em[221]. JENTSCHKE[21], for example, predicted that this branching should occur but estimated it as something less than 0.1 per cent.

[19] F. S. Stephens, Jr., Ph.D. Thesis, University of California, June 1955; also published as *Univ. of Calif. Radiation Lab. Report UCRL-2970*, June 1955.

[20] D. Strominger and J. O. Rasmussen, *Phys. Rev.* **100**, 844 (1955).

[21] W. Jentschke, *Phys. Rev.* **77**, 99 (1930).

FEATHER[22] estimated a branching of 0.7 per cent. MOMYER AND HYDE[23] estimated a somewhat lower value of 5×10^{-4} to 5×10^{-5}. KARLIK'S[24] prediction was 3.5×10^{-4}. MOMYER AND HYDE[23] have prepared the way for an experimental measurement of this branching by determining the

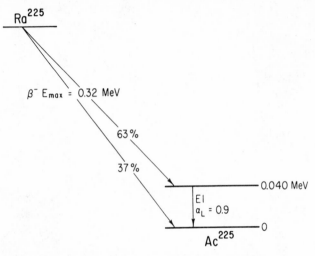

FIG. 7.3. Decay scheme of Ra[225] as drawn by Stephens.

properties of Em[221]. This isotope was prepared by bombardment of thorium with 110 MeV protons. Em[221] decays with a half-life of 25 minutes, 80 per cent by beta decay to Fr[221] and 20 per cent by the emission of 6.0 MeV alpha particles to produce Po[217]. Beta branching is not observed in the emanation isotopes of the three natural series. The product, Po[217], has a half-life of less than 10 seconds and decays by emission of 6.54 MeV alpha particles to produce Pb[213]. Pb[213] has not been directly observed but it must be a beta emitter with a decay energy of approximately 1.8 MeV and a minimum half-life of a minute.[24a] The decay sequence arising from Em[221] and its relationships to the $4n + 1$ series is shown in Fig. 7.4.

MALKIN, NIKOL'SKAYA, AND PETRZHAK[24b] searched for the alpha branching of Ra[225] and set an upper limit of 10^{-4} per cent corresponding to a partial alpha half life of $\geqslant 50{,}000$ years. Since it is not likely that the α-decay energy of Ra[225] is less than 5.0 MeV, it follows that α-decay is highly hindered.

Actinium-225. Samples of the 10.0 day alpha-emitter, Ac[225], can be

---

[22] N. Feather, *Reports Prog. Phys.* **11**, 19 (1948).

[23] F. F. Momyer, Jr. and E. K. Hyde, *Phys. Rev.* **101**, 136 (1956).

[24] B. Karlik, *Acta. Phys. Australi.* **2**, 181 (1948).

[24a] Butement, Robinson, and Quaim report a half-life of 10.2 ± 0.3 min., *J. Inorg. Nucl. Chem.* **26**, 491 (1964).

[24b] L. Z. Malkin, E. B. Nikol'skaya and K. A. Petrzhak, *Radiokhimiya*, **2** 632 (1960).

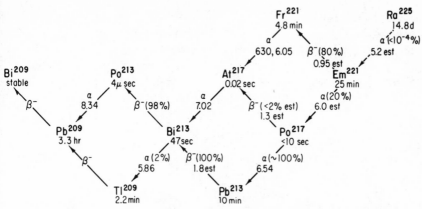

FIG. **7.4.** The decay sequence arising from Em^{221} showing the relationship of Em^{221} to the 4*n* + 1 series. The predicted but as-yet-unobserved alpha branching of Ra^{225} is sketched in. The alpha particle energies rather than total decay energies are shown.

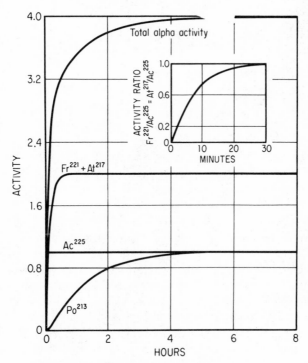

FIG. **7.5.** Growth of alpha activity into initially pure Ac^{225}. The main decay sequence is

$$Ac^{225} \xrightarrow[\text{10.0 days}]{\alpha} Fr^{221} \xrightarrow[\text{4.8 min}]{\alpha} At^{217} \xrightarrow[\text{.018 sec}]{\alpha}$$

$$Bi^{213} \xrightarrow[\text{47 min}]{\beta^-} Po^{213} \xrightarrow[\text{4.2} \times 10^{-6} \text{ sec}]{\alpha}$$

isolated radiochemically from old U^{233} sources. The alpha activity of freshly isolated Ac^{225} grows rapidly over the first few minutes as the 4.8-minute Fr^{221} daughter grows in, climbs more slowly as the 47-minute Bi^{213} grows in, and reaches a maximum after several hours. It then decays logarithmically with a half-life of 10.0 days. The change in alpha activity over the first few hours is shown in Fig. 7.5.

The alpha spectrum of Ac^{225} was carefully measured by HUMMEL, STEPHENS, ASARO, AND PERLMAN[25,26] in a magnetic spectrograph with the results summarized in Table 7.3. Similar results were obtained by DZHELEPOV, IVANOV, AND MOSKVIN[25a]. STEPHENS[19] studied the gamma radiations

TABLE 7.3. Alpha groups of Ac[225]. HUMMEL, ET AL.[25, 26]

Energy (MeV)	Abundance (per cent)	Energy of Fr[221] Level (keV)
5.818	54 (54)	0
5.782	28 (30.7)	37
5.721	9.5 (8.1)	99
5.713	2.6 (2.1)	107
5.672	0.8 (0.95)	149
5.627	3.8 (2.9)	195
5.599	0.6 (0.5)	223
5.570	0.07 (0.6)	253
5.543	0.07 (0.08)	280
	(0.02)	(341(?))
	(0.06)	(388)
	(0.05)	(544)

Data in parentheses are those of DZHELEPOV, ET AL.[25a] These authors report that the main alpha group may be complex.

of Ac^{225} using scintillation techniques. Direct examination of the gamma spectrum did not provide reliable information because of the presence of daughter activity. Similarly, alpha-gamma coincidence methods were of little use when the gross alpha activity was used to gate the coincidence circuit because of the presence of alpha-emitting daughters. This difficulty was eliminated by gating the alpha-gamma coincidence circuit with alpha particles of the proper energy to identify them as Ac^{225} alpha-particles. The alpha-particle detector used in the experiment was a crystal of potassium

[25] J. P. Hummel, Ph.D. Thesis, Univ. of Calif. Aug. 1956; also published as *Univ. of Calif. Rad. Lab. Report, UCRL-3456*, August 1956.

[25a] B. S. Dzhelepov, R. B. Ivanov, and L. N. Moskvin, *Zhur. Eksp. Teor. Fiz.* **43**, 2077 (1962).

iodide mounted on a photomultiplier tube. Energy selection was achieved by submitting the pulses from the photomultiplier tube to a pulse height analysis and selecting only those of a certain value. Gamma rays of 100, 150 and 187 keV energy were observed in coincidence with alpha groups of Ac^{225}. STEPHENS AND ASARO[26] studied the conversion electrons of the gamma rays in high-resolution permanent magnet spectrographs and found transitions with energies 36.60 keV, 38.53 keV, 62.97 keV and 99.53 keV.

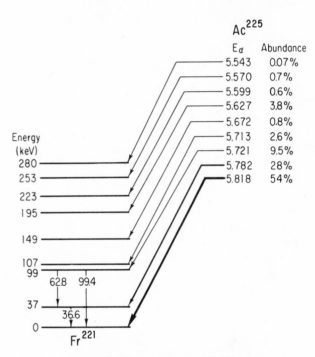

FIG. 7.6. Decay scheme of Ac^{225}.

A partial decay scheme of Ac^{225} is shown in Fig. 7.6; all the alpha groups, but only a few of the gamma transitions are shown. It is certain that considerable additional complexity exists in the gamma radiations of Ac^{225}. Further work is required to explore this complexity and to develop a complete decay scheme.

It is possible to prepare samples of Ac^{225} by cyclotron reactions as well as by isolating it from U^{233} sources. Ac^{225} can be prepared in good yield by bombarding Ra^{226} with deuterons of 20 to 30 MeV energy:

$$Ra^{226}(d, 3n) Ac^{225}$$

[26] J. P. Hummel, F. S. Stephens, F. Asaro, and I. Perlman, unpublished results, 1957.

At the same time, large amounts of Ac^{226} are prepared by the $(d, 2n)$ reaction. However, the difference in half-lives is such (10.0 days compared to 29 hours) that if the actinium fraction is repurified after one or two weeks of decay the sample is nearly pure Ac^{225}. Furthermore, the fission cross section of radium when bombarded with deuterons is quite small so that decontamination from fission products, particularly rare earths, is not a problem.

Ac^{225} is prepared with a cross section of about 10–20 millibarns[27] when thorium is bombarded with protons in the energy range 100–350 MeV. Ac^{226} is produced with a similar cross section. In this case considerable fission occurs and special chemical separations to remove rare-earth activity are necessary.

Francium-221. The $4n + 1$ series differs from the three natural series in that the main line of decay goes through the elements francium and astatine. Unfortunately, the isotopes of these elements which occur in the decay are quite short-lived. The 4.8 minute Fr^{221} is an alpha emitter. STEPHENS[19] found two alpha particle groups; 6.332 MeV (83.8 per cent) and 6.116 MeV (16.2 per cent). BASTIN-SCOFFIER AND WALEN[28a] report somewhat higher values of 6.340 and 6.125 MeV respectively. The excited state at 220 keV reached by the lower energy alpha group is deactivated by emission of a prominent 220 keV photon which is $E2$ in nature. MAGNUSSON AND CO-WORKERS[28] have also characterized this gamma transition.

Fr^{221} can be isolated radiochemically from a sample containing any of its longer-lived precursors. It can be isolated from a thin sample of Ra^{225} or Ac^{225} mounted on a metallic plate by heating the plate briefly to red heat; francium is volatile enough to be removed by this treatment and can be collected on a plate held above.

Astatine-217. The half-life of At^{217} was measured[15,16] by determining the time interval between successive alpha-particle emissions by Fr^{221} and At^{217} with an electronic technique. The value obtained was 18 milliseconds.[16] STEPHENS[19] measured the alpha particle energy to be 7.051 MeV. BASTIN-SCOFFIER and WALEN[28a] found the value 7.066 MeV. No complexity was observed in the spectrum and no gamma rays assignable to At^{217} have been observed.

Bismuth-213. The isotope Bi^{213} has a half-life of 47 minutes and can be isolated by radiochemical techniques from samples of U^{233}, Th^{229}, Ra^{225} or Ac^{225}. The principal decay is by beta emission, but alpha branching is noted in 2 per cent of the disintegrations.[15,16] Bi^{213} could be called neptunium C by analogy to RaC, AcC and ThC. Measurable branching has been observed in all four cases. WAGNER, FREEDMAN, ENGELKEMEIR,

---

[27] S. Skirvin and E. K. Hyde, unpublished information (1952).

[28a] Bastin-Scoffier and R. J. Walen, unpublished results, 1962.

[28] L. B. Magnusson, F. Wagner, Jr., D. Engelkemeir, and M. Friedman, *Argonne National Lab. Report ANL-5386*, January 1955 (unpublished).

AND MAGNUSSON[29] found two components in the beta spectrum; 1.39 MeV (68 per cent) and 0.959 MeV (32 per cent). The two levels of Po^{213} defined by these data differ by 430 keV and a gamma ray of 435 keV was observed in the proper abundance. The energy of the alpha particles of Bi^{213} is 5.86 MeV. A sample of Bi^{213} comes to equilibrium instantly with the Po^{213} daughter (4.2 × 10^{-6} sec half-life), and the 8.35 MeV alpha particles of Po^{213} are always present.

Polonium-213. The half-life of Po^{213} is 4.2 × 10^{-6} seconds as determined by JELLEY[30] using delayed coincidence techniques. Decay is entirely by the emission of alpha particles of 8.35 MeV (STEPHENS[19]). Po^{213} is the C'-product of the neptunium series, comparable to RaC′, AcC′ and ThC′ of the other series.

Thallium-209. The small alpha branching of Bi^{213} gives rise to 2.2 minute Tl^{209} first studied by HAGEMANN[31]. Tl^{209} could be called neptunium C'' by analogy to RaC″ and AcC″. It can be isolated radiochemically in a pure state from any sample containing any of the longer-lived members of the $4n + 1$ series. WAGNER, ET AL.[29] found a beta end-point energy of 1.99 MeV and a gamma ray of 120 keV. STEPHENS[19] found gamma rays of 120, 450, and 1560 keV, and by beta-gamma and gamma-gamma coincidence studies he showed that all these were in cascade following the 1.99 MeV beta transition. This leads to a disintegration energy of 3.92 MeV. The position of the transitions in the cascade was determined with the help of the studies of HARVEY[32] on the energy levels of Pb^{209} revealed from (d, p) reactions on Pb^{208}. He found levels at 1.56 and 2.03 MeV. Combining the results of all these studies the decay scheme can be written as in Fig. 7.7.

STROMINGER, STEPHENS AND RASMUSSEN[33] have performed beta-gamma coincidence experiments on this nuclide and have shown that the level at 2.13 MeV in Pb^{209} to which the beta particle decay of Tl^{209} leads is a metastable state with a half-life of (3.1 ± 1.0) × 10^{-9} seconds. These authors discuss possible assignments of neutron and proton configurations which might account for this metastable state and for other features of the decay scheme of Tl^{209}.

Lead-209. The isotope Pb^{209} is produced by the alpha-decay of Po^{213} and the beta decay of Tl^{209}. It was identified by HAGEMANN ET AL.[16] and by ENGLISH ET AL.[15] in the first detailed study of the decay products of U^{233}. Before this work, Pb^{209} had been produced and identified by FAJANS AND

---

[29] F. Wagner, Jr., M. S. Freedman, D. W. Engelkemeir, and L. B. Magnusson, *Phys. Rev.* **88**, 171A (1952).

[30] J. V. Jelley, *Can. J. Res.* **26A**, 255 (1948).

[31] F. Hagemann, *Phys. Rev.* **79**, 534 (1950).

[32] J. A. Harvey, *Can. J. Phys.* **31**, 278 (1953).

[33] D. Strominger, F. S. Stephens, Jr., and J. O. Rasmussen, *Phys. Rev.* **103**, 748 (1956).

VOIGHT[34] who produced it by a (d, p) reaction on Pb^{208}.   It has a half-life of 3.22 hours and decays by the emission of beta particles with end-point energy of 635 keV.[35]   No gamma rays are known[35] and none should be expected because apparently the first excited state of Bi^{209} lies at about 900 keV.   RAMLER AND CO-WORKERS[36] have measured the excitation function for Pb^{209} produced by the reaction, $Pb^{208}(d, p)Pb^{209}$.   See Section 5.2 of Chapter 5.

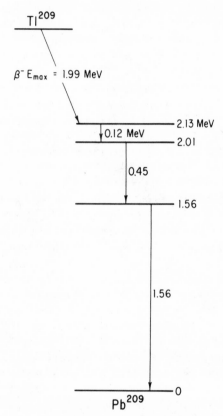

FIG. 7.7. Decay scheme of Tl[209].

Bismuth-209. This stable isotope is the termination point for the neptunium family of isotopes. Bi^{209} is the sole isotope found in ordinary terrestrial bismuth.   Ordinary bismuth is a mixture of the Bi^{209} formed directly at the time of nucleogenesis plus an unknown amount which was formed by

[34] K. Fajans and A. F. Voight, *Phys. Rev.* **60**, 619 (1941).
[35] A. H. Wapstra, *Phys. Rev.* **86**, 562 (1952); *Arkiv Fysik* **6**, 263 (1953).
[36] Ramler, Wing, Henderson, and Huizenga, *Phys. Rev.* **114**, 154 (1959).

the decay of all nuclides beyond bismuth of the $4n + 1$ mass type. Bi^{209} is unstable toward alpha decay by about 3 MeV, but the alpha half-life is so extremely long that the only feasible experimental method for its measurement is the search for alpha tracks in a nuclear emulsion impregnated with bismuth and permitted to stand for periods of time of the order of years. Several authors have made experiments of this type with somewhat conflicting results except that all agree that the half-life is extremely long.

JENKNER AND BRODA[37] found no evidence for α-activity of bismuth and set a lower limit for the half-life of 3×10^{15} years.   FARAGGI AND BERTHELOT[38] observed a few alpha particles tracks which they assigned to Bi^{209} and concluded that Bi^{209} emits 3.15 MeV alpha particles with a half-life of 2.7×10^{17} years.   HINCKS AND MILLAR[39a] did a similar experiment and found no tracks which could be attributed unambiguously to bismuth. However, RIEZLER AND PORSCHEN[39b] carried out an experiment with bismuth-impregnated emulsions which supported the report of FARAGGI AND BERTHELOT[38].   They reported an alpha particle energy of 3.0 ± 0.2 MeV and calculated a half-life of 2×10^{17} years.   They suggested that the plates of HINCKS AND MILLAR[39a] might have been insensitive to the low energy alpha particles of Bi^{209}.   However, HINCKS AND MILLAR[39c] carefully reconsidered their data, re-examined their tests for sensitivity, range calibration, etc., and reaffirmed their conviction that the true half-life was greater than 2×10^{18} years.   They estimated a decay energy of 2.93 ± 0.11 MeV by the method of reaction cycles and on the basis of alpha decay theory and systematics they predicted a half-life between 5×10^{19} and 5×10^{22} years.

The very great difficulty in this emulsion experiment can be appreciated from the specific activity figures; there are only 0.02 disintegrations $minute^{-1}$ $gram^{-1}$ Bi^{209} if the half-life is 3×10^{17} years and 3.6×10^{-5} disintegrations $minute^{-1}$ $gram^{-1}$ if the half life is 10^{20} years.

7.2 THE COLLATERAL SERIES

Among the heavy element nuclides there are several groups of genetically related, radioactive nuclides which are non-existent in nature and not in the direct line of decay of the four heavy-element radioactive families.   These have come to be known as "collateral series" since they are collateral to one of the four radioactive families which cover the four possible mass types. These series are of arbitrary length, since no matter which isotope is chosen as the beginning, there is nearly always a possible progenitor of the same or

[37] K. Jenkner and E. Broda, *Nature* **164**, 412 (1949).
[38] H. Faraggi and A. Berthelot, *Compt. Rend.* **232**, 2093 (1951).
[39a] E. P. Hincks and C. H. Millar, *Proc. Roy. Soc. Can.* **46**, 143 (1952).
[39b] W. Riezler and W. Porschen, *Z. Naturforsch* **7A**, 634 (1952) and **11A**, 143 (1956).
[39c] E. P. Hincks and C. H. Millar, *Can. J. Phys.* **36**, 231 (1958).

of higher mass.   In the following treatment these series will be described in much the same way as they were originally reported upon their discovery, since it is likely that any future study of these nuclides will be done on samples prepared in about the same way.   These particular series start with neutron deficient isotopes whose half-lives are sufficiently long to permit radiochemical isolation of the isotope.   These isotopes are usually prepared by the bombardment of the convenient starting materials, thorium or uranium, with high energy particles.   The half-lives in general become shorter as the radioactive decay proceeds down the series.   It should be mentioned that there are many instances, especially in the transuranium region, where a number of nuclides were discovered separately and then later pieced together into a decay sequence; these could also be regarded formally as collateral chains but are not treated here in this manner since the experimental study of them did not follow this pattern.   There are also many single isotopes which could be regarded as collateral members of one of the four radioactive families. As stated, the collateral series singled out for treatment in this section are those which are experimentally produced and studied as decay sequences and the members of which will most probably continue to be studied as units of these decay sequences.

The first such collateral series was that beginning with Pa^{230}, discovered by STUDIER AND HYDE[40], working at the wartime Metallurgical Laboratory (now the Argonne National Laboratory) on thorium samples which had been bombarded with deuterons in the 60-inch cyclotron of the Crocker Laboratory at the University of California.   This was followed by the discovery by MEINKE, GHIORSO, AND SEABORG[41] of about a half-dozen similar collateral series beginning in the thorium-uranium region.   For example, thorium was bombarded with higher energy deuterons and helium ions in the 184-inch cyclotron at the Radiation Laboratory in Berkeley to produce such isotopes as Pa^{228} and U^{228} which decay through a series of daughters until they reach the main radioactive families.   These series have come to be named after the long-lived parent activity directly isolated from the target.   Thus the series mentioned here are known as the "Pa^{230} series," the "Pa^{228} series" and the "U^{228} series."

In the next several sub-sections the properties of these collateral series will be summarized.   The long-lived parent of each of these series is prepared by bombardment of thorium or uranium with very high energy particles. The high energies required for their preparation, ranging up to hundreds of MeV, means that quite a mixture of radioactivities are produced.   In many cases proper choice of bombardment energy, and of timed chemical separations make it possible to isolate the desired activity in high purity.   In others, it is impossible to avoid working with samples heavily contaminated with

---

40 M. H. Studier and E. K. Hyde, *Phys. Rev.* **74**, 591 (1948).
41 W. W. Meinke, A. Ghiorso, and G. T. Seaborg, *Phys. Rev.* **81**, 782 (1951).

interfering radioactivity. There are sometimes no alternate methods of preparation which avoid these difficulties other than the use of an isotope separator. The main instrument used in these studies was the gridded ion-chamber connected to a pulse-height analyzer because nearly all the nuclides involved were alpha-emitters. This permitted a rough determination of the alpha-particle energies and assisted greatly in the assignment of certain isotopes. Much information remains to be collected on the gamma radiations of members of these series but severe experimental difficulties must be faced in such studies.

With reference to the discussion in Chapter 1 (Section 1.4.2) regarding the relationship of alpha decay to the mass energy surface, some general comments can be made about the collateral series. All the parent nuclides giving rise to these collateral series are neutron deficient and some, such as U^{227}, are extremely neutron deficient. This places them high up on the neutron deficient side of the Heisenberg mass valley, a region of the mass surface where the slope even of the line of beta stability is quite steep. In this location they are unstable toward electron capture decay but most of them are also unstable toward alpha decay with such large alpha decay energy that this process predominates. The typical series is a cascade of four rapid alpha processes dropping down the left side of the mass surface. Since an α decay step occurs skew to the direction of the valley of beta stability a succession of such steps inevitably leads to the region of beta stability where the main line series lie. However, each of the collateral series discussed here joins the main series only near its termination. These comments are illustrated in Fig. 1.9 of Chapter 1 by the placement of Th^{226} and its decay products.

The collateral series will be discussed in the following order:

Section	Collateral Series
7.2.1	Pa^{230} series, including collateral members, Ac^{226} and Fr^{222}
7.2.2	Pa^{228} series
7.2.3	Pa^{227} series
7.2.4	Pa^{226} series
7.2.5	Pa^{225} series
7.2.6	U^{229} series
7.2.7	U^{228} series
7.2.8	U^{227} series

7.2.1 The Pa^{230} Collateral Series

STUDIER AND HYDE[40] produced Pa^{230} by bombarding thorium with 22 MeV deuterons. This isotope has substantial β^- branching leading to U^{230} which then proceeds to decay through a series of 5 alpha emitting isotopes. The chief decay characteristics of this series of isotopes are given in Table 7.4. The series is of the $4n + 2$ mass type and the relationship of the collateral series to the uranium-radium $(4n + 2)$ series is shown in Fig. 7.8.

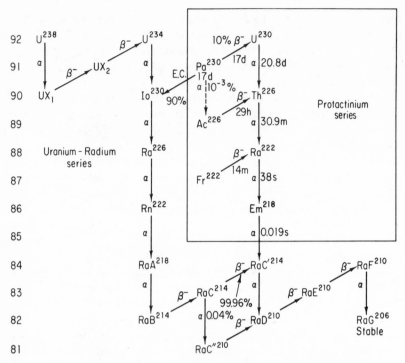

FIG. **7.8.** Relation of the protactinium series to the uranium-radium series.

Protactinium-230 The half-life of this nuclide has been reported as 17.0 $\pm$ 0.5 days[40] and 17.7 $\pm$ 0.5 days.[42]   It decays in three ways.   The most readily observed is that of beta emission because of the prominence of the alpha radiation of the daughter products.[40]   Beta decay accounts for only 10 per cent of the decay, however.   STUDIER AND BRUEHLMAN[43] proved that 90 per cent of the disintegrations go by orbital electron capture to produce ionium, but because of its long half-life, ionium is not easily identified in a source of Pa^{230}.   MEINKE AND SEABORG[45] have identified the Ac^{226} daughter formed by the alpha decay of Pa^{230} which occurs in ~ 0.003 per cent of the disintegrations.   It is also possible that Pa^{230} decays slightly by positron emission; ONG[44] estimates this decay as somewhat less than 0.1 per cent.

[42] D. W. Osborne, R. C. Thompson, and Q. Van Winkle, "The Transuranium Elements," NNES Volume **14B**, p. 1397, McGraw-Hill Book Co. (1949).

[43] M. H. Studier and R. J. Bruehlman, reported in *Argonne National Laboratory Report ANL-4252* (1949); in a later determination ONG[44] found the branching ratio to be 80 per cent electron capture and 20 per cent β^- emission.

[44] Ong Ping Hok, Thesis, University of Amsterdam (1955); see also Ong, Kramer, Meiser, Fennema, and Zisp, *Physica* **21**, 719 (1955).

[45] W. W. Meinke and G. T. Seaborg, *Phys. Rev.* **78**, 475 (1950).

TABLE **7.4.** Pa^{230} collateral series.

Isotope	Half-life	Mode of decay	Energy and abundance of α or β groups (MeV)	Energy and photon abundance of gamma rays (keV)
Pa^{230}	17.7 day	$\beta^-(\sim 10\%)$ $K(\sim 90\%)$ $\alpha(10^{-3}\%)$ $\beta^+(\sim 0.1\%)$	0.4051 5.14 (est.)	Very complex γ spectrum summarized in Section 8.3.6 Chapter 8.
U^{230}	20.8 day	α	5.884 (67.2%) 5.813 (32.1%) 5.658 (0.7%)	72.13 $\pm$ 0.06 (0.75%) 158 (0.16%) 232 (0.24%)
Th^{226}	30.9 min	α	6.330 (79%) 6.222 (19%) 6.095 (1.7%) 6.029 (0.6%)	111.1 $\pm$ 0.3 (4.8%) 131 (0.4%) 197 (0.4%) 242 (1.2%)
Ra^{222}	38 sec	α	6.551 (95%) 6.23 (4.4%) deduced from γ	325 (3.6%)
Em^{218}	0.030 sec	α	7.127 (99.8%) 6.53 (0.2%) inferred from γ	609 (0.2%)
†Ac^{226}	29 hr	β^- (80%) K (20%)	~ 1.2	With β^- 72.1, 158.1, 230.3 With K 67.6, 185.0, 253
*Fr^{222}	14.8 min	β^-	2.05	

* Fr^{222} is a collateral member of the Pa^{230} series and is most logically listed here because of its close relationship to the series.

† Ac^{226} appears in the Pa^{230} series as a product of rare α-branching of Pa^{230}. It is most readily prepared in an independent way as discussed later in this section.

The radiations of Pa^{230} are very complex. All discussion of these radiations and of the decay schemes of the isotope is collected in Section 8.3.6 of Chapter 8.

Uranium-230. This 20.8 day isotope can be prepared in high radiochemical purity by preparing a sample of Pa^{230}, letting it stand 20–35 days, and then isolating the U^{230} daughter activity. The growth and decay of U^{230} in Pa^{230} is shown in Fig. 7.9, from which it can be seen that 26 days after purification is the optimum time of isolation of U^{230}. If the protactinium fraction contains a large amount of Pa^{232} the final purification of the protactinium should not be carried out until the Pa^{232} has decayed sufficiently so that only negligible amounts of U^{232} are produced. Contamination of the protactinium by Pa^{233}, Pa^{231} and Pa^{229} causes no difficulty in the preparation of radioactively-pure U^{230}.

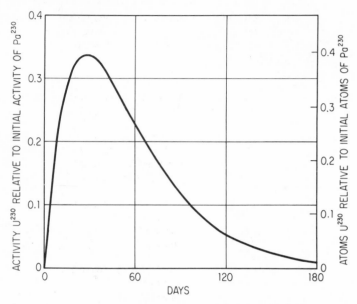

FIG. **7.9.** Growth and decay of U^{230} in initially pure Pa^{230}.

$$Pa^{230} \xrightarrow{\text{17 days}} U^{230} \xrightarrow{\text{20.8 days}}$$

U^{230} decays entirely by alpha emission with a half-life of 20.8 days.[40] Immediately after purification the alpha counting rate of a U^{230} sample rapidly increases because of the growth of daughters, the controlling rate being the 30.9 minute half-life of Th^{226}. After a few hours, the counting rate levels off at a value five times the initial rate and then decays slowly with a 20.8 day half-life. After transient equilibrium is reached the alpha spectrum, as determined in a gridded ionization chamber with pulse height analysis, is as shown in Fig. 7.10. When large samples are examined in a magnetic spectrograph of high resolution the spectrum is seen to be considerably more complex. The results of ASARO AND PERLMAN[46] are quoted in Table 7.4 and displayed schematically in Fig. 7.11.

The complexity of the U^{230} alpha spectrum suggests that gamma radiation must accompany the decay of this isotope. Gamma rays of 72.1,

---

[46] F. Asaro and I. Perlman, *Phys. Rev.* **104,** 91 (1956).

154.3, 158, and 232 keV have been reported. These radiations, their placement in a decay scheme, and the interpretation of that decay scheme are
discussed in Section 8.4.4 of Chapter 8.

Thorium-226. This isotope can be readily separated from its U^{230} parent
by radiochemical methods. Alternatively, the beta emitter Ac^{226} can be

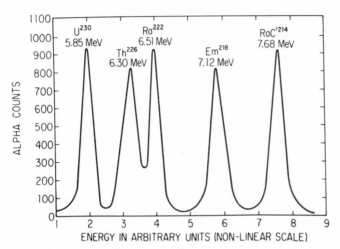

FIG. 7.10. Alpha spectrum of U^{230} and daughters as determined
in a gridded ion-chamber. The moderate resolution achieved
in this technique does not reveal the more complex structure seen
in data from magnetic spectrometers. See, for example,
Fig. 7.11.

made by deuteron bombardment of Ra^{226} or by high energy spallation of
thorium or uranium with protons of energy greater than 100 MeV; Th^{226}
daughter activity can then be isolated from the actinium fraction. The alpha
recoil method can be used for a quick and clean separation of Th^{226} from a
source of U^{230}. In this method a weightless sample of U^{230} on a metallic
plate is placed immediately below a metallic collector plate maintained at a
few hundred volts of negative potential. Preferably the collection is carried
out in a vacuum. The recoil momentum from the alpha disintegration of
U^{230} is sufficient to eject the Th^{226} daughter atoms as positively charged
ions and these are collected on the negatively-charged collector plate.

A sample of Th^{226} always has with it its short-lived decay products.
The radiations of Th^{226} itself are discussed in Section 8.2.4 of Chapter 8
where the decay scheme appears as Fig. 8.2.

Radium-222. This 38-second nuclide can be isolated in a pure state
(except for its short-lived daughters) by rapid radiochemical separation of a
radium fraction from a sample of Pa^{230}, U^{230} or Th^{226}. It can be separated
quickly and cleanly from a weightless sample of Th^{226} by the alpha-recoil

collection technique. ASARO AND PERLMAN[46] reported the energy of the main alpha particle group to be 6.551 MeV and its abundance to be 95 per cent. They also found a single gamma ray of 325 ± 3 keV energy which could be attributed to the de-excitation of the first excited state of Em^{218}.

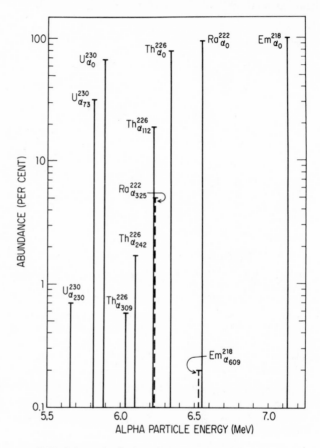

FIG. **7.11.** Schematic display of the complex alpha-spectrum of U^{230} and of its daughters. A logarithmic scale is used to permit the clearer presentation of low intensity groups.

From this they deduced that alpha particles of 6.232 MeV energy and 4.4 per cent abundance were present in the alpha spectrum of Ra^{222}. This particular alpha particle group falls at about the same energy as one of the alpha groups of Th^{226}. The energy of this main gamma ray of Ra^{222} was later remeasured[47] more accurately and found to be 324.6 keV. RUIZ, ASARO,

---

[47] W. G. Smith, F. Asaro, and J. M. Hollander, *Phys. Rev.* **104**, 99 (1956).

AND PERLMAN[48] later worked out a technique for the preparation of Ra^{222} samples which permitted a better determination of its spectrum. They made a direct observation of the α_{321} group and reported the revised value of 3.2 ± 0.4 per cent for its intensity.

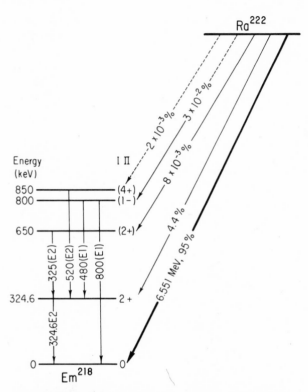

FIG. **7.12.** Decay scheme of Ra^{222} as formulated by STEPHENS, ASARO, AND PERLMAN.[49] Quantities enclosed in parentheses are not experimentally proved, but are probably correct.

STEPHENS, ASARO, AND PERLMAN[49] examined Ra^{222} for very low intensity gamma radiations by alpha-gamma and gamma-gamma coincidence techniques. They found the following gamma rays in addition to the prominent 324.6 keV transition: 325 keV (8×10^{-3} per cent), 480 keV (7×10^{-3} per cent), 520 keV (2×10^{-3} per cent), and 800 keV (0.02 per cent). A tentative decay scheme which is supported by gamma-gamma coincidence studies is given in Fig. 7.12. The decay scheme of Ra^{222} is quite similar to those of

[48] C. P. Ruiz, F. Asaro, and I. Perlman, unpublished results, 1960; C. P. Ruiz, Ph.D. Thesis, *Univ. of Calif. Lawrence Rad. Lab. Report UCRL-9511*, April 1961.

[49] F. S. Stephens, Jr., F. Asaro, and I. Perlman, unpublished results (1955).

Ra^{224} and Ra^{226} and systematic trends in the level systematics of the even-even emanation daughters are apparent.   These decay schemes are compared in Fig. 3.14 of Chapter 3.   These daughter emanation isotopes lie in a region intermediate between the closed shell region around lead where the shell model gives a good description of the observed energy levels and the region above mass 230 where the nuclear shape is stabilized in a spheroidal deformation.   In the intermediate region the ground state is probably spherical but the nucleus is soft toward the deformations in shape.   The two 2+ states in Em^{218} seen in the decay of Ra^{222} result from collective vibrations

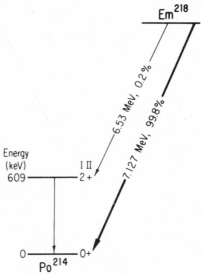

FIG. 7.13.   Decay scheme of Em²¹⁸.

of the type first pointed out by GOLDHABER AND WENESER.[50]   (Refer to Section 3.3.3 in Chapter 3.)   The negative parity state at 800 keV is also caused by collective motions and is probably similar to the negative parity states seen in heavier mass even-even nuclei.   These states are discussed in Section 3.4.4 of Chapter 3.

Emanation-218.   The original determination of the half-life, determined by an electronic technique, gave a value of 19 milliseconds.[51]   Many years later a better value of 30 ± 3 milliseconds was measured.[48]   The simple decay scheme is shown in Fig. 7.13.   Presumably the 609-keV state of Po^{214} seen here is the same one which leads to the well-known gamma ray of this energy in the beta-decay of Bi^{214} (RaC).

Actinium-226.   The nuclide Ac^{226} is collateral to the Pa^{230} series and

50 Scharff-Goldhaber and J. Weneser, *Phys. Rev.* **98**, 212 (1955).
51 M. H. Studier and E. K. Hyde, *Phys. Rev.* **74**, 591 (1948).

will be discussed here. It is possible to prepare Ac^{226} by high energy bombardment of thorium or uranium. SKIRVIN AND HYDE[52] have studied the cross section for formation of Ac^{226} by bombardment of thorium with protons. As the energy of the protons rises from 100 MeV to 340 MeV the cross section rises from 5 millibarns to 14 millibarns. LINDNER AND OSBORNE[53] have made a similar study with uranium targets. For 100 MeV protons the cross section is only 0.02 millibarns; it rises to 0.5 millibarns for protons of 340 MeV energy. In both types of bombardment equivalent yields of neighboring actinium isotopes are produced. The most troublesome of these, because of its roughly similar half-life, is 10.0 day Ac^{225}. Also in both cases a large fraction of the nuclear reaction cross section goes into fission, which results in the production of rare earth fission products which must be separated from the actinium. This separation is somewhat difficult because of the similarity in chemical properties of actinium and the rare earths, but there are several radiochemical methods by which a clean separation can be effected.

A preparative method which avoids many of those problems is the bombardment of radium with deuterons since the yield of interfering fission products is quite low.

$$Ra^{226}(d, 2n)\ Ac^{226}$$

Some 10.0-day Ac^{225} is also produced by the $(d, 3n)$ reaction, but by selecting a deuteron energy which emphasizes the $(d, 2n)$ relative to the $(d, 3n)$ reaction and by performing the chemical separation immediately after bombardment, one can obtain a high relative yield of Ac^{226}.

Ac^{226} has a half-life of 29 hours. It decays 80 per cent by β^- emission to produce Th^{226} and 20 per cent by orbital electron capture to produce Ra^{226}.

STEPHENS, ASARO, AND PERLMAN[54] have studied the gamma rays of Ac^{226} in a scintillation spectrometer and the conversion electrons in a permanent magnet electron spectrometer. They also performed gamma-gamma coincidence studies. From their results they constructed the decay scheme shown in Fig. 7.14. All of the states shown are also known from the α-decay of U^{230} and Th^{230} (see Chapter 8). The 1-states observed in both daughter nuclei represent collective excitations and may represent an excitation of a pear-shaped nuclear shape deformation. This same 1-state occurs systematically throughout the heavy element region.

Francium-222. This isotope does not appear in the decay chain of Pa^{230} but is so closely related (collateral member) to this series that it is most

[52] S. Skirvin and E. K. Hyde, unpublished results (1952).

[53] M. Lindner and R. N. Osborne, *Phys. Rev.* **103**, 378 (1956).

[54] F. S. Stephens, Jr., F. Asaro, and I. Perlman, *Phys. Rev.* **100**, 1543 (1956) and unpublished results (1957).

logically reviewed here. HYDE AND GHIORSO[55] prepared Fr^{222} by bombardment of Th^{232} with 100 MeV protons. When protons of 348 MeV were used the amount of Fr^{222} relative to Fr^{221} was too low to permit easy observation of Fr.^{222} Francium^{222} decays by beta emission to Ra^{222}. This is made certain by the observation of the characteristic alpha particles of Ra^{222}, Em^{218}, and $Po^{214}(RaC')$ in the chemically-purified francium fraction; all alpha peaks decayed with the 14.8-minute half-life of Fr^{222}.

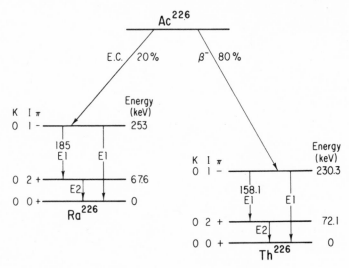

FIG. **7.14.** Decay scheme of Ac^{226}.

The radiations of Fr^{222} itself have not been observed because of interference from cesium fission-product activities. The beta decay energy is estimated from closed decay energy cycles to be 2.05 MeV. Francium-222 may be expected to undergo slight alpha-branching with the emission of 6.0 MeV alpha particles, but these have not been observed.

7.2.2 *The Pa²²⁸ Series*

MEINKE, GHIORSO, AND SEABORG[56] used 80 MeV deuterons to produce 22 hour Pa^{228} by the reaction, Th^{232} $(d, 6n)$ Pa^{228}. They waited several hours after the irradiation before purifying the protactinium and proceeding with measurements on Pa^{228} because, during the period immediately after bombardment, much 38 minute Pa^{227} activity was present. Pa^{228} gives rise

55 E. K. Hyde and A. Ghiorso, *Univ. of Calif. Rad. Lab. Report UCRL-593*, February 1950 (unpublished).

56 W. W. Meinke, A. Ghiorso, and G. T. Seaborg, *Phys. Rev.* **81**, 782 (1951).

to a series of daughter activities which join the thorium decay chain at Bi^{212} by the following decay sequence.

$$Pa^{228} \xrightarrow[23\ hr]{\alpha\ (2\%)} Ac^{224} \xrightarrow[2.9\ hr]{\alpha\ (10\%)} Fr^{220} \xrightarrow[27.5\ sec]{\alpha} At^{216} \xrightarrow[3 \times 10^{-4}\ sec]{\alpha}$$

$$\downarrow EC(98\%) \qquad \downarrow EC(90\%)$$

$$Th^{228}\ (RdTh) \rightarrow Ra^{224}\ (ThX)$$
$$1.9\ year \qquad 3.64\ days$$

$$Bi^{212}(ThC) \begin{array}{c} \xrightarrow{34\%\alpha} Tl^{208}\ (ThC'') \xrightarrow[3.1\ min]{\beta^-} \\ \xrightarrow{66\%\beta^-} Po^{212}\ (ThC') \xrightarrow[3 \times 10^{-7}\ sec]{\alpha} \end{array} Pb^{208}\ (stable)$$
$$60.5\ min$$

The half-lives of the several members were determined by isolating part of the chain by chemical methods, by recoil collection, and in the case of At^{216}

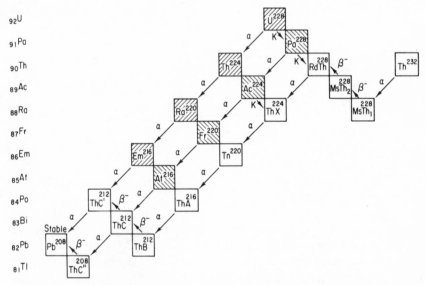

FIG. **7.15.** Block diagram of the Pa^{228} series and the U^{228} series, both collateral to the thorium $(4n)$ series.

by delayed coincidence counting. The branchings in the decay of Pa^{228} and of Ac^{224} were measured by obtaining the yield ratios of their products. The relationship of the Pa^{228} series to the thorium series is illustrated in Fig. 7.15.

Pa^{228} produced in the way suggested is necessarily contaminated with several other protactinium isotopes; Pa^{233}, Pa^{232}, Pa^{230}, and Pa^{229}. For measurements of the alpha particles of Pa^{228} this is not serious since Pa^{229} is the only contaminant which contributes extraneous alpha particles in a freshly purified sample. The 2.9 hour Ac^{224} daughter is conveniently prepared in an almost pure state by the alpha recoil collection technique from a Pa^{228} source. It can also be isolated by standard radiochemical techniques. Such a sample quickly comes to equilibrium with Fr^{220} and At^{216} and more slowly with Bi^{212}(ThC), Tl^{208}(ThC″) and Po^{212}(ThC′). Samples of

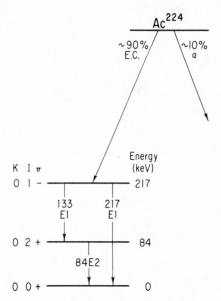

FIG. **7.16.** Electron capture decay scheme Ac^{224}.

27.5 second Fr^{220} can be prepared by the alpha recoil collection technique from a parent sample of Ac^{224} or of Pa^{228}. If Pa^{228} is used, some Ac^{224} will also be collected, but if the exposure time is limited to a few minutes, the major activity collected will be Fr^{220}.

The original crude measurements[56] on the alpha spectrum of Pa^{228} by the ion-chamber technique showed only two groups with energies 6.09 and 5.85 MeV. Later more careful experiments in a magnetic alpha spectrometer showed that the alpha spectrum of Pa^{228} is exceedingly complex. The gamma spectrum of Pa^{228} has been studied by several investigators and it also is known to be very complex. These studies are discussed more fully in the next chapter, Section 8.3.4.

Although the α-spectrum of Ac^{224} is likely to be complex it has only been studied with low resolution techniques and only a single α-group of 6.17 MeV has been reported.[56] HILL, STEPHENS, ASARO AND PERLMAN[57] studied the electron-capture branch decay of Ac^{224} because of their interest in negative parity states in even-even nuclei. The alpha decay of Th^{228}(RdTh) is known[58] to include some alpha emission to a $1-$ state in Ra^{224}(ThX) and it was of interest to know whether the same state was reached in the electron-capture decay of Ac^{224}. Their studies revealed that Ac^{224} decays primarily to this $1-$ state at 216 keV. This state is then deactivated by two parallel electric dipole (E1) transitions, one of 216 keV energy leading to the ground state and one of 133 keV leading to the first excited $2+$ state. The $2+$ state is then de-excited by an 84 keV electric quadrupole (E2) transition. These facts are summarized in Fig. 7.16.

The decay schemes of Fr^{220} and of At^{216} appear to be quite simple. Although both are undoubtedly β-unstable, their α-decay half-lives are too short to permit observation of other modes of decay.

The alpha spectrum of each consists of a single alpha-particle group presumed to lead directly to the ground state. The alpha particle energies are 6.69 ± 0.03 MeV and 7.79 ± 0.03 MeV, respectively.[56]

7.2.3 The Pa²²⁷ Collateral Series

MEINKE, GHIORSO, AND SEABORG[56] investigated 38.3 minute Pa^{227} produced by the reactions

$$Th^{232}\,(p,\,6n)\,Pa^{227}$$
$$Th^{232}\,(d,\,7n)\,Pa^{227}$$
$$Th^{232}\,(\alpha,\,p8n)\,Pa^{227}$$
$$U^{238}\,(p,\,\alpha8n)\,Pa^{227}$$

At the particle energies required to obtain these reactions in favorable yield, a number of other protactinium isotopes are also produced but these do not contribute greatly to the total alpha activity in the protactinium fraction for some hours after bombardment. Of the isotopes of heavier mass (i.e., Pa^{228} through Pa^{233}) the shortest-lived is 22-hour Pa^{228}. All the isotopes of lighter mass usually decay completely before the chemical purification is completed. Hence, Pa^{227} is relatively easier to study than, for example, Pa^{228}. It decays 85 per cent by alpha emission and gives rise to a series of four short-lived alpha-emitters, whose energies were measured by the ion-chamber technique.

[57] M. W. Hill, F. S. Stephens, Jr., F. Asaro, and I. Perlman, unpublished results. See abstract in *Bull. Amer. Phys. Soc. II* 2, 394 (1957); see also M. W. Hill, *Report UCRL-8423*, August 1958.

[58] F. Asaro, F. S. Stephens, Jr., and I. Perlman, *Phys. Rev.* 92, 1495 (1953), see also Section 8.2.6 of Chapter 8.

$$\text{Pa}^{227} \xrightarrow[\substack{38.3 \text{ min}}]{\alpha \,(85\%)} \text{Ac}^{223} \xrightarrow[2.2 \text{ min}]{\alpha} \text{Fr}^{219} \xrightarrow[0.02 \text{ sec}]{\alpha} \text{At}^{215} \xrightarrow[10^{-4} \text{ sec}]{\alpha}$$

$$\text{EC} \downarrow (15\%)$$

$$\text{Th}^{227}$$

$$\text{Bi}^{211}(\text{AcC}) \xrightarrow[2.16 \text{ min}]{\alpha} \text{Tl}^{207}(\text{AcC}'') \xrightarrow[4.76 \text{ min}]{\beta^-} \text{Pb}^{207}(\text{stable})$$

TABLE 7.5. Properties of members of the Pa^{227} collateral series.

Nuclide	Type of radiation	Half-life	Energy of radiation (MeV)
Pa^{227}	$\alpha \,(\sim 85\%)$	38.3 ± 0.3 min	6.46 (main group*)
	E.C. $(\sim 15\%)$		0.38 γ
Ac^{223}	$\alpha \,(99\%)$	2.2 ± 0.1 min	6.657 (37.5%), 6.643 (42.1%)
	E.C. (1%)		6.561 (13.3%), 6.52 (3.8%), and
			6.47 (3.2%)**
Fr^{219}	α	0.02 ± 0.002 sec	7.30 ± 0.02
At^{215}	α	10^{-4} sec $\pm 20\%$	8.00 ± 0.02
$\text{Bi}^{211}(\text{AcC})$	$\alpha \,(99.7\%)$	2.16 min	6.617 (83%), 6.273 (17%)
$\text{Tl}^{207}(\text{AcC}'')$	β^-	4.76 min	1.47 γ, 0.870γ
Pb^{207}	stable		

* Pa^{227} has a complex alpha spectrum containing at least 11 separate groups. Details are given in Section 8.3.3 of the next chapter.
** Relative to Bi^{211} $\alpha_0 = 6.620$ MeV.

Decay characteristics are listed in Table 7.5 and the relationship of the Pa^{227} series to the actinium series is illustrated in Fig. 7.17.

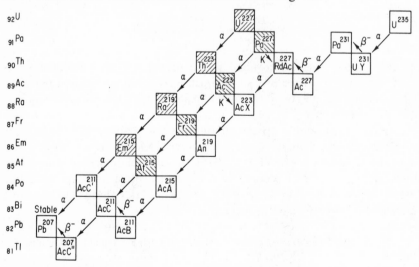

FIG. 7.17. Block diagram showing relationship of the Pa^{227} series and U^{227} series, both collateral to the actinium $(4n + 3)$ series.

HILL, ASARO, AND PERLMAN[59] remeasured the alpha spectrum of Pa^{227} in a magnetic spectrograph and found a complex spectrum containing at least 11 groups. This is discussed in Section 8.3.4 of Chapter 8. The electron capture branching decay of Pa^{227} was established by radiochemical isolation of the Th^{227} daughter.[56]

The 2.2 minute Ac^{223} can be separated radiochemically or by the alpha recoil collection technique from its parent Pa^{227} but it cannot be examined independently from its immediate descendants, Fr^{219} and At^{215}, which grow into equilibrium instantly. HILL'S[59] and SUBRAHMANYAM'S[60] measurements of the alpha spectrum of Ac^{223} are included in Table 7.5.

The half-life of Fr^{219} was measured by collecting α-recoils from a source of Pa^{227} onto a rotating disc. If the characteristic time constant of the rotating disc (relative to the point of collection and the position of counter) is of the same order as the decay constant of an isotope collected, the decay of that species will stand out clearly from others and its decay rate can be measured by varying the rate of rotation of the disc. A series of counters at different positions with constant disc velocity accomplishes the same purpose. A rough half-life of 20 milliseconds was measured by noting the decrease in counting rate with distance from the point of collection.[56] SUBRAHMANYAM[60] determined a more exact value of 21.5 milliseconds. The half-life of At^{215} was determined to be $\sim 10^{-4}$ sec by a delayed coincidence method.[56]

7.2.4 *The* Pa^{226} *Collateral Series*

The alpha emitting isotope Pa^{226} can be produced by bombardment of thorium with high energy deuterons. The reaction is $Th^{232}(d, 8n)$ Pa^{226} and the optimum deuteron energy for thick thorium targets is about 150 MeV. Pa^{226} has a half-life of only 1.8 minutes and gives rise to the alpha emitters Ac^{222}, Fr^{218}, and At^{214} which decay with even shorter half-lives. With the alpha decay of At^{214} the series reaches Bi^{210}(RaE) and hence ties into the uranium-radium $(4n + 2)$ series. This collateral chain relationship is illustrated in Fig. 7.18. The meager data on the members of this series are summarized in Table 7.6. These data are taken from the work of MEINKE, GHIORSO, AND SEABORG.[56,61]

Great difficulties attend the study of short-lived Pa^{226} and its descendants. The high energy reactions required for the production of Pa^{226} lead to the production of large amounts of radioactivity in the target which completely obscures the Pa^{226} radiations so that chemical separation of a protactinium

---

[59] M. Hill, F. Asaro, and I. Perlman, unpublished results. See M. Hill thesis, University of California, 1958; also printed as report *UCRL-8423*, August 1958.

[60] V. Subrahmanyam, Thesis, University of California (1963); also issued as *University of California Radiation Laboratory Report UCRL-11082* (1963).

[61] W. W. Meinke, A. Ghiorso, and G. T. Seaborg, *Phys. Rev.* **85**, 429 (1952).

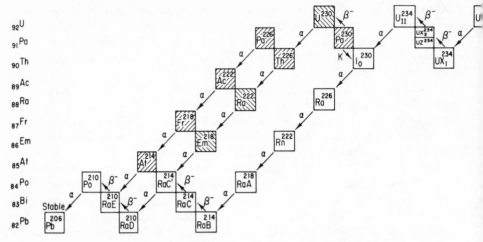

FIG. 7.18. Block diagram of Pa^{226} collateral series showing its relationship to the Pa^{230} collateral series and to the uranium-radium $(4n + 2)$ series.

fraction is essential. MEINKE, GHIORSO, AND SEABORG[56] found it necessary to bombard thorium nitrate (which could be more quickly dissolved than thorium metal) in a special target which could be blown from the cyclotron area in a compressed air line into the chemistry laboratory in a matter of seconds. By rapid chemical separations the protactinium could be extracted, purified sufficiently for the purpose, and mounted for counting in less than 3.5 minutes. Even so, there was considerable interference from the radio-activity of other protactinium isotopes. By bombarding the target for only a few minutes the build-up of Pa^{233}, Pa^{232}, Pa^{230}, Pa^{229}, and Pa^{228} was not serious, but the amount of 38-minute Pa^{227} produced was comparable to the amount of Pa^{226}. Hence, any delay in chemical processing meant that the Pa^{226}-series radiations became obscured by those of the Pa^{227} series. The information available on the Pa^{226} series as shown in Table 7.6 was obtained by measuring the α-particles of the four short-lived

TABLE 7.6. Properties of members of Pa^{226} collateral series.

Nuclide	Type of radiation	Half-life	Energy of radiation (MeV)
Pa^{226}	α	1.8 ± 0.2 min	6.81 ± 0.05
Ac^{222}	α	5.5 sec	6.96 ± 0.05
Fr^{218}	α	est. 5×10^{-3} sec	7.85 ± 0.05
At^{214}	α	est. 2×10^{-6} sec	8.78 ± 0.05
$Bi^{210}(RaE)$	β^-	5.0 day	1.17
$Po^{210}(RaF)$	α	138 day	5.298
Pb^{206}	stable		

members in an ionization chamber.   The half-life for Ac^{222} was measured after separating it by the recoil method.

7.2.5 *The* Pa^{225} *Collateral Series*

The Pa^{225} collateral series was first produced and partially identified by KEYS[62] who produced it at the McGill University cyclotron by the reaction:

$$Th^{232}(d, 9n) Pa^{225}$$

Because of the short half-life of the parent Pa^{225} (2 seconds), radiochemical separation was out of the question and it was necessary to use a technique in which observations could be made during the bombardment or shortly after; the photographic emulsion method was used.   The decay of the four members of this series, all of which decay by alpha emission, was observed as a four-pronged star in the emulsion.   The energies were allocated to the individual members and half-lives were estimated for them through the application of the systematics of alpha decay.   The observation of the expected unique value for the alpha particle energy of At^{213} (9.2 MeV) is important for the identification of the sequence of mass numbers.   The radioactive properties are summarized in Table 7.7.   The relationship to the

TABLE 7.7. Properties of members of Pa^{225} collateral series.

Nuclide	Type of radiation	Half-life	Energy of radiation (MeV)
Pa^{225}	α	2 sec	—
Ac^{221}	α	$\leqslant 1$ sec	7.6
Fr^{217}	α	$\leqslant 1$ sec	8.3
At^{213}	α	$\leqslant 1$ sec	9.2
Bi^{209}	stable		

neptunium ($4n + 1$) family and the U^{229} series is shown in the following Figure 7.19.   The information on the Pa^{225} is naturally regarded as only preliminary data for which more evidence needs to be collected.

7.2.6 *The* U^{229} *Collateral Series*

The isotope, 58-minute U^{229}, can be prepared in rather high radiochemical purity by bombardment of thorium with high energy helium ions (MEINKE, GHIORSO, AND SEABORG)[56]

$$Th^{232}(\alpha, 7n) U^{229}$$

If the bombardment time is short the contaminating activity from uranium isotopes of higher mass is quite small because of the longer half-lives of these

---

[62] J. D. Keys, Ph.D. Thesis, McGill University (1951).

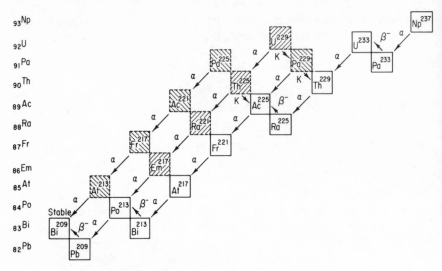

FIG. 7.19. Block diagram showing relationship of Pa^{225} series and U^{229} series to the neptunium ($4n + 1$) series.

isotopes. The only uranium isotope which interferes is 9.3-minute U^{228} and this interference is eliminated simply by delaying the final uranium purification for a suitable length of time, say one hour.

Uranium-229 decays 20 per cent by alpha emission and in so doing gives rise to a series of four additional alpha emitters of short life:

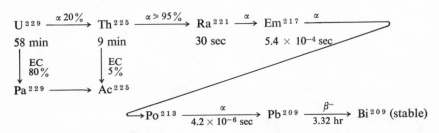

The relationship of the series to the neptunium ($4n + 1$) series is shown in Fig. 7.19.

The partial decay of U^{229} by capture of an orbital electron was established by chemical isolation of daughter Pa^{229} activity; similarly the partial decay of Th^{225} by orbital electron capture was established by isolating Ac^{225}. 8.0-minute Th^{225} can be isolated chemically from U^{229} or it can be isolated from U^{229} samples by the alpha recoil collection technique. The 30-second Ra^{221} can be separated by very rapid radiochemical methods from a U^{229} sample or by the recoil collection technique. The 5.4×10^{-4} second half-life of Em^{217} was measured by delayed coincidence techniques.[63]

Ruiz, Asaro, and Perlman[63] started a more intensive study of the radiations and decay schemes of these nuclides with the preliminary results summarized in Table 7.8. Only a start has been made on the construction of detailed decay schemes.

TABLE 7.8. Alpha and gamma radiation in the U^{229} collateral series.

Nuclide	Alpha group energy (MeV)[a]	Excited state energy of daughter (keV)	Abundance (per cent)	Hindrance factor	γ-ray energy (keV)	γ-ray abundance (photons/α)
U^{229}	6.355 ± 0.003	0	64	1.5		
	6.327	29 ± 2	20 ± 2	3.7		
	6.292	65 ± 2	11 ± 1	4.6		
	6.255	102 ± 3	1 ± 0.5	35		
	6.218	139 ± 3	3 ± 1	7.9		
	6.180	178 ± 4	1 ± 0.5	16		
Th^{225}	6.793 ± 0.005	0	9 ± 1	180	90 ± 2	0.33 ± 0.03
	6.739	55	7 ± 1	140	246	0.05
	6.695	98	2 ± 1	340	322	0.30
	6.645	151	3 ± 1	140	362	0.05
	6.622	174	3 ± 1	110	450	0.01
	6.496	301	14 ± 1	7.3	490	0.01
	6.473	324	43 ± 2	1.9		
	6.436	361	15 ± 1	3.8		
	6.340	460	2 ± 1	11		
	6.307	494	2 ± 1	7.7		
Ra^{221}	6.754 ± 0.005	0	30 ± 2	14	89 ± 2	0.15 ± 0.02
	6.661	9.1	20 ± 2	10	152	0.13
	6.606	151	34 ± 2	3	176	0.02
	6.584	174	8 ± 1	11	219	0.001
	6.574	184	3 ± 1	28	293	0.006
	(6.46)	300	0.4 ± 0.3	70	320	0.007
	(6.40)	360	0.3 ± 0.2	50	415	0.005
	6.25	500	0.7 ± 0.3	6		
	(6.16)	600	0.3 ± 0.2	5		
Em^{217}	7.735 ± 0.004	0	>99.8	1.59		
Po^{213}	8.37 ± 0.10	0	>99.8			

[a] Alpha particle energies are expressed relative to Th^{226} α_0 and Ra^{222} α_0 taken as 6.330 and 6.552 MeV, respectively. In the case of Em^{217} and Po^{213} the energy standard was Po^{214} taken as 7.680 MeV.

These data from C. P. Ruiz, thesis study, *Univ. Calif. Lawrence Rad. Lab. Report UCRL-9511*, 1961.

[63] C. P. Ruiz, F. Asaro, and I. Perlman, unpublished results. C. P. Ruiz, Ph.D. Thesis, *Univ. Calif. Lawrence Rad. Lab. Report UCRL-9511*, April 1961.

7.2.7 *The* U^{228} *Collateral Series*

Bombardment of thorium with high energy helium ions (120 MeV, for example) produces 9.3 minute U^{228} by the reaction, Th^{232} $(\alpha, 8n)$ U^{228} (MEINKE, GHIORSO, AND SEABORG).[56] This isotope decays chiefly by alpha emission and gives rise to a series of four alpha emitters with half-lives of less than one second. The series terminates at Pb^{208} and hence is collateral to the thorium (4*n*) family. The decay sequence is as follows:

Energy data on the alpha particles as obtained in a magnetic spectrometer by RUIZ, ASARO, AND PERLMAN[63] are summarized in Table 7.9. The relationship of the series to the Pa^{228} series and the thorium family is shown in the previous Fig. 7.15. Uranium-228 also decays by orbital electron capture to produce Pa^{228} to an extent measured as $\leqslant 5$ per cent.[63]

The uranium fraction isolated from a thorium target bombarded with 120 MeV helium ions contains several other uranium isotopes. However, if the

TABLE 7.9. Alpha and gamma radiations of the U^{228} collateral series.

Nuclide	Alpha particle energy (MeV)	Abundance (per cent)	Excited state energy (keV)	Energy (keV)	Abundance (photons/α)
U^{228}	6.68 ± 0.01	70	0	152 ± 3	0.002 ± 0.0005
	6.59	29 ± 4	93 ± 4	187 ± 3	0.003 ± 0.001
	6.44[a]	0.7 ± 0.3[b]	246 ± 3	246 ± 3	0.004 ± 0.001
	6.40[a]	0.5 ± 0.2[b]	280 ± 6		
Th^{224}	7.17 ± 0.01	79	0	90 ± 2	0.02 ± 0.09
	7.00	19 ± 2	177 ± 3	177 ± 2	0.09 ± 0.02
	6.77	1.5 ± 0.6[b]	410 ± 4	235 ± 3	0.004 ± 0.002
	6.70	0.5 ± 0.3[b]	475 ± 5	297 ± 3	0.003 ± 0.001
				410 ± 3	0.008 ± 0.003
Ra^{220}	7.45 ± 0.01	99	0	465 ± 4	0.01
	6.90[a]	1 ± 0.4[b]	465 ± 4		
Em^{216}	8.04 ± 0.01	100	0		

[a] Existence of groups and their energy inferred from gamma ray data.
[b] Abundance obtained from gamma ray intensities.

bombardment time is restricted to a few minutes, the radioactivity due to U^{235}, U^{234}, U^{233}, U^{232}, U^{231}, and U^{230} is quite low owing to their long decay periods. The principal contaminant is 58 minute U^{229}; the radiations of this isotope obscure those of U^{228} if the time spent in chemical processing is greater than a few minutes. The decay schemes of the members of this family of nuclides are incompletely known.

ORTH, GHIORSO, AND SEABORG[64] have produced 36 minute Pu^{232} by bombardment of U^{235} or U^{233} with high energy helium ions. Since it decays into U^{228} it can be considered part of this collateral series. The isolation of U^{228} from Pu^{232} offers a method for the preparation of small samples of U^{228} free of contamination from other uranium isotopes.

7.2.8 *The U^{227} Collateral Series*

MEINKE, GHIORSO, AND SEABORG[65] obtained evidence for a U^{227} collateral series by studying the uranium fraction of thorium targets bombarded with 150-MeV helium ions. The nuclear reaction involved is:

$$Th^{232} (\alpha, 9n) U^{227}$$

Uranium-227 has a half-life of 1.3 minutes and the decay sequence is

$$U^{227} \xrightarrow{\alpha} Th^{223} \xrightarrow{\alpha} Ra^{219} \xrightarrow{\alpha} Em^{215} \xrightarrow{\alpha} Po^{211} \xrightarrow{\alpha} Pb^{207}$$

The meager data on these isotopes are summarized in Table 7.10. The relationship of the U^{227} series to the Pa^{227} collateral series and to the actinium series is shown in the previous Fig. 7.17.

TABLE **7.10.** Properties of members of the U^{227} collateral series.

Nuclide	Type of radiation	Half-life	Energy of radiation (MeV)
U^{227}	α	1.3 ± 0.3 min	6.8 ± 0.1
Th^{223}	α	est $\sim 10^{-1}$ sec	7.55 ± 0.1
Ra^{219}	α	est $\sim 10^{-3}$ sec	8.0 ± 0.1
Em^{215}	α	est $\sim 10^{-6}$ sec	8.6 ± 0.1
Po^{211}	α	0.52 sec	7.434
Pb^{207}	stable		

The experiments to determine the data of Table 7.10 were carried out in the following manner. Thorium nitrate powder was bombarded for one

[64] D. Orth, A. Ghiorso, and G. T. Seaborg, unpublished results (1950); See D. A. Orth, Ph.D. Thesis, University of California, January 1951; also published as UCRL-1059 (Rev.) Nov. 1951.

[65] W. W. Meinke, A. Ghiorso, and G. T. Seaborg, *Phys. Rev.* **85**, 429 (1952).

or two minutes in a special target assembly which was blown from the cyclotron tank to the chemical laboratory in another building in a special compressed air line. The transit time was 12 seconds. The thorium nitrate was instantly dissolved and the uranium extracted with ethyl ether. The ether layer was washed several times with ammonium nitrate-nitric acid solution and then evaporated on platinum plates for alpha spectrum analysis in a gridded ion chamber coupled to a 48-channel analyzer. Some measurements were made as soon as 1.4 minutes after the end of the bombardment. The alpha spectrum showed the peaks due to U^{227} and to its short-lived daughters. These peaks were superimposed on a background due to the U^{228} series; the U^{228} alpha activity was about equivalent in intensity to the 1.3-minute U^{227} activity at the start of the measurements. Obviously, only a limited amount of data can be taken under such severe experimental handicaps. More extensive information on members of the U^{227} collateral series will have to come from new experimental approaches.

7.3 REFERENCE COLLECTION OF ALPHA SPECTRA

A common problem encountered by laboratory scientists working with heavy elements for research, for contamination control, for process development, and numerous other purposes is the identification of alpha emitter in a sample of unknown origin or composition. If the unknown sample happens to be a member of one of the radioactive families discussed in this chapter and the preceding one, the alpha particles emitted by the sample will consist of many groups of particles with characteristic energies and relative abundances. It is useful to have a set of reference spectra which may be compared with the spectrum observed in a sample of unknown identity. We present such a set of reference spectra in a series of drawings (Figs. 7.20–7.25).

In each of these drawings the energy (in MeV) and the relative intensity (in per cent) of the major groups are shown under the assumption that all the daughter products are in equilibrium with the parent of the series. The intensity of the parent emitter is taken equal to 100. Those alpha groups present in 5 per cent or less intensity are indicated in a lower section of the drawings because in an alpha detector of low or moderate resolution used for the identification of a sample of low disintegration rate these groups would ordinarily not be resolved.

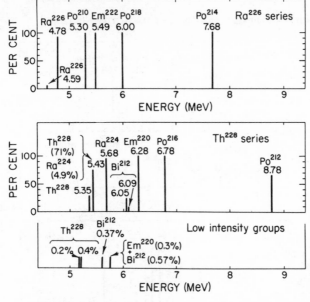

FIG. **7.20.** Reference alpha spectra of Ra[226] and Th[228] (RdTh) and daughter products in equilibrium.

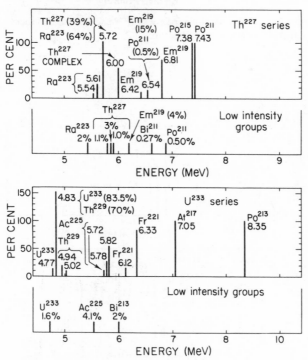

FIG. **7.21.** Reference alpha spectra of Th[227] and U[233] and of their daughter products in equilibrium.

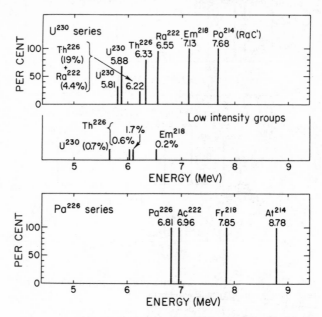

FIG. 7.22. Reference alpha spectra of U^{230} and Pa^{226} and of their daughter products in equilibrium.

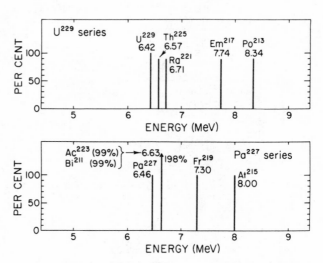

FIG. 7.23. Reference alpha spectra of U^{229} and Pa^{227} and of their daughter products in equilibrium.

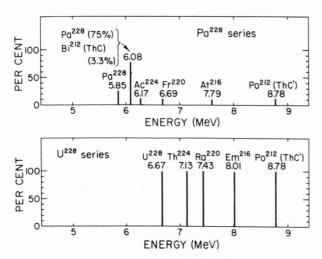

FIG. **7.24.** Reference alpha spectra of Pa²²⁸ and U²²⁸ and of their daughter products in equilibrium.

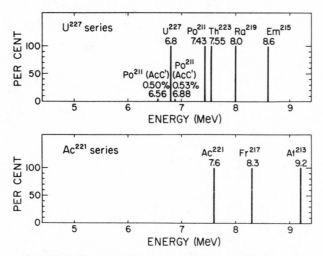

FIG. **7.25.** Reference alpha spectra of U²²⁷ and Ac²²¹ and of their daughter products in equilibrium.

8

THE ISOTOPES OF

THORIUM, PROTACTINIUM, AND URANIUM

8.1 GENERAL CONSIDERATIONS

This chapter consists of a systematic and detailed review of the radio-active properties of the isotopes of thorium, protactinium, and uranium. In the previous two chapters the presence of many of these isotopes in the heavy element decay series both natural and synthetic has been mentioned, but a complete discussion of their decay schemes has been reserved for this chapter. Appropriate cross references to the two previous chapters are made in the following material.

It may be useful first to speak of some general features of these decay schemes which may make it easier to understand what otherwise might be a confusing compilation of data. Since general features are more clearly discernible in the nuclear disintegrations leading to an even-even daughter product, we start with comments about such cases. Figure 8.1 shows all the identified levels lying below 600 keV in the even-even nuclei on which data have been obtained by a study of the decay of isotopes of thorium, protactinium, and uranium. The most common feature is a group of even parity states with the spin sequence 0+, 2+, 4+, etc. This series represents rotational excitation of the spheroidally deformed ground state nucleus. The spacing of the levels follows the rotational formula,

$$E_I = \frac{h^2}{2\Im} I(I + 1),$$

where $\Im$ is the effective moment of inertia. There is a steady decrease in the energy of the levels and hence a steady increase in the effective moment of

623

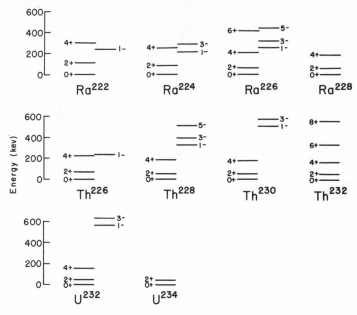

FIG. 8.1. System of levels up to 600 keV of excitation observed in nuclei produced by the decay of isotopes of thorium, protactinium, or uranium. Only observed levels are shown. In the case of Th^{232}, the level scheme was obtained from Coulombic excitation experiments. This figure is meant to show the great regularity in the observed levels, all of which are interpreted as rotational excitation of the $0+$ ground state and of a $1-$ vibrational state.

inertia as the mass number increases from 222 to 234. At mass number 232 the value of $\hbar^2/2\mathfrak{J}$ is about 7.5 keV and this value prevails nearly unchanged throughout the whole transuranium element group of even-even nuclei. Such nuclei are strongly stabilized in a deformed shape. In the case of the lightest nuclei here considered $\hbar^2/2\mathfrak{J}$ is about 15–20 keV. These nuclei may be just barely stabilized in a non-spherical shape.

The various features of the ground state rotational band, which are discussed fully in Chapter 3, are observed in the cases under discussion here. For example, the pattern of gamma ray de-excitation is in every case a series of $E2$ cascade transitions. The spectrum of α-groups of an even-even emitter which leads to such a band reflects this regularity. The most prominent alpha group is that leading to the ground state and has an intensity of about 70 per cent. About 30 per cent of the transitions populate the first-excited $(2+)$ state. Higher lying states are populated in very small intensity, in large part because of the sensitive dependence of the lifetime upon the available energy for α-decay but also because of other effects discussed in Chapter 4.

The only other states lying below about 600 keV comprise a negative-parity group for which the spin sequence is 1, 3, 5.   Much of the evidence as cited in Chapter 3 suggests that the base state represents an octupole vibration of the ground state.   The higher members behave like a rotational band, a common feature of which is the $I(I + 1)$ dependence of the level spacing. The energy of excitation above the ground state at which the 1− state lies varies considerably from nucleus to nucleus, a feature which has not yet been explained.

The groups of states so far mentioned stand out clearly in studies of the α-decay of the parent even-even nuclei.   Study of β-unstable odd-odd nuclei have extended this picture considerably.   In general, these odd-odd nuclei do not populate directly these low-lying states but rather others which lie at about 1 MeV of excitation.   This follows probably from the statistical fact that an unpaired neutron and unpaired proton are not likely to define a configuration closely allied to the ground state structure of an even-even nucleus.   The unified model of the nucleus suggests that one may expect to find a number of different vibrational modes appearing as energy levels at about 1 MeV.   These are discussed in Chapter 3 and examples will be found in the discussion of individual decay schemes in the present chapter.   (See, for example, the electron-capture decay of Pa^{228} from which much has been learned of the level structure of Th^{228}.)

When we consider the energy levels of those nuclei which have unpaired neutrons and protons, the picture is far less clear.   The spectra are quite complex and an adequate amount of experimental nuclear spectroscopy has not been done.   It is also likely that the region will prove difficult to analyze theoretically as is the case in other regions where the nuclear potential is neither strongly spherical nor strongly axial.   There is some reason to believe, however, that a number of the nuclei considered here can still be treated by a modification of Nilsson orbital treatment.   There is growing evidence that part of the complexity can be removed by postulating pairs of rotational bands of opposite parity related to the same particle configuration in the same sense that the low-lying 1− states in the even-even nuclei are related to the ground states.

8.2 THE ISOTOPES OF THORIUM

8.2.1 *Thorium-223*

This isotope is a member of the U^{227} collateral series (see Section 7.2.8) and the only information available on its properties is that it emits alpha particles with an energy of 7.55 ± 0.1 MeV.[2]   The half-life, as measured by TOVE,[1] is 0.9 ± 0.1 seconds.

---

[1] P. A. Tove, *Arkiv. Fysik.* **13**, 549 (1958).

8.2.2 *Thorium-224*

This isotope is a member of the U^{228} collateral series. (See Section 7.2.7.) The first measurements on Th^{224} were made by MEINKE, GHIORSO, AND SEABORG[2] who reported the emission of 7.13 MeV alpha particles. They estimated a half-life of 1 second from systematic trends in alpha decay half-lives. TOVE[1] measured a half-life of 1.05 ± 0.05 sec by an electronic technique. Later work by RUIZ, ASARO, AND PERLMAN[3] led to the construction

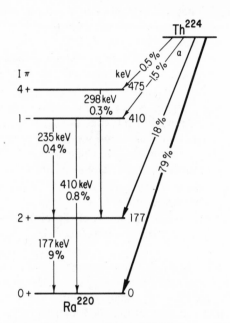

FIG. **8.2.** Decay scheme of Th[224].

of the decay scheme shown in Fig. 8.2. The energy of the most energetic alpha group is 7.17 ± 0.01 MeV as measured in an ionization chamber. Other data on the alpha particles is summarized in Table 7.9.

8.2.3 *Thorium-225*

This isotope is a member of the U^{229} collateral series discussed in Section 7.2.6 of the previous chapter.[2] It decays with a half-life of 8.0 ± 0.5 minutes. Approximately 5 per cent of total disintegrations go by orbital electron capture and the remainder by alpha emission. Ten alpha groups are listed

---

[2] W. W. Meinke, A. Ghiorso, and G. T. Seaborg, *Phys. Rev.* **85**, 429 (1952); *Phys. Rev.* **81**, 782 (1951).

[3] C. P. Ruiz, F. Asaro, and I. Perlman, unpublished results, 1961; see C. P. Ruiz, Ph.D. thesis, *Univ. Calif. Rad. Lab. Report, UCRL-9511*, April 1961.

in Table 7.8 in Section 7.2.6.[3]   Gamma rays with energies of 90, 246, 322, 362, 450 and 490 KeV have been identified.[3]   Some of these have been placed in a decay scheme with the aid of alpha-gamma coincidence experiments but, because of the experimental difficulties, the decay scheme is incompletely known.

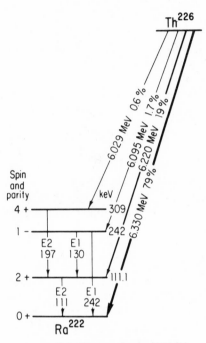

FIG. **8.3**. Decay scheme of Th[226].

8.2.4 *Thorium-226*

This isotope is a member of the Pa[230] collateral series[4] (see Section 7.2.1). It is an alpha emitter with a half-life of 30.9 minutes. The alpha spectrum as measured by ASARO AND PERLMAN[5] consists of four groups as indicated in the decay scheme of Fig. 8.3. Examination of the gamma ray spectrum with a scintillation crystal spectrometer[5] showed gamma rays of energy 112, 130, 197, and 242 keV belonging to Th[226]. Other gamma radiations present in the sample were due to short-lived daughter activities. Gamma-gamma coincidence studies showed that the 112 keV gamma ray was in coincidence with the 130 and the 197 keV gamma rays but not with the 242 keV radiation.

[4] M. H. Studier and E. K. Hyde, *Phys. Rev.* **74**, 591 (1948).
[5] F. Asaro and I. Perlman, *Phys. Rev.* **104**, 91 (1956).

All the alpha particle and gamma ray data on energies and abundances fit neatly the decay scheme shown in Fig. 8.3. The prominent 112 keV radiation was characterized as an electric quadrupole transition by its conversion coefficient,[5] and its high conversion in the L_{II}, L_{III}, M_{II}, and M_{III} shells,[6] and its angular correlation with the alpha particles leading to the state. SMITH, ASARO, AND HOLLANDER[6] report a more precise energy value of 111.1 ± 0.3 keV.

STROMINGER[7] performed alpha-gamma coincidence experiments which established that the 112, 197, and 242 keV gamma rays were emitted within a period of less than 1.4×10^{-9} seconds.

The $1-$ assignment of the 242 keV state was made definite by the alpha-gamma angular correlation experiments of STEPHENS, ASARO, AND PERLMAN[8] who found a clear correlation of the type predicted for the sequence:

$$0^+ \xrightarrow{\alpha} 1^- \xrightarrow{\gamma} 0^+$$

All the levels seen in the decay of Th^{226} are clearly assignable to collective modes of motion of the nucleus. The $0+$, $2+$, $4+$ sequence and the $1-$ state seen in this instance are of similar origin to comparable states seen in the decay of Th^{228}, Th^{230}, U^{230} and other even-even nuclei in this mass region.

8.2.5 *Thorium-227* (*Radioactinium*)

Radioactinium, the direct decay product of actinium, was found by HAHN[9] in 1906. HAHN was led to this discovery by noting that the regrowth of actinium X into an actinium sample freed from actinium X was much less rapid than was to be expected if actinium were transformed directly into this activity. This observation suggested the existence of an intermediate activity whose half-life HAHN found to be 19.5 days.

Growth curves showing the relationship of radioactinium to its parent, Ac^{227}, and to its descendants appear in Chapter 6. (See Fig. 6.40 and 6.41.)

Radioactinium is an alpha emitter whose half-life according to a recent redetermination is 18.17 days.[10] The alpha spectrum is exceedingly complex. Already in studies summarized by LEWIS AND BOWDEN[11] in 1934, eleven distinct alpha groups had been found. ROSENBLUM, VALADARES, PEREY, AND GUILLOT[12] restudied the spectrum in 1952 and obtained a

[6] W. G. Smith, F. Asaro, and J. M. Hollander, *Phys. Rev.* **104**, 99 (1956).

[7] D. Strominger, *Univ. Calif. Rad. Lab. Report, UCRL-3374* (1956).

[8] F. Stephens, Jr., F. Asaro, and I. Perlman, *Phys. Rev.* **96**, 1568 (1954).

[9] O. Hahn, *Phil. Mag.* (6) **12**, 244, 1906; **13**, 165 (1907); *Ber. D. Chem. Ges.* **39**, 1605 (1906).

[10] G. R. Hagee, M. L. Curtis, and G. R. Grove, *Phys. Rev.* **96**, 817A (1954).

[11] W. B. Lewis and B. V. Bowden, *Proc. Roy. Soc.* (London) **145A**, 235 (1934).

[12] S. Rosenblum, M. Valadares, M. Perey, and M. Guillot as quoted in Table of Isotopes, Hollander, Perlman, and Seaborg, *Rev. Mod. Phys.* **25**, Number 2, 1953.

somewhat revised list of energies and intensities.   The alpha spectroscopy of
radioactinium is complicated by the close spacings of the groups and by the
rapid ingrowth of the daughter, Ra^{223}, which also has a complex alpha
spectrum in the same energy region.   Later measurements were made by
HUMMEL[13] and by PILGER.[14]   We show the spectrum obtained by the latter
in Fig. 8.4 and list his results in Table 8.1.   Pilger confirmed the main

TABLE **8.1.** The alpha groups of radioactinium (Th^{227}).

Energy (MeV)	Decay energy to ground	Abundance (per cent)
6.036*	0.0	23
6.007	30.0	2.8
5.976	61.5	24
5.958	79.9	3.5
5.914	124.2	0.9
5.865	174.4	3.0
5.805	234.9	1.0
5.793	247.1	0.3
5.761	280.0	0.3
5.755	286.1	21
5.712	329.8	5.0
5.708	334.2	8.7
5.699	342.6	4.0
5.692	350.4	1.5
5.667	376.0	1.9

*Based on 6.110 MeV energy for $Cm^{242}\alpha_0$
Results of R. Pilger
Q value $= 6.218$

features of the spectrum reported by the ROSENBLUM group and found
additional groups through higher resolution techniques.   In all, he reported
fifteen alpha groups.   Such a complex spectrum is possible because a large
number of excited levels are present in the daughter nucleus in the 0–400
kilovolt region and because alpha decay is for some reason highly hindered
to the lowest-lying levels.

Since the alpha decay of Th^{227} leaves an appreciable number of daughter
Ra^{223} atoms in 15 different excited states, it is quite understandable that the
gamma ray and conversion electron spectrum of Th^{227} should be exceedingly
complex.   FRILLEY[15] reported nine gamma rays from studies made with a

---

[13] J. P. Hummel, thesis, University of California 1956; also printed as *Univ. Calif.
Rad. Lab. Report UCRL-3456*, July 1956.

[14] R. C. Pilger, Jr., thesis, University of California 1957; also printed as *Univ. Calif.
Rad. Lab. Report UCRL-3877*, July 1957.

[15] M. Frilley, *J. Phys. Rad.* **1**, 34 (1940).

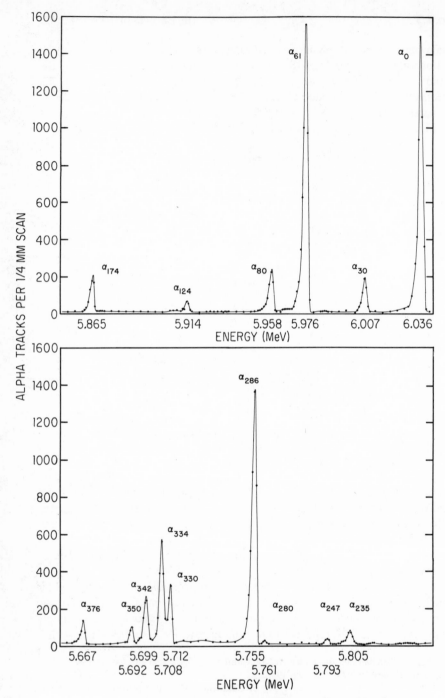

FIG. **8.4.** Alpha decay of radioactinium. The alpha spectrum as recorded photographically in a magnetic spectrograph of high resolution by PILGER.[14]

crystal spectrometer.   In later studies of the conversion electrons FRILLEY, ROSENBLUM, VALADARES, AND BOUISSIÈRES[16] found evidence for 14 gamma rays between 30 and 335 kilovolts energy.   PILGER recorded over 140 conversion electrons corresponding to more than 26 gamma rays lying in this same range of energies.   The energies and intensities of these gamma rays are listed in Table 8.2.

TABLE **8.2.** Internal transitions in decay of Th^{227}.

Energy (keV)	Intensity (per cent)	Multipolarity
29.8	27	$M1–E2$
31.6	12	$M1–E2$
48.2	2.7	$E2$
50.0	13.6	$E1(M2)$
61.3	9.0	$E2$
79.7	4.6	$E1$
100.1	1.0	$E2$
113.0	4.2	$E2$
173.3	~1	$E2$
205.0	0.4	$M1$
234.9	2.0	$M1$
236.1	10.6	$E1$
247.7	weak	$(E2?)$
250.3		$M1$[a]
256.4	7.1	$E2$
280.0		$M1$[a]
281.8	~2	$M1–E2?$
286.1	1.5	$M1$
289.7	~0.9	$E2?$
296.8	~2.5	$E2$
300.0	~1	$E2?$
304.5	~2	$M1(E2)?$
312.7	3.5	$E2$
329.7	1.6	$E2$
334.3	5.2	$E2$

[a] An $E1$ of the same energy probably also exists.
Data of PILGER[14]

PILGER[14] has constructed the decay scheme shown in Fig. 8.5.   Even with the precise knowledge of 15 excited levels of Ra^{223} given by the alpha groups all of the known gamma ray transitions cannot be placed with certainty in the decay scheme.   From the viewpoint of the unified model of nuclear structure, the daughter isotope Ra^{223} lies in a transition group of

[16] M. Frilley, S. Rosenblum, M. Valadares, and G. Bouissières, *J. Phys. Rad.* **16,** 378 (1955); *J. Phys. Rad.* **15,** 45 (1954).

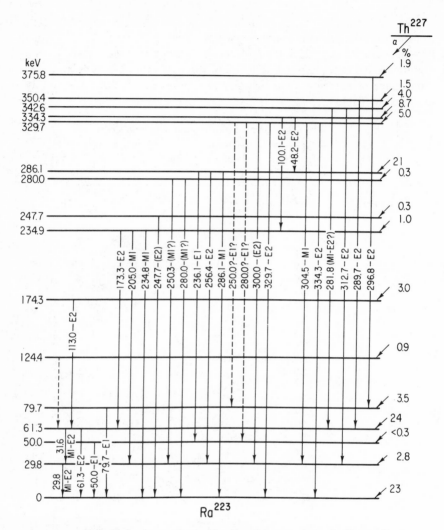

FIG. **8.5**. Alpha decay scheme of radioactinium as drawn by PILGER.[14]

nuclei between the strongly deformed transthorium nuclei, which show well-developed rotational bands, and the nuclei lying close to the double closed shell at Pb^{208}. It is difficult to classify nuclear levels in nuclei such as Ra^{223} which belong to this transition group. There is some evidence for rotational levels based on the ground state but the evidence is not conclusive.

PETIT[17,18] measured the angular distribution of the 236 keV γ-ray around

[17] G. Y. Petit, *J. Phys. Rad.* **21**, 447 (1960).

[18] F. Bragança, R. Foucher, and G. Y. Petit, *J. Phys. Rad.* **22**, 289 (1961).

a direction defined by time-coincident alpha particles and the angular distribution of the coincident 236 and 50 keV gamma rays. The study led to spin and parity assignments of 3/2+ and 1/2+ to the ground states of Th^{227} and Ra^{223}, respectively, and of 3/2+ and 3/2− to excited states at 286 keV and 50 keV in Ra^{223}.

8.2.6 Thorium-228 (Radiothorium)

Thorium-228 is a beta-stable alpha-emitter with a half-life[19] of 1.910 years occurring in nature as a member of the Th^{232} family. Its position in that family is discussed in Section 6.3 of Chapter 6. In the older literature of natural radioactivity thorium-228 bears the name radiothorium (symbol RdTh).

Isotopically-pure samples of Th^{228} can be prepared from thorium ores or aged thorium compounds by isolating Ra^{228} (mesothorium 1) and allowing Th^{228} to grow into the separated radium. For the success of this method the original radium-thorium separation must be exceptionally good. Thorium-228 may also be isolated from a U^{232} sample which has stood for some time; if the U^{232} is mixed with U^{233} there will be some contamination of the thorium daughter fraction with 7340 year Th^{229}. A third source of Th^{228} is the irradiation of radium or actinium with an intense flux of neutrons.[19]

$$Ra^{226} (n, \gamma) Ra^{227} \qquad Ra^{227} \xrightarrow[41 \text{ min}]{\beta^-} Ac^{227}$$
$$\sigma = 18 \text{ barns}$$

$$Ac^{227} (n, \gamma) Ac^{228} \qquad Ac^{228} \xrightarrow[6.13 \text{ hr}]{\beta^-} Th^{228}$$
$$\sigma = 495 \text{ barns}$$

The amount of contamination of the Th^{228} with the 18 day Th^{227} daughter of actinium depends on the neutron flux and the time elapsed between the pre- and post-bombardment separation of actinium and thorium.

The decay of Th^{228} to Ra^{224} is rather well known. The alpha spectrum has been studied in some detail with a magnetic spectrograph[20-22] and several groups have measured the gamma-ray and conversion electron spectra.[22-26] The results of the most recent and thorough study are summarized in the decay scheme shown in the Fig. 8.6.

[19] H. W. Kirby, G. R. Grove, and D. L. Timma, Phys. Rev. 102, 1140 (1956).
[20] S. Rosenblum, M. Valadares, and M. Perey, Compt. Rend. 228, 385 (1949).
[21] F. Asaro, F. S. Stephens, and I. Perlman, Phys. Rev. 92, 1495 (1953).
[22] F. S. Stephens, F. Asaro, and I. Perlman, Phys. Rev. 107, 1091 (1957).
[23] S. Rosenblum, M. Valadares, and M. Guillot, J. Phys. Rad. 15, 129 (1954).
[24] J. O. Newton and B. Rose, Phil. Mag. 45, 58 (1954).
[25] F. Demichelis and B. Chinaglia, Atti Acad. Nazl Lincei Rend. Classe Sci. Fis. mat. e nat. 22, 613 (1957).
[26] G. Bouissières, et al., Compt. Rend. 236, 1874 (1953).

Five alpha groups of Th^{228} have been identified, having energies and intensities as follows: 5.421 MeV (71%), 5.338 MeV (28%), 5.208 MeV (0.4%), 5.173 MeV (0.2%), and 5.137 MeV (0.03%). An upper limit of 0.01 per cent has been set on the intensity of any lower energy alpha groups. The positions of these groups in the decay scheme are indicated in Fig. 8.6.

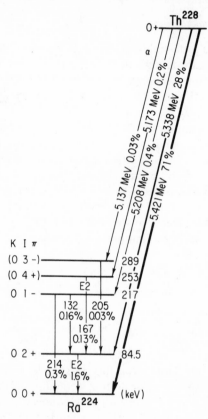

FIG. **8.6.** Decay scheme of Th^{228}. (Gamma intensity figures refer to photon intensities.)

The gamma-ray spectrum of Th^{228} is well known and the results are summarized as follows: 84 keV (1.6%), 132 keV (0.16%), 167 keV (0.13%), 205 keV (0.03%), and 214 keV (0.30%). The intensity of any gamma ray of energy greater than 275 keV has been shown to be less than 0.001 per cent. Coincidence measurements have established that the 132, 167, and 205 keV transitions are all in coincidence with the 84 keV transition. The placement of the gamma rays in the decay scheme is very straightforward. The agreement between the alpha-particle and gamma-ray spectra is unusually good in this case. In addition, the L conversion lines of the 84 keV transition have been studied and these indicate rather conclusively that this transition is $E2$. The total conversion coefficient of this gamma ray supports this assignment and the lifetime of the 84 keV level, which has been measured as 7.6×10^{-10} seconds[27] falls in line with other enhanced $E2$ transitions between members of a rotational band.

Radium-224, the daughter of Th^{228} alpha decay, lies on the edge of the region of nuclei in the heavy elements that have stable spheroidal deformations. This region extends from mass number approximately 220 up to the heaviest elements yet discovered. The fact that Ra^{224} lies just within this region means that a rotational band based on the ground state is still present, but that the equation

$$E_I = \frac{\hbar^2}{2\mathfrak{J}} I(I + 1)$$

is no longer exactly valid. The ground state rotational band in Ra^{224} is apparent in Fig. 8.6, the $2+$ and $4+$ members lying at energies 84.5 and 253 keV, respectively. The $4+$ assignment of the 253 keV level cannot be considered certain, but seems very likely because (1) the 167 keV gamma ray appears to be $E2$ from its total conversion coefficient, (2) there is no crossover transition from the 253 keV level to ground, and (3) the systematics of other even-even nuclei in this region strongly suggest a $4+$ level at approximately this energy. The value of $\hbar^2/2\mathfrak{J}$ in the equation above, as calculated from the energy of the 84.5 keV level, is 14.1 keV. This is considerably larger than is found for nuclei located well within the heavy-element spheroidal region, where $\hbar^2/2\mathfrak{J}$ is nearly constant and equal to ~ 7 keV. The larger value $\hbar^2/2\mathfrak{J}$ for Ra^{224} indicates a smaller moment of inertia, $\mathfrak{J}$, which presumably is the case because the spheroidal deformation is not so large as it becomes for heavier nuclei. If one uses the value of 14.1 keV for $\hbar^2/2\mathfrak{J}$ and calculates the energy of the $I = 4$ member of the band, this energy is 282 keV, almost 30 keV larger than is found. This deviation from the calculated value is characteristic for nuclei near the edge of regions of spheroidal deformation and in such regions higher terms must be added to the equation above. The second term $BI^2(I + 1)^2$, where B is a constant, will necessarily give agreement with the data on Ra^{224}, since only two energy spacings are known. In cases where more levels are seen, it is sometimes also necessary to add a third term.

Of the two remaining levels in Ra^{224}, the one at 217 keV has been assigned spin and parity $1-$, with a K value of 0. The spin and parity assignments are made on the basis of conversion coefficient arguments and angular correlation data. The earlier conversion coefficient arguments are simply that the sum of the intensities of the 214 and 132 keV gamma rays is

---

[27] Bell, Bjørnholm, and Severiens, *Dan. Mat.-fys. Medd.* **32**, No. 12 (1960).

0.46 per cent, and when this is compared with the alpha population of the 217 keV level, 0.4 per cent, it is clear that the conversion coefficients of the gamma rays must be quite small. On this basis it was argued that the gamma rays are very likely $E1$, and since one of them terminates at the ground, $0+$, level, the spin of the 217 keV level must be $1-$. The angular correlation data[28] are more definite and show unambiguously that the spin is 1; and an odd state populated directly by alpha decay must have odd parity. The assignment of the K value as 0 is made because the ratio of the intensities of the two gamma rays de-exciting the level is that predicted by the collective model of the nucleus if $K = 0$. The model demands that the ratio of the reduced transition probabilities for the $E1$ transitions to the $0+$ state and to the $2+$ state, respectively, should be 2 if $K = 1$ and 0.5 if $K = 0$. The observed value is 0.44, rather clearly indicating a K value of 0. A number of such $1-$ ($K = 0$) levels have been found at low excitation energies in just this region of the periodic table. It so happens that the 217 keV level in Ra^{224} is the lowest energy at which such a state is known to occur. These states are generally ascribed to octupole vibrations of the nucleus, but why they occur at such low energies only in the region of radium is not yet fully understood. It is interesting to note that this state receives most of the electron capture decay of Ac^{224} (see Section 7.2.2 in Chap. 7).

The level at 289 keV in Ra^{224} has been suggested to have spin and parity $3-$ by the following reasoning. A comparison of the intensity of the 205 keV photons with the alpha population to the 289 keV state shows that the conversion coefficient of this transition must be very small and therefore the probable assignment is $E1$ ($E2$ is also possible). If the $E1$ assignment is correct, the spin of the 289 keV level must be $1-$, $2-$, or $3-$. A spin of $2-$ is ruled out since the state receives direct alpha population, and this is not possible from a $0+$ parent to a $2-$ final state. A spin of $1-$ seems unlikely since no cross-over transition to the ground state is observed. The spin of $3-$ is not unexpected, as the rotational band based on the $1-$ ($K = 0$) state has been found in other nuclei and is expected to have members $1-$, $3-$, $5-$,.... Thus the levels of Ra^{224} can be accounted for in terms of two rotational bands, one based on the ground state, and the other based on the $1-$ state, which, itself, is presumably due to an octupole vibration of the ground state configuration.

8.2.7 *Thorium-229*

This isotope is a member of the neptunium ($4n + 1$) series[29,30] where it appears as the daughter product of U^{233}. The discovery experiments and

[28] F. S. Stephens, F. Asaro, and I. Perlman, *Phys. Rev.* **96**, 1568 (1954).

[29] A. C. English *et al.*, *Phys. Rev.* **72**, 253 (1947).

[30] F. Hagemann, *et al.*, *Phys. Rev.* **72**, 254 (1947), a preliminary note; and *Phys. Rev.* **79**, 435 (1950).

the family relationships are discussed in Chapter 7 (see section 7.1). Thorium-229 is an alpha emitter with a half-life of 7340 years.[30]

The alpha spectrum was measured in a magnetic spectrometer of high resolution by GOL'DIN, NOVIKOVA, PIROGOVA, AND TRETYAKOV[31] and in a gridded ion chamber and in a solid state detector, both of moderate resolution, by ENGELKEMEIR AND GINDLER.[32] KOCHAROV AND CO-AUTHORS[33] also studied the α-spectrum with an ion chamber. The results of two of these studies are compared in Table 8.3. The agreement is good for the more in-

TABLE 8.3 Alpha groups of Th[229].

ENGELKEMEIR AND GINDLER (1960)				GOL'DIN AND CO-WORKERS (1959)			
E_α (keV)	Energy Ra[225] state (keV)	Intensity (per cent)	α Hindrance	E_α (keV)	Energy Ra[225] state (keV)	Intensity (per cent)	α Hindrance
>5070	—	<0.2	>9000	—	—	—	—
5051	0	8.0	220	5048	0	6.7	330
—	—	—	—	5028	20	~0.2	~10⁴
—	—	—	—	5003	45	~0.1	~10⁴
4975	77	5.6	110	4971	78	3.4	200
4966	87	5.7	90	4961	88	6.0	100
—	—	—	—	4925	125	0.25	~1000
4901	153	10.6	18	4894	156	10.7	25
4845	210	56.1	1.5	4837	214	58.2	1.5
4814	241	10.1	5.2	4806	246	11.4	7
4797	259	2.0	20	4788	264	1.0	40
4763	293	1.5	16	4751	302	1.5	20
4695	363	0.4	20	4678	376	0.4	25
4608	451	0.05	40	—	—	—	—
4480	581	0.03	8	—	—	—	—

tense groups. There appears to be a systematic difference in the calibration of the energy scale by the two laboratories since the reported values for the highest energy alpha groups differ by 3 keV and for the lowest energy groups by 17 keV.

Both research groups report preliminary studies of the complex gamma spectrum. GOL'DIN ET AL.[31] report well established transitions with energies 17.2, 42.8, 69.9, 75.5, 137.2, 156.6, 193.4, and 210.5 keV. Others are reported with less certainty at 29.1, 31.6, 56.8, 58.9, 85.0, 132.1, 154.4, 179.6,

[31] L. L. Gol'din, G. I. Novikova, N. I. Pirogova, and E. F. Tretyakov, Zhur. Eksp. Teor. Fiz. 37, 1155 (1959).

[32] D. Engelkemeir and J. Gindler, unpublished results, Argonne National Laboratory, 1960.

[33] G. E. Kocharov, A. P. Komar, G. A. Korolev, I. N. Marov, and Yu. A. Surkov, Izvest. Akad. Nauk SSSR, Ser. Fiz. 23, 855–58 (1959) July.

and 242.0 keV. ENGELKEMEIR AND GINDLER[32] report L and K x-rays and gamma-rays with energies 25.3, 27.9, 31.5, 44.3, 75.1, 86.2, 136.7, 152.4, 193.7, and 210.2. Neither group in its original study had been able to construct a detailed decay scheme, but a few features were mentioned.

The favored alpha decay proceeds to a level in Ra^{225} at 214 keV. Since the ground state of Th^{229} has spin 5/2 and the Nilsson wave function assignment 5/2+ [633], for reasons which are discussed in the U^{233} review (see Section 8.4.6), the Nilsson assignment of the 214 keV level in Ra^{225} may also be 5/2+ [633]. There is some evidence for rotational structure based on this level but the level spacing does not follow the $I(I + 1)$ rule closely. There is a compression of the rotational spacings caused by the interaction with near-lying Nilsson states of similar K value. The close spacing of Nilsson levels and the distortion of rotational spacings is observed for many nuclei in this range of mass numbers.

The alpha transition of the highest observed energy is greatly hindered and there is evidence that the true ground state transition may be even higher in energy and in hindrance. ENGELKEMEIR AND GINDLER[32] report that L_α, L_β, and L_γ x-rays are in coincidence with the 5.051 MeV alpha group. This result places the ground state of Ra^{225} at least 19 keV below the level populated by the 5.051 MeV alpha particles.

TRETYAKOV, PIROGOVA, AND GOL'DIN[34] carefully reinvestigated the conversion electron spectrum of Th^{229}, identified the transitions listed in Table 8.4, and made multipolarity assignments on the basis of K/L ratios or

TABLE **8.4.** γ-transitions between levels of Ra^{225} seen in the α-decay of Th^{229}

(TRETYAKOV, PIROGOVA, and GOL'DIN).

Energy (keV)	Intensity relative to α-decay (per cent)	Multipolarity	Energy (keV)	Intensity relative to α-decay (per cent)	Multipolarity
17.3	30	$M1$	131.9	3	
23.7	5		137.0	10	$M1$
25.3	70	$E1$	143.0	3	
32	5	$M1 + E2$	154.2	4	$M1(?)$
42.7	26	$E1$	156.5	6	$M1$
56.7	3	$M1$	179.9	0.5	
68.9	3	$M1 + E2$	193.4	16	$M1$
75.1	18	$E2$	210.7	10	$M1$
86.3	15	$M1$	217.0	0.7	
107.2	1		242.2	0.3	
124.4	12	$M1$	269	0.10	

[34] E. F. Tretyakov, N. I. Pirogova, and L. L. Gol'din, *Izvest. Akad. Nauk SSSR, Ser. Fiz.* **25**, 274 (1961).

L-subshell electron ratios. They used coincidence techniques to obtain information on alpha-electron and photon-electron coincidences. From detailed arguments, not reproduced here, which were based on a consideration of their own results and on the alpha spectrum measurements of

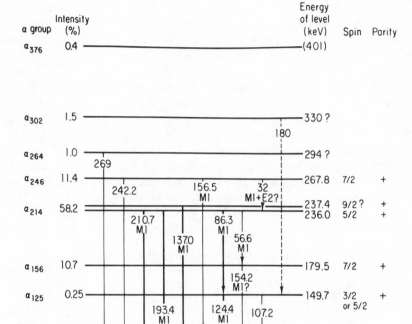

FIG. **8.7**. Scheme of the lower excited levels of Ra[225] involved in the alpha decay of Th[229]. The α-groups and intensities of Gol'din *et al.* are shown at the left of the levels. This figure is redrawn from one by TRETYAKOV, PIROGOVA, AND GOL'DIN.

GOL'DIN AND CO-WORKERS[31] these authors arrived at the tentative decay scheme shown in Fig. 8.7. In addition to the Ra[225] levels revealed in the alpha spectrum it was necessary to postulate a ground state level lying 25.3 keV lower in energy than the level populated by the most energetic of the observed alpha particles. It was also necessary to insert a pair of excited levels lying 236.0 and 237.4 keV above ground which are unresolved in the alpha spectrum.

8.2.8 Thorium-230 (Ionium)

Thorium-230 is an alpha-emitter with a half-life of 8.0×10^4 years, reported most recently as $(8.0 \pm 0.3) \times 10^4$ years[35] and $(7.52 \pm 0.16) \times 10^4$ years.[36] It is a member of the naturally occurring U^{238} family (see Section 6.2 of Chapter 6), and may be prepared simply by separation from uranium ores. For samples of high isotopic purity, however, the Th^{230} must be mass separated from the Th^{232} impurities present in the ores. Owing to the low specific activity of Th^{230}, high-resolution alpha-particle and conversion-electron spectroscopy have been difficult. Nevertheless the decay scheme has received rather extensive study, and is, for the most part, well established.

The alpha-particle spectrum of Th^{230} has been studied by several groups[37-40] using both magnetic spectrographs and ionization chambers. There is not complete agreement among the experiments at the present time; however, at least four alpha groups seem to be clearly established. These have energies and intensities as follows: 4.682 MeV (76%), 4.615 MeV (24%), 4.476 MeV (0.12%), and 4.437 MeV (0.03%). (See Table 8.5.) The

TABLE 8.5. Alpha groups of Th^{230} (Ionium).

Alpha particle energy* (MeV)	Alpha intensity (per cent)	Alpha decay hindrance factor	Final state	
			Energy (keV)	spin and parity
4.682	76	(1)	0	0+
4.615	24	1.1	67.76	2+
4.476	0.12	12	210	4+
4.437	0.03	38	253	1−
(4.368)	0.001	370	320	3−
(4.273)	$\sim 5 \times 10^{-6}$	8200	416	6+
(4.245)	$\sim 5 \times 10^{-6}$	4900	445	5−

* Alpha groups in parentheses were detected only indirectly via γ-ray measurements.[42]

[35] E. K. Hyde, National Nuclear Energy Series—Plutonium Project Record "The Transuranium Elements" (New York: McGraw-Hill Book Co.). 14B, 1435 (1949).

[36] R. W. Attree, M. J. Cabell, R. L. Cushing, and J. J. Pieroni, Can. J. Phys. 40, 194 (1962).

[37] G. Valladas and R. Bernas, Compt. Rend. 236, 2230 (1953).

[38] S. Rosenblum, M. Valadares, and J. Vial, Compt. Rend. 227, 1088 (1948).

[39] S. Rosenblum, M. Valadares, J. Blandin-Vial, and R. Bernas, Compt. Rend. 238, 1496 (1954).

[40] J. P. Hummel, Ph.D. Thesis, UCRL-3456 (July 1956).

placement of these groups in the decay scheme is indicated in Fig. 8.8 by the solid lines. The dashed lines indicate alpha groups inferred from the gamma ray studies.

Eight gamma rays accompanying Th^{230} decay have been found from studies of the singles gamma-ray spectrum and the gamma-gamma coincidences.[41–44] The gamma rays as given in one of the most recent

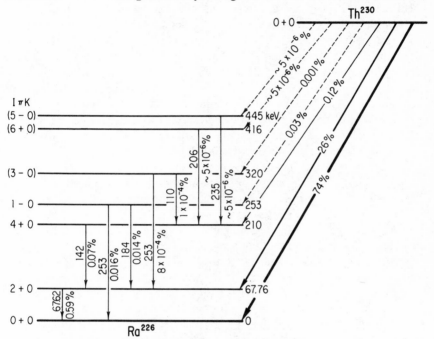

FIG. 8.8. Decay scheme of Th[230] (ionium) as drawn by STEPHENS, ASARO, AND PERLMAN. Note that the observed levels of Pa[226] are interpreted as a rotational band with 0+, 2+, 4+, and 6+ spin states based on an $I = 0$, $K = 0$ ground state and a second rotational band with 1−, 3−, and 5− spin states based on an $I = 1$, $K = 0$ fundamental state. (Gamma ray intensity figures are photon intensities.)

studies[42] are: 68 keV (0.59%), 110 keV (1×10^{-4}%), 142 keV (0.07%), 184 keV (1.4×10^{-2}%), 206 keV ($\sim 5 \times 10^{-6}$%), 235 keV ($\sim 5 \times 10^{-6}$%), and two gamma rays of 253 keV having intensities of 1.7×10^{-2}% and $\sim 8 \times 10^{-4}$%. An upper limit of 7×10^{-6}% has been set on any radiations between 300 and 700 keV. Of the observed gamma rays, only four can be seen in the singles spectrum. These have energies of 68, 142, 184, and

[41] S. Rosenblum, M. Valadares, and R. Bernas, *Compt. Rend.* **239**, 759 (1954).
[42] F. S. Stephens, F. Asaro, and I. Perlman, *Phys. Rev.* **107**, 1091 (1957).
[43] E. Booth, L. Madansky, and F. Rasetti, *Phys. Rev.* **102**, 800 (1956).
[44] F. Rasetti and E. C. Booth, *Phys. Rev.* **91**, 315 (1953).

253 keV. It was further shown that of these the 142 and 184 keV transitions are in coincidence with the one of 68 keV. These four gamma rays can easily be fitted into the decay scheme established by the alpha spectrum as shown in the Fig. 8.8. Next it was shown that some of the 253 keV photons were in coincidence with a 68 keV transition, indicating a new level at 320 keV. An experiment aimed at deciding whether (1) another gamma ray of 253 keV was present in coincidence with the established 68 keV transition, or (2) another 68 keV gamma ray was present in coincidence with the established 253 keV transition, indicated that the former, (1), is probably the correct situation. Thus the second 253 keV transition is characterized. A 110 keV transition in coincidence with the 142 keV gamma ray was also found to de-excite the new 320 keV level. Finally, also in coincidence with the 142 keV gamma ray two very low intensity transitions of energy 206 and 235 keV were found. These were interpreted as establishing the levels at 416 and 445 keV. The reasoning behind these placements of the two weak transitions is discussed in more detail below.

Only the 68 keV transition has been seen in the conversion electron spectrum of Th^{230}.[41] The energy of this transition has been placed as 67.7 keV from these studies and, also, since the conversion was found to be principally in the L_{II} and L_{III} subshells, an $E2$ assignment can be made. This assignment is confirmed by the total conversion coefficient of the transition (found by comparing the 68 keV photon intensity with the alpha population to the 68 keV level)[43] and by the lifetime of the 68 keV level, which has been measured to be 6.3×10^{-10} sec.[45] Thus the 68 keV level must have spin and parity assignments $2+$, as is found generally for the first excited state of an even-even nucleus.

As is indicated in Fig. 8.8, the levels of Ra^{226} have been interpreted in terms of two rotational bands based on the ground, $0+$, state and the $1-$ state. In the ground state band, spins of $2+$ and $4+$ have been clearly established for the 67.7 and 210 keV levels. This has been done by a combination of conversion coefficient and angular distribution arguments.[43,46-48] Both gamma-gamma and alpha-gamma angular distribution measurements have been made to establish the spin of the 210 keV level, and this assignment is one of the few that is well established for the third member of the ground state rotational band. In many other cases the spin assignment of this level rests largely on the agreement with the expected spacing of states in a rotational band Bohr-Mottelson formula. The assignment of the $6+$ member of the ground state band is by no means so clearly established. Here the arguments are (1) the decay to the $4+$ state and to no other is consistent with a

[45] H. Vartapetian and R. Foucher, *Compt. Rend.* **246**, 939 (1958).
[46] G. M. Temmer and J. M. Wyckoff, *Phys. Rev.* **92**, 913 (1953).
[47] Valladas, Teillac, Falk-Viarant, and Benoist, *J. Phys. Rad.* **16**, 125 (1955).
[48] Asaro, Stephens, and Perlman, unpublished data.

spin of 6+, and (2) the systematic trends in energy levels of other even-even nuclei in this region suggest that there should be a 6+ level in Ra^{226} at about this energy. These arguments are model dependent and the parentheses around the spin in Fig. 8.8 indicate the absence of independent proof.

Because Ra^{226} lies rather near the edge of the region of spheroidal nuclei in the heavy elements significant deviations occur from the $I(I + 1)$ energy dependence. In order to fit the three spacings as observed, a second term, $BI^2(I + 1)^2$, and a third term $CI^3(I + 1)^3$ must be added to the leading term. In this case the constants $\hbar^2/2\mathfrak{J}$, B, and C may be evaluated to be: 11.74 ± 0.10 keV, 0.080 ± 0.010 keV, and 0.00085 ± 0.00025 keV, respectively. Since there are only three spacings, it is necessary that three constants will fit the experimental data, and the fit obtained indicates nothing about the physical validity of such an expansion in terms of powers of $I(I + 1)$.

The level in Ra^{226} at 253 keV has been shown to have spin and parity 1−, and a K value of zero. The 1− assignment is based on angular distribution measurements (the $0+ \xrightarrow{\alpha} 1- \xrightarrow{\gamma} 0+$ pattern is very distinctive) and is quite conclusive.[49] The $K = 0$ assignment is made because the reduced transition probability of the transition from this level to the 0+ state divided by that to the 2+ state is 0.47. The unified model predicts a value of 2 for this ratio if $K = 1$ and 0.5 if $K = 0$. A number of such low-lying 1− ($K = 0$) states have been found in this region of the periodic table, and they are generally ascribed to octupole vibrations of the ground state configuration.

The 3− and 5− spin assignments (both with $K = 0$) are tentative and are based on the facts that (1) the decay of the levels is consistent with these assignments, (2) even spin states with odd parity could not receive direct alpha decay from a 0+ parent, and (3) such levels are expected to be present as rotational band members based on the 1− ($K = 0$) state. The $K = 0$ assignment for the 3− level is supported by the ratio of reduced transition probabilities (assuming the transitions to be $E1$) to the 2+ and 4+ levels, respectively, experimentally 0.7, and theoretically 0.75. The low limit set on the abundance of the possible (320 keV) crossover transition from this level to the ground state effectively rules out any spin lower than 3 for this level. Because of the small energy difference between the assigned 5− and 6+, one expects to see only the 5− →4+ transition if $K = 0$, as is observed.

If the 320 and 445 keV levels do, indeed, comprise the rotational band based on the 1− state, this band has two interesting features. First, the value of $\hbar^2/2\mathfrak{J}$ is 6.7 keV for this band compared with 11.7 keV for the ground state band, and second, there is no significant deviation from $I(I + 1)$ dependence, compared with large deviations for the ground state band. Both of these features can possibly be explained by a rather large mixing of this

[49] P. Falk-Vairant and G. Petit, *Compt. Rend.* **240**, 296 (1955).

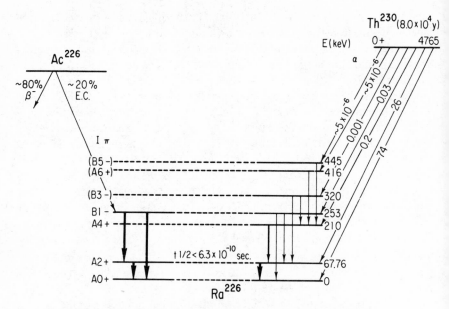

FIG. 8.9. Levels of Pa[226] observed in the electron capture decay of Ac[226] and the alpha decay of Th[230] (ionium). The vertical arrows representing the experimentally observed gamma transitions indicate qualitatively by their width the relative transition intensities. In the Ac[226] decay scheme, the Ra[226] levels are dotted except for those which have been found in the decay of Ac[226].

$I = 1$, $K = 0$ band with the other expected octupole vibrational bands, specifically in this case with the $I = 1$, $K = 1$ band. It will be interesting to see if such $K \neq 0$ octupole bands occur systematically in the even-even nuclei of this region.

The $1-$ level of Ra[226] plays a prominent role in the electron capture decay of Ac[226]. This is illustrated in Figure 8.9. A study of the decay of Ac[226] has helped to confirm the assignment of the level at 253 keV.[50]

8.2.9 Thorium-231 and Uranium-231

Thorium-231, a beta-emitter of 25.6 hours half-life, is well known as the "UY" of classical radioactivity, the immediate decay product of U[235]. Its early history and its relationship to the U[235] decay chain are discussed in Chapter 6. Thorium-231 can be isolated from U[235] sources (preferably enriched U[235] sources) or it can be conveniently made by the neutron irradiation of ionium.

$$Th^{230}(n, \gamma)Th^{231}$$

---

[50] F. S. Stephens, F. Asaro, and I. Perlman, *Phys. Rev.* **100**, 1543 (1955).

The beta decay of Th^{231} has been studied by several groups. There are a number of older papers in the literature reporting the radiations of Th^{231} as determined by absorption curve methods or by nuclear spectrometers of low resolution. References to this literature are made in a paper by JAFFEY, LERNER, AND WARSHAW.[51] In recent years nuclear spectrometers of high resolution have been used to investigate the moderately complex decay of Th^{231}.[52-56] Particularly important has been the measurement of conversion electrons in permanent magnet spectrometers of 0.1 per cent resolution. The analysis of the radiations and the decay scheme given here are based chiefly on a paper by HOLLANDER, STEPHENS, ASARO, AND PERLMAN.[56] It is convenient to discuss the electron capture decay of U^{231} at the same time since both U^{231} and Th^{231} decay to the same daughter nucleus and many of the same gamma transitions in Pa^{231} are seen in the decay of both nuclides. Uranium-231 is a 4.2 day activity prepared by bombardment of Pa^{231} with deuterons, protons or helium ions.

The photons emitted by Th^{231} and U^{231} were studied[56] with a NaI scintillation detector coupled to a 50-channel pulse-height analyzer with the results shown in Table 8.6. This analysis was useful for obtaining the photon intensity of several of the important gamma rays but could not reveal the true complexity of the gamma spectrum. The permanent magnet spectrographs were able to reveal the conversion electrons of the numerous gamma rays which are also listed in Table 8.6. In the case of U^{231} a prominent spectrum of Auger electrons was seen.[56] These electron energies are listed in Table 8.7. The multipolarity assignments were made chiefly on the basis of the comparisons of the L- or M-subshell conversion electron ratios with theoretical predictions for the various multipoles. In some instances the absolute values for the conversion coefficients were used to select or to corroborate the multipolarity.

Two sodium iodide detectors were used in a coincidence arrangement to detect photons emitted within 5 microseconds of each other.[56] One important fact brought out by this work was that the 26 keV and the 84 keV transitions are *not* in coincidence with each other, and that the high energy spectra coincident with both are identical. These facts suggest that the 26 keV and the 84 keV transitions originate at the same level. This conclusion is strengthened by the finding in other coincidence experiments that the 26 keV and 84 keV have measurable and identical half-lives.

[51] A. H. Jaffey, J. Lerner, and S. Warshaw, *Phys. Rev.* **82**, 498 (1951).

[52] J. P. Mize and J. W. Starner, *Bull. Am. Phys. Soc.*, Ser. II, **1**, 171 and unpublished results (1956).

[53] M. S. Freedman, A. H. Jaffey, F. Wagner, and J. May, *Phys. Rev.* **89**, 302 (1953).

[54] D. Strominger and J. O. Rasmussen, *Phys. Rev.* **100**, 844 (1955).

[55] J. O. Juliano, *Univ. Calif. Rad. Lab. Report*, UCRL-3733, April 1957, unpublished.

[56] J. M. Hollander, F. S. Stephens, F. Asaro, and I. Perlman, "Energy Levels of Pa²³¹," unpublished information (1961).

STROMINGER AND RASMUSSEN[54] report a value of 4.1×10^{-8} seconds for this half-life while MIZE AND STARNER[52] report 4.5×10^{-8} seconds. HOLLANDER, STEPHENS, ASARO, AND PERLMAN[56] measured the half-life of the 84 keV transition in the decay of U^{231} and found a value of 4.1×10^{-8} seconds.

TABLE 8.6. Gamma transitions in decay of Th²³¹ and U²³¹.

Decay of Th²³¹					Decay of U²³¹		
Measured photon energy (keV)	Photon intensity per 100 disintegrations	Transition energy from conversion electrons (keV)	Multipole order	Total transition intensity	Measured photon energy (keV)	Photon intensity per 100 disintegrations	Transition energy from conversion electrons (keV)
17 (L x-rays		17.21			17 (L x-rays)		18.05
		18.07					
26 ± 2	12.5 ± 2	25.65	E1	73%	26	12	25.64
		58.53	E2	74%			58.54
		63.8					
		68.5					68.5
		76.1					
	{ 4 ± 2	{ 81.16	M1	10%			81.3
		82.01	M1	8%			82.1
84 ± 3	{ 7.2 ± 1	84.17	E1	23%	84	7	84.18
		89.8					
95 ± 4 (includes x-rays)	2.4 ± 0.5	99.28			93 (includes x-rays)		108.2
		{ 135.8		~0.3%			
140	0.2	146.1		~0.3%			
160	0.2	163.3	M1	1.5%			
~180	~0.06						
218 ± 3	0.05				220 ± 4	~1	
~310	0.004						

Data taken from Hollander, Stephens, Asaro, and Perlman.[56] In the case of Th²³¹ data on many of these gamma rays were reported by Mize and Starner,[52] by Freedman, Jaffey, Wagner, and May,[53] and by Baranov[57] (see Table 8.7).

Gamma-gamma coincidence measurements were made on U^{231} with K x-rays as gate pulses.[56] These revealed the 26- and 84-keV photons in abundances of about 12 and 7 per cent, respectively, per K x-ray gate pulse. The 220 keV photon was found to be in coincidence with both 26 and 84 keV radiation.

Beta-gamma measurements were made in the case of Th²³¹ decay with a double detector system consisting of an anthracene crystal and a NaI crystal.

These were useful chiefly for setting the abundance of the 25.6 keV photon as 12.5 $\pm 2\%$ of the beta decay events and, by indirect estimates, for setting the abundances of several other gamma rays. These abundance values are given in Table 8.6. Another important fact established by the beta-gamma experiments was that the highest energy beta group was in coincidence with 84 keV photons.

TABLE 8.7. Auger electrons from U^{231} decay.

KLX transitions	Energy (exp) keV
KL_IL_I	70.05
KL_IL_{II}	70.87
KL_IL_{III}	74.45
$KL_{II}L_{II}$	—
$KL_{II}L_{III}$	75.21
$KL_{III}L_{III}$	78.78
KL_IM_I	85.88
KL_IM_{II}	86.29

From Hollander, Stephens, Asaro, and Perlman.[56]

The beta spectrum of Th^{231} was studied by FREEDMAN, JAFFEY, WAGNER, AND MAY[53] who observed three beta groups: 302 keV (44%), 216 keV (11%) and 94 keV (45%). JULIANO[55] obtained a somewhat different resolution as follows: 299 keV (39%), 218 keV (33%), 134 keV (20%) and 90 keV (8%). BARANOV AND CO-WORKERS[57] reported the resolution: 302 keV (52%), 218 keV (20%), 138 keV (22%), and ~90 keV (6%).

HOLLANDER AND CO-WORKERS[56] summarized their measurements on Th^{231} and U^{231} in the decay scheme reproduced here as Fig. 8.10. This scheme differs substantially from those suggested earlier by other authors. We mention here some of the arguments regarding the placement of levels, but refer the reader to the original paper for detailed justification.

The following facts establish clearly that there are levels in Pa^{231} at 58.5 and 84.2 keV.

1. The transition sum $58.53 + 25.65 = 84.18$ is in excellent agreement with the measured crossover energy 84.17 keV.

2. The 26 and 84 keV photons have the same half-life.

3. The 58 keV has been excited in Pa^{231} target samples by the Coulombic excitation process.[58]

[57] S. A. Baranov, R. M. Polevoi, Yu. F. Rodionov, G. V. Shishkin and V. M. Shubko, *Izvest. Akad. Nauk SSSR, Ser. Fiz.* **24**, 261 (1960); *Bull. Acad. Sci. USSR, Phys. Ser.*, Columbia Translation Series, **24**, No. 3, p. 241 (1961).
[58] J. O. Newton, *Nucl. Phys.* **3**, 345 (1957); **5**, 218 (1958).

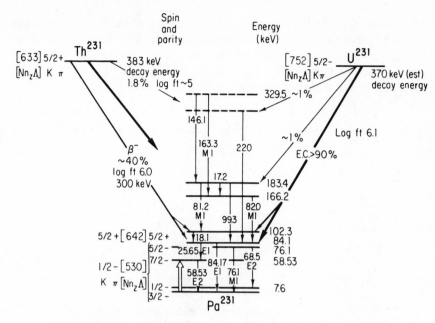

FIG. 8.10. Decay schemes of Th²³¹ and U²³¹ as drawn by HOLLANDER, STEPHENS, ASARO, AND PERLMAN. The half-lives are 25.6 hours and 4.2 days, respectively.

Three other sets of gamma energy sums were regarded as significant in the construction of the decay scheme.

$$18.07 + 81.16 = 99.23$$

$$17.21 + 82.01 = 99.22$$

$$\text{crossover} = 99.28$$

$$146.1 + 17.2 = 163.3$$

$$\text{crossover} = 163.3$$

The ground state spin of Pa²³¹ is 3/2 as measured by hyperfine structure analysis.[59]

We turn now to a discussion of the assignment of Pa²³¹ levels to Nilsson orbitals. It is convenient in this connection to examine the Nilsson diagram in which the calculated energies of single particle orbits in a spheroidal potential are plotted as a function of a nuclear eccentricity. In the case of Pa²³¹ the important Nilsson states are those available to the 91-st proton. A diagram showing the Nilsson states for proton number greater than 82 is located in Chapter 3. (See page 119.)

59 J. E. Mack, Revs. Mod. Phys. 22, 64 (1950).

The state labeled 1/2-[530] is suggested by the Nilsson diagram, and HOLLANDER, STEPHENS, ASARO, AND PERLMAN[56] select it for the ground state of Pa^{231}. When the K-quantum number is 1/2 the energies of rotational states are given by the formula

$$E_I = \frac{\hbar^2}{2\mathfrak{J}} [I(I + 1) + a(-1)^{I+1/2}(I + 1/2)]$$

where
$\mathfrak{J}$ is the effective moment of inertia
I is the spin of the state, and
a is a decoupling parameter which takes account of the partial decoupling of the $K = 1/2$ odd particle from the collective motion. This formula is discussed in Chapter 3. If a happens to be < -1 an interesting inversion of the order of rotational states can occur; the 3/2 level can drop below the 1/2, the 7/2 below the 5/2, etc. Apparently, just this situation occurs in Pa^{231} so that the ground state (with measured spin 3/2) is the 3/2 member of a $K = 1/2$ band. Similarly, the 7/2− level lies below the 5/2 level.

The same 1/2− [530] Nilsson assignment has been made to the ground state of Pa^{233} from an analysis of decay scheme data for Np^{237} (see Section 9.1.9 of Chapter 9). The same inversion occurs in the ground state rotational band of Pa^{233} so that the lowest-lying level is the state with spin 3/2. In this case also the 7/2 level lies below the 5/2 level of rotational excitation. Since Pa^{231} and Pa^{233} both have 91 protons this similarity in the lowest-lying levels is natural.

The 84.1 keV level in Pa^{231} decays by electric dipole transitions to the 3/2− ground state and the 7/2− state at 58.5 keV. Thus the 84.1 keV level has even parity and spin 5/2. An assignment of Nilsson quantum numbers to the 84 keV level is easily made since the 5/2+ [642] state lies immediately above state 1/2− [530] on the Nilsson diagram. It is consistent with this interpretation that the ground states of Np^{237} and Np^{239} with two additional protons have also the configuration 5/2+ [642].

There is no direct beta decay observed from Th^{231} to the ground state rotational band of Pa^{231} in spite of the fact that spin states 3/2, 1/2, 7/2, and 5/2 are available. This is attributed to the operation of the K-quantum number selection rule which states that ΔK must not exceed the multipolarity, ΔL, of the beta transition. The ground state assignment for Th^{231} (141 neutrons) is 5/2+ [633]. This assignment is also made to the ground state of U^{233} which also has 141 neutrons. The beta spectrum analysis given by FREEDMAN AND CO-WORKERS[53] or by JULIANO[55] cannot be reconciled in detail with the level system or transition abundances derived from the cited measurements on the gamma transitions, so the beta transitions are shown in incomplete form in Fig. 8.10.

Uranium-231 decays chiefly to the 84 keV level and/or the 102 keV level of Pa^{231} although there is a very small direct population of the upper states. Uranium-231 has 139 neutrons. The state predicted from the Nilsson diagram for the 139th neutron is 5/2− [752]; this assignment is consistent with the observed log ft value of 6.1, since the transition would be of the type forbidden ($\Delta I = 0$) unhindered.

The 84 keV transition which is found in the decay of both Th^{231} and U^{231} is worthy of special comment. It was mentioned above that the half-life of this transition has been found to be 4.1×10^{-8} seconds. This half-life is very long compared to the predictions of "single-particle" transition probability formulas. In fact, the photon retardation factor is 2.8×10^6.

TABLE **8.8**. Energies (in keV) of gamma transitions in Pa^{231} from decay of Th^{231} (BARANOV, ET AL.[57]).

β-spectrometer	Proportional counter	Scintillation spectrometer	β-spectrometer	Proportional counter	Scintillation spectrometer
(11.1)	11.0		81.2(E1)	81.0	
(17.2)	17		82.1	(82)	
(18.1)			84.2(E1)	84.1	~84
19.8	19.8		85.1		
25.6(E1)	25.6	25	89.8		
30.6	(30.6)		—	~92	
52.1	52.0	~51	95.2		
58.5(E2)	58.5		99.2	99	95.99
59.0(E2)			106.5	106.5	
62.0			135.8		(136)
63.3	(63)		145.6		145
(66.0)	(66)		163.3		163
68.5	(68)		169.2		
(73.2)			177.1		180
(76.0)					218
					~250
					~310

This E1 transition belongs to a group of E1 transitions with anomalously long half-lives which occur in the odd mass isotopes of heavy elements. In this particular case the chief part of the retardation may be attributed to violation of the selection rule in K. In other cases the retardation has been qualitatively explained in terms of violations of selection rules in the asymptotic quantum numbers N, n_z, and Λ as is discussed in Section 3.5.7 of Chapter 3. These transitions also show anomalies in the L-shell conversion coefficients. In the case of the 84 keV E1 transition in Pa^{231} the L_{III} conversion coefficient agrees with theoretical calculations, whereas the L_I and L_{II} are 21 and 15 times larger than the theoretical values. This interesting case and other similar anomalies in other $E1$ transitions are discussed critically in a paper by Asaro, Stephens, Hollander, and Perlman.[60] Another detailed study of the radiations of Th^{231} was made by Baranov, Polevoi, Rodionov, Shishkin, and Shubko.[57] They measured conversion electrons in a precision beta spectrometer and gamma ray photons in a proportional counter and a NaI scintillation spectrometer. Some of their results are summarized in Table 8.8. They determined the multipole order of 5 transitions by comparison of conversion electron coefficients with theoretical values. In these assignments they agree with those of Hollander, et al. except for the 81.2 keV transition to which they assign $E1$ instead of $M1$ character. These authors constructed a level scheme for Pa^{231} which is remarkably similar to that shown in Fig. 8.9 in the region below 110 keV and gave identical Nilsson assignments to the levels. In the region above 110 keV they made tentative assignments of more levels and of more transitions inter-connecting them. Their scheme shows levels at 139.7, 169.3, 177.1, 208, 248, 302 and 310 keV.

It is perhaps worth mentioning at this point that the levels of Pa^{231} are also involved in the alpha decay of Np^{235}. The favored alpha decay proceeds to the level at 84.2 keV. Refer to the discussion in Section 9.1.6 of Chapter 9.

8.2.10 Thorium-232

Natural thorium consists of the isotope Th^{232}. This isotope gives rise to the thorium series of radioactive isotopes which is thoroughly discussed in Chapter 6. Determinations of the half-life of thorium are quoted in Table 6.11 of that chapter. The "best value" is 1.39×10^{10} years, which corresponds to a specific activity of only 246 alpha disintegrations per minute for each milligram. The main alpha-particle group has an energy of 4.007 MeV according to the ion chamber measurements of Harvey, Jackson, Eastwood, and Hanna.[61] The intensity of the main group is about 76 per cent. A second group appears at 55–65 kilovolts lower energy in about 24 per cent abundance. Kocharov, Komar, and Korolev[62] have also observed this alpha particle group in some careful ion-chamber measurements. This result is amply confirmed by the observation[63–65] of electron tracks paired with alpha particle tracks in nuclear emulsions impregnated with thorium

[60] F. Asaro, F. S. Stephens, J. M. Hollander, and I. Perlman, *Phys. Rev.* **117**, 492 (1960).

[61] B. G. Harvey, H. G. Jackson, T. A. Eastwood, and G. C. Hanna, *Can. J. Phys.* **35**, 258 (1957).

[62] G. E. Kocharov, A. P. Komar, and G. A. Korolev, *Zhur. Eksp. Teor. Fiz.* **36**, 68 (1959); *Sov. Phys. JETP* **36** (9) 48 (1959).

[63] S. W. Peat and M. A. S. Ross, *Proc. Phys. Soc.* (London) **68A**, 923 (1955).

[64] G. Albouy, *J. Phys. Rad.* **13**, 309 (1952); *Ann. Phys.* **1**, 99 (1955).

[65] D. C. Dunlavey and G. T. Seaborg, *Phys. Rev.* **87**, 165 (1952).

salts. The electron tracks have the proper energy to be identified with the conversion of a 55 keV gamma ray. KOCHAROV, KOMAR, AND KOROLEV[62] also saw alpha particles in 0.2 ± 0.08 per cent intensity which populate a level at 185 ± 5 keV in the Ra^{228} daughter nucleus. The 60 keV level and the 185 keV levels in Ra^{228} can be assigned with some confidence to the $2+$ and $4+$ states of rotational excitation of a non-spherical ground state. Some alpha decay may occur in even smaller intensity to other levels of collective excitation of the Ra^{228} daughter but the low specific activity of thorium makes it extremely difficult to look for these low-intensity transitions.

Excited levels in Th^{232} have been produced by the Coulombic excitation process. These levels are discussed in connection with the comments on U^{236} in Section 8.4.10 below. They are also mentioned in the discussion of the Unified Model of the nucleus in Chapter 3. See Fig. 3.45.

TABLE 8.9. Gamma radiations in decay of Th233.

γ-ray energy	γ's per transition	Conversion electrons per transition
29.2	2.1%	5.9%
56.7	0	8.4%
86.9	2.7%	2.3%
171	0.7%	
195	0.3%	
253		
359		
453	1%	
590		
670	0.25%	
751		
895	0.14%	
+higher		

Unpublished results of Freedman, Engelkemeir, Porter, Wagner, and Day.[72]

Thorium-232 has an extremely long half-life for spontaneous fission. PODGURSKAYA AND CO-WORKERS[66] set a lower limit of 10^{20} years. FLEROV AND CO-WORKERS[67] later raised this limit to 10^{21} years.

8.2.11 Thorium-233

The short-lived Th^{233} is prepared by the neutron irradiation of Th^{232}. The discovery of Th^{233} is briefly described in Section 7.1 of the last chapter

---

[66] Podgurskaya, Kalashnikova, Stolyarev, Vorob'ev, and Flerov, *Zhur. Eksp. Teor. Fiz.* **28**, 503 (1955).

[67] Flerov, Klochkov, Skobkin, and Terent'ev, *Sov. Phys. Doklady* **3**, 79 (1958).

where the $4n + 1$ series of isotopes is described. The half-life is usually quoted as 23.5 minutes, but a determination by JENKINS[68] led to the value 22.12 minutes. Thorium-233 decays by emission of 1.24 MeV[69-72] beta particles directly to the ground state of Pa[233] in the majority of its disintegrations.

The work of FREEDMAN AND CO-WORKERS[72] on intense sources of Th[233] prepared in a high-flux reactor has shown that the beta spectrum is complex and that many low intensity gamma rays accompany the decay. These authors find a main beta group at 1.245 ± 0.003 MeV in somewhat less than 87 per cent abundance while the remaining beta transitions are divided among the following groups: 1.158, 1.073, 0.88, 0.79, and 0.58 MeV. In experiments using magnetic and scintillation spectrometers the gamma rays shown in Table 8.9 were found but these gamma rays have not been placed in a decay scheme. There should be some similarity in the gamma radiations of Th[233] and Np[237] since both these nuclides populate excited levels of Pa[233]. The decay scheme of Np[237] is discussed in Section 9.1.10 of Chapter 9. It can be noted that the 29.2 keV, 56.7 keV, and 86.9 keV radiations reported by FREEDMAN AND CO-WORKERS[72] in the decay of Th[233] may correspond to the de-excitation of the first two excited levels of Pa[233] which lie at 57 and 86 keV.

8.2.12 Thorium-234 and the UX₁-UX₂-UZ Complex

Thorium-234 is the daughter product of U[238] decay and is readily isolated from uranium compounds by chemical separation of a thorium fraction. It bears the classical name of UX₁. The important role it played in the history of radioactivity and its genetic relationship to the rest of the uranium family of natural radioactivities are discussed in Chapter 6. We are concerned here solely with the details of the radiations of UX₁. Because the radiations of UX₂ and UZ are almost always associated with those of UX₁ it is convenient to discuss all three activities in one place. The relationships of the members of the UX complex to each other are shown in Fig. 8.11.

Thorium-234 is a beta emitter with a half-life of 24.10 days.[73] The main group of beta particles in its spectrum has an endpoint energy of 191 keV but there is another group (complex) of about 103 keV energy. Several

[68] E. N. Jenkins, *Analyst* **80**, 301 (1955).

[69] M. E. Bunker, L. M. Langer, and R. J. D. Moffat, *Phys. Rev.* **80**, 468 (1950).

[70] W. C. Rutledge, J. M. Cork, and S. B. Burson, *Phys. Rev.* **86**, 775 (1952).

[71] B. S. Dropesky and L. M. Langer, *Phys. Rev.* **108**, 90 (1957).

[72] M. S. Freedman, D. W. Engelkemeir, F. T. Porter, F. Wagner, Jr., and P. Day, unpublished results (1957); as quoted in Strominger, Hollander, and Seaborg, *Revs. Mod. Phys.* **30**, 794 (1958).

[73] G. B. Knight and R. L. Machlin, *Phys. Rev.* **74**, 1540 (1948).

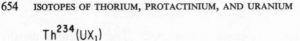

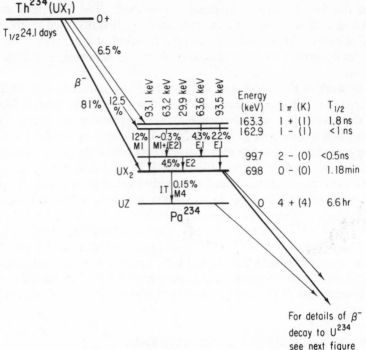

For details of β^-
decay to U^{234}
see next figure

FIG. 8.11. Decay scheme of Th²³⁴ (UX₁) based on FOUCHER, MERINIS, DE
PINHO, AND VALADARES.

determinations[74-80,89,94] of the beta spectrum are summarized in Table 8.10.
Gamma transitions with energies of 30, 63, and 93 keV have been reported
and studied by many investigators.[76-78,80,81-88] The energy values and

[74] H. Brandt and P. Sherrer, *Helv. Phys. Acta* 18, 405 (1945); *Phys. Rev.* 71, 141A (1947).
[75] P. H. Stoker, M. Heershap, and Ong Ping Hok, *Physica* 19, 433 (1953).
[76] Ong Ping Hok, J. Th. Verschoor, and P. Born, *Physica* 22, 465 (1956).
[77] M. Heershap, Ong Ping Hok, and G. J. Sizoo, *Physica* 16, 767 (1950).
[78] E. F. DeHaan, G. J. Sizoo, and P. Kramer, *Physica* 21, 803 (1955).
[79] M. G. Bouissières, Mme. N. Marty, and M. J. Teillac, *Compt. Rend.* 237, 324 (1953).
[80] S. A. E. Johansson, *Phys. Rev.* 96, 1075 (1954).
[81] H. Vartapetian, L. Dick, R. Foucher, and N. Perrin, *J. Phys. Rad.* 17, 537 (1956).
[82] R. Foucher, *Compt. Rend.* 248, 1800 (1959); *J. Phys. Rad.* 20, 508 (1959) Thèse, Paris (1961).
[83] G. T. Wood, unpublished results, Copenhagen (1960).
[84] F. S. Stephens, unpublished results, Copenhagen (1960).
[85] Ong Ping Hok, "The Beta Decay of Protactinium Isotopes," Thesis, Amsterdam (1955).
[86] J. P. Briand, *Compt. Rend.* 254, 84 (1962).
[87] A. M. Adamson, M. Duquesne, and R. Foucher, *J. Phys. Rad.* 23, 581 (1962).
[88] A. M. Adamson, Thèse, Paris (1962).

TABLE **8.10**. Beta transitions of the UX-complex.

Nuclide	HEERSHAP[77] keV	Int. (per cent)	STOKER[75] keV	Int. (per cent)	BRANDT[74] keV	Int. (per cent)	FOUCHER[89] from γ-ray intensities keV	Int. (per cent)	ONG[76] from decay scheme keV	Int. (per cent)	JOHANSSON[80] from γ-ray intensities keV	Int. (per cent)	DE HAAN[78] keV	Int. (per cent)	BJØRNHOLM[93,94] from γ-ray intensities keV	Int. (per cent)
UX₁	192	56	193	67	205	80	191	81	193	79	193	72	191	65		
	104	44	10?	33	112	20	97.9	12.5	103	21	101	28	100	35		
							97.5	6.5								
UX₂	2320	80	2305	90					2310	96	2320	98.8	2305	96	2290	98
	1500	13	1500	9					1500	1.0	1500	0.63	1500	2.3	2246	~1
									1300	1.6	1300	0.49	1300	1.2	1480	0.72
	600	7	580	1					480	1	600	0.04	500	1.4	1245	0.74
													100	0.5		
UZ	BOUISSIÈRES[79]						ONG[76] (measured)									
	1350	7			1200	10	1130	13	1130	16	1200	10			1080	7
	900	18					530	27	530	34					730	11
	500	75			450	90	320	32	320	40	450	90			410–520	66
							155	28	155	10					190	14

Note: SCHNEIDER ET AL.[91] also report a Fermi analysis of the UX₂ spectrum into 11 components; this analysis is inconsistent with the decay scheme described here.

the results of coincidence measurements indicated that the two transitions of lower energy were in cascade relationship and that the 93 keV transition was a crossover. But detailed study of the electron conversion characteristics and of the multipolarity assignments based on them uncovered some inconsistencies which could be explained only if the conversion characteristics of one or two of the transitions were very abnormal, or if the gamma spectrum were more complex than was first thought.

The latter turned out to be the case. FOUCHER, MERINIS, DE PINHO, AND VALADARES[89] reinvestigated the electron spectrum with a magnetic spectrometer of high resolution and showed that the 93 keV gamma was in fact a doublet (a 93.1 keV $M1$ transition plus a 93.5 keV $E1$ transition), and that the 63 keV transition was also double (a 63.6 keV $E1$ transition plus a 63.2 keV $M1 + E2$? transition). The decay scheme to which their results lead is shown in Fig. 8.11.

These authors[90] have proposed an interpretation of the level scheme of the odd-odd nucleus Pa^{234} in terms of Nilsson orbital assignments to the odd-neutron and the odd-proton. (See Section 3.5.6 of Chapter 3 for general discussion.) They considered specific Nilsson proton states available to the 91st proton from the Nilsson diagram and known from decay scheme analysis of odd mass protactinium isotopes. Further, they considered Nilsson states previously identified for the 143rd neutron. They concluded that the 4+ ground state (UZ) is composed of a $1/2 - [530]$ proton and a $7/2 - [743]$ neutron coupled according to the Gallagher-Moskowski rule to 4+. To UX_2 they assigned the same proton state, but combined it with a $1/2 - [631]$ neutron state to give a resultant 0−. The opposite coupling of these orbitals gives the resultant 1− and this may represent the level at 162.9 keV. The level at 99.7 keV is believed to be a rotational excitation of the 69.8 keV level.

We now turn to a discussion of the β-decay of UX_2 and UZ. The isomeric species UX_2 (1.17 minutes) and UZ (6.7 hours) were discovered in 1913 and 1921 and numerous investigations of them have been made in past decades, particularly in the last two. Nonetheless, there has been a remarkable lack of agreement on the decay schemes proposed by various authors. It is perhaps worth mentioning some of the experimental problems which hinder a definitive study of these nuclides.

1. The 1.17 minute UX_2 decays directly to the ground state of U^{234} in 98 per cent of its transitions. The continuous beta spectrum accompanying this decay has the high end-point energy of 2300 keV. It is difficult to study the weak conversion electrons in the presence of this beta spectrum. It

[89] R. Foucher, J. Merinis, A. G. De Pinho, and M. Valadares, *Compt. Rend.* **255**, 882, 1916 (1962).

[90] R. Foucher, J. Merinis, A. G. De Pinho, and M. Valadares, *J. Phys.* **24**, 203 (1963).

is particularly difficult to detect the electrons corresponding to the weak (0.13 per cent) isomeric transitions to UZ.

2. UZ has an extremely complex beta, gamma, and conversion electron spectrum which should be studied with spectrometers of high resolution. High resolution implies low transmission, however, and hence a need for intense sources. But UZ is produced in only 0.13 per cent of the decay events of UX_2 which corresponds to a loss in intensity of a factor of 700. To prepare UZ sources of millicurie strength one would have to isolate the UX_1 in equilibrium with tons of uranium. The published and unpublished studies cited here were all done with sources of microcurie or smaller intensity so that the necessary high resolution could not be utilized.

Many articles have been published on the radiations of UX_2 and UZ. Work published before 1955 is well reviewed by DE HAAN, SIZOO, AND KRAMER.[78] Later detailed discussions are given by ONG, VERSCHOOR, AND BORN,[76] and by SCHNEIDER, DE LANGE, AND DE VILLIERS.[91,92] Rather than attempt a review of these many publications or a resolution of the conflicting interpretations, we shall accept the experimental results and interpretation of BJØRNHOLM AND NIELSEN[93,94] as representative of a recent comprehensive study of UX_2 and UZ, and summarize it briefly here. These authors used the Copenhagen six-gap "orange" type beta spectrometer to measure the electron spectra. They used the same spectrometer in coincidence with a crystal spectrometer to measure beta-gamma, and electron-gamma coincidences. Also they relied on gamma-gamma coincidence and gamm-gamma angular correlation experiments of Wood.[95]

The beta decay scheme of UX_2 is shown in Fig. 8.12. This scheme was constructed in the following way.

The decay energy is set by the end point energy of the intense (98 per cent) ground state beta transition. The several determinations of the end point energy listed in Table 8.10 cluster around 2300 keV. The other beta group energies and intensities come chiefly from the analysis of gamma transitions. The gamma transitions are listed in Table 8.11.

The 43.5 keV transition is without much question identical with the 43.5 keV transition observed in the alpha decay of Pu^{238} and identified as the de-excitation of the first $(2+)$ level of the ground state rotational band of U^{234}. The 811 keV transition is very strongly converted, as was established by JOHANSSON,[80] and must be electric monopole in character.

[91] H. Schneider, P. W. DeLange, and J. W. L. DeVilliers, *Nuovo Cim.* X, **14**, pp. 11–28 (1959).

[92] P. W. De Lange, H. Schneider, and J. W. L. De Villiers, *Nuovo Cim.* X, **14**, pp. 681–702 (1959).

[93] S. Bjørnholm and O. B. Nielsen, *Nucl. Phys.* **42**, 642 (1963).

[94] S. Bjørnholm and O. B. Nielsen, *Nucl. Phys.* **30**, 488 (1962).

[95] G. T. Wood, *Phys. Rev.* **119**, 2004 (1960).

TABLE 8.11. Internal transitions following the beta-decay of UX₂
(BJØRNHOLM and NIELSEN[93]).

Energy (keV)	Multipolarity	Total Intensity (per cent)
43.5	E2	2
K x-ray		
236	E0	0.09
255 ± 5	E1	0.05
746 ± 5	E1	0.04
765	E2	0.30
790 ± 5	E1	0.02
(806)?	E0	≤0.03
811	E0	0.51
1001	E2	0.60
1045	E0	<0.001
1160		—
1440		~0.03
1750		~0.03

Consequently there must exist a level at 811 keV with spin and parity 0+. The same 0+ level has been observed in the alpha decay of Pu^{238} and the electron capture decay of Np^{234}. (See Chapter 9.)

The placement of the other gamma rays in the figure follows chiefly from the electron-gamma and gamma-gamma coincidence results listed in

TABLE 8.12. Gamma-rays observed in coincidence with conversion electrons and gamma-rays in the decay of UX₂

Selected transition	Gamma-rays found in coincidence with selected transition			Level indicated at: keV
	Peak energy (keV)	Interpreted as: keV	No. of coincidences (per cent)	
L 43.5	765	746 + 765	18	811
	1000	1001	32	1045
K 236	765	765	45	1045
	(1000)		0	
255 γ	765	746 + 790		790
770 γ component 746 + 765 + 790	100	{ K x-rays { from 236	~12	
	250	255	~10	
	765	?	≤1	

Results of BJØRNHOLM and NIELSEN[93] and of WOOD.[95]

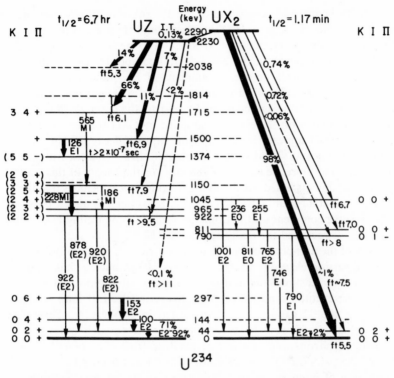

FIG. **8.12.** Decay scheme of UX₂ and of UZ as formulated by Bjørnholm and Nielsen. Only the most certain features of the schemes are shown.

Table 8.12 and from beta-gamma coincidence results listed in Table 8.13. An important fact in the interpretation of the gamma-gamma coincidence data was the recognition that the 236 keV transition is electric monopole in character. This fact also sets the spin and parity of the level at 1045 as 0+. The spin and parity of the level at 790 keV was set at 1− by a measurement

TABLE **8.13.** Beta-gamma coincidence results on UX₂ decay
(Bjørnholm and Nielsen).

End point energy of beta group (keV)	Gamma rays in coincidence		Level indicated at: keV
	Peak energy (keV)	Interpreted as	
∼ 1500	767	765	811
1250	250	255	⎱ 1045
			+
	1000	1001	⎰ 790

of the K-shell conversion coefficient of the 255 keV transition which indicated that it was electric dipole ($E1$) in character. This assignment was fully confirmed by the experiments of WOOD[95] who performed gamma-gamma correlation experiments on the 250 − "770" composite cascade in order to provide a crucial check on the assignments of K, I, and π to the levels at 1045 keV and 790 keV. The results confirm the assignments given in the figure. The K, I, π assignments of $(0, 1, -)$ to the level at 790 $\pm$ 5 keV is also in agreement with the evidence supplied by GALLAGHER AND THOMAS[96] that such a level appears in the electron capture decay of Np^{234}. GALLAGHER AND THOMAS[96] had intense sources of Np^{234} to work with and were able to set a more precise energy of 788 keV for the energy of this state.

From arguments based chiefly on log ft values one concludes that the most likely ground state spin of Pa^{234} (UX_2) is zero, but 1 is also a possibility.

We reserve comment on the isomeric transition connecting UX_2 and UZ until we have reviewed the decay scheme of UZ.

Many of the authors cited before have contributed valuable measurements of the conversion electrons and gamma rays of UZ but we shall again refer chiefly to the measurements and interpretations of BJØRNHOLM AND NIELSEN.[94] These authors measured 51 conversion electron lines which they assigned to the 32 gamma transitions listed in Table 8.14. Several pairs of the listed gamma rays have energies so close to each other that their conversion electrons were not in fact resolved from each other. The existence of the pairs (or in some cases of triplets) was deduced from a careful examination of intensity balances and from a detailed consideration of the decay scheme. All these transitions were placed in a tentative self-consistent decay scheme but we reproduce here as Fig. 8.12 only that part of it which is established with reasonable certainty; hence only a few of the levels and the gamma transitions are shown. The continuous beta spectrum could not be cleanly separated from the complex conversion electron spectrum which contained 225 conversion electrons for every 100 beta particles. Nonetheless a crude resolution of the beta spectrum into five groups was of considerable assistance in the construction of the decay scheme. It is interesting to note that while the beta decay of UX_2 goes 98 per cent to the ground state of U^{234}, the beta decay of UZ goes by several low-energy partial beta groups to excited levels lying between 1000 keV and 2100 keV. A 500 keV beta-group accounts for about 2/3 of the decays. There is no beta-intensity to the ground state rotational band (log ft > 11) which fact may be attributed to K-forbiddenness. A comparison of the decay schemes of UX_2 and UZ suggests a low spin, probably zero (or 1) spin for UX_2 and a high spin, probably 4 for UZ.

The ground state rotational band is represented by the 0+, 2+, 4+, and 6+ levels. There seems little question about the correct assignment of

[96] C. J. Gallagher and T. D. Thomas, *Nucl. Phys.* **14**, 1 (1959/60).

TABLE **8.14**. Gamma transitions in the decay of UZ
(BJØRNHOLM AND NIELSEN).

Energy (keV)	Multipolarity	K/L Exp.	K/L Theor.	Total transition intensity
44	$E2$	—	—	(92)
100	$E2$	—	—	71
126	$E1$			32
153	$E2$	≤0.2	~0.2	25
186	$M1$	5.8	4.4	13
197	$M1$ or $E2$	—	—	~9
(208)	($E1$)			(15)
224	($M1$) ⎫			(7)
228	$M1$ ⎬	4.3	4.4	33
287	$E1$			(12)
(323)	—	—	—	3
(355)	$E1$	—	—	(6)
369	$M1$	4.0	4.5	8.4
565	$M1$	3.9	4.5	17
694	($M1$)	≥2.9	4.5	(6)
727	$M1$	≥2.5	4.5	10
791	($E2$)	—	—	4
804	($E0$)	3.6	—	(0.6)
822	($E2$)	—	—	(4)
873 ⎫				(10)
875 ⎬	($E2$)	4.8	3.5	(5)
878 ⎭				(12)
920 ⎫	($E2$)	≥3.2	3.5	(18)
922 ⎭				
941	($E2$)	~4	3.5	13
976	($E2$)	—	—	3
1020	($E2$)	—	—	(5)
(1130)	—	—	—	—
(1340)	—	—	—	—
(1410)	—	—	—	—
(1620)	—	—	—	3
(1850)	—	—	—	1

these levels and of the well-characterized $E2$ cascade radiations by which they are de-excited because the $E2$ radiations are so intense and because they coincide with those determined in the alpha decay of Pu^{238}. (See Section 9.2.8 of Chapter 9.)

The next level of excitation observed in the decay of UZ lies at 922 keV and this is assigned by BJØRNHOLM AND NIELSEN[94] to a collective quadrupole vibration of the gamma-vibrational type. Their measurements indicate that no level appears between 297 keV and 922 keV which is at variance with several decay schemes published by other authors. The first rotational level of excitation of the gamma-vibrational band appears at 965 keV

($KI\pi = 2$, $3+$). BJØRNHOLM AND NIELSEN[94] and HANSEN, WILSKY, AND BJØRNHOLM,[100] have tentative evidence for several additional rotational members of the band lying at 1020 keV $(4+)$, 1087 keV $(5+)$ and 1167 keV $(6+)$. Each level must de-excite by $E2$ transitions to the ground state rotational band. Because the spacings in the two bands are similar many of these transitions are nearly identical in energy. Hence, their conversion electrons were not resolved at the 1.5 per cent instrumental resolution which had to be used because of the low intensity of the sources. The nature of the levels at 1150, 1379, 1500, and 1715 keV which are strongly populated by direct beta decay is not established. The spin values are high and the log ft values suggest a spin of 4 with positive parity for UZ. The level at 1374 keV has special interest because of its long half-life ($\tau > 2$ $\times 10^{-7}$ seconds). This delay was discovered when it was noted that the prominent 126 keV $E1$ transition, present in 32 per cent of all disintegrations, was not in coincidence with any radiation within the ground state rotational band. The 126 keV transition is coincident with beta particles. The conclusion is that the level to which the 126 keV transition decays, namely the 1374 keV level, is long-lived. This was confirmed in a restudy by HANSEN, WILSKY, AND BJØRNHOLM[100] who reported the value 33.5 $\pm$ 2.0 microseconds for the half-life of the state.

There has been considerable confusion in the literature as to whether UX_2 or UZ is the isomeric state and what the energy of separation is. Most authors conclude that UX_2 is the higher lying of the two. BJØRNHOLM AND NIELSEN agree with this choice and set the energy difference as 60 $\pm$ 30 keV. FOUCHER AND CO-WORKERS[89,90] give the more precise value of 69.8 keV. If the suggested spins of $0-$ and $4+$ for UX_2 and UZ, respectively, are correct then the two isomers are connected by an $M4$ transition.

In the older literature[74,97] the branch decay of UX_2 by isomeric transition to UZ was given as 0.15 per cent. In 1954 ZIJP, TOM, AND SIZOO[98] reported the much higher value of 0.63 per cent. However, a careful restudy of this branching by BJØRNHOLM AND NIELSEN[93] reestablished the validity of the earlier determination; they reported 0.13 $\pm$ 0.03 per cent. FOREST, LYLE, MARTIN, AND MAULDEN[99] report a value of 0.18 $\pm$ 0.02 per cent and ADAMSON[88] reports 0.15 per cent.

8.2.13 Thorium-235

Only sketchy information is available on Th^{235}. HARVEY AND PARSONS[101] prepared it by placing a sample of UX_1, which had been separated

---

[97] N. Feather and E. Bretscher, *Proc. Roy. Soc.* (London) **165A**, 530 (1938).

[98] W. L. Zijp, Sj. Tom, and G. J. Sizoo, *Physica* **20**, 727 (1954).

[99] J. H. Forest, S. J. Lyle, G. R. Martin, and J. J. Maulden, *J. Inorg. Nucl. Chem.* **15**, 210 (1960).

[100] P. G. Hansen, K. Wilsky, and S. Bjørnholm, *Nucl. Phys.* **45**, 417 (1963).

[101] B. G. Harvey and B. I. Parsons, *Phys. Rev.* **80**, 1098 (1950).

from one kilogram of uranium, in a flux of 6×10^{13} neutrons. The reactions are:

$$\text{Th}^{234}(n,\gamma)\text{Th}^{235}; \quad \text{Th}^{235} \xrightarrow[\text{short}]{\beta^-} \text{Pa}^{235} \xrightarrow[\text{23 min}]{\beta^-} \text{U}^{235}$$

Within a few minutes after the end of the irradiation a protactinium fraction was isolated from the thorium and Pa^{235} was identified. No additional Pa^{235} grew into the thorium sample, from which it was concluded that Th^{235} is a beta emitter with a half-life of much less than 5 minutes. The beta decay energy of Th^{235} is estimated as 1.77 MeV from decay cycles.

8.3 THE ISOTOPES OF PROTACTINIUM

8.3.1 Protactinium-225

This isotope is the parent of the Pa^{225} collateral series discussed in Chapter 7.[102] It is believed to be an alpha emitter with a half-line of 2 seconds. The alpha particle energy is estimated as 7.3 MeV. Protactinium-225 is prepared by the bombardment of thorium with high energy protons. The very tentative information on this isotope needs to be confirmed and extended by additional experimental studies.

8.3.2 Protactinium-226

This isotope is the parent of the Pa^{226} collateral series discussed in Chapter 7.[103] Our total information on Pa^{226} is that it emits alpha particles of 6.81 MeV energy with a half-life of 1.8 minutes.

8.3.3 Protactinium-227

The discovery of Pa^{227} is discussed in Section 7.2.3 of Chapter 7 because of its significance as the parent of the Pa^{227} collateral series. Protactinium-227 decays partially (85 per cent) by alpha emission and partially (15 per cent) by capture of an orbital electron.[104] The resultant half-life is 38.3 ± 0.3 minutes.[104] Orbital electron capture was proved[104] by isolation of Th^{227} daughter activity.

HILL, ASARO, AND PERLMAN[105,106] measured the alpha spectrum of Pa^{227} on samples prepared by the bombardment of thorium with 280 MeV protons. Their results are summarized in Table 8.15.

[102] J. D. Keyes, Ph.D. Thesis, McGill University (1951), unpublished.

[103] W. W. Meinke, A. Ghiorso, and G. T. Seaborg, *Phys. Rev.* **75**, 314 (1949); *Phys. Rev.* **81**, 782 (1951); *Phys. Rev.* **85**, 429 (1952).

[104] W. W. Meinke, A. Ghiorso, and G. T. Seaborg, *Phys. Rev.* **81**, 782 (1951).

[105] M. W. Hill, F. Asaro, and I. Perlman, unpublished results, 1957.

[106] M. W. Hill, Ph.D. thesis, *Univ. Calif. Lawrence Rad. Lab. Report, UCRL-8423* (1958).

TABLE 8.15. Pa^{227} alpha groups (HILL, ASARO, AND PERLMAN).

Alpha-particle energy (MeV)^a	Excited-state energy (keV)	Abundance (per cent)	Hindrance factor
6.460	0	50.7	3.1
6.418	42.4	11.8	8.8
6.410	50.5	15.2	6.3
6.396	64.7	9.6	8.8
6.371	90.6	2.6	24
6.351	110.3	8.0	6.6
6.331	131.3	0.7	60
6.321	141.3	0.4	95
6.294	168.3	0.8	36

^{a} Relative to $Bi_{\alpha 354}^{211} = 6.273$ MeV.

Note: In the original references[105,106] the 6.460 keV group was reported to populate a level at 67.3 keV, because a higher energy group at 6.526 MeV was present in low intensity in the α-spectrum. Later work by SUBRAHMANYAM, ET AL.[107] showed that the 6.526 MeV group belonged to Ac^{223}.

SUBRAHMANYAM, MOSIER, ASARO, AND PERLMAN[107,108] studied the gamma radiations by an α-γ coincidence technique in which energy selection was made both on the alpha particles and the γ-ray photons. Complete information on the decay scheme was not obtained, but a number of the chief radiations were identified and placed as shown in Fig. 8.13. The multi-polarity assignments were based on the α-particle intensities and the inten-sities of photons and conversion-produced x-rays observed in coincidence with specific alpha groups.

Although it is by no means certain that a nucleus of mass number 223 is sufficiently deformed to be described by the Nilsson wave-functions (see Chapter 3) the evidence from this work and from a study of Pa^{229} indicates that the Nilsson description may still be appropriate. The nine levels shown in Fig. 8.13 can be placed in two $K = 5/2$ rotational bands of opposite parity. The alpha decay hindrance factors are quite low which suggests that both bands fall in the category "favored transitions," which implies that the initial (Pa^{227}) and final (Ac^{223}) states have the same intrinsic configuration. The NILSSON wave function $5/2 - [523]$ is given as a suggested assignment. It is tempting to say (as has also been suggested for the decay of Pa^{229}) that both bands have the odd proton in the $K = 5/2$ state and that the change of parity is caused by a collective octupole vibrational excitation. Such octupole excitations are a common feature of the low-lying excited states

---

[107] V. Subrahmanyam, D. F. Mosier, F. Asaro, and I. Perlman, unpublished results, 1963.

[108] V. Subrahmanyam, thesis, University of California, 1963; also published as Univ. Cal. Radiation Laboratory Report UCRL-11082 (1963).

of even-even nuclei (see Chapter 3), but have not been identified in odd-nuclei. The fact that the $E1$ transitions are fast (they compete with the enhanced intra-band $E2$ transitions) is taken as supporting evidence for this conclusion.

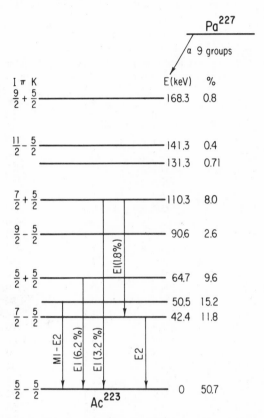

FIG. **8.13.** Partial decay scheme of Pa²²⁷. (Gamma intensity figures refer to photon intensities.)

8.3.4 *Protactinium-228*

The discovery of the 22 hour Pa²²⁸ and its position as the first member of the Pa²²⁸ series of radioactive isotopes is discussed in Section 7.2.2 of Chapter 7. Protactinium-228 is prepared by the bombardment of thorium with high energy protons or deuterons and all samples are necessarily contaminated with some of the higher-mass protactinium isotopes. This interferes with the careful study of its complex radiations particularly its gamma radiations. This contamination can be minimized by proper selection of the energy of the bombarding particles; for protons an energy of 65 MeV is best. The contamination can also be eliminated entirely by electromagnetic separation of

Pa^{228} in a suitable isotope separator.   Protactinium-228 disintegrates 98 per cent by capture of an orbital electron and two per cent by alpha decay.

HILL, ASARO, AND PERLMAN[109,110] have studied the alpha spectrum of Pa^{228} in a double-focusing magnetic spectrometer of high resolution and have found it to be exceedingly complex.   Table 8.16 lists twenty-seven

TABLE **8.16.** Alpha groups of Pa^{228}.

Alpha-particle energy (MeV)	Excited-state energy (keV)	Abundance (per cent)	Hindrance factor
6.138	0	2.5	3200
6.114	24.0	10.5	580
6.101	38.1	12.0	350
6.087	52.1	2.3	2000
6.074	66.3	20.7	190
6.062	77.2	1.0	3400
6.037	102.8	2.3	1100
6.024	116.4	9.0	260
6.007	133.6	0.8	2300
5.994	146.2	0.3	5400
5.985	155.8	1.1	1300
5.978	163.3	2.8	480
5.971	170.0	2.7	460
5.943	198.8	0.6	1500
5.937	204.6	0.5	1700
5.918	224.4	0.8	850
5.903	239.5	1.1	520
5.870	272.6	1.4	280
5.854	289.6	0.3	1100
5.839	304.3	0.4	610
5.801	343.2	7.3	24
5.795	349.4	11.3	14
5.775	369.9	1.4	92
5.761	383.7	2.0	55
5.756	388.4	1.4	73
5.752	393.5	2.5	43
5.707	439.4	1.0	57

These energies were measured relative to $U_{\alpha 0}^{230} = 5.884$.   From thesis of HILL.[110]

alpha groups.   The Ac^{224} levels revealed by these alpha groups are also listed in the table and shown in Fig. 8.14.   No interpretation of these levels was advanced by these authors.

Obviously, the gamma transitions resulting from the de-excitation of these many excited levels must be numerous.   HILL[110] measured the gamma

---

[109] M. W. Hill, F. Asaro, and I. Perlman, unpublished information, 1957.

[110] M. W. Hill, thesis, University of California 1958; *Univ. Calif. Rad. Lab. Report*, *UCRL-8423*, August 1958.

spectrum in coincidence with Pa^{228} alpha particles. A complex spectrum was noted in the energy region 90 to 400 keV which was roughly resolved into the components listed in Table 8.17. These gamma rays were not placed in the decay scheme.

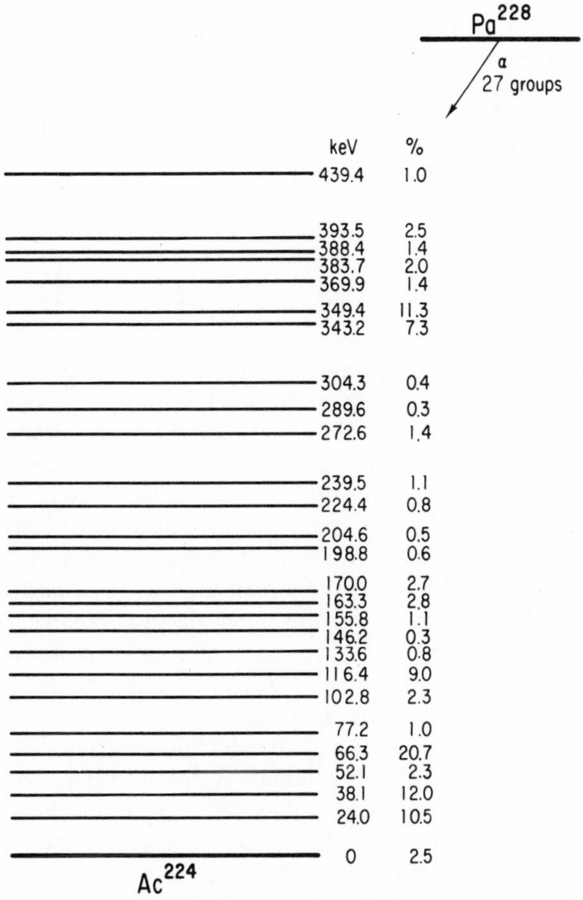

$$Pa^{228}$$

α
27 groups

keV	%
439.4	1.0
393.5	2.5
388.4	1.4
383.7	2.0
369.9	1.4
349.4	11.3
343.2	7.3
304.3	0.4
289.6	0.3
272.6	1.4
239.5	1.1
224.4	0.8
204.6	0.5
198.8	0.6
170.0	2.7
163.3	2.8
155.8	1.1
146.2	0.3
133.6	0.8
116.4	9.0
102.8	2.3
77.2	1.0
66.3	20.7
52.1	2.3
38.1	12.0
24.0	10.5
0	2.5

$$Ac^{224}$$

FIG. 8.14. Alpha decay scheme of Pa^{228}.

The electron capture decay of Pa^{228} have been studied by several authors. ONG[111,112] and HILL[109,110] and HILL, HOLLANDER, AND PERLMAN[113] measured conversion electron lines in magnetic spectrometers and gamma ray

[111] Ong Ping Hok, thesis "The Beta Decay of Protactinium Isotopes," the Free University of Amsterdam, 1955.
[112] Ong Ping Hok and E. Arbman, *Arkiv Fysik* 11 [9] 193 (1956).
[113] M. W. Hill, J. M. Hollander, and I. Perlman, unpublished information, 1956.

photons in sodium iodide crystals. From intensity, multipolarity, and coincidence measurements these authors were able to construct partial decay schemes and to interpret the low-lying levels in the daughter nucleus Th^{228}. A later and more complete study was made by ARBMAN, BJØRNHOLM, AND NIELSEN.[114] We quote here exclusively from this study.

TABLE 8.17. Gamma rays in Pa^{228} alpha decay as roughly resolved by HILL[110] from gamma spectrum in coincidence with alpha particles.

E_γ (keV)	Relative intensity	E_γ (keV)	Relative intensity
95	240	220	10
130	27	240	55
150	34	280	49
170	11	310	100
200	14	345	21

These authors studied the conversion electrons in an 18.5 cm double focusing electron spectrometer adjusted to a resolution of 0.2 per cent and a transmission of 0.2 per cent. They also used a six-gap, orange type spectrometer adjusted to a resolution of 0.4 per cent and a transmission of one per cent. The gamma ray transition energies deduced from these measurements are listed in Table 8.18. One hundred fifty three conversion lines from 72 gamma transitions were observed. The transitions below 500 keV were characterized in multipolarity by their $L_I + L_{II}/L_{III}$ and K/L electron ratios. Some information on photon intensities was obtained from a NaI scintillation spectrometer. Very important information on the decay scheme was obtained by electron-gamma coincidence experiments in which the coincidence circuit was gated by the detection of electron lines of a specific energy (resolution 1.5 per cent) and the gamma spectrum coincidence was measured with a multichannel scintillation spectrometer. About 50 coincidence spectra were recorded involving the conversion lines of 32 transitions and the photo peaks of 50 different gamma-rays. These measurements were aided by the fact that there was no beta spectrum to provide an interfering background.

From a detailed consideration of all the evidence ARBMAN, BJØRNHOLM, AND NIELSEN[114] constructed the very detailed decay scheme shown in Fig. 8.15. This scheme has 22 levels ranging in energy from 57.5 keV to 1943 keV. Considerable help in interpreting the data relating to the lower levels was obtained from a consideration of the alpha decay of U^{232} and the beta decay of Ac^{228} to the same Th^{228} daughter nucleus. For a discussion of these nuclides see Sections 8.4.6 and 6.3, respectively. Figure 8.12 accounts

---

[114] E. Arbman, S. Bjørnholm, and O. B. Nielsen, *Nucl. Phys.* **21**, 406 (1960).

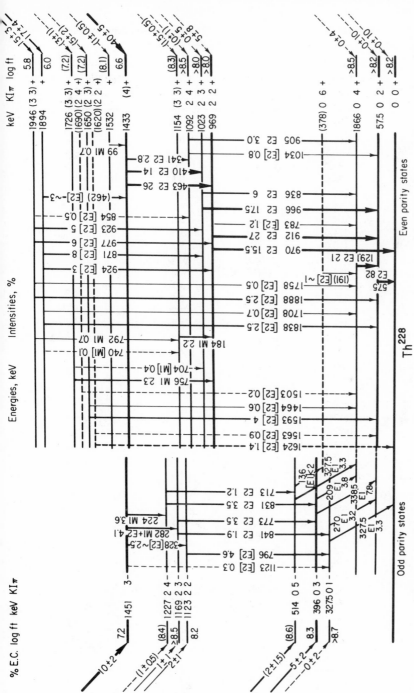

FIG. 8.15. The decay scheme of Pa[228] for capture of an orbital electron as formulated by ARBMAN, BJØRNHOLM, AND NIELSEN. The odd parity levels have been separated from those of even parity and grouped to the left. The electron capture transitions are therefore seen to come in from both sides. Transitions and levels for which only tentative evidence is obtained are dotted. Similarly, numbers in parentheses are tentative.

TABLE 8.18. Gamma transitions in the electron capture decay of Pa[228].
ARBMAN, BJØRNHOLM, AND NIELSEN[114]

Energy (keV)	Multipolarity	Total intensity	Placed in decay scheme
57.5	E2	82	+
99.4	M1	0.7	+
129.1	E2	21	+
137.8	M1	2.0	
178.0	M1	0.85	
184.5	M1	2.2	+
(191.3)	(E2)	~1	(+)
209.0	E1	3.8	+
224.0	M1	3.6	+
270.0	E1	3.2	
(278)	(E2)	(0.9)	
282.2	(M1 + E2)	4.0	+
327.5	E1	3.3	+
327.5	[E2]	2.5	+
327.5	E1	3.3	+
338.5	E1	7.8	+
341.1	E2	2.8	+
(397)			
409.7	E2	14	+
(462)	(E2)	3	+
463.3	E2	26	+
(469.2)			
(617)			
(622)			
641			
662			
666			
(670)			
680			
694			
704	[M1]	0.4	(+)
713	E2	1.2	+
732			
739.6	[M1]	0.13	(+)
745.6			
756.2	M1	2.3	+
773.4	E2	3.5	+
782.6	[E2]	1.2	+
792.2	M1	0.7	+
795.8	[E2]	4.6	+
817.4			
831.4	E2	3.5	+
835.8			
836.4	E2	6.0	+

Energy (keV)	Multipolarity	Total intensity	Placed in decay scheme
841.0	E2	1.9	+
853.8	[E2]	0.5	(+)
871.0	(E2)	8.0	+
889.0			
905.2	E2	3.0	+
912.2	E2	27	+
923	(E2)	5	+
924	(E2)	3	+
966	E2	17.5	+
970	E2	15.5	+
976.8	E2	6	+
1034.1	(E2)	0.8	+
(1123)	(E2)	0.3	(+)
1168			
1253	(M1)		
(1293)			
(1423)			
1464	(E2)	0.6	+
(1489)			
(1503)	(E2)	0.2	+
1563	(E2)	0.9	+
1593	(E2)	4	+
1624	(E2)	1.4	(+)
1678			
1708	(E2)	0.7	+
1744	(E2)		
1758	(E2)	0.5	+
1838	(E2)	2.5	+
1888	(E2)	2.5	+

for 47 of the 72 transitions found. The intensity of this fraction of the transitions amounts to 310 per 100 electron capture decays, whereas the 25 transitions not included represent 30 out of 100 transitions. Most of the levels shown in the scheme were cross checked in many ways and are firmly established. The intensity balance for the flow of transitions through the excited states to the ground state comes out in a consistent way. Table 8.19 gives a list of the levels and the intensity of feeding and de-excitation of each level. By difference the electron capture intensity and log ft values were calculated.

The level system of Th^{228} has been interpreted in the language of the collective model of the nucleus. It is one of the best examples in the whole heavy element region of an even-even nucleus with many levels which can be correlated with the rotational and vibrational excitations predicted by the theory. We now mention several of these features.

The level structure clearly shows the presence of rotational bands built on

TABLE **8.19**. Levels in Th[228]. (ARBMAN, BJØRNHOLM, AND NIELSEN).

Total intensities of internal transitions feeding and de-exciting each level.
Electron-capture intensities and log ft-values: Pa[228] : $t_{1/2} = 22 \pm 1$ h; $Q_{0EC} = 2.10 \pm 0.05$ MeV

Level (keV)	$K, I\pi$	Pa[228] Internal transitions: feeding level (%)	de-exciting level (%)	EC directly feeding level (%)	log ft	Ac[228] log ft
0	0,0 +	101	0	0 ± 10	> 8.2	> 8.8
57.5	0,2 +	86	82	0 ± 10	> 8.2	8.8
186.6	0,4 +	20	21	0 ± 4	> 8.5	—
327.5	0,1 +	6.8	6.5	0 ± 2	> 8.7	> 9.5
395.8	0,3 +	7.0	11.6	5 ± 2	8.3 ± 0.3	8.5
514.1	0,5 +	1.2	3.3	(2 ± 1.5)	(8.6 ± 0.4)	—
969.5	2,2 +	39.5	43.7	5 ± 8	≥ 8.0	7.3
1023.2	2,3 +	27.5	23.5	0 ± 5	> 8.0	≥ 8.0
1091.8	2,4 +	3.3	3.8	0 ± 1	> 8.5	—
1123.4	2,2 +	2.5	4.6	2 ± 1	8.2 ± 0.3	8.0
1168.8	2,3 +	4.0	5.4	1 ± 1	> 8.5	—
1227.0	2,4 +	(3.6)	4.7	(1 ± 0.5)	(8.4 ± 0.3)	—
1154.0	(3,3) +	(0.8)	2.2	(1.5 ± 0.5)	(8.3 ± 0.3)	7.7
1432.8	(4) +	3.7	42.8	40 ± 5	6.6 ± 0.1	> 8.0
1451.0	(3) +	0	10.1	10 ± 2	7.2 ± 0.1	≥ 8.3
1532.2	(4) +	0	0.7	(1 ± 0.5)	(8.1 ± 0.4)	7.1
(1620)	(2,2) +	(0)	(2.3)	(2 ± 1)	(7.6 ± 0.5)	—
1650	(2,3) +	0	4.6	(3 ± 2)	(7.2 ± 0.3)	6.8
(1690)	(2,4) +	(0)	(0.2)	(0.2 ± 0.1)	(8.5 ± 0.5)	—
1726	(3,3) +	0	2.7	(3 ± 1)	(7.2 ± 0.3)	—
1894.0	+	0	17	17 ± 4	6.0 ± 0.4	—
1946.3	(3,3) +	0	15	15 ± 3	5.8 ± 0.4	—
Total		206	307	111 ± 20		

the ground state $(0+)$, the 327.5 keV level $(1-)$, the 969 keV level $(2+)$, the 1123 keV level $(2-)$, and possibly on a 1620 keV level $(2+)$. Three members of each band are excited and it is possible to fit them all to the standard rotational formula,

$$E_{rot} = E_0 + \frac{\hbar^2}{2\mathfrak{J}} I(I+1) + BI^2(I+1)^2,$$

where I is the spin, $\hbar$ is Planck's constant divided by 2π, $\mathfrak{J}$ is the effective moment of inertia, and B is a constant giving the magnitude of a small second order correction for the effects of particle-rotation interaction. See Chapter 3 for a more complete discussion of this formula. The constants of this equation are fitted to the 5 observed rotational bands as shown in Table 8.20.

TABLE **8.20**. Rotational bands in Th^{228}.
ARBMAN, BJØRNHOLM, AND NIELSEN[114]

$$E_{rot} = E_0 + AI(I+1) + BI^2(I+1)^2$$

Band head		$A = \hbar^2/2\mathfrak{J}$	$-B$
keV	$KI\pi$	(keV)	(keV)
0	0 0+	9.70 ± 0.03	0.020 ± 0.002
327.5	0 1−	6.96 ± 0.03	0.009 ± 0.001
969	2 2+	9.43 ± 0.07	0.027 ± 0.003
1123	2 2−	7.93 ± 0.08	0.021 ± 0.004
(1620)	(2 2+)	(5.0 ± 0.5)	

The ground state rotational band is very plainly seen in the decay of Ac^{228} and U^{232} and resembles that observed in all neighboring even-even nuclei; i.e., it has the level sequence $0+, 2+, 4+ \ldots$ and each excited level is de-excited by an $E2$ transition to the level below. The K-quantum number for the band is 0. BELL, BJØRNHOLM, AND SEVERIENS[115] have measured the life-time of the first excited 57.5 keV state by a delayed coincidence technique and have found a value $t_{1/2} = 4.0 \times 10^{-10}$ seconds. From this they calculated an intrinsic electric quadrupole moment, $Q_0 = (8.5 \pm 0.3) \times 10^{-24}$ cm^2. This transition is enhanced by a factor of 200 compared to the single particle estimate, which conforms with the prediction of the collective model.

The even parity band with the 969 keV 2+ base state is assigned to a quadrupole gamma-vibration of the nuclear shape. The K-value for this band is 2. The level sequence of the 969, 1023, 1092 keV levels has the spacing, the $2+, 3+, 4+$ sequence, and the gamma-ray de-excitation pattern expected for the gamma-vibrational band. See the discussion of this point

[115] R. E. Bell, S. Bjørnholm, and J. C. Severiens, *Dan. Mat.-fys. Medd.* **32**, No. 12 (1960).

in Chapter 3. The de-excitation occurs by $E2$ transitions to the ground state rotational band. When 2 or more of these electric quadrupole transitions originate in one state and terminate in different members of the ground state rotational band, the relative intensities, according to theory, are given by simple geometrical factors (Clebsch-Gordan coefficients) after the energy dependence is factored out. Several comparisons of experimental with theoretical ratios were carried out by ARBMAN, BJØRNHOLM, AND NIELSEN[114] for transitions originating in the gamma-band and in the other bands.

In addition to the quadrupole collective nuclear vibrations, the collective model predicts the probable occurrence of octupole vibrations having negative parity and $K = 0, 1, 2,$ or 3. The negative parity state at 327.5 keV is believed to be the $K = 0$ octupole vibration. It is observed in the alpha decay of U^{232} (see Section 8.3.5). It decays by a pair of $E1$ transitions to the $0+$ and $2+$ levels of the ground state band and hence is well characterized as a $1-$ state. The rotational levels based on this $1-$ state should, according to theory, have spin and parity values $1-, 3-, 5-$, etc. and an energy spacing given by the $I(I + 1)$ rule. The levels at 396 and 514 keV are identified as the predicted $3-$ and $5-$ levels.

The $2-, 3-, 4-$, rotational series based on the $2-$ level at 1123 keV may represent a $K = 2$ octupole vibration. However, the evidence for this is not clear and it has also been suggested that this group of levels represents a gamma-vibration superimposed on the $K = 0$ octupole band.[114]

Some speculative suggestions have been made concerning the collective nature of some other levels in the decay scheme but these are not recorded here.

A consideration of the decay scheme and the spin values, parities, and log ft values of Table 8.19 leads to the assignment of spin 3 and positive parity to Pa^{228}. One can make a logical correlation of this assignment with the Nilsson diagrams for odd neutron and proton states in the following way. From the Nilsson diagrams given in Chapter 3 one finds for the 137th neutron the orbit $5/2 - [752]$ and for the 91st proton the orbit $1/2 - [530]$. The deformation parameter (the β parameter defined in Chapter 3) corresponding to these choices is 0.225. The spin-coupling rule for odd-odd nuclei formulated by GALLAGHER AND MOSZKOWSKI,[116] leads to the desired value $3+$.

The decay scheme of Ac^{228} has an overall similarity to that of Pa^{228} which is explained by the fact that Ac^{228} also probably has spin 3 with positive parity.[114]

The applicability of the collective model to the description of the Pa^{228} decay scheme is also shown in the operation of the K-selection rules. It is clear from a short examination of the scheme that some selection rules other than the usual ones depending on total spin and parity must be in

116 C. J. Gallagher and S. A. Moszkowski, *Phys. Rev.* **111**, 1282 (1958).

operation. For example, those states having quantum number $K = 0$ are poorly populated or missed entirely in the direct electron decay process. One striking feature is the complete absence of the expected beta-vibrational band with $K = 0$ which would be expected at approximately 1 MeV of excitation. In addition the K-selection rule serves to explain why the high energy states decay chiefly by multiple cascade instead of decaying directly to the appropriate levels in the ground state band.

For further details on the decay of Pa^{228} the references cited, particularly the paper by ARBMAN, BJØRNHOLM, AND NIELSEN[114], should be consulted.

8.3.5 Protactinium-229

This isotope was first produced[117] by the bombardment of ionium with deuterons, which gives rise to 1.4-day Pa^{229} by the reaction:

$$Th^{230}(d, 3n)Pa^{229}$$

The Pa^{231} prepared simultaneously by the (d, n) reaction does not interfere in radioactivity measurements because of its low specific activity. There is more interference from 17-day Pa^{230} prepared by the $(d, 2n)$ reaction. If the ionium contains a large isotopic impurity of Th^{232}, as it usually does, then Pa^{232} and Pa^{233} radioactivity is also produced and interferes with a detailed study of Pa^{229}.

Protactinium-229 decays almost entirely by electron capture, and has an alpha-branching of only 0.25 per cent.[118] In spite of its small alpha-branching, the proof of the mass assignment of Pa^{229} was made by the identification of its Ac^{225} and Fr^{221} daughter activities.[117]

The electron-capture decay of Pa^{229} has been studied by ONG[119] and by HILL, HOLLANDER, AND PERLMAN[120] who recorded the conversion electrons on photographic emulsions placed in permanent magnet spectrometers. ONG found L_{II} and L_{III} conversion lines of a 41.7 keV transition, and HILL AND CO-WORKERS found L_I, L_{II}, L_{III}, M_I, M_{II}, M_{III}, N_{II}, N_{III} lines corresponding to a transition of 42.37 keV. The L_I/L_{II} and L_{III}/L_{II} ratios indicate that the multipolarity of the transition is 95 per cent $E2$, 5 per cent $M1$. This transition energy is in good agreement with the results of alpha-decay studies[121] of U^{233}, which define levels in Th^{229} at 0, 42.8, and 98.9 keV as being members of a rotational band with spins of 5/2, 7/2, and 9/2. However, the $E2$-$M1$ mixing ratio is quite different from that reported for the

---

[117] E. K. Hyde, M. H. Studier, H. H. Hopkins, Jr., and A. Ghiorso, Paper No. 19.17, "The Transuranium Elements," Nat. Nucl. Energ. Ser., Division IV, 14B (New York: McGraw-Hill Book Company, Inc., 1949).

[118] L. M. Slater and G. T. Seaborg, unpublished data (Aug. 1951).

[119] Ong Ping Hok, thesis, Free University of Amsterdam (March, 1955).

[120] M. W. Hill, J. M. Hollander, and I. Perlman, unpublished information (1956).

[121] L. L. Gol'din, G. I. Novikova, and E. F. Tretyakov, Phys. Rev. 103, 1004 (1956).

same transition in the decay of U^{233}, as pointed out by RUIZ.[122] RUIZ reported an additional gamma ray of 146 keV energy. The fact that the electron-capture decay of Pa^{229} populates the $I = 7/2$ member of the rotational band is consistent with the assignment of spin 5/2 to Pa^{229} rather than 3/2 as is the case in Pa^{231} and Pa^{233}. The Nilsson level assignment of $5/2 - [523]$ has been suggested for the ground state of Pa^{229} where the quantum numbers in brackets are $[N, n_z \Lambda]$.

The alpha spectrum of Pa^{229} has been investigated by HILL[123,124] in a high-resolution, double-focusing magnetic spectrometer. He found a very complex spectrum with the groups listed in Table 8.21 and shown in Fig. 8.16. HILL[124] also performed alpha-gamma coincidence experiments to determine what gamma rays occurred in the alpha-branching decay of Pa^{229}. The gamma rays detected had the following energies and abundances per alpha transition: 40 keV (0.10), 69 keV (0.05), 81 keV (0.02), 92 keV (0.16), 107 keV (0.05), and 120 keV (0.02). From crude estimates of the upper limits to the conversion coefficients for these gamma rays it is probable that the prominent

TABLE 8.21. Alpha groups of Pa^{229}.

Alpha-particle energy (MeV)	Excited-state energy (keV)	Abundance (per cent)	Hindrance factor
5.665	65	19.1	23
5.625	105	9.8	28
5.610	121	13.4	17
5.586	146	4.7	36
5.575	157	36.8	4
5.560	172	3.9	31
5.531	202	8.9	9.4
5.512	221	0.60	110
5.496	237	0.74	73
5.474	259	1.77	23
5.417	317	0.07	280
5.408	329	0.15	115
5.315	420	0.05	100

This table reprinted from Hill's thesis[124] but with ground state located by SUBRAHMAN-YAM.

Standard used in setting energy scale—$U^{230}_{\alpha_0} = 5.884$ MeV and $Ra^{224}_{\alpha_0} = 5.681$ MeV.

The hindrance factor is the factor by which the observed partial alpha half-life differs from that calculated by simple barrier penetration theory.

---

[122] C. P. Ruiz, Ph.D. thesis, University of California, 1961. See *Univ. Calif. Rad. Lab. Report*, *UCRL-9511*, April 1961.

[123] M. W. Hill, Frank Asaro, and I. Perlman, unpublished information (1957).

[124] M. W. Hill, "Nuclear Decay Studies of Protactinium Isotopes," University of California thesis, see *Univ. Calif. Rad. Lab. Report*, *UCRL-8423*, August 1958.

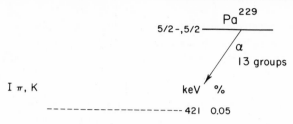

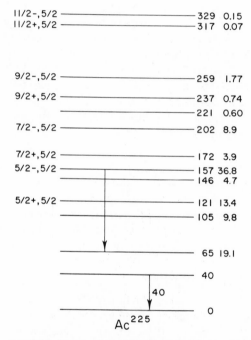

FIG. **8.16.** Decay scheme for the alpha decay of Pa[229] as given by HILL[124] and SUBRAHMANYAM.[125] The spin, parity, and K quantum number assignments on the left of each level are speculative.

40 and 92 keV transitions are electric dipole ($E1$) in nature and probable that the others also are $E1$. SUBRAHMANYAM[125] performed α-γ coincidence experiments which showed that a 5.69 MeV alpha group populated a level 25 keV below the ground state as given originally by HILL, and that this level was de-excited by a 40 keV γ to the true ground state. From the complexity

[125] V. Subrahmanyam, F. Asaro, and I. Perlman, unpublished results, 1963, see also Ref. 108.

of the alpha spectrum it is certain that a larger number of gamma rays accompany the alpha decay of Pa^{229} than have been identified so far, but the experimental difficulties in the way of a careful study of these low intensity transitions are large.

It is likely that the numerous observed levels of Ac^{225} can be accounted for by rotational bands of levels based on only a few states of intrinsic excitation of nucleonic motion. HILL[124] has attempted such an analysis. He concludes that the favored alpha decay proceeds to the 157 keV level in Ac^{225} to which he assigns the Nilsson level $5/2 - [523]$. The rotational band based on this intrinsic state gives rise to a $7/2-$ level at 202 keV, a $9/2-$ level at 259 keV and an $11/2-$ level at 329 keV. To the level at 121 keV he assigns K-quantum number $5/2-$ and parity positive and concludes that rotational levels with character $7/2+$, $9/2+$, and $11/2+$ occur at 172 keV, 237 keV, and 317 keV. The ground state of Ac^{225} is believed to have spin 3/2 and probably has the same Nilsson assignment as does Ac^{227}, namely $3/2 + [651]$. HILL relied on the energy spacing formula for rotational bands in odd-A nuclei as discussed in Chapter 3 and the considerations of BOHR, FRÖMAN, AND MOTTELSON[126] on the pattern of alpha abundances to various members of a rotational band.

8.3.6 Protactinium-230

This isotope is the parent activity of the Pa^{230} collateral series. The discovery of Pa^{230} by STUDIER AND HYDE[127] and its relationship to the other members of the series are discussed in Section 7.2.1 of Chapter 7.

Samples of Pa^{230} can be made by bombardment of thorium with protons. The energy should be chosen so as to emphasize the reaction,

$$Th^{232}(p, 3n)Pa^{230}$$

TEWES[128] reports an excitation function with a peak yield of 400 millibarns at a proton energy of 24 MeV. Some production of Pa^{232} by the (p, n) reaction cannot be avoided but this isotope decays out more rapidly than Pa^{230}. A smaller amount of Pa^{233} produced by the (p, γ) reaction may be more troublesome because of the similarity in half-lives.

Protactinium-230 can also be produced by the reactions:

$$Th^{232}(d, 4n)Pa^{230}$$
$$Io^{230}(d, 2n)Pa^{230}$$
$$Io^{230}(p, n)Pa^{230}$$
$$Pa^{231}(n, 2n)Pa^{230}$$
$$Pa^{231}(d, p2n)Pa^{230}$$
$$Pa^{231}(p, pn)Pa^{230}$$
$$Th^{232}(\alpha, p5n)Pa^{230}$$

126 A. Bohr, P. O. Fröman, and B. R. Mottelson, *Dan. Mat.-fys. Medd.* **29**, No. 10 (1955).
127 M. H. Studier and E. K. Hyde, *Phys. Rev.* **74**, 591 (1948)
128 H. A. Tewes, *Phys. Rev.* **98**, 25 (1955)

The half-life of Pa^{230} has been reported as 17.0 ± 0.5 days[127] and 17.7 ± 0.5 days.[129] The radioactive decay of Pa^{230} proceeds by three distinct modes. The most readily apparent is that of beta emission because the alpha radiation of the daughter resulting from the beta-decay mode is so prominent.

In fact, however, only 10 per cent of the decay goes by this mode. Approximately 90 per cent of the decay is by electron capture to produce ionium, a long-lived product (STUDIER AND BRUEHLMAN[130]). In addition, MEINKE AND SEABORG[131] have shown that in ~0.003 per cent of the disintegrations, an alpha particle is emitted and Ac^{226} is produced. It is possible that Pa^{230} undergoes positron emission to an extent somewhat less than 0.1 per cent.[132,133]

The numerous gamma radiations emitted in the electron capture branch have been studied by ONG,[132,133] by HILL[134] and by NIELSEN, NORDBY, AND BJØRNHOLM[135]. Since the work of the last-mentioned group is the most thorough we shall quote almost exclusively from it.

These workers measured the conversion electron spectrum carefully in an iron-free six gap beta spectrometer adjusted to a resolution of 0.5 per cent. The photon spectrum was measured with a sodium iodide scintillation spectrometer. Coincidence experiments were performed in which the coincidence circuit was triggered by pulses from the beta spectrometer registering a specific conversion line and the entire coincident photon spectrum was measured with a sodium iodide spectrometer. These experiments were very useful in the construction and checking of the decay scheme and were carried out for every principal gamma transition. In addition some electron-electron coincidences were studied.

Table 8.22 lists the gamma transitions together with their multipolarities and their total intensity. The multipolarity assignments were made by a comparison of experimental conversion coefficients with theoretical values. The level scheme of Th^{230} which is deduced from this work is shown in Fig. 8.17. This nucleus is a fine example of the experimental confirmation of the collective excitations predicted by the unified model of the nucleus for even-even nuclei.

[129] D. W. Osborne, R. C. Thompson, and Q. VanWinkle, "The Transuranium Elements," *Nat. Nucl. Energ. Ser.* **14B**, p. 1397 (New York: McGraw-Hill Book Co., Inc., 1949).
[130] M. H. Studier and R. J. Bruehlman, reported in *Argonne National Laboratory Report, ANL-4252* (Feb. 1949); revised values of the beta and electron capture branching of ~15 per cent and ~85 per cent, respectively, were reported by ONG.
[131] W. W. Meinke and G. T. Seaborg, *Phys. Rev.* **78**, 475 (1950).
[132] Ong Ping Hok, thesis, University of Amsterdam (1955).
[133] Ong, Kramer, Meijer, Fennema, and Zijp, *Physica* **21**, 719 (1955).
[134] M. W. Hill, *Univ. Calif. Rad. Lab. Report, UCRL-8423* (1958).
[135] O. B. Nielsen, H. Nordby, and S. Bjørnholm, unpublished results (1961).

TABLE **8.22.** Gamma transitions in the electron capture decay of Pa^{230} (NIELSON, NORDBY, AND BJØRNHOLM).

E_γ	Shell	I_{e^-}	I_γ	α_{exp}	Multipolarity assignment	$\alpha_{Theoretical}$			I_{Total}
						$E1$	$E2$	$M1$	
53	L	3680			E2		200		5300
122	L	120			E2		3.5		200
230	K	39	⩽6	⩾6	E0		0.12	1.50	40
379	K	2.0			(E2)		4.6^{-2}		45
398			135		(E1)	1.62^{-2}			135
401	K	19	100	⩾0.15	M1 +E2		4.2^{-2}	0.33	125
444	K	111	900	⩾0.10	M1 +E2		3.4^{-2}	0.25	900
456	K	8.3	500	⩽1.7^{-2}	E1	1.21^{-2}	3.3^{-2}		700
464	K	19			M1 +E2		3.15^{-2}	0.22	200
508	K	4.7	420	11.2^{-3}	E1	9.8^{-3}	2.7^{-2}		490

520	K	1.5	150	10.0^{-3}	E1	9.5^{-3}	2.65^{-2}		160
572	K	2.7	100	2.7^{-2}	E2	7.9^{-3}	2.3^{-2}	0.13	100
624	K	16.4	⩽20	⩾1	E0			0.10	
634	K	11.9	⩽50	⩾0.2	E0			0.098	
730	K	2.8	210	1.3^{-2}	E2		1.39^{-2}		200
783	K	2.1	160	1.3^{-2}	E2		1.20^{-2}		175
901	K	2.8 ⎫	1600	3.9^{-3}	E1	3.45^{-3}	8.5^{-3}		820
920	K	3.4 ⎭			E1	3.30^{-3}	8.3^{-3}		1020
954	K	11.8	~3500	3.4^{-3}	E1	3.10^{-3}	7.6^{-3}		3800
1012	K	1.1			(E2)		6.6^{-3}		150
1027	K	0.5	240	2^{-3}	E1	2.7^{-3}	6.5^{-3}		250

I_γ is the photon intensity found in coincidence experiments, I_{e^-} is the conversion line intensity.

Multipole assignments given in brackets are deduced from the decay scheme and not from measurements of the γ-ray.

I_{total} refers to the total intensity of the transition; it includes the γ-ray intensity, measured conversion electrons and calculated values for conversion in shells other than those measured.

The negative exponent in the $\alpha_{Theoretical}$ values refers to the power of 10 by which the number should be multiplied.

The lowest levels are the $0+$, $2+$, $4+$ members of the ground state rotational band observed universally for even-even nuclei in the mass region above mass ~ 226. The typical cascade of $E2$ transitions is observed. HILL, HOLLANDER, AND PERLMAN[136] thoroughly characterized these $E2$ transitions

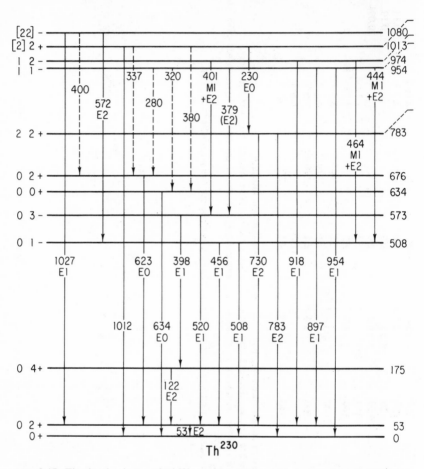

FIG. 8.17. The level scheme of Th[230] and the pattern of gamma ray de-excitation observed in the orbital electron capture of Pa[230]. All energies are given in keV. The 954 keV level is most strongly populated. Figure obtained from O. B. NIELSEN.

and measured precise values of 53.15 keV and 120.8 keV for their energy. ONG[137] called attention to the presence of the ground state rotational band in Th[230]. The next group of levels is a negative parity rotational band

[136] M. Hill, J. M. Hollander, and I. Perlman, unpublished information, 1956. See Ref. 134.

[137] Ong Ping Hok, *Phys. Rev.* **99**, 1613 (1955).

consisting of the two states at 508 and 573 keV. The spin and parity of these are firmly fixed as $1-$ and $3-$, respectively, by their pattern of de-excitation via pairs of electric dipole transitions to the ground state rotational band. The K-quantum number of this band was found to be 0 from the ratio of the reduced transition probabilities of the two $E1$ transitions de-exciting these levels. According to theory this ratio is simply the ratio of squares of

TABLE **8.23**. Conversion ratios in the γ-transitions of $Pa^{230} \rightarrow Th^{230}$.

NIELSEN, NORDBY, AND BJØRNHOLM[135]

E_γ	Ratio	Exp.	Theoretical		
			$E1$	$E2$	$M1$
53	$L_I + L_{II}/L_{III}$	1.15 ± 0.10		1.14	175
122	$L_I + L_{II}/L_{III}$	1.70 ± 0.15		1.65	210
230	K/L	4.8 ± 0.3	5.4	0.60	4.8
444	K/L	4.6 ± 0.2	5.5	1.80	4.8
456	K/L	5.5 ± 1.5	5.5	1.85	4.8
464	K/L	~ 5	5.5	1.90	4.8
508	K/L	>3	5.5	2.15	4.8
572	K/L	~ 3	5.5	2.5	4.7
623	K/L	4.8 ± 0.4	5.5	2.7	4.7
634	K/L	4.7 ± 0.4	5.5	2.7	4.7
954	K/L	6.2 ± 0.5	5.6	3.7	4.5

TABLE **8.24**. Evaluation of K-quantum numbers from Clebsch-Gordan coefficient ratios in the electron capture decay of Pa^{230}.

NIELSEN, NORDBY, AND BJØRNHOLM[135]

Transitions		Branching Ratios		
	Exp.	Theoretical		
		$K=0$	$K=1$	$K=2$
From 954 keV $\dfrac{B(E1)\ 1\rightarrow 0}{B(E1)\ 1\rightarrow 2}$	3.9 ± 0.3	0.5	2.0	
From 573 keV $\dfrac{B(E1)\ 3\rightarrow 4}{B(E1)\ 3\rightarrow 2}$	1.8 ± 0.2	1.33	0.66	
From 508 keV $\dfrac{B(E1)\ 1\rightarrow 0}{B(E1)\ 1\rightarrow 2}$	0.43 ± 0.05	0.5	2.0	
From 783 keV $\dfrac{B(E2)\ 2\rightarrow 0}{B(E2)\ 2\rightarrow 2}$	0.60 ± 0.05	1.8	3.2	0.7

Clebsch-Gordan coefficients.   This negative parity, $K = 0$, band is believed to represent an octupole vibration of the nuclear shape.   A negative parity rotational band of this nature is a general feature of neighboring even-even nuclei.

Another generally occurring collective vibration is the so-called beta-vibration of the quadrupole type.   In the Th^{230} nucleus the $0+$ level at 634 keV is of this type.   The spin and parity of this level is fixed at $0+$ by the observation of conversion lines of an $E0$ transition of 634 keV energy and the determination that these electrons are *not* in coincidence with electrons of the 53 keV transition in the ground state rotational band.   The $E0$ nature of the transition was confirmed by the establishment of a lower limit of ~ 7 for the K-conversion coefficient.   The first rotational excitation of the beta-vibrational band occurs 42 keV higher at 676 keV where a $2+$ level exists.   This level was identified by observing electrons of a 623 keV transition in such abundance that the multipolarity could only be electric monopole and by observing that these electrons were in coincidence with the electrons of the 53 keV transition in the ground state rotational band.   This level was also identified independently in quite a different way by CLASS AND CO-WORKERS.[138]   They produced this state by Coulomb excitation of ionium with low energy protons.   They observed the conversion electrons of the 623 $E0$ transition.

The gamma mode of the quadrupole vibrations may be identified with the $2+$ level at 783 keV.   The placement of this state is confirmed by two $E2$ transitions of 730 keV and 783 keV energy, the first of which is in coincidence with the 53 keV transition in the ground state band.

The level at 954 keV is very important in the decay of Pa^{230} as it is this level which is most strongly populated.   It is strongly de-excited by a 954 keV electric dipole transition going directly to the ground state which fixes the spin and parity of the 954 keV state as $1-$.   This transition is seen in about half the disintegrations of Pa^{230}.   The $2-$ level at 974 may be a rotational excitation of the 954 keV level.   This band may represent another mode of octupole vibration.

The decay scheme shows a number of dotted transitions with energy 280, 337, 320, and 380 keV which are not observed in the conversion electron or singles gamma spectrum.   Gamma rays of approximately this energy are plainly seen in the photon spectrum coincident with the conversion electrons of the two $E0$ transitions.

The decay scheme leads to the selection of $2-$ as the most likely spin and parity for Pa^{230}.   One can account for this choice by selecting the Nilsson orbit $1/2 - [530\uparrow]$ for the 91st proton (by analogy to the 91st proton in Pa^{231}) and the orbit $5/2 + [633\downarrow]$ for the 139th neutron (by analogy to the

---

[138] C. M. Class, Rice Institute, unpublished results (1960). See *Proc. Int. Conf. on Nucl. Struc.*, Kingston, Ont., 1960, Univ. of Toronto Press.

139th neutron in Th^{229}). By the GALLAGHER-MOSZKOWSKI[139] coupling rule these choices lead to the resultant spin and parity, $2-$, for the ground state. The Nilsson assignments cannot be considered proved on this evidence alone.

The absence of any direct beta population to the lower levels of ionium below 700 keV is explained by the K-selection rule.

Very little is known about the beta decay branch of Pa^{230}. ONG[132,133] has reported an end-point energy of 410 kilovolts for the beta spectrum. HILL[134] has measured conversion electrons of a 51.67 keV transition with the L_{II}, L_{III}, M_{II}, and M_{III} spacings corresponding to conversion in uranium. Hence this transition occurs in U^{230} following beta decay and undoubtedly represents the de-excitation of the $2+$ rotational state.

TABLE **8.25.** Alpha groups of Pa^{231}

ROSENBLUM, COTTON, and BOUISSIÈRES[140]		GOL'DIN, TRETYAKOV, AND NOVIKOVA[141]		HUMMEL, ASARO, AND PERLMAN[142,143]			
Energy (MeV)	Abundance (per cent)	Energy (MeV)	Abundance (per cent)	Energy (MeV)	Abundance (per cent)	Energy of Ac^{227} level (keV)	Hindrance factor
5.042	11	5.0490	12	5.046	10	0	230
		5.0205	23	5.017	23	29.4	68
5.002	47						
		5.0060	26	5.001	24	46.1	51
		4.9740	1.5	4.971	2.3	76.3	330
4.938	25	4.9420	24	4.938	22	110.1	21
				4.921	2.8	127	130
4.838	3	4.8476	1.5	4.839	1.4	211	73
4.720	11	4.7270	10	4.722	11	329	1.5
		4.7040	0.8	4.696	1.4	356	7.6
4.660	1–3	4.6710	1.3	4.666	2.1	387	3.2

[139] C. J. Gallagher and S. A. Moszkowski, *Phys. Rev.* 111, 1282 (1958).

[140] S. Rosenblum, E. Cotton, G. Bouissières, *Compt. Rend.* 229, 825 (1949); E. Cotton, *Ann. Phys.* 6, 481 (1951).

[141] L. I. Gol'din, E. F. Tretyakov, and G. I. Novikova, *Proc. of the Moscow Conference on the Peaceful Uses of Atomic Energy*, July 1–5, 1955. Available in English translation, Superintendent of Documents, U.S. Government Printing Office, Washington, D.C.

[142] J. P. Hummel, F. Asaro, and I. Perlman, *Phys. Rev.* 98, 261A (1955); and unpublished results.

[143] J. Hummel, thesis, University of California, July 1956. See *Univ. Calif. Rad. Lab. Report*, *UCRL-3456*, July 1956.

TABLE **8.25.** (continued)

S. A. BARANOV AND CO-WORKERS[144]

Energy* (MeV)	Abundance (%)	Energy of Ac^{224} level (keV)	Hindrance Factor
5.045$_3$	11.0	0	205
5.018$_5$(?)	~2.5	~27.4	640
5.016$_4$	≤20.0	29.4	70
5.012 $\Big\}$(?) 5.010	?	$\Big\}$ ~34(?)	
4.999$_3$	25.4	45.9	45
4.972$_2$	1.4	73.1	525
4.961$_5$	0.4	84.4	1600
4.938$_0$ (standard)*	22.8	107.1	20
4.920$_7$	3.0	126.8	120
4.887$_0$	2 × 10^{-3}	~160	~10^5
4.839$_4$	1.4	209.5	75
4.781$_7$	4 × 10^{-2}	268.2	1050
4.724$_0$	8.4	327.0	2
4.699$_7$	~1	351.7	12
4.667$_5$	1.5	384.5	5
4.630$_2$	~10^{-1}	422.4	~40
4.618$_7$	~10^{-1}	434.0	30
4.586$_0$	1.5 × 10^{-2}	467.4	120
4.553$_3$	8 × 10^{-3}	501.0	120
4.494$_8$	3 × 10^{-3}	560.0	135

* The 4.938 keV group as measured by ROSENBLUM, COTTON, AND BOUISSIÈRES[140] was used as a standard.

8.3.7 *Protactinium-231*

This isotope is found in all uranium minerals where it occurs as a member of the actinouranium decay chain. The history of protactinium and its relationship to the rest of the actinouranium family is described thoroughly in Chapter 6.

Protactinium-231 is an alpha-emitter with a half-life of 34,800 ± 300 years as recalculated by ELSON[145] from the data of VAN WINKLE, LARSON, AND KATZIN.[146] This value is confirmed by KIRBY[147] who obtained the value 34,480 ± 260 years from a calorimetric measurement. It is the longest-lived of the isotopes of protactinium.

The alpha spectrum of Pa^{231} is complex so that magnetic spectrometers

---

[144] S. A. Baranov et al. *Sov. Phys. JETP* **14** 1053 (1962).

[145] R. Elson in Chapter 5, "The Actinide Elements," J. J. Katz and G. T. Seaborg, editors. *Nat. Nucl. Energ. Ser.* **14A** (New York: McGraw-Hill Book Co., Inc., 1954).

[146] Q. VanWinkle, R. G. Larson, and L. I. Katzin, *J. Am. Chem. Soc.* **71**, 2585 (1949).

[147] H. W. Kirby, *J. Inorg. Nucl. Chem.* **18**, 8 (1961).

of high resolution are required to make a significant analysis of it. The results of four recent studies are shown in Table 8.25. It can be seen that each succeeding study has resulted in the resolution of more groups. It seems likely that further groups will be revealed by future studies although the low specific activity of Pa^{231} is a deterrent to the observation of groups in low intensity.

The complexity of the alpha spectrum implies a complex gamma spectrum. Here again, repeated re-examination of the radiations with more care and better instruments has successively revealed more and more transitions. MEITNER[148] first examined the conversion electron spectrum and reported electron energies corresponding to gamma transitions of 95.2, 294, and 323

TABLE **8.26**. Gamma ray transitions in decay of Pa^{231}
deduced from study of conversion electrons.

Results of FALK-VAIRANT[155]		Results of STEPHENS[156]	
Energy (keV)	Multipolarity assignment	Energy (keV)	Multipolarity assignment
		18.88	$M2$
		25.31	$M1$
		27.28	$E1$ ($M2$)
		29.88	$M2$
33.6			
38.0	$E2$	38.12	
		44.04 (?)	
		52.60	($M2$)
56.9	$E2$	57.08	$E2$
63.5	$E2$	63.51	$E2$
		74.04	$E2$
82.3	$M1$ or $M2$		
		77.22	$M1$
		96.68	$E2$
		100.66	$E2$
102	$E2$	102.55	$E2$
198	$E2$		
259	$M1$	259.8	
		283.1	
		299.4	
301	$M1$	302.0	
331	$M1$	329.2	
357	$M1$	356.3	
383	$E1$ or $M2$		

Note: MOORE[154] reinterpreted several of the conversion shell assignments of FALK-VAIRANT[155] which had the result of removing the 82.3 keV gamma-ray and inserting gamma-rays of 280, 96.6, 118, and 67.5 keV.

---

[148] L. Meitner, *Z. Physik*, **50**, 15 (1928).

TABLE **8.26.** (continued)

Results of BARANOV AND CO-WORKERS[144]

Energy (keV)	Multipolarity assignment	Intensity
11.0		11
16.5	$M1$	~20
19.6		~2
22.7		~2
25.4	$M1$	11
27.0		<2
27.4	$E1$	~50
29.4	$M1 + E2$ ⎫	40
34.0	$M1$ ⎭	
38.2	$E1 + M2(?)$	~15
57.0	$E2$ ⎫	13
63.3	$E1$ ⎭	
96.0	$E2(?)$	weak
97.1		~1.5
102.5	$E2$	~0.5
126.8		weak
260.5		weak
285		weak
300	$M2$	2.2
303		weak
330	$M2$	1
354		weak
~380		weak

keV. Her results were later confirmed by HAGGSTROM.[149] SCHARFF-GOLDHABER AND McKEOWN[150] examined the low-energy photons in proportional counters and found a prominent 27 keV gamma ray in addition to L x-rays with energies of 13, 16, and 20 keV. TEILLAC[151] saw electron tracks in a Wilson cloud chamber corresponding to gamma-rays with energy 44 and 66 keV. RIOU[152] used absorption curves taken with proportional counters and Geiger counters to resolve out L x-rays and gamma ray energies of 27, 100, and 300 keV energy. His values for the abundances per 100 alpha disintegrations were 36, 9, 2.5, and 4, respectively, for these photon groups. MOUHASSEB AND RIOU[153] gave slightly different relative abundances. RIOU[152] decided that the 100 keV photon group was a complex mixture of K x-rays and a gamma ray of about 87 keV. The 300 keV

[149] E. Haggstrom, *Phys. Rev.* **62**, 144 (1942).
[150] G. Scharff-Goldhaber and M. McKeown, *Phys. Rev.* **82**, 123 (1951).
[151] J. Teillac, *Ann. Phys.* **7**, 396 (1952).
[152] M. Riou, *Compt. Rend.* **234**, 1157 (1952); and *Ann. Phys.* **8**, 535 (1953).
[153] A. Mouhasseb and M. Riou, *Compt. Rend.* **238**, 2520 (1954).

gamma ray component was also suspected of being complex. Moore[154] examined the gamma rays with a NaI spectrometer and found peaks at 27, 95, and 280 keV. Hummel[146] did a similar study but found a value of 300 keV instead of 280 for the highest energy peak.

The most detailed information on the gamma transitions has come from recent studies of the conversion electrons with magnetic spectrometers of high resolution. The results of Falk-Vairant[155] are given in Table 8.26. The energies of the transitions are given together with the multipolarity assignments which are based on subshell conversion ratios and K/L conversion ratios. The later results of Stephens[156] and of Baranov and co-workers[147] also are given in Table 8.26.

Moore[154] carried out alpha-gamma and gamma-gamma coincidence studies and introduced a variable time delay between the two detectors in order to detect possible delayed transitions. In the alpha-gamma experiments he measured a delay half-life of $(3.7 \pm 0.1) \times 10^{-8}$ seconds for the 27 keV photons. Teillac, Riou, and Desneiges[157] and Foucher, Dick, Perrin, and Vartapetian[158] have also measured the delay in the emission of the 27 keV photons following alpha emission; their values of the half-life are 4.2×10^{-8} and 3.7×10^{-8} seconds, respectively. The multipolarity of the 27 keV transition has been firmly assigned as $E1$ by many authors on the basis of its conversion coefficient. This assignment, the possibility of some $M2$ admixture, and possible anomalies in the conversion coefficients and the half-life are discussed by Asaro, Stephens, Hollander, and Perlman.[159]

Strominger[160] set an upper limit of 1.5×10^{-9} seconds to the half-life of the 300 keV gamma ray (or gamma ray complex) in an alpha-gamma delayed-coincidence experiment.

Albouy[161] measured conversion electrons in coincidence with alpha particles. Hummel[146] performed a few exploratory alpha-gamma coincidence experiments in which the more intense alpha particle groups were singled out in a magnetic spectrometer and the coincident gamma spectrum was measured in a NaI crystal spectrometer. His results are summarized in Table 8.27. Gil and Petit[162] performed coincidence experiments on the 300 keV–27 keV γ-cascade.

[154] R. L. Moore, thesis (Ohio State University) Angular Correlation and Coincidence Studies of Alpha-Gamma Cascade from Pa231, Cm242, and Am241. AECU-2757 (1953).
[155] P. Falk-Vairant, Compt. Rend. 235, 796 (1952).
[156] F. S. Stephens, Jr., unpublished results (1958).
[157] Teillac, Riou, Desneiges, Compt. Rend. 237, 41 (1953).
[158] R. Foucher, L. Dick, N. Perrin, and H. Vartapetian, J. Phys. Rad. 17, 581 (1956).
[159] F. Asaro, F. S. Stephens, J. M. Hollander, and I. Perlman, Phys. Rev. 117, 492 (1960).
[160] D. Strominger, Univ. Calif. Rad. Lab. Report, UCRL-3374 (1956).
[161] G. Albouy, Ann. Phys. 1, 99 (1956).
[162] F. B. Gil and G. Y. Petit, J. Phys. Rad. 22, 680 (1961).

Decay schemes for Pa^{231} have been proposed from time to time on the basis of the available data. A notable publication in this respect is that of FALK-VAIRANT AND RIOU[163] in 1953. But subsequent data have forced revisions in these decay schemes. It is still impossible to present a revised decay scheme for the complex decay of this isotope with any confidence that

TABLE 8.27. Alpha-gamma coincidence results of HUMMEL.[146]

Pa^{231} Alpha-group	Gamma rays in coincidence
$\alpha_{29} + \alpha_{46}$	L x-rays $+ 27$ keV γ
α_{110}	L x-rays $+ 27$ keV γ
α_{329}	K x-rays 300 keV γ (complex)
α_{387}	K x-rays ~ 260 keV γ 300 keV γ ~ 360 keV γ

it will not require some revision or extension as more precise data become available. However, the alpha spectrum does provide a rather firm skeleton of levels on which to build. Furthermore the rather precise data on the conversion electrons permit one to place many gamma transitions with considerable confidence. Some of the alternate choices of gamma ray placement can be ruled out by consideration of the available alpha-gamma or gamma-gamma coincidence results. Figure 8.18 shows a tentative decay scheme constructed in this fashion by STEPHENS[156]. One interesting feature is the presence of pairs of close-lying levels near 30 keV which were not resolved in HUMMEL's alpha spectrum measurements, but were observed in the later work of BARANOV ET AL[144].

The excellent measurements of BARANOV, KULAKOV, SAMOILOV, ZELENKOV, RODIONOV, AND PIROZHKOV[144] on the alpha and electron spectra of Pa^{231} permit a considerable amplification of the decay scheme drawn earlier by STEPHENS. In Fig. 8.19 we show the level scheme obtained from the α-spectrum and the placement of the gamma rays between these levels as given by the Russian authors.

It is quite clear that the level system of Ac^{227} is very complex and that it will not be easy to learn the nature of all the excitations. Some of the levels can be given assignments in the Nilsson scheme of single particle levels for non-spherical nuclei as we shall see below. Many of the levels may represent rotational levels based on the Nilsson levels of intrinsic motion, but the interaction of bands of levels from two or more Nilsson states may be

163 P. Falk-Vairant and M. Riou, *J. Phys. Rad.* **14**, 65 (1953).

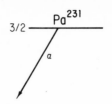

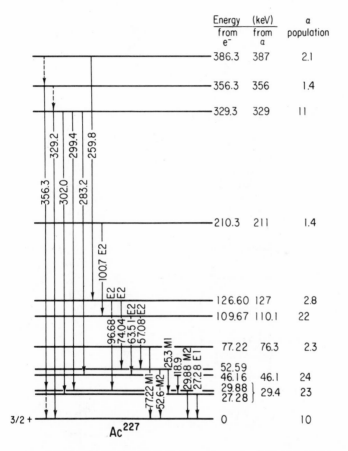

FIG. **8.18.** Decay scheme for Pa^{231} as drawn by STEPHENS (1958).

expected to be severe and the rotational energy spacings and other properties may be so altered as to make identification and analysis difficult.

The nuclear spin of Pa^{231} is 3/2 as determined from atomic spectra.[164] MOTTELSON AND NILSSON[165] discuss the possible NILSSON state assignment of

---

[164] J. E. Mack, *Revs. Mod. Phys.* **22**, 64 (1950).

[165] B. R. Mottelson and S. G. Nilsson, *Mat. Fys. Skr. Dan. Vid. Selsk.* **1**, 8 (1959).

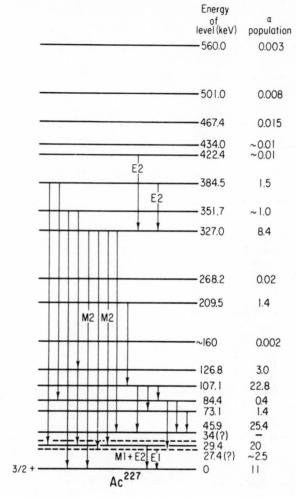

FIG. **8.19.** Decay scheme for Pa[231] redrawn according to the scheme of BARANOV AND CO-WORKERS.

the Pa^{231} ground state and conclude that this state is the 3/2 member of an anomalous $K = 1/2$ band in which the decoupling constant a in the equation

$$E = \frac{\hbar^2}{2\Im} \left[I(I + 1) + a(-1)^{I+1/2}(I + 1/2)\delta_{K,1/2} \right]$$

is negative and sufficiently large to drop the 3/2 level below the 1/2 level. (Compare discussion of "anomalous" $K = 1/2$ rotational bands in Chapter 3.) The $[Nn_z\Lambda]$ quantum numbers are [530]. This assignment is based on a consideration of the common features of the decay of Pa^{231} and Pa^{233} and of the results of NEWTON's experiments on the excitation of levels in Pa^{231} by the Coulomb excitation process.[166]   A similar assignment is made by STEPHENS, ASARO, AND PERLMAN[167] on similar considerations.

Favored alpha decay appears to be that which populates the level at 327 keV.   According to the BOHR, FRÖMAN, AND MOTTELSON[168] hypothesis favored alpha decay of an odd proton alpha-emitter populates that state in the daughter nucleus in which the odd proton is in the same configuration. Hence we may assign[144,165,167] to the 327 keV level the Nilsson quantum numbers $K = 1/2$, $I = 3/2$, [530].   BARANOV AND CO-WORKERS[144] suggest that the levels at 352, 385, 434 and possibly 501 keV may be rotational levels of this band.

The ground state of Ac^{227} has measured spin 3/2.   The multipolarity of the 330 keV gamma-ray connecting the 327 keV level to the ground state is $M2$ which fixes the parity of the ground state as even.   The most likely Nilsson assignment[167,144] is 3/2 + [651].

Some other assignments have been made to other of the levels below 100 keV (see Refs. 167, 144) but they are too tentative to discuss here.

8.3.8 *Protactinium-232*

This nuclide may be made by the following reactions:*

$$Th^{232}(d, 2n)Pa^{232}$$
$$Th^{232}(p, n)Pa^{232}$$
$$Th^{232}(\alpha, p3n)Pa^{232}$$
$$Pa^{231}(d, p)Pa^{232}$$

An additional method of preparation is the neutron irradiation of Pa^{231},

$$Pa^{231}(n, \gamma)Pa^{232} \qquad \sigma = 293 \text{ barns}$$

This last is the best method for the preparation of samples for detailed study of the Pa^{232} radiations since large amounts can be produced and the contamination can be kept low.

GOFMAN AND SEABORG[169] were the first to produce and study this isotope. Protactinium-232 is a beta emitter with a half-life of 1.32 days.[170]   It is also unstable toward electron capture decay but the branching is apparently

[166] J. O. Newton, *Nucl. Phys.* **3**, 345 (1957).

[167] F. S. Stephens, F. Asaro, and I. Perlman, *Phys. Rev.* **113**, 212 (1959).

[168] A. Bohr, P. Fröman, and B. R. Mottelson, *Dan. Mat.-fys. Medd.* **29**, No. 10 (1955).

[169] J. W. Gofman and G. T. Seaborg, Paper No. 19.14, "The Transuranium Elements," *Nat. Nucl. Energ. Ser.*, Division IV, **14B**, (New York: McGraw-Hill Book Company, Inc., 1949)

[170] A. H. Jaffey and E. K. Hyde, *Phys. Rev.* **79**, 280 (1950).

* An indication of the cross sections is given in Table 5.9 of Chapter 5.

TABLE **8.28.** Gamma transitions in the decay of Pa^{232}.
(as summarized by BJØRNHOLM ET AL.[175])

$E\gamma$ (keV)	Multipolarity	L_{I-II}/L_{III} exp.	L_{I-II}/L_{III} theor.	K/L exp.	K/L theor.	γ-intensity from total γ-spectrum	from coinc. γ-spectra	calc. from conv. data	adopted value	Total intensity (per cent)
47.6	E2	1.2	1.2			<1		0.2		78
80.2	E1								0.13	0.16
81.2									0.02	
K x-ray								3.0		
105.4	E1					} 9.6	2.5		2.1	2.5
109.0	E2		1.7					3.3	3.0	26
132.5	E2	1.9							0.02	0.08
139.2	E1							0.7		0.9
150.1	E1	3.4	4.1	3.4	5.0	12	13	12	12	14
174.9	E2						0.025		0.025	0.05
178	E2						0.020		0.020	0.04
183.9	E1								1.65	1.85
388.0	{ M1+ / E2 }	4.0	250 / 4.4	2.1	4.6 / 1.3	} 4.8	7.3	0.5 / 6.7	0.5* / 6.7*	} 8.0
422.0	{ M1+ / E2 }			≈3	4.6 / 1.5	≦3	2.5		0.5* / 2.0*	} 2.8
454.2	{ M1+ / E2 }	10	260 / 5.8	2.6	4.6 / 1.6	} 8.4	5.0	1.1 / 6.3	1.3* / 3.7*	} 5.7
472.8	E1			≈2	5.2		4.2	4.0	4.1	4.2
516.1	E1					2.4	3.3	≈4	3.3	3.4
564.5	E1			4	5.2	} 6.0		2.3		2.3
583.8	E1				5.2		6.4	6.0	6.2	6.3
645	(E2)							0.033	0.033	0.034
676.5	E0			3		} <3	<0.03	0	0	0.016
687.5	E0			3.6			<0.10	0	0	0.056
692.9	E0			4			<0.04	0	0	0.029
711.6	E2					<2	<0.5		0.23	0.23
757.0	E2			3	3.1	<2	<1		0.67	0.67
819.6	E2			3.3	3.3	} 30		8.2	8.2	8.3
865.3	E2							2.8	2.8	2.8
868.0	E2			3.3	3.5			6.3	6.3	6.4
894.8	E1			6.0	5.3		21	21	21	21
971.0	E1			5.8	5.4	40		42	41	41

Column one lists the energy of the internal transitions.   Column two gives the multipolarity, assigned to each transition on the basis of the data presented in the following columns.   First theoretical and experimental L_{I-II}/L_{III} and K/L ratios are compared.   In the subsequent columns the γ-intensities determined from 1) the total scintillation γ-spectrum, 2) the e-γ coincidence measurements and 3) a calculation based on conversion line intensities (assuming the multipolarity given in column two) are compared.   In the last column the sum of conversion line and adopted γ-ray intensities, the total intensity, is given.   The intensities are in per cent of all β-decays.

---

* The adopted values for the three mixed $M1 + E2$ transitions are calculated by combining K and L conversion line intensities with the γ-intensity found from coincidence spectra.
This table reproduced from Ref. 175.

small.　Several groups of investigators[171-174] have contributed to a preliminary study of the very complex radiations of Pa^{232}.　A quite definitive
study has been carried out by BJØRNHOLM, BOEHM, KNUTSEN, AND NIELSEN[175]
and we quote here almost exclusively from their work.

Approximately 60 conversion lines have been identified.　These lines are
superimposed on a complex beta spectrum.　The total intensity of the conversion electrons is greater than the beta spectrum electron intensity.　Accurate measurement of the conversion lines was made on a six-gap beta spectrometer with resolution adjusted to 0.2 per cent.　The absolute accuracy of the
energy determinations was 0.2 per cent.　The gamma transitions deduced
from the conversion lines are listed in Table 8.28.　This table also shows the
multipolarity assignments made on the basis of $L_I + L_{II}/L_{III}$ and K/L
electron ratios, and K-conversion coefficients.　The Fermi analysis of the
beta spectrum made by these workers is shown in Table 8.29.　Valuable

TABLE 8.29. Fermi analysis of the Pa^{232} β-spectrum.　$Q_\beta = 1345 \pm 20$ keV

Max energy keV	Intensity (per cent)	Leading to excited levels at: keV
1295 ± 20	0.7	47.6 ±20*
1190 ± 20	0.8	156.6 ±20*
600 ± 100	<1	(750 ± 100)
320 ± 30	98	1005 ± 30

Table prepared by BJØRNHOLM, BOEHM, KNUTSEN, AND NIELSEN.[175]

* The value of Q_β is based on the assumption that the two high energy β-groups populate
the 2+ and 4+ members of the ground-state rotational band at 47.6 keV and 156.6 keV.
This is suggested by the energy difference, 105 ± 20 keV; and by the observation that high
energy β-rays are only coincident with low energy (conversion) electrons and weak γ-rays
of $\approx$ 109 keV.

information on the arrangement of these gamma rays into a decay scheme
was obtained by beta-gamma and $e - \gamma$ coincidence measurements.　In these
experiments the gating signal was provided by pulses from the detector of the
six-gap beta spectrometer with the spectrometer focused on a specific

[171] C. I. Browne, Jr., D. C. Hoffman, H. L. Smith, M. E. Bunker, J. P. Mize, J. W.
Starner, R. L. Moore, and J. P. Balagna, Phys. Rev. 96, 827A (1954).

[172] Ong Ping Hok, Thesis, Free University of Amsterdam, March, 1955.

[173] Ong Ping Hok and G. J. Sizoo, Physica 20, 77 (1954).

[174] M. W. Hill, Thesis, University of California, 1958; also published as Univ. Calif. Rad.
Lab. Report, UCRL-8423, August 1958.

[175] S. Bjørnholm, F. Boehm, A. Knutsen, and O. B. Nielsen, Nucl. Phys. 42, 469 (1963).

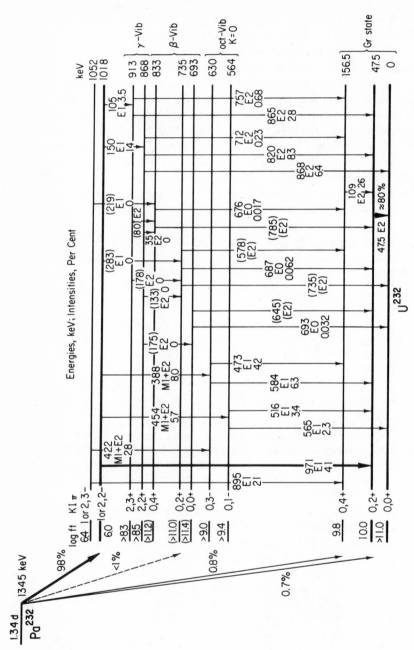

FIG. **8.20.** The decay scheme of Pa²³² as formulated by Bjørnholm, Boehm, Knutsen, and Nielsen. The log ft values were determined from the in-out intensity balance of each level from which the intensities of the individual beta branches were calculated. The β⁻ branches to the ground state band were, however, measured directly. The gamma energies given in parentheses are very weak in intensity and are not identified with certainty.

electron line. The coincident gamma spectrum was measured with a sodium iodide crystal in combination with a multichannel analyzer.

The decay scheme as formulated by BJØRNHOLM, BOEHM, KNUTSEN, AND NIELSEN[175] is shown in Fig. 8.20. The more intense gamma rays can be placed, without benefit of the coincidence experiment results, by the following considerations. Uranium-232, like all even-even nuclei in this region of mass numbers, has a deformed shape and its lowest levels of excitation represent rotational excitation with a spin sequence $0+$, $2+$, $4+$, etc. This ground state rotational band is known to occur in U^{232} from a study of the alpha-decay of Pu^{236} (see Section 9.2.6 of Chapter 9). Hence in the decay of Pa^{232} there is no question about the placement of the intense $E2$ transitions with energy 47.5 keV and 109 keV. HILL, HOLLANDER, AND PERLMAN[176] have measured the precise values 47.48 and 108.9 keV for these energies. The next step is to note that many of the more energetic transitions occur in pairs which differ in energy precisely by the 47.5 or 108.9 keV difference of the levels of the ground state rotational band. Each such pair of transitions can be used to set the energy of an excited level; for example the levels at 564, 630, 868, and 913 keV are fixed with certainty in this way. The energies of other transitions are then found to be equal to the energy difference of two of these higher levels and can be placed in the scheme. In the case of the three levels at 693, 735, and 833, which are labeled beta-vibrational band in the figure, the additional information obtained from $e^-\gamma$ and e^-e^- coincidence experiments was crucial in the proof of their correct placement in the scheme. The multipolarity assignments of the gamma rays were used in the assignment of spins and parities to all levels. It is beyond the scope of this summary to include all the experimental results and detailed arguments which entered into the construction and interpretation of the Pa^{232} decay scheme, but these can be found in the original paper.[175] We shall, however, call attention to several interesting features of the level system of U^{232}.

The U^{232} level system is an excellent example of the types of collective excitation described by the collective model of the nucleus. There is first the ground state rotational band with the level spacings, the spins and parity sequence, and the pattern of electric quadrupole cascade de-excitation which are universally observed in the mass region above mass 225. At 564 and 630 keV there are levels with spin and parity $1-$ and $3-$, respectively. These are interpreted as an excitation of an octupole vibrational mode. The K-quantum number of this excitation is zero. The $1-$ level is the base state for one phonon of vibrational excitation and the $3-$ level is the first rotational excitation of this base state. Both states de-excite by a pair of $E1$ transitions to two members of the ground state rotational band. According to theory the ratio of the reduced transition probabilities should be given by ratios of squares of Clebsch-Gordan coefficients. This proves to be the

---
[176] M. W. Hill, J. M. Hollander, and I. Perlman, unpublished results (1956).

case as shown in Table 8.30. The levels at 693, 735, and 833 keV are believed to be a rotational band of levels based on a 693 keV level which represents the beta-vibrational mode of quadrupole collective excitation. These levels decay by $E2$ and $E0$ transitions to the ground state rotational band. These levels are very weakly populated if at all by direct beta decay. This fact receives a natural explanation in terms of K-forbiddenness since the spin and K-value of Pa^{232} is most likely 3. The weak population of the

TABLE **8.30**. Reduced branching ratios in U^{232} as analyzed by BJØRNHOLM, ET AL.[175]

Upper level		Multi-polarity	Lower levels		Branching intensities		z
(keV)	$K, I\pi$		(keV)	K, I, π	exp.	theor.	
564	$0,1^-$	$E1$	0	0.0^+	1	1	
			47.6	0.2^+	1.9 ± 0.2	2.0	
630	$0,3^-$	$E1$	47.6	0.2^+	1	1	
			156.6	0.4^+	1.24 ± 0.05	1.33	
868	$2,2^+$	$E2$	0	0.0^+	0.69 ± 0.05	0.70	0.003 ± 0.007
			47.6	0.2^+	1	1	
			156.6	0.4^+	0.057 ± 0.006	0.05	0.009 ± 0.007
913	$2,3^+$	$E2$	47.6	0.2^+	1	1	
			156.6	0.4^+	0.47 ± 0.10	0.40	0.012 ± 0.015
1018	$2,2^-$	$E1$	868	2.2^+	1	1	
			913	2.3^+	0.50 ± 0.06	0.50	
1052	$2,3^-$	$E1$	868	2.2^+	1.0 ± 0.3	0.72	
			913	2.3^+	1	1	
			972	2.4^+	1.0 ± 0.5	1.3	
1018	$1,2^-$	$M1$	564	0.1^-	1	1	
			630	0.3^-	0.6 ± 0.1	0.67	
1018	$1,2^-$	$E2$	same	0.1^-	1	1	
				0.3^-	4 ± 1	4.0	
868	$2,2^+$	$E2$	693	0.0^+	0.32 ± 0.08	0.70	0.14 ± 0.04
			735	0.2^+	1	1	
			833	0.4^+	0.15 ± 0.05	0.05	0.10 ± 0.06
913	$2,3^+$	$E2$	735	0.2^+	1	1	
			833	0.4^+	0.9 ± 0.4	0.40	0.07 ± 0.05

The table gives the reduced intensities of the γ-transitions from the upper level listed in column one to the lower levels in column four, the reduction factor being $(E_\gamma)^{2L+1}$, where L is the multipole order. One intensity in each branching has been normalized to unity.

The quantity z in the last column is derived from the discrepancy between theoretical and experimental branching intensities and is a relative measure of mixing between the bands (see Chapter 3).

levels of the beta-vibrational band makes it difficult to identify with certainty all the $E2$ transitions which de-excite them or to determine reduced transition probability ratios. The gamma-vibrational mode of quadrupole excitation is represented by the levels at 868 and 913 keV. Theory predicts that these levels will de-excite by $E2$ transitions to members of the ground state band. This de-excitation is observed and the ratios of reduced transition probabilities for pairs of these $E2$ transitions agree with the theoretical calculation from Clebsch-Gordan coefficient ratios. See Table 8.30. The nature of the very heavily populated levels of 1018 and 1052 keV is not identified with certainty. Between them they receive about 98 per cent of the total beta intensity.

Table 8.31 summarizes the rotational constants for the four rotational bands seen in the U^{232} level system.

TABLE 8.31. Rotational bands $E_{rot} = A(I\,(I+1)) + B(I\,(I+1))^2$ in U^{232}.

Band head		$\dfrac{\hbar^2}{2\mathfrak{J}} = A$	$-B$
keV	$K, I\pi$	keV	keV
0	0,0+	7.86 ± 0.03	0.008 ± 0.002
564	0,1−	6.6 ± 0.1	
693	0,0+	7.0 ± 0.2	0.002 ± 0.006
868	2,2+	7.55 ± 0.03	0.005 ± 0.002

One puzzling feature of the decay scheme is the existence of several electric quadrupole transitions from levels in the gamma-vibrational band to levels in the beta-vibrational band. Such transitions would be forbidden if the vibrational states were pure; hence there must be some mixing of the β and γ wave functions.

BARANOV AND CO-WORKERS[177] have also made a detailed study of the conversion electrons and photons of the Pa^{232} gamma radiations. There is agreement with the work of BJØRNHOLM, BOEHM, KNUTSEN, AND NIELSEN[175] in many of the details but there are some strong disagreements between the two studies in the multipolarity assignments of certain gamma rays and in the designation of certain levels as β and γ vibrational states.

8.3.9 Protactinium-233

The production of Pa^{233} by neutron irradiation of thorium and its original identification as a 27.4 day beta emitter are mentioned in the discussion of the $4n + 1$ series of radioactive elements in Section 7.1 of the preceding

---

[177] S. A. Baranov, P. S. Samoilov, Yu. F. Rodionov, S. N. Belen'kii and S. V. Pirozhkov, *Sov. Phys. JETP* **14**, 1237 (1962).

TABLE **8.32.** Energy (in keV) of gamma transitions in decay of Pa[233].

	From measurements of conversion electrons						Crystal spectrometer photon measurements	
	Ong Ping Hok[180,181]	Brodie[182]	Elliott and Underhill[183]	Keller and Cork[184]	Schultze and Ahlf[188]*	Albridge, Hill, and Hollander[179,185]	Albridge, et al.[179]	Browne and Perlman[178]
1	15.8	—	—	—	17.18	17.26	—	—
2	27.5	28.6	—	28.9	28.5	28.54	—	28.7(100)
3	40	40.7	—	40.6	40.3	40.29	40.35	40.5(75)
4	—	—	—	—	—	—	41.65	—
5	58	58	—	58.1	58.0	57.90	—	—
6	75	75.6	76	75.7	75.3	75.13	75.28	75.4(3)
7	86	87	88	87.1	86.6	86.45	86.59	87.0(3)
8	104	104	105	104.5	103.8	103.6	103.86	—
9	—	—	—	—	—	—	145.42	—
10	272	—	—	272.6	272	271.5	271.62	—
11	301	302	298	301.5	300	299.8	300.20	—
12	313	314	310	313.1	312	311.7	311.91	—
13	341	343	339	342	340	340.3	340.51	—
14	376	—	—	376.6	376	375.5	375.35	—
15	400	—	398	399.9	398	398.3	398.57	—
16	417	—	415	416.4	416	415.6	415.87	—
17	476	—	474	—	—	—	—	—

* These authors report several additional gamma rays of low intensity not listed in this table.

chapter. As a precursor of the important $4n + 1$ series isotope, U^{233}, it is an important collateral member of the $4n + 1$ series. The radiations of Pa^{233} are complex. There are numerous gamma rays ranging in energy from 28 to 416 keV. Many of these give rise to strong conversion electron lines and Auger electrons superimposed on a complex beta spectrum. Gamma ray spectrum analysis by the sodium iodide scintillation spectrometer technique is not very useful because of the complexity of the spectrum and the limited resolving power of the method. Photon energies can be accurately measured in bent crystal spectrometers. The L x-ray and gamma ray photons up to 100 keV were measured by BROWNE AND PERLMAN[178] with such a spectrometer; their values for four gamma rays are listed in Table 8.32. Several years later this study was repeated and extended to much higher energies by ALBRIDGE, HOLLANDER, GALLAGHER, AND HAMILTON[179]; their results are also listed in the table. Many authors have contributed to the accurate measurement and interpretation of the conversion electron spectrum of Pa^{233}, and, except for a few doubtful points, the agreement on the major transitions has been gratifying. The gamma ray transition energies reported by several authors[178-185] are summarized in Table 8.32. The multipolarity assignments of BISGÅRD, DAHL, AND OLESEN,[186] of ALBOUY AND VALADARES,[187] and of ALBRIDGE AND HOLLANDER[179] and of SCHULTZE AND AHLF[188] are summarized in Table 8.33.

It has been difficult to make a detailed analysis of the beta spectrum because so many conversion electrons are superimposed on the beta continuum; attempts at such a resolution were made by BRODIE[182] and by ONG PING HOK[180,181] with results which agree very well as to end-point energies but only roughly as to relative intensity. BRODIE'S[182] values are: 568 ± 5 keV (5 per cent), 256 ± 4 keV (57 per cent) and 140 ± 14 keV (38 per cent). Each of these groups may be unresolved mixtures of two groups separated by 16

[178] C. I. Browne and I. Perlman, unpublished results quoted in *Revs. Mod. Phys.* **25**, 469 (1953).

[179] R. G. Albridge, J. M. Hollander, C. J. Gallagher, and J. H. Hamilton, *Nucl. Phys.* **27**, 529 (1961); See also thesis report of R. G. Albridge, University of California report *UCRL-8642*, 1960.

[180] Ong Ping Hok, Thesis, University of Amsterdam, March 1955.

[181] Ong Ping Hok and P. Kramer, *Physica* **21**, 676 (1955).

[182] W. D. Brodie, *Proc. Phys. Soc.* **67A**, 397 (1954).

[183] L. G. Elliott and A. B. Underhill, *Atomic Energy Research Establishment Report*, *HAR-761* (Harwell) (1952).

[184] H. B. Keller and J. M. Cork, *Phys. Rev.* **79**, 1030 (1950).

[185] R. G. Albridge, Jr., M. W. Hill, and J. M. Hollander, unpublished measurements made with permanent magnet spectrographs.

[186] K. M. Bisgård, P. Dahl, and K. Olesen, *Nucl. Phys.* **12**, 612 (1959) and K. M. Bisgård, P. Dahl, P. Hornshøj, and A. B. Knutsen, *Nucl. Phys.* **41**, 21 (1963).

[187] G. Albouy and M. Valadares, *J. Phys. Rad.* **20**, 816 (1959).

[188] G. Schultze and J. Ahlf, *Nucl. Phys.* **30**, 163 (1962)

TABLE **8.33.** The decay of Pa^{233}—multipolarity assignments of various workers.

E_γ (keV)	Conversion ratio	Experimental Values		Theoretical values[a]			Multipolarity (per cent)			
		Bisgård, et al.[b]	Albridge and Hollander[d]	$E1$	$E2$	$M1$	Bisgård, et al.[a]	Albouy and Valadares[c]	Albridge and Hollander[d]	Schultze and Ahlf[e]
28	$\dfrac{M_I + M_{II}}{M_{III}}$	~9	4.3	2.2	0.7	170	$M1 + E2$	$M1 + E2$	98 $M1$ 2 $E2$	99 $M1$ 1 $E2$
	$\dfrac{M_{III}}{M_{IV}}$	>20	—	1.9	62	7.6				
40	$\dfrac{L_I + L_{II}}{L_{III}}$	1.0	1.7	1.1	1.1	230	$M1 + E2$	20 $M1$ 80 $E2$	70 $M1$ 30 $E2$	46 $M1$ 54 $E2$
	$\dfrac{L_I}{L_{II}}$	~0.4	0.27	0.7	0.03	13				
	$\dfrac{M_I + M_{II}}{M_{III}}$	1.7	—	2.0	1.1	200				
	$\dfrac{M_{III}}{M_{IV}}$	≳50	—	2.8	46	7.3				
76	$\dfrac{L_I + L_{II}}{L_{III}}$	>130	74	2.2	1.3	223	$M1$	$M1(< 1\ E2)$	98 $M1$ 2 $E2$	<0.5 $E2$
	$\dfrac{L_I}{L_{II}}$	~13	7.1	1.4	0.06	12				

87	$\frac{L_I + L_{II}}{L_{III}}$	>20	40	2.4	1.3	207	M1	M1(<1 E2)	97 M1	<0.2 E2
	$\frac{L_I}{L_{II}}$	~9	7.4	1.5	0.06	11			3 E2	
104	$\frac{L_I + L_{II}}{L_{III}}$	>30	30	1.9	1.6	229	M1	M1(<1 E2)	95 M1	<3 E2
	$\frac{L_I}{L_{II}}$	~9	5.6	0.9	0.06	11			5 E2	
273	K/L	0.55	≧0.59	5.2	0.67	4.6	E2	E3,E4, or E5 or M1 + E2	E2	100 E2
	$\frac{L_I + L_{II}}{L_{III}}$	2.8	≧1.3	6.7	3.3	274				
301	K/L	5.0	4.1	5.2	0.84	4.5	M1	M1	90 M1	<3 E2
									10 E2	
313	K/L	5.1	3.9	5.1	0.9	4.5	M1	M1	M1	<3 E2
341	K/L	5.0	4.0	5.2	1.1	4.5	M1	M1	95 M1	92 M1
	$\frac{L_I + L_{II}}{L_{III}}$	>100	—	8.2	4.2	277			5 E2	8 E2

TABLE **8.33**—*continued*

E_γ (keV)	Conversion ratio	Experimental Values		Theoretical values[a]			Multipolarity (per cent)			
		Bisgård, et al.[b]	Albridge and Hollander[d]	E1	E2	M1	Bisgård, et al.[a]	Albouy and Valadares[c]	Albridge and Hollander[d]	Schultze and Ahlf[e]
377	K/L	1.2	0.90	5.1	1.2	4.6	E2	—	E2	E2
	$\dfrac{L_I+L_{II}}{L_{III}}$	3.1	3.0	9.0	4.9	287				
400	K/L	~2.4	1.0	5.2	1.3	4.5	E2	—	E2	E2
	$\dfrac{L_I+L_{II}}{L_{III}}$	4.0	5.1	9.2	5.1	294				
417	K/L	3.9	2.8	5.1	1.5	4.4	M1	—	22 M1 78 E2	4 M1 9.6 E2
	$\dfrac{L_I+L_{II}}{L_{III}}$	>20	9.0	9.9	5.5	297				

This table is a copy of one presented by BISGÅRD, ET AL., with the data of other workers included for comparison.

[a] M. E. Rose, Internal Conversion Coefficients 1958.
[b] Bisgård, Dahl, and Olesen, *Nucl. Phys.* **12**, 612 (1959).
[c] Albouy and Valadares, *J. Phys. Rad.* **20**, 816 (1959).
[d] Albridge, Hollander, Gallagher and Hamilton, *Nucl. Phys.* **27**, 529 (1961).
[e] G. Schultze and J. Ahlf, *Nucl. Phys.* **30**, 163 (1962).

to 40 kilovolts.   The beta component intensities and log ft values shown in
the decay scheme were derived from gamma ray transition intensities, which
clearly seem to indicate this greater complexity in the beta spectrum.
The gamma transitions listed in Tables 8.32 and 8.33 can be arranged in
the decay scheme of Fig. 8.21.   This scheme was prepared by ALBRIDGE AND
HOLLANDER[179] but in general features it is based on the earlier scheme of
BRODIE[182] which was supported by ONG AND KRAMER.[181]   SCHULTZE AND
AHLF[188] also published a decay scheme essentially identical to Fig. 8.21 except
for some gamma transition intensities.   This scheme accounts for all the
gamma rays listed except for the doubtful weak ray of 476 keV energy and

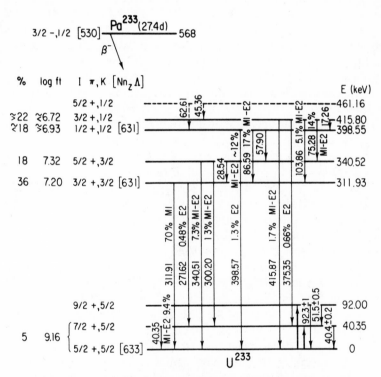

FIG. 8.21.   A tentative decay scheme for Pa[233].   The per cent beta populations listed were deduced by ALBRIDGE et al.[179] from the gamma transition
intensities which were in turn deduced from relative electron and photon
intensities.   The log ft values were calculated from the beta populations
by the method of Moszkowski.   The percentage figures given for the
gamma transitions refer to the percentage of Pa[233] disintegrations in which
the transition appears.   The level at 461.16 keV was assigned on the basis
of two weak electron lines which could be assigned to transitions of 62.11
and 45.36 keV.   ALBRIDGE ET AL.[179] also discuss the possible assignments
of two weak photon transitions of 41.65 and 145.42 keV to a level at
270.3 or 457 keV.

gives a good "in-out" intensity balance for each level. The scheme receives support from additional pieces of evidence. ELLIOTT AND UNDERHILL[183] observed coincidences between the conversion electrons of the 312 keV transition and those of the 75, 87, and 104 keV transitions. UNIK[189] performed similar electron-electron coincidence experiments with similar results. He also showed that the 75 keV transition is in coincidence with a 151 ± 4 keV beta group and the 86 keV transition is in coincidence with a 166 ± 5 keV beta group. The beta spectrum in coincidence with the 312 keV transition is complex and comprises beta groups with end point energies of 250 ± 5 keV and 168 ± 8 keV.

The nuclear spin of Pa^{233} has been determined to be 3/2 by the atomic beam resonance technique by WINOCUR.[190] The Nilsson orbital assignment for the ground state is believed[191] to be 1/2 − [530] where these numbers represent the following quantum numbers, $K\pi[Nn_z\Lambda]$. The rotational band based on this $K = 1/2$ level has an anomalous ordering and the $I = 3/2$ member of the band lies lowest. The arguments upon which this assignment is based are cited in the discussion of the decay scheme of Np^{237} in Chapter 9, Section 9.1.9.

The Nilsson assignments shown in the diagram for the levels of U^{233} follow those given by NEWTON.[192] He contributed greatly to the identification of the lowest-lying levels in U^{233} by Coulomb excitation of levels at 40.1 and 92 keV and by identification of these as the 7/2 and 9/2 rotational states of a $K = 5/2$ ground state. This Coulombic excitation is shown in the figure by upward-pointing arrows. The ground state of U^{233} is known to have spin 5/2 from atomic spectra and paramagnetic resonance studies. (See Section 8.4.6.) NEWTON[192] assigned the Nilsson wave function 5/2 + [633] to the ground state and this is considered to be well established. NEWTON'S identification of the levels at 312 and 398 keV with Nilsson orbitals were made with much less certainty at the time but later data on the multipolarity assignments[179,186] of the gamma rays in the decay of Pa^{233} have served to confirm them. See especially the discussion of ALBRIDGE.[179] Other discussions of the U^{233} Nilsson assignments can be cited.[191,193,188]

If these Nilsson assignments are accepted as correct, both for Pa^{233} and U^{233}, it is possible to interpret many details of the decay scheme in terms of the selection rules pertinent to the collective model of the nucleus. For example the high log ft values for beta transitions to the ground state rotational band are explained by K-forbiddenness and violation of the selection

[189] J. Unik, Thesis, University of California 1960; also published as *Univ. Calif. Rad. Lab. Report, UCRL-9105*, 1960.

[190] J. Winocur, Thesis, University of California, 1960; R. Marrus, W. A. Nierenberg, and J. Winocur, *Nucl. Phys.* **23**, 90 (1961).

[191] B. R. Mottelson and S. G. Nilsson, *Mat. fys. Skr. Dan. Vid. Selsk.* **1**, 8 (1959).

[192] J. O. Newton, *Nucl. Phys.* **5**, 218 (1958)

[193] F. S. Stephens, F. Asaro, and I. Perlman, *Phys. Rev.* **113**, 212 (1959).

rules in the asymptotic quantum numbers. Also many of the branching ratios in the gamma ray de-excitation of a higher level of U^{233} can be calculated theoretically by Clebsch-Gordan coefficient ratios. Details of this type are discussed by ALBRIDGE ET AL.[179]

8.3.10 Protactinium-234

In the decay chain of U^{238}, the species Pa^{234} occurs in two isomeric forms known as UX_2 and UZ. UX_2 has a half-life of 1.18 minutes and UZ has a half-life of 6.7 hours; both are beta-emitters. The discovery of these interesting nuclides during the early history of radioactivity is mentioned in Section 6.1 of Chapter 6, and the genetic relationships within the uranium decay chain are covered in Section 6.2 of that chapter. The radiations of UX_2 and of UZ are usually studied in a mixture of the $UX_1 - UX_2 - UZ$ complex and it is convenient to discuss the radiations of all three nuclides in one place; hence the radiations of the isomers of Pa^{234} are discussed in Section 8.2.12 entitled Thorium-234 and the $UX_1 - UX_2 - UZ$ Complex.

8.3.11 Protactinium-235

HARVEY AND PARSONS[194] prepared Th^{235} and Pa^{235} by neutron irradiation of $Th^{234}(UX_1)$. The reactions are:

$$Th^{234}(n, \gamma)Th^{235} \xrightarrow{\beta^-} Pa^{235}$$

The 24-day Th^{234} was extracted from one kilogram of natural uranium and thoroughly separated from uranium and protactinium immediately before neutron irradiation. Ten minutes after the completion of the irradiation, a protactinium fraction was purified and examined. A 23-minute beta-emitting protactinium isotope which could only be Pa^{235} was found. From milking experiments, an upper limit of 5 minutes was set on the half-life of Th^{235}.

MEINKE AND SEABORG[195] prepared Pa^{235} by bombardment of uranium with 19-MeV deuterons and 9.5-MeV protons:

$$U^{238}(d, \alpha n)Pa^{235} \quad \sigma \approx 2 \times 10^{-27} \, cm^2$$

$$U^{238}(p, \alpha)Pa^{235} \quad \sigma \approx 3 \times 10^{-29} \, cm^2$$

They reported a half-life of 23.7 minutes. The beta end-point energy was set at 1.4 MeV by absorption measurements. No gamma rays were observed. LINDNER AND OSBORNE[196] have prepared Pa^{235} by proton bombardment of uranium at higher energies. They report the following cross sections: 100

194 B. G. Harvey and B. I. Parsons, Phys. Rev. **80**, 1098 (1950).
195 W. W. Meinke and G. T. Seaborg, Phys. Rev. **78**, 475 (1950).
196 M. Lindner and R. N. Osborne, Phys. Rev. **103**, 378 (1956).

MeV, 5.7 mb; 175 MeV, 7.3 mb; 250 MeV, 15 mb; 340 MeV, 21 mb. It remains to be determined whether the decay of Pa^{235} involves the 26 minute isomer of U^{235} (see Section 8.4.8).

8.3.12 *Protactinium-236*

WOLZAK AND MORINAGA[197] identified a protactinium isotope of 12.5 ± 1.0 minute half-life in the products of the bombardment of natural uranium with 26 MeV deuterons. They assigned this activity to Pa^{236} on the basis of its likely production by the (d, α) process. Also, they measured an end point energy of 3.35 ± 0.10 MeV for the beta particles, which is much higher than the expected decay energy of Pa^{237}. The authors point out that the same activity had been observed earlier by CRANE AND IDDINGS[198] who had assigned it to Pa^{237}. See next section.

8.3.13 *Protactinium-237*

CRANE AND IDDINGS bombarded uranium with high energy deuterons (40–190 MeV) and found in the protactinium fraction the 23.5-minute Pa^{235} produced by the $(d, \alpha n)$ reaction and in addition, a small amount of a 10.5 ± 1 minute beta emitter which they assigned to Pa^{237}, formed by the reaction:

$$U^{238}(d, 2pn)Pa^{237}$$

The isotope identification and the half-life measurement were made by the repeated separation of U^{237} daughter activity. (But see Section 8.3.12.)

TABLE **8.34.** Beta groups of Pa^{237}.
TAKAHASHI AND MORINAGA[199]

E_0 (MeV)	Intensity (per cent)	Log ft	Classification
3.30	60	7.2	1u
1.35	23	7.3	1u
	7	7.4	ah
≈ 0.8	$\leqslant 10$	$\geqslant 6.5$	ah

TAKAHASHI AND MORINAGA[199] prepared Pa^{237} by the bombardment of uranium with a 25 MeV bremsstrahlung beam

$$U^{238}(\gamma, p)Pa^{237}$$

---

[197] G. Wolzak and H. Morinaga, *Radiochem. Acta* **1**, 225 (1963).
[198] W. W. T. Crane and G. M. Iddings, *Phys. Rev.* **95**, 1702 (1954).
[199] K. Takahashi and H. Morinaga, *Nucl. Phys.* **15**, 664 (1960).

In the decay of a radiochemically purified protactinium fraction they observed a prominent component with a half-life of 39 ± 3 minutes. It is difficult to understand this discrepancy in half-life values, but the determination of TAKAHASHI AND MORINAGA is the more direct.[200]

These authors studied the beta spectrum with an anthracene scintillation spectrometer with the results summarized in Table 8.34. They studied the complex gamma spectrum with a sodium iodide scintillation spectrometer and found the gamma rays listed in Table 8.35. They performed a few

TABLE 8.35. Gamma rays of Pa^{237} (Takahashi and Morinaga[199]).

Energy (keV)	Relative intensity	Relative intensity coincident with 145 keV gamma-ray
90	50	5
145	45	3
205	55	3
275	20	2.5
330	40	1.5
405	30	(5)*
460	100	3.5
550	30	—
590	25	(5)*
750	50	2.5
805	45	
860 ⎫ 880 ⎭	100	
915	100	
1045	35	
1320	10	
1420	15	

* Possibly caused by Pa^{234}(UZ) contamination.

gamma-gamma coincidence experiments. The low source strengths made it impossible to study the conversion electron spectrum. TAKAHASHI AND MORINAGA constructed the decay scheme shown in the Figure 8.22. The Nilsson orbital assignments were based almost entirely on an examination of Nilsson diagrams and by examination of systematic trends in Nilsson orbitals in neighboring nuclei. Hence, it is a highly tentative decay scheme, useful as a guide to future work.

---

[200] It may be worth mention that Pate and Poskanzer [*Phys. Rev.* **123**, 648 (1961)] found the 10 minute activity but no 39 minute activity among the protactinium isotopes isolated from uranium targets bombarded with high energy protons.

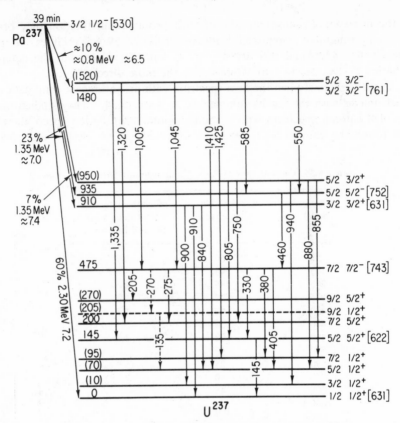

FIG. 8.22. Decay scheme of Pa²³⁷ as formulated by TAKAHASHI AND MORINAGA.

8.4 THE ISOTOPES OF URANIUM

8.4.1 Uranium-227

This isotope is the parent activity of the U^{227} collateral series which is discussed in Section 7.2.8 of the previous chapter.[201]   Our knowledge of U^{227} is limited to the facts that it emits alpha-particles of 6.8 ± 0.1 MeV energy and it has an apparent half-life of 1.3 ± 0.3 minutes.

8.4.2 Uranium-228

This isotope is the parent activity for the U^{228} collateral series discussed in Section 7.2.7 of the previous chapter.[202]   The reported data on its alpha particle spectrum and gamma spectrum are summarized in Table 7.9.

201 W. W. Meinke, A. Ghiorso, and G. T. Seaborg, *Phys. Rev.* **85**, 429 (1952).
202 W. W. Meinke, A. Ghiorso and G. T. Seaborg, *Phys. Rev.* **81**, 782 (1951).

These data and the results of alpha-gamma coincidence experiments performed by Ruiz[203] lead to the decay scheme shown in Fig. 8.23.

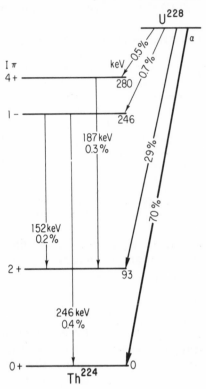

FIG. **8.23.** Decay scheme of U[228] as drawn by Ruiz.

8.4.3 *Uranium-229*

The 58-minute isotope, U^{229}, is the first member of the U^{229} collateral series.[204]   The preparation of U^{229} and the characteristics of all members of the decay series to which it gives rise are treated in Section 7.2.6.   Uranium-229 decays by the emission of alpha particles in about 20 per cent of its disintegrations.   It decays by orbital electron capture in the remaining 80 per cent of its decay events.   Ruiz[205] reports the alpha spectrum summarized in Table 8.36.   A preliminary analysis based on the alpha spectrum

[203] C. P. Ruiz, F. Asaro and I. Perlman, unpublished results, 1960; C. P. Ruiz, Ph.D. thesis, *Univ. Calif. Lawrence Rad. Lab. Report, UCRL-9511,* April 1961.

[204] W. W. Meinke, A. Ghiorso, and G. T. Seaborg, *Phys. Rev.* **81**, 782 (1951).

[205] C. P. Ruiz, F. Asaro, I. Perlman, unpublished results 1960–1961. See C. P. Ruiz, Ph.D. thesis, *Univ. Calif. Lawrence Rad. Lab. Report, UCRL-9511,* April 1961.

712 ISOTOPES OF THORIUM, PROTACTINIUM, AND URANIUM

and some alpha-gamma coincidence experiments indicates that the lowest four levels of Th^{225} populated in alpha decay are members of a rotational band with base spin of 3/2. The tentative Nilsson orbital assignment is

TABLE 8.36. Alpha groups of U^{229} reported by Ruiz.

Alpha-particle energy (MeV)*	Excited state energy (keV)	Abundance (per cent)	Hindrance factor
6.355 ± 0.003	0	64	1.5
6.327	29 ± 2	20 ± 2	3.7
6.292	65 ± 2	11 ± 1	4.6
6.255	102 ± 3	1 ± 0.5	35
6.218	139 ± 3	3 ± 1	7.9
6.180	178 ± 4	1 ± 0.5	16

* Alpha particle energies are expressed relative to Th^{226} α_0 and Ra^{222} α_0 taken as 6.330 and 6.552 MeV, respectively.

3/2 + [631]. Since unhindered alpha decay goes directly to the ground state of Th^{225}, the identical orbital assignment is given to the ground state of U^{229}.

8.4.4 Uranium-230

The 20.8 day alpha-emitter U^{230} is a member of the Pa^{230} collateral series[206] which is discussed in Section 7.2.1. The methods of preparation of samples of U^{230} are treated there. Uranium-230 is always associated with its four short-lived alpha-emitting daughters so that its alpha spectrum is complex as shown in Fig. 7.10 and 7.11 presented in Section 7.2.1. Here we are concerned only with the details of the radiations of U^{230} itself.

TABLE 8.37. Alpha groups of uranium-230

Group energy (MeV)	Excited state energy (MeV)	Relative abundance (per cent)
5.884	0	67.2
5.813	72.13	32.1
5.658*	230	0.7
5.662	226.4	0.4
5.658	230.4	0.3

* This is an unresolved doublet consisting of the following two groups.

---

[206] M. H. Studier and E. K. Hyde, *Phys. Rev.* **74**, 591 (1948).

A study of the alpha spectrum in a magnetic spectrometer of high resolution by ASARO AND PERLMAN[207] revealed the complex structures shown in Table 8.37.

The four gamma rays shown in the decay scheme of Fig. 8.24 have been identified and subjected to study with NaI crystal spectrometers and high resolution permanent magnet electron spectrographs.[207–209] An interesting feature of the decay scheme is that the alpha particle group of 5.658 MeV energy seen by ASARO AND PERLMAN[207] must actually be an unresolved pair of alpha particles differing by only 4 kilovolts and populating a 4+ level and 1− level. This decay scheme is supported by many pieces of evidence.

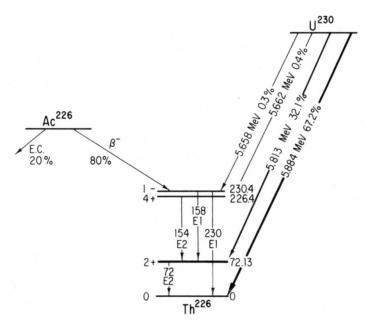

FIG. **8.24.** Decay scheme of U[230] including the beta decay scheme of Ac[226].

The 0+, 2+, 4+ sequence of levels is the familiar rotational band of levels seen in every even-even nucleus in the heavy element region. The $E2$ nature of the 72.13 keV and 154.3 keV gamma transitions is shown[209] by the prominent conversion in the L_{II} and L_{III} and in the M_{II} and M_{III} shells and the extremely weak conversion in the L_I and M_I shells. The conversion coefficient of the 72 keV transition as determined by the population of the

[207] F. Asaro and I. Perlman, *Phys. Rev.* **104**, 91 (1956).

[208] F. Stephens, Jr., F. Asaro, and I. Perlman, *Phys. Rev.* **96**, 1568 (1954).

[209] W. G. Smith, F. Asaro, and J. M. Hollander, *Phys. Rev.* **104**, 99 (1956).

alpha decay to the state and the number of photons is correct for an electric quadrupole transition[207]; (alpha population 32.6 per cent, 72 keV photons 0.75 per cent, $\alpha_{L,M,...} = 42$.)

Angular correlations between alpha particles of a selected energy range and gamma rays of a specific energy were studied by STEPHENS, ASARO, AND PERLMAN.[208]   A thin crystal of NaI was used as the alpha detector and a thick crystal was used as the gamma detector.   The signals from both detectors were submitted to pulse height analysis for energy discrimination. The observed correlation for α_{72} of U^{230} with the 72 keV gamma ray photons was the correct one for a sequence $0+\xrightarrow{\alpha} 2+\xrightarrow{\gamma} 0+$.   On the other hand the observed correlation between α_{230} of U^{230} and the 230 keV gamma ray photons was entirely different but in agreement with that to be expected of the sequence $0+\xrightarrow{\alpha} 1-\xrightarrow{\gamma} 0+$.   The 154.1 and 158 keV photons could not be resolved by the NaI crystal spectrometer; when the α_{230}-160 keV gamma angular correlation was studied no variation of counting rate with angle was observed.   This is consistent with the supposition that the 230 keV "level" consists of unresolved $4+$ and $1-$ states and therefore the sequence measured is a mixture of $0+\xrightarrow{\alpha} 1-\xrightarrow{\gamma} 2+$ and $0+\xrightarrow{\alpha} 4+\xrightarrow{\gamma} 2+$.

Other strong evidence for the presence of two states near 230 keV comes from a study[210] of the beta decay of Ac^{226}.   This isotope decays to the $1-$ state in Th^{226} and not at all to the close-lying $4+$ state.   The relative abundance of the 158 keV gamma ray to that of the 230 keV gamma ray in the decay of Ac^{226} is lower by a factor of two than it is in the alpha-decay of U^{230}.

The $1-$ state in Th^{226} is a result of a collective excitation of the nucleus. This same $1-$ state appears in the excited levels of many even-even nuclei among the heavy elements and may represent octupole vibrations.   In this case as in the others the $K = 0$ assignment for the $1-$ state is supported by the ratio of the reduced transition probabilities of the two $E1$ transitions. See the discussion of Chapter 3.

8.4.5 *Uranium-231*

OSBORNE, THOMPSON, AND VAN WINKLE[211] prepared U^{231} by deuteron and helium ion bombardment of protactinium by the reactions:

$$Pa^{231}(d, 2n)U^{231}$$

$$Pa^{231}(\alpha, p3n)U^{231}$$

[210] J. Grover, G. T. Seaborg, and F. Stephens, Jr., unpublished information (1954); quoted by Stephens, Asaro, and Perlman, *Phys. Rev.* **100**, 1543 (1955).

[211] D. W. Osborne, R. C. Thompson, and Q. Van Winkle, Paper No. 19.11, "The Transuranium Elements," *Nat. Nucl. Energ. Ser.*, Division IV, **14B** (New York: McGraw-Hill Book Company, Inc., 1949).

It has also been prepared by helium-ion bombardment of thorium by the reaction:

$$Th^{232}(\alpha, 5n)U^{231}$$

In either case it is contaminated somewhat by other uranium isotopes. Uranium-230 is most similar in half-life and hence most likely to interfere in the measurement of the radiations. Uranium-231 decays almost entirely by orbital electron capture with a half-life of 4.2 days. Some preliminary measurements indicate the presence of gamma rays of 51-, 64-, and 76-keV energy. CRANE AND PERLMAN[212] found alpha particles of 5.45-MeV energy in an abundance corresponding to an alpha branching of 5.5 × 10⁻³ per cent. HOLLANDER, STEPHENS, ASARO, AND PERLMAN[213] studied the gamma ray photons and conversion electrons emitted by U^{231} and constructed a decay scheme. This work is discussed together with the studies of the same authors on the beta decay of Th^{231} since in both cases the daughter product is Pa^{231}. See Section 8.2.10.

8.4.6 Uranium-232

The uranium isotope U^{232} is a beta-stable, alpha-particle emitter with a half-life of 73.6 years.[214] It was first identified[215] following its growth from the shorter-lived β^- emitter Pa^{232} which had been prepared by the deuteron bombardment of thorium as follows:

$$Th^{232}(d, 2n)Pa^{232} \xrightarrow[\beta^-]{1.32 \text{ days}} U^{232}$$

It has also been produced by other cyclotron-induced reactions:

$$Th^{232}(p, n)Pa^{232} \xrightarrow{\beta^-} U^{232}$$
$$Th^{232}(\alpha, 4n)U^{232}$$
$$Pa^{231}(\alpha, p2n)U^{232}$$

The cross sections for several of these reactions are given in Table 5.5 of Chapter 5. Uranium-232 can also be prepared by intense neutron irradiation of ionium or protactinium* as follows:

212 W. W. T. Crane and I. Perlman, unpublished results cited in *Revs. Mod. Phys.* **25**, 469 (1953).

213 J. M. Hollander, F. S. Stephens, F. Asaro, and I. Perlman, "Energy Levels of Pa²³¹" unpublished paper 1961.

214 P. A. Sellers, C. M. Stevens, and M. H. Studier, *Phys. Rev.* **94**, 952 (1954).

215 J. W. Gofman and G. T. Seaborg, Paper No. 19.14, "The Transuranium Elements," *Nat. Nucl. Energ. Ser.*, Division IV, **14B** (New York: McGraw-Hill Book Company, Inc., 1949).

* Oak Ridge National Laboratory reported the isolation of 33 milligrams of U²³² containing only 180–350 ppm of U²³³ and 1 gram containing only 0.72 weight per cent U²³³. These samples were made by neutron irradiation of 45 grams of Pa²³¹. See report *ORNL-3452*, p. 239 (1963). This material was used to determine a new half-life of 71.7 ± 0.9 years.

$$\text{Th}^{230}(n,\gamma)\text{Th}^{231} \xrightarrow{\beta^-} \text{Pa}^{231}(n,\gamma)\text{Pa}^{232} \xrightarrow{\beta^-} \text{U}^{232}$$

Any Th^{232} present in the ionium will cause the formation of considerable U^{233} by the first order reaction, but the U^{232} alpha activity may still be predominant because of the longer (1.6×10^5 year) half-life of U^{233}.

A careful study of the alpha spectrum of U^{232} has been carried out by ASARO AND PERLMAN.[216]   The gamma radiations have been most thoroughly studied and interpreted by these workers and by SCHARFF-GOLDHABER AND CO-WORKERS.[217]

The alpha spectrum[216] consists of three directly observed groups: 5.318 MeV (68 per cent), 5.261 MeV (32 per cent) and 5.132 MeV (0.32 per cent). A fourth group with energy 4.998 MeV and intensity 0.01 per cent is deduced from gamma ray measurements.[216,217]   Gamma rays of 57.9, 131, 268, and 326 keV have been observed with the aid of sodium iodide scintillation spectrometers. The photon abundances of these gamma transitions are 0.21 per cent, 0.75 per cent, 4×10^{-3} per cent, and 4×10^{-3} per cent, respectively.[216]   It will be useful to refer to Fig. 8.25 in discussing these alpha and gamma radiations further.

The alpha spectrum of U^{232} follows the familiar pattern for even-even nuclei in this mass region. The principal decay is to the $0+$ ground state of Th^{228} with lower abundance groups proceeding to members of a rotational band of levels based on this ground state. The 131-keV transition is an electric quadrupole transition connecting the $4+$ and $2+$ levels while the 57.9 keV transition is an electric quadrupole transition from the $2+$ level to ground. The electric quadrupole nature of both transitions was established by calculating the conversion coefficient from the observed photon intensities and the known alpha group intensities. The cascade arrangement of the 57.9 and 131 keV gamma rays was verified by gamma-gamma coincidence measurements.[216,217]

The level at 326 keV is deduced from the observation of low intensity gamma rays of energy 326 keV and 268 keV which differ by 58 keV. The intensity of these gamma transitions is $\sim 4 \times 10^{-3}$ of the total alpha disintegrations. The $1-$ spin and parity assignment of the 326 keV level is based on analogy to well characterized $1-$ levels found in the decay of other even-even alpha emitters in this region such as U^{230}, Th^{226}, and Th^{228}.

The beta decay of MsTh_2 (Ac^{228}) also gives information on the levels of Th^{228}. The studies of KYLES, CAMPBELL, AND HENDERSON,[218] and of

[216] F. Asaro and I. Perlman, *Phys. Rev.* **99**, 37 (1955).

[217] G. Scharff-Goldhaber, E. der Mateosian, G. Harbottle, and M. McKeown, *Phys. Rev.* **99**, 180 (1955)

[218] J. Kyles, C. G. Campbell, and W. J. Henderson, *Proc. Phys. Soc.* (London), **A66**, 519 (1953).

BRODIE[219] indicate that $E2$ transitions of 56.75 keV and 127.5 keV also appear in the decay of Ac[228]. A puzzling feature of the 58-keV transition is that two groups[219,220] of authors have reported the lifetime of the state as > 10 microseconds. The work of ASARO AND PERLMAN[216] on U[232] sources and of SCHARFF-GOLDHABER AND CO-WORKERS[217] on U[232] and Ac[228] sources indicates that this transition has a half-life shorter than 0.2 microseconds.

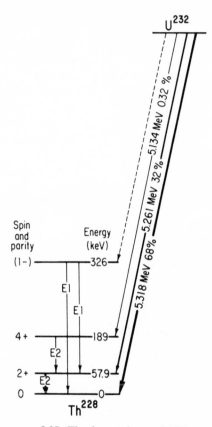

FIG. **8.25.** The decay scheme of U[232].

BOX AND KLAIBER[221] also found a pair of gamma rays in the decay of Ac[228] differing by 58 keV (their gamma energies were 336 keV and 278 keV) which may be identical with those observed in U[232] decay. Further discussion of Ac[228] appears in Section 6.3.2 of Chapter 6.

A third nuclide which decays to Th[228] is Pa[228] as discussed in Section

[219] W. D. Brodie, *Proc. Phys. Soc.* (London), **A67**, 265 (1954).
[220] M. Lecoin, M. Perey, and J. Teillac, *J. Phys. Rad.* **10**, 33 (1949).
[221] H. C. Box and G. S. Klaiber, *Phys. Rev.* **95**, 1247 (1954).

TABLE **8.38**. Alpha groups of U^{233}.

Gol'din, Novikova, Tretyakov 1955[a]			Ruiz, Asaro, Perlman 1960[b]				Dzhelepov, Ivanov, Nedovesov and Shishin 1959[c]			Dzhelepov, Ivanov, Nedovesov, Puzynovich[d]	
E_α (MeV)	Energy level in Th^{229} daughter (keV)	Intensity (per cent)	E_α (MeV)	Energy level in Th^{229} daughter (keV)	Intensity (per cent)	Hindrance factor	E_α (MeV)	Energy level in Th^{229} daughter (keV)	Intensity (per cent)	Energy level in Th^{229} daughter (keV)	Intensity (per cent)
4.816	0	83.5	4.8157	0	83.7	1.17	—	0	83.4	0	83
										29 ± 2	0.48
4.773	43.2	14.9	4.773	43	14.1	3.66	—	43	14.9	42 ± 3	14.6
							—	71.4	~0.3	72 ± 2	0.3
										97	1.5
4.717	100	1.6	4.719	99	1.9	10.5	—	100	1.6		
										126 ± 2	0.08
										(145 ± 5)	≤0.01
										163 ± 2	0.06
4.655	164	0.07	4.652	166	0.05 ± 0.03	200	—	166 ± 3	0.06 ± 0.015		
										195 ± 3	0.015
4.582	237	0.04*	not seen	237	<0.02	>100	?	234 ± 5	<0.007		
										(240 ± 5)	≤0.004
4.489	333 ± 5	0.03	4.500	320	0.04 ± 0.02	10	—	316 ± 3	0.033 ± .008	316 ± 2	0.033
							—	364 ± 5	<.005	(364 ± 5)	≤0.004

[a] L. L. Gol'din, E. F. Tretyakov, and G. I. Novikova, *Proceedings of a Conference on Peaceful Uses of Atomic Energy*, Moscow, July 1955, *Acad. Sci. USSR*; see also *Phys. Rev.* **103**, 1004 (1956).

[b] C. Ruiz, F. Asaro, and I. Perlman, unpublished results (1960); see C. Ruiz, Ph.D. Thesis, *Univ. Calif. Rad. Lab. Report, UCRL-9511* (1961).

[c] B. S. Dzhelepov, R. B. Ivanov, V. G. Nedovesov, and B. P. Shishin, *Izvest. Akad. Nauk. SSSR. Ser. Fiz.* **23**, 782, 788 (1959); see translation in *Bull. Acad. Sci. USSR, Physical Series* **23**, No. 7.

[d] B. S. Dzhelepov, R. B. Ivanov, V. G. Nedovesov, and Yu. T. Puzynovich, *Izvest. Akad. Nauk. SSSR Ser. Fiz.* **24**, 258 (1960).

[e] E. F. Tretyakov, M. P. Anikina, L. L. Gol'din, G. I. Novikova, and N. I. Pirogova, *Sov. Phys., JETP* **37** (10), 656 (1960).

* These authors later revised this intensity downward to 0.007 per cent. (See Ref. e above).

8.3.4.   All the radiations shown in Fig. 8.25 are also observed in the decay of Pa^{228} but in addition there are many gamma rays dropping down from higher-lying levels of Th^{228} which are not reached in the alpha-decay of U^{232}.

8.4.7 *Uranium-233*

This long-lived alpha-emitter is made by the irradiation of thorium with neutrons:

$$Th^{232}(n, \gamma)Th^{233}; \; Th^{233} \xrightarrow[23 \text{ min}]{\beta^-} Pa^{233} \xrightarrow[27.4 \text{ day}]{\beta^-} U^{233}$$

It is beta stable and has a half-life of 1.62×10^5 years.[222,223,224] The discovery of U^{233} and its importance as a member of the $4n + 1$ series of radioactive isotopes is discussed in Section 7.1.4 of the preceding chapter. Uranium-233 is of great technical importance because its high cross section for fission when irradiated with thermal neutrons and its other physical properties make it one of the few suitable materials for the industrial or military release of nucelar energy.   The fission characteristics of U^{233} are thoroughly reviewed in Volume III, Part 1.

The first careful measurements of the alpha particles of U^{233} were reported by CRANSHAW AND HARVEY[225] and by ASARO.[226]   These reports have been superseded by the four studies summarized in Table 8.38.   From the study of the gamma radiations emitted by U^{233} it is quite clear that other alpha particle groups are emitted with an intensity of ~ 0.01 per cent. RUIZ[227], for example, examined the alpha spectrum in an ionization chamber alpha spectrometer operated in a gamma-alpha coincidence arrangement so that only those alpha particles in coincidence with gamma rays were recorded.   This largely eliminated the interference ("tailing") from the very intense α_0 group and made it possible to detect alpha transitions with 142, 210, and 318 keV less decay energy than the ground state transition.   The intensity of these groups was estimated as ~ 0.01 per cent, ~ 0.02 per cent, and ~ 0.04 per cent, respectively.

The intense gamma transitions which de-excite the 99 keV and 42.8 keV

[222] E. K. Hyde, paper 19.15, p. 1431, *Nat. Nucl. Energ. Ser.* **14B** "The Transuranium Elements," edited by Seaborg, Katz, and Manning (New York: McGraw-Hill Book Company, Inc., 1949).

[223] Dokuchayev and Osipov, *Atomnaya Energ.* **6**, 73 (1959).

[224] D. S. Popplewell, *React. Sci. and Tech.* **14**, 50 (1961).

[225] T. E. Cranshaw and J. A. Harvey, *Can. J. Res.* **26A**, 243 (1948).

[226] F. Asaro, *Univ. Calif. Rad. Lab. Report*, UCRL-3180, June (1953).

[227] C. Ruiz, F. Asaro, and I. Perlman, unpublished results (1960); see C. Ruiz, Ph.D. Thesis, *Univ. Calif. Rad. Lab. Report UCRL-9511* (1961).

levels in the Th^{229} daughter nucleus have been carefully studied by many authors$^{228-232}$ of whom we cite only a few. STUDIER^{230} observed gamma ray photons of 40 and 80 keV and their corresponding conversion electrons. He also reported a gamma ray of 310 keV energy in 0.1 per cent intensity.

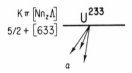

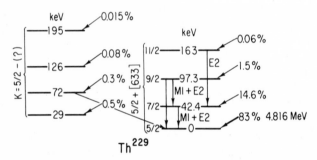

FIG. 8.26. Partial decay scheme of U^{233} drawn in a way to emphasize the rotational band interpretation of the observed levels of Th^{229}. The interpretation of the levels at the left as members of a $K = 5/2 -$ band is speculative. See especially Ref. 246. The interpretation of the four levels at the right as members of a $K = 5/2 +$ band seems well established.

BISGÅRD^{229} found electrons corresponding to 43, 56, and 99 keV gamma transitions in coincidence with alpha particles. WEST, DAWSON, AND MANDELBERG^{228} found L x-rays, a 42.8 $\pm$ 0.3 keV gamma ray and a 56.1 keV gamma ray with intensities of 4 $\times$ 10^{-2}, 5 $\times$ 10^{-4}, and 1 $\times$ 10^{-4} photons per alpha, respectively. TRETYAKOV AND CO-WORKERS^{233} studied conversion electron energies and assigned energies of 42.4 $\pm$ 0.2, 54.7 $\pm$ 0.5, and 97.3

228 D. West, J. K. Dawson, and C. J. Mandelberg, *Phil. Mag.* **43**, 875 (1952).

229 K. M. Bisgård, *Proc. Phys. Soc.* (London), **65A**, 677 (1952).

230 M. H. Studier, paper 1.3 in *Report TID-5223* "Production and Separation of U^{233}"; see also *Report AECD-2444*.

231 D. C. Dunlavey, *Univ. Calif. Rad. Lab. Report, UCRL-1911*, August 1952.

232 C. A. Prohaska, *Univ. Calif. Rad. Lab. Report, UCRL-1395* (1951).

$\pm$ 0.3 keV to the three transitions under discussion. ANDERSEN, BISGÅRD, AND HANSEN[234] also carefully restudied the conversion electrons of these transitions. The placement of these three gamma rays in the decay scheme seems well established and is shown in Fig. 8.26.

We turn now to a discussion of the less intense gamma rays. The gamma transitions deduced by TRETYAKOV AND CO-WORKERS[233] from conversion electron spectra are given in Table 8.39.

TABLE **8.39**. Gamma ray transition energies in the decay of U^{233} from conversion electron spectrum.

Energy (keV)	Multipolarity
29.1 $\pm$ 0.2	$M1$?
42.4 $\pm$ 0.2	80% $M1$ ⎤
	20% $E2$ ⎬ *
54.7 $\pm$ 0.5	$M1 + E2$ ⎦ †
66.0 $\pm$ 1.0	
71.4 $\pm$ 0.6	
97.3 $\pm$ 0.3	$E2$
103.0 $\pm$ 1.0	—
121.0 $\pm$ 0.3	$E2$
245.3 $\pm$ 0.5	$M1$
248.6 $\pm$ 0.8	$M1$?
277.8 $\pm$ 1.5	$M1$?
291.5 $\pm$ 0.5	$M1$
317.0 $\pm$ 1.5	$M1$
321.0 $\pm$ 1.5	$M1$?
366.0 $\pm$ 2.0	$M1$?

From Tretyakov, Anikina, Gol'din, Novikova, and Pirogova, *Sov. Phys. JETP* **37**, (10), 656 (1960).

* Andersen, *et al.*[234] report 86% $M1$ + 14% $E2$ for this transition.

† Andersen *et al.*[234] report 85% $M1$ + 15% $E2$ for this transition.

RUIZ, ASARO, AND PERLMAN[227] used scintillation spectrometer techniques to study the gamma rays. In addition to an analysis of the "singles" spectrum they performed gamma-alpha, alpha-gamma, and gamma-gamma coincidence experiments which revealed the presence of photons with energies of 43, 57, 72, 94, 102, 118, 146, 164, 182, 211, 242, 282, 318, and 367 keV.

---

[233] E. F. Tretyakov, M. P. Anikina, L. L. Gol'din, G. I. Novikova, and N. I. Pirogova, *Sov. Phys. JETP* **37** (10), 656 (1960).

[234] T. Andersen, K. M. Bisgård, and P. G. Hansen, *Nucl. Phys.* **27**, 673 (1961).

The coincidence experiments suggested that a majority of these transitions terminated at the ground state of Th^{229}. These workers as well as the Russian authors cited above have formulated tentative decay schemes which include many more alpha and gamma transitions than are shown in the decay scheme given here.

Some progress has been made in the assignment of Nilsson orbitals to the odd neutron in U^{233} and in Th^{229}. The spin of U^{233} has been measured as 5/2 by interpretation of atomic spectra[235-238] and by a nuclear paramagnetic resonance study.[239]   The magnetic moment is 0.51 magnetons.[239] A Nilsson state with $K = 5/2$ which would be a natural choice[240] for neutron number 141 is 5/2 + [633] where the brackets refer to the asymptotic quantum numbers $[Nn_z\Lambda]$. The prominent alpha decay goes to the ground state of Th^{229} and to the rotational levels based on this intrinsic state. According to the concept of favored alpha decay put forth by BOHR, FRÖMAN, AND MOTTELSON[241], this fixes the assignment of the Th^{229} ground state also as 5/2 + [633]. A spin measurement[242] by the optical hyperfine measurement technique gave a preliminary value $\geqslant 3/2$ and probably 5/2. This is an interesting case because usually the favored decay in an odd-A alpha emitter proceeds to an excited intrinsic state in the daughter.   The fact that Th^{229} and U^{233} both have the same ground state configurations implies that the odd-particle state filled for Th^{229} is vacated when the particle becomes paired.   The $K = 5/2$ assignment of the ground state of U^{233} has been further confirmed by the Coulombic excitation studies of NEWTON.[240]   His results are summarized in Fig. 8.27.   The energy spacing and gamma ray pattern correspond to that expected for a 5/2, 7/2, 9/2 rotational sequence.   Information on other intrinsic states of excitation in U^{233} comes from a study of the decay of Pa^{233}.   (See Section 8.3.9.)

Several of the lowest-lying levels of Th^{229} can be interpreted as rotational levels based on the $K = 5/2$ ground state.   The levels at 42.8 and at 98.9 keV are almost certainly the 7/2+ and 9/2+ levels, respectively, of this band and the 164 keV level is probably the 11/2 member of the band.   The levels

235 K. L. Vander Sluis and J. R. McNally, Jr., *J. Opt. Soc. Amer.* **44**, 87 (1954); **45**, 65 (1955).

236 N. I. Kaliteevskii and M. P. Chaika, *Doklady, Akad. Nauk SSSR*, **103**, 49 (1955); *Optika i Specktroskopiya* **1**, 809 (1956); AEC-tr-2890.

237 L. A. Korostyleva, A. R. Striganov, and N. M. Iashin, *Sov. Phys., JETP*, **1**, 310 (1955).

238 A. G. Zimin and N. M. Yashin, *Doklady, Akad. Nauk SSSR* **109**, 283 (1956); *Sov. Phys., Doklady*, **1**, 419 (1957).

239 P. B. Dorain, C. A. Hutchison, Jr., and E. Wong, *Phys. Rev.* **105**, 1307 (1957).

240 J. O. Newton, *Nucl. Phys.* **5**, 218 (1957).

241 Bohr, Fröman, and Mottelson, *Kgl. Dan. Videnskab. Selskab. Mat.-fys. Medd.* **29**, No. 10 (1955).

242 M. Fred and F. Tomkins, private communication from D. Engelkemeier.

at 237 keV and 320 keV were interpreted at one time[243,244] as the 13/2 and 15/2 levels of this same band, but later experimental evidence[227,233,245] proved that these assignments could not be correct. It is clear from the gamma ray evidence[227,233] that additional intrinsic Nilsson states of Th[229] are reached in the alpha decay of U[233] but no very definite assignments have been made.

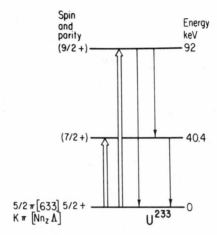

FIG. 8.27. Coulombic excitation of rotational levels in U[233] (after Newton).

In the alpha spectrum studies of DZHELEPOV, IVANOV, NEDOVESOV AND PUZYNOVICH[246] reported in Table 8.34 special attention was given to low intensity groups not detected in previous studies. These workers found evidence for Th[229] levels at 29, 72, 126 and 195 keV which they interpreted as a rotational band of levels based on a $K = 5/2$, negative parity state at 29 keV.

8.4.8 Uranium-234

This isotope appears in the natural uranium decay chain in which context it has traditionally borne the name Uranium-II. In natural uranium its

---
[243] L. L. Gol'din, E. F. Tretyakov, and G. I. Novikova, *Proceedings of a Conference of the Academy of Sciences of the USSR on the Peaceful Uses of Atomic Energy*, July 1955; English translation available from Superintendent of Documents, U.S. Government Printing Office, Washington 25, D.C.

[244] L. L. Gol'din, G. I. Novikova, and E. F. Tretyakov, *Phys. Rev.* **103**, 1004 (1956).

[245] B. S. Dzhelepov, R. B. Ivanov, V. G. Nedovesov, and B. P. Shishin, *Izvest. Akad. Nauk SSSR Ser. Fiz.* **23**, 782, 788 (1959).

[246] B. S. Dzhelepov, R. B. Ivanov, V. G. Nedovesov, and Yu. T. Puzynovich, *Izvest. Akad. Nauk SSSR, Ser. Fiz.* **24**, 258 (1960); English translation, *Bull. Acad. Sci. USSR, Phys. Ser.* **24**, 247 (1961).

abundance is only 0.0055 atom per cent. Its position as a member of the uranium series is discussed in Chapter 6. It can be isolated in high isotopic purity as a daughter product from large samples of 90-year Pu^{238} after a suitable decay period. It is a beta-stable alpha-emitter with a half-life of 2.48×10^5 years. (Refer to Table 6.2 in Section 6.2 of Chapter 6.) The alpha particle energy was reported by HARVEY, JACKSON, EASTWOOD, AND HANNA[247] to be 4.768 MeV on the basis of careful ionization chamber measurements. GOL'DIN, NOVIKOVA, AND TRETYAKOV[243] measured the alpha spectrum in an enriched sample of 7 per cent abundance and found two groups; the main group of energy of $4.768 \pm .001$ MeV energy was in 72 per cent abundance; a second group 51.5 keV lower in energy was in 28 per cent abundance. BARANOV, ZELENKOV, AND KULAKOV[248] found an additional α_{173} group in an abundance $\leqslant 0.37 \pm 0.11$ per cent. Their values for the α_0 and α_{53} groups were 72.5 per cent and 27.5 per cent, respectively. By means of an alpha-electron coincidence technique KOMAR, KOROLEV, AND KOCHAROV[249] also observed the α_{173} group in an abundance of 0.35 per cent.

TEILLAC[250] saw the conversion electrons of a gamma ray of about 50 keV energy. BELL AND CO-WORKERS[251] reported gamma rays of 53 and 118 keV as well as K x-rays from the conversion of the 118 keV gamma ray. VALLADAS[251a] performed coincidence experiments between alpha particles and gamma rays and concluded that there were at least three alpha groups in the U^{234} spectrum with the following abundances: α_0 (77 per cent), α_{56} (23 per cent), and α_{170} (~ 0.3 per cent). SCHARFF-GOLDHABER[252] also reports the presence of the gamma rays of 50 and 117 keV energy.

These observations are summarized in the decay scheme of Fig. 8.28. This is a typical spectrum for an even-even alpha-emitter in the heavy element region. There seems little doubt that the observed alpha groups populate three members of the ground state rotational band of Th^{230} (ionium) and that the $4+$ level is de-excited with the usual cascade of electric quadrupole transitions, the second of which is very highly converted.

Proceeding on the assumption that some alpha decay should occur to the

---

[247] B. G. Harvey, H. G. Jackson, T. A. Eastwood, and G. C. Hanna, *Can. J. Phys.* **35**, 258 (1957).

[248] S. A. Baranov, A. G. Zelenkov, and V. M. Kulakov, *Bull. Acad. Sci. USSR, Phys. Ser.*, Columbia Translations **24**, 1045 (1960).

[249] A. P. Komar, G. A. Korolev, and G. E. Kocharov, *Bull. Acad. Sci. USSR, Phys. Ser.*, Columbia Translations **22**, 818 (1958).

[250] J. Teillac, *Compt. Rend.* **230**, 1056 (1950), *Ann. Phys.* **7**, 396 (1952).

[251] P. R. Bell, *et al.*, reported in *Oak Ridge National Laboratory Report, ORNL-1164*, April, 1952 (unpublished).

[251a] G. Valladas, *Compt. Rend.* **237**, 1673 (1953).

[252] G. Scharff-Goldhaber, reported in *Brookhaven National Laboratory Report BNL-103*, June, 1951 (unpublished).

states of vibrational excitation of Th^{230} identified in the decay scheme of Pa^{230}, BJØRNHOLM, LEDERER, ASARO, AND PERLMAN[252] searched for evidence for such decay by alpha-gamma and alpha-electron coincidence techniques.

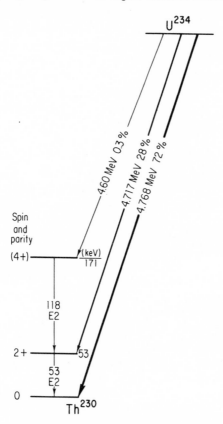

FIG. **8.28.** Decay scheme of U^{234}. The slight population of levels at 508 and 634 keV is not shown.

Evidence was found for alpha particles of 4.12 MeV in $(2.1 \pm 0.5) \times 10^{-5}$ per cent intensity populating the 650 ± 20 keV state which they identified with the known beta vibrational state at 634 keV ($KI\pi = 0, 0, +$). Evidence was also found for alpha particles of 4.27 MeV energy in $(4 \pm 1) \times 10^{-5}$ per cent intensity populating a level at 505 keV identified with the known $1-$ state at 508 keV previously identified as a state of octupole vibrational excitation.

Information on other levels of Th^{230} has been obtained from the gamma

[252] S. Bjørnholm, M. Lederer, F. Asaro, and I. Perlman, *Phys. Rev.* **130**, 2000 (1963).

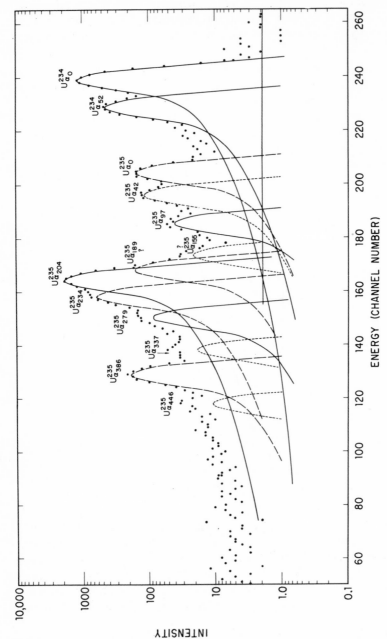

FIG. **8.29.** Alpha spectrum of U[235] as recorded with solid-state detectors by Pilger, Stephens, Asaro, and Perlman. Solid dots are experimental points. The curves show the resolution of the spectrum into the groups labeled at the peaks.

radiations seen in the electron capture branch of the decay of Pa^{230} (see Section 7.3.1 of the preceding chapter).

8.4.9 Uranium-235

All uranium minerals contain U^{235} in about 0.720 per cent isotopic abundance.* Uranium-235 is the parent activity of the actinouranium family of natural radioactivities which is thoroughly discussed in Section 6.4 of Chapter 6. The fission characteristics of U^{235} are thoroughly discussed in Volume III, Part 1.

Uranium-235 is an alpha emitter with a half-life of 7.13×10^8 years. The low specific activity of 4.5 disintegrations per minute per microgram causes considerable difficulty in the determination of the alpha spectrum. A number of analyses of this spectrum have been carried out by absorption or ionization chamber techniques[253] but these have been superseded by the work of PILGER, STEPHENS, ASARO, AND PERLMAN,[254,255] D. J. SKILLINGS[256] and BARANOV, ZELENKOV, AND KULAKOV.[257] PILGER, ET AL. used highly enriched samples of U^{235} containing ~ 60 per cent U^{235} and ~ 40 per cent U^{234} by alpha activity. These authors measured the alpha spectrum with a magnetic spectrograph at a resolution of ~ 15 keV and with a Au-Si surface barrier spectrometer at a resolution of 25 keV. D. J. SKILLINGS used a sample of U^{235} of similar composition. He measured the alpha spectrum with a P-Si diffused-junction solid state spectrometer at a resolution of 25 keV. BARANOV, ET AL. used a sample containing ~ 90 per cent U^{234} and ~ 10 per cent U^{235} by alpha activity. They measured the alpha spectrum in a magnetic spectrograph at a resolution of ~ 8 keV.

Figure 8.29 shows a spectrum of U^{235} taken by PILGER, ET AL. with a solid state spectrometer and Fig. 8.30 shows a spectrum taken with the magnetic spectrograph of BARANOV, ET AL.[257] For the more intense alpha groups, the high resolution spectrum taken with the magnetic spectrograph gives more definitive results; for low intensity groups the better statistics of the spectra taken with the solid state counter give better results. A summary of the data and a choice of the best values are shown in Table 8.40.

The gamma rays associated with the decay of U^{235} have been studied by a number of groups; among recently published studies are those of PILGER,

---

[253] See, for example, the work of A. Ghiorso, *Phys. Rev.* **82**, 979 (1951).

[254] R. C. Pilger, Jr., Thesis, *UCRL-3877*, July 1957.

[255] R. C. Pilger, F. S. Stephens, F. Asaro, and I. Perlman, unpublished data 1961, 1962.

[256] D. J. Skillings, reported by P. R. Tunnicliffe, Atomic Energy of Canada, Limited, *Chalk River Project Progress Report*, *PR-RRD-27*, July 1, 1961 to September 30, 1961, unpublished.

[257] Baranov, Zelenkov, and Kulakov, *Izvest. Akad. Nauk* **24**, 1035 (1960).

* Variations up to about 0.1 per cent have been reported.

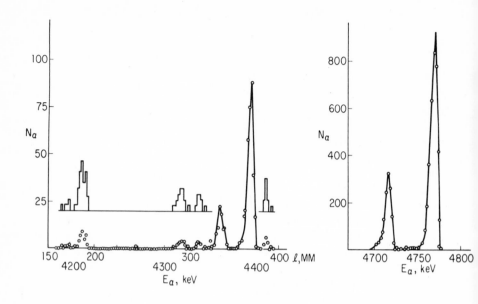

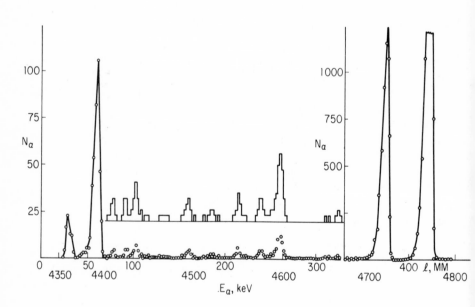

FIG. **8.30.** Alpha spectrum of U^{235} as determined in a magnetic spectrometer by BARANOV, ZELENKOV, AND KULAKOV.[257]

TABLE **8.40**. Alpha-particle spectra of U^{235}.

	Baranov, Zelenkov, and Kulakov — Magnetic α spect.		Skillings — P-Si spect.		Pilger, Stephens, Asaro and Perlman — Magnetic α spect.		Pilger, Stephens, Asaro and Perlman — Au-Si spect.		Best values		
	Energy (MeV)*	Int. (%)	Energy (MeV)*	Int. (%)	Energy (MeV)	Int. (%)	Energy (MeV)*	Int. (%)	Energy (MeV)	Excited state Energy (keV)	Int. (%)
α_0	(4.592)	<1	4.593	4.5 ± 0.3	4.592 (assumed)**	6.7 ± 1.4	4.592	4.7	4.592	0	4.6
	4.578	1.5	†					<0.5			
α_{42}	4.550	3	4.550	4.0 ± 0.3	4.553	2.7 ± 0.6	4.551	3.7	4.551	42	3.7
	4.522?	<1	†					<0.1			
α_{97}	4.496	1	4.500 ††	1.8 ± 0.5	4.499?	0.9 ± 0.4	4.497	1.2	4.497	97	1.2
	4.438	3	†								
α_{155}	4.426?	1.5					4.440?	~0.6	4.440?	~155	0.6
								<2			
α_{185}	4.412	2	4.408	5 ± 1			4.414?	~4?	4.410	185	4
α_{204}	4.394	62	4.389	55 ± 1		84	4.391	58	4.391	204	57
	4.368 } 6		†								
α_{234}	4.326 } 11		4.357	19 ± 1			4.361	19	4.361	234	18
	4.339	1.5	†								
α_{279}	4.320	3	4.313	4.5 ± 0.4			4.318	2.9	4.318	279	3.4
							4.261	0.6	4.261	337	0.6
α_{387}	4.214	5.5	4.200	6.5 ± 0.6	4.210	5.8 ± 1	4.210	5.5	4.211	387	5.7
α_{448}			4.136	0.8 ± 0.3			4.153	~0.3	4.152	448	~0.5

* The energy standard was the 4.768 MeV alpha group of U^{234}.
** A substantially different energy tentatively reported earlier[260] was found to be due to a computational error.
† Could not have been seen.
†† Should have been seen.

STEPHENS, ASARO, AND PERLMAN,[258] of MALICH,[259] of JOHANSSON,[260] and of STEPHENS,[261] and of FILIMONOV AND PSHENICHNIKOV.[262]   The energies and intensities from the work of PILGER, ET AL. are: (K x-rays) (11 per cent), 110 keV (2.5 per cent), 143 ± 2 keV (11 per cent), 163 keV (5 per cent), 180 keV (0.5 per cent) 185 ± 2 keV (54 per cent), 201 keV (0.8 per cent) and 204 keV (5 per cent).   Other gamma rays have been reported but the data are

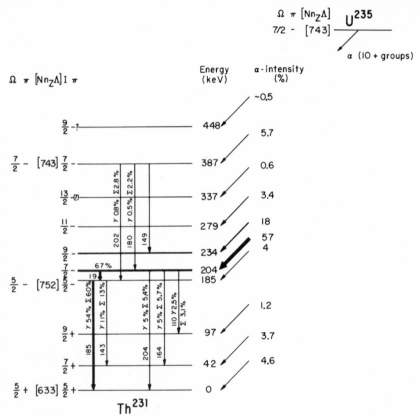

FIG. 8.31. Decay scheme of U[235] as drawn by PILGER, STEPHENS, ASARO, AND PERLMAN showing principal α and γ transitions.   Other lower intensity transitions are certainly present.   Gamma transition arrows are labeled with energy (in keV), photon intensity, and total transition intensity.

[258] R. C. Pilger, F. S. Stephens, F. Asaro, and I. Perlman, *Bull. Am. Phys. Soc.*, *Ser. II* **2**, 394 (1957).

[259] C. W. Malich, *Bull. Am. Phys. Soc.*, *Ser. II*, **1**, 43 (1956).

[260] S. A. E. Johansson, *Arkiv Fysik* **10**, 97 (1956).

[261] F. S. Stephens, Thesis, University of California (1955); also published as *Univ. Calif. Rad. Lab. Report*, *UCRL-2970*, June 1955.

[262] Yu. I. Filimonov and B. V. Pshenichnikov, *Zhur. Ekspt. Teor. Fiz.* **35**, 548 (1958).

not so conclusive as for those mentioned above. The low specific activity of U^{235} makes it quite difficult to study the conversion electrons. Coincidence studies have established that the 201 keV and 180 keV gamma rays are in coincidence with both the 143 and 185 keV gamma rays. STROMINGER[263] has measured the half-life of the 185 keV $E1$ transition and reports the value $(0.77 \pm 0.12) \times 10^{-9}$ seconds. This transition is slower by a factor of 6×10^4 than the single proton life-time prediction. This hindrance can be understood qualitatively in terms of a violation of selection rules in the asymptotic quantum numbers. Such delays are a general phenomenon for $E1$ transitions in the heavy element region as discussed in Section 3.5.8 of Chapter 3.

The alpha and gamma radiation data have been combined by PILGER, STEPHENS, ASARO, AND PERLMAN[255] into the decay scheme which is shown here as Fig. 8.31. In this scheme the data have been interpreted in terms of three rotational bands having base states at 0, 185, and 387 keV. Specific assignments of NILSSON states have been made for reasons which will be briefly discussed.

The ground state of Th^{231} and the excited states at 42 and 97 keV comprise an energy level pattern which can be interpreted as a single rotational band. From the energy separations of 42.4 ± 0.5 and 54.5 ± 1.2 keV, PILGER ET AL. have calculated the spin of the base state of the rotational band (and hence the quantum number Ω) to be 2.5 ± 0.4, in excellent agreement with the value 5/2. The value of the rotational constant $\hbar^2/2\Im$ is 6.05 ± 0.07 in good agreement with the values found for odd-neutron even-parity rotational bands in neighboring nuclei. Thus the ground state of Th^{231} and the excited states at 42 and 97 keV can be assigned spins of 5/2, 7/2 and 9/2, respectively, and are readily interpreted as members of a rotational band with Ω and π of 5/2+. The most likely Nilsson assignment for the ground state band of Th^{231} is the same as for U^{233}, 5/2 + [633].

The ground state of U^{235} has a measured spin of $7/2^{264,265}$ and has been given the Nilsson assignment 7/2 − [743] by NEWTON,[266] ASARO AND PERLMAN,[267] and others. This assignment can be considered quite well established. It is supported by the Coulombic excitation studies of NEWTON[266] who excited the 9/2 and 11/2 rotational levels, and by the alpha decay of Pu^{239} which takes place predominantly to a $K = 1/2$ intrinsic state of U^{235} which lies within 100 electron volts of the ground state. This state decays to the ground state by an $E3$ transition with a half-life of 26

[263] D. Strominger, *Phys. Rev.* **114**, 502 (1959).

[264] K. L. Vander Sluis and J. R. McNally, Jr. *J. Opt. Soc. Am.* **45**, 65 (1955).

[265] C. A. Hutchison, Jr., P. M. Llewellyn, E. Wong, P. Dorain, *Phys. Rev.* **102**, 292 (1956)

[266] J. O. Newton, *Nucl. Phys.* **3**, 345 (1957); *Physica* **22**, 1129 (1956).

[267] F. Asaro and I. Perlman, *Phys. Rev.* **107**, 318 (1957).

minutes.   This evidence is discussed in connection with the alpha decay of
Pu^{239} in Section 9.2.9 of the next chapter.

The 4.211 MeV alpha particle emission is unhindered.   According to
the concept of favored alpha transitions formulated by BOHR, FRÖMAN, AND
MOTTELSON,[268] unhindered alpha decay in odd-A alpha emitters proceeds to
a state in the daughter nucleus with the same intrinsic state assignment as the
parent.   On this basis the 387 keV level in Th^{231} would also be given the
assignment 7/2 − [743].   This level decays to several members of the
group of levels around 185 keV by transitions which appear to be predominantly $M1$.[261]   As the level at 185 keV is fed by an $M1$ transition from
the 7/2− state at 387 keV and in turn decays to the 5/2+ ground state by an
$E1$ transition, its spin and parity should be either 5/2− or 7/2−.   The only
Nilsson state which could give either of these values is 5/2 − [752].
The observed states at 185, 204, 234, 274 and possibly 337 were therefore
assigned spins of 5/2 → 13/2 as members of a 5/2− rotational band.

TABLE **8.41.** Calculation of effects of the Coriolis force on energy levels
of Th^{231} and their alpha particle population.

K	π	I	Excited state energy (keV)		Alpha decay hindrance factors	
			Calc.[270]	Exp.	Calc.[255]	Exp.
5/2	−	5/2	185(norm)	185	4×10^2	1×10^2
		7/2	204(norm)	204	5.7(norm)	5.7
		9/2	238	234	14	11
		11/2	280	279	35	25
		13/2	341	337	250	50
7/2	−	7/2	383	387	2.0(norm)	2.0
		9/2	454	448?	9	~7?

The main features of the decay scheme shown in Fig. 8.31 have now been
developed, and there remains only the problem of the very closely spaced
members of the 5/2 − [752] band.   This can be accounted for by the
interaction between the 7/2 − [743] and 5/2 − [752] rotational bands brought
about by the Coriolis forces.   This type of interaction has been discussed by
KERMAN.[269]   The effect is unusually large in this case for two reasons.
First, the levels involved are both derived from the j 15/2 single particle
level; and second, these two bands in Th^{231} are unusually close together
because the ground state of Th^{231} (5/2 + [633]) lies between them on the
Nilsson diagram.   The effects of the Coriolis force on the energies of the
Th^{231} levels have been calculated by F. S. STEPHENS[270] using Nilsson's wave

[268] A. Bohr, P. O. Fröman, and B. R. Mottelson, *Dan. Mat.-fys. Medd.* **29**, 10 (1955).
[269] A. K. Kerman, *Dan. Mat.-fys. Medd.* **30**, No. 15 (1956).
[270] F. S. Stephens, unpublished data, 1960.

functions with some modifications for pairing considerations. The principal effect of the pairing correlations in this case is substantially to reduce the Coriolis matrix element between the $7/2 - [743]$ and $5/2 - [752]$ bands. The actual reduction in this matrix element, a factor of 3, was treated as an arbitrary parameter to give the appropriate energy for the 204 keV state. The results of STEPHENS' calculations are shown in Table 8.41. The agreement is good qualitatively, but further refinements will be necessary for quantitative agreement.

It was mentioned earlier that the 4.211 MeV alpha group populated the 387 keV state by an essentially unhindered transition. The alpha transition probabilities to the rotational states based on the 387 keV state can also be calculated from the known hindrance factors in adjacent even-even nuclides. PILGER, STEPHENS, ASARO, AND PERLMAN[255] used the same type of approach to calculate the alpha populations in the $K = 5/2$ and $K = 7/2$ bands caused by the Coriolis interaction. They used the equation:

$$P/P_E = \frac{1}{N} \sum_{L=0,2,4} \frac{\left(\sum_{K=5/2,7/2} a_{KI_i} a_{KI_f} \langle I_i L K O | I_i L I_f K_f \rangle \right)^2}{HF_{L(e-e)}}$$

where P is the alpha transition probability, P_E is the transition probability calculated from the spin-independent alpha decay theory, $H_{L(e-e)}$ are the hindrance factors for various moment alpha-particle waves in the adjacent uranium even-even nuclides, a_{KI} are the admixtures of various K in the states of spin I, and i and f refer to initial and final states, respectively. N is a parameter between 1 and 2 which is usually determined empirically although it can be calculated by the theoretical treatment of MANG.[271] The ratio P/P_E is essentially a reduced alpha transition probability. The results of the calculation of PILGER ET AL. are shown in Table 8.41. N was chosen as 2 in order to give the appropriate hindrance factor for the transition to the 387 keV state. The pairing calculations made by STEPHENS indicated the Coriolis matrix element which leads to the admixtures of the $K = 5/2$ and $K = 7/2$ states in each other should be reduced from the Nilsson value by a factor of 3. In order for the alpha group to the 204 keV state to have the correct hindrance factor, that particular matrix element was reduced by only a factor of 2.

The discrepancy in the population to the 185 keV state and possibly to the 337 keV state may be explained by intrinsic alpha decay between the $\Omega = 7/2$ parent and the $\Omega = 5/2$ daughter. MANG[271] has calculated that the intrinsic alpha decay to the 185 keV state should have a hindrance factor of ~ 200.

[271] H. J. Mang and J. O. Rasmussen, *Mat.-Fys. Skr. Dan. Vid. Selsk.* **2**, No. 3 (1962); H. J. Mang, Abstract of paper presented at the Washington Meeting of the American Physical Society, 1963.

8.4.10 *Uranium-235m*

The primary product of the alpha decay of Pu^{239} is an isomeric form of U^{235} with a half-life of 26.5 minutes.   This isomer lies less than 100 electron volts above the ground state and decays to the ground state by an $E3$ gamma transition.   The formation and decay of U^{235m} are thoroughly discussed in connection with the alpha decay of Pu^{239}.   See Section 9.2.9.

8.4.11 *Uranium-236*

WILLIAMS AND YUSTER[272] first detected U^{236} by mass spectrographic analysis of an enriched sample of U^{235} which had been irradiated with slow neutrons.   GHIORSO, BRITTAIN, MANNING, AND SEABORG[273] first detected the alpha particles which U^{236} was expected to emit, and set a value of about 2×10^{7} years for the half-life.   Uranium-236 is beta stable.   FLEMING, GHIORSO, AND CUNNINGHAM[274] measured the specific activity of U^{236} samples which had been enriched to 97 per cent isotopic purity by electromagnetic separation.   The specific activity is $(1.406 \pm 0.011) \times 10^{5}$ disintegrations per minute per milligram corresponding to a half-life of $(2.391 \pm 0.018) \times 10^{7}$ years.   This value supersedes an earlier determination which yielded the value 2.457×10^{7} years.[275]   The half-life of U^{236} is too short for any U^{236} to have survived since the formation of the elements but it is long enough that U^{236} may have contributed significantly to the heating of the earth during its early history.   ROSENBLATT[276] has put forward this suggestion, but KOHMAN[277] is inclined to discount it.

The energy of the main alpha particle group has been measured[273] by the ion chamber method to be 4.499 ± 0.004 MeV.   Evidence for other groups has been found indirectly.   DUNLAVEY AND SEABORG[278] impregnated photographic emulsions with U^{236} and found conversion electrons from a ~ 50-keV gamma ray in coincidence with 27 per cent of the alpha particles.   GROVER AND SEABORG[279] found a gamma ray of 163 keV energy in ~ 0.5 per cent abundance.   From these results, the principal alpha groups are believed to be the following: 4.499 MeV (73 per cent), 4.45 MeV (27 per cent), and 4.337 MeV (~ 0.5 per cent).   Further work on U^{236} may be expected to

---

[272] D. Williams and P. Yuster, *Los Alamos Scientific Laboratory Report LAMS-195*, January 1945, unpublished.

[273] A. Ghiorso, J. W. Brittain, W. M. Manning, and G. T. Seaborg, *Phys. Rev.* **82**, 558 (1951).

[274] E. H. Fleming, Jr., A. Ghiorso, and B. B. Cunningham, *Phys. Rev.* **88**, 642 (1952).

[275] A. H. Jaffey, H. Diamond, J. Hirsch, and J. Mech, *Phys. Rev.* **84**, 785 (1951).

[276] D. B. Rosenblatt, *Phys. Rev.* **91**, 1474–75 (1953).

[277] T. P. Kohman and N. Saito, *Ann. Rev. Nucl. Sci.* **4**, 439 (1954).

[278] D. C. Dunlavey and G. T. Seaborg, *Phys. Rev.* **87**, 165 (1952).

[279] J. R. Grover and G. T. Seaborg, unpublished information.

show that the decay scheme of U^{236} is closely similar to those of all even-even alpha emitters in this mass region.*

Further information on the excited levels of Th^{232} has been obtained from the excitation of nuclear states by the Coulombic excitation method with charged particle beams of energy below the potential barrier for nuclear reactions. The first excited 2+ level at 53 keV was produced by several investigating teams.[280-283] STEPHENS, DIAMOND, AND PERLMAN[284] bombarded thorium targets with argon ions of high energy but of insufficient energy to penetrate the Coulomb barrier and were able to excite several levels of the ground state rotational band up to a 10+ level at 825 keV. These results are summarized in Figure 8.32. STELSON AND MCGOWAN[282,283] were also able to excite a 2+ state at 790 keV which decays by $E2$ radiation to the 0+ and 2+ members of the ground state rotational band. This level at 790 keV is probably the first γ-vibrational state of the collective excitation of the Th^{232} nucleus. DURHAM, RESTER, AND CLASS[285] confirmed the excitation of the 790 keV level and its assignment as a state of vibrational excitation. In addition they reported the excitation of a level at 773 keV which they assigned to the 2+ member of the beta-vibrational band. An interesting feature of this study was the presence of prominent conversion electrons of a 723 keV transition connecting the vibrational level at 773 keV with the 2+ level of the ground state rotational band at 50 keV. The prominent conversion electrons arise from a strong $E0$ component in this gamma transition. These results were confirmed by DIAMOND AND ELBEK.[286] These last-named authors also have unpublished data on the excitation of states of negative parity by the Coulomb excitation process. These lie about 1 MeV above ground. The well-established levels of Th^{232} are summarized in Figure 8.32.

The chief method of preparation of U^{236} is by the neutron capture reaction on U^{235} for which the cross section is 107 barns. Samples of high isotopic purity are prepared by the intense neutron irradiation of U^{235} followed by electromagnetic separation. The formation of U^{236} by the

[280] G. M. Temmer and N. P. Heydenburg, *Phys. Rev.* **93**, 351 (1954).

[281] R. H. Davis, A. S. Divatra, D. A. Lind, and R. D. Moffat, *Phys. Rev.* **103**, 1801 (1956).

[282] P. H. Stelson and F. K. McGowan, *Phys. Rev.* **99**, 112, 616A (1955).

[283] F. K. McGowan and P. H. Stelson, *Bull. Am. Phys. Soc. Ser.* II **2**, 207 (1957). F. K. McGowan and P. H. Stelson, p. 765–771 *Proceedings of the International Congress on Nuclear Physics*; see also *Phys. Rev.* **120**, 1803 (1960).

[284] F. S. Stephens, Jr., R. M. Diamond, and I. Perlman, *Phys. Rev. Letters* **3**, 435 (1959).

[285] F. E. Durham, D. H. Rester, and C. M. Class, *Bull. Am. Phys. Soc.* II **5**, 110 (1960). *Phys. Rev. Letters* **5**, 202 (1960).

[286] R. M. Diamond and B. Elbek, unpublished results, 1960.

* KOMAR, KOROLEV, AND KOCHAROV, *Sov. Phys. JETP* **11**, 1038 (1960), report the following alpha groups: α_0 (74 %) α_{50} (26 %) and α_{160} (0.26 %). They give 4.488 ± .003 MeV as the energy of the ground state transition.

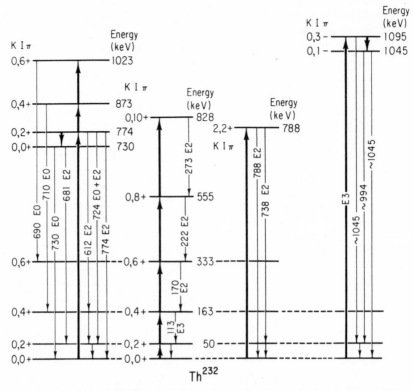

FIG. 8.32. Levels of Th²³² revealed by the Coulombic excitation process. The energy of each level is given in keV at the right of the level. The heavy arrows indicate major steps in the Coulombic excitation process. Figure prepared with advice of F. STEPHENS JR. AND R. DIAMOND.

reaction $U^{235}(n, \gamma) U^{236}$ is an important factor in the operation of nuclear reactors burning U^{235} not only because of the change in isotopic composition of the fuel but because U^{236} is an intermediate in the production of other heavy element nuclides such as Np^{237}.

8.4.12 Uranium-237

Uranium-237 is a beta emitter with a half-life of 6.75 days. This nuclide is a collateral member of the $4n + 1$ series by virtue of its decay into Np^{237}. The discovery of U^{237} is discussed in connection with the discovery of Np^{237} in Section 7.1 of the preceding chapter.

Uranium-237 is usually prepared by fast neutron bombardment of U^{238} by the reaction:

$$U^{238}(n, 2n)U^{237}$$

It is a prominent component in the radioactive debris from the testing of nuclear explosive devices in which an intense fast neutron flux is generated in the vicinity of U^{238}. The nuclide can also be prepared by the following cyclotron reactions:

$$U^{238}(d, t)U^{237}$$

$$U^{238}(\alpha, \alpha n)U^{237}$$

$$U^{238}(p, pn)U^{237}$$

We turn now to a detailed review of its complex radiations.

Of those nuclei in the heavy-element region whose spectroscopic properties have been widely studied, few are as interesting as Np^{237} the daughter of U^{237}; its levels have provided a wealth of information with which to test the Bohr-Mottelson theory, both in its general and in its more detailed aspects. The Np^{237} levels are populated by the alpha decay of Am^{241}, by the beta decay of U^{237}, and by the electron capture decay of Pu^{237}; this section on U^{237} decay will supplement the more detailed discussion presented in the Section 9.3.6 covering Am^{241} decay. The study of U^{237} neatly supplements the work on Am^{241}, since the decay of the former populates chiefly some high-lying levels of Np^{237}, whereas the alpha decay leads overwhelmingly to the low-lying levels.

Spectroscopic studies of U^{237} decay have been carried out by WAGNER, FREEDMAN, ENGELKEMEIR, AND HUIZENGA,[287] BARANOV AND SHLYAGIN,[288] BUNKER, MIZE, AND STARNER,[289] and by RASMUSSEN, CANAVAN, AND HOLLANDER.[290] Figure 8.33 shows the Np^{237} energy level scheme as summarized by RASMUSSEN, CANAVAN, AND HOLLANDER,[290] which includes both the Am^{241} and U^{237} information. The discussion here will follow closely that given in their paper.

The principal electromagnetic radiations observed in the U^{237} spectrum are photons of 60 keV (38 per cent), K x-rays (55 per cent), 163 keV (3.6 per cent), 208 keV (24 per cent), 266 keV (0.9 per cent), 332 keV (~ 2 per cent), and 365 keV (~ 0.1 per cent); the 60 keV photon is familiar because of its prominent position in the decay of Am^{241}. The other transitions shown in Figure 8.33 and listed in Table 8.42 are either highly converted or too weak to appear in the scintillation spectrum. These are discussed thoroughly by RASMUSSEN, ET AL.[290] The end point of the main spectrum is 248 keV.[287,288,290] A low limit of 0.1 per cent has been set on beta particles leading directly to the ground state or low-lying levels of Np^{237}. The

[287] F. Wagner, Jr., M. S. Freedman, D. W. Engelkemeir, and J. R. Huizenga, *Phys. Rev.* **89**, 502 (1953).

[288] S. A. Baranov and K. N. Shlyagin, *Zhur. Eksp. Teor. Fiz., SSSR* **30**, 225 (1956); translation *Sov. Phys., JETP* **3**, 200 (1956).

[289] M. E. Bunker, J. P. Mize, and J. W. Starner, *Bull. Am. Phys. Soc. Ser.* II **2**, 104 (1957).

[290] J. O. Rasmussen, F. L. Canavan, and J. M. Hollander, *Phys. Rev.* **107**, 141 (1957).

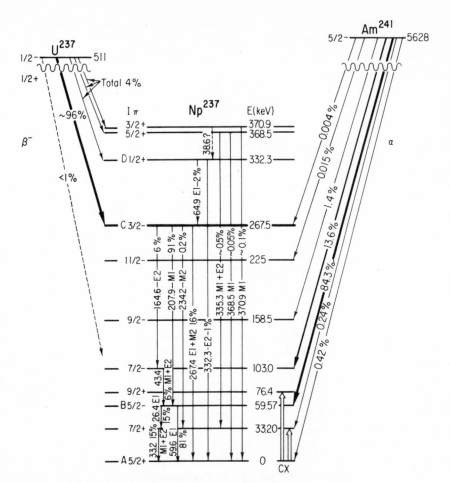

FIG. **8.33.** Decay scheme of U[237]. The alpha transitions of Am[241] to the
same daughter nucleus shown for comparison. Note that U[237] populates
primarily the level at 267.5 keV. Transition energies, multipolarities, and
gross abundances are shown. Nilsson state assignments are given for
intrinsic particle states. The levels at 225 and 158.5 keV which appear in
Am[241] alpha decay and the level at 76.4 keV excited Coulombically (symbol
CX) are not observed in the decay of U[237].

chief beta decay goes almost entirely ($\sim$96 per cent) to the 267.5 keV level
but minor branching to higher-lying states must occur.

The level at 267.5 keV de-excites by four transitions, all of different
multipole orders (a most unusual and interesting situation). Of these, the
207.9 keV magnetic dipole transition is the most prominent. From our
knowledge of the spins and parities of the lower states in Np[237] (from Am[241]

decay) and from the multipolarity information on the transitions which de-
excite the 267.5 keV state, the spin and parity assignments of this state are 3/2−.

The eight levels populated directly or indirectly by the beta decay of
U^{237} can be grouped into four rotational bands; these are displayed schematically in Figure 8.34.   Band A, based on the ground state, has $K = 5/2$
with positive parity; Band B based on the 59.6 keV level has $K = 5/2$ with

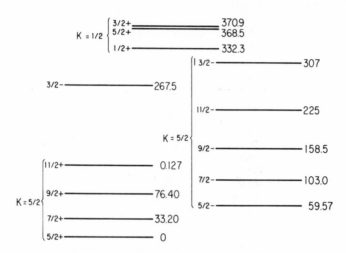

FIG. **8.34.** Levels of the Np^{237} nucleus grouped as rotational bands.   Each
group of levels represents collective rotational excitation of a base state
which is an eigenstate of the odd proton in an anisotropic harmonic oscillator potential.   Levels here shown are seen in the decay of U^{237} and Am^{241}
or both.   The only levels not seen in the decay of U^{237} are the levels at
225, 158.5, and 387.5 keV.

negative parity; Band C with one known level at 267.5 keV has $K = 3/2$ with
negative parity; Band D based on the 332.3 keV level has $K = 1/2$ with
positive parity.   Energies of levels in a $K = 1/2$ type band are given by the
following formula (see Chapter 3):

$$E_I = \frac{\hbar^2}{2\mathfrak{J}} [I(I + 1) + a(-)^{I + 1/2}(I + 1/2)]$$

Using the three level energies, 332.3, 368.5, and 370.9 keV and the spins
1/2, 3/2, and 5/2, respectively, one calculates a value of the rotational constant
$\hbar^2/2\mathfrak{J} = 6.2$ keV which compares closely with that of Band B.   One cannot,
however, in this case test the accuracy with which the equation fits the
experimental energy ratios, because knowledge of just two excited states of a
$K = 1/2$ rotational band serves only to define the two parameters in the
equation.

The experimental levels of Np^{237} provide some interesting comparisons with the "branching-ratio rule" of ALAGA, ALDER, BOHR, AND MOTTEL-SON.[291] This rule states that in photon transitions of a single multipole type which originate at a common level and terminate at the various levels of a rotational band, the intrinsic nuclear transition probabilities are identical and observable differences in the photon intensities should result only from the different energies and angular momenta involved; both are independent effects and easily computed.

TABLE **8.42.** Gamma transitions of U^{237} decay.

Energy (keV)	Multipolarity assignment*	Total estimated transition intensity
26.35	$E1$	15
33.20	$M1 + E2$	15
43.46	$M1 + E2$	7
59.57	$E1$	81
64.8	$E2$	3
113.9		
164.6	$E2$	7
207.9	$M1$	89
234.2	$M2$	~ 0.2
267.5	$E1 + M2$	1.7
332.3	$E2$	1.5
335.3	$M1 + E2$	~ 0.2
368.5	$M1$	~ 0.05
370.9	$M1$	~ 0.10

*Chiefly from L-subshell conversion ratios.

Two pairs of gamma-rays may be compared in the Np^{237} levels; these are the 26.4-59.6 keV pair of electric dipole transitions, and the electric quadrupole components of the 164.6 and 207.9 keV photons. The agreement with theory in both cases is poor, and in the latter pair there is at least a factor of ten discrepancy. The key to understanding the lack of agreement lies in the recognition that these cases involve transitions much retarded from the single-particle rates. The disagreement is interpreted within the framework of the Bohr-Mottelson theory as an indication that those components of initial or final wave functions actually contributing to the transition matrix element have a different K value from the main components of the wave function. In general, such disagreement is found in abnormally retarded transitions; those transitions proceeding at nearly the single particle rate generally show good agreement with the branching ratio rules.

---

[291] Alaga, Alder, Bohr, and Mottelson, *Kgl. Dan. Vidensk. Selskab. Mat.-fys. Medd.* **29**, No. 9 (1955).

Explanation of the factors causing the retardation of the transitions mentioned here has been advanced in terms of selection rules involving the Nilsson eigenfunctions (states) appropriate to these highly deformed nuclei, represented by an asymptotic limit in the theory. The low energy $E1$ transitions all violate these selection rules, as do also the $E2$ transitions mentioned above. In addition, very strong $M1$ radiation from the 267.5 keV state (207.9 keV) is retarded by more than 10^4 from the single particle rate, and this transition also violates the "asymptotic" selection rules.

There are interesting cases in Np^{237} of anomalous electric dipole conversion coefficients. The retarded 60 keV transition to ground has a normal L_{III} conversion coefficient but abnormally high values for conversion in the L_I and L_{II} subshells. The retarded 267.5 keV transition appears to have a high K-conversion coefficient. However, in the same nucleus, the 65 keV transition from the 322 keV level seems to have normal conversion coefficients. Anomalies due to dynamic nuclear structure effects can arise by virtue of the fact that different nuclear matrix elements can produce internal conversion when electron density lies within the nuclear volume. The anomalous contributions are observable only when the normal radiative process is highly retarded and the "anomalous" conversion process is not, and it is consistent with this interpretation that in the case of electric dipole anomalies only the penetrating electrons ($s_{1/2}$ and $p_{1/2}$) show definite anomalies. A discussion of such conversion anomalies is given in Section 3.5.8 of Chapter 3.

For further details on the radiations of U^{237} or the interpretation of the U^{237} decay scheme the reader is referred to the comprehensive paper of RASMUSSEN, CANAVAN, AND HOLLANDER.[290]

UNIK[292] has studied the angular correlation of the gamma rays in the 64.9–207.9 and 207.9–59.6 keV cascades. From the results he determined limits on the small amount of $E2$ contribution in the predominantly $M1$ 207.9 keV transition. His results also confirm the 1/2 spin assignment of the 332 keV level.

8.4.13 *Uranium-238*

This is the chief constituent of natural uranium and the progenitor of the uranium series of radioelements. Its properties are fully discussed in Section 6.2 of Chapter 6.

The decay scheme of U^{238} is very simple and can be briefly recapitulated here. Uranium-238 is beta stable. Its half-life for alpha decay is $(4.51 \pm 0.01) \times 10^9$ years corresponding to a specific activity of 738.6 ± 1.6 disintegrations per minute per milligram. The energy of the main group of alpha particles, emitted in 77 per cent abundance, is 4.195 MeV. Conversion

---

[292] J. Unik, Ph.D. thesis printed as *Lawrence Radiation Laboratory Report UCRL-9105*, March 1960.

electrons of a 48 keV gamma ray have been observed indicating that the alpha decay is complex; an alpha group 48 keV lower in energy than the main group is present in 23 per cent abundance. This 48 keV state in the daughter Th^{234} is undoubtedly the (2+) member of the ground state rotational band. There is also evidence for emission of 4.038 MeV alpha particles in 0.23 per cent abundance to populate the 4+ rotational level at 160 keV. Uranium-238 very probably undergoes slight alpha branching decay to higher-lying members of the ground state rotational band but this branching has not been observed because of experimental difficulties stemming from the low specific activity of U^{238}.

8.4.14 Uranium-239

In 1937 HAHN, MEITNER, AND STRASSMAN[293] noted that a new isotope of uranium with a 23-minute half-life was produced when natural uranium was irradiated with slow neutrons. They correctly identified this activity as U^{239}. The decay of U^{239} produces Np^{239}, the first form of element 93 to be identified. The discovery of neptunium via the reactions:

$$U^{238}(n, \gamma)U^{239}; \quad U^{239} \xrightarrow[\text{23 min}]{\beta^-} Np^{239}$$

is treated in Section 9.1.11 of Chapter 9.

Uranium-239 emits beta particles with an end-point energy of 1.21 MeV.[294-296] A single gamma ray of 73.6 keV has been observed.[294-296] The isotope Am^{243} also decays to Np^{239} and additional information on the excited levels of Np^{239} comes from studies of the gamma radiations accompanying Am^{243} decay. Refer to Section 9.1.11, Chapter 9.

8.4.15 Uranium-240

The isotope U^{240} was found by HYDE, STUDIER, AND MANNING[297] in uranium samples which had been irradiated with a high flux of neutrons.

$$U^{238}(n, \gamma)U^{239}(n, \gamma)U^{240}$$

This isotope decays with a half-life of 14 hours to a 7.3 minute isomer of Np^{240}. Uranium-240 has also been isolated[298,299] as the daughter of Pu^{244}.

293 L. Meitner, O. Hahn, and F. Strassmann, Z. Physik **106**, 249 (1937).

294 M. Freedman, unpublished information (1953).

295 H. Slätis, Nature **160**, 579 (1947); Arkiv Mat. Astron. Fysik **35A**, No. 3 (1948).

296 N. Feather and R. S. Krishnan, Proc. Cambridge Phil. Soc. **43**, 267 (1947); N. Feather, Nature **160**, 749 (1947).

297 E. K. Hyde, M. H. Studier, and W. M. Manning, Argonne National Laboratory Reports, ANL-4143, April 15, 1948, and ANL-4182, August 4, 1948 (unpublished).

298 H. Diamond and R. F. Barnes, Phys. Rev. **101**, 1064 (1956).

299 J. P. Butler, T. A. Eastwood, T. C. Collins, M. E. Jones, F. M. Rourke, and R. P. Schuman, Phys. Rev. **103**, 634 (1956).

BUNKER, DROPESKY, KNIGHT, STARNER, AND WARREN[300] studied the
decay of this β-emitter and that of its daughter; their findings on Np^{240} are
summarized in Chapter 9, Section 9.1.12.

BUNKER ET AL. proposed a simple decay scheme for U^{240}, but this has been
modified in important respects by ASARO AND CO-WORKERS.[301]   Both
schemes are shown in Figure 8.35.   There are difficulties in the determination
of the decay properties of this isotope stemming from the presence of interfering radiations from the short-lived Np^{240} daughter and from U^{237}.

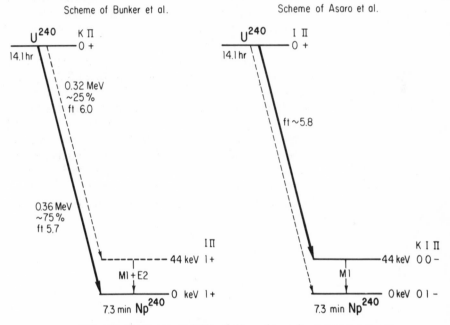

FIG. **8.35.** Decay scheme of U[240]: (*left*) as drawn by BUNKER AND CO-
WORKERS,[300] and (*right*) by ASARO AND CO-WORKERS.[301]

ASARO AND CO-WORKERS[301] found that most of the beta decay of U^{240}
leads to the 44 keV state.   Furthermore they found that the 44 keV transition
is $M1$ with no detectable $E2$ admixture (<2 per cent).   This information is
well explained by the following orbital assignments for the base state and the
44 keV state of 7.3 minute Np^{240}.   The lowest lying proton orbitals for
Np^{240} (proton number 93) should be 5/2 + [642] and 5/2 − [523] while the
neutron orbital (neutron number 147) should be 5/2 + [622].   The possible

[300] M. E. Bunker, B. J. Dropesky, J. D. Knight, J. W. Starner, and B. Warren, *Phys.
Rev.* **116**, 143 (1959), earlier results given in *Phys. Rev.* **91**, 889 (1953).

[301] F. Asaro, F. S. Stephens, J. M. Hollander, K. Hulet, R. Hoff, and I. Perlman, unpublished results.

couplings of these orbitals will give rise to a quartet of levels. Employing the GALLAGHER-MOSZKOWSKI coupling rules discussed in Chapter 3, Section 3.5.6, one would expect the lowest state to be $K = 5+$, the highest of the quartet to be $K = 5-$, and states of $K = 0+$ and $K = 0-$ to be in between. The $K = 5+$ configuration is interpreted as the ground state of the 60-minute isomer of Np^{240} discussed in Section 9.1.13. The $K = 0-$ configuration is assigned as the base state of 7.3 minute Np^{240}.

It is known that the rotational band of a $K = 0$ state in an odd-odd nucleus can have an unusual ordering of levels such that the spin 1 rotational member lies below the spin zero fundamental state, and it is this interpretation which is given to the ground state and the 44 keV state of the 7.3 minute isomer. With these assignments, the following observations fall into line.

1. The principal mode of β-decay has log ft ≈ 5.8. According to the assignments just discussed this transition corresponds to a paired 5/2 + [622] neutron of U^{240} changing to a 5/2 − [523] proton in Np^{240}. The corresponding beta decay has been observed in Pu^{241} and in Am^{239} and for these the log ft values have been determined as 5.7 and 5.9, respectively.

2. The log ft value for the decay of 7.3 minute Np^{240} to the ground state of Pu^{240} is 6.6. This is hard to explain by the earlier decay scheme[300] which indicates that the state decaying to the ground state of Pu^{240} is the same as that which receives β-decay from U^{240} with log ft = 5.7.

3. The pure $M1$ character of the 44 keV transition is to be expected with ASARO'S assignments.

9.

THE TRANSURANIUM ELEMENTS

In this chapter we present a comprehensive description of the nuclear properties of each of the transuranium elements. For each element we include an introductory section which treats the history of the first synthesis and identification of an isotope of that element. Following this there is a section on each isotope. These sections discuss the first identification of that particular isotope, the alternate methods for its preparation, measurements of its half-life and, where pertinent, of its alternate modes of radioactive decay. Alpha, beta and gamma-ray data are summarized. If a decay scheme has been formulated this scheme is presented and various features of it are interpreted by application of the nuclear models outlined in Chapter 3. A careful citation to the original literature is maintained throughout.

9.1 THE ELEMENT NEPTUNIUM (ELEMENT 93)

9.1.1 *The Discovery and Early History of Neptunium*

The first attempts to prepare an isotope of neptunium were made in the 1930's by the bombardment of uranium with neutrons. This was a logical approach because experiments with many other elements had shown that a β-unstable isotope is formed which, of course, decays to the next heaviest element. We now know that when natural uranium is irradiated with slow neutrons, neutron capture by U^{238} does indeed yield a β^--unstable isotope which decays to an identifiable isotope of element 93. During the neutron irradiation, however, the rare uranium isotope, U^{235}, undergoes nuclear fission resulting in the production of numerous radioactive isotopes. This was not known at the time of the first attempts to prepare element 93 by the neutron capture method and, of course, caused considerable confusion.

Another cause of confusion was the incorrect placement of element 93 in the Periodic System of the Elements. Most experimentalists at the time thought that element 93 should resemble rhenium, and the radiochemical methods for isolation of element 93 were based on this false supposition. With these dual difficulties some mistaken conclusions were reached in the period before the discovery of fission. As early as 1934, FERMI[1] and his co-workers at Rome had isolated a 13-minute activity from a uranium sample after neutron irradiation and had separated it chemically from all elements of atomic number 82 to 92. This led them to the logical conclusion that this 13-minute activity was an isotope of element 93, particularly since it seemed to have chemical properties resembling rhenium. Additional experiments by these investigators and by experimentalists in other countries resulted in the discovery of many additional activities which appeared to be isotopes of transuranium elements. Some of these were believed to have atomic numbers as large as 96. In addition to the transuranium element isotopes other activities were found which had the properties of thorium, protactinium, actinium and other elements of smaller atomic number than the target uranium. It was difficult to understand why such a variety of products should come from the irradiation of uranium with neutrons when nothing of this nature had been observed with the irradiation of lighter elements.[2] At this point HAHN AND STRASSMANN[3] performed their definitive radiochemical experiments which proved beyond question that uranium undergoes a unique nuclear reaction in which the nucleus is split to form radioactive isotopes of medium weight elements. It became evident at once that all the previous reports of transuranium elements had to be reinterpreted and the search for element 93 had to begin anew.

Following the announcement of HAHN AND STRASSMANN'S[3] discovery of fission in 1939, MCMILLAN[4] at the University of California carried out a study of the range of the radioactive fission products collected from a thin foil of uranium oxide irradiated with neutrons. The neutrons were produced by the reaction of 16 MeV deuterons with a beryllium target. Although the experiment was necessarily crude, it showed clearly that the fission products possessed high momentum as expected and that there was a distribution of ranges with a similar pattern of half-lives associated with the different range intervals. (It was not certain from this study that the distribution of ranges could not be explained by the thickness of the uranium oxide grains.)

[1] E. Fermi, Nature 133, 898 (1934); E. Amaldi, O. D'Agostino, F. Rasetti, and E. Segrè, Proc. Roy. Soc. A146, 483 (1934).
[2] For a more complete account of the status of "the transuranium elements" one year before the discovery of nuclear fission, see the review article by Quill, Chem. Rev. 23, 87–155 (1938).
[3] O. Hahn and F. Strassmann, Naturwiss 27, 11, 89 (1939).
[4] E. McMillan, Phys. Rev. 55, 510 (1939).

However, the striking finding was that there remained within the uranium a fraction which had little or no recoil momentum. This fraction contained an activity of 23 min half-life, previously identified as an isotope of uranium,[5] and a new ~ 2-day activity. None of the recoiling fractions had a 2-day component with anything like the intensity of the non-recoiling activity. This suggested that this activity might be the sought-after element 93 arising from the β-decay of the 23 min. uranium isotope or some other isotope which had not been observed.

SEGRÈ[6] attempted to make this identification but was misled as were others by attributing rhenium-like properties to element 93. He found that the 2.3-day activity followed most closely the rare earth fraction and felt that it could not be a transuranium element. In the meantime, Abelson in Washington and McMillan renewed the efforts on the chemical identification of the non-recoiling 2.3-day activity. Soon they combined their efforts in Berkeley and jointly published the discovery of the first transuranium element.[7] They showed that the new activity had great similarity to uranium with the important difference that the oxidation state corresponding to quadrivalent uranium is more stable than U^{+4} and that it is this property which made it follow the rare earths in the precipitation of rare earth fluorides. They were able to separate it from rare earths by carrying out the precipitation in the presence of strong oxidizing agents. Further convincing proof came from the demonstration that the new activity resulted from the β^- decay of the 23-min uranium, an observation that had eluded other experimenters. Supporting confirmation also came from the finding that when slow neutrons were filtered from the uranium by wrapping it in cadmium, the fission products were much reduced relative to the 23-min and 2.3-day activities and these latter two retained their same relative abundances. The reaction sequence resulting from this work could be most logically written:

$$U^{238}(n,\gamma)U^{239}; \quad U^{239}\xrightarrow[\text{23 min}]{\beta^-} Np^{239}\xrightarrow[\text{2.3 days}]{\beta^-}$$

Further chemical experiments showed a distinct similarity of the new element to hexapositive uranium in the oxidized state and further similarity to Th^{+4} and U^{+4} in the reduced state. There was no resemblance to rhenium, contrary to the expectations of most experimenters seeking at this time to identify element 93. McMILLAN AND ABELSON suggested that neptunium was to be considered a member of a transition series of elements starting in this region of the periodic chart, probably with the element uranium, in which series the 5f inner shell of electrons is filled. McMILLAN AND ABELSON originated the lanthanum fluoride oxidation-reduction cycle (coprecipitation of neptunium on an insoluble fluoride compound precipitated from reducing

[5] L. Meitner, O. Hahn, and F. Strassmann, Z. Physik 106, 249 (1937).

[6] E. Segrè, Phys. Rev. 55, 1104 (1939).

[7] E. McMillan and P. H. Abelson, Phys. Rev. 57, 1186 (1940).

solution followed by non-coprecipitation of neptunium on an insoluble fluoride compound precipitated under aqueous oxidizing conditions) which was to be a mainstay of neptunium purification for many years to come.

MCMILLAN later chose the name neptunium for element 93 from the planet Neptune which is the first planet beyond Uranus in our solar system. The symbol Np was suggested somewhat later.

STARKE[8] apparently made an independent discovery of Np^{239} at about the same time. He bombarded a large sample of uranium in the form of the complex compound, uranylbenzoylacetone, with neutrons from a weak neutron source. By the Szilard-Chalmers effect the U^{239} product of the n, γ reaction was obtained in 10^5-fold enrichment. STARKE then observed that a 2.4 day activity was formed on the decay of the 23 minute U^{239}.

A second isotope of neptunium, the 2.0-day beta-emitter Np^{238}, was discovered later in 1940 by SEABORG, MCMILLAN, KENNEDY, AND WAHL[9] at the University of California. This isotope was produced by the bombardment of natural uranium with 16 MeV deuterons by the reactions:

$$U^{238}(d, 2n)Np^{238}; \quad Np^{238}\xrightarrow[\text{2.0 days}]{\beta^-} Pu^{238}$$

The beta decay of Np^{238} produces Pu^{238} which is an alpha emitter of some 90 years half-life. The isolation of this long-lived daughter of Np^{238} by the above research team constituted the discovery of element 94.

Much of the initial tracer work on the chemistry of neptunium was performed with Np^{239} prepared by neutron irradiation of uranium or with the $Np^{239} - Np^{238}$ mixture produced by the deuteron bombardment of uranium.

The longest-lived isotope of neptunium and the isotope which must be considered the most important from the standpoint of chemical investigations of neptunium is Np^{237} which has a half-life of 2.20×10^6 years. Its discovery in 1942 was an outgrowth of the study of U^{237}. In 1940, NISHINA AND CO-WORKERS[10] found a 6.5 day uranium period when uranium oxide was bombarded with fast neutrons from a cyclotron. This activity remained with the uranium when the fission product activities were removed. They assigned the new activity correctly to U^{237} produced by the reaction:

$$U^{238}(n, 2n)U^{237}$$

Since U^{237} is a beta emitter, it must decay into 93^{237}, and NISHINA AND CO-WORKERS[10] attempted to isolate the new element. They were unsuccessful because of the weakness of their sources and because they assumed chemical properties for neptunium similar to rhenium.

---

[8] K. Starke, *Naturwiss.* **30**, 107 (1942); **30**, 577 (1942); and private communications (1949).

[9] G. T. Seaborg, E. M. McMillan, J. W. Kennedy, and A. C. Wahl, *Phys. Rev.* **69**, 366 (1946), paper originally written January 1941.

[10] Y. Nishina, T. Yasaki, H. Ezoe, K. Kimura, and M. Ikawa, *Phys. Rev.* **57**, 1182 (1940).

Independently, at the same time, McMillan[11] had also studied the new isotope U^{237}. He too looked for the 93^{237} daughter using the fluoride oxidation-reduction coprecipitation cycle which he and Abelson had developed for their studies of Np^{239}. Using U^{237} sources of 80 microcurie strength they were unable to detect any radiations due to Np^{237} because of the long half-life of Np^{237}.

In 1942, Wahl and Seaborg[12] in a continuation of the experiments of McMillan prepared a much larger source of U^{237} (97 millicuries) by irradiating 1,200 grams of uranyl nitrate with the fast neutrons produced in a 15,000 microampere hour bombardment of beryllium with 16 MeV deuterons. Using ether extractions to remove the bulk of the uranium and numerous rare earth fluoride coprecipitation cycles to remove and purify the neptunium fraction these workers succeeded in isolating and identifying 300 alpha counts per minute of Np^{237}. Using the ratio of U^{237} to the daughter Np^{237} activity they calculated a half-life of 3×10^6 years, which agrees within their experimental error with the presently accepted value of 2.20×10^6 years.

The principal source of Np^{237} is now the uranium reactor. When natural uranium or uranium of only moderate U^{235} enrichment is used the Np^{237} is produced almost entirely through the U^{238} $(n, 2n)$ reaction which can proceed with that part of the fission-neutron distribution having energies beyond the $n, 2n$ threshold, about 7 MeV. In the original Hanford reactors, for example, the amount of Np^{237} produced was approximately 0.3 percent of the amount of Pu^{239} produced. Therefore, neptunium can be made available in kilogram quantities by suitable modification of plutonium chemical processing methods. This is fortunate for it means that this element, whose complex chemical and physical properties are of such great scientific interest, can be subjected to careful study in many laboratories. In reactors operating on uranium highly enriched in U^{235} the principal reaction path giving rise to Np^{237} is the following reaction sequence which was first studied by Manning and Brittain[13].

$$U^{235}(n,\gamma)U^{236}(n,\gamma)U^{237}\xrightarrow[\text{6.7 days}]{\beta^-}Np^{237}$$

The first isolation of a weighable amount of Np^{237} was carried out by Magnusson and La Chapelle[14] in October 1944. These workers purified neptunium by the rare-earth fluoride coprecipitation technique and then

[11] E. McMillan, *Phys. Rev.* **58**, 178 (1940).

[12] A. C. Wahl and G. T. Seaborg, Paper No. 1.5, "The Transuranium Elements," *Nat. Nucl. Energ. Ser.*, Division IV **14B**, (New York: McGraw-Hill Book Co., Inc., 1949); *Phys. Rev.* **73**, 94 (1948); paper originally written April 1942.

[13] W. M. Manning and J. W. Brittain, unpublished results (1944).

[14] L. B. Magnusson and T. J. LaChapelle, Paper No. 1.7, "The Transuranium Elements," *Nat. Nucl. Energ. Ser.*, Division IV **14B** (New York: McGraw-Hill Book Co., Inc., 1949); *J. Am. Chem. Soc.* **70**, 3534 (1948).

eliminated the rare earth carrier by precipitating pure neptunium compounds such as sodium neptunyl acetate. Since they had only a few micrograms of material available to them these precipitations were carried out with ultramicrochemical techniques. The half-life was measured by determining the counting rates of accurately weighed samples of NpO_2 whose identity and purity were checked by x-ray crystallographic analysis. The weight of one of the NpO_2 samples was only 3.8 micrograms. These experiments constituted the first chemical isolation of a weighable amount of neptunium.

The isotope Np^{237} is the only beta-stable isotope of neptunium, a fact which agrees with the general rule that all the odd elements have, at most, one or two beta-stable isotopes. An isotope such as Np^{237}, which is unstable only because of its alpha-particle lability, is therefore analogous to the "stable" nuclides in the region below lead.

Identification of further isotopes of neptunium could not be accomplished easily until target materials other than U^{238} were available or cyclotron beam energies were increased beyond the 16 MeV deuteron maximum prevailing in 1942. By 1944 milligram quantities of U^{233} and U^{235} became available for cyclotron bombardments, and JAMES, FLORIN, HOPKINS, AND GHIORSO[15] identified Np^{236}, Np^{235}, and Np^{234} as products of deuteron bombardments of U^{235}. The isotope Np^{234} was also made[16] by deuteron bombardment of U^{233}. A few years later the Berkeley synchrocyclotron went into operation. This greatly extended the complexity of spallation reactions which could be carried out. MAGNUSSON, THOMPSON, AND SEABORG[17] took advantage of the new beam energy to produce and identify Np^{233}, Np^{232}, and Np^{231} by (d, xn) type reactions using U^{233}, U^{235}, and U^{238} targets. At the other end of the mass range new studies have been aided by the high neutron fluxes available in modern nuclear reactors. The isotope Np^{240} can be prepared by successive capture of neutrons starting with U^{238} as was first shown by HYDE, STUDIER, AND MANNING.[18]

$$U^{238}(n, \gamma)U^{239}(n, \gamma)U^{240} \xrightarrow[\text{14 hours}]{\beta^-} Np^{240}$$

The isotope Np^{241} was first identified by LESSLER AND MICHEL[19] who prepared it by the reaction

$$U^{238}(\alpha, p)Np^{241}$$

15 R. A. James, A. E. Florin, H. H. Hopkins, Jr., and A. Ghiorso, Paper No. 22.8 "The Transuranium Elements," *Nat. Nucl. Energ. Ser.*, Division IV **14B** (New York: McGraw-Hill Book Co., Inc., 1949).

16 E. K. Hyde, M. H. Studier and A. Ghiorso, Paper No. 22.15, "The Transuranium Elements," *Nat. Nucl. Energ. Ser.*, Division IV **14B** (New York: McGraw-Hill Book Co., Inc., 1949).

17 L. B. Magnusson, S. G. Thompson, and G. T. Seaborg, *Phys. Rev.* **78**, 363 (1950).

18 E. K. Hyde, M. H. Studier, and W. M. Manning, *Argonne National Laboratory Report*, *ANL-4143*, April 15, 1948 and *ANL-4182*, August 4, 1948 (unpublished).

19 R. M. Lessler and M. C. Michel, *Univ. Calif. Rad. Lab. Report*, *UCRL-8757*, August 1959.

In the sections which follow we discuss the properties of the isotopes of neptunium in a systematic fashion. The isotopes of neptunium follow the normal pattern with regard to beta instability; those with mass greater than 237 are unstable toward negative beta particle emission while those with smaller mass numbers are unstable toward decay by orbital electron capture. The isotopes Np^{238} and Np^{236} should exhibit both types of beta-instability since each lies between β-stable isobars of uranium and plutonium. So far, only for Np^{236} has electron capture branching been observed. All neptunium isotopes are alpha unstable but the alpha activity of Np^{238} and higher mass isotopes has not been detected because negative beta particle emission is so much more rapid. Similarly for Np^{236} and lighter-mass isotopes the rate of decay by capture of an orbital electron is so fast that alpha-particle emission is often difficult to detect. For isotopes which are extremely deficient in neutrons such as Np^{231}, the alpha decay energy becomes large and the partial alpha half-life short enough that alpha-particle emission again becomes prominent.

9.1.2 *Neptunium-231*

MAGNUSSON, THOMPSON, AND SEABORG[20] produced Np^{231} by bombardment of natural uranium with 100 MeV deuterons or of enriched U^{235} with 45–100 MeV deuterons.

$$U^{238}(d, 9n)Np^{231}$$
$$U^{235}(d, 6n)Np^{231}$$

This isotope decays principally by electron capture to U^{231} with a half-life of about 50 minutes although the radiations corresponding to this decay cannot be observed directly because of interference from the electromagnetic radiation of the several other neptunium isotopes produced in the bombardment. It decays also by the emission of 6.28 MeV alpha particles. These alpha particles can be readily distinguished by measurements in an ion chamber because the alpha branching of the heavier neptunium isotopes present in the sample is so slight. The mass identification depends on the observation of the growth of Pa^{227} and of the Pa^{227} daughters comprising the Pa^{227} collateral series (see section 7.2.3). The alpha branching is probably about one per cent.

9.1.3 *Neptunium-232*

In the experiments of MAGNUSSON, THOMPSON, AND SEABORG[20] cited above, preliminary evidence for Np^{232} was found indicating a half-life of 13 minutes for decay by electron capture. Further confirmatory experiments are necessary; one essential experiment is the production of

[20] L. B. Magnusson, S. G. Thompson, and G. T. Seaborg, *Phys. Rev.* **78**, 363 (1950).

detectable yields of U^{232} daughter activity. No alpha radioactivity was observed. This is in agreement with alpha systematics which would predict that the degree of alpha branching should be smaller than could have been detected in experiments described.

9.1.4 *Neptunium-233*

MAGNUSSON, THOMPSON, AND SEABORG[20] produced 35 minute Np^{233} by bombardment of U^{235} targets with deuterons of 45–100 MeV energy. In the case of U^{233} targets the yield of Np^{233} was still detectable when the deuteron energy was lowered to as low as 15 MeV. The reactions involved are:

$$U^{235}(d, 4n)Np^{233}$$
$$U^{233}(d, 2n)Np^{233}$$

The decay is >99 per cent by electron capture. Absorption curve measurements revealed the presence of K x-radiation and some gamma radiation and conversion electrons. It was possible to look for alpha particles emitted by Np^{233} in samples prepared by the bombardment of U^{233} with 15 MeV deuterons because at this beam energy no Np^{231} alpha activity was produced. Alpha particles of 5.53 MeV energy were observed in amounts corresponding to a branching ratio of only 10^{-5}.

LESSLER[22] prepared Np^{233} by the reaction:

$$U^{234}(d, 3n)Np^{233}$$

and studied the gamma radiations in a NaI spectrometer. Peaks were observed at 95, 150, 170, 205 and 410 keV. Broad peaks indicating two or more unresolved gamma rays were observed from 230–310 keV and from 500–560 keV. The most prominent photons were K x-rays. Other gamma rays are probably present, but the presence of some Np^{234} activity interfered with their measurement. No detailed decay scheme has been proposed for Np^{233}.

LESSLER[22] set an upper limit of 3×10^{-5} for the α-decay branching.

9.1.5 *Neptunium-234*

The 4.40 day isotope Np^{234} was discovered by JAMES, FLORIN, HOPKINS, AND GHIORSO[23] who found that the neptunium fraction chemically isolated from a U^{235} target bombarded with 20 MeV deuterons contained in addition to Np^{238} and Np^{239} (from the U^{238} present) an activity decaying with a half-life of about 4 days. This activity was characterized by soft electrons, x-rays and energetic gamma radiation. Shortly afterward, HYDE, STUDIER,

[22] R. M. Lessler, *Univ. Calif. Rad. Lab. Report, UCRL-8439*, October 1958.

[23] R. A. James, A. E. Florin, H. H. Hopkins, Jr., and A. Ghiorso, Paper No. 22.8, "The Transuranium Elements," *Nat. Nucl. Energ. Ser.*, Division IV **14B** (New York: McGraw-Hill Book Co., Inc., 1949).

AND GHIORSO[24] found that Np^{234} could be prepared in a purer state by bombarding U^{233} with 20 MeV deuterons. These authors reported high energy gamma radiation in high abundance. An upper limit of 0.01 per cent was set on the alpha branching of Np^{234} by the failure to isolate Pa^{230} from the neptunium fraction. OSBORNE, THOMPSON, AND VAN WINKLE[25] prepared Np^{234} by bombarding Pa^{231} with 40 MeV helium ions.

The reactions by which Np^{234} has been formed include:

$$U^{236}(d, 4n)Np^{234}$$

$$U^{235}(d, 3n)Np^{234}$$

$$U^{235}(\alpha, p4n)Np^{234}$$

$$Pa^{231}(\alpha, n)Np^{234}$$

$$U^{234}(d, 2n)Np^{234}$$

$$U^{233}(d, n)Np^{234}$$

$$U^{233}(\alpha, p2n)Np^{234}$$

$$U^{233}(\alpha, 3n)Pu^{234} \xrightarrow{EC} Np^{234}$$

$$U^{235}(p, 2n)Np^{234}$$

The cross sections for several of these reactions are given in Table 5.5 of Chapter 5.

The various modes of formation limited the mass number assignment to 234 or 233. The assignment 234 was confirmed by the fissionability measurements of HYDE, BENTLEY, AND HAGEMANN[26] who found a slow neutron fission cross section of 900 barns for Np^{234}. The fissionability of the sample decreased with a half-life of 4.4 days and did not level out as would have been expected if the highly fissionable U^{233} had been the daughter product. In the case of U^{233} bombarded with helium ions the formation of Np^{234} by the electron capture decay of Pu^{234} has been directly observed.[27] This bombardment yields a plutonium activity of approximately 8 hour half-life that is known to be Pu^{234}, which decays principally ($\sim$96 per cent) by electron capture. The genetic relationship between the 8-hour plutonium and the 4-day neptunium has been demonstrated.

---

[24] E. K. Hyde, M. H. Studier, and A. Ghiorso, Paper No. 22.15, "The Transuranium Elements," *Nat. Nucl. Energ. Ser.*, Division IV **14B** (New York: McGraw-Hill Book Co., Inc., 1949).

[25] D. Osborne, R. C. Thompson, and Q. Van Winkle, Paper No. 19.11, "The Transuranium Elements," *Nat. Nucl. Energ. Ser.*, Division IV **14B** (New York: McGraw-Hill Book Co., Inc., 1949).

[26] E. K. Hyde, W. C. Bentley, and F. Hagemann, *Argonne National Laboratory Report ANL-4152*, May 20, 1948.

[27] I. Perlman, P. R. O'Connor, and L. O. Morgan, Paper No. 22.30, "The Transuranium Elements," *Nat. Nucl. Energ. Ser.*, Division IV **14B** (New York: McGraw-Hill Book Co., Inc., 1949).

A number of workers[28-33] have contributed to the measurement of the gamma ray photons, the x-rays and the conversion electrons emitted by Np^{234}. We quote here chiefly from the study of GALLAGHER AND THOMAS[34] which is considerably more comprehensive than those published earlier. Np^{234} emits a large number of gamma rays ranging in energy from 43 to 1606 keV. Measurements by the NaI scintillation method do not resolve these gamma rays cleanly. The most fruitful approach has been the measurement of the conversion electrons in permanent magnet spectrographs of high resolution and in electromagnetic beta spectrometers of moderate to high resolution.

GALLAGHER AND THOMAS[34] measured more than 150 conversion lines and deduced the gamma rays listed in the table from the energies and relative intensities of these lines. In addition, a number of plutonium Auger electrons were observed as well as a few lines which could not be definitely assigned to a gamma transition.

GALLAGHER AND THOMAS[34] constructed the decay scheme shown in Fig. 9.1. In constructing this figure, they were able to use information on the low-lying levels obtained from the α-decay of Pu^{238} (see Section 9.2.8). They also relied partially on sum and difference relationships between their observed gamma rays and partially on some gamma-gamma coincidence data reported by HUIZENGA AND CO-WORKERS.[31] In many respects this decay scheme is incomplete and tentative. The spin of Np^{234} is unknown (although restricted to the values 0, 1, or 2) and the primary electron-capture branching to the levels of U^{234} is also unknown. The spin and parity assignments of several of the highest-lying levels are uncertain. Nonetheless this decay scheme contains a great deal of information on the level structure of U^{234} and it is worthwhile calling attention to several interesting points.

The lowest levels constitute a rotational band based on the 0+ ground state. The spin sequence is 0+, 2+, 4+, ..., the energy spacing follows the $I(I+1)$ rule, and the pattern of de-excitation is a cascade of E2 transitions. In the decay scheme of Pu^{238} which is shown in section 9.2.8 the 6+ and 8+ members of this rotational band of levels are also observed.

[28] G. D. O'Kelley, Ph.D. Thesis, University of California, June 1951; also published as *Univ. Calif. Rad. Lab. Report, UCRL-1243* (1951).

[29] R. W. Hoff, Ph.D. Thesis, University of California, Sept. 1953; also published as *Univ. Calif. Rad. Lab. Report, UCRL-2325* (1953).

[30] F. S. Stephens, Jr., unpublished results.

[31] Huizenga, Engelkemeir, Freedman, Porter, and Gindler, *Bull. Am. Phys. Soc.*, Ser. II, **1**, 171 (1956).

[32] R. J. Prestwood, H. C. Smith, C. I. Browne, and D. C. Hoffman, *Phys. Rev.* **98**, 1324 (1955).

[33] D. A. Orth, Ph.D. Thesis, University of California, Sept. 1953; also published as *Univ. Calif. Rad. Lab. Report, UCRL-1059* (1953).

[34] C. J. Gallagher, Jr. and T. D. Thomas, *Nucl. Phys.* **14**, 1-20 (1959/1960).

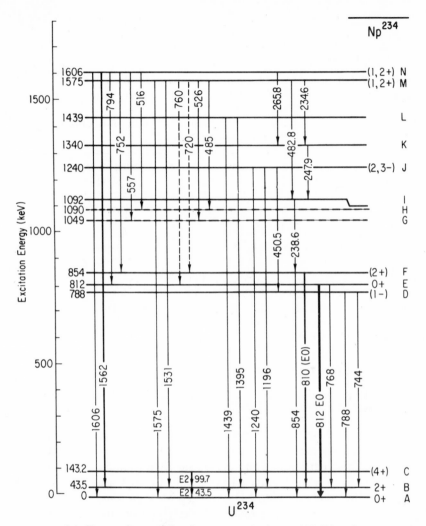

FIG. **9.1.** Decay scheme of the electron-capture decay of Np[234] as formulated by GALLAGHER AND THOMAS.

Furthermore, the 4+ and 6+ levels are seen in the beta decay of Pa[234] (UZ).

The 1− level at 788 is the first 1− level to be reported in an even-even nucleus of uranium, but it is a commonly observed level in the spectra of even-even nuclei of neighboring elements (see discussion in Chapter 3). It is assigned to a collective mode of excitation. This level de-excites by a pair of E1 transitions to the 0+ and 2+ levels of the ground state rotational band. These gamma rays are also seen in the beta decay of Pa[234] (UX₂); See discussion in Section 8.2.12.

The level at 812 keV is given the spin assignment 0+ and is believed with some confidence to be the first β-vibrational level of excitation in U^{234}. (See Chapter 3 for a discussion of collective β and γ vibrations in even-even nuclei.)   The level at 854 is believed to be the first rotational level in a band based on the 812 keV state.   This interpretation for both levels is strongly based on the observance of the completely converted $E0$ transitions

TABLE 9.1.   Transitions in U^{234} following Np^{234} decay as reported by Gallagher and Thomas.*

Energy of gamma (keV)	Energy of gamma (keV)	Energy of gamma (keV)
43.49 ± 0.5	485.1 ± 1	811.6 ± 0.8
99.7 ± 0.1	515.7 ± 0.5	853.6 ± 1
233.6 ± 0.2	525.9 ± 0.5	1003 ± 2
234.6 ± 0.2	556.8 ± 0.6	1105 ± 2
238.6 ± 0.4	744.1 ± 0.7	1196 ± 2
247.9 ± 0.2	751.7 ± 0.8	1240 ± 2
265.8 ± 0.5	768.0 ± 0.8	1395 ± 3
297.6 ± 0.5	787.8 ± 0.8	1439 ± 3
450.5 ± 0.5	793.8 ± 0.8	1531 ± 3
482.8 ± 1ᵍ	810.0 ± 0.8	1562 ± 3
		1575 ± 3
		1606 ± 3

* Electron lines observed on a series of permanent magnet spectrographs with fields of 99, 160, and 350 gauss.

which de-excite them.   The observation of these $E0$ transitions is one of the most interesting results of the study of the decay of Np^{234}.   Further information on these particular levels and on the $E0$ transitions de-exciting them comes from the work of DURHAM, RESTER, AND CLASS[35] who excited the level at 854 keV by bombardment of U^{234} with 5 MeV protons.

$E0$ transitions proceed completely by emission of conversion electrons. Hence the dominant feature of the conversion electron spectrum of Np^{234} is the K and L electron lines of these prominent $E0$ transitions.   The transition from the 0+ level to the ground state has also been identified in the α-decay of Pu^{238} and in the β-decay of Pa^{234} (see Sections 9.2.8 and 8.0.0, respectively).   This particular transition connects an 0+ state with an 0+ state and is pure $E0$.   The other $E0$ connecting the 2+ level at 854 keV with the 2+ level at 43.5 keV competes with $E2$ de-excitation.   This was the first observation in the heavy element region of an $E0$-admixed transition between two

---

[35] F. E. Durham, D. H. Rester, and C. M. Class, *Proceedings of Kingston Conference on Nuclear Structure*, Univ. of Toronto Press, 1960, p. 594.

states with $I \neq 0$. CHURCH AND WENESER[36] had predicted such transitions on theoretical grounds.

GALLAGHER AND THOMAS[34] also suggested that the levels at 1049 and 1090 (MeV) may be the expected $2+$ and $3+$ ($K = 2$) states corresponding to collective excitation of the first γ-vibrational mode. This interpretation is probably incorrect in view of the later studies of BJØRNHOLM AND NIELSEN[37] on the decay of Pa^{234} (UZ) which indicates that the γ-vibrational level falls at 922 keV. Refer to the discussion in Section 8.2.12 of Chapter 8.

PRESTWOOD AND CO-WORKERS[32] have investigated the radiations of Np^{234} with a trochoidal analyzer and have identified positrons with an end point energy of 0.8 MeV. The ratio of positron emission to electron capture was found to be 4.6×10^{-4}. This is the first observation of the emission of positrons by a nuclide of atomic number higher than 80. This measurement set a lower limit of 1.8 MeV to the disintegration energy.

9.1.6 *Neptunium-235*

JAMES, FLORIN, HOPKINS, AND GHIORSO[38] found that the neptunium fraction from uranium bombarded with 20 MeV deuterons, after thorough decontamination, exhibits a long-lived activity characterized by low-energy electromagnetic radiation such as would be emitted by an electron-capturing species. Bombardments of uranium targets of varying isotopic composition have established the responsible target isotope as U^{235}. It is now certain that this activity is due to Np^{235}, produced by the reaction $U^{235}(d, 2n)Np^{235}$.

Bombardment of U^{235} and U^{233} with 40 MeV helium ions[38,39] also produces Np^{235} by the reactions:

$$U^{235}(\alpha, p3n)Np^{235}$$

$$U^{235}(\alpha, 4n)Pu^{235} \xrightarrow{\text{electron capture}} Np^{235}$$

$$U^{233}(\alpha, pn)Np^{235}$$

$$U^{233}(\alpha, 2n)Pu^{235} \xrightarrow{\text{electron capture}} Np^{235}$$

Failure to find long-lived neptunium activity from the bombardment of U^{233} with deuterons[39] is confirmation of the isotopic assignment of the activity as Np^{235}.

---

[36] E. L. Church and J. Weneser, *Phys. Rev.* **103**, 1035 (1956).

[37] S. Bjørnholm and O. B. Nielsen, *Nucl. Phys.* **30**, 488 (1962).

[38] R. A. James, A. E. Florin, H. H. Hopkins, Jr., and A. Ghiorso, Paper No. 22.8, "The Transuranium Elements," *Nat. Nucl. Energ. Ser.*, Division IV, **14B** (New York: McGraw-Hill Book Co., Inc., 1949).

[39] E. K. Hyde, M. H. Studier, and A. Ghiorso, Paper No. 22.15, "The Transuranium Elements," *Nat. Nucl. Energ. Ser.*, Division IV, **14B** (New York: McGraw-Hill Book Co., Inc., 1949).

The best estimate of the half life,[40] obtained from the decay of several samples over a period of 2 years, is 410 ± 10 days; these particular samples were prepared by the bombardment of 95 per cent U^{235} with 20 MeV deuterons. The observed radiations consist chiefly of the characteristic L x-rays of uranium.[40]

The total disintegration energy is low and the ratio of L-electron to K-electron capture is large. JAMES, GHIORSO, AND ORTH[40] set the ratio at approximately 10. Later HOFF, OLSEN, AND MANN[41] reported the value 30 ± 2. The most careful measurement was made by GINDLER, HUIZENGA, AND ENGELKEMEIR[42] who arrived at the value of 36.7 for the L/K electron capture ratio. They also observed M x-rays and set 0.46 as the ratio of M-electron to L-electron capture. The L/K electron capture ratio is a sensitive measure of the decay energy for a nuclide with low disintegration energy. For the experimentally observed L/K ratio of 36.7 the calculated decay energy, based on an allowed transition, is 123 keV. The estimates of decay energy from closed decay-energy cycles are imprecise by comparison. FOREMAN AND SEABORG[43] calculate a value of 210 kilovolts while GINDLER, HUIZENGA, AND ENGELKEMEIR[42] estimate 70 kilovolts.

The electron capture decay of Np^{235} leads to U^{235} whose low-lying levels are well known. They consist of a $7/2-, 9/2-, 11/2-$ rotational band based on a $K = 7/2$ ground state and a $1/2+, 3/2+$ and $5/2+$ rotational band based on a $K = 1/2$ based level lying within a few electron volts of the ground state. The $K = 1/2, I = 1/2$ state has a half-life of 26.17 minutes as has been learned from a study of alpha decay of Pu^{239} (see Section 9.2.9). GINDLER, HUIZENGA, AND ENGELKEMEIR[42] examined the radiations of Np^{235} very carefully to see whether any of the decay events led to the low-lying excited states of U^{235}. They attempted a chemical isolation of the 26 minute U^{235m} but found no evidence for decay to any state other than the ground state of U^{235}; they set a lower limit of 97.9 per cent for decay to this state. Their conclusions are summarized in Fig. 9.2. A ground state assignment of $I = 5/2+, K = 5/2$ for Np^{235} is consistent with the decay scheme.

Neptunium-235 also decays to a slight extent by alpha emission. JAMES, GHIORSO, AND ORTH[40] first observed the emission of 5.06 ± 0.02 MeV alpha particles and reported a branching ratio of 5×10^{-5}. HOFF ET AL.[41] reported a value of the branching ratio of 3.5×10^{-5}. More recent values by THOMAS[44] and by GINDLER ET AL.[42] are $(1.23 \pm 0.10) \times 10^{-5}$ and 1.59×10^{-5},

[40] R. A. James, A. Ghiorso, and D. A. Orth, *Phys. Rev.* **85**, 369 (1952).

[41] R. W. Hoff, J. L. Olsen, and L. G. Mann, *Phys. Rev.* **102**, 805 (1956).

[42] J. E. Gindler, J. R. Huizenga, and D. W. Engelkemeir, *Phys. Rev.* **109**, 1263 (1958).

[43] B. M. Foreman, Jr., and G. T. Seaborg, *Univ. Calif. Rad. Lab. Report, UCRL-8015* (Rev.), January 1958. *J. Inorg. Nucl. Chem.* **7**, 305 (1958).

[44] T. D. Thomas, Ph.D. Thesis, University of California, Sept. 1957; also published as *Univ. Calif. Rad. Lab. Report, UCRL-3791* (July 1957).

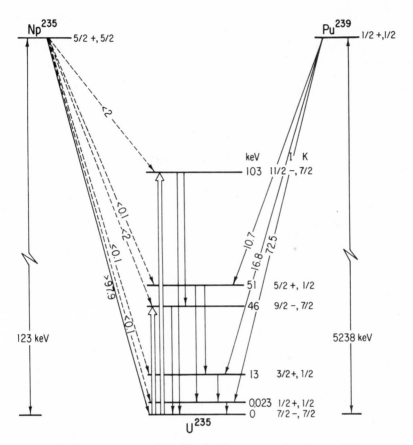

FIG. 9.2. Decay scheme of Np^{235} showing quantitative decay (within experimental error) to the ground state of U^{235}. The three levels in U^{235} with spins and parities 1/2+, 3/2+, and 5/2+ comprise a rotational band and are populated by Pu^{239} alpha decay. The base state 1/2+ has a half-life of 26 minutes. Levels at 46 and 103 keV are reached by Coulomb excitation of U^{235} and are assumed to have spins and parities of 9/2− and 11/2−, respectively.

respectively.   The latter corresponds to a partial alpha half-life of 7.0 × 10^4 years.   The alpha spectrum is complex as was first shown by HOFF, OLSEN, AND MANN[41] who found gamma rays of 26 keV and 85 keV and L x-rays to be in coincidence with alpha particles.   These gamma rays were shown to arise from a metastable state with a half-life of 37 millimicroseconds. GINDLER AND ENGELKEMEIR[45] confirmed these findings and also noted a coincidence with K x-radiation in small intensity.   Intensities of (0.15 ± 0.02),

[45] J. E. Gindler and D. W. Engelkemeir, *Phys. Rev.* **119**, 1645 (1960).

(0.088 ± 0.008) and (0.006 ± 0.002) photon per alpha disintegration were found for the 26 keV, 84 keV, and K x-radiation, respectively.

Direct measurement of the alpha spectrum is extremely difficult because of the low percentage of events going by alpha decay. Nonetheless, by means of precise technique with the ion chamber method GINDLER AND ENGELKEMEIR[45] achieved a partial resolution of the spectrum. Their results are displayed in Figure 9.3. It is possible to interpret these results in some

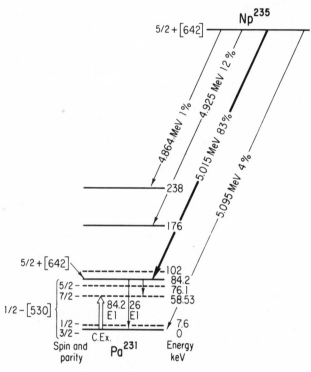

FIG 9.3. Alpha decay scheme of Np235. Dotted levels of Pa231 and Nilsson state assignments based on discussion of Section 8.2.10. Total alpha branching is 1.59 × 10⁻⁵.

detail because the low-lying excited levels of Pa²³¹ are well-known from a study of the decay schemes of U²³¹ and Th²³¹ and from Coulombic excitation of Pa²³¹ targets with low energy beams of charged particles. The lower part of the excitation spectrum as deduced from these studies is shown as dotted lines in the figure. The detailed arguments on which these levels and their Nilsson wave function assignments are based are given in Section 8.2.10 of Chapter 8.

It is apparent that the favored decay of Np^{235} leads to the Nilsson state 5/2 + [642] which lies at 84.2 kilovolts above ground. On the basis of the principle of favored alpha decay between parent and daughter nuclei bearing identical Nilsson wave function assignments,[46] it is clear that the ground state of Np^{235} is 5/2+ [642]. The quantum numbers being referred to here are K, π [N $n_z\Lambda$]. It is rather likely that the alpha groups shown in the figure are still not completely resolved and that alpha population is distributed over several members of the rotational bands of each intrinsic state of Pa^{231}. The alpha decay of Np^{235} closely resembles that of Np^{237} discussed below in Section 9.1.9 and it is reasonable that the greater complexity observed in Np^{237} decay is also in fact present in Np^{235} decay.

9.1.7 Neptunium-236

The isotope Np^{236} was discovered by JAMES, FLORIN, HOPKINS, AND GHIORSO.[47] In the neptunium fraction isolated from a target of U^{238}, depleted with respect to U^{235}, which had been bombarded with 20 MeV deuterons, they observed the growth of alpha particles of 4.3-cm range known from other evidence to belong to Pu^{236}. Consequently, there was indicated the formation of Np^{236} and its beta decay to Pu^{236} as follows:

$$U^{238}(d, 4n)Np^{236} \xrightarrow{\beta^-} Pu^{236}$$

The same phenomenon was found in the bombardment of U^{235} with 20 MeV deuterons and 40 MeV helium ions:[47]

$$U^{235}(d, n)Np^{236} \xrightarrow{\beta^-} Pu^{236}$$

$$U^{235}(\alpha, p2n)Np^{236} \xrightarrow{\beta^-} Pu^{236}$$

This isotope is also produced in 40 MeV helium-ion bombardments of $Np^{237,48}$ and $U^{233,49}$

$$Np^{237}(\alpha, \alpha n)Np^{236} \xrightarrow{\beta^-} Pu^{236}$$

$$U^{233}(\alpha, p)Np^{236} \xrightarrow{\beta^-} Pu^{236}$$

[46] A. Bohr, P. O. Fröman, and B. R. Mottelson, Dan. Mat.-fys. Medd. 29, 10 (1955).

[47] R. A. James, A. E. Florin, H. H. Hopkins, Jr., and A. Ghiorso, Paper No. 22.8, "The Transuranium Elements," Nat. Nucl. Energ. Ser. 14B (New York: McGraw-Hill Book Co., Inc., 1949).

[48] R. A. James, S. G. Thompson, and H. H. Hopkins, Jr., Paper No. 22.16, "The Transuranium Elements," Nat. Nucl. Energ. Ser. 14B (New York: McGraw-Hill Book Co., Inc., 1949).

[49] E. K. Hyde, M. H. Studier, and A. Ghiorso, Paper No. 22.15, "The Transuranium Elements," Nat. Nucl. Energ. Ser. 14B (New York: McGraw-Hill Book Co., Inc., 1949).

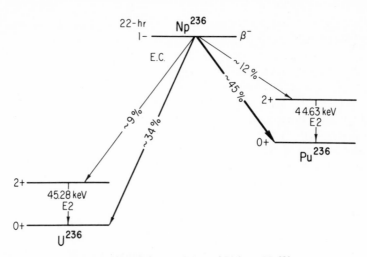

FIG. **9.4.** Partial decay scheme of 22-hour Np²³⁶.

In the helium-ion bombardments of U^{235} and U^{233} it was possible to observe in the neptunium fraction not only the growth of Pu^{236} alpha particles but also the decay of the beta particles of Np^{236}. From the rate of growth of Pu^{236} alpha particles in a bombardment of U^{235} with helium ions, a half-life of 22 hours was derived for Np^{236}. Analysis of the decay curve from the U^{235} experiment gave an independent value of the Np^{236} half-life of 21 hours.[47] JAMES, FLORIN, HOPKINS, AND GHIORSO[47] were unable to produce samples of Np^{236} free of excessive amounts of Np^{238} and Np^{239}, and therefore could set only wide limits on the beta energy. ORTH AND O'KELLEY,[50] using highly purified U^{235} (99.4 per cent), repeated the deuteron bombardments and prepared sufficient activity for absorption measurements and a beta ray spectrometer analysis. At a later time JAFFE[51] and PASSELL[52] prepared Np^{236} in a similar way for study of the radiations. The results of ORTH AND O'KELLEY had to be reinterpreted by the later workers and will not be quoted here. JAFFE[51] and PASSELL[52] constructed the decay scheme shown in Fig. 9.4. The L_{II} and L_{III} conversion lines and the M and N conversion lines of the 43.4-keV transition in Pu^{236} and the 44.2 keV transition in U^{236} were resolved from the electron spectrum.[52] HOLLANDER,[53] studying the decay of Np^{236}, has remeasured the energy of the first excited states of U^{236} and Pu^{236} and found 45.28 ± 0.06 keV and 44.63 ± 0.1

[50] D. A. Orth and G. D. O'Kelley, *Phys. Rev.* **82**, 758 (1951).

[51] H. Jaffe, Ph.D. Thesis, University of California, April 1954; also published as *Univ. Calif. Rad. Lab. Report, UCRL-2537*, April 1954.

[52] T. O. Passell, Ph.D. Thesis, University of California, March 1954; also published as *Univ. Calif. Rad. Lab. Report, UCRL-2528*, March 1954.

[53] J. M. Hollander, *Phys. Rev.* **103**, 1590 (1956).

keV, respectively.   The beta decay of Np^{236} appears to proceed to the $0+$ and $2+$ levels of the ground state rotational band of Pu^{236}; the electron capture decay appears to proceed to the $0+$ and $2+$ levels of the ground state rotational band of U^{236} which are familiar from the alpha decay of Pu^{240} to the same nucleus.   The log ft values for these four transitions are 7.1, 6.6, 7.5, and 7.0 respectively, indicating first forbidden transitions.   On this basis one can assign a spin and parity of 1− to 22 hour Np^{236}.   This is consistent with the measured spin of Np^{237} (93 protons), which is 5/2, and of U^{235} (143 neutrons), which is 7/2.   The Nilsson orbital assignments of the odd nucleon in the ground states of these nuclei are known on rather sure evidence to be 5/2+ [642] and 7/2 − [743], respectively.   Neptunium-236 with 93 protons and 143 neutrons might then be expected to be represented by (5/2+, 7/2−) leading to 1− or 6−.   It is logical to assign 1− to the 22 hour form of Np^{236} and 6− to the long lived isomer.   The $M5$ transition between the two isomers would have a very long lifetime and would account for the occurrence of isomerism.   It is known, however, that a 5/2− level identified as the Nilsson state 5/2 − [523] occurs at 59.6 keV above ground in Np^{237}.   This state could possibly be the ground state for the 93rd proton in Np^{236}.   This in combination with the 143rd neutron state 7/2 − would lead to spins of 1+ and 6+ for the isomers of Np^{236}, which would be an alternative set of assignments.   The negative parity set may be preferred on the basis of the log ft values.

GRAY[54] sets the ratio of negatron emission to K-electron capture as 57/43 in Np^{236}.   GINDLER, HUIZENGA, AND ENGELKEMEIR[55] suggests a 15 per cent correction for the contribution of L-electron capture to the electron capture branch.   This reduces the β^-/EC ratio to 1.2.   GINDLER AND SJOBLOM[57] report the even lower value of 0.95.

The energy of the most energetic beta particle group is about 520 keV.[54] GALLAGHER AND THOMAS[56] observed conversion lines of gamma rays with 641.7 and 687.0 keV energy which defined a level at 687 keV in U^{236}.

9.1.8 *Long-lived Isomer of Np²³⁶*

Evidence for the existence of a long-lived isomer of Np^{236} was first obtained by STUDIER, HOPKINS, GHIORSO, AND BENTLEY[58] from a 22 MeV

[54] P. R. Gray, *Phys. Rev.* **101**, 1306 (1956).

[55] J. E. Gindler, J. R. Huizenga, and D. W. Engelkemeir, *Phys. Rev.* **109**, 1263 (1958).

[56] C. J. Gallagher and T. D. Thomas, *Nucl. Phys.* **14**, 1–20 (1959/1960).

[57] J. E. Gindler and R. Sjoblom, *J. Inorg. Nucl. Chem.* **12**, 8 (1959).

[58] M. H. Studier, H. H. Hopkins, Jr., A. Ghiorso, and W. C. Bentley—*Atomic Energy Commission Report CF-3762*, 1947; reviewed by G. T. Seaborg, Chapter 11, "The Transuranium Elements," *Nat. Nucl. Energ. Ser.* **14A** (New York: McGraw-Hill Book Co., Inc., 1954).

deuteron bombardment of uranium metal in which the U^{235}/U^{238} ratio was only 1/2800. Neptunium prepared in a bombardment of long duration was isolated chemically, and measurements were made of the fission rate of the sample in a calibrated flux of slow neutrons. These showed the fission-ability to decrease with a two day half-life characteristic of Np^{238}. In addition to the fission events due to Np^{238} a long-lived fissionable material was present even after further chemical separations had been performed which should have removed any other element. Since the slow-neutron fission cross section of long-lived Np^{237} was too small to account for the observed number of fission events, and since the long-lived fissionability was found only in the upper 3 mil layer of the uranium metal target where the $(d, 4n)$ reaction was energetically possible, it had to be concluded that this fission-ability was due to a Np^{236} isomer.

In a followup experiment STUDIER, GINDLER, AND STEVENS[59] prepared a larger sample of the suspected isomer in a similar way. Fifteen months after bombardment, the neptunium fraction was isolated from the U^{238} and subjected to analysis in a mass spectrometer. Masses 236 and 237 were observed in the mass ratio 0.062. The alpha activity of the sample was entirely due to Np^{237}. Beta activity was observed and assigned to Np^{236} (long-lived). A beta decay half-life of ≥ 5000 years was derived. This is a highly forbidden transition (log ft > 12). The cross section for fission with slow neutrons was measured to be 2800 barns. GINDLER, HUIZENGA, AND ENGELKEMEIR[60] repeated the experiment of STUDIER, GINDLER, AND STEVENS with the same results. They found that the 22 hour isomer was produced in a 7-fold greater yield than the long-lived isomer.

Further research is required to determine the relationship of the 5000-year Np^{236} to the 22-hour Np^{236} but a tentative spin of 6 can be assigned to the isomer on the basis of the considerations discussed in the preceding section.

9.1.9 Neptunium-237

The discovery of Np^{237} by WAHL AND SEABORG[61] is mentioned in the introductory Section 9.1.1. There is also some discussion of Np^{237} in Section 7.1.2 of Chapter 7 where the $4n + 1$ decay chain is treated. Np^{237} is an alpha-emitter with a half-life reported by MAGNUSSON AND LACHAPELLE[62] as $(2.20 \pm 0.10) \times 10^6$ years and by BRAUER AND CO-WORKERS[63] as $(2.14 \pm$

[59] M. H. Studier, J. E. Gindler, and C. M. Stevens, Phys. Rev. 97, 88 (1955).

[60] J. E. Gindler, J. R. Huizenga, and D. W. Engelkemeir, Phys. Rev. 109, 1263 (1958).

[61] A. C. Wahl and G. T. Seaborg, Phys. Rev. 73, 94 (1948); paper originally written April 1942.

[62] L. B. Magnusson and T. J. LaChapelle, "The Transuranium Elements," Nat. Nucl. Energ. Ser., Paper 1.7, 14B (New York: McGraw-Hill Book Co., Inc., 1949).

[63] F. P. Brauer, R. W. Stromatt, J. D. Ludwick, F. P. Roberts and W. L. Lyon, J. Inorg. Nucl. Chem. 12, 234 (1960).

0.01) × 10^6 years. This latter value corresponds to a specific activity of 1562 ± 7 disintegrations per minute per microgram. The spontaneous fission rate is less than 5 fissions per gram-hour, corresponding to a half-life limit of greater than 4 × 10^{16} years.[64] Np^{237} is beta stable. This isotope is the longest lived species of the element neptunium and the most suitable species for investigation of the chemical properties of the element. It is isolated in gram and kilogram amounts by the special processing of spent reactor fuel elements made of natural or enriched uranium.

A measurement of the details of the alpha spectrum is a matter of some difficulty because of the low specific activity. MAGNUSSON, ENGELKEMEIR, FREEDMAN, PORTER, AND WAGNER[65] studied the spectrum with a gridded ionization chamber connected to a multichannel pulse height analyzer. Close attention was paid to important details,[66] such as sample collimation, to get the best resolution of which this method is capable. Their results are summarized in Table 9.2. These same authors used scintillation, proportional and magnetic spectrometers to get information on transitions with the energies, 20, 29, 56.8, 86.9, 145, 175, and 200 MeV. Transition assignments derived from α-e$^-$, α-γ and γ-γ coincidence measurements were used to construct the decay scheme shown in the figure. STEPHENS[67] also contributed to the measurement of the gamma transitions by scintillation spectrometer determinations and γ-γ coincidence measurements.

Alpha spectrum measurements by KONDRAT'EV, NOVIKOVA, VOROB'EV AND GOL'DIN,[68] unpublished measurements by ASARO, STEPHENS, AND PERLMAN,[69] and published data of BARANOV, KULAKOV, SAMOILOV, ZELENKOV, AND RODIONOV[69a] are also included in the table.

The decay scheme shown in Fig. 9.5 is incomplete and no detailed assignments of the spins, parities and excitation character has been given to the majority of the levels in the Pa^{233} daughter nucleus. There are interesting experimental facts and suggested interpretations of the lower-lying levels and of the transitions which de-excite them which we should like to mention. As an aid to the discussion we show Fig. 9.6 which emphasizes the similarity in the lowest levels of Pa^{231} and Pa^{233}.

[64] E. Segrè, *Phys. Rev.* **86**, 21 (1952).

[65] L. B. Magnusson, D. W. Engelkemeir, M. S. Freedman, F. T. Porter, and F. Wagner, Jr., *Phys. Rev.* **100**, 1237A (1955).

[66] D. W. Engelkemeir and L. B. Magnusson, *Rev. Sci. Instr.* **26**, 295 (1955).

[67] F. S. Stephens, Jr., Ph.D. Thesis, University of California, June 1955. Also published as *Univ. Calif. Rad. Lab. Report, UCRL-2970*, (1955).

[68] L. N. Kondrat'ev, G. I. Novikova, A. M. Vorob'ev, L. L. Gol'din, *Izvest. Akad. Nauk SSSR, Ser. Fiz.* **20**, 875 (1956); Columbia Tech. Transl. p. 795.

[69] F. Asaro, F. S. Stephens, Jr., and I. Perlman, unpublished results 1956–58.

[69a] S. A. Baranov, *et al.*, *Sov. Phys., JETP* **14**, 1232 (1962); *Zhur. Eksp. Teor. Fiz.* **41**, 1733 (1961).

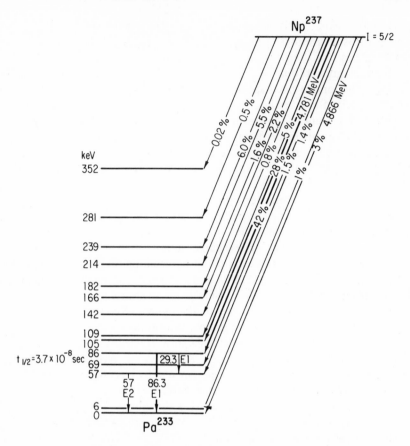

FIG. **9.5.** Decay scheme of Np[237] based on data of ASARO, STEPHENS, AND PERLMAN (unpublished data). Only the most thoroughly studied gamma transitions are included.

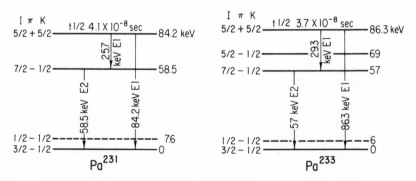

FIG. **9.6.** Partial level schemes of Pa[231] and Pa[233]. The lowest-lying levels of Pa[233] as seen in the α-decay of Np[237] are shown on the right.

TABLE 9.2. Alpha particle groups emitted by Np^{237}.

Magnusson et al.* Alpha particle energy (MeV)	Energy of Pa^{233} excited state (keV)	Abundance (per cent)	Kondrat'ev et al.† Alpha particle energy (MeV)	Abundance (per cent)	Asaro et al.‡ Alpha particle energy (MeV)	Energy of Pa^{233} excited state (keV)	Abundance (per cent)	Baranov et al.§ Alpha particle energy (MeV)	Energy of Pa^{233} excited state (keV)	Abundance (per cent)
4.872	0	3.1	4.867	2.5	4.866	0	3	4.872_3	0	0.44
					4.860	6	1	4.869_8	~2	0.92
								4.861_8	~10.6	0.24
4.816	57	3.5	4.803	3.4	4.810	57	1.4	4.816_3	57.0	1.49
					4.798	69	1.5	4.802_3	71.2	1.56
4.787	86	53	4.781	54	4.781	86	42	4.787_0	86.3	51.42
4.767	107	29	4.761	29.5	4.764	105	28	4.769_8	104.2	19.38
					4.759	108	5	4.764_7	109.5	16.82
								4.740_3	~134.3	0.02
					4.726 (?)	142	0.8			
4.713	162	1.7	4.701	2.3	4.703	166	2.2	4.711_3	163.8	0.13
								4.707_3	167.9	0.29
								4.698_2?	177.1	0.07
					4.687	182	1.6	4.693_4	182.0	0.18
4.674	201	3.3	4.643	8.3	4.656	214	5.5	4.663_0	212.0	1.6
			(several unresolved groups)					4.658_1	217.3	0.57
4.644	232	6.0			4.631	239	6.0	4.638_4	238.6	4.62
								4.597_6	279.5	0.06
								4.593_9	283.2	0.08
4.589	288	0.5			4.59	281	0.5	4.580_0	297.3	0.02
								4.572_7	304.8	0.05
4.52	~360	0.02			4.52	352	0.02	4.513_5	~365	0.01
								4.385_0	496	0.02

* Data of Magnusson and co-workers, *Phys. Rev.* **100**, 1237A (1955).   Relative to Th^{230} $E_\alpha = 4.682$ MeV and Po^{209} $E_\alpha = 4.877$ MeV.

† Data of Kondrat'ev and co-workers[68] relative to Po^{210} $E_\alpha = 5.2984$ MeV.

‡ Data of Asaro, Stephens and Perlman (unpublished) relative to Kondrat'ev's value of 4.781 MeV for α_{86}.

§ S. A. Baranov, *et al.*, *Sov. Phys. JETP* **14**, 1232 (1962). All α-energies relative to Magnusson, *et al.*'s value of 4.7870 for $\alpha_{86\cdot3}$.

First let us consider the 86.3 keV level in Pa^{233} which plays a prominent role in the decay of Np^{237}, since it is populated in 90 ± 5 out of every 100 alpha decay events. ENGELKEMEIR AND MAGNUSSON[70] have shown that this level is metastable by measuring an apparent half-life of $(3.69 \pm 0.04) \times 10^{-8}$ seconds for the 86.3 and 29.6 keV transitions. The true partial half-lives are 2.6×10^{-7} seconds and 3.0×10^{-7} seconds, respectively. STROMINGER AND RASMUSSEN[71] confirmed these results and speculated on their significance. Both the 86.3 and the 29.6 keV transitions are believed to be $E1$ in nature from the measured conversion coefficients and from other lines of evidence.[72] The half-lives of these transitions are enormously longer than would be predicted by the "single particle" transition probability formulas. The retardation in these cases is 1.4×10^6 and 7.2×10^4, respectively. These transitions belong to a class of $E1$ transitions observed in the decay of heavy deformed nuclei of odd mass which have anomalously long decay periods and anomalous L-shell and M-shell conversion coefficients. The 84.2 keV and 25.7 keV transitions in the decay of the 84.2 keV level of excitation of Pa^{231} (shown in the figure) also show these anomalous characteristics. Experimental data on this class of $E1$ transitions is discussed in a paper by ASARO, STEPHENS, HOLLANDER, AND PERLMAN.[72] Some of the theoretical implications are discussed by NILSSON AND RASMUSSEN.[73]

Now let us discuss the spin and parity assignments of the Pa^{233} levels. The ground state spin of Pa^{233} is deduced to be 3/2 from the decay scheme of Np^{237} and of Pa^{233}. This assignment is confirmed by the measurement[79] of spin 3/2 for the ground state of Pa^{233}. In each case this ground state is probably the $I = 3/2$ member of a rotational band of levels with $K = 1/2$. In the discussion of the collective model in Chapter 3 it is pointed out that $K = 1/2$ rotational bands can have an "anomalous" ordering of levels. The Nilsson orbital assignment for the ground state of both Pa^{231} and Pa^{233} is 1/2– [530]. For details of these assignments see Section 3.5.5 of Chapter 3 or other references.[69,74,75] The levels at 6, 57 and 69 keV are assigned as $I = 1/2$, 7/2 and 5/2 members of this same band. Note the inversion of the 5/2 and 7/2 members. In the Pa^{231} case only the $I = 3/2$ and $I = 7/2$ members have been identified by decay scheme analysis but the others are believed to exist. The NILSSON state assignment of the 86.3 keV level in Pa^{233} is $5/2 +$ [642]. A somewhat uncertain assignment of $3/2 +$ [651]

[70] D. Engelkemeir and L. B. Magnusson, *Phys. Rev.* **94**, 1395 (1954).

[71] D. Strominger and J. O. Rasmussen, *Phys. Rev.* **100**, 844 (1955).

[72] F. Asaro, F. S. Stephens, Jr., J. M. Hollander and I. Perlman, *Phys. Rev.* **117**, 492 (1960).

[73] S. G. Nilsson and J. O. Rasmussen, *Nucl. Phys.* **5**, 617 (1958).

[74] F. S. Stephens, Jr., F. Asaro, and I. Perlman, *Phys. Rev.* **113**, 212 (1959).

[75] B. R. Mottelson and S. G. Nilsson, *Mat.-fys. Skr. Dan. Vid. Selsk.* **1**, No. 8 (1959).

has been made for the 200 keV level. BARANOV ET AL.[69a] speculate on the assignments of additional levels.

The ground state spin of Np^{237} has been determined to be 5/2 by hyperfine structure analysis[76] and by the method of paramagnetic resonance.[77] The Nilsson state assignment of the Np^{237} ground state is firmly made to 5/2 + [642] for reasons which are discussed in connection with the decay scheme of Am^{241} below. The identity of this Nilsson assignment with that of the 86.3 keV level in Pa^{233} accounts for the high percentage of the alpha transitions which go to this level.

The neptunyl ion, NpO_2^{++}, is paramagnetic because of its unpaired $5f$ electron. It is possible to grow crystals of such compounds as rubidium neptunyl acetate and by cooling such crystals to temperatures in the vicinity of absolute zero to align the nuclei of Np^{237}. The angular distribution of the alpha particles of such aligned nuclei of Np^{237} has been studied and found to be anisotropic by ROBERTS, DABBS, AND CO-WORKERS.[78] It was found that Np^{237} emits its alpha particles preferentially through the tips of the Np^{237} nucleus, a prolate spheroid.

9.1.10 Neptunium-238

It is mentioned in the historical introduction that 2.10-day Np^{238} was the second isotope of neptunium to be discovered and that it was first produced[80,81] by the cyclotron-induced reaction:

$$U^{238}(d, 2n)Np^{238}$$

It can also be produced by helium ion bombardment of uranium:[82]

$$U^{238}(\alpha, p3n)Np^{238}$$
$$U^{235}(\alpha, p)Np^{238}$$

[76] F. S. Tomkins, *Phys. Rev.* **73**, 1214 (1948).

[77] B. Bleaney, P. M. Llewellyn, M. H. L. Pryce, and G. R. Hall, *Phil. Mag.* **45**, 992 (1954).

[78] S. H. Hanauer, J. W. T. Dabbs, C. D. Roberts, and G. W. Parker, *Bull. Am. Phys. Soc.* II, **5**, 22 (1960); see also Roberts, Dabbs, and Parker, *Proceedings of the Second International Conference on the Peaceful Uses of Atomic Energy*, United Nations, Geneva (1958) **15**, p. 322, and Dabbs, Roberts, and Parker, *Physica* **24**, 569 (1958).

[79] J. Winocur, *Univ. Calif. Rad. Lab. Report*, UCRL-9174, April 1960.

[80] G. T. Seaborg, E. M. McMillan, J. W. Kennedy, and A. C. Wahl, *Phys. Rev.* **69** 366 (1946); article submitted Jan 28, 1941.

[81] G. T. Seaborg, A. C. Wahl, and J. W. Kennedy, Paper No. 1.4, "The Transuranium Elements," *Nat. Nucl. Energ. Ser.*, Division IV **14B** (New York: McGraw-Hill Book Co., Inc., 1949).

[82] R. A. James, A. E. Florin, H. H. Hopkins, Jr., and A. Ghiorso, Paper No. 22.8, "The Transuranium Elements," *Nat. Nucl. Energ. Ser.*, Division IV, **14B** (New York: McGraw-Hill Book Co., Inc., 1949).

Cross sections for these reactions are listed in Table 5.9, Chapter 5. The first evidence for the production of Np^{238} by the reaction $Np^{237}(n, \gamma)Np^{238}$ was the discovery of Pu^{238} in reactor produced plutonium.[83] This was produced by the neutron reaction sequence:

$$U^{238}(n, 2n)U^{237} \xrightarrow{\ \beta^-\ } Np^{237}(n, \gamma) \ Np^{238} \xrightarrow{\ \beta^-\ } Pu^{238}$$
$$\text{fast neutron} \qquad\qquad \text{slow neutron}$$

In reactors operating with enriched uranium another mechanism becomes important; namely

$$U^{235}(n, \gamma)U^{236}(n, \gamma)U^{237} \xrightarrow{\ \beta^-\ } Np^{237}(n, \gamma)Np^{238} \xrightarrow{\ \beta^-\ } Pu^{238}$$

The rate of buildup of Pu^{238} by this latter mechanism in a high flux pile is discussed in Section 9.2.8 of this chapter.

The production of Np^{238} from Np^{237} was first observed directly by JAFFEY AND MAGNUSSON.[84] The slow neutron capture cross section of Np^{237} is 172 barns.[85] An important feature of this reaction is that it provides a means of producing Np^{238} free from other short-lived neptunium isotopes and Pu^{238} free from other plutonium isotopes. However, in careful studies of the radiations of Np^{238} prepared in this way some attention must be paid to the growth of Pa^{233} activity from its Np^{237} parent.

TABLE 9.3. Beta groups of Np^{238}.

End point energy (MeV)	Abundance (per cent)	Reference	log ft	Reference
Determinations of the most energetic beta group				
1.272	47	89		
1.25	45	86	8.5	87
1.236	38	90	8.6	90
Determinations of lower energy beta groups				
0.258	53	89		
0.27	55	86	5.8	87
0.28 and	20		6.6)	
0.250	31 } 62	90	6.2)	90
0.200?	8			
1.139?	2.8)			

---

[83] J. A. Crawford reported in *Metallurgical Laboratory Report, CN-2767* (April 13, 1945). Unpublished.

[84] A. H. Jaffey and L. B. Magnusson, Paper No. 14.2, "The Transuranium Elements," *Nat. Nucl. Energ. Ser.*, Division IV, **14B** (New York: McGraw-Hill Book Co., Inc., 1949).

[85] J. Halpern, *et al.*, *Nucl. Sci. Eng.* **1**, 108 (1956).

The early studies of Np^{238} were complicated by the fact that the isotope, when produced by the deuteron bombardment of uranium, was always accompanied by comparable amounts of Np^{239}. Since the half-life of the latter, 2.33 days, is close to that of Np^{238}, differentiation by following the decay is difficult. Extensive studies of the complex beta-rays, gamma-rays, x-rays and conversion electrons have been carried out in recent years with many modern techniques. These studies have been carried out on pure Np^{238} made from neutron irradiation of Np^{237} and with the Np^{238} –Np^{239} mixture made from cyclotron bombardment. We shall not try to review the experimental evidence exhaustively but will summarize the most important results. In this we follow closely the treatment of RASMUSSEN, SLÄTIS, AND PASSELL,[86] of RASMUSSEN, STEPHENS, STROMINGER, AND ÅSTRÖM,[87] and of ALBRIDGE AND HOLLANDER.[88] Others who have also done detailed work on this isotope are FREEDMAN, JAFFEY, AND WAGNER[89] and BARANOV AND SHLYAGIN.[90] Data on the beta groups which may be resolved from the electron spectrum are summarized in Table 9.3. Data on the numerous conversion electron lines which are superimposed on the complex continuous beta spectrum are given in Table 9.4. The half-life of Np^{238}, which was originally reported[81] as 2.0 days has since been revised slightly to 2.10 days.[89]

The gamma rays revealed by a NaI scintillation spectrometer include an unresolved photopeak near 1 MeV made up of 4 high energy gamma-rays, a photopeak near 100 keV made up of 102-keV gamma-rays plus K x-rays, and L-shell x-rays of about 20 keV. A number of gamma-gamma, gamma-x-ray, and beta-gamma coincidence measurements have been made[87] to clarify the decay scheme.

Figure 9.7 presents a decay scheme based on all these measurements. This decay scheme is not completely established in spite of the detailed experiments which have been done to test it. One of our purposes in presenting it here is to discuss a possible interpretation of the higher-lying levels of Pu^{238} since this nucleus was the first in the heavy element region to provide evidence for the vibrational states at ~ 1 MeV predicted by the unified model of the nucleus.

The lower-lying states of Pu^{238} are firmly established by the study of the alpha decay of Cm^{242}. A ground state rotational band with levels $0+$, $2+$,

[86] J. O. Rasmussen, H. Slätis, and T. O. Passell, *Phys. Rev.* **99**, 42 (1955).

[87] J. O. Rasmussen, F. S. Stephens, D. Strominger, and B. Åström, *Phys. Rev.* **99**, 47 (1955).

[88] R. G. Albridge and J. M. Hollander, *Nucl. Phys.* **21**, 438 (1961); see also R. G. Albridge, Thesis, *Univ. Calif. Rad. Lab. Report UCRL-8642*, April 1960.

[89] M. S. Freedman, A. H. Jaffey, and F. Wagner, Jr., *Phys. Rev.* **79**, 410 (1950).

[90] S. A. Baranov and K. N. Shlyagin, *Atomnia Energ.* **1**, 52 (1956); UCRL translation-270. Also see *J. Nucl. Energ. II* **3**, 132 (1956).

[91] H. Slätis, J. O. Rasmussen, and H. Atterling, *Phys. Rev.* **93**, 646 (1954).

TABLE 9.4. Np^{238} conversion electron data.

Electron energy (keV)	Conversion shell	Transition energy[a] (keV) ALBRIDGE AND HOLLANDER[g]	Selected transition energy[b] (keV)	Abundances per 100 beta disintegrations FREEDMAN et al.[c]	SLÄTIS et al.[d]	RASMUSSEN et al.[e]	Relative intensities[h] BARANOV AND SHLYAGIN[f]	ALBRIDGE AND HOLLANDER[g]
21.76	L_{II}	44.01		38	28.7	—	23.1	—
25.96	L_{III}	44.02		20	21.0	—	21.1	—
38.44	M_{II}	44.00		14	—	—	11.6	—
39.40	M_{III}	43.96		—	15.2	—	5.72	—
42.58	N_{II}	43.96		3.2	—	—	3.71	—
42.84	N_{III}	43.97		—	—	—	—	—
43.71	O	~44.0	(44.11)[j]	—	—	—	—	—
79.52	L_{II}	101.8		1.9	1.4	—	1.21	—
83.74	L_{III}	101.8		—	0.9	—	0.64	—
96.20	M_{II}	101.8		1.2	0.7	—	0.40	—
97.17	M_{III}	101.7		—	—	—	0.36	—
100.3	N_{II}	101.7		—	—	—	—	—
101.4	O	101.7	101.7	—	—	—	—	—
96.79	L_I	119.9		—	—	—	—	—
113.9	M_I	119.8		—	—	—	—	—
118.1	N_I	119.7	119.8	—	—	—	—	—
99.22	K	221.0	221.0	—	—	—	—	0.09
170.8	K	292.6	292.6	—	—	—	—	(?)
748.8	K	870.6	870.6	—	—	—	—	<0.01
762.8	K	884.6	884.6	—	—	—	—	0.014
803.6	K	925.4	925.4	—	—	0.04	—	0.034
818.8	K	940.6		—	0.05	0.07	—	0.072
917.9	L_I, L_{II}	940.2		—	0.10	—	0.09	0.021
934.4	M_I, M_{II}	940.0	940.4	—	0.06	—	—	0.0075

821.3	K	943.1	943.1	0.3	—	—	—	0.0093
864.0	K	985.8		—	0.26	0.20	0.20	0.20
963.1	L_I, L_{II}	985.4		—	0.13	0.06	0.06	0.059
967.8	L_{III}	985.9		—	—	—	—	0.010
980.2	M_I, M_{II}	985.8		—	—	—	—	0.020
985.3	N	~986	985.7	—	—	—	—	0.0090
867.3	K	989.1	989.1	0.3[j]	0.22[j]	0.20[j]	0.16[j]	0.012
905.6	K	1027.4		—	0.08	0.04	0.03	0.048
1005.1	L_I, L_{II}	1027.4		—	0.06	0.02	—	0.018
1021.7	M	~1027	1027.4	—	—	—	—	extremely weak
908.1	K	1029.9		—	—	—	0.08	0.15
1007.3	L_I, L_{II}	1029.6		—	—	—	0.03	0.039
1024.8	M	~1030	1029.9	—	—	—	—	0.011
912.1	K	1033.8	1033.8	—	—	—	—	<0.01
973.5	K	1095.3	1095.3	—	—	—	—	?

[a] Electron binding energies were taken from Hill, Church, and Mihelich, *Revs. Sci. Instr.* **23**, 523 (1952).

[b] The selected values are weighted averages of the experimental values.

[c] Ref. 89

[d] Ref. 91

[e] Ref. 86

[f] Ref. 90

[g] Ref. 88

[h] For purposes of comparison, the relative intensities from Baranov and Shlyagin and from Albridge and Hollander were normalized to Rasmussen's value of 0.20 for the K line of the 985-keV transition. In the last column question marks indicate uncertainty as to the actual existence of the lines.

[i] The weighted average is 44.00. The value 44.11 had been reported previously by Smith and Hollander by measurement of Cm^{242} in which the same transition occurs and is considered more accurate.

[j] The intensities listed for the 1027-keV transition by Freedman, Slätis, and Rasmussen include those of the unresolved 1030-keV transition. The division of intensities by Baranov and Shlyagin between 1027 and 1030 is reported as only approximate.

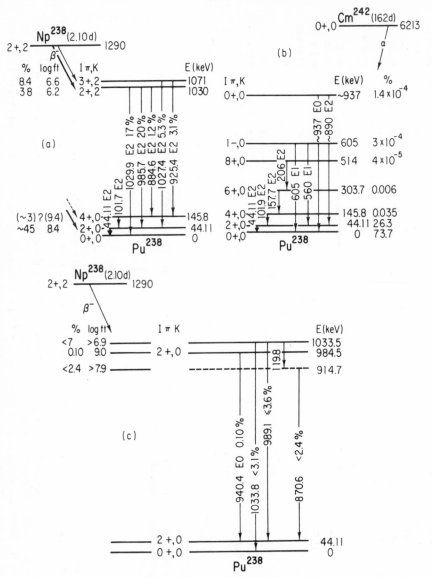

FIG. 9.7. Decay scheme of Np²³⁸. The more certain features are shown in (a), the more speculative in (c). The decay scheme of Cm²⁴² is also shown in (b) since it strengthens the interpretation of the level system seen in the decay of Np²³⁸. All observed levels of Pu²³⁸ are interpreted as arising from a single (ground) state of intrinsic particle motion. The lowest levels clearly constitute a rotational band based on the ground state. Several of the 6 levels at around 1 MeV may be assigned to two rotational bands based on a $K = 0$, beta-vibrational level at 937 keV and a $K = 2$, gamma-vibrational level at 1030 keV, but this interpretation is speculative.

4+, 6+, and 8+ has been observed. (See Section 9.4.6 and the figures therein.) These states are connected by a series of cascading $E2$ transitions which have been precisely measured and characterized. In agreement with the spin and parity assignments there are no crossover transitions. Only the first three members of this band are involved in the decay of Np^{238}. There is a 1-level of Pu^{238} at 605 keV but this plays no role in the decay of Np^{238}.

The levels at about 1 MeV which are populated by the lower energy beta groups of Np^{238} are interpreted as a gamma-vibrational band and a beta-vibrational band. Beta-vibration refers to oscillations of the spheroidal nucleus in which the eccentricity is changed but the shape is preserved; gamma-vibration refers to oscillations entailing shape changes. A general account of collective oscillations is given in Chapter 3. An excited vibrational state can have rotational excitation superimposed on it so that in general each such state can give rise to a whole family of levels. A strong indication that rotational excitation of two of the higher lying levels may be occurring in the present case is the fact that two sets of these high-lying levels are separated in energy by about 45 keV or the same amount as the lowest members of the ground state rotational band. The higher levels of Pu^{238} are interpreted as a (0+, 2+) rotational band based on a $K = 0$, beta-vibrational level at 937 and a (2+, 3+) rotational band based on a $K = 2$, gamma-vibrational level at 1030 keV. It has been suggested that two other levels exist at 914.7 and 1033.5 keV and are perhaps related to an octupole vibrational band[88] with a base state spin and parity 2−.

Several lines of evidence suggest the above interpretations:

1. The spins and parities as determined by the multipolarity of the gamma transitions.

2. The close spacing of the levels above 900 keV; in particular the 48 keV spacing in the beta-vibrational pair and the 41 keV spacing in the gamma-vibrational pair are quite close to the 44.11 keV spacing of the 2+ level in the ground state rotational band.

3. Another strong piece of evidence concerns the ratio of the reduced transition probabilities for the energetic gamma rays which depopulate the level at 1030 keV. (The reduced transition probability is obtained by correcting for the fifth power energy dependence.) Since these gamma rays originate at a common level and go to levels in the same rotational band, the relative intensities of the gamma rays do not depend on the details of the nuclear wave functions but only on the squares of the appropriate vector addition coefficients (CLEBSCH-GORDAN coefficients) involving I- and K-quantum numbers. The experimental intensity ratios and the ratios calculated theoretically by the equation given in Chapter 3 for three different values for $K_{initial}$ are compared in Table 9.5. The assignment, $K = 2$, is

TABLE 9.5. Experimental and theoretical relative reduced $E2$ transition probabilities from the 1030-keV level $(2+)$. of Pu^{238}.

Final state	Experimental $\dfrac{B(2\longrightarrow I_f)}{B(2\longrightarrow 0)}$		Theoretical $\dfrac{B(2\longrightarrow I_f)}{B(2\longrightarrow 0)}$		
I_f	RASMUSSEN[87]	ALBRIDGE[88]	$K_i = 0$	$K_i = 1$	$K_i = 2$
2+ (44.11 keV)	1.3	1.5	1.4	0.36	1.4
4+ (145.8 keV)	<0.3	0.15	2.6	1.1	0.071

clearly indicated for the 1030-keV level. With this assignment the absence of $M1$ character in the 985.7 keV gamma ray finds a natural explanation in K-forbiddenness; the $K = 2$ exceeds the multipolarity, L. The weakness of the gamma ray from the 1030 $(2+)$ level to the 146 keV $(4+)$ level also receives a natural explanation.

The spin of Np^{238} was determined to be 2 by the atomic beam magnetic-resonance method.[92] ALBRIDGE AND HOLLANDER[88] calculated the log ft values of beta decay to the various levels which are given in the figure. It is to be emphasized that these calculations are not independent of the present assignment of multipole orders of the various transitions; however, the only ft values which are sensitively dependent are those of the beta decay to the 985- and 1089-keV levels. If the transitions which de-excite these states should prove to be of $M1$ character instead of $E0$ character, then the log ft values will decrease by one unit.

The log ft values are of importance as an indication of the parity of Np^{238}. The most reasonable choice, based upon the existing data, seems to be even parity. The log ft values of 6.2 and 6.6 to the 1030- and 1071-keV levels, respectively, indicate either slow allowed transitions $(I = 0$ or 1, no) or rather fast first-forbidden transitions $(I = 0$ or 1, yes). As pointed out by RASMUSSEN, ET AL.,[87] the nuclear rearrangement accompanying the decay to the vibrational levels may tend to hinder these transitions; thus the interpretation of the transitions as slow allowed, with even parity for Np^{238}, has been chosen.

One can make use of the 2+ (or possibly 2−) assignment of Np^{238} to draw conclusions concerning the nature of the single-particle states that comprise the ground state of this nucleus. It is simplest to assume that the odd proton and odd neutron in Np^{238} have the same Nilsson orbitals as

[92] R. G. Albridge, J. C. Hubbs, and R. Marrus, *Phys. Rev.* **111**, 1137 (1958)

are seen in the ground state or the very low-lying states in the neighboring odd mass isotopes or isotones. The 93rd proton in Np^{235}, in Np^{237}, and in Np^{239} has the Nilsson assignment 5/2 + [642] so it seems likely that the odd proton in Np^{238} also is in this state. The 145th neutron in Pu^{239} is in the 1/2 + [631] Nilsson orbital so perhaps the 145th neutron in Np^{238} is also in this state. It is also possible that the proton is in the 5/2 − [523] state found in Np^{237} at 60 keV and in Np^{239} at 75 keV. Another possibility for the odd neutron is 1/2 − [501], which is the assignment favored for the 145th neutron in U^{237}. GALLAGHER AND MOSKOWSKI[93] have formulated coupling rules for the angular momentum of individual particle states in odd-odd nuclei.* According to these rules the possible combinations of the above cited states which give a resultant ground-state spin of 2 are the following:

Proton	Neutron	Final state
5/2 + [642]	1/2 + [631]	2+
5/2 + [642]	1/2 − [501]	2−

Thus the coupling rules predict for the proton state in Np^{238} the unique assignment 5/2 + [642]. If the choice of parity (even) is correct, the neutron state is 1/2 + [631].

Closed decay energy cycles (see chapter 2) indicate that Np^{238} is unstable toward electron capture decay to U^{238} but only by about 120 keV so that K-electron capture is energetically impossible. JAFFE[94] has looked for possible L-electron capture by studying the L x-rays using a Cauchois-type bent-crystal spectrometer. With the high resolution of this instrument the L x-rays of uranium should have been observable in the presence of L x-rays of plutonium. His failure to find L x-rays of uranium allowed him to set an upper limit of 4 per cent for L_I electron capture and 2 per cent for L_{II} electron capture. Since the log ft value for the transition to the ground state of U^{238} would be expected to be ∼8.5, the failure to observe electron capture decay is readily understood.

9.1.11 Neptunium-239

In the historical description of the element neptunium presented in Section 9.1.1 we discussed the early experiments on Np^{239} by McMILLAN AND

---

* See the discussion of this matter in Section 3.5.6. of chapter 3, Volume 1.

[93] C. J. Gallagher and S. A. Moszkowski, *Phys. Rev.* **111**, 1282 (1958).

[94] H. Jaffe, Ph.D. Thesis, University of California, April 1954; also published as *Univ. Calif. Rad. Lab. Report*, UCRL-2537 (1954).

ABELSON[95] which constituted the discovery of neptunium. The isotope Np^{239} was made by them by neutron irradiation of uranium; it can also be made by a number of reactions carried out in a cyclotron. These synthetic methods are summarized by the reactions:

$$U^{238}(n, \gamma)U^{239} \xrightarrow[23\ min]{\beta^-} Np^{239}$$

$$U^{238}(d, n)Np^{239}$$

$$U^{238}(d, p)U^{239} \xrightarrow{\beta^-} Np^{239}$$

$$U^{238}(\alpha, p2n)Np^{239}$$

Some reaction cross section values are given in Table 5.5, Chapter 5. The isotope Np^{238} is an impurity in any neptunium sample prepared by deuteron or helium ion bombardment and it has to be considered in any study of the radiations of Np^{239} in such material.

The half-life of Np^{239} is 2.35 days.[96,97] The disintegration scheme is complex involving four or more partial beta spectra, nineteen or more gamma-rays, x-rays, a large number of conversion electron and Auger-electron lines. A number of the more complete studies are summarized in Tables 9.6 and 9.7. Early spectroscopic studies were carried out by FULBRIGHT,[98] SLÄTIS,[99] TOMLINSON, FULBRIGHT, AND HOWLAND,[100] and

TABLE 9.6. Beta ray groups of Np[239]

	SLÄTIS[99] 1947	GRAHAM AND BELL[102] 1951	TOMLINSON, FULBRIGHT, AND HOWLAND[100] 1951	FREEDMAN et al.[101] 1952	BARANOV AND SHLYAGIN[107] 1956	CONNOR AND FAIRWEATHER[109] 1959
End point	288	310 (47%)	330	329 (52%)	327 (45%)	332 (28%)
energy	403	435 (46%)	440	380 (10%)	382 (27%)	393 (13.5%)
(keV) and	676	705 (7%)	654	441 (31%)	439 (21%)	437 (48%)
abundances			715	655 (1.7%)	655	654 (4%)
(per cent)				718 (4.8%)	723 } (7%)	713 (6.5%)

[95] E. McMillan and P. H. Abelson, *Phys. Rev.* **57**, 1186 (1940).

[96] L. Wish, *Nucleonics* **14**, No. 5, 102 (1956). The half-life value reported in this Ref. is 2.345 ± 0.004 days.

[97] D. Cohen, J. C. Sullivan, and A. J. Zielen, *J. Inorg. Nucl. Chem.* **11**, 159–161 (1959). The half-life value reported in this reference is 2.359 ± 0.010 days.

[98] H. W. Fulbright, Paper 14.5 of "The Transuranium Elements," *Nat. Nucl. Energ. Ser.* **14B** (New York: McGraw-Hill Book Co., Inc., 1949).

[99] H. Slätis, *Nature* **160**, 579 (1947); *Arkiv. Mat. Astron. Fysik*, **33A** No. 3 (1948).

[100] E. P. Tomlinson, H. W. Fulbright, and J. J. Howland, Jr., *Phys. Rev.* **83**, 223 (1951).

TABLE **9.7.** Gamma ray energies in Np^{239} decay as shown by conversion electron data.

FULBRIGHT[98] 1944	TOMLINSON, FULBRIGHT, AND HOWLAND[100] 1951	GRAHAM AND BELL[102] 1951	FREEDMAN et al.[101] 1952	BARANOV AND SHLYAGIN[107] 1956	HOLLANDER, SMITH, AND MIHELICH[106] 1956	EWAN, GEIGER, GRAHAM, AND MACKENZIE[108] 1959
			13	12		
			19			
	44.2		44	44.4	44.64	44.65
49.1	49.0	49	49	49.3	49.40	49.41
57.3	57.0	57	57	57.2	57.25	57.26
61.2	61.4	61	61	61.4	61.4	61.46
67.5	67.5	67	67	67.9	67.82	67.86
			77			88.06
105.5	105		105	106.2	106.12	106.14
						106.47
						166.39
					181.8	181.71
209.3	209	210	209	210.3	209.9	209.76
227.8	228	227	228		226.4	226.42
				228.4	228.4	228.20
	254		254		254.6	254.41
					273.1	272.87
277.4	277	276	277	278.1	277.7	277.62
	286		285		285.6	285.47
			316		316.1	315.91
			334	334	334.5	334.33

Note: A number of estimates of beta ray end-points and gamma ray energies were made by absorption techniques in early publications on Np^{239} but these may be regarded as superseded by the spectrometer work quoted above.

FREEDMAN ET AL.[101] GRAHAM AND BELL[102] used a thin lens spectrometer to study the electrons. Delayed coincidence measurements by these experimenters established that the 210-, 227- and 276-keV transitions de-excite a state with a half-life of $(1.1 \pm 0.1) \times 10^{-9}$ seconds. ENGELKEMEIR AND MAGNUSSON[103] discovered a 193 millimicrosecond metastable level in Pu^{239} by the delayed coincidence technique in which anthracene and sodium

---

[101] M. S. Freedman, F. Wagner, Jr., D. W. Engelkemeir, J. R. Huizenga, and L. B. Magnusson, private communication, 1952.

[102] R. L. Graham and R. E. Bell, *Phys. Rev.* **83**, 222 (1951).

[103] D. W. Engelkemeir and L. B. Magnusson, Jr. *Phys. Rev.* **99**, 135 (1955).

iodide scintillation crystals were used as beta and gamma detectors, respectively. The delayed state is populated by a (343 ± 15)-keV beta group and is de-excited mainly by $E1$ transitions of 61- and 105- keV energy which lead to the state giving rise to the three γ-rays just mentioned. LEFEVRE, KINDERMAN, AND VAN TUYL[104] observed the gamma-rays with the aid of a NaI scintillation crystal and found 440-keV and 490-keV photons in low abundance which had not previously been reported. Their values for the abundances of these gamma rays were 1.6×10^{-4} and 1.9×10^{-4} per disintegration. CONNOR AND MACKENZIE[105] confirmed the presence of these photons but report the lower abundances of 3.6×10^{-5} and 2.0×10^{-5}, respectively. HOLLANDER, SMITH, AND MIHELICH[106] studied the conversion electron spectrum with $180°$ permanent magnet spectrographs utilizing photographic recording. BARANOV AND SHLYAGIN[107] have studied Np^{239} with a double focusing spectrometer, a scintillation gamma spectrometer, a proportional counter, and other equipment. EWAN, GEIGER, GRAHAM, AND MACKENZIE[108] have studied the conversion electron spectrum with an iron-free double-focusing spectrometer and the beta spectrum has been re-examined by CONNOR AND FAIRWEATHER.[109]

A number of decay schemes which have been proposed on the basis of part of the data quoted above have had to be modified in the light of later more complete information. In the discussion which follows we accept the interpretation of HOLLANDER, SMITH, AND MIHELICH.[106] (See also the review of PERLMAN AND RASMUSSEN.[110]) In constructing a level scheme for Pu^{239} based on the beta decay of Np^{239} one is aided by information obtained from the electron capture decay of Am^{239} and, particularly, the alpha decay of Cm^{243}. Coulombic excitation of Pu^{239} has also been of considerable importance in setting a location of the ground state. A decay scheme consistent with all known information on Np^{239} is shown in Fig. 9.8. For comparison the levels of Pu^{239} revealed by Np^{239} beta decay, Am^{239} electron capture decay, and Cm^{243} alpha-decay are shown in the figure.

The levels of Pu^{239} have been interpreted as 4 sets of rotational levels.

[104] H. W. Lefevre, E. M. Kinderman, and H. H. Van Tuyl, *Phys. Rev.* **100**, 1374 (1955).

[105] R. D. Connor and D. R. MacKenzie, *Can. J. Phys.* **39**, 1595 (1961).

[106] J. M. Hollander, W. G. Smith, and J. W. Mihelich, *Phys. Rev.* **102**, 740 (1956).

[107] S. A. Baranov and K. H. Shlyagin, *Atomnia Energ.* **1**, 52 (1956); English translation in *J. Nucl. Energ.* **3**, 132 (1956).

[108] G. T. Ewan, J. S. Geiger, R. L. Graham, and D. R. MacKenzie, *Phys. Rev.* **116**, 950 (1959); see also G. T. Ewan, J. W. Knowles, D. R. MacKenzie, *Phys. Rev.* **108**, 1308 (1957).

[109] R. D. Connor and I. L. Fairweather, *Proc. Phys. Soc.* (London), **74**, 161–9 (1959).

[110] I. Perlman and J. O. Rasmussen, "Alpha Radioactivity," contribution to *Handbuch der Physik* **42**, Springer Verlag 1956.

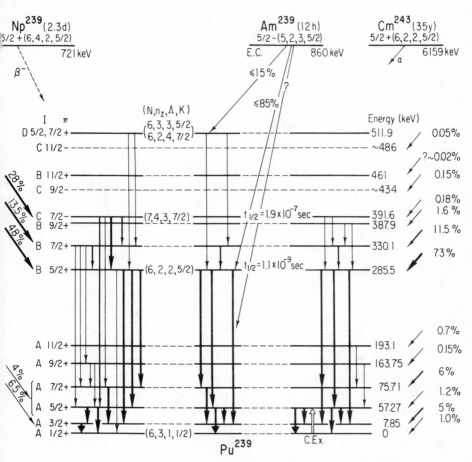

FIG. 9.8. Decay schemes of Np[239], Am[239], and Cm[243] shown on a common plot. The Coulombic excitation scheme of Pu[239] is also shown. All known gamma rays of Np[239] are placed with the exception of the very weak gamma rays of 440 and 490 keV energy found by LEFEVRE, KINDERMAN, AND VAN TUYL which may originate at the 511.9 keV level.

The vertical arrows in each scheme are drawn only for experimentally observed transitions. Assignments of the asymptotic quantum numbers (N, n_z, Λ, K) are given as well as spins and parities. Rotational levels in a common band are designated by a common letter (A, B, C, or D).

The separation of the levels into rotational bands is shown more clearly in Fig. 9.9 which is free of all the details concerning gamma transitions.

The ground state and the first five excited levels comprise one band. The measured ground state spin of 1/2 (BLEANEY, LLEWELLYN, PRYCE, AND

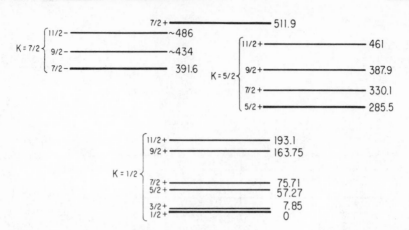

FIG. 9.9. Energy levels of Pu^{239} displayed to emphasize their interpretation as rotational bands based on four intrinsic states.

HALL[111]) identifies this band, with its irregular spacings, as an "anomalous" $K = \Omega = 1/2$ band with energy level spacings given by the special rotational formula, applicable to $K = 1/2$ cases.

$$E_I = \frac{\hbar^2}{2\mathfrak{J}}[I(I + 1) + (-)^{I+1/2}a(I + 1/2)]$$

The quantity a, the decoupling parameter, depends on details of the intrinsic nucleonic structure. The discussion of this paragraph follows the language of the Bohr-Mottelson unified model according to which K is the projection of the total angular momentum on the symmetry axis of the deformed (spheroidal) nucleus and Ω is the component of the total nucleonic angular momentum along the symmetry axis. $\mathfrak{J}$ is the moment of inertia of the collective wave motion of the nucleus and I is the angular momentum of a given level. These quantities are discussed in Chapter 3.

EWAN ET AL.[108] have shown that the simple rotational formula is inadequate to fit the precisely known energies of the ground state rotational band and that at least one additional parameter is required. They add a "rotation-vibration" term to the level spacing formula:

$$E_I = \frac{\hbar^2}{2\mathfrak{J}}[I(I + 1) + a(-1)^{I+1/2}(I + 1/2)]$$
$$- B[I(I + 1) + a(-1)^{I+1/2}(I + 1/2)]^2$$

Table 9.8 shows the experimental and calculated energy levels.

If the values 7.85 keV and 57.27 keV, respectively, are substituted for the energies of the 3/2 and 5/2 levels into the simpler rotational formula given

---

111 B. Bleaney, P. M. Llewellyn, M. H. L. Pryce, and G. R. Hall, *Phil. Mag.* **45**, 773, 991 (1954).

above the value of the rotational splitting constant $\hbar^2/2\mathfrak{J}$ turns out to be 6.28 keV which is close to the value, 6.20 keV, found for the $K = 5/2$ band in Np^{237} but somewhat smaller than the 7.37-keV value found for the $K = 0$ band in Pu^{238}. This is in accord with the expectation that this quantity for odd-A nuclei should be less than for neighboring *even-even* nuclei. The value of the decoupling parameter a is -0.58 from the above substitution.

TABLE 9.8. Energy levels in ground state $K = 1/2$ band, in keV (Pu^{239}).

Level	Theoretical (Simple rotational model formula)*	Theoretical (Including rotation-vibration term)†	Experimental
1/2	0	0	0
3/2	7.85	7.88	7.85
5/2	57.27	57.37	57.27
7/2	75.59	75.65	75.71
9/2	164.51	163.75	163.75

From EWAN, ET AL.[108]
* $\hbar^2/2\mathfrak{J} = 6.284$ keV, $a = -0.581$.
† $\hbar^2/2\mathfrak{J} = 6.290$ keV, $a = -0.582$, and $b = 0.0024$ keV.

In early versions of the decay scheme of Np^{239} the ground state of Pu^{239} was placed 7.85 keV above its designated position in the figures shown here. Later, however, it was found that the most reasonable interpretation[106] of the gamma ray cascades could be made if the location of the ground state was lowered by 7.85 keV. This implied that a transition of 7.85 keV had been overlooked. This assignment was later confirmed by the Coulombic excitation experiments of NEWTON,[112] who observed 57.5 keV and 49.6 keV gamma rays (difference 7.8 keV). BARANOV AND SHLYAGIN[107] directly observed the conversion electrons of the 7.85 keV transition, but these workers interpreted the observed lines as due to M and L conversion lines of a 12.3 keV transition; they are here reinterpreted as N and O conversion lines of the 7.85 keV transition.[113]

The levels labeled B in Fig. 9.8 are rotational levels based on an excited state with a K-value tentatively assigned as 5/2. The 285.5 keV base level of the $K = 5/2$ rotational band has a measured half-life of 1.1×10^{-9} seconds. This is interesting since it represents a retardation from the value calculated from the Weisskopf single-particle formula of about a factor of 10^4 for the $M1$ transitions to the ground state band. The long half-life of these transitions finds a natural explanation in the fact that transitions between the upper ($K = 5/2$) and lower ($K = 1/2$) bands involve a ΔK of two. This violates

[112] J. O. Newton, *Nature* 175, 1028 (1955).
[113] J. M. Hollander, private communication.

the K-selection rule which states that ΔK must be equal to or less than the multipolarity of the transition.[114,115]

The level at 391.6 keV has a measured half-life[103] of 1.9×10^{-7} seconds representing a retardation of $\sim 2 \times 10^6$ from the single-proton lifetime estimate for an $E1$ transition. This slowness is rather commonly observed for $E1$ transitions in the heavy element region and may be associated with a violation of selection rules in the asymptotic quantum number N_Z or Λ. The experimental data for these anomalous transitions between Pu^{239} levels and for many other $E1$ transitions in odd mass heavy deformed nuclei are summarized by ASARO, STEPHENS, HOLLANDER, AND PERLMAN.[116] (See Chapter 3 for discussion of these quantum numbers.) It has been suggested that the long life of the level at 391.6 keV may be attributed to a violation of the selection rule in n_Z, since on the basis of reasonable assignments of Nilsson wave functions to the intrinsic particle states Δn_Z is 3, which is greater than the multipolarity of the transition.

The decay scheme of Np^{239} provides several other opportunities to test the selection rules for beta and gamma transitions for strongly-deformed nuclei. A number of these are discussed in detail elsewhere.[106,114]

The spin of 5/2 is required for the ground state of Np^{239} in order to make a consistent interpretation of the observed transitions. A suitable orbital with $\Omega = 5/2$ is predicted by Nilsson's calculations; specifically the favored assignment is $\Omega\pi \ (Nn_Z\Lambda) = 5/2 + (642)$. The log ft values for the beta transitions are readily interpreted[114] using Alaga's selection rules[115] together with the orbital assignments given in the figure; the log ft values definitely *cannot* be understood in terms of the ordinary selection rules of beta decay. This 5/2 spin value for Np^{239} has been confirmed by the atomic beam measurement of HUBBS AND MARRUS.[117] All of this evidence suggests that the value 1/2 obtained earlier by the optical experiments of CONWAY AND MCLAUGHLIN[118] is probably in error. Another early assignment of the spin value 1/2 by a paramagnetic resonance technique[119] has been withdrawn[120] after a restudy of the determination.

The following Nilsson orbital assignments have been made to the important levels of Pu^{239}. The ground state is $1/2 + [631]$; the level at 285.5

[114] J. M. Hollander, *Phys. Rev.* **105**, 1518 (1957).

[115] G. Alaga, *Phys. Rev.* **100**, 432 (1955).

[116] F. Asaro, F. S. Stephens, J. M. Hollander, and I. Perlman, *Phys. Rev.* **117**, 492 (1960). "Anomalous Electric Dipole Conversion Coefficients in Odd-Mass Isotopes of the Heavy Elements."

[117] J. C. Hubbs and R. Marrus, *Phys. Rev.* **110**, 287 (1958).

[118] J. G. Conway and R. D. McLaughlin, *Phys. Rev.* **96**, 541 (1954).

[119] M. Abraham, C. D. Jeffries, R. W. Kedzie, and J. C. Wallmann, *Phys. Rev.* **106**, 1357 (1957); see also Ref. 120.

[120] M. Abraham, C. D. Jeffries, R. W. Kedzie, and J. C. Wallmann, *Phys. Rev.* **112**, 553 (1958).

keV is 5/2 + [622]; the level at 391.6 keV is 7/2 − [743] and the level at 511.9 is 7/2 + [624]. The arguments on which these assignments are based are covered elsewhere[114,124] and references 105 and 108 should be consulted for a more detailed discussion of the radiations of Np^{239} and their interpretation in terms of the unified model.

A close inspection of Fig. 9.8 will reveal that Pu^{239} levels at 193.1, 387.9, ~434 and ~486 keV are populated in the α-decay of Cm^{243} but not in the decay of Np^{239}.

9.1.12 Neptunium-240

The isotopes U^{240} and Np^{240} were found by HYDE, STUDIER, AND MANNING[125] in natural uranium which had been irradiated in the high neutron flux of one of the Hanford piles. U^{240} was produced by the capture sequence,

$$U^{238}(n, \gamma,)U^{239}(n, \gamma)U^{240}$$

U^{240} and its daughter, Np^{240}, were identified by standard radiochemical techniques and found to be beta-emitters with half-lives of 14 ± 2 hours and 7.3 ± 0.3 minutes, respectively. No further characterization of these nuclides was made with these samples because of their low intensity and because of interference from the radiations of U^{237}, which isotope was prepared by a side reaction,

$$U^{238}(n, 2n)U^{237}$$

The most careful study of the radiations of U^{240} and Np^{240} has been made by BUNKER, DROPESKY, KNIGHT, STARNER, AND WARREN[126,127] who made use of U^{240} sources of high strength and high specific activity produced by irradiation of U^{238} with the very high instantaneous neutron fluxes available during nuclear weapons testing.

The half-life of U^{240} was more precisely determined as 14.1 ± 0.2 hours.

The β-spectrum of the U^{240}– Np^{240} mixture was studied in a β-spectrometer and the observed complex spectrum was analyzed by Fermi plots into the groups shown in Table 9.9. From the gamma ray studies and the decay scheme to be discussed below it is certain that these observed β groups contain unresolved components. The right hand side of the table shows a postulated breakdown of the Np^{240} β spectrum into its primary components. An intense low-energy component of the U^{240}– Np^{240} mixture with an end-point energy of 0.36 ± 0.02 MeV was assigned to U^{240}.

[124] F. Stephens, F. Asaro, and I. Perlman, *Phys. Rev.* **113**, 212 (1959).

[125] E. K. Hyde, M. H. Studier, and W. M. Manning, *Argonne National Laboratory Report*, *ANL-4143*, April 15, 1948 and *ANL-4182*, August 4, 1948 (unpublished).

[126] J. D. Knight, M. E. Bunker, B. Warren, and J. W. Starner, *Phys. Rev.* **91**, 889 (1953).

[127] M. E. Bunker, B. J. Dropesky, J. D. Knight, J. W. Starner, and B. Warren, *Phys. Rev.* **116**, 143 (1959).

TABLE 9.9. Beta-ray transitions of Np^{240}.

Observed groups*			Postulated transitions†		
End-point energy (MeV)	Intensity (per cent)	End-point energy (MeV)	Intensity (per cent)	Log ft	I, π final state
2.18 ± 0.02	52 ± 3	2.18	41 ± 5	6.68	0+
		2.14	12 ± 4	7.18	2+
1.60 ± 0.03	31 ± 2	1.60	32 ± 2	6.28	1−
1.30 ± 0.05	10 ± 1	1.32	3.9 ± 0.5	6.86	0+
		1.28	2.3 ± 0.3	7.05	2+
		1.24	3.3 ± 0.5	6.86	(2+)
0.65 ± 0.10	7 ± 3	0.76	0.3 ± 0.1	7.15	$(1\pm, 2\pm)$
		0.65	3.8 ± 0.5	5.83	$(1, 2)+$
		0.57	0.7 ± 0.1	6.33	$(1\pm, 2+)$

* Deduced from Fermi-Kurie analysis of the β spectrum.
† Deduced from analysis of γ-ray spectra.

BUNKER, DROPESKY, KNIGHT, STARNER, AND WARREN[127] studied the conversion electron spectrum in 180° permanent magnet spectrographs and in a uniform-field, ring-focusing solenoidal spectrometer. They studied the γ-ray photons in a NaI scintillation spectrometer. γ-γ coincidence measurements were made with two NaI crystal spectrometers in coincidence.

TABLE 9.10. Conversion electron lines from 7.3 minute Np^{240}.
(as observed by ASARO ET AL.[128])

Electron energy (keV)	Conversion shell (Pu)	Transition energy (keV)	Relative electron intensity (visual estimate)
20.6	L_{II} ⎫	42.9	Strong
24.8	L_{III} ⎬		
435.3	K ⎫	557	100
	L_I ⎬		10
477.7	K ⎫	599.5	50
576.4	L_I ⎬		
638.3	K	760.1	
670.1	(K)	(791.9)	
722.6	(K)	(844.4)	
738.1	K ⎫	859.9	40
836.8	L_I ⎬		4
740.9	(K)	(862.7)	20
823.6	(K)	(945.4)	8
969.3	(K)	(1091.9)	4

β-γ coincidences were also studied.   Asaro and co-workers[128] also studied the radiations of Np^{240}.   We first tabulate the principal results, then present the derived decay scheme and discuss its interesting features.

TABLE **9.11.** Internal-conversion electron lines in decay of Np^{240} as measured on permanent magnet spectrograph by Bunker.

Electron energy (keV)	Conversion shell	Transition energy (keV)	Relative intensity (visual estimate)
20.6	$L_{II}(Pu)$	42.9	~2
21.6	$L_I(Np)$	44.0	~2
22.4	$L_{II}(Np)$	44.0	~0.5
24.8	$L_{III}(Pu)$	42.9	~2
38.3	$\begin{cases} M_{III}\,Pu \\ M_I\,Np \end{cases}$	$\left.\begin{matrix} 42.9 \\ 44.0 \end{matrix}\right\}$	~1

Tables 9.10 and 9.11 show the conversion electron lines seen in the 180° permanent magnet spectrographs by Asaro[128] and by Bunker[127].   Table 9.12

TABLE **9.12.** Internal-conversion electron data in decay of Np^{240} obtained by Bunker et al.[127] with a beta-ray spectrometer.

Electron energy (keV)	Assigned shell	Transition energy (keV)	Intensity* $\times 10^4$
432.4	K	554.1	19.6 ± 1.5
530.7	L_I	553.8	3.8 ± 0.7
474.8	K	596.5	9.8 ± 1.0
573.3	L_I	596.4	2.0 ± 0.6
636.5	K	758.2	1.8 ± 0.6
694.3	K	816.0	2.2 ± 0.6
736.2	K	857.9	14.0 ± 1.2
835.4	L_I	858.5	2.7 ± 0.6
776.0	K	897.7	1.5 ± 0.7
819.9	K	941.6	3.5 ± 0.7

* Area of the conversion line relative to the area of the total Np^{240} β-ray spectrum.

shows conversion electron data taken by the latter authors in a beta-spectro-meter and Table 9.13 shows their summary of the data and assignments for all the gamma ray transitions of 7.3 minute Np^{240}.

[128] F. Asaro, F. S. Stephens, Jr., J. M. Hollander, E. K. Hulet, R. W. Hoff, and I. Perlman, *Univ. Calif. Rad. Lab.*, unpublished results.

From these data and from coincidence data and detailed arguments not reproduced here the decay scheme of Fig. 9.10 was constructed. Pu^{240} is an even-even nucleus and like all other even-even nuclei in this mass region has for its first levels of excitation a rotational band of levels with a familiar $0+, 2+, 4+ \dots$ sequence and the familiar energy spacing proportional to $I(I+1)$.   This is very well established in the case of Pu^{240} because the $2+$ and $4+$ levels have been observed in the electron capture decay of Am^{240}

TABLE **9.13.** Transitions in Pu^{240} which follow the decay of 7.3-min Np^{240}.
As reported by BUNKER ET AL.[127]

Energy (MeV)	Transi- tion	Photon intensity*	K conversion coefficient × 10²		Assigned multi- polarity	Total estimated transition intensity*
			Exptl.	Theor.†		
0.0429	BA				E2	39 ± 5
0.0989‡	CB				E2	1.3 ± 0.2
0.260	ED	1.9 ± 0.3		4.3	E1	2.0 ± 0.3
0.304	FD	0.9 ± 0.2		3.1	E1	0.9 ± 0.2
0.554	DB	21.4 ± 1.5	0.92 ± 0.09	0.94	E1	21.6 ± 1.5
0.597	DA	12.6 ± 1.4	0.78 ± 0.12	0.81	E1	12.7 ± 1.4
0.758	FC	1.3 ± 0.2	1.4 ± 0.5	1.50	E2	1.3 ± 0.2
0.816	EB	1.6 ± 0.3	1.4 ± 0.5	1.32	E2	1.6 ± 0.3
0.82	HD	0.3 ± 0.1		(0.45)	(E1)	0.3 ± 0.1
0.858	EA	<0.17	>80		E0	0.14 ± 0.01
0.898	GB	1.2 ± 0.3	1.2 ± 0.7	1.16	E2	1.2 ± 0.3
0.936	ID	0.3 ± 0.1		(0.36)	(E1)	0.3 ± 0.1
0.942	GA	1.9 ± 0.5	1.8 ± 0.7	0.94	E2	1.9 ± 0.5
1.49	IB	1.5 ± 0.3		(0.46)	(E2)	1.5 ± 0.3
1.53	IA	1.9 ± 0.5		(0.44)	(E2)	1.9 ± 0.5
1.62	JA	0.7 ± 0.1		(0.40)	(E2)	0.7 ± 0.1

* Per 100 disintegrations.
† Values obtained from the tables of L. A. Sliv and I. M. Band, *Leningrad Physico-Technical Institute Report*, 1956 [translation: *Report 57 ICC K1*, issued by Physics Department, University of Illinois, Urbana, Illinois (unpublished)] for the multipolarities shown in the next column.
‡ Not observed in the present experiments.

(see Section 9.3.5) and the $2+$, $4+$ and $6+$ levels have been seen in the α-decay of Cm^{244} (see Section 9.3.8). The $4+$ and $2+$ levels are de-excited by $E2$ transitions with energy 98.9 and 42.9 keV.   These are almost completely converted in the L_{II} and L_{III} shells so that these transitions are revealed chiefly through the electrons and through L x-rays.   These abundant L x-rays are very useful in fixing the placement of the higher-energy gamma rays in the decay scheme through a consideration of L x-rays versus γ-ray

coincidence spectra. γ-rays which decay directly to ground do not show an
L x-ray coincidence, while those which populate the 42.9 keV level show a
strong L x-ray coincidence.

At 597 keV there occurs a 1− level which is strongly populated in the β-
decay of Np^{240}. This 1− level is believed to represent collection oscillations

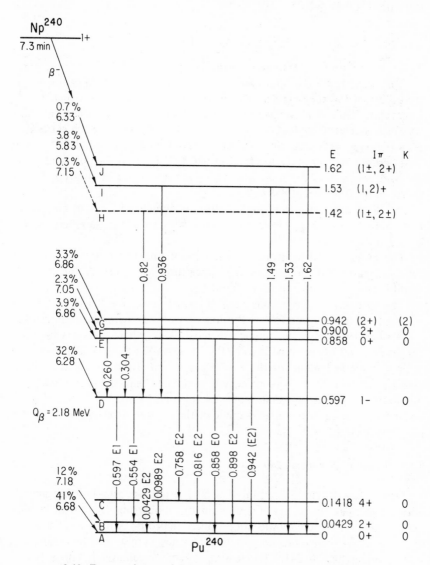

FIG. 9.10. Decay scheme of 7.3 minute Np^{240} (as drawn by BUNKER,
DROPESKY, KNIGHT, STARNER, AND WARREN). ASARO AND CO-WORKERS
construct a slightly different scheme and made a 1− assignment to Np^{240}.

of the Pu^{240} nucleus of the octupole type. Such $1-$ collective states have been observed at about this energy above ground for several other even-even nuclei. (See discussion in Chapter 3.) The spin and parity are firmly fixed by the proved $E1$ character of the 597 and 554 keV gamma rays which de-excite it. The ratio of the reduced transition probabilities of these two transitions is 0.47 ± 0.05.

$$\frac{B\ (E1;\ 1-\ \longrightarrow\ 0+)}{B\ (E1;\ 1-\ \longrightarrow\ 2+)} = 0.47$$

This fixes the K-quantum number of the $1-$ level as $K = 0$.

The level at 858 has spin and parity $0+$ with near certainty because of the occurrence of the completely-converted $E0$ transition which goes directly to ground. This level is believed to be a vibrational state of the β-classification discussed in Chapter 3. $(n_\beta = 1, n_\gamma = 0$ and $K = 0)$. Such states have been observed at about this level of excitation in Pu^{238} and U^{234}. With considerably less certainty the level at 900 keV is given the spin and parity $2+$ and assigned as the first rotational state in a band of rotational levels based on the $0+$ level at 858 keV.

The level at 942 is given the tentative assignment of $2+$ and may be the first Bohr-Mottelson γ-vibrational level with quantum numbers $n_\beta = 0$, $n_\gamma = 1$ and $K = 2$.

The experimental evidence does not point unambiguously to a definite spin and parity for any one of the upper three levels (H, I, and J). The possible choices are shown in the figure.

The structure of Np^{240} has been discussed in Section 8.4.15 of Chapter 8 in terms of the decay of U^{240}. BUNKER ET AL.[127] analyzed their information and deduced that a $1+$ assignment is most likely, whereas ASARO ET AL.[128] consider the 7.3 minute Np^{240} to be the $1-$ level of a $K = 0-$ configuration. A part of the argument for the $K = 0$ assignment is the finding that the 43 keV $2+$ state in Pu^{240} is more heavily populated than the ground state, an observation opposite to that made by BUNKER ET AL.[127] This $K = 0-$ assignment can be interpreted as made of the Nilsson orbitals, proton $5/2 -$ [523], neutron $5/2 + [622]$.

9.1.13 Isomer of Neptunium-240

ORTH AND STREET[129] produced a 60 ± 2 minute beta-emitting activity with the chemical properties of neptunium by bombarding U^{238} with 35 MeV helium ions. This activity was not produced in proton or deuteron bombardments of U^{238}; hence this 60 minute neptunium activity can be assigned to mass number 240 or 241. ORTH AND STREET[129] tentatively chose Np^{241}

---

129 D. A. Orth and K. Street, Jr., unpublished data (1951).

but later work of LESSLER AND MICHEL[130] favored Np^{240}. These latter authors carried out a mass separation of neptunium activities produced in a helium ion bombardment of U^{238} using a mass spectrometer based on a time-of-flight principle. If this assignment is correct the 60 minute activity is an isomer of 7.3 minute Np^{240}.

RITSEMA[131] determined the excitation function for the production of 60-minute neptunium from U^{238} bombarded with helium ions. LESSLER[132] determined an excitation function for neptunium produced by the (d, γ) reaction on U^{238}. LEFEVRE, KINDERMAN, AND VAN TUYL[133] produced both Np^{240} isomers by bombarding Np^{239} with pile neutrons and set an upper limit of < 5 per cent for the genetic linkage between the two isomers.

Measurements with a beta-ray spectrometer[129] showed a beta spectrum of upper energy limit 0.89 ± 0.03 MeV and conversion electrons corresponding to gamma rays of energies 0.15, 0.20, 0.26 and 0.58 MeV. Gamma ray measurements by LESSLER AND STEPHENS[134] with a NaI scintillation spectrometer showed gamma rays of energies 1160, 1000, 915, 580 and 435 keV, but additional gamma rays of less than 350 keV were obscured by the Np^{239} background. By gamma-gamma coincidence techniques LESSLER AND STEPHENS[134] found additional gamma rays of 160, 245 and 85 keV. The 580-keV gamma ray was shown to be a complex with components of 595 and 565 keV in coincidence with each other. The most energetic beta particle group has an end point energy of 900 keV and is in coincidence with 1160 keV gamma radiations. LESSLER estimated the decay energy as 2.06 MeV; this is consistent with the mass assignment, since from closed decay-energy cycles, one would estimate only 1.32 MeV for the decay energy of Np^{241}, whereas over 2 MeV is available in the case of Np^{240}.

Further work remains to be done before the decay scheme of the 60 minute isomer and the relationship between the isomers can be written with certainty. However it is possible to suggest structures for the two isomers which are consistent with what is known about odd-odd nuclei in the neighboring nuclei. This has been done in the discussion of U^{240} in Section 8.4.15 of Chapter 8. From the arguments presented there the 60 minute isomer is the ground state of Np^{240} It is a $K = 5+$ state constructed of the Nilsson proton orbital $5/2 + [642]$ and the Nilsson neutron orbital $5/2 + [622]$.

[130] R. Lessler and M. C. Michel, *Univ. Calif. Rad. Lab. Report*, *UCRL-2709* (September 1954), unpublished, and *Phys. Rev.* **118**, 263 (1960).

[131] S. E. Ritsema, *Univ. Calif. Rad. Lab. Report*, *UCRL-3266* (January 1956); also included in *Phys. Rev.* **111**, 1358 (1958).

[132] R. M. Lessler, *Univ. Calif. Rad. Lab. Report*, *UCRL-8439* (October 1955).

[133] H. W. Lefevre, E. M. Kinderman, and H. N. Van Tuyl, *Bull. Am. Phys. Soc.* II, **1**, 62 (1956).

[134] R. Lessler and F. S. Stephens, Jr., *Univ. Calif. Rad. Lab. Reports*, *UCRL-2531* (April 1954), and *UCRL-2647* (July 1954).

9.1.14 *Neptunium-241*

LESSLER AND MICHEL[135,136] identified a 16 minute beta-emitter in the mass 241 fraction of a neptunium sample carefully isolated from a U^{238} target bombarded with 35 MeV helium ions. The mass separation was performed in a time-of-flight isotope separator. In addition, another beta activity of 3.4 hours half-life was found in the 241 fraction and assigned tentatively to an isomeric form of Np^{241}.

VANDENBOSCH[137] confirmed the existence of a 16 minute species of neptunium of high mass by isolating and identifying such an activity from an uranium target bombarded with helium ions.

$$U^{238}(\alpha, p)Np^{241}$$

The 60 minute Np^{240} and 2.3 day Np^{239} were also produced in this bombardment but no 3.4 hour neptunium activity was seen (upper limit to production cross section 0.2 mb). The beta spectrum of the 16 minute neptunium activity was studied with an anthracene crystal-photomultiplier tube detector. The end point of the beta spectrum was 1.36 MeV. No gamma rays or K x-rays were observed which could be attributed to the 16 minute neptunium activity. Hence, the 1.36 MeV beta group may represent decay to the ground state of Pu^{241}. This is consistent with the 1.32 MeV decay energy estimated for Np^{241} from closed decay-energy cycles (see Chapter 2). The log ft value is 5.8 on this assumption.

The measured spins of Np^{237} and Np^{239} are both 5/2 and the Nilsson orbital assignments with considerable certainty are 5/2 + [642] for the ground states of these two nuclei. Hence, one might predict the same spin and orbital assignment for the ground state of Np^{241}.

9.2 THE ELEMENT PLUTONIUM (ELEMENT 94)

9.2.1 *The Discovery and Early History of Plutonium*

MCMILLAN AND ABELSON[138] found that Np^{239}, formed by the beta decay of U^{239}, underwent radioactive decay by the emission of beta particles, but they were hindered in the search for the 94^{239} daughter in their samples because of the long half-life of this daughter isotope. They did observe some alpha particles in their samples but did not have the opportunity to pursue their investigation to make a complete identification of the daughter

---

[135] R. M. Lessler and M. C. Michel, *Univ. Calif. Rad. Lab. Report, UCRL-2709*, September 1954, unpublished, and *Phys. Rev.* **118**, 263 (1960).

[136] R. M. Lessler, Ph.D. Thesis, University of California, October 1958; also available as *Report UCRL-8439*, October 1958, unpublished.

[137] R. Vandenbosch, *Phys. Rev.* **113**, 259 (1959).

[138] E. M. McMillan and P. H. Abelson, *Phys. Rev.* **57**, 1185 (1940).

product.   The first isotope of element 94 to be identified was Pu^{238} produced in the experiments of SEABORG, McMILLAN, KENNEDY, AND WAHL[139] by the bombardment of uranium with 16-MeV deuterons in the University of California 60-inch cyclotron:

$$U^{238}(d, 2n)Np^{238} \xrightarrow[2.1 \text{ days}]{\beta^-} Pu^{238}$$

The isotope Pu^{238} was shown to emit alpha particles with a half-life of approximately 50 years (best present value = 86.4 years).   The discoverers[146] later proposed the name plutonium (symbol Pu) taken from the planet Pluto, the second planet beyond Uranus in our solar system.

In 1941, KENNEDY, SEABORG, SEGRÈ, AND WAHL[140] isolated and identified Pu^{239} as the decay product of a very intense source of Np^{239}.   A target of about 1.2 kilograms of uranyl nitrate hexahydrate was distributed in a large paraffin block and irradiated with the neutrons produced when a beryllium target was struck with 16 MeV deuterons from the Berkeley 60-inch cyclotron.   It was necessary to bombard for a total of 3500 microampere-hours of deuteron current to obtain a sufficiently active sample of Np^{239}, about 125 millicuries.   This was isolated by the fluoride coprecipitation method of McMILLAN AND ABELSON[138] to free it from all impurities.   Alpha particles were observed to grow into this neptunium sample with a growth half-life of 2.3 days.   From the number of alpha particles which grew in, the half-life of Pu^{239} was estimated to be 30,000 years.   (The presently accepted value is 24,400 years.)   These experimenters used this sample of Pu^{239} (about 0.5 micrograms) to investigate the slow neutron fissionability of this isotope.   It was established that Pu^{239} undergoes fission with slow neutrons and that the fission cross section is somewhat larger than that of U^{235}.   This measurement immediately gave this isotope great importance because it meant that if Pu^{239} could be produced and isolated in appreciable quantities, it might possibly be used in the release of huge amounts of nuclear energy.   It was recognized that the slow neutron fission of large amounts of U^{235} in a suitably designed assembly might provide a neutron source of sufficient strength to allow the conversion of appreciable quantities of natural uranium to Pu^{239} via the neutron capture reaction:

$$U^{238}(n, \gamma)U^{239} \xrightarrow[23 \text{ min}]{\beta^-} Np^{239} \xrightarrow[2.3 \text{ days}]{\beta^-} Pu^{239}$$

On the strength of this hope, the secret plutonium project was set up

---

[139] G. T. Seaborg, E. M. McMillan, J. W. Kennedy, and A. C. Wahl, *Phys. Rev.* **69**, 366 (1946); G. T. Seaborg, A. C. Wahl, and J. W. Kennedy, *Phys. Rev.* **69**, 367 (1946). Original reports written early in 1941.

[140] J. W. Kennedy, G. T. Seaborg, E. Segrè, and A. C. Wahl, *Phys. Rev.* **70**, 555 (1946). Original report written in May 1941.

by the Uranium Committee, an agency of the United States Government, established early in World War II to explore the possibility of utilizing the energy of the fission reaction for military purposes. During 1941 and the early part of 1942 cyclotron-produced Pu^{238} was used at the University of California to investigate the chemical properties of plutonium by the tracer method. Following this initial work, the investigation of plutonium was taken up by other laboratories. Chief among these were the Metallurgical Laboratory of the University of Chicago, where the program got underway during the first half of 1942, the Los Alamos Laboratory in New Mexico, where work began early in 1943, the Clinton Laboratories in Oak Ridge, Tennessee, which opened late in 1943, and the Hanford Engineer Works in Washington, which began operation in the latter half of 1944. The goal of these investigations was to design a chemical process workable on an industrial scale for the isolation of plutonium from uranium fuel elements irradiated in a chain-reacting pile. Other groups of investigators at these same laboratories were concerned with the demonstration of the feasibility of a chain-reacting pile and the design of the large reactors ultimately constructed at Hanford, Washington.

The organizational and administrative history of this effort is recorded in the SMYTH[141] report and, in considerably more detail, in the official historical volume, *The New World*, by HEWLETT AND ANDERSON.[142] The scientific findings of these American laboratories on the nuclear and chemical properties of plutonium and other transuranium elements are detailed in the volumes of the National Nuclear Energy Series—Plutonium Project Record.[143] SEABORG[144] has traced the history of the wartime developments in plutonium isolation from the Hanford pile fuel elements in another volume. The important contributions of British, French, and Canadian workers at the Canadian Chalk River Laboratory are described in other publications.

Prior to the establishment of the organized attack on plutonium chemistry some of the important features of the chemical behavior of plutonium were established by SEABORG, WAHL, AND KENNEDY[145] and SEABORG AND WAHL[146] working at the University of California. Plutonium could be

[141] H. D. Smyth, "Atomic Energy for Military Purposes." Princeton University Press, Princeton, New Jersey, 1945.

[142] "The New World," *History of the United States Atomic Energy Commission* 1, R. G. Hewlett and O. E. Anderson, Jr., Pennsylvania State University Press, 1962.

[143] The *Nat. Nucl. Energ. Ser.*, **14A** Plutonium Project Record (New York; McGraw-Hill Book Co., Inc., 1954) "The Actinide Elements," G. T. Seaborg and J. J. Katz, editors, 1954. **14B** "The Transuranium Elements," G. T. Seaborg, J. J. Katz, and W. M. Manning, editors, 1949.

[144] G. T. Seaborg, "The Transuranium Elements" Silliman Lectures, Yale University Press, 1958.

[145] G. T. Seaborg, A. C. Wahl, and J. W. Kennedy, *Phys. Rev.* **69**, 367 (1946).

carried from acid solution on rare earth fluorides, on thorium fluoride, on the peroxyhydrate of thorium, and on insoluble iodates. In basic solution it would coprecipitate on insoluble hydroxides. However, in the presence of a powerful oxidizing agent such as peroxydisulfate ion the plutonium tracer could be oxidized to a higher oxidation state which did not coprecipitate with insoluble fluorides in acid solution. In order to estimate oxidation-reduction potentials, a number of oxidizing and reducing agents were tested for their ability to oxidize or reduce tracer plutonium. Historically, an important difference between neptunium and plutonium in trace concentrations was the faster rate of oxidation of neptunium to the fluoride-soluble higher oxidation state by bromate ion at room temperature. Neptunium is quantitatively oxidized in 20 minutes whereas plutonium is not and thus plutonium could be removed from solution by precipitation of an insoluble fluoride such as lanthanum fluoride. This bromate-lanthanum fluoride cycle was a mainstay of neptunium and plutonium separation for some time.

SEABORG AND WAHL,[146] in the first detailed paper on the chemistry of plutonium, emphasized the conclusion that plutonium was a member of a new rare earth-like series which included neptunium and uranium. It was regarded as an open question whether this series began with actinium, thorium or uranium.

Very soon after the discovery of plutonium, G. T. SEABORG AND M. PERLMAN[147] made a search for Pu^{239} in natural sources. Their work and the later work of others, which is described in the section entitled "The Natural Occurrence of Transuranium Elements in Trace Amounts" in the chapter on the Natural Radioactivities (Chapter 6), shows that traces of Pu^{239} are present in minerals containing uranium as a result of the action of naturally occurring neutrons on U^{238}.

During 1942, when the main effort to develop a process for plutonium isolation was centered at the Metallurgical Laboratory, a process which later came to be known as the bismuth-phosphate process, was originated by the tracer scale experiments of S. G. THOMPSON.[148] Since the chemical behavior of an element on the tracer scale and the macroscopic scale is not always the same, it was important to test the behavior of plutonium at the

[146] G. T. Seaborg and A. C. Wahl, Paper No. 1.6, page 25, "The Transuranium Elements," Nat. Nucl. Energ. Ser., Division IV 14B (New York: McGraw-Hill Book Co., Inc., 1949). Original report written March, 1941. Also published in J. Am. Chem. Soc. 70, 1128–1134 (1948).

[147] G. T. Seaborg and M. L. Perlman, Paper No. 1.3, "The Transuranium Elements," Nat. Nucl. Energ. Ser., Division IV 14B (New York: McGraw-Hill Book Co., Inc., 1949).

[148] For a description of the historical bismuth phosphate process for plutonium isolation see a paper by S. G. Thompson and G. T. Seaborg in Prog. Nucl. Energ., Ser. 3, 3 "Process Chemistry," edited by F. R. Bruce, J. M. Fletcher, H. H. Hyman, and J. J. Katz, Pergamon Press, Ltd. 1956.

concentrations expected in the chemical plant. At this time only microgram quantities of plutonium were available and hence such experiments
had to be done by ultramicrochemical techniques. The first chemically
pure plutonium, free from carrier material and all other foreign matter, was
prepared by CUNNINGHAM AND WERNER[149] in August, 1942. This was the
first isolation of any synthetic element. The half-life of plutonium was
determined by these authors by direct weighing of a few micrograms of
plutonium oxide and direct counting of the alpha particle emission rate.
A value of 24,300 years was obtained. By direct analysis of a 1.7 microgram sample of plutonium iodate using microscale analytical methods
CUNNINGHAM AND WERNER[149] established the formula $Pu(IO_3)_4$. This
was the first direct chemical proof of any of the oxidation states of plutonium.

A year or two later plutonium became available in milligram quantities
from the operation of the Clinton, Tennessee and Hanford, Washington
reactors and it was possible to initiate chemical studies by ordinary bench-
top techniques (albeit modified somewhat because of the physiological
hazard). The chemistry of plutonium on the tracer scale and at ordinary
concentrations is summarized by KATZ AND SEABORG[150] and by HYDE AND
SEABORG.[151]

For a few years after the discovery of plutonium the only isotopes available for study were Pu^{238} and Pu^{239}; then the isotope Pu^{240} was found by
CHAMBERLAIN, FARWELL, AND SEGRÈ[152] in samples of Pu^{239} subjected to
long neutron bombardment. Cyclotron bombardment of uranium targets
with high-energy helium ions resulted in the identification of Pu^{237}, Pu^{236} and
lighter isotopes. When higher-flux reactors were built, the production of a
number of higher isotopes of plutonium by successive neutron capture reactions
became feasible. Some of the plutonium isotopes of very high mass number were first identified during nuclear weapons test programs. In the following pages the individual isotopes of plutonium will be discussed in detail.

9.2.2 Plutonium-232

This isotope was first produced by ORTH AND STREET[153] who bombarded

[149] B. B. Cunningham and L. B. Werner, Paper No. 1.8, "The Transuranium Elements,"
Nat. Nucl. Energ. Ser., Division IV 14B (New York: McGraw-Hill Book Co., Inc., 1949);
see also J. Am. Chem. Soc. 71, 1521 (1949).

[150] J. J. Katz and G. T. Seaborg, "The Chemistry of the Actinide Elements," (New
York: Wiley and Sons, 1957).

[151] E. K. Hyde and G. T. Seaborg, "The Transuranium Elements," Handbuch der
Physik 42, S. Flügge, editor, Springer-Verlag, Berlin, 1957.

[152] O. Chamberlain, G. Farwell, and E. Segrè, unpublished information, 1944.

[153] D. A. Orth, Ph.D. Thesis, University of California, January 1951 (unpublished);
also published as Univ. Calif. Rad. Lab. Report, UCRL-1059 (Rev.) March, 1952. D. A.
Orth and K. Street, unpublished information, 1951.

uranium targets enriched in U^{235} to make it by the reaction:

$$U^{235}(\alpha, 7n)Pu^{232}$$

The maximum yield occurred when the energy of the helium ions was 110 MeV. At such an energy several other isotopes of plutonium are produced and pure samples of Pu^{232} can not be made. Pu^{232} has also[154] been prepared by the reaction:

$$U^{233}(\alpha, 5n)Pu^{232}$$

The half-life of Pu^{232} is 36 minutes. The alpha decay of Pu^{232} produces 9.3 minute U^{228} which in turn decays through a series of short-lived alpha emitting descendants; this U^{228} collateral series is discussed in Chapter 7 (Section 7.2.7). The growth of this series of isotopes into the plutonium fraction is strong evidence for the presence of Pu^{232}. The U^{228} can be separated chemically, and observed to decay with a 9.3-minute half-life. The alpha particle energy of Pu^{232} was found to be 6.58 MeV in a gridded ion chamber; the resolution of this peak from the 6.67-MeV peak of U^{228} presents some difficulty.

The isotope Pu^{232} is very far on the neutron-deficient side of beta stability and decays also by capture of an orbital electron although it is quite difficult to establish this mode of decay by direct measurement of x-rays because of the presence of Pu^{235} and Pu^{234} in the available samples. Attempts were made to determine the amount of electron capture by separating the 13 minute Np^{232} daughter but no positive results were obtained. An upper limit of 60 was placed on the EC/α branching ratio.[153] The half-life of an even-even nucleus for alpha decay can be reliably estimated, if the energy is known, by the methods outlined in Chapter 4, Volume I. Based on an alpha disintegration energy of 6.60 MeV the alpha decay half-life of Pu^{232} is about 5 hours. From this the EC/α ratio is approximately 8.

9.2.3 Plutonium-233

The isotope Pu^{233} was discovered years after the first identification of Pu^{232}, Pu^{234}, and Pu^{235} even though it is always produced when Pu^{232} is made and frequently produced when Pu^{234} or Pu^{235} is made. This delay was due to the fact that the radiations of Pu^{233} are obscured by those of the other plutonium isotopes and are unobserved unless careful experiments are performed. THOMAS, VANDENBOSCH, GLASS, AND SEABORG[154] identified

---

[154] T. D. Thomas, R. Vandenbosch, R. A. Glass, and G. T. Seaborg, *Phys. Rev.* **106**, 1228 (1957).

Pu^{233} in the plutonium fraction from targets of U^{233} bombarded with helium ions of 40–45 MeV energy:

$$U^{233}(\alpha, 4n)Pu^{233}$$

Fig. 9.11 shows a pulse-height analysis of the output of a gridded ionization chamber used to examine the alpha activity of the mixture of plutonium isotopes produced in such a bombardment. (The Pu^{239} was added to the target after the end of the bombardment to serve as a monitor of the chemical yield.) An alpha particle group was regularly observed at 6.3 MeV as a shoulder on the high energy side of the Pu^{234} alpha peak. This 6.30-MeV activity, which decayed with a 20 ± 2 minute half-life, was assigned to Pu^{233}.

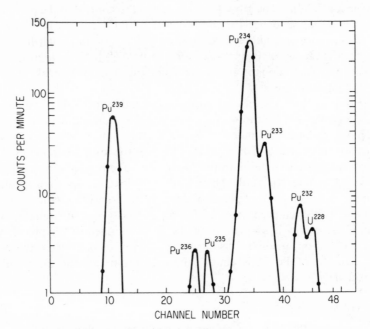

FIG. 9.11. Alpha spectrum of plutonium fraction isolated from a U^{233} target bombarded with 45.2 MeV helium ions.

The mass assignment is based on three lines of evidence: (1) the change in the yield of the new activity with the helium ion energy in agreement with that expected for an (α, $4n$) reaction, (2) the identification of U^{229} daughter activity, (3) the identification of Np^{233} daughter activity.

The Np^{233} daughter activity was isolated quantitatively and the x-radiation of this 35-minute isotope was counted. From the amount of Np^{233} isolated the alpha-decay branching of Pu^{233} was set at (1.2 ± 0.5)

$\times\,10^{-3}$, the major mode of decay being orbital electron capture. The partial alpha half-life is 11 ± 4 days.

9.2.4 Plutonium-234

HYDE, STUDIER, AND GHIORSO[156] produced Pu^{234} by bombardment of U^{233} with 40 MeV helium ions:

$$U^{233}(\alpha, 3n)Pu^{234}$$

The isotope was shown to decay partially by the emission of alpha particles of 6.0 MeV energy to produce U^{230} and partially by orbital electron capture to produce Np^{234}; the observed half-life was 8 hours. The U^{230} and the alpha-emitting daughters of U^{230} had previously been well characterized (see the discussion in Section 7.3, Chapter 7) so that identification of such isotopes as U^{230} and Th^{226} could be made with certainty. PERLMAN, O'CONNOR, AND MORGAN[157] extended these measurements using larger samples and revised the half-life to 8.5 hours, the alpha-particle energy to 6.2 ± 0.1 MeV. They isolated and identified the 4.40-day Np^{234} produced by orbital electron capture. ORTH AND STREET[158] made additional experiments on Pu^{234} produced by the above reaction and also prepared it from U^{235} as follows:

$$U^{235}(\alpha, 5n)Pu^{234}$$

These authors report a half-life of 9.0 ± 0.5 hours and an alpha-particle energy of 6.19 ± 0.01 MeV. A later study of the alpha spectrum by HOFF, ASARO, AND PERLMAN[159] revealed the following complex spectrum: 6.196 MeV (68 per cent), 6.145 MeV (32 per cent) and 6.025 MeV (0.4 per cent).

HOFF AND ASARO[160] have found that there are 0.09 alpha disintegrations per K-electron capture and 0.3 L-electron captures per K-electron capture. From these figures and an estimated value of the amount of electron capture from the M shell and higher shells, it is possible to calculate a ratio of electron capture decay to alpha particle emission of 16, corresponding to a partial

[156] E. K. Hyde, M. H. Studier, and A. Ghiorso, Paper No. 22.15, "The Transuranium Elements," *Nat. Nucl. Energ. Ser.*, Division IV **14B** (New York: McGraw-Hill Book Co., Inc., 1949).

[157] I. Perlman, P. R. O'Connor, and L. O. Morgan, Paper No. 22.30, "The Transuranium Elements," *Nat. Nucl. Energ. Ser.*, Division IV **14B** (New York: McGraw-Hill Book Co., Inc., 1949).

[158] D. A. Orth, Ph.D. Thesis, University of California, January, 1951; also published as *Univ. Calif. Rad. Lab. Report, UCRL-1059* (Rev.), March 1952. D. A. Orth and K. Street, Jr., unpublished results.

[159] R. W. Hoff, F. Asaro, and I. Perlman, unpublished results, 1960.

[160] R. W. Hoff and F. Asaro, unpublished data, University of California, 1956.

alpha half-life of 6 days. The electron capture decay goes directly to the ground state[161] of Np^{234}. For a calculated decay energy of 460 keV this corresponds[161] to a log ft value of 5.6.

Pu^{234} has been observed as the daughter of 2.5-hour Cm^{238} by HIGGINS.[162]

9.2.5 Plutonium-235

ORTH AND STREET[158] found that a 26 ± 2-minute plutonium isotope was produced by helium-ion bombardments of U^{233} together with 8.5-hour Pu^{234} and 2.7-year Pu^{236}. The best relative yield of the 26-minute plutonium isotope occurred when the helium ion energy was in the range 28–30 MeV. The most reasonable mass assignment is Pu^{235}. It is possible to produce Pu^{235} from U^{235} targets as well. The reactions are:

$$U^{233}(\alpha, 2n)Pu^{235}$$

$$U^{235}(\alpha, 4n)Pu^{235}$$

From the work of ORTH AND STREET[158] the radiations appear to consist primarily of L x-rays, a small amount of harder electromagnetic radiation and few, if any, conversion electrons of energy greater than 100 keV. Alpha activity of energy 5.85 ± 0.03 MeV was observed in amounts corresponding to about 0.002 per cent branching decay by this process.

Further work on the radiations of Pu^{235}, done by THOMAS, VANDENBOSCH, GLASS, AND SEABORG,[164] has confirmed the half-life and alpha particle energy measured by ORTH AND STREET.[158] By measuring the K x-rays accompanying the electron capture and using an estimated value of 0.23 for the ratio of L-electron to K-electron capture, these authors were able to calculate an alpha branching ratio of $(3.0 \pm 0.6) \times 10^{-5}$, corresponding to a partial alpha half-life of 1.7 ± 0.4 years.

9.2.6 Plutonium-236

JAMES, FLORIN, HOPKINS, AND GHIORSO[165] observed, in the plutonium fraction from the bombardment of natural uranium with 40-MeV helium

---

161 R. W. Hoff and S. G. Thompson, *Phys. Rev.* **96**, 1350 (1954).

162 G. H. Higgins, Ph.D. Thesis, University of California, June, 1952; also published as *Univ. Calif. Rad. Lab. Report, UCRL-1796*, June 1952.

164 T. D. Thomas, R. Vandenbosch, R. A. Glass, and G. T. Seaborg, *Phys. Rev.* **106**, 1228 (1957).

165 R. A. James, A. E. Florin, H. H. Hopkins, Jr., and A. Ghiorso, Paper No. 22.8, "The Transuranium Elements," *Nat. Nucl. Energ. Ser.*, Division IV, **14B** (New York: McGraw-Hill Book Co., Inc., 1949).

ions, an alpha-particle group of 5.75-MeV energy and proved it to be due to Pu^{236}, formed by the reaction:

$$U^{235}(\alpha, 3n)Pu^{236}$$

That this is the principal reaction was confirmed by the relative yields from targets of enriched U^{235} and of U^{238}, depleted with respect to U^{235}, but the evidence indicated in addition the occurrence of the reaction:

$$U^{238}(\alpha, 6n)Pu^{236}$$

Several other cyclotron reactions[166-168] can be used to produce Pu^{236}:

$$Np^{237}(d, 3n)Pu^{236}$$

$$Np^{237}(\alpha, p4n)Pu^{236}$$

$$Np^{237}(\alpha, 5n)Am^{236} \xrightarrow{EC} Pu^{236}$$

$$U^{233}(\alpha, n)Pu^{236}$$

This isotope has repeatedly been observed as the daughter of the 22-hour beta-emitter Np^{236} produced by the several reactions discussed in Section 9.1.7. Similarly, this plutonium isotope has been observed as the alpha decay daughter of 27-day Cm^{240} which is discussed in Section 9.4.4. Confirmation of the mass assignment of Pu^{236} comes from the isolation and identification of U^{232} daughter activity.[165]

Small amounts of Pu^{236} have been detected in reactor-produced plutonium and are presumably accounted for by the following sequence of fast neutron reactions.

$$U^{238}(n, 2n)U^{237} \xrightarrow[\text{6.8 days}]{\beta^-} Np^{237}(n, 2n)Np^{236} \xrightarrow[\text{22 hour}]{\beta^-} Pu^{236}$$

The half-life of Pu^{236} as determined by direct decay is 2.85 years.[169] The spontaneous-fission rate as measured by GHIORSO AND CO-WORKERS[170] is $(5.8 \pm 2) \times 10^7$ fissions per gram-hour corresponding to a half-life of $(3.5 \pm 1) \times 10^9$ years for this process. Pu^{236} is the lightest of the beta stable isotopes of plutonium.

The alpha particle spectrum of Pu^{236} has been measured on a magnetic

[166] R. A. James, S. G. Thompson, and H. H. Hopkins, Jr., Paper No. 22.16, "The Transuranium Elements," Nat. Nucl. Energ. Ser., Division IV, 14B (New York: McGraw-Hill Book Co., Inc., 1949).

[167] E. K. Hyde, M. H. Studier, and A. Ghiorso, Paper No. 22.15, "The Transuranium Elements," Nat. Nucl. Energ. Ser., Division IV, 14B (New York: McGraw-Hill Book Co., Inc., 1949).

[168] I. Perlman, P. R. O'Connor, and L. O. Morgan, Paper No. 22.30, "The Transuranium Elements," Nat. Nucl. Energ. Ser., Division IV, 14B (New York: McGraw-Hill Book Co., Inc., 1949).

[169] D. C. Hoffman, G. P. Ford, and F. O. Lawrence, J. Inorg. Nucl. Chem. 4, 143 (1957).

[170] A. Ghiorso, G. A. Higgins, A. E. Larsh, G. T. Seaborg, and S. G. Thompson, Phys. Rev. 87, 163 (1952).

spectrograph by HUMMEL AND CO-WORKERS:[171] 5.763 MeV (68.9 per cent),
5.716 MeV (30.9 per cent) and 5.610 MeV (0.18 per cent).   By alpha-gamma
coincidence experiments it was established that a further group must exist
with energy 5.448 MeV and 0.002 per cent abundance.

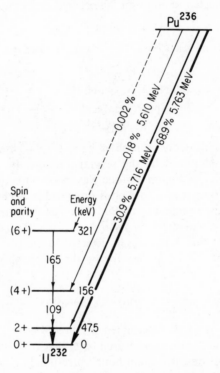

FIG. **9.12.** Decay scheme of Pu[236].

The isotope Pu^{236} is an *even-even* nucleus and the energy levels of U^{232}
observed in its decay follow a familiar pattern for *even-even* nuclei in this
mass region.   The lowest lying levels of U^{232} defined by the alpha spectrum
of Pu^{236} are the following: ground state $(0+)$, 47.5 keV $(2+)$, 156 keV $(4+)$
and 321 $(6+)$.   A decay scheme is given in Fig. 9.12. Pa^{232} decays to the
same daughter nucleus, U^{232}, and several of the same $E2$ gamma rays are
seen in its decay.   Refer to Section 8.3.8.

---

171 J. P. Hummel, F. Asaro, G. H. Higgins, and I. Perlman, unpublished results (1956);
see J. P. Hummel, Ph.D. Thesis, University of California, August, 1956; also published as
Univ. Calif. Rad. Lab. Report, UCRL-3456, August, 1956.

9.2.7 *Plutonium-237*

JAMES, FLORIN, HOPKINS, AND GHIORSO[172] found that the plutonium fraction from natural uranium bombarded with 40-MeV helium ions emitted a considerable amount of electromagnetic radiation of energy similar to characteristic K and L x-rays of a heavy element, which suggested the presence of a nuclide decaying by electron capture. This activity decayed with a half-life of about 40 days. By bombardments of different uranium targets, some enriched and some depleted with respect to U^{235}, it was established that the U^{235} was the target isotope principally responsible for the formation of the activity but that it originated to a small extent from U^{238} as well. The same activity was produced later[173] by the action of 20-MeV deuterons on Np^{237}, but was not found when U^{233} was bombarded with helium ions.[174] Neptunium isolated from an aged plutonium fraction[172] failed to show radioactivity due to Np^{235} indicating that the 40-day plutonium cannot be Pu^{235}. Consequently this activity is assigned to Pu^{237} produced by the reactions:

$$U^{235}(\alpha, 2n)Pu^{237}$$

$$U^{238}(\alpha, 5n)Pu^{237}$$

$$Np^{237}(d, 2n)Pu^{237}$$

More recent work by HOFFMAN[175] has established the half-life as 45.63 ± 0.20 days.

For several years after its discovery no alpha radiation was found for Pu^{237} although it was obviously alpha unstable. The reason for this was the low branching ratio for this mode of decay and the unavoidable presence of Pu^{238}, and often of Pu^{239} and Pu^{236}, in the plutonium samples available for examination. Later search for the alpha radiation by THOMAS, VANDENBOSCH, GLASS, AND SEABORG[176] and by HOFFMAN[175] was successful. The former reported alpha particles of 5.65 ± 0.02 MeV in 21 ± 4 per cent abundance and of 5.36 ± 0.02 MeV in 79 ± 8 per cent abundance. HOFFMAN[175] has observed an alpha group at 5.34 ± 0.01 MeV and has reported evidence for

[172] R. A. James, A. E. Florin, H. H. Hopkins, Jr., and A. Ghiorso, Paper No. 22.8, "The Transuranium Elements," *Nat. Nucl. Energ. Ser.*, Division IV, **14B** (New York: McGraw-Hill Book Co., Inc., 1949).

[173] R. A. James, S. G. Thompson, and H. H. Hopkins, Jr., Paper No. 22.16, "The Transuranium Elements," *Nat. Nucl. Energ. Ser.*, Division IV, **14B** (New York: McGraw-Hill Book Co., Inc., 1949).

[174] E. K. Hyde, M. H. Studier, and A. Ghiorso, Paper No. 22.15, "The Transuranium Elements," *Nat. Nucl. Energ. Ser.*, Division IV, **14B** (New York: McGraw-Hill Book Co., Inc., 1949).

[175] D. C. Hoffman, *J. Inorg. Nucl. Chem.* **4**, 383 (1957).

[176] T. D. Thomas, R. Vandenbosch, R. A. Glass, and G. T. Seaborg, *Phys. Rev.* **106**, 1228 (1957).

a group at 5.60–5.65 MeV and for a group at 5.20–5.25 MeV. Her value for the branching ratio of the 5.34 MeV group is $(2.0 \pm 0.4) \times 10^{-5}$ in agreement with that determined by THOMAS AND CO-WORKERS,[176] $(2.6 \pm 0.3) \cdot 10^{-5}$.

HOFFMAN AND DROPESKY[177] have studied in detail the conversion electron spectrum, the K-Auger electron spectrum, and the photon spectrum of Pu^{237}. They found evidence for K and L x-rays and for gamma rays of energies 26.36, 33.20, 43.46, 59.57, 55.56, and 76.4 keV. The data indicate that the previously established levels of Np^{237} at 33.20, 59.57, 103.0, and 158.5 keV are fed by the electron-capture decay of Pu^{237}. These authors measured the following intensity ratios: K x-radiation; L x-radiation; 59.6-keV gamma radiation = 1.00; 0.75; 0.14. On the basis of their results, they have calculated a value of 0.06 ± 0.01 for the K-Auger coefficient. Both K- and L-electron capture populate the level in Np^{237} at 59.6 keV, with a ratio of L- and K-electron capture to this level of 2.8. From this ratio HOFFMAN AND DROPESKY[177] have calculated an electron-capture decay energy of 0.21 MeV, in good agreement with the value of 0.22 MeV calculated from closed cycles. The relative intensities of the electron capture transitions and the log ft values for these transitions are shown in the decay scheme for Pu^{237} given in Fig. 9.13. The spins, parities and asymptotic quantum numbers are those assigned by HOLLANDER, SMITH, AND RASMUSSEN[178] on the basis of the alpha decay of Am^{241} and by RASMUSSEN, CANAVAN, AND HOLLANDER[179] on the basis of the beta decay of U^{237}. The paper of HOFFMAN AND DROPESKY represents a very thorough study of the electron capture decay of Pu^{237} and should be consulted for details. GINDLER, GRAY, AND HUIZENGA[180] found the ratio of K-electron capture to total electron capture to be 0.38 ± 0.06.

STEPHENS, ASARO, AMIEL, AND PERLMAN[181] have identified an isomer of Pu^{237} with a half-life of 0.18 ± 0.02 seconds. This nuclide was isolated by collecting recoils from the alpha decay of Cm^{241}. The isomer is 145 keV above the ground state and is thought to have spin 1/2. A more detailed description of this isomer is found in the discussion of the decay of Cm^{241}, Section 9.4.5.

9.2.8 *Plutonium-238*

In the description of the discovery and early history of plutonium, which appears earlier in this chapter, it is mentioned that Pu^{238} was the first isotope

177 D. C. Hoffman and B. J. Dropesky, *Phys. Rev.* **109**, 1282 (1958).
178 J. M. Hollander, W. G. Smith, and J. O. Rasmussen, *Phys. Rev.* **102**, 1372 (1956).
179 J. O. Rasmussen, F. L. Canavan, and J. M. Hollander, *Phys. Rev.* **107**, 141 (1957).
180 J. E. Gindler, J. Gray, Jr., and J. R. Huizenga, *Phys. Rev.* **115**, 1271 (1959).
181 F. S. Stephens, Jr., F. Asaro, S. Amiel, and I. Perlman, *Phys. Rev.* **107**, 1456 (1957).
182 J. O. Newton, *Nature* **175**, 1027 (1955).

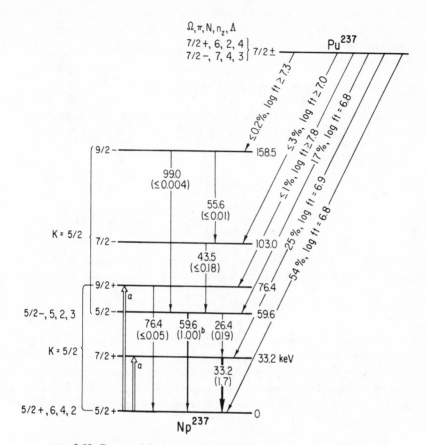

FIG. **9.13.** Proposed decay scheme for the electron capture decay of Pu[237] as given by HOFFMAN AND DROPESKY.[177] The spins, parities and asymptotic quantum numbers assigned to the levels of Np[237] are those given by HOLLANDER ET AL[178] and RASMUSSEN ET AL[179] from a study of the decay of Am[241] and U[237] (refer to the discussion of these nuclides). The symbol *a* denotes Coulomb excitation experiments of NEWTON.[182] The values in parentheses give estimates of the intensities of the various transitions relative to the 59.6 keV transition.

of element 94 to be identified. SEABORG, MCMILLAN, KENNEDY, AND WAHL[183] prepared it by bombarding normal uranium with 16 MeV deuterons. KENNEDY, PERLMAN, SEGRÈ, AND WAHL[184] made the mass assignment

---

[183] G. T. Seaborg, E. M. McMillan, J. W. Kennedy, and A. C. Wahl, *Phys. Rev.* **69**, 366 (1946); G. T. Seaborg, A. C. Wahl, and J. W. Kennedy, *Phys. Rev.* **69**, 367 (1946). Original reports written in 1941.

[184] J. W. Kennedy, M. L. Perlman, E. Segrè, and A. C. Wahl, Paper No. 1.9, "The Transuranium Elements," *Nat. Nucl. Energ. Ser.*, Division IV **14B** (New York: McGraw-Hill Book Co., Inc., 1949).

certain by bombarding U^{238}, depleted with respect to U^{235}, and noting that the yield was proportional to the U^{238} content. ENGLISH AND JAMES[185] determined the yield as a function of deuteron energy and showed that it varied in a manner expected for the reaction:

$$U^{238}(d, 2n)Np^{238} \xrightarrow[2.1\,\text{days}]{\beta^-} Pu^{238}$$

Subsequent experiments with helium ion bombardments of U^{238} and U^{235} targets have resulted in the formation of Pu^{238} by the following reactions:[186]

$$U^{238}(\alpha, 4n)Pu^{238}$$

$$U^{238}(\alpha, p3n)Np^{238} \xrightarrow{\beta^-} Pu^{238}$$

$$U^{235}(\alpha, n)Pu^{238}$$

$$U^{235}(\alpha, p)Np^{238} \xrightarrow{\beta^-} Pu^{238}$$

Preparation of Pu^{238} by Neutron Reactions. This isotope is also produced[187,188] as a result of neutron capture by Np^{237}:

$$Np^{237}(n, \gamma)Np^{238} \xrightarrow{\beta^-} Pu^{238}$$
$$\sigma = 172 \text{ barns}$$

This is a convenient method for the preparation of isotopically-pure Pu^{238} provided the irradiation is not prolonged to the point where appreciable amounts of Pu^{239} are made. Pu^{238} produced in quantity in this manner is used in isotopic heat sources as a compact source of electric power. A small amount of Pu^{238} is formed in reactor-produced plutonium via the reaction sequence:

$$U^{238}(n, 2n)U^{237} \xrightarrow[6.8\,\text{days}]{\beta^-} Np^{237}(n, \gamma)Np^{238} \xrightarrow[2.1\,\text{days}]{\beta^-} Pu^{238}$$

The amount of Pu^{238} so produced is small on a weight ratio basis but it is readily detectable because its alpha half-life is short compared to Pu^{239}. The calculation of the yield of Pu^{238} by this mechanism depends on knowledge of the distribution of neutron energies in the reactor. In high-flux reactors containing plutonium operating at neutron fluxes of the order of 10^{14} neutrons cm^{-2} sec^{-1} and higher, measurable amounts of Pu^{238} may be produced by another mechanism. If the integrated flux is high enough to

[185] S. G. English and R. A. James in Report CN-261, September 15, 1942. Unpublished.

[186] R. A. James, A. E. Florin, H. H. Hopkins, Jr., and A. Ghiorso, Paper No. 22.8, "The Transuranium Elements," *Nat. Nucl. Energ. Ser.*, Division IV **14B** (New York: McGraw-Hill Book Co., Inc., 1949).

[187] A. H. Jaffey, L. B. Magnusson, and J. A. Crawford, unpublished results, 1945.

[188] G. C. Hanna and B. G. Harvey, unpublished results in *Report CRR-443*, June 20, 1950.

produce Cm^{242} via the successive neutron-capture sequence given below, some Pu^{238} will appear in the sample as a result of the alpha decay of Cm^{242}.

$$Pu^{239}(n,\gamma)Pu^{240}(n,\gamma)Pu^{241} \xrightarrow[13 \text{ years}]{\beta^-}$$

$$Am^{241}(n,\gamma)Am^{242} \xrightarrow[16 \text{ hours}]{\beta^-} Cm^{242}$$

$$Pu^{238} \xleftarrow[162 \text{ days}]{\alpha}$$

Figure 9.14 shows the production of Pu^{238} by this mechanism. If the flux is very high very little Pu^{238} is formed, because the Pu^{241} is burned out quickly to form higher mass isotopes before much can decay to Am^{241}. If the irradiation is continued for several years at lower fluxes the production of Pu^{238} also goes down, because most of the matter is converted to higher mass

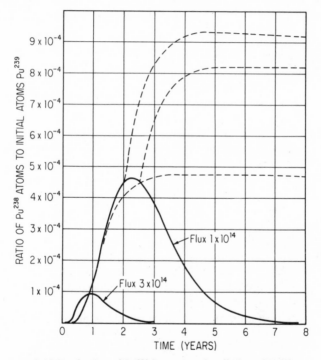

FIG. **9.14.** Production of Pu²³⁸ by neutron irradiation of Pu²³⁹ at fluxes of 3×10^{14} and 1×10^{14} neutrons cm⁻² sec⁻¹. The neutron capture and radioactive decay steps are given in the text. Curves are approximate because of approximations in the neutron capture and fission cross section. The dotted lines indicate the formation of Pu²³⁸ by alpha decay of Cm²⁴² after the sample is removed from the reactor (shown for the case of samples removed after 1 year, 2 years, and 2.5 years).

nuclides or to fission products, and the Pu^{238} itself is converted back to Pu^{239} by neutron capture. It is interesting to note the dotted lines in the figure which show that the amount of the Pu^{238} may increase by more than a factor of two after the sample is removed from the reactor because of the subsequent decay of Cm^{242}. At a flux of 1×10^{14} neutrons cm^{-2} sec^{-1} the maximum production of Pu^{238} occurs for an irradiation of about 2 years time. The chief isotopes of plutonium in the sample at this time will be Pu^{242} and Pu^{240}.

The amount of Pu^{238} by mass will be roughly one-half per cent. In Fig. 9.14 we neglected the possibility of producing Pu^{238} by the Pu^{239} $(n, 2n)$ Pu^{238} path, since the Pu^{239} is burned out quickly and any Pu^{238} so produced during the first two weeks of irradiation is converted back to Pu^{239} by neutron capture.

Gram quantities of Am^{241} are now available in many laboratories so that pure Pu^{238} can be made from Am^{241} by conversion of the Am^{241} to Cm^{242} as shown in Fig. 9.15. For the highest isotopic purity the Cm^{242} should

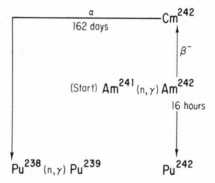

FIG. **9.15.** Path of conversion of Am²⁴¹ to Pu²³⁸.

be first isolated and purified and the Pu^{238} separated after decay; the reason for this indirect procedure is that Pu^{242} is produced by the electron capture decay of Am^{242} and also some Pu^{238} is converted to Pu^{239} in the reactor.

In reactors operating on U^{235} some Pu^{238} is produced via the reaction sequence:

$$U^{235}(n, \gamma)U^{236}(n, \gamma)U^{237} \xrightarrow[6.8 \text{ days}]{\beta^-} Np^{237}(n, \gamma)Np^{238} \xrightarrow[2.1 \text{ days}]{\beta^-} Pu^{238}$$

The rate of buildup of Pu^{238} by this sequence is shown in Fig. 9.16.

The formation of heavy element isotopes by successive neutron-capture reactions in high flux reactors is discussed in more detail in Chapter 5.

The Radiations of Pu^{238}. The best measurements of the half-life of Pu^{238} have come from direct observation of Pu^{238} alpha activity over a period of a few years. An accurate determination is that of JAFFEY and LERNER[189] who followed four samples over a period of 31 months and obtained a value of 89.59 ± 0.37 years. A later determination was made by HOFFMAN,

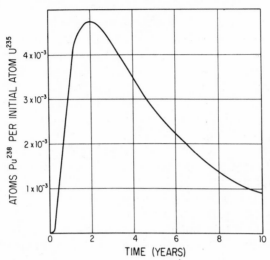

TIME (YEARS)

FIG. 9.16. Buildup of Pu^{238} in a thin sample of pure U^{235} irradiated at a neutron flux of 3×10^{14} neutrons cm^{-2} sec^{-1}. The neutron capture and beta decay sequence and the reaction cross sections are as follows:

$$U^{235} (n,\gamma) \ U^{236} (n,\gamma) \ U^{237} \xrightarrow[6.8\,d]{\beta^-} Np^{237} (n,\gamma) \ Np^{238} \xrightarrow[2\,d]{\beta^-} Pu^{238} (n,\gamma) \ Pu^{239}$$

| | 112 | 24 | | 170 | | 489 |

Fission   Fission   Fission
582   1600   18

FORD, AND LAWRENCE[190] who measured the Pu^{238} activity growing into a Cm^{242} sample. They reported a half-life of 86.41 ± 0.3 years for Pu^{238} based on a Cm^{242} half-life of 162.7 days.

Several early reports on the energy of the alpha particles of Pu^{238} are superceded by those of ASARO AND PERLMAN[191] and of KONDRAT'EV, NOVIKOVA, DEDOV, AND GOL'DIN.[192] The former group reported the following energies and abundances: 5.495 MeV* (72 per cent), 5.452 MeV (28 per cent)

[189] A. H. Jaffey and J. Lerner in *Argonne National Laboratory Report, ANL-4411*, February 13, 1950 (unpublished).

[190] D. C. Hoffman, G. P. Ford, and F. O. Lawrence, *J. Inorg. Nucl. Chem.* **5**, 6 (1957).

[191] F. Asaro and I. Perlman, *Phys. Rev.* **94**, 381 (1954).

[192] L. N. Kondrat'ev, G. I. Novikova, V. D. Dedov, and L. L. Gol'din, *Izvest. Akad. Nauk USSR*, **21**, 907 (1957).

* A restandardization of α_0 by Asaro and Perlman in 1961 led to the result 5.491 MeV and slightly revised abundance which we show in Fig. 9.17.

and 5.352 MeV (0.095 per cent).   The latter group reported 5.491 MeV (71.1 per cent), 5.448 MeV (28.7 per cent), 5.352 MeV (0.13 per cent), and 5.208 MeV (5×10^{-3} per cent).   These values are relative to Po^{210} $E_\alpha = 5.2978$ MeV.

ASARO AND PERLMAN[191] studied the gamma radiation of Pu^{238} with a scintillation crystal spectrometer and found a large number of 17-keV L x-rays (from the conversion of gamma rays) and gamma rays at 43.8, 99, and 150 keV.   NEWTON, ROSE, AND MILSTED[193] measured these gamma rays with somewhat greater accuracy by the proportional counter pulse-height analysis technique and reported gamma ray energies of 43.49 ± 0.08, 99.8 ± 0.4 and 153.1 ± 0.6 keV with relative intensities of 100:28:3.   HOLLANDER[194] examined the conversion electrons of the lowest energy transition.   His value of 43.50 keV checks closely the value of NEWTON, ROSE, AND MIL-STED.[193]   The $L_{II}L_{III}M_{II}M_{III}$ pattern of conversion confirms the $E2$ nature of the transitions.

DUNLAVEY AND SEABORG[195] found by the photographic plate technique, with emulsions soaked with a solution containing Pu^{238}, that 23 per cent of the Pu^{238} alpha particles are in coincidence with electrons corresponding to an ~ 40-keV gamma ray.   ASARO AND PERLMAN[191] conclude from comparison of the conversion coefficients, estimated from the experimental data, with the theoretical conversion coefficients that these radiations are $E2$ in nature. CHURCH AND SUNYAR[196] confirmed the electric quadrupole character of these gamma rays by detailed study of relative conversion in the L and M subshells.   They report the values 43.6 and 100.0 keV for the gamma ray energies.   MILTON AND FRASER[197] measured the angular correlations of the 43.6-keV photons with the 5.45 MeV alpha particles of Pu^{238} and obtained the correlation expected for a $0+ \xrightarrow{\alpha} 2+ \xrightarrow{\gamma} 0+$ sequence.   The 153-keV gamma ray is also believed to be an electric quadrupole radiation although with less certainty.   These results are summarized in the decay scheme shown in Fig. 9.17.   TRET'YAKOV, KONDRAT'EV, KHLEBNIKOV, AND GOL'DIN[198] measured conversion electrons in coincidence with the alpha-particles of Pu^{238} and found evidence for a gamma transition of energy 152.6 ± 0.3 keV with a subshell conversion ratio typical of an $E2$ transition.   They interpret this as evidence for a $6+$ level at 295.9 ± 0.4 keV populated in $(4.3 \pm 0.4) \times 10^{-3}$ per cent of the alpha events.

[193] J. O. Newton, B. Rose and J. Milsted, *Phil. Mag.* **1**, 981 (1956).

[194] J. M. Hollander, *Phys. Rev.* **103**, 1590 (1956)

[195] D. C. Dunlavey and G. T. Seaborg, *Phys. Rev.* **87**, 165 (1952).

[196] E. L. Church and A. W. Sunyar, *Phys. Rev.* **98**, 1186A (1955).

[197] J. C. D. Milton and J. S. Fraser, *Phys. Rev.* **95**, 628A (1954).

[198] E. T. Tret'yakov, L. N. Kondrat'ev, G. I. Khlebnikov, and L. L. Gol'din, *Zhur. Eksp. Teor. Fiz.* (USSR) **36**, 362 (1959); *Sov. Phys. JETP* **36**, (9) 250 (1959).

By gamma-gamma coincidence experiments it was established by ASARO, STEPHENS, AND PERLMAN that the 153 keV gamma ray is in cascade with the 99.8-keV gamma ray.[199] Placement of this gamma ray in the scheme as

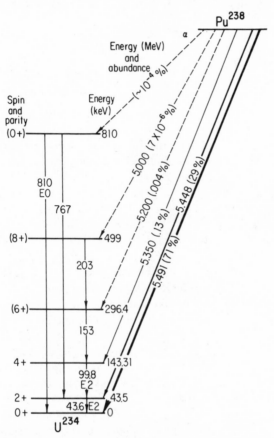

FIG. **9.17.** Decay scheme of Pu[238]. The decay of the UX₂–UZ complex and of Np[234] also involves these levels of U[234], plus other levels not shown, which are not reached in the alpha decay of Pu[238].

shown in the figure requires that an unobserved alpha particle group of 5.204 MeV energy and 0.004 per cent abundance be emitted by Pu[238]; an alpha particle group with this low intensity would have been missed in the direct examination of the alpha spectrum.   Later work by ASARO, STEPHENS, AND PERLMAN[199] led to the discovery of a 203 ± 5 keV gamma ray in very low abundance (4×10^{-6} per cent) which is in coincidence with the 150-keV

---

[199] F. Asaro, F. S. Stephens, Jr., and I. Perlman, unpublished results, 1956.

gamma rays. This gamma ray is shown as a transition from an 8+ level at 499 keV to a 6+ level at 296.4 keV in the figure. This assignment, which is very reasonable but not definitely proved, requires that an undiscovered alpha-particle group of 5.004 MeV energy and 7×10^{-6} per cent abundance be emitted by Pu^{238}.

ASARO, STEPHENS, AND PERLMAN[199] have found strong evidence for an electric monopole ($E0$) transition occurring in low abundance in the decay of Pu^{238}. An examination of the conversion electron spectrum using an anthracene crystal as detector showed K and L electrons of an 0.82-MeV transition. The total electron abundance was roughly 10^{-6} electrons per alpha disintegration. No gamma-ray photons of this energy were seen with a sodium iodide crystal detector. In an electric monopole transition photon emission is forbidden and the transition occurs entirely by electron emission. This 0.820-MeV transition is in all likelihood identical with the 810 keV (or 803 keV) 0+ → 0+ transition to the ground state of U^{234} which has been identified in the beta decay of UX_2 (Pa^{234}) to U^{234} (see Section 5.2.12), and it is so drawn in the decay scheme. This same $E0$ transition is seen in the electron capture decay of Np^{234}. See Fig. 9.7 in Section 9.1.5. If this is correct, one would expect to observe an $E2$ transition of 767 keV energy from the 0+ level at 810 keV to the 43.5-keV 2+ level. ASARO[199] observed photons of 763-keV energy in abundance corresponding to $\sim 5 \times 10^{-7}$ photons per alpha. These photons were shown to be in coincidence with L x-rays, presumably from the conversion of the 43.5-keV gamma ray, and not to be in coincidence with photons of 100-keV energy.

BJØRNHOLM, LEDERER, ASARO, AND PERLMAN[200] used α-γ coincidence techniques to search for alpha transitions to levels above 810 keV and set extremely low upper limits corresponding to an alpha hindrance factor of > 20 for decay to a known level at 922 keV and to a hindrance factor of > 10 for decay to a known level at 1044 keV.

The energy levels of U^{234} observed from the alpha decay of Pu^{238} resemble those of several other *even-even* nuclei in this mass region in conforming in a remarkable fashion with the predictions of the unified nuclear model as developed by BOHR AND MOTTELSON. The 0+, 2+, 4+ sequence has the correct energy spacings for the first members of the ground state rotational band with the splitting constant $\hbar/2\mathfrak{J}$ set equal to 7.30 keV. The levels at 296 and 499 keV have the correct energy values for the 6+ and 8+ levels of this rotational band. The 0+ level at 810 represents a collective vibrational excitation of the nucleus.

Early measurements by SEGRÈ AND CO-WORKERS[201,202] on the rate of

[200] S. Bjørnholm, M. Lederer, F. Asaro, and I. Perlman, *Phys. Rev.* **130**, 2000 (1963).

[201] E. Segrè, *Phys. Rev.* **86**, 21 (1952).

[202] G. W. Farwell, E. Segrè, A. Spano, and C. E. Wiegand, *Los Alamos Scientific Laboratory Report*, LA-490, April 25, 1946.

spontaneous fission of Pu^{238} gave a value of $(5.1 \pm 0.8) \times 10^6$ fissions per gram-hour corresponding to a spontaneous fission half-life of about 3.8×10^{10} years. A more recent measurement by JAFFEY AND HIRSCH[203] gave a value of $(4.0 \pm 0.34) \times 10^6$ fissions per gram-hour corresponding to a half-life of 4.9×10^{10} years.

9.2.9 *Plutonium-239*

The discovery of Pu^{239} through the work of McMILLAN AND ABELSON[204] and of KENNEDY, SEABORG, SEGRÈ, AND WAHL[205] is described in Section 9.2.1. The fission properties of Pu^{239} are discussed in Volume III, Part 1.

The most important method of preparation of Pu^{239} is the neutron capture reaction involved in its original synthesis:

$$U^{238}(n, \gamma)U^{239}; \quad U^{239} \xrightarrow[23.5 \text{ min}]{\beta^-} Np^{239} \xrightarrow[2.33 \text{ days}]{\beta^-} Pu^{239}$$

Plutonium-239 is made in large quantities in nuclear reactors by this reaction for industrial or military purposes. Reactor-produced plutonium contains small amounts of other plutonium isotopes as a result of side reactions. In reactors operating at very high fluxes the amounts of higher-mass plutonium isotopes produced by multiple neutron capture can be quite sizeable. (See Chapter 5.)

Plutonium-239 is produced by a number of cyclotron reactions with U^{238} as a target:

$$U^{238}(d, p)U^{239}; \quad U^{239} \xrightarrow{\beta^-} Np^{239} \xrightarrow{\beta^-} Pu^{239}$$

$$(d, n)Np^{239}; \qquad\qquad Np^{239} \xrightarrow{\beta^-} Pu^{239}$$

$$(\alpha, 3n)Pu^{239};$$

$$(\alpha, p2n)Np^{239}; \qquad\quad Np^{239} \xrightarrow{\beta^-} Pu^{239}$$

The yields for several of these reactions are given in Table 5.5 in Chapter 5.

The Half-life of Pu^{239}. Considerable effort has been expended in the determination of the half-life of Pu^{239}. The first determination[205] of 30,000 years was obtained by counting the beta particles of Np^{239} and the alpha particles of its daughter. It was subject to considerable uncertainty because of the complexity of the radiations of Np^{239}. A later refinement of the same method[206] gave the value 23,000 years; in this determination the Pu^{239} alpha activity was compared with the corresponding beta activity of its parent, U^{239}, whose radiations are simpler than those of Np^{239}.

[203] A. H. Jaffey and A. Hirsch, *Argonne National Laboratory Report ANL-4286*, May 12, 1949.

[204] E. M. McMillan and P. H. Abelson, *Phys. Rev.* **57**, 1185 (1940).

[205] J. W. Kennedy, G. T. Seaborg, E. Segrè, and A. C. Wahl, *Phys. Rev.* **70**, 555 (1946). Report originally written in May, 1941.

[206] A. C. Wahl and G. T. Seaborg, *Report CN-266*, September 14, 1942.

The first accurate value for the half-life was derived from the experiments of CUNNINGHAM AND WERNER,[207] who determined the specific alpha activity by weighing a pure compound of Pu^{239} and counting its alpha particles. These experiments constituted the first isolation of plutonium and the first preparation and isolation of a weighable amount of a synthetic atomic species.   In spite of the small quantity of material available, which was of the order of 100 μg, the accuracy of weighing and volumetric aliquoting was so great that the limiting factor in these experiments was the uncertainty in the alpha-counting yield (ratio of counts to disintegrations) of the instruments used.   This quantity is needed in order to convert the observed alpha-particle counting rate of the samples to the absolute alpha-disintegration rate. Experimental work of CUNNINGHAM, GHIORSO, AND HINDMAN[208] and theoretical calculations of CRAWFORD[209] led to the discovery that, in a parallel-plate ionization chamber, the alpha-particle counting yield may be greater than 50 per cent as a result of back-scattering of some of the particles from the sample mount.   The early specific-activity measurements were in error because counting yields of 47 to 50 per cent were assumed, whereas measurements[208] indicate that the counting yield of an extremely thin sample of Pu^{239} on a flat platinum plate in a parallel-plate counting ionization chamber operating in air is about 52 per cent.   However, most of the back-scattering alpha particles leave the plate at low angles, and the calculations indicate that, normal to the surface of the plate, there are virtually no back-scattering particles.   Consequently, in a counter with a low geometry factor, in which only those particles traversing a small aperture at the end of an evacuated collimating tube normal to the plane of the sample mount are counted, the counting yield is identical with the geometry factor and can be calculated by careful geometrical measurements.   Such counters were therefore used for calibration in connection with the accurate specific-activity determinations.

The weighing experiments of CUNNINGHAM AND CO-WORKERS[207,208] led to a half-life of 24,300 years.   Careful redeterminations by WESTRUM, HINDMAN, AND GREENLEE[210] have given 24,400 ± 70 years, and FARWELL, ROBERTS, AND WAHL[211] have also obtained the value of 24,400 years.   The

---

[207] B. B. Cunningham and L. B. Werner, *J. Am. Chem. Soc.* **71**, 1521 (1949).

[208] B. B. Cunningham, A. Ghiorso, and J. C. Hindman, Paper No. 16.3, "The Transuranium Elements," *Nat. Nucl. Energ. Ser.*, Division IV **14B** (New York: McGraw-Hill Book Co., Inc., 1949).

[209] J. A. Crawford, Paper No. 16.55, "The Transuranium Elements," *Nat. Nucl. Energ. Ser.*, Division IV **14B** (New York: McGraw-Hill Book Co., Inc., 1949.)

[210] E. F. Westrum, Jr., J. C. Hindman, and R. W. Greenlee, *Report CC-3894*, Nov. 1946.

[211] G. W. Farwell, J. E. Roberts, and A. C. Wahl, *Los Alamos Scientific Laboratory Report LAMS-293*, October 11, 1945; *Phys. Rev.* **94**, 363 (1954).

calorimetric measurements of JONES AND STOUT[212] have resulted in the value 24,100 ± 240 years, based on 5.23 MeV as the disintegration energy of the alpha decay. A later specific activity determination, carried out by WALL-MANN[213] yielded the value 24,360 ± 100 years. DOKUCHAEV[214] made specific activity measurements on 12 speciments of Pu^{239} having isotopic composition varying from 91.26 to 99.11 per cent Pu^{239} and obtained a value of 24,390 ± 30 years. MARKIN[215] solved the problem of the correction for Pu^{240} by using electromagnetically separated Pu^{239} with an isotopic purity of 99.92 per cent. He prepared and weighed a series of samples as the compounds, $Pu(SO_4)_2$ and $PuCl_3$, and by specific activity measurements found a half-life value of 24,413 ± 30 years.

It should be pointed out that one of the chief complications in the determination of the specific activity of Pu^{239} is the presence of small amounts of Pu^{240} which contribute to the alpha activity. The Pu^{240} content must be measured in some manner such as by measuring the spontaneous-fission rate of the sample. The Pu^{240} content of Pu^{239} is dependent on the neutron irradiation history of the sample. Small amounts of Pu^{238} may also be present in Pu^{239} prepared in a reactor because of the side reactions discussed in the last section. Because of the 86-year half-life of Pu^{238} its contribution to the specific activity can be appreciable even when its weight per cent is quite low.

The Alpha-Particle Spectrum of Pu^{239}. A number of measurements of the energy of the main alpha-particle group of Pu^{239} have been carried out, but the earliest measurements will not be reviewed here. Three groups have made careful measurements by the ionization chamber method; JESSE AND FORSTAT[216] obtained a value 5.137 MeV, CRANSHAW AND HARVEY[217] found 5.159 ± 0.005 MeV, and CONJEAUD AND NAGGIAR[218] gave the value 5.134 ± 0.015 MeV for the main group. The most accurate measurements have been made by the magnetic-deflection method and these have revealed complex structure in the alpha spectrum. ROSENBLUM, VALADARES, AND GOLDSCHMIDT[219] report a main group at 5.147 MeV in 70 per cent abundance and a second group at 5.097 MeV in 30 per cent abundance. ASARO AND PERLMAN[220] report three groups with the energies and abundances, 5.150 MeV

[212] W. M. Jones and J. W. Stout, *Los Alamos Scientific Laboratory Report LA-347*, August 17, 1945; *Phys. Rev.* **71**, 582 (1947).

[213] J. C. Wallmann, Ph.D. Thesis, University of California, April, 1951; also published as *Univ. Calif. Rad. Lab. Report, UCRL-1255*, April, 1951.

[214] Ya. P. Dokuchaev, *Atomnaya Energ.* **6**, 74 (1959).

[215] T. L. Markin, *J. Inorg. Nucl. Chem.* **9**, 320 (1959).

[216] W. P. Jesse and H. Forstat, *Phys. Rev.* **73**, 926 (1948).

[217] T. E. Cranshaw and B. G. Harvey, *Can. J. Res.* **A26**, 243 (1948).

[218] M. Conjeaud and V. Naggiar, *Compt. Rend.* **232**, 499 (1951).

[219] S. Rosenblum, M. Valadares, and B. Goldschmit, *Compt. Rend.* **230**, 638 (1950).

[220] F. Asaro and I. Perlman, *Phys. Rev.* **88**, 828 (1952).

(69 per cent), 5.137 MeV (20 per cent) and 5.099 MeV (11 per cent). Gol'din, Tret'yakov, and Novikova[221] report the same three groups, their figures being 5.1474 MeV (72.5 per cent), 5.1344 MeV (16.8 per cent), and 5.0963 MeV (10.7 per cent); no other alpha groups in greater than 0.2 per cent abundance in the energy region 4.9 to 5.33 MeV were found. Novikova, Kondrat'ev, Sobol'ev, and Gol'din[222] reported additional groups with the following energies and intensities: 5.064 ± 0.002 MeV (0.037 ± 0.005 per cent), 4.999 ± 5 MeV (0.013 ± 0.005 per cent), 4.975 MeV (0.005 per cent), 4.917 ± 0.005 MeV (0.005 ± 0.001 per cent), 4.780 MeV (~0.002 per cent), and 4.728 MeV (~0.005 per cent). New studies reported by Dzhelepov,

TABLE **9.14.** Alpha particle groups of Pu^{239} as reported by
BARANOV, KOULAKOV, AND BELENKI.[224]

Group	Energy of α-particle (MeV)	Intensity (per cent)	Hindrance factor	Energy of excited level in daughter (keV)
α_0, α_0'	5.157	73.3	3	$\gtrsim 0.008$
α_1	5.145	15.1	12.8	12.7
$\alpha(?)$	—	$<3 \times 10^{-2}$	—	~46
α_2	5.107	11.5	9.4	51.0
α_3	5.078	3.2×10^{-2}	2.1×10^3	81
α_4	5.066	9×10^{-4}	6.5×10^4	93
α_5	5.056	2.1×10^{-2}	2.5×10^3	103
α_6	5.031	5×10^{-3}	6.9×10^3	129
α_7	5.010	8×10^{-3}	3.1×10^3	150
α_8	5.001	6×10^{-4}	4×10^4	160
α_9	4.988	5×10^{-3}	4.1×10^3	172
α_{10}	4.963	3×10^{-3}	4.1×10^3	198
α_{11}	4.957	5×10^{-4}	2.5×10^4	204
α_{12}	4.937	3×10^{-3}	3.2×10^3	224
α_{13}	4.914	8×10^{-4}	7.8×10^3	248
α_{14}	4.873	7×10^{-4}	4.9×10^3	290
α_{15}	4.830	1.5×10^{-3}	1.2×10^3	333
α_{16}	4.801	6×10^{-4}	1.8×10^3	363
α_{17}	4.743 ⎱	2.6×10^{-3}		422
α_{18}	4.739 ⎰			426
α_{19}	4.695	4×10^{-4}	5×10^2	470
α_{20}	4.636	2×10^{-4}	3×10^2	530

The α_0 group of Pu^{238} was used as the energy standard and set equal to 5.4950 MeV.

[221] L. L. Gol'din, E. F. Tret'yakov, and G. I. Novikova, *Conf. Acad. Sci. of the USSR on Peaceful Uses of Atomic Energy, Phys. Math. Sci.* p. 226, July, 1955; available in English translation from Superintendent of Documents, U.S. Government Printing Office, Washington 25, D.C.

[222] G. I. Novikova, L. N. Kondrat'ev, Yu. N. Sobol'ev, and L. L. Gol'din, *Sov. Phys. JETP* (English translation) **5**, 832 (1957).

IVANOV, AND NEDOVESOV[223] and by BARANOV, KOULAKOV, AND BELENKI[224] in 1962 revealed even more complexity in the less abundant α-groups in the Pu^{239} alpha spectrum. The results of the latter groups are summarized in the accompanying table. It should be pointed out that the discrepancies in the energy of the principal groups which are evident when all the above-cited references are examined is partly caused by the use of different values for primary or secondary alpha standards.

The Gamma Radiations of Pu^{239}. A number of studies have been made of the electromagnetic and electron radiations of Pu^{239}. Absorption curve measurements carried out by early workers showed that the electromagnetic radiation included uranium K and L x-rays and apparently some gamma rays of 400 keV and lower energy. The most energetic gamma ray was reported to exist in approximately 10^{-4} of the disintegrations and x-rays were reported to be emitted in about one-tenth to one-hundredth of the disintegrations. The electrons are of low energy and consist of internal conversion and Auger electrons. Using photographic emulsions, ALBOUY AND TEILLAC[225] found conversion electrons corresponding to gamma rays of 50 keV and also found 100-keV electrons (0.1 to 1 per cent); by the same technique DUNLAVEY AND SEABORG[226] found the conversion electrons of 35- and 50-keV gamma rays (0.12 gamma ray per alpha particle) and also 100-keV conversion electrons (0.5 per cent). WEST, DAWSON, AND MANDELBERG,[227,228] using a proportional counter, found the corresponding gamma ray photons with energies 52.0 ± 0.3 kev (7×10^{-5} gamma ray per alpha particle) and 38.5 ± 0.4 kev (2×10^{-5} gamma ray per alpha particle). FREEDMAN, WAGNER, AND ENGELKEMEIR[229] have assigned gamma rays of 39, 53.1, 100, 124, and 384 keV to the alpha decay of Pu^{239} from conversion-electron and scintillation-spectrometer measurements. The ratio of L x-rays of uranium to the last four of these is about $100:0.56:0.25:0.14:0.08$. These investigators,[227,228,229] as well as ISRAEL[230] have made measurements of sufficient accuracy to assign the L x-rays to the daughter uranium. ASARO AND PERLMAN[231] have studied the gamma rays with a scintillation spectrometer and found photons with energies of 37, 52, 120, 207, 340, 380, and 415 keV

[223] B. S. Dzhelepov, R. B. Ivanov, and V. G. Nedovesov, *Sov. Phys. JETP* **14**, 1227 (1962).

[224] S. A. Baranov, V. M. Koulakov, and S. N. Belenki, *Zhur. Eksp. Teor. Fiz.* **43**, No. 4, 1135 (1962); *Nucl. Phys.* **41**, 95 (1963).

[225] G. Albouy and J. Teillac, *Compt. Rend.* **232**, 326 (1951).

[226] D. C. Dunlavey and G. T. Seaborg, *Phys. Rev.* **87**, 165 (1952).

[227] D. West and J. K. Dawson, *Proc. Phys. Soc.*, London **A64**, 586 (1951).

[228] D. West, J. K. Dawson, and C. J. Mandelberg, *Phil. Mag.* **43**, 875 (1952).

[229] M. S. Freedman, F. Wagner, Jr., and D. Engelkemeir, *Report AECD-3304*, November 1951; *Phys. Rev.* **88**, 1155 (1952).

[230] H. I. Israel, *Phys. Rev.* **88**, 682 (1952).

[231] F. Asaro and I. Perlman, unpublished results, 1956.

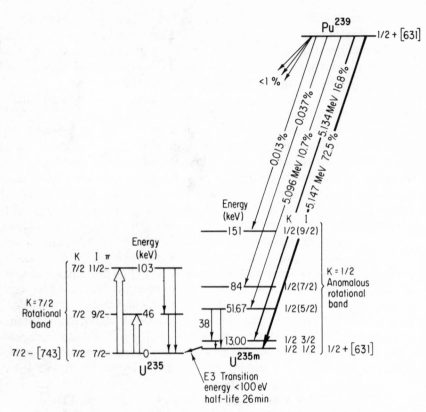

FIG. **9.18.** Decay scheme of Pu²³⁹. The alpha decay populates several levels of a $K = 1/2$ "anomalous" rotational band. The ground state of this band is an isomeric state of U²³⁵ lying only a few volts above the $I = 7/2-$ ground state. The isomeric state decays by a highly converted E3 isomeric transition with a half-life of 26 minutes. The higher-lying levels of the $K = 7/2$ ground state rotational band are known from Coulombic excitation studies. Gamma rays (not shown) and α-groups in low abundance indicate that some low intensity alpha groups of Pu²³⁹ populate higher-lying levels. The Nilsson wave function assignments of U²³⁵ (ground state) and U²³⁵ᵐ are 7/2 − [743] and 1/2 + [631]. Other levels of U²³⁵ populated by very rare alpha transitions are shown in Fig. 9.19.

in addition to K_α and K_β x-rays. The relative intensity of the gamma ray photons is $130 : 320 : 70 : 20 : 30 : 60 : 40$. Gamma-gamma coincidence studies established that L x-rays are in coincidence with the 207-, 340-, and 380-keV gamma rays and that the 120- and 207-keV gamma rays are in coincidence with each other. SHLYAGIN²³² studied the conversion electrons of gamma

---

²³² K. N. Shlyagin, *Zhur. Eksp. Teor. Fiz.* (SSSR) **30**, 817 (1956); in translation *Sov. Phys. JETP* **3**, 663 (1956).

rays with energies 12.5, 38.3, 50.8, and 117 keV. ALBRIDGE AND HOL-LANDER[233] report precise values of 13.00 keV and 51.67 keV for these two important transitions. MURRI AND CLINE[234] provide energy and abundance data on 13 transitions.

BJØRNHOLM, LEDERER, ASARO, AND PERLMAN[235] looked for evidence of lower-energy alpha groups and higher-energy gamma transitions in very low intensity by use of sensitive alpha-gamma and alpha-electron coincidence techniques. They found evidence for an alpha intensity of $(2.5 \pm 0.8) \times 10^{-7}$ for population of a state or rotational band at 780 keV excitation in U^{235}. This level decays partly by an $E0$ transition which identifies the 780 keV level as a collective state of excitation (beta vibrational level or band) such as is observed generally in even-even nuclei. The $1/2+$ assignment is given to this level. They also found evidence for a level at 650 ± 20 keV de-excited by an $E1$ gamma ray with an intensity $(8 \pm 3) \times 10^{-7}$. It was tentatively assigned $K = 1/2-$ and assigned to collective octupole vibrational excitation of the $K = 1/2+$ isomeric state near the ground state of U^{235} discussed in the next section.

Decay Scheme of Pu^{239} *and the Discovery of* U^{235m}. It is simple to construct a reasonable partial decay scheme of Pu^{239} incorporating the known alpha groups and the most prominent gamma transitions of energy 38 and 51 keV which have been reported by most experimentalists. This partial decay scheme is shown on the right side of Fig. 9.18. It is evident, however, from the repeated observation of low intensity gamma rays of higher energy that one or more alpha groups in very low abundance (less than 0.1 per cent), with lower energy than any yet reported, must be present in the alpha spectrum of Pu^{239}. It is reasonable to identify the observed spectrum of U^{235} levels as an "anomalous" rotational band based on a $K = 1/2$ base level. This is consistent with the spacings of the levels, the known ground state spin of $1/2$ for Pu^{239} and the low hindrance factor of 3 for the highest energy alpha group suggesting favored alpha decay to a daughter nucleus of very similar intrinsic particle structure. This interpretation was first suggested by BOHR, FRÖMAN, AND MOTTELSON.[236]

The formula given by BOHR AND MOTTELSON (see Chapter 3) for the level spacings of an anomalous $K = \Omega = 1/2$ band is

$$E_I = \frac{\hbar^2}{2\Im} [I(I + 1) + (-)^{I + 1/2} a(I + \tfrac{1}{2})]$$

The lowest 5 levels of U^{235} populated by the alpha-groups of Pu^{239} fit this

    [233] R. G. Albridge and J. M. Hollander, unpublished results, 1956.
    [234] E. L. Murri and J. E. Cline, *Bull. Am. Phys. Soc.* II, **6**, 239 (1961).
    [235] S. Bjørnholm, M. Lederer, F. Asaro, and I. Perlman, *Phys. Rev.* **130**, 2000 (1963).
    [236] A. Bohr, P. O. Fröman, and B. R. Mottelson, *Dan. Mat.-fys. Medd.* **29**, No. 10 (1955).

formula closely if the constant, a, is set equal to -0.276 and $\hbar^2/2\mathfrak{J}$ is 6.1 keV.[222] ALBRIDGE AND HOLLANDER[233] give slightly different values of -0.28 and 6.04 keV based on their values of 13.00 and 51.67 keV for the first two levels.

For a long period of time this very reasonable interpretation of the alpha decay of Pu^{239} gave rise to a very puzzling discrepancy. The difficulty was that the measured spin[237] of the ground state of U^{235} is 7/2 instead of 1/2. Furthermore, the experiments of NEWTON[238] on the Coulombic excitation of U^{235} with helium ions clearly proved that levels with energy 46.2 keV and 103 keV were among the low-lying levels of U^{235}. He observed the gamma rays of 46.7, 57.8, and 103.8 keV shown in the figure. These experiments constitute strong evidence that a (7/2, 9/2, 11/2) rotational band based on a $K = 7/2$ ground state is being excited. It was realized by workers in several laboratories that the discrepancy between the two sets of observations could be resolved if some transition were observed in nearly 100 per cent abundance between the $K = 1/2$ and $K = 7/2$ states. This transition would be expected to be of the $\Delta I = 3$ type. A diligent search for the photons, the conversion electrons, or the x-rays from this transition lead at first only to the conclusion that the energy of the transition must lie below the L-shell binding energies of uranium. The possibility that this unobserved transition had a very long half-life was checked by HUIZENGA, ENGELKEMEIR, AND TOMKINS[239] who separated U^{235} which had grown into a 10-year old sample of Pu^{239}, and measured its spin. The optical spectrum was the same as that of normal uranium. From the limits of the experiment an upper limit of 4 months was set on the half-life for the transition between the two forms of U^{235}.

Following these observations the investigation took the form of a search for a short-lived transition of extremely low energy and was rewarded with immediate success. ASARO AND PERLMAN[240] and HUIZENGA, RAO, AND ENGELKEMEIR[241] almost simultaneously reported the separation by a recoil collection technique of an activity emitting very soft conversion electrons and decaying with a half-life of 26.5 minutes. The electron activity could also be isolated chemically using separation methods specific for uranium. Later measurements showed that the energy of the electrons was extremely low indeed. FREEDMAN, PORTER, WAGNER, AND DAY[242] set an upper limit of 19 electron volts and an upper limit of 23 electron volts to the transition

[237] K. L. Vander Sluis and J. R. McNally, Jr., *J. Opt. Soc. Am.* **45**, 65 (1955).

[238] J. O. Newton, *Physica* **22**, 1129 (1956); *Nucl. Phys.* **3**, 345 (1957).

[239] J. R. Huizenga, D. W. Engelkemeir, and F. Tomkins, *Bull. Am. Phys. Soc.* II, **2**, 198 (1957).

[240] F. Asaro and I. Perlman, *Phys. Rev.* **107**, 318 (1957).

[241] J. R. Huizenga, C. L. Rao, and D. W. Engelkemeir, *Phys. Rev.* **107**, 319 (1957).

[242] M. S. Freedman, F. T. Porter, F. Wagner, Jr., and P. P. Day, *Phys. Rev.* **108**, 836 (1957).

energy. MICHEL, ASARO, AND PERLMAN[243] found electrons of energy up to 70 volts. The great majority of the electrons are of much less energy. They are nearly completely absorbed in 2 micrograms of plastic film, which accounts for their non-observance in the numerous studies of the radiations of Pu^{239} which had been carried out earlier. This is by a large margin the lowest transition energy ever reported for an isomeric state. The short half-life is accounted for by the extremely large conversion coefficient which is estimated to fall in the range $10^{19} - 10^{21}$.

From a consideration of the nuclear level systems of Np^{239}, Pu^{239} and U^{235} it is possible to make a tentative assignment of Nilsson wave functions to the odd 143rd neutron in U^{235} (ground state) and in U^{235m}. In the $K\pi[Nn_z\Lambda]$ nomenclature of the unified nuclear model (see Chapter 3) these assignments are $7/2 - [743]$ and $1/2 + [631]$, respectively. The isomeric transition would accordingly be $E3$. The Nilsson orbital assignment of the ground state of Pu^{239} is $1/2 + [631]$. It is interesting to note that another case of $E3$ isomerism resulting from the close proximity of these same two Nilsson states is observed[244] in Pu^{237} which, like U^{235}, has 143 neutrons. See Section 9.4.5.

Not all of the levels of U^{235} populated in the alpha decay of Pu^{239} are shown in the figure. There is evidence from several published studies [222,223,224,231] for the population of numerous other levels of U^{235} by rare alpha transitions in the abundance range of 10^{-2} to 10^{-4} per cent. Some of these transitions are to high-lying levels of the two rotational bands shown in Fig. 9.18 whereas others lead to different rotational

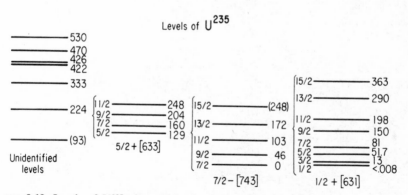

Levels of U^{235}

FIG. **9.19.** Levels of U^{235} observed in the decay of Pu^{239} including many levels populated in less than 0.01 per cent intensity. Separation of levels into rotational bands as given by BARANOV, KOULAKOV, AND BELENSKI.

---

[243] M. C. Michel, F. Asaro, and I. Perlman, *Bull. Am. Phys. Soc.* II, **2**, 394 (1957).
[244] F. S. Stephens, Jr., F. Asaro, S. Amiel, and I. Perlman, *Phys. Rev.* **107**, 1456 (1957).

bands. An analysis by BARANOV, KOULAKOV, AND BELENKI[224] of their alpha spectral data (reproduced in Table 9.14 above) is summarized in Fig. 9.19. These authors assign the Nilsson state $5/2 + [633]$ to a group of levels with a base level at 129 keV.

Level System of Pu^{239}. The excited levels of Pu^{239} are discussed in connection with the decay of Np^{239} (see Section 9.1.10). The excitation of the 57 keV level of Pu^{239} by Coulombic excitation techniques is also covered there rather than here.

Spin of Pu^{239}. The nuclear spin of Pu^{239} has been measured to be $1/2$ by nuclear paramagnetic resonance,[245] by analysis of optical spectra,[246,247,248] and by atomic beam resonance studies.[249]

9.2.10 *Plutonium-240*

CHAMBERLAIN, FARWELL, AND SEGRÈ[250] provided the first direct evidence for the isotope Pu^{240}; this evidence was the observation that samples of Pu^{239} that had been exposed to strong neutron fluxes exhibited spontaneous fission activity and that the spontaneous fission rate was proportional to the irradiation received. From this relation it was deduced that the isotope responsible was Pu^{240} formed in the reaction $Pu^{239}(n, \gamma)Pu^{240}$; and this has been firmly established by subsequent experiments. BARTLETT, SWINE-HART, AND THOMPSON[251] established the presence of Pu^{240} in reactor produced plutonium by mass spectrographic analysis.

The alpha half-life of Pu^{240} has been measured several times by direct specific activity measurements although this approach is made difficult by the presence of Pu^{239} in the samples available for analysis. The method consists in the measurement of the specific activity of a weighed plutonium sample of known composition and correcting for the Pu^{239} contribution. The first careful studies had of necessity to be carried out on samples of plutonium containing only a few per cent of Pu^{240}. WESTRUM, HINDMAN, AND GREENLEE[252] obtained the value 6240 ± 120 years. FARWELL, ROBERTS,

[245] B. Bleaney, *et al.*, *Phil. Mag.* **45**, 773, 991 (1954).

[246] M. van den Berg, P. F. A. Klinkenberg, and P. Regnaut, *Physica* **20**, 37, 461 (1954).

[247] N. I. Kaliteevskii and M. P. Chaika, *Akad. Nauk SSSR Doklady* **103**, 49 (1955).

[248] L. A. Korostyleva, A. R. Striganov, and N. M. Iashin, *J. Exp. Theor. Phys.* (USSR) **28**, 471 (1955); translation *Sov. Phys. JETP* **1**, 310 (1955).

[249] J. C. Hubbs, R. Marrus, W. A. Nierenberg, and J. L. Worchester, *Phys. Rev.* **109**, 390 (1958).

[250] O. Chamberlain, G. W. Farwell, and E. Segrè, *Los Alamos Scientific Laboratory Report LAMS-131*, September 8, 1944.

[251] A. A. Bartlett, D. F. Swinehart, and R. W. Thompson, *Los Alamos Scientific Laboratory Reports LA-168* (November 7, 1944), *LA-327* (July 11, 1945), and *LA-561* (May 24, 1946).

[252] E. F. Westrum, Jr., J. C. Hindman, and R. W. Greenlee, *Metallurgical Laboratory Report CC-3894* (November 1946); see also *Phys. Rev.* **83**, 1250 (1951).

AND WAHL[253] reported a value of 6300 ± 600 years. DOKUCHAEV[254] published a value of 6620 ± 50 years.

At a later period, plutonium with a much higher Pu^{240} content became available. In Chapter 5 it is shown that plutonium samples containing as much as 45 atom per cent of Pu^{240} can be made in high flux reactors. CUNNINGHAM, THOMPSON, AND GHIORSO,[255] using samples containing as much as 34 per cent Pu^{240}, redetermined the half-life and reported a value of 6650 ± 150 years. WALLMANN[256] repeated these experiments with somewhat more care and obtained the value 6760 years. Corrections were applied for appreciable amounts of Pu^{238} alpha activity in the sample. BUTLER AND CO-WORKERS[257] report a value of 6600 ± 100 years.

An independent method of determining this quantity has been employed by INGHRAM, HESS, FIELDS, AND PYLE.[258] These workers carried out a mass spectrographic analysis of a plutonium sample which contained a substantial percentage of Pu^{240} and also mass analyzed the uranium daughters U^{235} and U^{236} which were formed by alpha decay of the plutonium isotopes over a several year period. From these ratios and from the known half-life of Pu^{239}, the half-life of Pu^{240} was calculated to be 6580 ± 40 years.

In uranium reactors some of the observed Pu^{240} results from the alternate reaction sequences:

$$U^{238}(n, \gamma)U^{239}(n, \gamma)U^{240} \xrightarrow[14\text{ h}]{\beta^-} Np^{240} \xrightarrow[7.3\text{ m}]{\beta^-} Pu^{240}$$

$$U^{238}(n, \gamma)U^{239} \xrightarrow[23.5\text{ m}]{\beta^-} Np^{239}(n, \gamma)Np^{240} \xrightarrow[7.3\text{ m}]{\beta^-} Pu^{240}$$

The first sequence, observed by HYDE AND STUDIER[259] in their experiments on the discovery of U^{240} and Np^{240}, opens up the possibility of preparing isotopically pure samples of Pu^{240} by purification of neutron-irradiated uranium at the proper time after bombardment and isolation thereafter of the Pu^{240} formed. This method was used by HULET AND CO-WORKERS[260] to prepare small samples of Pu^{240} for measurement of its fission cross section. The second sequence has never been specifically observed, although it undoubtedly occurs to some extent.

[253] G. W. Farwell, J. E. Roberts, and A. C. Wahl, *Phys. Rev.* **94**, 363 (1954).

[254] Ya. P. Dokuchaev, *Atomnaya Energ.* **6**, 74 (1959).

[255] B. B. Cunningham, S. G. Thompson, and A. Ghiorso, unpublished results, 1949.

[256] J. C. Wallmann, Ph.D. Thesis, University of California, April, 1951; also published as *Univ. Calif. Rad. Lab. Report, UCRL-1255*, April 1951, declassified, 1956.

[257] J. P. Butler, T. A. Eastwood, T. L. Collins, M. E. Jones, F. M. Rourke, and R. P. Schuman, *Phys. Rev.* **103**, 634 (1956).

[258] M. G. Inghram, D. C. Hess, P. R. Fields, and G. L. Pyle, *Phys. Rev.* **83**, 1250 (1951).

[259] E. K. Hyde and M. H. Studier, *Argonne National Laboratory Reports ANL-4143* (April 15, 1948) and *ANL-4182* (August 4, 1948), unpublished.

[260] E. K. Hulet, H. R. Bowman, M. C. Michel, and R. W. Hoff, *Phys. Rev.* **102**, 1621 (1956).

During the bombardment of uranium with 40-MeV helium ions, JAMES, FLORIN, HOPKINS, AND GHIORSO[261] observed the production of alpha activity attributed to Pu^{240} as a result of the reaction $U^{238}(\alpha, 2n)Pu^{240}$ and presumably:

$$U^{238}(\alpha, pn)Np^{240} \xrightarrow[7.3 \text{ m}]{\beta^-} Pu^{240}$$

These alpha particles had an energy hardly distinguishable from the energy of the alpha particles of Pu^{239}, but in a fission chamber the sample yielded a number of neutron-induced fissions different from a sample of pure Pu^{239}.

The energy of the main alpha-particle group of Pu^{240} is so close to that of the main 5.150 MeV group of Pu^{239} that the two cannot be distinguished when the ionization chamber—pulse height analysis method is applied. Hence, mass spectrographic or spontaneous-fission counting methods had to be used to assay mixtures of the two. ASARO AND PERLMAN,[262] using a magnetic spectrometer, found a main group of 5.162 ± 0.004 MeV (76 per cent) and a lower energy group of 5.118 MeV (24 per cent). ASARO[263] has also observed a third group at 5.014 MeV of 0.1 per cent abundance. GOL'DIN, TRET'YAKOV, AND NOVIKOVA[264,265] report three groups: 5.1589 (75.5 per cent), 5.1147 MeV (24.5 per cent) and 5.004 (0.085 per cent). This same Russian group[266] later restudied the Pu^{240} alpha spectrum and found an additional low intensity group plus two more tentatively assigned to Pu^{240}. Their revised alpha spectrum is given in Table 9.15. BARANOV, KOULAKOV, AND BELENKI[267] determined precisely the energy of the α_0 group of Pu^{240} relative to the main group of Pu^{239} and found it to lie exactly 12.10 ± 0.15 keV higher.

It is expected that Pu^{240} will resemble all other even-even alpha emitters in this mass region. On this basis the first alpha groups undoubtedly populate the $0+$, $2+$ and $4+$ states, respectively, of the daughter nucleus U^{236}. In addition, the excited state at 313 keV reached by the 4.851 MeV alpha group has the correct energy to be the $6+$ state. These states should

[261] R. A. James, A. E. Florin, H. H. Hopkins, Jr., and A. Ghiorso, Paper No. 22.8, "The Transuranium Elements," *Nat. Nucl. Energ. Ser.,* Division IV **14B** (New York: McGraw-Hill Book Co., Inc., 1949).

[262] F. Asaro and I. Perlman, *Phys. Rev.* **88**, 828 (1952).

[263] F. Asaro, Ph.D. Thesis, University of California, June 1952; also published as *Univ. Calif. Rad. Lab. Report UCRL-2180,* June, 1952.

[264] L. L. Gol'din, E. F. Tret'yakov, and G. I. Novikova, *Conf. Acad. Sci. USSR on Peaceful Uses of Atomic Energy, Phys. Math. Sci.,* p. 226, July 1955; available in English translation from Superintendent of Documents, U. S. Government Printing Office, Washington 25, D.C.

[265] L. L. Gol'din, G. I. Novikova, and E. F. Tret'yakov, *Phys. Rev.* **103**, 1004 (1956).

[266] L. N. Kondra'ev, G. I. Novikova, Iv. P. Sobolev, and L. L. Gol'din, *Zhur. Eksp. Teor. Fiz.* (SSSR) **31**, 771 (1956); in translation, *Sov. Phys., JETP* **4**, 645 (1957).

[267] Baranov, Koulakov, and Belenki, *Zhur. Eksp. Teor. Fiz.* **43**, 1135 (1962).

TABLE **9.15**. Alpha spectrum of Pu[240].

Group	Energy (MeV)	Per cent abundance	Energy of excited state (keV)
α_0	5.159	75.5	0
α_{45}	5.115	24.4	45
α_{147}	5.014	.091	147
α_{210}	4.952?	2.7×10^{-3}	210?
α_{239}	4.924?	3.1×10^{-3}	239?
α_{313}	4.851	3.2×10^{-3}	313

Data of Kondrat'ev, Novikova, Sobol'ev, and Gol'din, see Refs. 264, 265, 266.

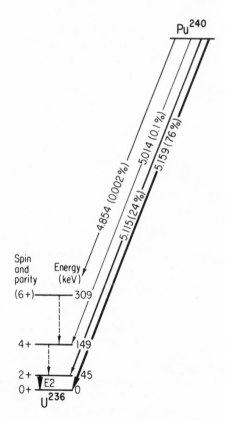

FIG. **9.20**. Decay scheme of Pu[240].

be de-excited by a cascade of electric quadrupole (E2) gamma rays with energies 166, 102, and 45 keV. The intensity of the first two as directly deduced from the alpha group intensities is very low. TRET'YAKOV AND

CO-WORKERS[267a] have seen conversion electrons of a gamma ray of 160 ± 1.5 keV energy in coincidence with the alpha particles of Pu^{240}. From this they deduce an energy of 309 keV for the 6+ level and an alpha population of $(2 \pm 1) \times 10^{-3}$ per cent. The 45 keV transition from the 2+ state to the ground state has been observed by several research groups.[268-270] HOLLANDER[270] found the expected conversion electron pattern for an $E2$ transition and measured a precise value of 45.28 ± 0.06 keV for the transition. This same transition is prominent in the electron capture decay of Np^{236}.

KONDRAT'EV AND CO-WORKERS[266] tentatively interpret the possible levels at 210 and 239 keV (see Table 9.15) as $1-$ and $3-$ states. It is unlikely that the interpretation is correct because the spacing of these levels is much too small and no odd parity states are found at such low energies for other nuclei close to Pu^{240}.

Plutonium-240 is beta stable. The spontaneous fission half-life has been reported to be 1.2×10^{11} years by CHAMBERLAIN, FARWELL, AND SEGRÈ[271], and 1.22×10^{11} years by BARCLAY AND CO-WORKERS.[272]

9.2.11 *Plutonium-241*

Evidence for the presence of Pu^{241} in samples of plutonium which had been strongly irradiated with neutrons was first obtained by SEABORG, JAMES, MORGAN, AND GHIORSO[273,274] in the late fall of 1944. These workers isolated two new alpha emitting radioactivities from the plutonium and attributed them to Am^{241} and Cm^{242}. It was postulated that beta-decaying Pu^{241}, formed by the reaction sequence:

$$Pu^{239}(n, \gamma)Pu^{240}(n, \gamma)Pu^{241}$$

was an intermediate in the reaction sequence leading to these activities. Subsequent experiments showed that the activity attributed to Am^{241} continued to grow in the irradiated plutonium after purification of the latter, indicating that the parent Pu^{241} was long-lived. Observations on the rate of Am^{241}

[267a] E. F. Tret'yakov, L. N. Kondrat'ev, G. I. Khlebnikov, and L. L. Gol'din, *Zhur. Eksp. Teor. Fiz* (SSSR) **36**, 362 (1959), *Sov. Phys. JETP* **36** (9) 250 (1959).

[268] M. S. Freedman, F. Wagner, Jr., and D. W. Engelkemeir, *Phys. Rev.* **88**, 1155 (1952).

[269] K. N. Shlyagin, *Zhur. Eksp. Teor. Fiz* (SSSR) **30**, 817 (1956); in English translation, *Sov. Phys. JETP* **3**, 663 (1956).

[270] J. M. Hollander, *Phys. Rev.* **103**, 1590 (1956).

[271] O. Chamberlain, G. W. Farwell, and E. Segrè, *Phys. Rev.* **94**, 156 (1954).

[272] F. R. Barclay, W. Galbraith, K. M. Glover, G. R. Hall, and W. J. Whitehouse, *Proc. Phys. Soc.* (London) **67A**, 646 (1954).

[273] A. Ghiorso, R. A. James, L. O. Morgan, and G. T. Seaborg, *Phys. Rev.* **78**, 472 (1950).

[274] G. T. Seaborg, R. A. James, and L. O. Morgan, Paper No. 22.1, "The Transuranium Elements," *Nat. Nucl. Energ. Ser.*, Division IV **14B** (New York: McGraw-Hill Book Co., Inc., 1949).

growth in various plutonium samples led to an early value[274] of about 10 years for the half-life of Pu^{241}. Later studies based on values determined mass spectrographically for the isotopic abundance of Pu^{241} in samples of neutron-irradiated plutonium, together with the best half-life of Am^{241}, led to the better values of 14 ± 1 years (THOMPSON AND CO-WORKERS)[275] and 13.0 ± 0.2 years (MACKENZIE, LOUNSBURY, AND BOYD)[276] and 12.77 ± 0.28 years (ROSE AND MILSTED).[277] HALL AND MARKIN[278] remeasured the half-life of Am^{241} on which the Pu^{241} half-life directly depends and revised the last two values of the Pu^{241} half-life to 13.32 ± 0.12 and 13.04 ± 0.28 years, respectively. BROWN AND CO-WORKERS[279] report the value 13.24 ± 0.24 years.

It is possible to prepare samples of plutonium containing up to about 20 atom per cent of Pu^{241} by bombardment of Pu^{239} to an integrated flux of approximately 4×10^{21} neutrons per square centimeter. Such a sample will contain about 40 atom per cent of Pu^{240}, 25 atom per cent of Pu^{242} and 15 atom per cent of Pu^{239}. This is illustrated in Fig. 5.7 in Chapter 5. With further neutron irradiation the Pu^{241} isotopic abundance decreases and in order to obtain samples of Pu^{241} of isotopic purity approaching 100 per cent it is necessary to resort to electromagnetic separation. Samples of 78 per cent isotopic purity have been reported by English workers.[279,280]

The isotope Pu^{241} has also been prepared[274] in the cyclotron by the reaction:

$$U^{238}(\alpha, n)Pu^{241}$$

It has also been isolated[281] as the daughter product of Cm^{245}.

The beta particles of Pu^{241} are of low energy. The first estimate of the maximum energy was approximately 20 keV.[274] Observations of the Pu^{241} beta particles is difficult in samples of low isotopic abundance because of interference from the intense alpha activity, the conversion electrons, and the Auger electrons accompanying the disintegration of the Pu^{239}. FREEDMAN, WAGNER, AND ENGELKEMEIR[282] have studied the electrons of Pu^{241} in a double lens spectrometer and report an end-point energy of 20.5 keV; their Kurie plot exhibits an allowed shape down to 14 keV below which

---

[275] S. G. Thompson, K. Street, Jr., A. Ghiorso, and F. L. Reynolds, *Phys. Rev.* **80**, 1108 (1950).

[276] D. R. MacKenzie, M. Lounsbury, and A. W. Boyd, *Phys. Rev.* **90**, 327 (1953).

[277] B. Rose and J. Milsted, *J. Nucl. Energ.* **2**, 264 (1956).

[278] G. R. Hall and T. L. Markin, *J. Inorg. Nucl. Chem.* **4**, 137 (1957).

[279] F. Brown, G. G. George, D. E. Green, and D. E. Watt, *J. Inorg. Nucl. Chem.* **13**, 192 (1960).

[280] H. M. Davis, et al., *Prog. Nucl. Energ.*, Ser. 9, *Analytical Chemistry*, Vol. 1, p. 5 (London: Pergamon Press, 1959).

[281] A. M. Friedman, et al., *Phys. Rev.* **95**, 1501 (1954).

[282] M. S. Freedman. F. Wagner, Jr., and D. W. Engelkemeir, *Phys. Rev.* **88**, 1155 (1952).

instrumental effects distort it. These workers also detected gamma rays of 100 and 145 keV energy which they assigned to Pu^{241}. The 100 keV peak may be K x-rays from the conversion of the 145 keV gamma ray. The intensity of the 145 keV gamma ray is only 2 photons per 10^6 Pu^{241} beta disintegrations which probably means the gamma ray is to be associated with the alpha branching of Pu^{241}. SHLYAGIN[283] reports an end-point energy of 20.8 keV for the beta particles.

The alpha branching of Pu^{241} was established by KOHMAN, SWARTOUT, AND SULLIVAN[284] and by SEABORG, JAMES, AND MORGAN[274] who isolated and characterized the daughter U^{237} from plutonium produced at high neutron-irradiation levels. THOMPSON, STREET, GHIORSO, AND REYNOLDS[275] have observed a low-abundance group of alpha particles by analysis of ionization chamber pulses with the energy 4.91 ± 0.03 MeV. This group was present in the plutonium samples in the amount expected for the isotope Pu^{241}. From the alpha particle intensity and the isotopic abundance, the alpha branching was calculated to be ~ 0.003 per cent and the alpha half-life $\sim 4 \times 10^5$ years. These values are in agreement with the predictions of alpha systematics. ASARO[285] applied the more accurate magnetic deflection method to samples of plutonium with a higher Pu^{241} content and found two alpha-particle groups, 4.893 MeV (75 per cent) and 4.848 MeV (25 per cent) for Pu^{241}. His estimate of the alpha branching is 0.005 per cent corresponding to an alpha half-life of 2.7×10^5 years.

The α-decay of Pu^{241} has been interpreted[285a] as follows: The favored α-transition (4.893 MeV group) populates an excited state at 145 keV in U^{237} which has the orbital assignment $5/2 +$ [622] and the 4.848 MeV group goes to the first rotational member. The ground state of U^{237} is assigned to the orbital $1/2 +$ [631] which is the same as the ground state for Pu^{239}. The α-transitions of Pu^{241} directly to the ground state band are presumably hindered.

The older values for the α half-life of Pu^{241} have been improved by more recent measurements of BROWN, GEORGE, GREEN, AND WATT[279] on samples containing 77 per cent Pu^{241}. They reported a value of $(5.72 \pm 0.10) \times 10^5$ years. This value is supported by the measurements of SMITH[286] on a plutonium sample containing 96.19 atom per cent of Pu^{241}. She reports an α/β ratio of $(2.31 \pm 0.10) \times 10^{-5}$, a partial β half-life of 13.3 ± 0.3 years

283 K. N. Shlyagin, *Zhur. Eksp. Teor. Fiz.* (SSSR) **30**, 817 (1956); in English translation *Sov. Phys. JETP* **3**, 663 (1956).

284 T. P. Kohman, J. A. Swartout, and W. H. Sullivan, Report (H) CN-3213, October 10, 1945, unpublished.

285 F. Asaro, Ph.D. Thesis, University of California, June, 1952; also published as *Univ. Calif. Rad. Lab. Report UCRL-2180*, June, 1952.

285a F. S. Stephens, Jr., F. Asaro, and I. Perlman, *Phys. Rev.* **113**, 212 (1959).

286 H. L. Smith, *J. Inorg. Nucl. Chem.* **17**, 178 (1961).

and a partial alpha half-life of $(5.6 \pm 0.2) \times 10^5$ years. Two groups[287,288] have calculated the alpha branching by determining the amount of U^{237} daughter activity in equilibrium with a plutonium sample of known Pu^{241} content. Both report a partial alpha half-life of $(2.9 \pm 0.5) \times 10^5$ years. The discrepancy between the different α-decay half-lives has not yet been explained.

The nuclear spin of Pu^{241} has been determined to be $5/2$ by the paramagnetic resonance method.[289]

HORROCKS AND STUDIER[290] describe the use of liquid scintillation techniques to measure the Pu^{241} content of plutonium samples. The lower limit of detection is 10^{-15} grams.

9.2.12 *Plutonium-242*

THOMPSON, STREET, GHIORSO, AND REYNOLDS[291] first observed the isotope Pu^{242} in a mass-spectrographic analysis of neutron-irradiated plutonium. The Pu^{242} content of this original sample was quite low. In modern high-flux reactors, however, it is rather simple to prepare Pu^{242} with isotopic purity of 98 per cent or higher. For example, in Fig. 5.9 of Chapter 5 we note that a Pu^{239} sample irradiated at a flux of 3×10^{14} neutrons per cm^2 per second for 1.5 years is converted to plutonium which is nearly pure Pu^{242}. At a higher neutron flux this result is achieved in a shorter time. A typical analysis[292] for a plutonium sample irradiated to a total integrated flux of 1.4×10^{22} neutrons per cm^2 is given in Table 9.16.

Another method of preparation of Pu^{242}, the method which historically was used to provide samples for the first examination of the properties of this isotope, is based on the conversion of Am^{241} to Am^{242} by neutron irradiation followed by the partial decay of Am^{242} by electron capture to form Pu^{242}. The electron capture decay of 16 hr Am^{242} upon which this synthesis is based was first observed by O'KELLEY, BARTON, CRANE, AND PERLMAN.[292a] The Am^{241} starting material is carefully purified from plutonium and then placed in a reactor. After the irradiation the plutonium is isolated

[287] M. Jones, *et al.*, *Knolls Atomic Energy Laboratory Report, KAPL-1378* (1955), unpublished.

[288] M. W. Gift, *Report HW-34431*, February, 1955, abstracted in *Nucl. Sci. Abs.* **10**, page 529 (1956).

[289] B. Bleaney, P. M. Llewellyn, M. H. L. Pryce, and G. R. Hall, *Phil. Mag.* **45**, 773, 991 (1954).

[290] D. L. Horrocks and M. H. Studier, *Anal. Chem.* **30**, 1747–50 (1958).

[291] S. G. Thompson, K. Street, Jr., A. Ghiorso, and F. L. Reynolds, *Phys. Rev.* **80**, 1108 (1950).

[292] W. C. Bentley, *et al.*, Paper P/809, Vol. 7, "Peaceful Uses of Atomic Energy, Proceedings of the Geneva Conference," United Nations, August, 1955.

[292a] G. D. O'Kelley, G. Barton, W. W. Crane and I. Perlman, *Phys. Rev.* **80**, 293 (1950).

TABLE **9.16** Isotopic composition of plutonium prepared by irradiation of pure Pu^{239} to an integrated flux of 1.4×10^{22} neutrons/cm^2.

Isotope	Abundance in atom per cent	Composition by alpha activity
Pu^{238}	0.16 ± 0.02	81.9 ± 0.3
Pu^{239}	0.068 ± 0.004	
Pu^{240}	0.633 ± 0.006	5.3 ± 0.3
Pu^{241}	0.308 ± 0.006	
Pu^{242}	98.77 ± 0.03	12.8 ± 0.2
Pu^{244}	$0.052 \pm 0\,004$	

From W. C. Bentley, *et al.*, see Ref. 292.

chemically from the americium. The Pu^{242} will be contaminated somewhat with Pu^{238} formed by the alpha decay of Cm^{242}. Samples of Pu^{242} of 98 atom per cent or higher are formed when the irradiation time is short (i.e., a few days or less) and the plutonium isolation step is carried out quickly after the irradiation before much of the Cm^{242} has decayed. Larger samples of Pu^{242} are produced by longer irradiation of Am^{241} at the expense of increased Pu^{238} content. This method is well described by BUTLER, LOUNSBURY, AND MERRITT.[293]

THOMPSON AND CO-WORKERS[291] first prepared Pu^{242} by this mechanism and obtained samples which were 50 per cent Pu^{242} and 50 per cent Pu^{238}. Alpha-particle analysis using the ionization chamber method showed the presence of alpha particles of 4.88 MeV attributable to Pu^{242} and in an abundance corresponding to a half-life of roughly 5×10^5 years. ASARO[294] redetermined the alpha spectrum in a magnetic spectrograph and found two groups of 4.898 MeV (80 per cent) and 4.854 MeV (20 per cent). HUMMEL[295] checked these energies but revised the abundances to 74 per cent and 26 per cent, respectively. Three accurate determinations of the half-life of Pu^{242} have been made: $(3.73 \pm 0.05) \times 10^5$ years,[296] $(3.79 \pm 0.05) \times 10^5$ years,[297] and $(3.88 \pm 0.10) \times 10^5$ years.[298]

The two alpha groups of Pu^{242} define an excited state of the U^{238} daughter lying 45 keV above ground. This state is unquestionably a 2+ state representing the first state of rotational excitation of the U^{238} nucleus.

[293] J. P. Butler, M. Lounsbury, and J. S. Merritt, *Can. J. Chem.* **34**, 253 (1956).

[294] F. Asaro, Ph.D. Thesis, University of California, June, 1952; also published as *Univ. Calif. Rad. Lab. Report UCRL-2180*, June, 1952.

[295] J. P. Hummel, Ph.D. Thesis, University of California, July, 1956; also published as *Univ. Calif. Rad. Lab. Report UCRL-3456*, July, 1956.

[296] J. P. Butler, M. Lounsbury, and J. S. Merritt, *Can. J. Phys.* **35**, 147 (1957).

[297] J. P. Butler, T. A. Eastwood, T. L. Collins, M. E. Jones, F. M. Rourke, and R. P. Schuman, *Phys. Rev.* **103**, 634 (1956).

[298] J. F. Mech, *et al.*, *Phys. Rev.* **103**, 340 (1956).

When the alpha decay of Pu^{242} is re-examined it probably will be possible to detect some slight alpha branching to higher-lying levels of the ground-state rotational band of U^{238}. It is known[299] from the Coulombic excitation of U^{238} with energetic ions of Ar^{40} that U^{238} levels of rotational excitation are present at 44.7 keV (2+), 148 keV (4+), 310 keV (6+), 520 keV (8+), 790 keV (10+) and 1100 keV (12+).

The spontaneous fission half-life of Pu^{242} as measured by BUTLER, LOUNSBURY, AND MERRITT[293] on samples of 98.2 per cent isotopic purity is $(6.64 \pm 0.10) \times 10^{10}$ years. MECH AND CO-WORKERS[298] report a value of $(7.06 \pm 0.19) \times 10^{10}$ years from measurements on a sample with a similar isotopic purity.

9.2.13 Plutonium-243

When samples of plutonium containing Pu^{242} are irradiated with slow neutrons, the isotope Pu^{243}, which decays by beta emission with a 4.98 ± 0.02 hour half-life, is formed. This was first established by SULLIVAN AND CO-WORKERS[300] and confirmed by THOMPSON AND CO-WORKERS[301] and O'KELLEY.[302] The cross section for formation of Pu^{243} is 18.6 barns for thermal neutrons.[303]

Determination of the beta-particle energy by absorption curve techniques[300] gave a rough value of 0.5 MeV while beta-ray spectrometer measurements[301,302] gave an early value of 0.4 MeV and a later value[304] of 0.560 MeV. Gamma rays of 95 and 120 keV were reported by early investigators.[301,302] A more detailed study by ENGELKEMEIR, FIELDS, AND HUIZENGA[304] showed that the beta spectrum is complex. The most energetic group, present in 53 per cent abundance, has an end-point energy of 566 keV. No gamma radiation is in coincidence with it. A second beta group in about 35 per cent abundance has an energy of 468 keV and is followed by 85-keV gamma ray. Gamma-gamma coincidence studies showed that the 85-keV gamma ray is in coincidence with gamma rays of about 92-, 107-, and 160-keV energy. The abundance of these higher energy gamma rays suggests that lower energy beta transitions with total abundance approximately 12 per cent must be present. The total disintegration energy appears to be 566 keV, the energy of the most energetic beta-ray group.

[299] F. S. Stephens, Jr., R. M. Diamond, and I. Perlman, *Phys. Rev. Letters* **3**, 435 (1959).

[300] J. C. Sullivan, G. L. Pyle, M. H. Studier, P. R. Fields, and W. M. Manning, *Phys. Rev.* **83**, 1267 (1951).

[301] S. G. Thompson, K. Street, Jr., A. Ghiorso, and F. L. Reynolds, *Phys. Rev.* **84**, 165 (1951).

[302] G. D. O'Kelley, Ph.D. Thesis, University of California, May, 1951; also published as *Univ. Calif. Rad. Lab. Report UCRL-1243*, May, 1951.

[303] J. P. Butler, M. Lounsbury, and J. S. Merritt, *Can. J. Phys.* **35**, 147 (1957).

[304] D. W. Engelkemeir, P. R. Fields, and J. R. Huizenga, *Phys. Rev.* **90**, 6 (1953).

STEPHENS AND ASARO[305] have studied the gamma rays of Pu^{243} by scintillation spectrometer techniques and have measured conversion electrons in a permanent magnet spectrograph. The exact energy of the ~ 85 keV transition is 83.9 keV and from the conversion coefficient and the subshell conversion ratios it is an electric dipole transition. Another transition with energy 42.2 keV was found to be electric quadrupole in nature from the subshell conversion coefficient ratios. Gamma rays of 340 keV and 381.2 keV were observed. Only the K-conversion line of the 381.2 keV transition was seen in the conversion electron spectrum.

STEPHENS, ASARO, AND PERLMAN[306] have interpreted the decay scheme of Pu^{243} in terms of the unified nuclear model and have made Nilsson orbital assignments to the ground state of Pu^{243} and to several of the levels of the Am^{243} daughter. These assignments were made on the basis of the incomplete published and unpublished information on Pu^{243}, on the data for the alpha decay of Bk^{247} to the same daughter nucleus, and also to a large part on the systematic trends in the Nilsson orbitals in neighboring nuclei. These assignments are reviewed very briefly here and are summarized in Fig. 9.21. More details are given in the reference cited.[306]

States in Am^{243} having spins 5/2, 7/2, and probably 9/2 seem to receive direct beta population from Pu^{243} so that a spin of 7/2 for Pu^{243} seems most reasonable. The expected Nilsson orbital is $7/2 + [624]$ expressed in the quantum numbers K, parity $[N\ n_z\ \Lambda]$. The 84 keV level decays by a prominent $E1$ transition to the ground state and by a very weak $E1$ transition to an ~ 40 keV level—presumably the first member of the ground state rotational band. Since the ground state has a measured spin[307] of 5/2 this fixes the spin and parity of the 84 keV level at $5/2+$ or $7/2+$. Assignment is made to $K = 5/2$, in particular to $5/2 + [642]$, because the energy spacing with respect to the ground state, $5/2 - [523]$, is similar to that seen in neptunium isotopes except that the ordering of the states is reversed. The 465 keV level decays by a predominantly $M1$ transition to the 84 keV level and to the band based on the 84 keV level. Thus the parity of the 465 keV level is even and the spin is probably 7/2 or 9/2, although 5/2 is also a possibility. The assignment $7/2 + [633]$ is consistent with these data and with the proposed $7/2+$ spin of Pu^{243}. There is no other Nilsson level that seems to be satisfactory for this state. The level at 265 keV is not seen in the β decay of Pu^{243}. From arguments not given here this level is assigned spin and parity $3/2 -$ and may be the $3/2 -$ level of the Nilsson state $1/2 - [530]$. The decay scheme is shown in Fig. 9.21.

---

[305] F. S. Stephens, Jr. and F. Asaro, unpublished information (1956); see also UCRL-8376.

[306] F. S. Stephens, Jr., F. Asaro, and I. Perlman, *Phys. Rev.* **113**, 212 (1959).

[307] J. G. Conway and R. D. McLaughlin, *Phys. Rev.* **94**, 498 (1954).

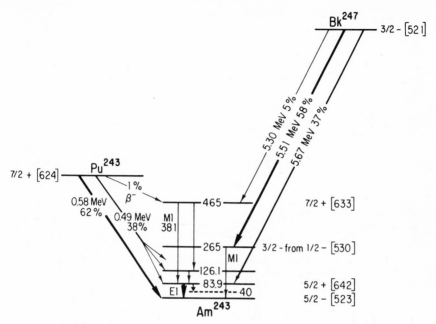

FIG. **9.21.** Decay scheme of Pu²⁴³ and Bk²⁴⁷ as interpreted by
STEPHENS, ASARO, AND PERLMAN.

9.2.14 *Plutonium-244*

In the course of an examination of the plutonium fraction isolated from
the debris of a November, 1952 thermonuclear test explosion the isotope
Pu²⁴⁴ was detected by mass spectrographic methods by HESS, PYLE, FRIED,
AND INGHRAM.[308] This experiment constituted the discovery of Pu²⁴⁴.
The neutron capture sequence in explosive devices of this type is discussed in
Section 5.4.3 of Chapter 5. The entire synthesis takes place with fast neutrons in a very brief period and no beta emitting steps occur until after the
initial reaction. The isotopic composition of a particular element prepared in
this way can be quite different from that which results when many neutrons
are added successively on a long time scale. It is concluded that Pu²⁴⁴
was formed by the successive additions of neutrons to U²³⁸ until the isotope
U²⁴⁴ was produced; after the explosion the beta decay chain gave rise to the
long-lived Pu²⁴⁴.

$$U^{244} \xrightarrow[\text{short}]{\beta^-} Np^{244} \xrightarrow[\text{short}]{\beta^-} Pu^{244}$$

[308] D. C. Hess, G. L. Pyle, S. Fried, and M. Inghram, unpublished results cited by
Engelkemeir, *et al., J. Inorg. Nucl. Chem.* **1**, 345 (1955).

The isotope Pu^{244} has also been found in small isotopic abundance by the mass spectrographic analysis of Pu^{239} samples which had been irradiated with an integrated flux of 4×10^{21} neutrons.[309]   The radiations of Pu^{244} could not be studied with this sample because of its long half-life and the presence of the other plutonium isotopes.   The reaction sequence leading to the

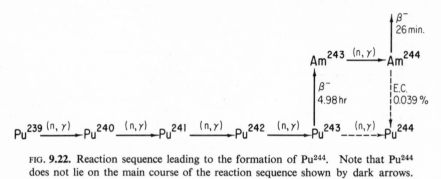

FIG. 9.22. Reaction sequence leading to the formation of Pu²⁴⁴. Note that Pu²⁴⁴ does not lie on the main course of the reaction sequence shown by dark arrows.

formation of Pu^{244} is summarized in Fig. 9.22.   It will be observed that Pu^{244} is off the main course of the neutron capture sequence and is formed only by side reactions.   The greater part of the yield comes from the $Pu^{243}(n, \gamma)Pu^{244}$ side reaction for which the cross section is about 170 barns, but the contribution of the electron-capture decay of Am^{244} is appreciable. This contribution increases as the irradiation is prolonged and the Am^{243} builds up in the sample.   Table 9.17 indicates how the Pu^{244} content builds up in Pu^{239} irradiated at a flux of 3×10^{14} neutrons per cm^{2}.

TABLE **9.17** Pu²⁴⁴/Pu²⁴² ratios in irradiated Pu²³⁹.   Data from Refs. 310 and 311.

Integrated flux	Pu²⁴² abundance in atom per cent	Pu²⁴⁴ abundance in atom per cent	Pu²⁴⁴/Pu²⁴²
4 × 10²¹	34.1	0.0018	5.28 × 10⁻⁵
1.1 × 10²²	96.33	0.037	3.84 × 10⁻⁴
1.4 × 10²²	98.77	0.052	5.26 × 10⁻⁴

[309] M. H. Studier, P. R. Fields, P. H. Sellers, A. M. Friedman, C. M. Stevens, J. F. Mech, H. Diamond, J. Sedlet, and J. R. Huizenga, *Phys. Rev.* **93**, 1433 (1954).

[310] P. R. Fields, J. F. Gindler, A. L. Harkness, M. H. Studier, J. R. Huizenga, and A. M. Friedman, *Phys. Rev.* **100**, 172 (1955).

[311] W. C. Bentley, *et al.*, Paper P/809, Vol. 7 "Peaceful Uses of Atomic Energy, Proceedings of the Geneva Conference," United Nations, August, 1955.

The presence of Pu^{244} in such samples of neutron-irradiated plutonium has been proven[312,313] by isolation of the U^{240} formed by its alpha decay. Uranium-240 could be identified by the known radiations of U^{240} in equilibrium with its Np^{240} daughter. An interfering activity in this "milking" experiment is U^{237} which forms from the alpha decay of Pu^{241} present in the plutonium in much greater abundance. This is taken care of by the use of sufficient absorber over the uranium daughter fraction to cut out the weak beta radiation of U^{237} and U^{240}. Alternatively, the Np^{240} can be chemically isolated.

It is possible[310] to prepare plutonium samples with a much higher percentage of Pu^{244} by neutron irradiation of Am^{243} (see Fig. 9.23).

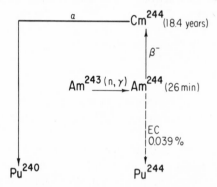

FIG. 9.23. Preparation of Pu^{244} by neutron irradiation of Am^{243}.

By quantitative separation and counting of the U^{240} daughter activity in equilibrium with a plutonium sample whose Pu^{244} content was known from mass spectrographic analysis, the alpha half-life of Pu^{244} has been found by DIAMOND AND BARNES[312] to be $(7.6 \pm 2) \times 10^7$ years, and by BUT-LER AND CO-WORKERS[313] to be $(7.5 \pm 2) \times 10^7$ years.

Since Pu^{244} is an *even-even* isotope it is expected to have an appreciable rate of decay by spontaneous fission; the half-life has been determined[310,311] as $(2.5 \pm 0.8) \times 10^{10}$ years.

The cross section of Pu^{244} for capture of thermal neutrons has been measured as 1.5 ± 0.3 barns[311] and as 2.1 ± 0.3 barns.[313]

DIAMOND AND BARNES[312] conclude from the limits of error on their measurement of the half-life of Pu^{244} and from an estimate of its primeval abundance that Pu^{244} might still be present in barely detectable amounts in the earth's crust. They also conclude that Pu^{244} might have been an important heat source in the early history of the earth. Later considerations

[312] H. Diamond and R. F. Barnes, *Phys. Rev.* **101**, 1064 (1956).
[313] J. P. Butler, T. A. Eastwood, T. L. Collins, M. E. Jones, F. M. Rourke, and R. P. Schuman, *Phys. Rev.* **103**, 634 (1956).

and calculations by KOHMAN[314] indicate that the heat contribution by Pu^{244} was never very significant compared to other radionuclides.

9.2.15 *Plutonium-245*

BROWNE AND CO-WORKERS[315] and FIELDS AND CO-WORKERS[316] first reported the existence of a 10.6-hour beta emitter assignable to Pu^{245}. This isotope is prepared by neutron irradiation of plutonium targets containing Pu^{244} or of other heavy element targets which can be converted to Pu^{244} and Pu^{245} by multiple neutron-capture reactions. The radiations of Pu^{245} itself were not studied by these authors because of conflicting radiations in the plutonium fractions. The half-life was measured by repeated isolation of the daughter, 2.08-hour Am^{245}, whose radiations are discussed in Section 9.3.10. BUTLER AND CO-WORKERS[317] confirm the production of Pu^{245} from plutonium samples containing Pu^{244}.

9.2.16 *Plutonium-246*

During the course of the examination of the plutonium fraction isolated from the debris of the November, 1952, thermonuclear test explosion the previously-unknown isotope Pu^{244} was detected by mass spectrometric methods.[318] This stimulated further investigation of the plutonium fraction for isotopes of higher mass and resulted in the discovery of the 11.2-day isotope, Pu^{246}, by groups of scientists at the Los Alamos Scientific Laboratory and at the Argonne National Laboratory.[319]

Examination of the radiations of the plutonium fraction indicated the presence of two beta activities, one of approximately 0.15 MeV and the other of 1.2 MeV energy. By chemical separation procedures it was possible to show that the more energetic beta-emitter was an isotope of americium with a half-life of 25 ± 0.2 minutes. The chemical identification was made certain by detailed chemical experiments during which the new activity was not separated from added Am^{241} tracer. The 25-minute americium isotope was proved to be the daughter of the 11.2-day beta emitter. This latter

314 T. P. Kohman, *J. Chem. Educ.* **38**, 73 (1961).

315 C. I. Browne, D. C. Hoffman, W. T. Crane, J. P. Balagna, G. H. Higgins, J. W. Barnes, R. W. Hoff, H. L. Smith, J. P. Mize, and M. E. Bunker, *J. Inorg. Nucl. Chem.* **1**, 254 (1955).

316 P. R. Fields, M. H. Studier, A. M. Friedman, H. Diamond, R. Sjoblom, and P. A. Sellers, *J. Inorg. Nucl. Chem.* **1**, 262 (1955).

317 J. P. Butler, T. A. Eastwood, T. L. Collins, M. E. Jones, F. M. Rourke, and R. P. Schuman, *Phys. Rev.* **103**, 634 (1956).

318 Unpublished results of Hess, Pyle, Fried, and Inghram cited by Engelkemeir, *et al.*, in Ref. 319.

319 D. Engelkemeir, P. R. Fields, S. Fried, G. L. Pyle, C. M. Stevens, L. B. Asprey, C. I. Browne, H. Louise Smith, and R. W. Spence, *J. Inorg. Nucl. Chem.* **1**, 345 (1955).

activity was proved to be a plutonium isotope by exhaustive chemical steps.

From the known properties of the plutonium isotopes it was certain that the mass number of the new 11.2-day isotope could not be less than 244. Several lines of evidence conclusively ruled out the mass number 244 and made the most likely assignment 245 or 246. The mass spectrographic analysis results reported later[320] established that the correct mass assignment was 246.

ENGELKEMEIR AND CO-WORKERS[319] reported that Pu^{246} emits gamma rays of 43, 111, 175, and 224 keV energy. The gamma rays of the 25-minute Am^{246} are also emitted by a sample of Pu^{246} because the daughter activity quickly comes to equilibrium with the parent.

HOFFMAN AND BROWNE[321], and SMITH AND CO-WORKERS[322] restudied the radiations of Pu^{246} using scintillation spectrometers and gamma-gamma and beta-gamma coincidence spectrometers. They report complexity in the beta spectrum with 73 per cent of the disintegrations going by means of a 150-keV beta transition to a 249-keV level in Am^{246}. In 27 per cent of the transitions the beta ray energy is 330 keV. There may be higher energy beta particles in low abundance. Evidence for gamma rays of 100 keV and 225 keV was also found.[322] HOFFMAN AND BROWNE[321] report the value 10.85 ± 0.02 days for the half-life.

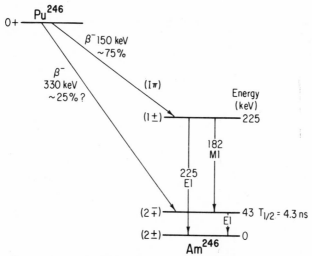

Decay scheme of Pu^{246} as drawn by ASARO, FRIED, STEPHENS, AND PERLMAN. Other radiations are present in lower intensity.

[320] P. R. Fields, M. H. Studier, A. Friedman, H. Diamond, R. Sjoblom, and P. A. Sellers, unpublished results (1953).

[321] D. C. Hoffman and C. I. Browne, *Nucl. Chem.* **2**, 209 (1956).

[322] H. L. Smith, *et al.*, *J. Inorg. Nucl. Chem.* **3**, 93 (1956).

ASARO, FRIED, STEPHENS, AND PERLMAN[323] re-examined the gamma
radiations of Pu^{246} by coincidence techniques and formulated the decay
scheme shown in the figure.   A particularly interesting feature is the delayed
$E1$ transition which may be added to the moderately long list of delayed $E1$
transitions observed in heavy nuclei and discussed in Chapter 3, Section 3.5.8.
In the present case the transformation involved in the 43-keV transition is
believed to be caused by the same change in the proton configuration that is
involved in the well-known 60-keV transition in Np^{237} following the α-decay
of Am^{241}.   The Nilsson proton states involved in the Np^{237} case are $5/2 -$
[523] transforming to $5/2 +$ [642].

9.3 THE ELEMENT AMERICIUM (ELEMENT 95)

9.3.1 The Discovery of Americium

The element americium was discovered in experiments conducted late
in 1944 and early in 1945 at the Metallurgical Laboratory (now Argonne
National Laboratory) of the University of Chicago by SEABORG, JAMES,
MORGAN, AND GHIORSO.[324,325]   The discovery of element 95 followed
shortly after the discovery of curium (element 96).   These investigators found
that a long-lived, alpha-emitting isotope could be separated chemically
from plutonium which had received extensive irradiation with neutrons.
From the known flux and time of irradiation and the predicted properties of
Pu^{240} and Pu^{241} it was clear that the reaction sequence responsible for the
results was the following:

$$Pu^{239}(n, \gamma)Pu^{240}(n, \gamma)Pu^{241} \xrightarrow[\text{long}]{\beta^-} 95^{241} \xrightarrow[\text{long}]{\alpha}$$

The plutonium was purified repeatedly and the growth of the new alpha-
emitter into the purified plutonium was clearly established.   Later irradiation
of samples of the supposed 95^{241} with neutrons resulted in the production
of the known isotope Cm^{242}.

Further proof of the mass assignment came from helium ion bombardments of U^{238} targets.   A beta-emitting plutonium isotope of long half-
life was produced with a yield which varied in a manner characteristic of
an (α, n) reaction as the energy of the helium ions striking the target was
changed.

$$U^{238} (\alpha, n) Pu^{241} \xrightarrow[\text{long}]{\beta^-} 95^{241}$$

Numerous chemical experiments were carried out to determine the

[323] F. Asaro, S. Fried, F. Stephens, and I. Perlman, unpublished results (1963).

[324] G. T. Seaborg, R. A. James, L. O. Morgan, Paper No. 21.1, "The Transuranium
Elements," Nat. Nucl. Energ. Ser., Division IV 14B (New York: McGraw-Hill Book
Co., Inc., 1949).

[325] A. Ghiorso, R. A. James, L. O. Morgan, and G. T. Seaborg, Phys. Rev. 78, 472 (1950).

properties of the new long-lived alpha-emitter assigned to 95^{241} and to provide the necessary proof that this activity could be separated chemically from all known elements. The chemical properties in aqueous solution were found to be those of a tripositive ion and in almost every particular to be very similar to those of lanthanide element ions. Indeed, considerable time elapsed before a completely satisfactory method for the separation of elements 95 and 96 from each other and from the rare earth elements was developed. Vigorous attempts to convert 95^{241} to a lower or a higher oxidation state were unsuccessful although a number of years later it was found that it could be converted to the oxidation states V and VI under suitable conditions. This oxidation is easier to perform with macro quantities of the element, but it can be done with tracer quantities.

The similarity of elements 95 and 96 to the rare-earth elements provided the first substantial clue that the new transition series of elements in the heavy element region should be considered to be an actinide series of elements. Indeed it was the adoption of this view as a working hypothesis[326] that led directly to the identification of Cm^{242} and Am^{241} after a number of fruitless experiments had been carried out under the assumption that elements 95 and 96 would resemble neptunium and plutonium in being readily oxidized to the VI oxidation state.

Element 95 was named americium (symbol Am) after the Americas on the basis of its position as the sixth member of the actinide rare-earth series, analogous to europium of the lanthanide rare earths.

Americium was first isolated in the form of a pure compound by CUNNING-HAM[327] who carried out the first measurement of the half-life by direct measurement of specific activity. This work was done with only a few micrograms of material. From the weight of this sample and from its alpha counting rate a half-life of 498 years was determined, which is very close to the modern value of 458 years. Since then americium in the form of 458 year Am^{241} has been produced in kilogram quantities from reactor produced plutonium. The many studies of the chemistry of the element which have been performed with this isotope are described elsewhere.[328,329,330]

---

[326] G. T. Seaborg, *Chem. Eng. News*, **23**, 2192 (1945); G. T. Seaborg, *Metallurgical Laboratory Memorandum MUC-GTS-858*, July 17, 1944, reproduced as an appendix in Paper 21.1, page 1517, *Nat. Nucl. Energ. Ser.* **14B**, "The Transuranium Elements," edited by Seaborg, Katz, and Manning (New York: McGraw-Hill Book Co., Inc., 1949).

[327] B. B. Cunningham, Paper No. 19.2, "The Transuranium Elements," *Nat. Nucl. Energ. Ser.*, Division IV **14B** (New York: McGraw-Hill Book Co., Inc., 1949).

[328] E. K. Hyde and G. T. Seaborg, "The Transuranium Elements," *Handbuch der Physik* **42**, Springer-Verlag, Berlin, 1957.

[329] J. J. Katz and G. T. Seaborg, "The Chemistry of the Actinide Elements" (London: Methuen and Co., Ltd., 1957); (New York: John Wiley and Sons, 1957).

[330] R. A. Penneman and T. Keenan, "The Radiochemistry of Americium and Curium," *Nucl. Sci. Ser. Report NAS-NS-3006* (1960). National Academy of Sciences.

The specific activity of Am^{241} is 7×10^{12} disintegrations per minute per gram so that the study of the chemistry of americium is severely hindered by the remarkable chemical effects caused by the intense alpha radiations. The isotope Am^{243} with a half-life of 7930 years is more suitable for chemical studies and has come into more widespread use as gram and larger quantities have become more generally available.

The nuclear properties of the individual isotopes of americium are described in the following pages of this chapter.

9.3.2 Americium-237

HIGGINS[331] found evidence for a 1.3-hour isotope Am^{237} formed with 30 to 50 MeV deuterons by the reaction $Pu^{239}(d, 4n)Am^{237}$. It decays chiefly by electron capture, but it also emits 6.01 MeV alpha particles to the extent of about 0.005 per cent. This isotope has not been carefully studied.

9.3.3 Americium-238

STREET, GHIORSO, AND SEABORG[332] found that the bombardment of Pu^{239} with 50-MeV deuterons results in the production of an americium activity of about 1.2-hour half-life in addition to 12-hour Am^{239} and 50-hour Am^{240}. Later work by HIGGINS[331] suggested that this activity was mixed with Am^{237} and that the half-life of Am^{238} is actually about 2.1 hours. CARR, GLASS, AND GIBSON[334] report a half-life value of 1.86 ± 0.09 hours. Reactions by which Am^{238} is prepared include:

$$Pu^{239}(d, 3n)Am^{238}$$
$$Pu^{239}(p, 2n)Am^{238}$$
$$Np^{237}(\alpha, 3n)Am^{238}$$

Peak yields are listed for these reactions in Table 5.5, Chapter 5.

The principal mode of decay of Am^{238} is orbital electron capture for which ~ 2.24 MeV of decay energy is available. An upper limit of 3×10^{-4} per cent has been set on the alpha branching.[333] CARR, GLASS, AND GIBSON[334] have studied the gamma rays of Am^{238} with scintillation spectrometers by use of gamma-gamma coincidence techniques. They observed gamma rays with energies 370, 580, 950, 980, and 1350 keV. There is a 580-370-980 cascade, a 580-1350 cascade, and a 950-980 cascade. These results define the decay scheme shown in Fig. 9.24. Electron capture

[331] G. H. Higgins, Ph.D. Thesis, University of California, June, 1952; also published as *Univ. Calif. Rad. Lab. Report UCRL-1796*, June, 1952.

[332] K. Street, Jr., A. Ghiorso, and G. T. Seaborg, *Phys. Rev.* 79, 530 (1950).

[334] R. J. Carr, R. A. Glass, and W. M. Gibson, *J. Inorg. Nucl. Chem.* 13, 181 (1960).

proceeds mainly to the Pu^{238} levels at 980 and 1930 but a few per cent of the transitions may lead to other high-lying levels.

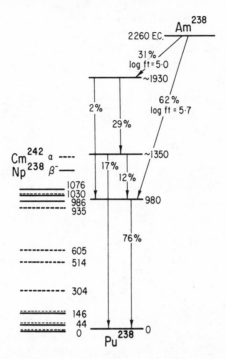

FIG. 9.24. Preliminary decay scheme of Am^{238}, as formulated by GLASS, CARR, AND GIBSON. Gamma-ray intensities and electron capture branching intensities are based on the assumption that one K x-ray is emitted per disintegration. Seven per cent of the transitions are unaccounted for because of errors in the data or in the above assumption or because of unobserved branching to a low-lying state of Pu^{238}. The Pu^{238} levels on the left are those populated from Np^{238} β^- decay or from Cm^{242} α-decay. The exact alignment of these levels with those seen in the decay of Am^{238} is not certain due to uncertainties in gamma-ray energies and in the precise levels near the ground state populated by the high energy gamma-rays.

A striking feature of this decay scheme compared to the decay of Np^{238} is that none of the several known excited levels of Pu^{238} below 900 keV appear to be reached directly or indirectly. A great deal of information on the levels of Pu^{238} is available from the beta decay of Np^{238} (Section 9.1.11) and the alpha decay of Cm^{242} (Section 9.4.6.).

There has been considerable success in the classification of neutron and proton states in odd-odd nuclei. (See the discussion in Section 3.5.6 of

Chapter 3, Volume I.) One may suggest possible assignments in the case of Am^{238}. The Nilsson state, $5/2 - $ [523], would be a likely one for the odd proton and $7/2 - $ [743] for the odd neutron. These would couple to $K = 1 +$ for the ground state and to $K = 6 +$ for an isomeric state, for which as yet no evidence has been reported. The absence of decay to the ground state rotational band of Pu^{238} may be a result of selection rules in N and n_z; the neutron and proton differ by 2 units in these quantum numbers. The observed decay with low log ft values is to excited states of Pu^{238} which are de-excited directly to ground. These excited states must have $K = 0$ or 2 but they presumably have strong admixtures of several N values.

9.3.4 Americium-239

The 12-hour radioactivity Am^{239} was first prepared by SEABORG, JAMES, AND MORGAN[335] by the following reactions:

$$Pu^{239}(d, 2n)Am^{239}$$
$$Np^{237}(\alpha, 2n)Am^{239}$$

The Am^{239} so prepared is not pure because it is contaminated with 53-hour Am^{240}. Other reactions which have been used for the preparation are:[336]

$$Pu^{239}(p, n)Am^{239}$$
$$Pu^{239}(\alpha, p3n)Am^{239}$$

Some cross sections for these reactions are listed in Table 5.5 of Chapter 5.

This isotope decays almost entirely by orbital electron capture although an alpha branching of 0.003 per cent was reported by HIGGINS.[337] This was confirmed by GLASS, CARR, AND GIBSON[338] who redetermined the branching as $(5.0 \pm 1.0) \times 10^{-3}$ per cent corresponding to a partial alpha half-life of 28 ± 5 years. The alpha particle energy has been reported as 5.78 MeV[339] and as 5.77 MeV[338]. STEPHENS AND CO-WORKERS[340,341] found the alpha particles of Am^{239} to be in coincidence with a 48 keV $E1$ transition indicating that the alpha decay of Am^{239} is similar to that of Am^{241} and Am^{243}. This similarity is shown in Fig. 9.25. The presence of low-lying states of

[335] G. T. Seaborg, R. A. James, and L. O. Morgan, Paper No. 22.1, "The Transuranium Elements," *Nat. Nucl. Energ. Ser.*, Division IV **14B** (New York: McGraw-Hill Book Co., Inc., 1949).

[336] K. Street, Jr., A. Ghiorso, and G. T. Seaborg, *Phys. Rev.* **79**, 530 (1950).

[337] G. H. Higgins, Ph.D. Thesis, University of California, June, 1952; also published as *Univ. Calif. Rad. Lab. Report UCRL-1796*, June, 1952.

[338] R. A. Glass, R. J. Carr, and W. M. Gibson, *J. Inorg. Nucl. Chem.* **13**, 181 (1960).

[339] W. M. Gibson, private communication, 1956.

[340] F. S. Stephens, Jr., Ph.D. Thesis, University of California, June, 1955; also published as *Univ. Calif. Rad. Lab. Report UCRL-2970*, June, 1955.

[341] F. Asaro, F. S. Stephens, Jr., W. M. Gibson, R. A. Glass, and I. Perlman, *Phys. Rev.* **100**, 1514 (1955).

opposite parity from that of the ground state is an interesting feature of the daughter neptunium isotopes in these three cases. The nuclear states of Np^{235} and of Am^{239} have been assigned to specific quantum states of single particle motion by STEPHENS, ASARO, AND PERLMAN.[342] The assignments

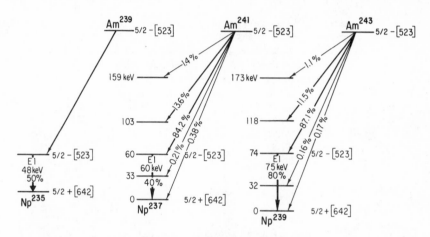

FIG. 9.25. Comparison of the decay schemes of Am²⁴³, Am²⁴¹, and Am²³⁹. Some Nilsson state assignments are given. Quantum numbers of these states are K, parity [N nz Λ].

are based on the great similarities of the decay of Am^{239} to that of Am^{241} for which Nilsson state assignments have been made on a variety of firm evidence. These Nilsson assignments are given in the figure. In all probability the alpha spectrum of Am^{239} is complex but a detailed study is made difficult by the low alpha branching and short half-life of the isotope.

Americium-239 is the electron capture decay product of the isotope 2.5-hour Cm^{239} and can be prepared in small quantities, free of contaminating Am^{240} activity, by isolation of americium from a curium sample containing Cm^{239}, since the Cm^{240} shows no observable decay by orbital electron capture to Am^{240}.

The radiations of Am^{239} include K and L x-rays and a number of gamma ray photons and conversion electrons. SMITH, GIBSON, AND HOLLANDER[343] have made precise measurements of the conversion electrons with permanent magnet spectrographs and have discussed the decay scheme of Am^{239}. GLASS, CARR, AND GIBSON[338] used scintillation spectrometers to measure the gamma rays singly and in coincidence. The electron capture decay of

342 F. S. Stephens, Jr., F. Asaro, and I. Perlman, *Phys. Rev.* 113, 212 (1959).

343 W. G. Smith, W. M. Gibson, and J. M. Hollander, *Phys. Rev.* 105, 1514 (1957).

Am^{239} proceeds to a number of the same excited levels of Pu^{239} that are reached in the beta decay of Np^{239} and the alpha decay of Cm^{243}. This is shown clearly in Fig. 9.8 in Section 9.1.11. The interpretation of the level scheme of Pu^{239} is discussed earlier in this chapter in connection with the radiations of Np^{239}.

TABLE **9.18** Gamma rays of Am^{239} from conversion electron data.*

Energy (keV)	Multipole order
44.70	$M1 + E2$
49.47	$M1 + E2$
57.31	$E2$
67.91	$E2$
181.8	$M1$
209.9	$M1$
226.5	$M1$
228.3	$M1$
277.6	$M1$

* See SMITH, GIBSON, AND HOLLANDER, Ref. 343.

The gamma rays of Am^{239} are listed in Table 9.18. The placement of these gamma rays in the decay scheme is shown in Fig. 9.8 accompanying the description of Np^{239} in Section 9.1.11. HOLLANDER[344] has discussed the operation of selection rules in the asymptotic quantum numbers as they affect the electron capture decay of Am^{239}.

9.3.5 *Americium-240*

The 53-hour isotope Am^{240} was first produced by deuteron bombardment of Pu^{239} and helium ion bombardment of Np^{237}.[345,346]

$$Pu^{239}(d, n)Am^{240}$$
$$Np^{237}(\alpha, n)Am^{240}$$

It may also be produced by the reaction:[345,347]

$$Pu^{239}(\alpha, p2n)Am^{240}$$

The Am^{240} prepared in these ways is contaminated with 12-hour Am^{239}.

[344] J. M. Hollander, *Phys. Rev.* **105**, 1518 (1957).

[345] G. T. Seaborg, R. A. James, and L. O. Morgan, Paper No. 22.1, "The Transuranium Elements," *Nat. Nucl. Energ. Ser.*, Division IV **14B** (New York: McGraw-Hill Book Co., Inc., 1949).

[346] K. Street, Jr., A. Ghiorso and G. T. Seaborg, *Phys. Rev.* **79**, 530 (1950).

[347] G. H. Higgins, Ph.D. Thesis, University of California, June, 1952; also published as *Univ. Calif. Rad. Lab. Report UCRL-1796*, June, 1952.

The main mode of decay of Am^{240} is orbital electron capture. Alpha branching is energetically possible but has not yet been observed; an upper limit of 0.2 per cent has been set.[347] This is consistent with an estimated partial alpha half-life of 10^3 years. This isotope is believed to be stable with respect to β^- decay to the extent of a few kilovolts. Because of the uncertainty regarding this, CARR[348,349] has searched for the Cm^{240} product of a possible beta transition in Am^{240} and has set an upper limit of 6×10^{-6} for the β^- branching; this corresponds to a lower limit of 1×10^5 years for the beta half-life.

The radiations of Am^{240} consist of x-rays, gamma rays and conversion electrons. The gamma transitions are of interest since they delineate the excited levels of the *even-even* nucleus Pu^{240}. The results can be compared to the level system deduced from the alpha decay of Cm^{244} and the β^- decay of Np^{240}. (See Sections 9.4.8 and 9.1.12.) SMITH, GIBSON, AND HOLLANDER[350] reported measurements on the $4+ \rightarrow 2+ \rightarrow 0+$ ground state gamma ray cascade in Pu^{240} following electron capture of Am^{240}. They saw L_{II}, L_{III}, M_{II}, M_{III}, N and O electrons corresponding to a 42.87-keV transition (the $2+ \rightarrow 0+$ transition) and L_{II}, L_{III}, M_{II}, M_{III}, N and O electrons from a 98.90 ± 0.2 keV transition (the $4+ \rightarrow 2+$ transition). Both transitions are $E2$. The levels of Pu^{240} deduced from this information are a $2+$ excited state at 42.88 keV and a $4+$ second excited state at 141.8 keV. These are members of a rotational band of levels based on the $0+$ ground state. The constant $\hbar^2/2\mathfrak{J}$ for the rotational spacing is 7.16 keV. GLASS, CARR, AND GIBSON[349,351] have found additional gamma rays of 0.90, 1.00 and 1.40 MeV by scintillation spectrometer studies. These are similar to gamma rays seen in the beta decay of Np^{240} to the same daughter nucleus Pu^{240}. These gamma rays are believed to de-excite levels of Pu^{240} at 0.900, 1.00, and 1.40 MeV populated directly by electron capture. It is a striking feature of the decay of Am^{240} that all or nearly all of the transitions proceed to levels lying above 900 keV even though many lower-lying levels of the ground state rotational band covering a wide range of spins are available. In this respect Am^{240} resembles Am^{238}.

KNIGHT[351a] offers a tentative explanation for this. According to his gamma ray measurements there are 990 and 890 keV transitions in 71 per cent and 29 per cent intensity, respectively. He postulates that these gamma rays de-excite a $K=3+$ level at 1033 keV in Pu^{240}. In Am^{240} the odd

---

[348] R. J. Carr, Ph.D. Thesis, University of California, April, 1956; also published as *Univ. Calif. Rad. Lab. Report UCRL-3395*, April 1, 1956.

[349] R. A. Glass, R. J. Carr, and W. M. Gibson, *J. Inorg. Nucl. Chem.* **13**, 181 (1960).

[350] W. G. Smith, W. M. Gibson, and J. M. Hollander, *Phys. Rev.* **105**, 1514 (1957).

[351] R. A. Glass, Ph.D. Thesis, University of California, April, 1954; also published as *Univ. Calif. Rad. Lab. Report UCRL-2560*, April, 1954.

[351a] J. Knight, private communication, 1963.

proton is assigned $5/2-[523]$ while the odd neutron is assigned $1/2+[631]$. These couple to $K=3-$ as the ground state of Am^{240}.

9.3.6 Americium-241

This isotope was first[352] produced by the reaction sequence:

$$Pu^{239}(n, \gamma)Pu^{240}(n, \gamma)Pu^{241} \xrightarrow[13 \text{ year}]{\beta^-} Am^{241}$$

and this remains the best method for its preparation. In some laboratories a sample of plutonium which has been strongly irradiated with neutrons is set up as a source or "Cow". The Am^{241} which builds up in this source is periodically removed by some simple chemical operation and the plutonium is set aside to produce more americium.[353] Plutonium sources containing up to 20 per cent Pu^{241} can be made by neutron irradiation of Pu^{239}. The Am^{241} can also be isolated from the reactor fuel elements during chemical

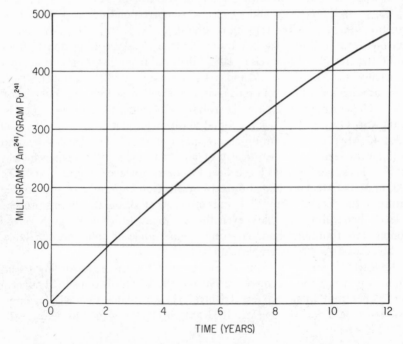

FIG. 9.26. The number of milligrams of Am²⁴¹ produced in a sample of plutonium containing one gram of 13-year Pu²⁴¹.

---

352 A. Ghiorso, R. A. James, L. O. Morgan, and G. T. Seaborg, *Phys. Rev.* **78**, 472 (1950).
353 See, for example, a report by Butler and Merritt on "Recovery of Am²⁴¹ from Kilogram Amounts of Plutonium," *Chalk River Project Report, AECL-353* (1956).

processing but this, for many reasons, is a more troublesome way to obtain large samples of this isotope. The amount of Am^{241} formed in a sample of plutonium containing one gram of Pu^{241} is shown in Fig. 9.26 as a function of the growth time.

The half-life of Am^{241} was determined originally by CUNNINGHAM[354] as 498 years. HALL AND MARKIN[355] have revised this value to 458.1 ± 0.5 years on the basis of careful determinations of the specific alpha activity of the compounds $Am_2(SO_4)_3$ and $AmCl_3$. For some reason the value obtained with the compound AmO_2 was slightly higher. WALLMANN, GRAF, AND GODA[356] check this closely with a value of 457.7 ± 1.8 years obtained by specific activity measurements on a weighed sample of pure americium metal. Am^{241} is stable with respect to orbital electron capture or beta decay and decays entirely by the emission of alpha particles.

The Alpha Spectrum of Am^{241}. The complex alpha particle spectrum of Am^{241} has been measured carefully by the magnetic deflection technique by four groups of experimentalists.[357-360] The closely agreeing results are summarized in Table 9.19.

These alpha data define several excited levels in the daughter nucleus Np^{237} and assist in the placement of the observed gamma rays in a decay scheme. Additional assistance in this task is obtained from a study of the β^- decay of U^{237} (see Section 8.4.10) and the decay of Pu^{237} by orbital electron capture (see Section 9.2.7), both of which lead to the same Np^{237} daughter nucleus. In addition, the gamma rays observed in the Coulombic excitation of Np^{237} have been of great help in the interpretation of the decay scheme. Figs. 9.27 and 9.28 summarize the level scheme of Np^{237} as deduced from these four distinctly different studies. The work of many experimentalists on the gamma radiations of Am^{241} is summarized in the decay schemes and in the following paragraphs. All the observed low-lying levels of Np^{237} are neatly explained in terms of four states of intrinsic excitation and their rotational bands. The discussion of the decay scheme will be reserved until some of the more important experimental data on the gamma transitions are summarized.

[354] B. B. Cunningham, Paper No. 19.2, "The Transuranium Elements," *Nat. Nucl. Energ. Ser.*, Division IV **14B**, (New York: McGraw-Hill Book Co., Inc., 1949).

[355] G. R. Hall and T. L. Markin, *J. Inorg. Nucl. Chem.* **4**, 137 (1957).

[356] J. Wallmann, P. Graf, and L. Goda, *J. Inorg. Nucl. Chem.* **7**, 199 (1958).

[357] S. Rosenblum, M. Valadares, and J. Milsted, *J. Phys. Rad.* **18**, 609 (1957).

[358] F. Asaro, F. L. Reynolds, and I. Perlman, *Phys. Rev.* **87**, 277 (1952); see correction in F. Asaro and I. Perlman, *Phys. Rev.* **93**, 1423 (1954).

[359] L. L. Gol'din, G. I. Novikova, and E. F. Tret'yakov, *Conf. Acad. Sci. USSR on Peaceful Uses of Atomic Energy*, July 1–5, 1955, p. 226; English translation available form Superintendent of Documents, U.S. Government Printing Office; See also *Phys. Rev.* **103**, 1004 (1956).

[360] S. A. Baranov, V. M. Koulakov, A. G. Zelenkov, and V. M. Chatinski, *Zhur. Eksp. Teor. Fiz.* **43**, No. 3, 795 (1962): see also *Nuc. Phys.* **43**, 547 (1963).

TABLE **9.19.** Alpha particle groups of Am^{241}.

ASARO, REYNOLDS, AND PERLMAN[358]			GOL'DIN, NOVIKOVA, AND TRET'YAKOV[359]			ROSENBLUM, VALADARES AND MILSTED[357]		BARANOV, KOULAKOV, ZELENKOV, AND CHATINSKI[360]		
Alpha particle energy (MeV) (see note 1 below)	Relative abundance (per cent)	Excited state energy (keV)	Alpha particle energy (MeV)	Relative abundance (per cent)	Excited state energy (keV)	Alpha particle energy (MeV)	Relative abundance (per cent)	Alpha particle energy (MeV) (Note 3)	Relative abundance (per cent)	Excited state energy (keV)
5.541	0.42	0	5.541	0.39	0	5.534	0.35	5.543	0.25	0
5.509	0.24	33	5.508	0.24	33.1	5.500	0.23	5.510	0.12	32.5
5.482	84.3	59.6	5.482	85.0	59.8	5.477	85.1	5.484	86.0	59.5
								5.468	0.04	76.5
5.439	13.6	103	5.439	12.8	103.2	5.435	12.6	5.442	12.7	102.5
5.416 (note 2)	0.008	127						5.416	$\sim 10^{-2}$	129(?)
5.385	1.4	158.6	5.386	1.66	157.2	5.378	1.74	5.387	1.33	158
5.318	0.018	226	5.321	0.015	224	5.311	0.013	5.320	1.5×10^{-2}	226
								5.291(?)	1×10^{-4}	256(?)
5.241 (note 2)	0.004	307	5.241	0.002	305			5.277	5×10^{-4}	270
5.239	0.0034	306						5.272(?)	3×10^{-4}	~ 275(?)
								5.242	2.4×10^{-3}	306
5.218(?) (note 2)	0.0018	328(?)						5.222	1.3×10^{-3}	327
5.174 (note 2)	0.0018	372						5.192	6×10^{-4}	357
5.150	0.0018	397						5.180	9×10^{-4}	369
								5.176	3×10^{-4}	372
								5.155	7×10^{-4}	395
								5.137(?)	3×10^{-4}	413(?)
								5.113	4×10^{-4}	437
								5.099	7×10^{-4}	452
								5.093	3×10^{-4}	458
								5.086	3×10^{-4}	464

Note 1: In the original reference all energies were measured relative to α_{60} reported at that time to be 5.476 MeV. Asaro redetermined the energy of α_{60} in 1960 and found the higher value of 5.482 relative to Briggs' values for Po^{210} and Rn^{222}.

Note 2: These groups were measured by Asaro and Perlman in 1961 (unpublished)

Note 3: The energy standard was E_{α_0} Pu^{238} = 5.495 keV.

The Gamma Transitions of Am^{241}. The low energy gamma rays have been studied carefully several times with a bent-crystal spectrometer, an instrument which permits measurement of photon energies with great pre-

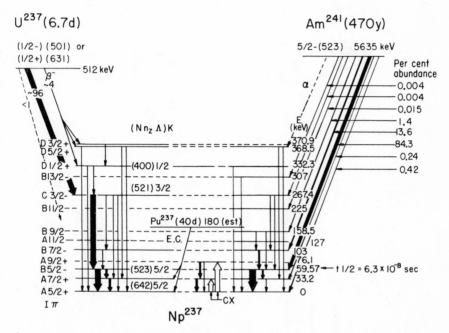

FIG. 9.27. Alpha decay scheme of Am²⁴¹, beta decay scheme of U²³⁷, and electron capture decay scheme of Pu²³⁷ to the common daughter nucleus Np²³⁷. Also shown is the Coulombic excitation scheme. The vertical arrows in each scheme are drawn only for experimentally observed transitions, but not all observed transitions are included. Proposed assignments of the asymptotic quantum numbers (N, n_z, Λ, K) are given as well as spins and parities. The decay scheme of U²³⁷ is displayed in somewhat more detail in Section 8.2.7 Several alpha groups of Am²⁴¹ present in very low intensity are not shown.

cision.[361,362] The results of DAY[362] are given in Table 9.20. The conversion electrons of these same transitions have been studied by several groups. The precise measurements of BARANOV AND SHLYAGIN[363] with a double-focusing

[361] H. Jaffe, T. O. Passell, C. I. Browne, and I. Perlman, *Phys. Rev.* **97**, 142 (1955).

[362] P. P. Day, *Phys. Rev.* **97**, 689 (1955).

[363] S. A. Baranov and K. N. Shlyagin, *Conf. Acad. Sci. USSR on Peaceful Uses of Atomic Energy*, July 1955, *Phys. Math. Sci.*, p. 251 (1955).

TABLE 9.20. Gamma transitions of Am^{241} (Low energy region).

Energy "best" value	Cauchois bent-crystal spectrometer results (Ref. 362)		Conversion electron measurements				Proportional Counter Results		
	Energy (keV)	Photon relative intensity	Transition Energy	Conversion electrons seen	Transition Type	Ref.	Energy	Photon Intensity per alpha	Ref.
26.36	26.363 ± 0.014	8.2	26.38	$L_{I\,II\,III}\,M_{I\,II\,III}\,N_I$	$E1$	363	26.3	0.028	368
			26.36	M_I		364	26.4	0.025	369
			26.34	$L_{I\,II\,III}\,M_I$ N_I	$E1$	357			
			26.36	$L_{I\,II\,III}\,M_{I\,II\,III\,IV\,V}\,N_I\,O_I$	$E1$	367			
27.0			27.00	$L_{I\,III}\,M_{I\,III}$	$M2$	367			
33.20	33.199 ± 0.021	0.5	33.22	$L_{I\,III}\,M_{I\,II\,III}\,N_I$	$M1+E2$	363			
			33.20	$L_{I\,II\,III}\,M_{I\,II\,III}\,N_{II}$ $N_{I\,III\,IV}\,O_{I\,II}$	$M1+E2$	364			
			33.14	$L_{I\,II\,III}\,M_{I\,II\,III}\,N_I\,O_I$	$M1+E2$	357			
			33.16	$L_{I\,II\,III}\,M_{I\,II\,III}\,N_I\,O_I$	$M1+E2$	367			
42.8			42.8	$L_{I\,III}\quad M_{III}\quad N_I$	$M3$	367			

43.46	43.463 ± 0.085	0.6	43.43	$L_{II\,III}\,M_{I\,II\,III}\,N_I\,O_I$	$E2+M1$	363	43.4	0.00073	369
			43.20	$L_{II\,III}\,M_{I\,II\,III}$ $N_{I\,II\,III}\,O_{I\,II\,III}$					
			43.34	$L_{II\,III}\,M_{III}\,N_{III}\,O_I$	$M1+E2$	364			
			43.48	$L_{II\,III}\,M_{III\,IV}\,N_{III}\,O_I$	$M1+E2$	357 367			
55.52			55.52	$L_{II}\,M_{I\,III\,IV}$		363			
			55.56	$L_{II\,III}\,M_{I\,II\,III}$		364			
			55.46	$L_{II}\quad M_{I\,II\,III}$	$M1+E2$	357			
			55.52	$L_{II\,III}\,M_{I\,II\,III}$	$M1+E2$	367			
59.57	59.568 ± 0.017	100	59.62	$L_{II\,III}\,M_{I\,II\,III}\,IV$ $N_I\,O_I$	$0.9\,E1$ $0.1\,M2$	363	59.7	0.40	368
			59.57	$L_{II\,III}\,M_{I\,II\,III\,IV\,V}$ $N_{I\,II\,III\,IV\,V}\,O_{I\,II}P$	$E1$	364	59.6	0.359	369
			59.54	$L_{II\,III}\,M_{I\,II\,III\,IV}\,N_{I\,II}\,O_{I\,II}$	$E1$	357			
			59.59	$L_{II\,III}\,M_{I\,II\,III\,IV\,V}\,N_{I\,II\,III}\,O_I$	$E1+M2+E3$	367			
			67.26	$L_{II\,III}$	$M3$	372			
			70.1(?)	$L_{II\,III}\,M_{I\,II\,III}$		372			
			75.9	$L_{III}\,M_{II\,III}$	$E2$	372			
			99.05	$L_{III}\,M_{II\,III}\,N_{II}\,O_{II}$	$E2$	372			
98.9			99.80	$L_{II\,III}\,M_{III}$		363			
			99.0	L_{III}					
			98.85	$L_{III}\quad M_{II\,III}\,N_{II\,III}$	$E1$	357			

spectrometer as well as the precise measurements of HOLLANDER, SMITH, AND RASMUSSEN[364] and of ROSENBLUM, VALADARES, AND MILSTED[357] made with permanent magnet spectrographs are summarized in the same table.

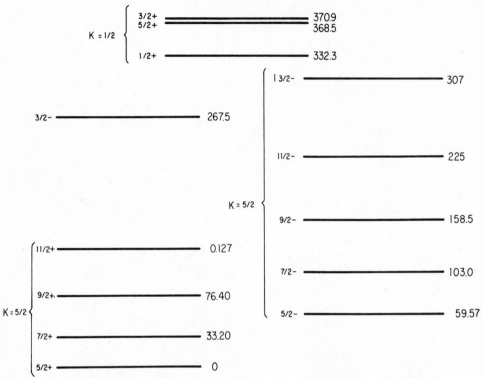

FIG. **9.28.** Level scheme of Np^{237} as drawn by HOLLANDER, RASMUSSEN, ALBRIDGE, AND SMITH except for the levels at 127 and 307 keV which were established later. In addition, the measurements of BARANOV AND CO-WORKERS indicate very slight alpha decay to several other higher-lying members of these rotational bands.

Other pertinent references are Refs. 365–367. The proportional counter measurements of BELING, NEWTON, AND ROSE[368] were also important in determining photon energies and abundances. In particular,

364 J. M. Hollander, W. G. Smith, and J. O. Rasmussen, *Phys. Rev.* **102**, 1372 (1956).

365 J. Milsted, S. Rosenblum, and M. Valadares, *Compt. Rend.* **239**, 259, 700 (1954).

366 J. F. Turner, *Phil. Mag.* **46**, 687 (1955).

367 P. S. Samoilov, *Bull. Acad. Sci. USSR—Physical Series* **23**, 1401 (1959), Columbia Translation Series.

368 J. K. Beling, J. O. Newton, and B. Rose, *Phys. Rev.* **86**, 797 (1952); **87**, 670 (1952); See also correction in **87**, 1144 (1952).

TABLE 9.21 Summary of the intensities of the Np L x-rays and gamma rays (as published by L. B. Magnusson).

Group	Line	Energy[a,i] keV	Relative intensity[b] Bent-Crystal spect. Day[c]	Relative intensity[b] Bent-Crystal spect. Day[d]	Relative intensity[b] Proportional spect. BELING, et al.[e]	Relative intensity[b] Proportional spect. Present[f]	Absolute intensity[g] photon/alpha	Absolute intensity[g] photon/alpha
Ll	l	11.89	0.83	1.32	—	2.2_4	0.008	0.008
$L\alpha$	α_2	13.78	1.89	2.61				0.013
	α_1	13.96	17.2	24.4				0.119
	$\frac{1}{2}\eta$	15.88	0.39	0.49				0.0024
			19.5	27.5	42.0	37.5	0.135	
$L\beta$	$\frac{1}{2}\eta$	15.88	0.39	0.49				0.0018
	β_6	16.14	0.38	0.50				0.0018
	β_2	16.86	4.60	6.03				0.022
	β_4	17.08	3.04	3.90				0.015
	β_5	17.52	0.74	0.99				0.0037
	β_1	17.76	26.1	34.2				0.127
	β_3	18.00	2.41	3.17				0.012
	$\frac{1}{2}\gamma_5$	20.12	0.11	0.15				0.0006
			37.8	49.5	66.0	51.2	0.184	
$L\gamma$	$\frac{1}{2}\gamma_5$	20.12	0.10	0.13				0.0005
	γ_1	20.80	6.42	7.92				0.031
	γ_2	21.11	0.71	0.86				0.0033
	γ_3	21.34	0.81	0.96				0.0037
	γ_6	21.48	1.73	2.01				0.0078
	γ_4	22.20	0.78	0.92				0.0036
			10.6	12.8	17.7	13.8		0.050

TABLE 9.21 Summary of the intensities of the Np L x-rays and gamma rays (cont.)

Group	Line	Energy[a,i] keV	Relative intensity[b] Bent-Crystal Day[c]	Day[d] spect.	Proportional spect. BELING, et al.[e]	Present[f]	Absolute intensity[g] photon/alpha
L_γ		26.36	10.6	12.8	17.7	13.8	0.050
		33.20	5.93	7.5	7.5	7.0	0.025
		43.46	0.40	0.40	—	—	0.0011
			0.22	0.26	—	0.20[h]	0.0007
		59.56	100	100	100	100[h]	0.359
		99.0	0.10[h]			0.064[h]	0.00023
		103.0				0.053[h]	0.00019

a P.P. Day, Phys. Rev. 97, 689 (1955).

b Photons per 100 59.6 keV photons.

c Relative intensities of Ref. a recalculated by Day with the topaz reflectivity dependence equal to $1/E^{1.35}$.

d Relative intensities of column 4 recalculated with mass absorption coefficients for the sample self-absorption extrapolated from the data in Phys. Rev. 24, 1 (1924); 27, 266 (1926); 28, 907 (1926); and 43, 527 (1933).

e Beling, Newton, and Rose, Phys. Rev. 86, 797 (1952).

f The preliminary intensities for the L x-ray groups were normalized to the absolute intensities of 0.376 L x-ray/α and 0.359 59.6-keV gamma-ray/α determined by NaI crystal spectrometry.

g The relative group intensities of column 7 were distributed by the relative line intensities within each group as given by column 5 and normalized to give the absolute total of 0.376 L x-ray/α.

h These values were measured by scintillation spectrometry.

i Better values of the energies of the neptunium L x-rays were later measured by J. J. Merrill by fluorescent excitation of x-rays in a sample of neptunium and the measurement of these x-rays in a carefully calibrated 2-crystal spectrometer. See Ph.D. Thesis, Calif. Inst. of Technology (1960). See also the section on x-ray energies in the appendix of Volume 1 of this book set.

the absolute abundance of the 59.57-keV gamma ray was determined by them to be 0.40 ± 0.015 photons per alpha. This measurement is important because this transition is the most prominent gamma ray in the decay of Am^{241} and because the 59.57-keV gamma ray is a widely used standard in nuclear spectroscopy for calibrating the energy scale and efficiency (or geometry) of counting equipment. MAGNUSSON[369] remeasured this quantity and got the slightly lower value of 0.359 photons per alpha.

The discussion in several published articles[357,361,364,367] may be consulted for detailed arguments leading to the following multipolarity assignments for these low energy gamma rays: 26.28 keV ($E1$), 33.2 keV ($M1 + E2$), 43.4 keV ($E2 + M1$), 59.57 keV ($E1$), and 99.0 keV ($E2$).

SAMOILOV[367] remeasured the conversion electrons of the above transitions and, in addition, identified conversion electrons of the following higher energy transitions: 102.8, 123, 126.6, 158.8, 166.5, 207.4, 234.4, 268.0, 304.5, 333.4, 369.4, and 429 keV. All of these are in very low abundance.

L x-rays of neptunium are produced in considerable abundance as a result of the emission of conversion electrons in the decay of Am^{241}. The accurate measurements of DAY[362] made on a bent-crystal spectrometer are presented in Table 9.21. When instruments of lesser resolution such as the proportional counter spectrometer are used, only the more abundant groups appear. The measurements of BELLING, NEWTON, AND ROSE[368] and of MAGNUSSON[369] on the Np L_α, Np L_β and Np L_γ groups of x-rays are summarized in Table 9.21. Scintillation spectrometer measurements of high energy gamma rays are listed in Table 9.22.

TABLE 9.22 Gamma ray photons in decay of Am^{241} (high energy region).

Energy	Relative abundance	Ref.
99	2.3×10^{-4}	369
103	1.9×10^{-4}	369
113	3.3×10^{-5}	362
130	5.3×10^{-5}	362
159	4.4×10^{-6}	362
210	8.4×10^{-6}	362
270	1.1×10^{-6}	362
328	3.0×10^{-6}	362
370	1.7×10^{-6}	362

The Decay Scheme of Am^{241}. We are now in a position to discuss the decay scheme of Figs. 9.27 and 9.28. We follow the discussion of PERLMAN

[369] L. B. Magnusson, *Phys. Rev.* **107**, 161 (1957).

AND RASMUSSEN[370] and others and interpret the decay scheme in terms of the Bohr-Mottelson unified model. The levels at 33.20 and 76.4 keV constitute a series of rotational levels based on the 5/2+ ground state. In the theory of Bohr and Mottelson the coupling of single particle motions and collective motions in a region of strong interaction leads to a limiting equation representing the energies of rotational levels in odd A nuclei (valid except for $K = 1/2$) which is

$$E_I = \frac{\hbar^2}{2\mathfrak{J}} [I(I + 1) - I_0(I_0 + 1)]$$

where $\mathfrak{J}$ = moment of inertia, I = spin, I_0 = spin of base level. The ground state rotational band comprising the three levels mentioned has a spacing constant $\hbar^2/2\mathfrak{J}$ of 4.75 keV. The effective moment of inertia is by far the largest one known for a rotational band. The value of $\hbar^2/2\mathfrak{J}$ is more than 20 per cent less than the corresponding value for the band based on the 59.6 keV level in the same nucleus. The 76.4-keV 9/2+ level is not observed in the alpha decay of Am^{241} or the beta decay of U^{237}, but it was revealed by the Coulombic excitation results of NEWTON.[371] His excitation of the 33.20 and 76.4 keV levels by bombardment of Np^{237} with low energy helium ions makes certain the collective nature of these levels. The base level, i.e., the ground state of Np^{237}, is given the Nilsson orbital assignment 5/2 + [642] where the numbers in brackets refer to the asymptotic quantum numbers $Nn_z\Lambda$.

The level at 59.57 keV which is so prominently observed in the decay of Am^{241}, being populated directly or indirectly in more than 99 per cent of the transitions, is the base state of a second rotational band of levels. The associated levels, which are labeled with the letter B in Fig. 9.27 are 59.57 keV (5/2−), 103 keV (7/2−), and 158.2 keV (9/2−). This level spacing corresponds to a value of 6.21 keV for the spacing constant. The next higher levels in this rotational band would be expected to be 225 keV (11/2−), 305 keV (13/2−), and 395 keV (15/2−). Alpha particle groups corresponding to two of these levels were found by GOL'DIN, NOVIKOVA, AND TRET'YAKOV[359] (and confirmed by ASARO AND PERLMAN[372]) as listed in Table 9.20 and interpreted as the higher members of this rotational band. BARANOV AND CO-WORKERS[360] found alpha groups corresponding to all three. The Nilsson assignment for this band is 5/2 − [523].

It is noteworthy that Am^{241}, with a ground state spin 5/2, is so highly hindered in alpha decay to the ground state rotational band of Np^{237} whose

[370] I. Perlman and J. O. Rasmussen, "Alpha Radioactivity," *Handbuch der Physik* 42, Springer-Verlag, Berlin (1957).

[371] J. O. Newton, *Nature* 175, 1028 (1955).

[372] F. Asaro and I. Perlman, unpublished results, 1960.

base spin is 5/2, whereas, on the other hand, alpha decay to the family of levels based on the 5/2 state at 59.57 keV accounts for the great majority of the transitions. RASMUSSEN[373] interpreted this as meaning that the wave function of the odd-proton (Nilsson eigenstate) in Am^{241} is the same as that for the 59.57 keV state in Np^{237} but distinctly different from the ground state of Np^{237}. Specifically, the 59.57 keV state in Np^{237} and the ground state of Am^{241} are both given the Nilsson assignment 5/2 − [523].

BOHR, FRÖMAN, AND MOTTELSON[374] have found this to be a general phenomenon in the alpha decay of odd mass nuclei and have developed a theory showing why certain alpha transitions are favored while others are hindered. These matters are discussed further in Chapters 3 and 4.

In Fig. 9.28 we note a group of levels at 332.3, 368.5, and 370.9 keV which are grouped together as a $K = 1/2$ rotational band. These levels were identified by RASMUSSEN, CANAVAN, AND HOLLANDER[375] in a study of the β-decay of U^{237}. They made the tentative Nilsson level assignment 1/2 + [400]. It was not until the work of BARANOV, KOULAKOV, ZELENKOV, AND CHATINSKI[360] that alpha groups of Am^{241} were found to populate these levels in very low intensity. The 9/2 and 7/2 levels of this rotational band would be expected to fall at 458 and 464 keV energy. Alpha groups in 3×10^{-4} per cent intensity are found to populate levels at these energies.

Several of the low-intensity alpha groups reported by BARANOV AND CO-WORKERS may represent transitions to several members of a rotational band based on the 3/2− level at 267.5 keV. Nilsson assignment of this band may be 1/2 − [530].

The 59.37 keV level in Np^{237} took on special significance with the discovery by BELING, NEWTON, AND ROSE[368] that it had a half-life of 6.3 × 10^{-8} seconds, a value which is $\sim 4 \times 10^5$ longer than that expected through the use of the Weisskopf single-proton formula for estimating the lifetimes of $E1$ transitions. It has been suggested that this retardation is caused by the violation of a selection rule in the asymptotic quantum number n_z. The general occurrence of highly retarded $E1$ transitions for heavy element nuclei is discussed in Section 3.5.7 of Chapter 3.

In addition to its unexpectedly long half-life the 59.37 keV (and the 26.4 keV) transition in Np^{237} is anomalous in another respect. The L-shell conversion coefficients do not agree with the theoretical conversion coefficients as given by ROSE[376] or by SLIV AND BAND[377]. The disagreement is in a

[373] J. O. Rasmussen, Arkiv Fysik **7**, 185 (1953).

[374] A. Bohr, P. O. Fröman, and B. R. Mottelson, Dan. Mat.-fys. Medd. **29**, No. 10 (1955).

[375] J. O. Rasmussen, F. L. Canavan, and J. M. Hollander, Phys. Rev. **107**, 141 (1957).

[376] M. E. Rose, Internal Conversion Coefficients (Amsterdam: North Holland Publishing Company; New York: Interscience Publishing Company, 1958).

[377] L. A. Sliv and I. M. Band, Table of γ-ray Conversion Coefficients, Part 2. Physico-Technical Institute, Academy of Science, Leningrad, USSR (1958).

TABLE 9.23 Summary of L-shell $E1$ conversion data for the "anomalous" transitions in Np^{237}. (From Ref. 378.)

Transition energy (keV)		$\alpha(L_I)$	$\alpha(L_{II})$	$\alpha(L_{III})$	$\alpha(L_{Total})$
59.57	Experimental	0.22 ± 0.02	0.46 ± 0.05	0.12 ± 0.03	0.80 ± 0.08
	theory—Rose	0.11	0.10	0.125	0.34
	theory—Sliv and Band	0.13	0.12	0.13	0.38
26.4	Experimental	2.0	3.9	1.2	7.1
	theory—Rose	0.22	0.55	1.25	2.0
	theory—Sliv and Band	0.55	1.1	1.4	3.1

direction which cannot be removed by postulating some suitable admixture of other multipole types. ASARO, STEPHENS, HOLLANDER, AND PERLMAN[378] have critically examined the data on 13 such anomalous $E1$ transitions in the region of heavy element deformed nuclei. Their summary of the transitions appearing in the decay of Am^{241} is presented in Table 9.23. The later work of SAMOILOV[367] on the L-conversion ratios may require some revision of this analysis.

KROHN, NOVEY, AND RABOY[379] measured the gyromagnetic ratio of the 59.57 keV level as $+(0.8 \pm 0.2)$ by the attenuation of the alpha-gamma angular correlation in an applied magnetic field. The magnetic moment of the state is $+2.0 \pm 0.5$ nuclear magnetons.

The ground state spin of Am^{241} has been proved to be 5/2 from a study of atomic spectra.[380-382] This assignment is fully confirmed by atomic beam experiments.[383] The decay scheme is also strengthened by the determination of the ground state spin of Np^{237} as 5/2 by atomic spectrum analysis[384] and paramagnetic resonance studies.[385] MANNING, FRED, AND TOMKINS[382] report a quadrupole moment of $+4.9$ barns and a magnetic moment of $+1.4$ nuclear magnetons.

The half-life of Am^{241} for spontaneous fission has been found by MIKHEEV, SKOBELEV, DRUIN, AND FLEROV[386] to be 2×10^{14} years.

---

[378] F. Asaro, F. S. Stephens, J. M. Hollander, and I. Perlman, *Phys. Rev.* 117, 492 (1960).

[379] V. E. Krohn, T. B. Novey, and S. Raboy, *Phys. Rev.* 98, 1187 (1955).

[380] M. Fred and F. S. Tomkins, *Phys. Rev.* 89, 318 (1953).

[381] R. Thorne, *Nature* 178, 484 (1956).

[382] T. E. Manning, M. Fred, and F. S. Tomkins, *Phys. Rev.* 102, 1108 (1956).

[383] R. Marrus, W. A. Nierenberg, and J. Winocur, *Phys. Rev.* 120, 1429 (1960).

[384] J. E. Mack, *Revs. Mod. Phys.* 22, 64 (1950).

[385] B. Bleaney, *et al.*, *Phil. Mag.* 45, 992 (1954).

[386] V. L. Mikheev, N. K. Skobelev, V. A. Druin, and G. N. Flerov, *Zhur. Eksp. Teor. Fiz.* 37, 859 (1959).

9.3.7 *The Isomers of Am²⁴²*

When Am^{241} is irradiated with slow neutrons two isomeric forms of Am^{242} are produced. The first to be discovered was a 16-hour β^--emitter (MANNING AND ASPREY[387]) whose half-life was later determined more precisely as 16.01 ± 0.02 hours.[388] Experiments by SEABORG, JAMES, AND MORGAN[389] showed that a long-lived form of Am^{242} was also produced. This isomer was identified by the isolation of its radioactive decay products (Cm^{242} and Np^{238}) and by mass spectrographic analysis.[389,390] The half-life was given as ~ 100 years,[390] later determined more precisely as 152 ± 7 years.[391]

The β^- and conversion electron spectra associated with both isomers were investigated[392-396] and the puzzling conclusion was reached that both had almost identical decay schemes involving transitions to the 0+ and 2+ states of Cm^{242}. The ratio of β^- emission/electron capture also appeared to be similar. This, of course, is out of keeping with their existence as isomers. On the basis of a small difference in the β^- spectra end points the 16-hour isomer was taken to be the metastable state.

This unsatisfactory situation was cleared up by ASARO, PERLMAN, RASMUSSEN, AND THOMPSON[397] who showed that the 152-year isomer is the metastable state and that its principal mode of decay is by a 48.6 keV isomeric transition to the ground state, which is the 16-hour β-emitter. This explains the similarity of β-decay properties, because in both cases only the decay associated with the ground state was under observation. The proof of the decay sequence consisted of an isomer separation in which it was shown that 16-hour isomer was present in equilibrium with the 152-year

[387] W. M. Manning and L. B. Asprey, Paper No. 22.7, "The Transuranium Elements," *Nat. Nucl. Energ. Ser.*, Division IV **14B** (New York: McGraw-Hill Book Co., Inc., 1949).

[388] T. K. Keenan, R. A. Penneman, and B. B. McInteer, *J. Chem. Phys.* **21**, 1802 (1953); *Phys. Rev.* **87**, 204A (1952).

[389] G. T. Seaborg, R. A. James, and L. O. Morgan, Paper No. 22.1, "The Transuranium Elements," *Nat. Nucl. Energ. Ser.*, Division IV **14B** (New York: McGraw-Hill Book Co., Inc., 1949).

[390] K. Street, Jr., A. Ghiorso, and G. T. Seaborg, *Phys. Rev.* **79**, 530 (1950).

[391] R. F. Barnes, D. J. Henderson, A. L. Harkness, and H. Diamond, *J. Inorg. Nucl. Chem.* **9**, 105 (1959).

[392] R. W. Hoff, H. Jaffe, T. O. Passell, F. S. Stephens, Jr., E. K. Hulet, and S. G. Thompson, *Phys. Rev.* **100**, 1403 (1955).

[394] S. A. Baranov and K. N. Shlyagin, *Conf. Acad. Sci. USSR on Peaceful Uses of Atomic Energy, Phys. Math. Sci.*, p. 251, July 1955; English translation, Superintendent of Documents, Washington, D.C.

[395] E. L. Church as reported in Ref. 391.

[396] J. M. Hollander, *Phys. Rev.* **103**, 1590 (1956).

[397] F. Asaro, I. Perlman, J. O. Rasmussen, and S. G. Thompson, *Phys. Rev.* **120**, 934 (1960).

isomer. The minor differences previously observed[392] in the decay properties (β^- populations to different energy levels; β^-/EC ratios) have dis-
appeared in the light of later measurements,[391,398] and only the apparent
difference in β^- end points (which have not been remeasured) remains.

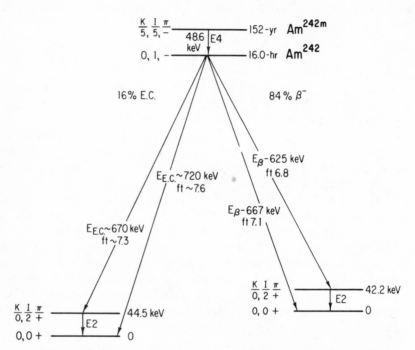

FIG. 9.29. Decay scheme of isomers of Am²⁴². The alpha decay of Am²⁴²ᵐ, known
to occur to the extent of 0.48 per cent, is discussed below and illustrated in Fig. 9.30.

The decay scheme embodying all available information is shown in
Fig. 9.29. The percentages of branching decay by orbital electron capture
and by β^--emission are taken from the work of BARNES, HENDERSON, HARK-
NESS, AND DIAMOND.[391]   A slight alpha decay of the long lived isomer was
noted by SEABORG, JAMES, AND MORGAN[389] as demonstrated by the chemical
separation of the daughter Np²³⁸.   An accurate value of 0.476 ± 0.014 per
cent, corresponding to a partial alpha half-life of 32,000 ± 1600 years, was
measured by BARNES, HENDERSON, HARKNESS, AND DIAMOND.[391]   The
discussion of the alpha spectrum and of the decay scheme associated with the
alpha decay of Am²⁴²ᵐ is deferred to the end of this section.

---

398 R. Hoff, E. K. Hulet, and M. C. Michel, *J. Nucl. Energ.* **8**, 224 (1959).

TABLE 9.24. Gamma transitions in decay of Am^{242} from conversion
electron measurements.

Transition	Energy	Ref.
	42.3	392
16 hr $Am^{242} \rightarrow Cm^{242}$	42.2	395
conversion in Cm subshells	42.12	396
	42.18	394
	42.20	397
	44.8	392
16 hr $Am^{242} \rightarrow Pu^{242}$	44.6	395
conversion in Pu subshells	44.50	396
	44.52	394
	44.50	397

It may be worthwhile to point out the difficulty responsible for the long delay in the discovery of the correct relationship of the two isomers. It happens that the long-lived Am^{242} isomer has a large neutron capture cross section so that a maximum concentration of only a few per cent by activity can be built up in a sample of Am^{241}. Since Am^{241} has abundant low-energy photon transitions associated with its alpha decay, the electrons associated with the isomeric transition are obscured unless special pains are taken to look for them. In addition, Am^{243} is always present and its decay product Np^{239} also obscures the picture. The best solution to these difficulties is magnetic separation of an enriched sample of Am^{242m}.

Table 9.24 summarizes the precise measurements of the gamma transitions seen in the β^- decay of the 16-hour isomer. The authors cited therein used electron spectrometers to measure the L, M, N, and O electrons of the two chief gamma transitions. The subshell conversion ratios clearly identify both transitions as $E2$. ASARO, PERLMAN, RASMUSSEN, AND THOMPSON[397] measured the electrons associated with an aged americium sample, which contained an appreciable amount of 152-year Am^{242}, and found L, M, N, and O conversion lines of a 48.63 keV transition converted in americium subshells. This is the isomeric transition by which the 152-year isomer is chiefly de-excited. The multipolarity of the transition was determined unambiguously as $E4$ by comparison of the experimental ratios of conversion lines, particularly those from the M-shell, with ratios calculated from theoretical conversion coefficients.

The spin of the 16-hour state was measured by the atomic beam resonance technique and found to be 1 by WINOCUR, MARRUS, AND NIERENBERG.[399]

---

[399] J. Winocur, R. Marrus, and W. Nierenberg, *Bull. Am. Phys. Soc.* II, **4**, No. 8, 451 (1959); see also J. Winocur, Ph.D. Thesis issued as *Univ. Calif. Rad. Lab. Report UCRL-9174*, April, 1960.

In combination with the $E4$ multipolarity assignment of the 48.63 keV transition this establishes a probable spin value of 5 for the 152 year Am^{242m}. The atomic beam experiment emphasized strongly the shortcomings of the earlier decay schemes for the Am^{242} isomers and provided a strong stimulus for the work of ASARO AND CO-AUTHORS.[397]

The beta decay properties of Am^{242} and Am^{242m} are summarized in Table 9.25.

TABLE 9.25. Beta decay properties of Am^{242} and Am^{242m}.

Isomer	Decay mode	Product state	Decay energy	Relative intensity (per cent)	Log ft
16-hour Am²⁴²	β⁻	Cm²⁴², 0+	0.667	34	7.1
	83.6%	Cm²⁴², 2+	0.625	50	6.8
	EC16%	Pu²⁴², 0+	0.72	~6 (K-cap., 4.4)	~7.6
		Pu²⁴², 2+	0.67	~10 (K-cap., ~7.6)	~7.3
152-year Am²⁴²ᵐ	β⁻	Cm²⁴², 4+	0.578	<2% of IT	>13

As summarized in Ref. 397.

The radiations of Am^{242} include a complex spectrum of x-rays resulting from the electron capture branching, and the gamma conversion process. Some precise measurements of the L x-ray spectrum on a bent crystal type x-ray spectrometer are given in Table 9.26. Since these measurements were made with samples of the 16 hour isomer, the L x-rays of americium cannot be attributed to the isomeric transition but only to the fluorescent excitation of americium x-rays in the bulk sample by the L x-rays of curium; all the samples subjected to study contained large amounts of Am^{241} because of the method of preparation.

Several features of the decay scheme were interpreted in terms of the unified model of nuclear structure by ASARO, PERLMAN, RASMUSSEN, AND THOMPSON.[397] Americium-242 lies within a group of nuclei which have large prolate nuclear deformation. It has one odd neutron and one odd proton and it is believed that the wave functions of these odd nucleons should be identifiable with Nilsson wave functions for nucleons in a deformed nucleus. The most likely Nilsson state for the odd neutron is the 5/2 + [622] state, which appears as the ground state of the isotonic nuclei Pu^{241} and Cm^{243}. The quantum numbers are the usual ones $K\pi[Nn_z\Lambda]$ appropriate to particles in spheroidal nuclei (see Chapter 3). The most likely proton orbital is 5/2 − [523], the ground state of Am^{241} and Am^{243}. The orbital 5/2 + [642], however, is rather near-lying and is also a possibility.

TABLE **9.26.** X-rays following the decay of Am^{242}. (From Hoff, Ref. 392.)

Line	Transition	Observed energy (keV)	Siegbahn's extrapolated energy (keV)	Corrected relative intensity
Cm $L\alpha_2$	$L_3 - M_4$	14.75 ± 0.03	14.74	4
Cm $L\alpha_1$	$L_3 - M_5$	14.97 ± 0.03	14.96	27
Cm $L\beta_2$	$L_3 - N_5$	18.09 ± 0.02	18.10	16
Cm $L\beta_1$	$L_2 - M_4$	19.47 ± 0.02	19.38	100
Cm $L\gamma_1$	$L_1 - N_3$	22.79 ± 0.04	22.63	40
Cm $L\gamma_3$	$L_1 - N_3$	23.30 ± 0.06	23.25	6
Cm $L\gamma_6$	$L_2 - O_4$	23.62 ± 0.12	23.46	12
Am $L\alpha_2$	$L_3 - M_4$	14.44 ± 0.06	14.41	1
Am $L\alpha_1$	$L_3 - M_5$	14.61 ± 0.03	14.61	4
Am $L\beta_1$	$L_2 - M_4$	18.89 ± 0.02	18.80	6
Pu $L\alpha_2$	$L_3 - M_4$	14.08 ± 0.03	14.08	2
Pu $L\alpha_1$	$L_3 - M_5$	14.28 ± 0.03	14.28	10
Pu $L\beta_2$	$L_3 - N_5$	17.29 ± 0.03	17.25	9
Pu $L\beta_1$	$L_2 - M_4$	18.33 ± 0.03	18.27	27
Pu $L\beta_3$	$L_1 - M_3$	18.62 ± 0.04	18.52	7
Pu $L\gamma_1$	$L_2 - N_4$	21.46 ± 0.04	21.38	16
Pu $L\gamma_3$	$L_1 - N_3$	22.06 ± 0.10	21.97	7
Pu $L\gamma_6$	$L_2 - O_4$	22.24 ± 0.10	22.13	7
Pu K x-rays		102		37

Note: For additional data on energies of heavy element x-rays refer to Appendix, Vol. I.

The K-quantum number is the projection of the total angular momentum on the nuclear symmetry axis. With two unpaired particles of $\Omega = 5/2+$ and $\Omega = 5/2-$ the values $K = 0-$ and $K = 5-$ are possible. According to the Nordheim coupling rules, as modified by GALLAGHER AND MOSZKOW-SKI,[400] in this particular case, the $K = 0-$ state should lie below the $K = 5-$ state.

Thus the spin 5 of the long-lived form of Am^{242} receives a natural explanation. Also the high log ft value, > 13, for the beta transition from this isomer to the $4+$ level of Cm^{242} receives a ready explanation in 5-fold change in K which this transition would entail. On the other hand, it seems hard to reconcile the $K = 0-$ prediction for the ground state with the observed spin of 1. The reconciliation is made by asserting that the spin 1 member of the rotational band of levels based on a $K = 0$ ground state appears as the lowest member of the $K = 0$ band. This surprising feature is strongly supported by the close correspondence of several of its theoretical implications with experimental data.

---

[400] C. J. Gallagher and S. A. Moszkowski, *Phys. Rev.* **111**, 1282 (1958).

For example, a traditional test for the K-quantum number involves comparisons of branching ratios of beta or gamma radiation to different members of the same rotational band, the reduced transition probabilities being proportional to the square of a Clebsch-Gordan coefficient. This test is fully described in Section 3.4.7 of Chapter 3. When this criterion is applied to the relative population of the $2+$ and $0+$ state of Cm^{242} in the beta decay of 16 hour Am^{242}, the $K = 0$ assignment for Am^{242} favors the population of the $2+$ first excited state by a factor of 2, whereas the $K = 1$ assignment favors the transition to the ground state by a factor of 2. Experiment (see log ft values in Table 9.25) clearly favors the $K = 0$ choice.

Even more striking evidence comes from consideration of quantities derived from atomic beam measurements.[399] These have fixed precisely the absolute value of the ratio of the magnetic moments of Am^{242} and Am^{241}, 0.236, and also the absolute value of the ratio of their spectroscopic quadrupole moments, 0.562. Furthermore, the measurements have established that either the magnetic moment or the quadrupole moment of Am^{242} is of opposite sign to the corresponding moment of Am^{241}. The optical spectrographic data of MANNING, FRED, AND TOMKINS[401] for Am^{241} gives $\mu = +1.4$ nuclear magnetons (nm) and $Q_{\text{spec}} = +4.9$ barns. Combining this information with that from the atomic beam measurements, we obtain for Am^{242}, $\mu = \pm 0.33$ nm and $Q_{\text{spec}} = \mp 2.75$ barns.

These nuclear moments may now be compared with the theoretical expectations for the $I = 1$, $K = 0$ assignment. An abundance of evidence has established the intrinsic quadrupole deformations of nuclei in the region of americium as prolate (positive). However, for nuclear states with $K^2 < I(I + 1)/3$ the signs of the intrinsic and spectroscopic moments will be opposite. The relation between these moments is as follows:

$$Q_{\text{spec}} = \frac{3K^2 - I(I + 1)}{(I + 1)(2I + 3)} Q_0$$

for $I = 1$, $K = 0$, $Q_{\text{spec}} = -Q_0/5$.
If we assume that Q_0 for Am^{242} is the same as that for Am^{241}, the $K = 0$ assignment gives $Q_{\text{spec}} = -2.74$ barns, which is in excellent agreement with the value ∓ 2.75 barns obtained as mentioned above. If, on the other hand, we assume $K = 1$ for Am^{242}, then Q_{spec} should be $+1.4$ barns.

The magnetic moment may also be analyzed. For the $K = 0$, $I = 1$ assignment the angular momentum is directed perpendicular to the symmetry axis, and there is no specific contribution to the magnetic moment from the odd nucleons. In this case we would expect a magnetic moment $\mu = g_R I$, where g_R is the gyromagnetic ratio for collective motion, usually estimated as $+Z/A$, the fraction of protons in the nucleus. From this we get $\mu = +0.39$

401 T. E. Manning, M. Fred, and F. S. Tomkins, *Phys. Rev.* **102**, 1108 (1956).

nm, which agrees in sign and magnitude with the measured value ($\mu = +0.33$ nm) if the sign for Q_{spec} is taken to be negative in accord with our theoretical prediction.

If we consider the assignment $I = 1$, $K = 1$, we must first of all postulate some possible orbital assignments for the neutron and proton. The most likely are $5/2 - [523]$ (or $5/2 + [642]$) for the proton, as before, and $7/2 + [624]$ for the neutron. This neutron orbital appears as a state at 172 keV in Pu^{241}. If the magnetic moments are calculated from Nilsson wave functions[402,403] (with a deformation parameter, η, of 4.8), the values for $5/2 - [523]$ and $5/2 + [642]$ proton orbitals are 0.2 nm and -1.2 nm, respectively. Thus the measured magnetic moment is not consistent with a $K = 1$ assignment with proton orbital $5/2 + [642]$, but cannot be used by itself to rule out $K = 1$ with proton orbital $5/2 - [523]$. With the latter assignment, however, the ratio of μ/Q_{spec} would be positive, in disagreement with the experimental results. It is seen, therefore, that not only is the magnitude of the measured quadrupole moment in better agreement with theory for $K = 0$ than for $K = 1$, but the sign of the ratio μ/Q_{spec} (as determined from theory) can only be negative for $K=0$. Thus, the atomic beam measurements reinforce the $K=0$ assignment.

The publication[397] from which the analysis of the Am^{242} isomers is taken also discusses the means by which the inversion of spin 1 and spin 0 levels of a $K = 0$ band may arise.

We turn now to a discussion of the alpha decay properties of 152 year Am^{242m}. Difficulties which hinder the measurement of the alpha disintegration properties of samples prepared by neutron irradiation of Am^{241} are (1) the great alpha activity of Am^{241}, (2) the very low isotopic abundance of Am^{242m} in such samples, and (3) the low branching ratio (0.48 per cent[391]) for this mode of decay. The first two difficulties can be overcome by isotopic separation of a suitable americium sample. We now quote from results obtained by ASARO, MICHEL, THOMPSON, AND PERLMAN[404] on samples prepared with the aid of the mass separator of the Institute of Theoretical Physics in Copenhagen.

The alpha spectra measurements showed groups of 5.404 (~ 1.6), 5.360 (~ 1.6), 5.308 (0.8), 5.28 (0.4)?, 5.244 (0.6), 5.201 (88), 5.136 (5.7 ± 0.2), 5.078 (0.30 ± 0.06), and 5.061 MeV (0.25 ± 0.06 per cent). The main group of Am^{241} at 5.482 MeV was used as an energy standard.

The electron spectra indicated only an 87 keV $M1$ transition which could be assigned to the Am^{242m} alpha decay.

[402] B. R. Mottelson and S. G. Nilsson, *Dan. Mat.-fys. Skr. Vid. Selsk* **1**, No. 8 (1959).
[403] S. G. Nilsson, *Kgl. Danske Videnskab Selskab Mat.-fys. Medd.* **29**, No. 16 (1955).
[404] F. Asaro, M. C. Michel, S. G. Thompson, and I. Perlman, *Proceedings of the Rutherford Conference*, Manchester, England 1961.

The main gamma ray studies consisted of delay measurements and co-incidence studies of the L x-ray and gamma-ray spectra occurring before and after two metastable states. The results of these experiments are shown in the decay scheme in Fig. 9.30. The dashed quantities, those in parentheses, and the relative positions of the 48 and 87 keV gamma rays are uncertain.

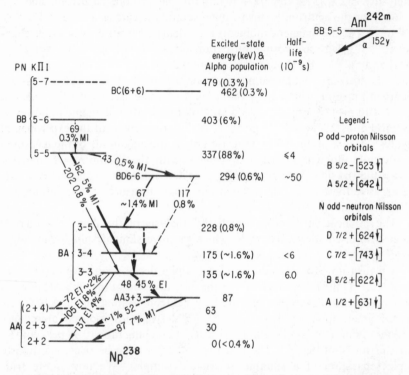

FIG. 9.30. The alpha decay scheme of 152-year Am^{242m} as drawn by ASARO, MICHEL, THOMPSON, AND PERLMAN. See text for explanation.

The assignment of spins and parities to the various Np^{238} levels depends considerably on the values assigned to the 337-keV level. The partial alpha half-life for the decay of this level is essentially unhindered. In the even-even and odd-mass nuclides the unhindered (or favored) type of decay populates states in the daughter nucleus having the same configuration as the parents. As K, π and I had been assigned 5–, 5 for Am^{242m}, the authors calculated the expected relative alpha intensities to the rotational members of a similar 5–, 5 band in Np^{238}. As is seen in Table 9.27 the agreement is very good, even with respect to the energy spacings, which will be discussed later.

In Fig. 9.30 the assigned rotational bands of Np^{238} are classified in terms of the adjacent odd-mass Nilsson orbitals. These orbitals are listed as A, B,

TABLE 9.27 Am^{242m} favored alpha decay to $5-$ band.[404]

$K\pi I$	Energy spacing (keV)		Calculated abundances[404] (per cent)				Exp. abundances (per cent)
	Calc.	Exp.	$L=0$	$L=2$	$L=4$	Sum	
$5-5$	—	—	65.2	22.8	0.023	88.0	88
$5-6$	66.0	65.7	—	5.6	0.021	5.6	5.66 ($\pm$0.17)
$5-7$	143.0	142	—	0.33	0.006	0.34	0.25 ($\pm$0.06)

etc., according to their increasing excited state energy in the appropriate odd-mass nuclides. All of the observed α and γ ray transitions shown in Fig. 9.30 can be interpreted as taking place between levels having at least one common Nilsson orbital. In five instances where comparisons could be made, the reduced γ-ray and α-particle transition probabilities were within a factor of 4 of the values for the corresponding odd-mass transitions in Cm^{243} and Am^{243} α decay.

The rotational energy spacings were calculated from the moments of inertia of the corresponding levels in Np^{237} modified by the difference between the even-even and the corresponding odd-neutron moments of inertia. The agreement was good for the bands $BB(5-)$ and $BA(3-)$ but the calculated spacings for the $AA(2+)$ band were about 15 per cent too small.

9.3.8 Americium-243

The neptunium fraction from a sample of Am^{241} that had been irradiated with slow neutrons in a reactor was shown by STREET, GHIORSO, AND SEABORG[405] to contain equilibrium amounts of both Np^{238} and Np^{239}. The presence of Np^{239} indicated the existence of the nuclide Am^{243} prepared by the reaction sequence:

$$Am^{241}(n, \gamma)Am^{242}(n, \gamma)Am^{243}$$

$$Am^{243} \xrightarrow{\alpha} Np^{239}$$

Mass spectrographic analysis of the irradiated americium sample confirmed the presence of Am^{243} in an amount of about 0.5 per cent. This, together with the chemical yield of Np^{239}, gave a partial half-life for alpha emission of about 10^4 years. Better values are cited below. It has also been possible[406] to produce Am^{243} by the reaction:

$$Pu^{242}(n, \gamma)Pu^{243}$$

$$Pu^{243} \xrightarrow[\text{5.0 hours}]{\beta^-} Am^{243}$$

[405] K. Street, Jr., A. Ghiorso, and G. T. Seaborg, *Phys. Rev.* **79**, 530 (1950).

[406] S. G. Thompson, K. Street, Jr., A. Ghiorso, and F. L. Reynolds, *Phys. Rev.* **84**, 165 (1951).

In high flux reactors Am^{243} can be produced in large quantity in the following way. Plutonium of mass number 239 or 240 is converted to Pu^{242} of high isotopic purity (>98 per cent) by prolonged neutron bombardment. The Pu^{242} can be repurified, principally to remove Am^{241}, and reinserted in a reactor to produce Am^{243} by the reaction outlined above.

This synthesis is important because Am^{243} is the longest-lived of the isotopes of americium; it is about 19 times longer in half-life than Am^{241}. The study of the chemistry of americium is severely hindered by the remarkable chemical effects caused by the intense alpha radiation of Am^{241}, since its specific activity is 7×10^{12} disintegrations per minute per gram. The much lower specific activity of Am^{243} extends the range of possible studies of the properties of americium.

The half-life of Am^{243} has been reported as 7600 years,[407,408] 8800 $\pm$ 600 years,[409] 7600 $\pm$ 370 years,[410] 7720 $\pm$ 160 years,[411] 7650 $\pm$ 50 years[412] and 7951 $\pm$ 48 years[413]. The last cited measurement was made by specific activity measurements on two weighed samples of americium metal in which the alpha activity was 99.35 per cent Am^{243}.

A careful study of the alpha spectrum of Am^{243} in a magnetic spectrograph was made by STEPHENS, HUMMEL, ASARO, AND PERLMAN[410] who report the following groups; 5.345 MeV (0.17 per cent), 5.314 MeV (0.16 per cent), 5.272 MeV (86.9 per cent), 5.230 MeV (11.5 per cent), and 5.175 MeV (1.3 per cent). The decay scheme based on these data is shown in the figure. The nuclear spin 5/2 has been assigned to Am^{243} on the basis of a study of the hyperfine structure of atomic spectral lines.[414] The quadrupole moment and the magnetic moment have been measured as $+4.9$ barns and $+1.4$ nuclear magnetons.[415]

---

407 F. Asaro and I. Perlman, *Phys. Rev.* **93**, 1423 (1954).

408 J. P. Butler, T. A. Eastwood, and R. P. Schuman, as quoted in *Can. J. Phys.* **35**, 147 (1957).

409 H. Diamond, P. R. Fields, J. Mech, M. Inghram, and D. C. Hess, *Phys. Rev.* **92**, 1490 (1953).

410 J. P. Hummel, Ph.D. Thesis, University of California, July, 1956; also published as *Univ. Calif. Rad. Lab. Report UCRL-3456*, July, 1956. F. Stephens, J. Hummel, F. Asaro, and I. Perlman, *Phys. Rev.* **98**, 261A (1955). The alpha particle energies quoted in these references were 6 keV lower than those cited in this chapter. The energies were determined relative to the α_{60} group of Am^{241} whose accepted value in 1956 was 5.476 MeV but was later raised to 5.482 MeV.

411 R. F. Barnes, D. J. Henderson, A. L. Harkness, and H. Diamond, *J. Inorg. Nucl. Chem.* **9**, 105 (1959).

412 A. B. Beadle, D. F. Dana, K. M. Glover, and J. Milsted, *J. Inorg. Nucl. Chem.* **12**, 359 (1960).

413 J. C. Wallmann, P. Graf, and L. Y. Goda, *J. Inorg. Nucl. Chem.* **7**, 199 (1958).

414 J. G. Conway and R. D. McLaughlin, *Phys. Rev.* **94**, 498 (1954).

415 T. E. Manning, M. Fred, and F. S. Tomkins, *Phys. Rev.* **102**, 1108 (1956).

The pattern of alpha group abundances and level spacings as far as it is known is remarkably similar to that of Am^{241}, as can be seen in Fig. 9.25 appearing in Section 9.3.4. This suggests that the interpretation of the decay scheme of Am^{243} should follow closely that of Am^{241}, about which much more evidence has been gathered. In particular the levels at 74, 117, and 173 keV in the daughter nucleus Np^{239} may constitute a rotational band of levels with spins 5/2, 7/2, and 9/2, respectively, based on the 5/2 level. The Nilsson assignment of this rotational band is $5/2 - [523]$ where the numbers have the meanings K, parity $[N, n_z, \Lambda]$.

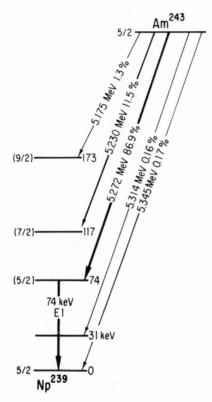

FIG. 9.31. Decay scheme of Am^{243}.

A prominent $E1$ gamma ray with energy 75 keV has been studied[407] by alpha-gamma coincidence techniques and shown to follow about 80 per cent of the alpha transitions. HOLLANDER[416] measured the L-shell conversion electrons, which characterize the transition as $E1$ and determined the energy to be 74.6 keV. This gamma ray is shown in Fig. 9.31. The

[416] J. M. Hollander, unpublished data.

half-life of this gamma ray is about 1.2×10^{-9} seconds[417,418]; this corresponds to a factor of 6000 retardation in the speed of this transition compared to the "single-proton" transition rate prediction. ASARO, STEPHENS, HOLLANDER, AND PERLMAN[419] have made a detailed comparison of the characteristics of this 74.6 keV transition with many other $E1$ transitions in the heavy element nuclei. Many of these are anomalous in their conversion and half-life characteristics.

Other low intensity gamma rays must certainly be present in the decay of Am^{243}.

The ground state spin of Np^{239} is known to be 5/2 from the atomic beam experiments of HUBBS AND MARRUS[420]. The ground state of Np^{239} is given the rather firm Nilsson orbital assignment of $5/2 +$ [642]. This assignment is based on a study of the decay scheme of Np^{239}, and on a comparison of Np^{239} with Np^{237}, as well as on a study of Am^{243}. The ground state of Am^{243} is given the Nilsson assignment $5/2 -$ [523] on the basis of a study of Am^{243} itself and of the decay of Pu^{243} and Bk^{247}. For a review of Nilsson orbital assignments see STEPHENS, ASARO, AND PERLMAN.[421]

We note that the favored alpha decay proceeds to a rotational band of levels in Np^{239} which has a Nilsson orbital assignment identical with that of the ground state of the parent in accordance with the ideas of BOHR, FRÖMAN, AND MOTTELSON.[422]

For some time it was not certain whether Am^{243} was stable with respect to beta decay to Cm^{243}. Using the decay energy cycle involving the alpha-disintegration energies of Am^{243} and Cm^{243} and the beta-disintegration energy of Np^{239}, FOREMAN AND SEABORG[423] found a value of the mass difference of Am^{243} and Cm^{243} which was smaller than the errors involved, and hence it was uncertain which member of this isobaric pair was the heavier. However CHOPPIN AND THOMPSON[424] found evidence for an electron capture decay of Cm^{243} to Am^{243} with a partial half-life of $(1.0 \pm 0.1) \times 10^4$ years.

[417] D. Strominger and J. O. Rasmussen, *Phys. Rev.* **100**, 844 (1955); see also D. Strominger, *Univ. Calif. Rad. Lab. Report UCRL-3374*, 1956 (unpublished).

[418] J. P. Unik, Ph.D. Thesis published as *Univ. Calif. Rad. Lab. Report UCRL-9105*, March 1960.

[419] F. Asaro, F. S. Stephens, J. M. Hollander, and I. Perlman, *Phys. Rev.* **117**, 492 (1960).

[420] J. C. Hubbs and R. Marrus, *Phys. Rev.* **110**, 287 (1958).

[421] F. S. Stephens, F. Asaro, and I. Perlman, *Phys. Rev.* **113**, 212 (1959); a similar review is given by B. R. Mottelson and S. G. Nilsson, *Mat.-fys. Skr. Dan. Vid. Selsk.* **1**, No. 8 (1959).

[422] A. Bohr, P. O. Fröman, and B. R. Mottelson, *Dan. Mat.-fys. Medd.* **29**, No. 10 (1955); see also the discussion of favored α-decay of odd mass nuclei in Chapters 3 and 4.

[423] B. M. Foreman, Jr. and G. T. Seaborg, *J. Inorg. Nucl. Chem.* **7**, 305 (1958).

[424] G. R. Choppin and S. G. Thompson, *J. Inorg. Nucl. Chem.* **7**, 197 (1958).

9.3.9 *The Isomers of Americium-244*

STREET, GHIORSO, AND SEABORG[425] found that neutron irradiation of a sample of americium containing approximately 10 per cent Am[243] produced a new americium activity. This activity decays by beta emission with a half-life of 26 minutes. The isotope was assigned to Am[244] produced by the reaction:

$$Am^{243}(n, \gamma)Am^{244}$$

Later work of GHIORSO, THOMPSON, CHOPPIN, AND HARVEY[426] confirmed this result. These workers studied the beta rays with an anthracene crystal spectrometer and found an end-point energy of 1.5 MeV. They found no prominent gamma rays in a study carried out with the aid of a sodium iodide crystal spectrometer. VANDENBOSCH AND DAY[427] measured a beta end-point of 1489 ± 10 keV and found evidence for a low intensity transition to a state 42.9 keV above ground.

Subsequently, VANDENBOSCH AND DAY[427] found convincing evidence that the neutron irradiation of Am[243] results in the production of a 10.1 hour isomeric form of Am[244]. They studied the gamma rays emitted by this isomer with a NaI spectrometer and found photons with energies of 105, 154, 746, and 900 keV. They measured conversion electrons in a double lens beta spectrometer and found transition energies of 42.9, 99.4, 154, 206, 540, 746, and 900 keV. Their intensity and conversion ratio data are summarized in Table 9.28. The data are in agreement with *E*2 multipolarity for every transition. These data plus the results of photon-photon and photon-electron coincidence studies support rather unambiguously the decay scheme shown in Fig. 9.32.

We note at once that the levels at 42.9, 142.3, 296, and 502 keV have the appearance of the usual ground state rotational band seen in every even-even nucleus in the transthorium group of nuclides. The energies of the levels agree with the rotational formula

$$E_I = \frac{\hbar^2}{2\Im} I(I + 1) + b[I(I + 1)]^2$$

where $\hbar^2/2\Im = 7.16$ keV and $b = -0.0025$ keV. The assignments of K, I, and parity are based on the strong presumption that those levels are indeed members of a rotational band.

The end-point energy of the beta spectrum of the 10.1 hour isomer is 387 ± 1 keV. There is no evidence for more than one component. Beta-photon coincidence experiments gave the curious result that none of the

[425] K. Street, Jr., A. Ghiorso, and G. T. Seaborg, *Phys. Rev.* **79**, 530 (1950).

[426] A. Ghiorso, S. G. Thompson, G. R. Choppin, and B. G. Harvey, *Phys. Rev.* **94**, 1081 (1954).

[427] S. E. Vandenbosch and P. Day, *Nucl. Phys.* **30**, 177 (1962).

TABLE 9.28. Comparison of experimental transition intensities with the theoretical $E2$ predictions; decay of Am^{244} (VANDENBOSCH AND DAY[427]).

Transition energy	Total e^-/β (per cent)	K/L Exp.	K/L Theo.	$L_I L_{II}/L_{III}$ Exp.	$L_I L_{II}/L_{III}$ Theo.	α_K Exp.	α_K Theo.	α_L Exp.	α_L Theo.	α_{total}[e] Exp.	α_{total}[e] Theo.	Transition intensity
42.9 ± 0.1	100			1.4	1.4				800	20	20	100
99.4 ± 0.1	100			1.7	1.8				15	2.7	3.0	100
154 ± 1	50	0.09	0.08			0.19	0.16	2.1	1.9			69
206 ± 4	(0.1)[a]		0.25				0.14		0.56			(0.5)[c]
540 ± 2	(0.2)[b]		1.5				0.03		0.02			(0.4)[d]
746 ± 1	5.8	4.5	2.9			0.06	0.017	0.01	0.0058			72
900 ± 1	0.41	3.3	3.3			0.01	0.012	0.003	0.0036			28

[a] Total L-electron intensity

[b] Total K-electron intensity

[c] Obtained by using total L-electron intensity and assuming theoretical α_L for an $E2$ transition

[d] Obtained by using K-electron intensity and assuming theoretical α_K for an $E2$ transition

[e] Obtained from gamma-gamma coincidence measurements

gammas are in coincidence with the beta particles. From this result and the resolving time of the circuitry it was concluded that all beta decay proceeds to a 1042 keV metastable state in Cm^{244} which has a half-life of > 10 microseconds. This level is de-excited by 900, 746, and 540 keV transitions to the $4+$, $6+$, and $8+$ levels of the rotational band, which strongly suggests a spin assignment of 6 for the 1042 keV level. The lifetime of > 10 microseconds corresponds to a hindrance in the $E2$ transitions of $> 10^7$ over the

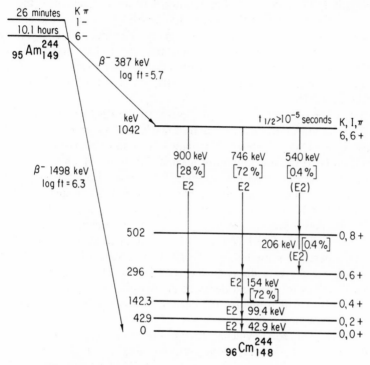

FIG. **9.32**. Decay scheme for the isomers of Am²⁴⁴ as drawn by VANDEN-BOSCH AND DAY.

theoretical lifetime estimates based on single particle transitions. The most likely explanation for this great hindrance is K-forbiddenness; VANDENBOSCH AND DAY[427] suggest a K assignment of 6.

These authors advance a plausible interpretation of the isomerism of Am^{244} and of the nature of the 1042 keV level in Cm^{244} in terms of Nilsson wave functions. In Am^{244} the most probable assignment of the odd (95th) proton is $5/2 - [523]$ and of the odd (149th) neutron is $7/2 + [624]$.* This

---

* The quantum numbers referred to here are K, parity $[N, n_z \Lambda]$ where those given in brackets are the Nilsson asymptotic quantum numbers. See Chapter 3.

statement is based on the analysis of the level schemes of neighboring odd mass nuclei, as reviewed in Section 3.5.5 of Chapter 3. The angular momenta of the odd neutron and odd proton can add parallel or anti-parallel to give spins of $6-$ and $1-$, respectively. The spin difference of 5 accounts for the isomerism. The decay characteristics of the two forms are consistent with assignment of $1-$ to the 26-minute form and $6-$ to the 10.1-hour form. According to the GALLAGHER-MOSZKOWSKI[428] modification of the Nordheim coupling rules, the favored orientation for the odd nucleons is the one in which the intrinsic spins of the nucleons are parallel. In the case of Am^{244} this rule predicts that the $6-$ state has the lower energy, which agrees with the decay scheme. The 26-minute isomer lies 69 ± 10 keV higher in energy.

It is noteworthy that an analogous set of arguments based on Nilsson's orbital assignments was used to explain the isomerism observed in Am^{242} (see Section 9.3.7).

It is hard to account for the high K value of the 1042 keV level in Cm^{244} as a collective vibration of the ground state of that deformed nucleus. VANDENBOSCH AND DAY[427] prefer to explain it as a state of particle excitation, corresponding to the uncoupling of a pair of protons which are coupled in the ground state configuration. Figure 9.33 shows how this might come about. It is postulated that in the beta decay process, instead of the unpaired, $7/2 + [624]$ neutron changing into a proton, a paired $5/2 + [622]$ neutron becomes a proton, resulting in two unpaired neutrons, which is the configuration of the 1042 keV level. The postulated structure of this level is shown in part (b) of the figure. This scheme is supported by the fact that the log ft value for beta decay to the 1042 keV level is in good agreement with log ft values for the beta decay of nearby odd-A nuclei (see part (c) of the figure) all of which involve the change of a $5/2 + [622]$ neutron into a $5/2 - [523]$ proton.

Strong confirmatory evidence for the decay scheme in Fig. 9.32 was provided by the work of HANSEN, WILSKY, BABA, AND VANDENBOSCH[429] who measured the angular correlation of the 746-154 keV γ-cascade and found it to be consistent only with a

$$6 \overset{M1 + E2}{\underset{(746 \text{ keV})}{\longrightarrow}} 6 \overset{E2}{\underset{(154 \text{ keV})}{\longrightarrow}} 4$$

sequence. They found the 746 keV γ-ray to be a mixture of 46 per cent quadrupole ($E2$) and 54 per cent dipole ($M1$). They measured the half-life of the 1042 keV state by measurement of delayed coincidences between β-particles and conversion electrons and found it to be 0.034 ± 0.002 seconds. Comparison with the single particle estimate shows that the $E2$ transitions from the delayed state are hindered by factors of about 10^{10}.

428 C. J. Gallagher and S. A. Moszkowski, *Phys. Rev.* **111**, 1282 (1958).

429 P. G. Hansen, K. Wilsky, C. K. Baba, and S. E. Vandenbosch, *Nucl. Phys.* **45**, 410 (1963).

From a consideration of closed decay-energy cycles FIELDS AND CO-WORKERS[430] concluded that Am^{244} was unstable toward electron capture. By isolation of the Pu^{244} daughter from samples of Am^{243} which had received extensive irradiation with neutrons, and by comparison of the amount

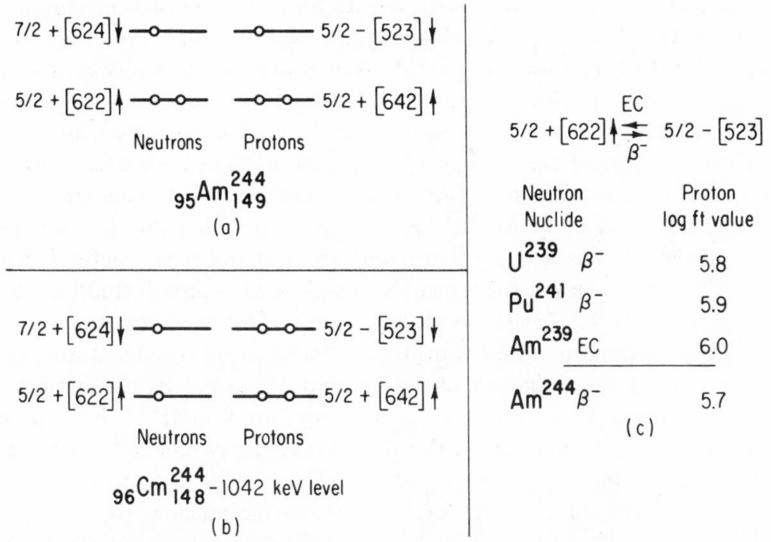

FIG. 9.33. (a) Schematic diagram by VANDENBOSCH AND DAY[427] showing occupation of Nilsson orbitals by the last few protons and neutron in Am^{244}. (b) Proposed configuration of the 1042 keV level in Cm^{244}. The Am^{244} configuration of part (a) can convert to the Cm^{244} configuration of part (b) by the change of a 5/2 + [622] neutron into a 5/2 − [523] proton. (c) Comparison of Am^{244} log ft value with the log ft values for decay of other nuclides involving change of a 5/2 + [622] neutron into a 5/2 − [523] proton or vice versa.

of Pu^{244} to the amount of Cm^{244} found in the sample they measured a value of 0.039 ± 0.003 per cent for the electron capture branching of Am^{244}. At the time of this work the existence of the 10.1-hour isomer was not known. Hence, this branching ratio must be regarded as an average value for the mixture of isomers formed in their sample.

Since large amounts of Am^{243} can be produced by prolonged neutron irradiation of plutonium (as was discussed in the previous section), it is possible to prepare high intensity samples of Am^{244} with considerable ease.

---

430 P. R. Fields, J. E. Gindler, A. L. Harkness, M. H. Studier, J. R. Huizenga, and A. M. Friedman, *Phys. Rev.* **100**, 172 (1956).

9.3.10 *Americium-245*

The isotope Am^{245} is a beta emitter with a half-life of 2.08 hours.   It is produced by the beta decay of Pu^{245} which has a half-life of 10.5 hours. The Pu^{245} parent can be produced by the neutron irradiation of plutonium samples containing appreciable concentrations of 7.6×10^7 year Pu^{244}; or by the irradiation of a heavy element with an extremely high instantaneous flux of neutrons such as is available in the explosion of thermonuclear devices.   The first reports on Am^{245} were provided by BROWNE AND CO-WORKERS[431] and by FIELDS AND CO-WORKERS[432].   Confirmatory evidence was provided by BUTLER AND CO-WORKERS[433].   The mass assignment was made on the basis of the method of preparation, the systematics of isotope properties in this mass region, and the isolation of Cm^{245} daughter activity.

The beta spectrum of Am^{245} has been studied with a thin lens magnetic spectrometer.   It has a single beta component of end-point energy 905 ± 5 keV.   The log ft value is 6.2 indicating an allowed or first forbidden transition.   The K and L conversion electrons of a 255 keV gamma ray are believed to correspond to an $E1$ transition.   Scintillation counter studies show prominent photons of 108 keV (K x-rays) and 248 keV.   By gamma-gamma coincidence methods several other gamma rays are found;[431] their energies are 36, 120, 143, 156 and 232 keV.   A tentative decay scheme[431] leads to a total disintegration energy of 1.32 MeV.   This energy leads to a gross discrepancy with the decay-energy cycle involving the nuclides Bk^{249}, Cf^{249}, Cm^{245}, and Am^{245} since only 860 keV should be available for the decay of Am^{245}.   The decay of Bk^{243} by electron capture also produces Cm^{245} as a daughter product but there is not much correspondence between the radiations seen in the two cases except for the common occurrence of a 255 keV gamma ray.   Compare Section 9.5.4 where Bk^{243} is described.

9.3.11 *Americium-246*

The isotope Am^{246} was first found in a study of the plutonium fraction isolated from the debris of the explosion of a thermonuclear device.[434] This was discussed under *Plutonium-246* in Section 9.2.16 of this chapter. The plutonium fraction was found to contain 10.8-day Pu^{246} decaying by

[431] C. I. Browne, D. C. Hoffman, W. T. Crane, J. P. Balagna, G. H. Higgins, J. W. Barnes, R. W. Hoff, H. L. Smith, J. P. Mize, and M. E. Bunker, *J. Inorg. Nucl. Chem.* **1**, 254 (1955).

[432] P. R. Fields, M. H. Studier, A. M. Friedman, H. Diamond, R. Sjoblom, and P. A. Sellers, *J. Inorg. Nucl. Chem.* **1**, 262 (1955).

[433] J. P. Butler, T. A. Eastwood, T. L. Collins, M. E. Jones, F. M. Rourke, and R. P. Schuman, *Phys. Rev.* **103**, 634 (1956).

[434] D. W. Engelkemeir, P. R. Fields, S. Fried, G. L. Pyle, C. M. Stevens, L. B. Asprey, C. I. Browne, H. L. Smith, and R. W. Spence, *J. Inorg. Nucl. Chem.* **1**, 345 (1955).

beta emission to Am^{246}. The Am^{246} has a half-life of 25 ± 0.2 minutes for the emission of beta particles. The genetic relationship of Am^{246} and Pu^{246} is firmly established.

The beta and gamma ray spectrum of Am^{246} has been studied in equilibrium mixtures of Pu^{246} and Am^{246} and in samples of radiochemically pure Am^{246}. The following resolution of the beta spectrum has been reported:[435] 1.35 MeV, 79 per cent, log ft = 6.1; 1.60 MeV, 14 per cent, log ft = 7.3; 2.10 MeV, 7 per cent, log ft = 8.0. Gamma rays were identified which have energies of 18.5, 103, 245, 795 (complex) and 1069 keV (complex). The 18.5- and 103-keV radiations are probably L and K x-rays, respectively. The beta ray spectrum in coincidence with 1069-keV gamma rays has an end-point energy of 1.222 MeV. Hence, the beta decay energy is at least 2.29 MeV. SMITH AND CO-WORKERS[435] have made an extensive study of gamma-gamma coincidences. More extensive studies are required before a complete decay scheme can be formulated.

9.4 THE ELEMENT CURIUM (ELEMENT 96)

9.4.1 The Discovery of Curium

The first isotope of curium was prepared by SEABORG, JAMES, AND GHIORSO[436] in mid-1944. These men worked at the Metallurgical Laboratory of the University of Chicago on cyclotron targets of plutonium which had been bombarded with helium ions at the 60-inch cyclotron at the University of California. Their goal was to identify an isotope of element 96 prepared by reactions of the (α, xn) type. At first these experiments were unsuccessful because the chemical steps chosen for the isolation of the element 96 fraction were based on the premise that this element should resemble uranium, neptunium, and plutonium in having a stable hexapositive oxidation state. The first successful experiments on element 96 occurred shortly after it was realized that this element might be a member of an actinide series of elements and, as such, might be oxidized beyond the tripositive state only with extreme difficulty, if at all. A new activity emitting alpha particles with a range of 4.75 centimeters of air and a half-life of five months was then isolated by coprecipitation on lanthanum fluoride and other carrier precipitates suitable for a rare-earth-like tripositive ion. This activity was Cm^{242} produced by the reaction:

$$Pu^{239}(\alpha, n)Cm^{242}$$

[435] H. L. Smith, C. I. Browne, D. C. Hoffman, M. E. Bunker, and J. P. Mize, "Radiations of Am^{246}," J. Inorg. Nucl. Chem. 3, 93 (1956).

[436] G. T. Seaborg, R. A. James and A. Ghiorso, Paper No. 22.2, "The Transuranium Elements," Nat. Nucl. Energ. Ser., Division IV 14B (New York: McGraw-Hill Book Co., Inc., 1949).

Shortly thereafter, late in 1944, the identification of element 95 followed as a result of the irradiation of Pu^{239} with reactor neutrons, the reactions being as follows:

$$Pu^{239}(n, \gamma)Pu^{240}(n, \gamma)Pu^{241}$$

$$_{94}Pu^{241} \xrightarrow[\text{long}]{\beta^-} {}_{95}Am^{241}$$

In the same samples the isotope Cm^{242} was formed by an additional neutron-capture step.

$$Am^{241}(n, \gamma)Am^{242}$$

$$_{95}Am^{242} \xrightarrow{\beta^-} {}_{96}Cm^{242}$$

The irradiated plutonium was processed chemically to separate a transplutonium element fraction with rare earth carriers. Alpha particles of 4.75 cm range and five months half-life were assigned to 96^{242} and alpha particles of 4.0 cm range were assigned to 95^{241}. This assignment was partially based on the ratio of the yields of the two alpha particle groups in plutonium samples bombarded with differing total numbers of neutrons. The Cm^{242} is produced by a second-order reaction whereas the Am^{241} is produced by a first-order reaction. The activity assigned to Cm^{242} was also identified by separating Pu^{238} daughter activity. A satisfactory chemical separation of curium from its neighboring element americium did not come until about one year later when the method of selective elution with a buffered citric acid complexing agent from a cation exchange resin was adopted. This system had already been used successfully in separating rare earth ions from each other.

The name for element 96 was chosen by SEABORG, JAMES, AND GHIORSO[436] to honor Marie and Pierre Curie and to emphasize the analogy of element 96 as the seventh member of the actinide series of elements to gadolinium, the seventh member of the lanthanide elements, whose name honored the Finnish chemist, J. Gadolin.

The first isolation of curium in a weighable quantity was carried through by WERNER AND PERLMAN.[437] Microgram quantities of curium were made by the intense neutron irradiation of 4.5 milligrams of americium in a nuclear reactor. The chief separation was made by the ion exchange method. The final sample was 40 micrograms of Cm_2O_3 of about 90 per cent purity.

Most chemical studies of curium up until the mid-1950's were carried out with samples of Cm^{242} prepared in this way. There are severe difficulties in working with weighable amounts of this isotope because of the high specific activity. Each milligram of Cm^{242} emits about 10^{13} alpha

437 L. B. Werner and I. Perlman, Paper No. 22.5, "The Transuranium Elements," *Nat. Nucl. Energ. Ser.*, Division IV **14B** (New York: McGraw-Hill Book Co., Inc., 1949); also published in *J. Am. Chem. Soc.* **73**, 5215 (1951).

particles of 6.110 MeV energy per minute. Water solutions of Cm^{242} are decomposed by this radiation; some of the decomposition products interfere with attempted chemical reactions or the complete study of the absorption spectrum. Precise temperature control of solutions or compounds as, for example, in magnetic susceptibility experiments is difficult because of heating effects. A massive chunk of such curium metal would be heated rapidly to incandescence, if it could be prepared, since the energy released is 123 watts per gram. Crystal lattices of compounds are disarranged by recoil effects of the alpha particles which makes it very difficult to perform crystallographic studies.

It is for these reasons that the isotope Cm^{242} has been replaced with longer-lived isotopes for laboratory studies of the chemical and physical properties as the longer-lived isotopes became available. The isotope Cm^{244} was the first of these longer-lived isotopes to be substituted because it could be prepared easily with rather high isotopic purity in milligram or greater quantities. The half-life is 19.4 years and the specific alpha activity is 43 times less than that of Cm^{242}. The isotopes Cm^{245}, Cm^{246}, Cm^{247} and Cm^{248} are made in milligram-to-gram quantities by the neutron irradiation procedures described later in this chapter. These isotopes are even longer-lived than Cm^{244} and hence are even more suitable for laboratory study of many chemical properties.

9.4.2 *Curium-238*

The isotope Cm^{238} was first prepared by the reaction,[438,439]

$$Pu^{239}(\alpha, 5n)Cm^{238}$$

This isotope decays by the emission of 6.52 MeV alpha particles and also by orbital electron capture. The alpha branching has been estimated to be about 0.4 per cent.[440] The observed half-life is 2.5 hours. It is probable that the measured alpha branching is too low, because, from the energy, the partial alpha half-life is estimated to be 100 hours, and this corresponds to an alpha branching of 2.5 per cent.

The Cm^{238} prepared by the above reaction is contaminated with 12-hour Cm^{239} and with higher mass curium isotopes. GLASS, CARR, COBBLE, AND SEABORG[439] have studied the yield of Cm^{238} as a function of helium ion energy for the reaction

$$Pu^{238}(\alpha, 4n)Cm^{238}$$

They report a cross section of only 0.26 millibarns at 47.4 MeV, the highest energy for which they could obtain data.

---

[438] K. Street, Jr., A. Ghiorso, D. A. Orth, and G. T. Seaborg, unpublished results (1948).

[439] R. A. Glass, R. J. Carr, J. W. Cobble, and G. T. Seaborg, *Phys. Rev.* **104**, 434 (1956).

[440] G. H. Higgins, Ph.D. Thesis, University of California, 1952; also published as *Univ. Calif. Rad. Lab. Report UCRL-1796*, June 1952.

880 THE TRANSURANIUM ELEMENTS

9.4.3 *Curium-239*

By bombardment of Pu^{239} with high energy (70–80 MeV) helium ions the 3-hour isotope Cm^{239} is produced.[441]

$$Pu^{239}(\alpha, 4n)Cm^{239}$$

A number of other curium isotopes are produced at the same time and interfere with the study of the radiations of Cm^{239}. This isotope decays by orbital electron capture to 12-hour Am^{239}. The genetic relationship of these two isotopes has been established by radiochemical experiments. An upper limit of 0.1 per cent has been set on alpha branching.

9.4.4 *Curium-240*

The second isotope of curium to be discovered[442] was the 26.8-day Cm^{240} produced when Pu^{239} was bombarded with 40 MeV helium ions:

$$Pu^{239}(\alpha, 3n)Cm^{240}$$

GLASS, CARR, COBBLE, AND SEABORG[443] report a cross section for this reaction at several values of the helium ion bombardment energy: 0.09 millibarns at 27.5 MeV, 0.22 millibarns at 33.3 MeV, and 1.6 millibarns at 37.2 MeV. The Cm^{240} is not produced in a pure state by the above reaction, since other curium isotopes are formed at the same time.

Curium-240 decays by the emission of alpha particles whose energy was first reported to be 6.26 MeV.[444] The mass assignment has been confirmed by the isolation of Pu^{236} daughter activity.[442] A redetermination[445] of the alpha spectrum gave the following results: 6.287 MeV (72 per cent,) 6.243 MeV (28 per cent), 6.143 MeV (0.04 per cent). Curium-240 is nearly beta stable but the best estimate from closed decay-energy cycles is that it is unstable toward orbital electron capture decay to Am^{240} by about 90 keV. HIGGINS AND STREET[446] have set an experimental upper limit of 0.5 per cent to this mode of decay. Curium-240 is the daughter of the alpha-emitter, 45-minute Cf^{244}.[447]

---

[441] G. H. Higgins, Ph.D. Thesis, University of California, June 1952; also published as *Univ. Calif. Rad. Lab. Report UCRL-1796* (1952).

[442] G. T. Seaborg, R. A. James, and A. Ghiorso, Paper No. 22.2, "The Transuranium Elements," *Nat. Nucl. Energ. Ser.*, Division IV **14B** (New York: McGraw-Hill Book Co., Inc., 1949).

[443] R. A. Glass, R. J. Carr, J. W. Cobble, and G. T. Seaborg, *Phys. Rev.* **104**, 434 (1956).

[444] R. A. Glass, R. J. Carr, and W. M. Gibson, *J. Inorg. Nucl. Chem.* **13**, 181 (1960).

[445] F. Asaro, F. S. Stephens, S. Amiel, and I. Perlman, unpublished results, 1960.

[446] G. H. Higgins and K. Street, Jr., *Phys. Rev.* **86**, 252 (1952).

[447] A. Chetham-Strode, Jr., G. R. Choppin, and B. G. Harvey, *Phys. Rev.* **102**, 747 (1956).

The spontaneous fission half-life of Cm^{240} has been measured by GHIORSO, HIGGINS, LARSH, AND SEABORG[448] to be $(1.9 \pm 0.4) \times 10^6$ years.

9.4.5 Curium-241

The isotope Cm^{241} was first produced by SEABORG, JAMES, AND GHIORSO[449] by bombardment of Pu^{239} with 40 MeV helium ions:

$$Pu^{239}(\alpha, 2n)Cm^{241}$$

These investigators reported a half-life of about 55 days for decay by orbital electron capture. HIGGINS AND STREET[450] redetermined a half-life of 35 ± 2 days and detected a small alpha branching decay. GLASS, CARR, COBBLE, AND SEABORG[451,452] obtained a value of 0.96 per cent for the alpha branching which corresponds to a partial alpha half-life of 10 years. They reported a value of 5.95 ± 0.02 MeV for the alpha-particle energy.

The discovery of an interesting case of isomerism in U^{235} during a study of the α-decay of Pu^{239} led to the speculation[453] that a similar isomerism might be involved in the alpha decay of Cm^{241} to Pu^{237}; U^{235} and Pu^{237} both have 143 neutrons. This isomerism in the U^{235} case is discussed under the description of the decay of Pu^{239} in Section 9.2.9 where it is shown that the chief α-decay of Pu^{239} goes to a state of spin 1/2 located less than one kilovolt above ground, and that this state decays by an $E3$ transition of 26 minute half-life to the $7/2-$ ground state. It was thought that Pu^{237} might have a similar $1/2-$ isomeric state, particularly since the ground state of Pu^{237} can be assigned[454] the same Nilsson orbital, namely $7/2 - [743]$, as the ground state of U^{235}. The decay scheme of Pu^{237} is described in Section 9.2.7.

Experiments of STEPHENS, ASARO, AMIEL, AND PERLMAN[453] did indeed prove that a 0.18 second isomeric state exists in Pu^{237}. Furthermore, the 145 keV delayed transition was shown to be $E3$ from its total K and L conversion coefficients. Thus, the analogy to U^{235} seems complete except that the energy of the transition is much larger in the case of Pu^{237}. The isomeric state of Pu^{237} is assigned to the $1/2 - [631]$ Nilsson orbital on the basis of the above data. Since the favored alpha decay is to this state, it seems logical to identify this same Nilsson orbital with the ground state of Cm^{241}.

[448] A. Ghiorso, G. H. Higgins, A. E. Larsh, Jr., and G. T. Seaborg, *Phys. Rev.* **87**, 163 (1952).

[449] G. T. Seaborg, R. A. James, and A. Ghiorso, Paper 22.2 "The Transuranium Elements," *Nat. Nucl. Energ. Ser.* **14B** (New York: McGraw-Hill Book Co., Inc., 1949).

[450] G. H. Higgins and K. Street, Jr., *Phys. Rev.* **86**, 252 (1952).

[451] R. A. Glass, R. J. Carr, J. W. Cobble, and G. T. Seaborg, *Phys. Rev.* **104**, 434 (1956).

[452] R. A. Glass, R. J. Carr, and W. M. Gibson, *J. Inorg. Nucl. Chem.* **13**, 181 (1960).

[453] F. S. Stephens, F. Asaro, S. Amiel, and I. Perlman, *Phys. Rev.* **107**, 1456 (1957).

[454] D. C. Hoffman and B. J. Dropesky, *Phys. Rev.* **109**, 1282 (1958).

These assignments are summarized in the decay scheme shown here.   Additional information on the alpha spectrum of Cm^{241} was obtained by ASARO, STEPHENS, AMIEL, AND PERLMAN[455] who found the following groups:

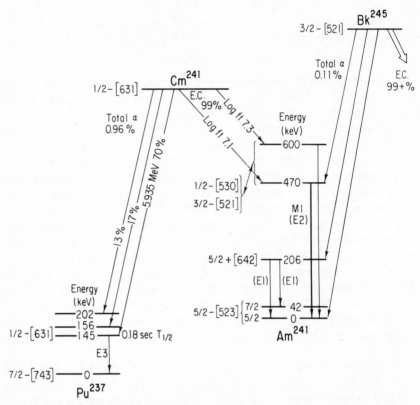

FIG. **9.34.** Decay scheme of Cm^{241}. The α-decay of Bk^{245} is also shown since knowledge gained from its study was essential to an understanding of the EC decay of Cm^{241}. The Nilsson orbital assignments are given to the left of the levels of intrinsic excitation.   In order, the quantum numbers are K, parity [N n_z Λ].

5.935 MeV (70 per cent), 5.925 MeV (17 per cent), and 5.879 MeV (13 per cent).

We now consider the electron-capture decay of Cm^{241}.   Our account follows the experimental findings and theoretical interpretation of STEPHENS, ASARO, AMIEL, AND PERLMAN.[455]

Two gamma rays have been shown to accompany the electron capture decay of Cm^{241} and coincidence data indicate that other weaker transitions

[455] F. Asaro, F. S. Stephens, S. Amiel, and I. Perlman, unpublished results.

are probably also present.[455,456]   The two gamma rays have energies of 470 and 600 keV.   The 470 keV transition has also been seen accompanying the alpha decay of Bk^{245} to Am^{241}.[457]   (See Section 9.5.4.)   This transition is quite strong in Cm^{241}, accounting for most of the decay.   It is assigned on the basis of its K conversion coefficient as principally $M1$, although the data indicate that there is some $E2$ admixture.   Since no strong transitions are in coincidence with this gamma ray, and also because of the data from Bk^{245} decay, it is thought to terminate at the ground state of Am^{241}, placing the excited state at 470 keV.   Less is known about the weaker 600 keV transition, but because there are no strong coincident transitions, it too is thought to terminate at the ground state, indicating a 600 keV level.

The ground state of Am^{241} has a measured spin of 5/2 and is known from its alpha decay properties to have the Nilsson configuration, $5/2 - [523]$. (See discussion of Am^{241} in Section 9.3.6.)   Another level in Am^{241} at 206 keV, populated from Bk^{245} decay, is thought to have the $5/2 + [642]$ assignment.   No decay to either of these levels from Cm^{241} is observed; this is consistent with the $K = 1/2$ assignment for Cm^{241}.   The 470 keV level in Am^{241} must have negative parity since it is connected with the ground state by an $M1$ ($E2$) transition; and the 600 keV level probably has negative parity also since higher-energy positive-parity levels would probably decay to the 206 keV level.   We would expect levels with K values of 1/2 and 3/2 to receive most of the decay since they are populated from a $K = 1/2$ parent.   Two such Nilsson states are available, the $1/2 - [530]$ which is the ground state for Pa^{231} and Pa^{233}, and the $3/2 - [521]$ which probably occurs as the ground state for the berkelium isotopes (except Bk^{249}).   It is not easy to decide which level in Am^{241} has which of these two assignments, particularly since this $1/2 - [530]$ band has its 3/2 member as the lowest state in the protactinium isotope.   (See discussion of Th^{231} decay in Chapter 8, Section 8.2.10.) Because of arguments hinging on a comparison of excited levels in Am^{239}, Am^{241} and Am^{243} which are summarized in Section 3.5.5 of Chapter 3, we prefer the $K = 1/2$ assignment for the 470 keV level, and the $K = 3/2$ assignment for the 600 keV level, but these arguments are not conclusive.   The electron capture decay scheme is also shown in the accompanying Fig. 9.34.

9.4.6 Curium-242

The first isotope of curium to be identified was Cm^{242}.   SEABORG, JAMES, AND GHIORSO[459] found that this alpha-emitting isotope was produced

[456] R. G. Albridge, Jr., *Univ. Calif. Rad. Lab. Report UCRL-8642*, April 1960.

[457] A. Chetham-Strode, Jr., Ph.D. Thesis, *UCRL-3322* (1956).

[459] G. T. Seaborg, R. A. James, and A. Ghiorso, Paper No. 22.2, "The Transuranium Elements," *Nat. Nucl. Energ. Ser.*, Division IV **14B** (New York: McGraw-Hill Book Co., Inc., 1949).

when Pu^{239} was bombarded with 32 MeV helium ions:

$$Pu^{239}(\alpha, n)Cm^{242}$$

The cross section for this reaction is close to one millibarn for helium ion energy in the range 20–37 MeV.[460]   Another cyclotron reaction useful in the preparation of Cm^{242} is the bombardment of Am^{241} with deuterons:

$$Am^{241}(d, n)Cm^{242}$$

The Cm^{242} is prepared in much larger quantities by neutron irradiation of plutonium or americium.   When Pu^{239} is irradiated with neutrons, Cm^{242} is formed via the reaction sequence:

$$Pu^{239}(n,\gamma)Pu^{240}(n,\gamma)Pu^{241} \xrightarrow[13\ \text{yrs}]{\beta^-} Am^{241}(n,\gamma)Am^{242} \xrightarrow[16\ \text{hrs}]{\beta^-} Cm^{242}$$

The curium isolated from neutron-irradiated Pu^{239} contains curium isotopes of higher mass produced by further addition of neutrons to Cm^{242} or by the sequence:

$$Pu^{241}(n,\gamma)Pu^{242}(n,\gamma)Pu^{243} \xrightarrow[5\ \text{hrs}]{\beta^-}$$

$$Am^{243}(n,\gamma)Am^{244} \xrightarrow[25\ \text{min}]{\beta^-} Cm^{244}(n,\gamma)Cm^{245}, \text{etc.}$$

The isotopic composition of the curium will depend on the neutron flux and on the total integrated flux through the sample.   However, it is possible to prepare samples which are almost pure Cm^{242} in terms of alpha activity.

The best way to prepare weighable quantities of Cm^{242} is to irradiate Am^{241} with thermal neutrons.

$$Am^{241}(n,\gamma)Am^{242} \xrightarrow[16\ \text{hrs}]{\beta^-} Cm^{242}$$

The cross section for this reaction is ~ 600 barns.

The half-life of Cm^{242} has been measured as 162.5 ± 2 days[461,462,463] and as 162.7 ± 0.1 days.[464]   This isotope is beta stable so that all disintegrations occur by the emission of alpha particles except for a small but measurable decay by spontaneous fission to be discussed later.   The alpha particle groups are summarized in Table 9.29.   These alpha particle groups

[460] R. A. Glass, Ph.D. Thesis, University of California, April 1954; also published as Univ. Calif. Rad. Lab. Report UCRL-2560, April 1954; see also Glass, Carr, Cobble, and Seaborg, Phys. Rev. 104, 434 (1956).

[461] G. C. Hanna, B. G. Harvey, and N. Moss, Phys. Rev. 78, 617 (1950).

[462] W. P. Hutchinson and A. G. White, Nature 173, 1238 (1954).

[463] K. M. Glover and J. Milsted, Nature 173, 1238 (1954).

[464] R. A. Penneman, L. H. Treiman, and B. Bevan, as reported by D. C. Hoffman, G. P. Ford, and F. O. Lawrence, J. Inorg. Nucl. Chem. 5, 6 (1957).

TABLE 9.29. Alpha particle groups of Cm^{242}.

Results of ASARO AND CO-WORKERS[465,466,467]			Results of KONDRAT'EV AND CO-WORKERS[469]			Results of IVANOV AND CO-WORKERS[469a]	
α-particle energy (MeV)	Energy of Pu^{238} state (keV)	Abundance (per cent)	α-particle energy (MeV)	Energy of Pu^{238} state (keV)	Abundance (per cent)	α-particle energy (MeV)	Abundance (per cent)
6.110	0	73.7	6.110	0	73.5	6.115 ± 0.001	—
6.066	44.11[b]	26.3	6.0656	45.1	26.5	6.071 ± 0.001	—
5.965	146.0[c]	0.035	5.967	145	0.03	5.971	0.035
5.811	303.7[c]	6×10^{-3}	5.809	306	4.6×10^{-3}		
5.605	514	4×10^{-5}					
5.515	605	3.2×10^{-4}					
5.184	941	6×10^{-5d}					

a Measured in magnetic α-spectrometer relative to Po^{218} taken as 5.998 MeV.
b This exact energy is the γ-transition energy.
c Deduced from gamma ray measurements.[465,466,467]
d Deduced from $\alpha\gamma$ and αe^- measurements.[468]
e Measured in magnetic α-spectrometer relative to Bi^{212} groups taken equal to 6.0898 and 6.0506 MeV.

[465] F. Asaro, S. G. Thompson, and I. Perlman, *Phys. Rev.* **92**, 694 (1953); **87**, 277 (1952).
[466] F. Asaro, B. G. Harvey, F. S. Stephens, Jr., and I. Perlman, unpublished data 1955–1956; *Bull Am. Phys. Soc. Series II*, **2**, 394 (1957).
[467] F. S. Stephens, Jr., F. Asaro, and I. Perlman, *Phys. Rev.* **100**, 1543 (1955).
[468] S. Bjornholm, M. Lederer, F. Asaro, and I. Perlman, *Phys. Rev.* **130**, 2000 (1963).
[469] L. N. Kondrat'ev, V.D. Dedov, and L. L. Gol'din, *Izvest. Akad. Nauk USSR, Ser. Fiz.* **22**, 99 (1958).
[469a] R. B. Ivanov, A. S. Krivokhatskii, and V. G. Nedovesov, *Izvest. Akad. Nauk USSR Ser. Fiz.* **26**, 976 (1962); *Sov. Phys. JETP* **18**, 937 (1964).

represent transitions to excited levels in Pu^{238} which are de-excited by gamma ray transitions.   Since the beta decay of Np^{238} and the electron capture decay of Am^{238} result in the same end product nucleus, it is instructive to compare the decay schemes of the three isotopes.   This is done in Fig. 9.35. The decay scheme of Cm^{242} is shown separately in another form in Fig. 9.36.

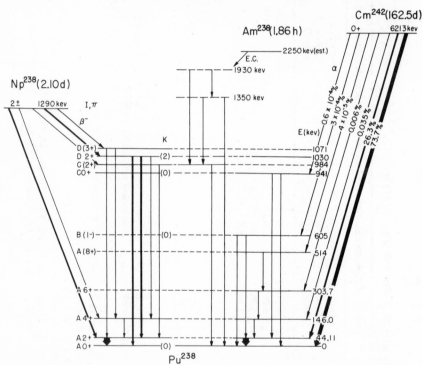

FIG. **9.35.** Level scheme of Pu^{238} deduced from decay schemes of Cm^{242}, Np^{238}, and Am^{238}.

By far the most prominent gamma transition is the 44.11 keV $E2$ transition from the first excited state to the ground state.   ASARO, THOMPSON, AND PERLMAN[465] found the L-shell conversion coefficient of this gamma ray to be 520.   O'KELLEY[470] and PASSELL[471] measured the conversion electrons of this transition in a double focusing beta ray spectrometer and found a transition energy of 44.9 keV.   NEWTON, ROSE, AND MILSTED[472] used a

[470] G. D. O'Kelley, Ph.D. Thesis, University of California, May 1951; also published as *Univ. Calif. Rad. Lab. Report UCRL-1243*, May 1954.

[471] T. O. Passell, Ph.D. Thesis, University of California, March 1954; also published as *Univ. Calif. Rad. Lab. Report UCRL-2528*, March 1954.

[472] J. O. Newton, B. Rose, and J. Milsted, "Gamma Radiation from the Decay of Pu^{238}, Cm^{242} and Cm^{243}," *Phil. Mag.* **1**, 981 (1956).

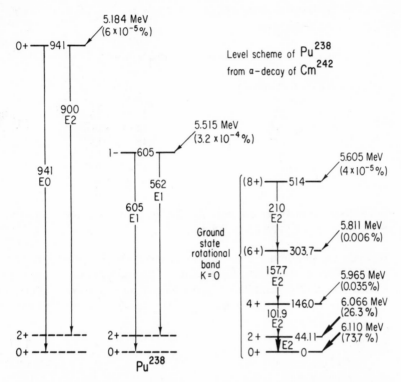

FIG. 9.36. Decay scheme of Cm²⁴² with gamma transitions isolated to clarify different features of the level scheme of Pu²³⁸.

proportional counter to measure a gamma energy of 44.03 ± 0.06 keV and an abundance of 3.9×10^{-4} photons per alpha particle. SMITH AND HOL-LANDER[473] measured the conversion electrons in a permanent magnet spectrograph and obtained a value of 44.11 ± 0.05 keV. BARANOV AND SHLYAGIN[474] report an energy of 44.1 keV. HUMMEL[475] measured an abundance of 2.9×10^{-4} 44 keV photons per alpha particle. These energy values are in close agreement with those reported for the identical transition which occurs in the beta decay of Np²³⁸. (See Section 9.1.10.) From the conversion coefficient and the L_{II}/L_{III} subshell ratio this transition is clearly electric quadrupole in nature.

The conversion of the 44.1 keV transition gives rise to L x-rays of plutonium which have been measured carefully in a Cauchois-type bent-crystal

[473] W. G. Smith and J. M. Hollander, *Phys. Rev.* **101**, 746 (1956).

[474] S. A. Baranov and K. N. Shlyagin, *Sov. J. Atom. Energ.*, **51**, No. 1 (1956).

[475] J. P. Hummel, Ph.D. Thesis, University of California, July 1956; also published as *Univ. Calif. Rad. Lab Report UCRL-3456*, July 1956.

spectrometer by BARTON, ROBINSON, AND PERLMAN.[476]   Table 9.30 lists the x-rays which were observed.

TABLE **9.30.** Plutonium x-rays emitted in the decay of Cm^{242}.

x-ray disintegration	Energy
L_{α_1}	14.31 ± 0.01
L_{α_2}	14.14 ± 0.01
L_{β_1}	18.35 ± 0.02
L_{β_5}	17.91 ± 0.02
L_{β_2}	17.28 ± 0.02
L_{γ}	21.46 ± 0.04
L_{γ_6}	22.20 ± 0.04

Barton, Robinson and Perlman, *Phys. Rev.* **81**, 208 (1951).   For fuller discussion of heavy element x-rays see Appendix II, Vol. I.

Whereas the plutonium L x-radiation constitutes the principal electromagnetic radiation of Cm^{242}, the photons of several gamma-ray transitions have been observed in scintillation spectrometer measurements.   These are summarized in Table 9.31.   It will be noted that these gamma rays are in very

TABLE **9.31.** Gamma rays of Cm^{242}.

Energy (keV)	Photon abundances relative to total alphas	Multipole order	Comments	Ref.
44.11	2.9×10^{-4}	$E2$		465, 470, 471, 472, 473, 475
101.9	4.1×10^{-5}	$E2$		465, 472, 473, 475
157.7	1.8×10^{-5}	$E2$	in cascade with 101.9 keV γ	465, 472, 473, 475
210	1.5×10^{-7}	$E2$	in cascade with 157.7, 101.9 keV γ's	466
562	1.8×10^{-6}	$E1$	de-excites $1-$ level at 605 keV; in cascade with L x-rays of 44 keV γ	467
605	1.4×10^{-6}	$E1$	de-excites $1-$ level at 605 keV	467
900	2.6×10^{-7}	$E2$	de-excites $0+$ level at 941 keV; in cascade with L x-rays of 44 keV γ	466, 468
941	none observed	$E0$	completely converted; de-excites $0+$ level at 941 keV	466

[476] G. W. Barton, H. P. Robinson, and I. Perlman, *Phys. Rev.* **81**, 208 (1951).

low abundance corresponding to very small intensities of alpha groups to excited levels of Pu^{238}. The intensity of some of these gamma rays is so low that gamma rays from the spontaneous fission of Cm^{242} interfere with the measurements. The spontaneous-fission gamma ray background may be decreased appreciably by anti-coincidence techniques.

These gamma rays are placed in the decay scheme of Figs. 9.35 and 9.36. Several interesting features of the level scheme of Pu^{238} may be mentioned. A well developed rotational band based on the 0+ ground state is observed with the levels at 44.11 (2+), 146.0 (4+), 303.7 (6+), and 514 keV (8+) following closely the rotational formula given in Chapter 3 where $\hbar^2/2\mathfrak{J}$ is set equal to 7.37 keV and the constant B of the second order correction term is set equal to 0.0033 keV. De-excitation by the predicted cascade of $E2$ transitions with no observable cross over transitions is verified.

The level at 605, assigned spin and parity 1−, was deduced[467] from a pair of gamma rays at 605 keV and about 560 keV. From the electron spectrum taken with the aid of an anthracene crystal,[466] the average K conversion coefficient for these gamma rays was found to be $\gtrsim 1$ per cent, indicating $E1$ or $E2$ transitions. The higher-energy component was not in coincidence with any photons and the lower energy component was in coincidence with L x-rays proving that it leads to the 2+ level at 44.11 keV. Such pairs of gamma rays have been seen[477] in other heavy even-even nuclei and have been proved to be $E1$ transitions arising from 1− states. In all cases examined in which the 1− assignment was established the reduced transition probabilities of the competing $E1$ transitions were found in the ratio, 0.5, expected for the K-quantum number assignment of 0 for the 1− state as well as for the rotational band based upon the ground state. This same relationship of the reduced transition probabilities was found in the present case. (Actual experimental value = 0.6.) A general discussion of these 1− states is given in Section 3.6.3 of Chapter 3.

The 900 keV $E2$ transition and the 941-keV $E0$ transition shown in Table 9.31 and Figs. 9.35 and 9.36 are quite interesting. The electric monopole transition goes entirely by the emission of conversion electrons. Hence, this transition was overlooked until considerations of excited-level systematics in heavy element nuclei (see discussion in Section 3.6.2 in Chapter 3) suggested that such an electric monopole transition might exist. Such a transition exists, for example, in the de-excitation of excited levels of U^{234}. (The 806-keV transition of the decay of UX_2.) CHURCH AND WENESER[478] emphasized the probable importance of $E0$ transitions in heavy nuclei. For these reasons and also because photons of an 890-keV $E2$ transition had been found in cascade with the L x-rays of the 44.11-keV transition discussed above, it

[477] F. S. Stephens, Jr., F. Asaro, and I. Perlman, *Phys. Rev.* **96**, 1568 (1954).
[478] E. L. Church and J. Weneser, *Phys. Rev.* **103**, 1035 (1956).

seemed worthwhile to look for conversion electrons of a completely converted transition from a 935 keV 0+ level to the 0+ ground state. ASARO
AND CO-WORKERS[466] found these conversion electrons using an anthracene

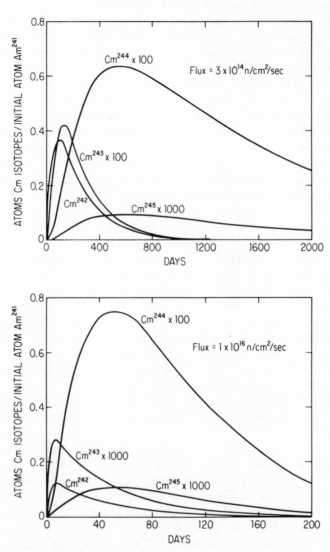

FIG. 9.37. Buildup of curium isotopes in Am^{241} by the neutron capture sequence:

$$Am^{241}(n, \gamma)Am^{242} \xrightarrow[\text{16 hr}]{\beta^-} Cm^{242}(n, \gamma)Cm^{243} \ (n, \gamma)Cm^{244}(n, \gamma)Cm^{245}$$

Curves are given for two neutron fluxes.

crystal spectrometer.   The assignment of the multipolarity is unambiguous. The ratio of the total transition rates of the 900-keV $E2$ gamma ray to the 941-keV $E0$ transition is 0.8.

The other higher levels of Pu^{238} are hard to characterize by studying α decay of Cm^{242} because of the extremely low α-branching to these levels. These are better studied in the β-decay of Np^{238}.   (See Section 9.1.12.)

GHIORSO AND ROBINSON[479] made the observation that the isotope Cm^{242} undergoes spontaneous fission at a high rate (3×10^{10} fissions per gram-hour), corresponding to a half-life for this process of about 7×10^6 years.   HANNA, HARVEY, MOSS, AND TUNNICLIFFE[480] report this half-life to be (7.2 ± 0.2) $\times 10^6$ years corresponding to 2.7×10^{10} fissions per gram-hour.   Many characteristics of the spontaneous fission of Cm^{242} have been measured. These experiments are thoroughly discussed in Volume III, Part 1.

9.4.7 *Curium-243*

When a sample of Am^{241} or Cm^{242} is strongly irradiated with slow neutrons, Cm^{243} is produced via the reactions

$$Am^{241}(n, \gamma)Am^{242} \xrightarrow[16\ hr]{\beta^-} Cm^{242}(n, \gamma)Cm^{243}.$$

REYNOLDS, HULET, AND STREET[482] first produced this isotope in this manner and identified it by mass spectroscopic analysis.   The conversion of Am^{241} to Cm^{242} and higher isotopes of curium is illustrated graphically in Fig. 9.37.

The isotope Cm^{243} has also been identified experimentally as the daughter of 4.6-hour Bk^{243}.

Curium-243 decays by emission of alpha particles.   An early publication[483] gave a half-life value of 35 years determined on an isotopically impure sample by a combination of mass spectrometric analysis, alpha spectrum analysis, and specific activity measurements.   However, later measurements[484] of the alpha spectrum showed that only 90 per cent of the alpha groups had been identified; a correction for this reduces the half-life value to 32 years.

ASARO, THOMPSON, STEPHENS, AND PERLMAN[484] measured the alpha spectrum of samples of curium containing varying amounts of Cm^{242}, Cm^{243}, and Cm^{244} and assigned to Cm^{243} the groups listed in Table 9.32.

[479] A Ghiorso and H. P. Robinson, unpublished results, 1947.

[480] G. C. Hanna, B. G. Harvey, N. Moss, and P. R. Tunnicliffe, *Phys. Rev.* **81**, 466 (1951).

[482] F. L. Reynolds, E. K. Hulet, and K. Street, Jr., *Phys. Rev.* **80**, 467 (1950).

[483] F. Asaro, Ph.D. Thesis, University of California, June 1953; also published as *Univ. Calif. Rad. Lab. Report UCRL-2180.*

[484] F. Asaro, S. G. Thompson, F. S. Stephens, Jr., and I. Perlman, *Bull. Amer. Phys. Soc.* **8**, 393 (1957); unpublished results (1956–1957); F. Asaro, S. G. Thompson, and I. Perlman, *Phys. Rev.* **92**, 694 (1953).

The alpha particle groups define excited levels of Pu^{239} as shown in Fig. 9.38. An interpretation of the level scheme of Pu^{239} is given in Section 9.1.12 where the decay of Np^{239} is described. The complex structure of the α-spectrum of Cm^{243} implies the existence of many low-intensity gamma rays. Experimental difficulties have retarded the investigation of many of these.

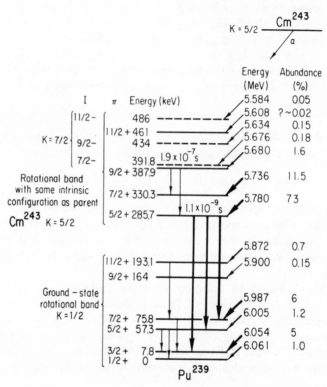

FIG. 9.38. Decay scheme of Cm^{243} including interpretation of Pu^{239} levels as three sets of rotational levels based on three states of intrinsic excitation (Nilsson orbitals).

The data of NEWTON, ROSE, AND MILSTED[485] on the gamma spectrum are summarized in Table 9.33. The 278 and 228 keV gamma rays have been shown[484] to be in coincidence with the most intense α-groups at about 5.78 MeV.

---

[485] J. O. Newton, B. Rose and J. Milsted, "Gamma Radiation from the Decay of Pu^{238}, Cm^{242} and Cm^{243}," *Phil. Mag.* 1, 981 (1956).

TABLE 9.32. Alpha groups of Cm^{243}.

6.061 MeV	1.0%
6.054 MeV	5%
6.005 MeV	1.2%
5.987 MeV	6%
5.900 MeV	0.15%
5.872 MeV	0.7%
5.780 MeV	73%
5.736 MeV	11.5%
5.680 MeV	1.6%
5.676 MeV	0.18%
5.634 MeV	0.15%
5.608 MeV (?)	~0.02%
5.584 MeV	0.05%

From Asaro, Thompson, Stephens and Perlman, *Phys. Rev.* **92**, 694 (1953); *Bull. Am. Phys. Soc.* **8**, 393 (1957); and unpublished results, 1956–1957; very similar results were published by B. S. Dzhelepov, R. B. Ivanov, V. G. Nedovesov, and V. P. Chechev, *Sov. Phys. JETP* **18**, 937 (1964).

TABLE 9.33. Gamma rays in decay of Cm^{243}.

Gamma ray energy (keV)	Relative intensity	
102.15 ± 0.2	3.6 ± 0.2	K_α Pu x-ray
117.3 ± 0.4	1.4 ± 0.2	K_β Pu x-ray
210 ± 1.5	0.5 ± 0.15	
228 ± 2	0.65 ± 0.15	
277 ± 2	1.00	

From Newton, Rose, and Milsted, *Phil. Mag.* **1**, 981 (1956).

TABLE 9.34. Cm^{243} alpha decay to 5/2+ band of Pu^{239} (unhindered decay)

$$P_\alpha \propto \sum_L \frac{1}{\text{H.F.}} \left[C^{I_i L \, I_f}_{K_i K_f - K_i K_f} \right]^2$$

I	E	Calculated abundances (per cent)					Experimental abundances
		L = 0	L = 2	L = 4	L = 6	Sum	
5/2	286	57.0 (norm)	16.0	0.0	—	73	73
7/2	330	—	9.2	0.0	0.0	9.2	11.5
9/2	388	—	1.57	0.01	0.0	1.58	1.6
11/2	461	—	—	0.0037	0.0026	0.006	~0.02?
13/2	547 (calc)	—	—	0.0004	0.0015	0.002	<0.02
Assumed relative hindrance factors from Cm^{242} and Cm^{244} decay		1.00	1.82	590	580		

ASARO, THOMPSON, STEPHENS, AND PERLMAN[484] have interpreted the alpha decay to the levels shown in Fig. 9.38 in terms of the theory of BOHR, FRÖMAN, AND MOTTELSON[486] for unhindered (favored) alpha decay.

Table 9.34 shows the calculated and experimental alpha particle populations to the rotational states with the same intrinsic configuration as the parent nucleus, Cm^{243}. The decay probabilities for alpha particles with various angular momenta were taken from the adjacent even-even nuclides. Table 9.35 shows the data for hindered (unfavored) alpha decay to states

TABLE 9.35. Cm^{243} alpha decay to 7/2— band

$$P_\alpha \text{ (reduced)} \propto \sum_L \frac{1}{\text{H.F.}} \left[C_{K_i K_f - K_i K_f}^{I_i L \ I_f} \right]^2 \ L < K_i + K_f$$

I	E (keV)	Calculated abundances (per cent)			Experimental abundances
		L = 1	L = 3	Sum	
7/2	392	0.07 (norm)	0.11	0.18 (norm)	0.18
9/2	434	—	0.15 (norm)	0.15 (norm)	0.15
11/2	485	—	0.042	0.042	0.05
Hindrance factor		4×10^2	59		

with a different intrinsic configuration than the parent nucleus. For this type of decay the relative decay probabilities are not known for alpha particles with different angular momenta and are arbitrarily normalized to give the proper experimental ratio for the 392 and 434 keV levels. The calculated population to the 485 keV level serves as an independent check of the method and is in satisfactory agreement with the experimental value. The hindered decay to the ground state rotational band is more complicated because an appreciable portion of the decay takes place by alpha particles whose angular momenta are equal to or less than the sum of $K_i + K_f$. Waves of a given angular momentum then populate levels with $\pm K_f$ and can interfere with each other. Table 9.36 shows the calculated and experimental abundances. Five of the experimental abundances were used to evaluate the parameters in the equations and the sixth value served as an independent check of the method.

CHOPPIN AND THOMPSON[487] found that Cm^{243} is slightly unstable toward electron capture decay with an electron capture half-life of $(1 \pm 0.1) \times 10^4$

[486] A. Bohr, P. O. Fröman, and B. R. Mottelson, *Dan. Mat.-fys. Medd.* **29**, No. 10 (1955).

[487] G. R. Choppin and S. G. Thompson, *J. Inorg. Nucl. Chem.* **7**, 197 (1958).

years.   Previously[488] a lower limit of 50,000 years had been placed on the electron capture half-life.

TABLE **9.36.** Alpha decay of Cm^{243} to $1/2+$ band of Pu^{239}

$$P_{\alpha,L}(\text{reduced}) \propto \left[C^{I_iLI_f}_{K_iK_f - K_iK_f} + b(-1)^{(I_f + K_f)} C^{I_iL\ I_f}_{K_i,-K_f-K_i,-K_f} \right]^2 L \gtrless K_f + K_i$$

		Calculated abundance (per cent)				
I	E (keV)	$L = 2$	$L = 4$ $b = 1.9$	$L = 6$ $b = 2.2$ $b = 0.3$	Sum	Experimental abundances
1/2	0	1.00 (norm)	—	—	1.00 (norm)	1.0%
3/2	8	1.05	3.78 (norm)	—	4.83 (norm)	4.8
5/2	57	0.33	0.86 (norm)	—	1.19 (norm)	1.2
7/2	76	0.08	5.22	0.45	5.75	6.1
9/2	164	0.00	0.03	0.12 (norm)	0.15 (norm)	0.15
11/2	193	—	0.21	0.49 (norm)	0.70 (norm)	0.70
Hindrance factor		1100	800	2300		

9.4.8 *Curium-244*

The long-lived curium isotope Cm^{244} was first identified[489] by mass spectrographic analysis of a curium sample produced by neutron irradiation of Am^{241}.   The Cm^{244} is produced in such an irradiation through four separate paths, because of the different modes of decay of Am^{242} and the existence of isomeric forms of Am^{242}.

$Am^{241}(n, \gamma)Am^{242}(100 \text{ yr}); Am^{242}(n, \gamma)Am^{243}(n, \gamma)Am^{244} \xrightarrow[25 \text{ min}]{\beta^-} Cm^{244}$

$Am^{241}(n, \gamma)Am^{242}(16 \text{ hr}); Am^{242}(n, \gamma)Am^{243}(n, \gamma)Am^{244} \xrightarrow[25 \text{ min}]{\beta^-} Cm^{244}$

$Am^{242} \xrightarrow[16 \text{ hr}]{\beta^-} Cm^{242}(n, \gamma)Cm^{243}(n, \gamma)Cm^{244}$

$Am^{242} \xrightarrow[16 \text{ hr}]{EC} Pu^{242}(n, \gamma)Pu^{243} \xrightarrow[5 \text{ hr}]{\beta^-} Am^{243}(n, \gamma)Am^{244} \xrightarrow[25 \text{ min}]{\beta^-} Cm^{244}$

Figure 9.37 in the previous section illustrates the rate of build-up of Cm^{244} as

---

[488] E. K. Hulet, Ph.D. Thesis, University of California, August 1953; also published as *Univ. Calif. Rad. Lab. Report UCRL-2283.*

[489] F. L. Reynolds, E. K. Hulet, and K. Street, Jr., *Phys. Rev.* **80**, 476 (1950).

a function of neutron irradiation. These curves are approximate because of uncertainties in the neutron capture cross sections of some of the isotopes in the chain.

The most satisfactory way to make large amounts of Cm^{244} in high isotopic purity is to irradiate Pu^{239} or Pu^{242} with neutrons in a high flux reactor.[490]   The main sequence of reactions leads directly to Cm^{244} as follows:

$$Pu^{239}(n, \gamma)Pu^{240}(n, \gamma)Pu^{241}(n, \gamma)Pu^{242}(n, \gamma)Pu^{243} \xrightarrow[5\,hr]{\beta^-}$$

$$Am^{243}(n, \gamma)\ Am^{244} \xrightarrow[25\,min]{\beta^-} Cm^{244}$$

The build-up of Cm^{244} by this mechanism when the neutron flux is 3×10^{14} $n/cm^2/sec$ is shown in Chapter 5. In an experiment[491] in which Pu^{239} was irradiated at this flux until the total integrated flux was 1.4×10^{22} neutrons/cm^2, it was found by mass spectrographic analysis that the isotopic composition of the curium fraction was the following:

Cm^{242}	0.68 per cent
Cm^{244}	96.29 per cent
Cm^{245}	1.14 per cent
Cm^{246}	1.86 per cent
Cm^{247}	0.028 per cent

If it is desirable to achieve a higher isotopic purity, the above neutron capture sequence can be interrupted when a good yield of Am^{243} has been achieved, the Am^{243} can be chemically purified and then reinserted in the reactor for the final transmutation to curium via the short sequence:

$$Am^{243}(n, \gamma)Am^{244} \xrightarrow[25\,min]{\beta^-} Cm^{244}$$

The half-life of Cm^{244} has been determined in three ways. THOMPSON, HULET, AND GHIORSO[492] followed the decay directly to obtain a value of 19 years. STEVENS AND CO-WORKERS[490] determined the atom ratio and alpha activity ratio of Cm^{244} to Cm^{242} in a mixture of the two isotopes and from the known half-life of 162.5 days for Cm^{242} were able to calculate an alpha half-life of 19.2 ± 0.6 years for Cm^{244}. FRIEDMAN AND CO-WORKERS[493] measured the atom ratio of Cm^{244} to Cm^{242} in a mixture of the two isotopes. After a certain decay period the plutonium daughters Pu^{240} and Pu^{238} were isolated and the ratio of the two determined mass spectrographically.

490 C. M. Stevens, M. H. Studier, P. R. Fields, J. F. Mech, P. A. Sellers, A. M. Friedman, H. Diamond, and J. R. Huizenga, *Phys. Rev.* **94**, 974 (1954).

491 W. C. Bentley, *et al.*, Paper No. P/809, *Proceedings of the International Conference on the Peaceful Uses of Atomic Energy* 7, United Nations, New York (1956).

492 S. G. Thompson, E. K. Hulet, and A. Ghiorso, unpublished data reported in *Revs. Mod. Phys.* **25**, 611 (1953).

493 A. M. Friedman, A. L. Harkness, P. R. Fields, M. H. Studier, and J. R. Huizenga, *Phys. Rev.* **95**, 1501 (1954).

From these data and the known half-life of Cm^{242}, the half-life of Cm^{244} was calculated to be 17.9 ± 0.5 years. CARNALL, FRIED, AND HARKNESS[494] measured the specific activity of a curium sample (in the form of $CmCl_3$) which was 94.57 per cent Cm^{244} in isotopic content and almost pure Cm^{244} by alpha activity. They reported a half-life of 17.59 ± 0.06 years.*

The alpha spectrum of Cm^{244} was first determined on a magnetic spectrometer by ASARO, THOMPSON, AND PERLMAN[495] who reported alpha groups of 5.798 MeV (75 per cent) and 5.755 MeV (25 per cent) with respect to an energy of 6.110 MeV for Cm^{242}. WHITE AND CO-WORKERS[496] later remeasured the energy of the main transition and obtained a value of 5.8025 ± 0.002 MeV with respect to an energy of 5.305 MeV for Po^{210}. More recently MICHEL, ASARO, AND PERLMAN[497] measured a value of 5.802 ± 0.001 MeV relative to a value of 5.8614 MeV for the α_0 group of Ra^{224}. HUMMEL, ASARO, AND PERLMAN[475] measured the energies and abundances of the alpha groups of Cm^{244} relative to the ground state. ASARO AND PERLMAN[498] measured the low intensity groups of Cm^{244} with respect to the 5.272 MeV alpha group as a standard. These results together with those of HUMMEL[495] and of MICHEL[497] are shown in Table 9.37. IVANOV AND CO-WORKERS[498a] published values for the three most prominent groups; these agree with the values in Table 9.37.

HUMMEL[475] has studied the gamma rays of Cm^{244} using a scintillation spectrometer. He found three gamma rays with the following abundances relative to the alpha disintegration rate: 43 keV (2.1×10^{-4}), 100 keV (1.3×10^{-5}) and 150 keV (1.4×10^{-5}). SMITH AND HOLLANDER[499] measured the conversion electrons of the first of these gamma rays. They found a transition energy of 42.88 ± 0.05 keV and defined the transition as $E2$ from the absence of L_I electrons and from an L_{II}/L_{III} conversion ratio of 1.10 in agreement with the theoretical prediction. In the electron capture decay of Am^{240} to the same Pu^{240} daughter nucleus the 42.88-keV gamma ray also appears as shown by SMITH, GIBSON, AND HOLLANDER.[500] The 100 keV gamma ray occurs also in Am^{240} decay and the conversion electron measurements show it to be a 98.90 ± 0.2 keV $E2$ transition.

---

* A more recent determination by W. C. Bentley gave 18.11 ± 0.07 years, as reported by D. Metta et al., J. Inorg. Nucl. Chem. (1964).

[494] W. T. Carnall, S. Fried, and A. L. Harkness, J. Inorg. Nucl. Chem. 17, 12 (1961).

[495] F. Asaro, S. G. Thompson, and I. Perlman, Phys. Rev. 92, 694 (1953).

[496] F. A. White, F. M. Rourke, J. C. Sheffield, R. P. Schuman, and J. R. Huizenga, Phys. Rev. 109, 437 (1958).

[497] H. V. Michel, F. Asaro, and I. Perlman, unpublished results, 1963.

[498] F. Asaro and I. Perlman, unpublished results, 1960.

[498a] R. B. Ivanov, A. S. Krivokhatskii, and V. G. Nedovesov, Izvest Akad. Nauk; Ser. Fiz. 26, 976 (1962); Sov. Phys. JETP 18 937 (1964)

[499] W. G. Smith and J. M. Hollander, Phys. Rev. 101, 746 (1956).

[500] W. G. Smith, W. M. Gibson, and J. M. Hollander, Phys. Rev. 105, 1514 (1957).

TABLE 9.37. Alpha particle groups of Cm[244].

Energy (MeV)	Abundance (per cent)	Energy of excited level in Pu[240] daughter (keV)
5.802 ± 0.001[a]	76.7[b]	0
5.760[b]	23.3[b]	42.9
5.663	$(2.3 \pm 0.2) \times 10^{-2}$	142.2
5.511	$(3.6 \pm 0.3) \times 10^{-3}$	296
5.316?	$\sim 1.5 \times 10^{-4}$	495
5.212	1.5×10^{-4}	600
4.953	$(1.55 \pm 0.16) \times 10^{-4}$	863
4.913	$(5.0 \pm 0.5) \times 10^{-5}$	904

(rows 5.663 through 4.913 grouped with label [c])

[a] Data of Michel, Asaro, and Perlman.[497]
[b] Data of Hummel, Asaro, and Perlman.[475]
[c] Data of Asaro and Perlman (1960–1).

These data on the alpha and gamma transitions of Cm^{244} lead to the decay scheme shown in the figure. This resembles the decay scheme of all other even-even nuclei in this mass region. The lowest lying excited levels of Pu^{240} are members of a rotational band of levels based on a $0+$ $(K = 0)$ ground state.

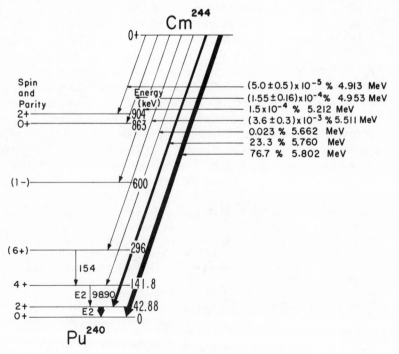

FIG. 9.39. Decay scheme of Cm[244].

Other information on the levels of Pu^{240} is based on the β-decay of Np^{240}. (See Section 9.4.13.) Excited levels at 600 keV $(1-)$, 863 keV $(0+)$, 903 keV $(2+)$, and possibly 942 keV $(2+)$ are known and have been tentatively identified as collective states of octupole, β-quadrupole and γ-quadrupole vibration, respectively. BJØRNHOLM, LEDERER, ASARO, AND PERLMAN[501] have looked for alpha decay to these Pu^{240} levels by sensitive $\alpha\gamma$ coincidence techniques. They found a population of the 600 keV $(1-)$ level plus possible contributions to the rotational excitation band of this state to be $(1.1 \pm 0.2) \times 10^{-6}$, corresponding to an alpha decay hindrance factor of 100 ± 20. They also observed a population of the 863 keV level and its rotational band members of $(2.3 \pm 0.4) \times 10^{-6}$ corresponding to a hindrance factor of 3. They set a very low upper limit on alpha decay to the $2+$ level at 942 keV, corresponding to a hindrance factor of >100. A direct measurement of the alpha spectrum in a magnetic spectrograph by ASARO AND PERLMAN[498] confirmed the presence of groups leading to the $0+$ state at 863 keV and to the first rotational excitation of the state, i.e., to the $2+$ state at 903 keV. The measured intensities were $(1.55 \pm 0.16) \times 10^{-6}$ and $(0.50 \pm 0.08) \times 10^{-6}$.

Curium-244 is beta stable.

The spontaneous fission rate of Cm^{244} is quite high compared to isotopes of lighter elements. GHIORSO AND CO-WORKERS[502] measured a spontaneous fission rate of $(1.4 \pm 0.2) \times 10^{10}$ fissions per gram hour, corresponding to a half-life of $(1.4 \pm 0.2) \times 10^7$ years.

9.4.9 Curium-245

The existence of Cm^{245} was first proved by REYNOLDS'[504] mass spectrographic analysis of samples of curium subjected to prolonged neutron irradiation in the Chalk River reactor. Pure but small samples of Cm^{245} were first obtained[505,506] by examining the curium daughter fraction from a sample of berkelium which contained 4.95-day Bk^{245}, an isotope which decays chiefly by electron capture. The curium fraction from Pu^{239} subjected to prolonged neutron irradiation also contains Cm^{245}. STEVENS AND CO-WORKERS[507] report the values quoted in Table 9.38 given in the next section for the isotopic composition of a curium fraction isolated from a sample of

[501] S. Bjørnholm, M. Lederer, F. Asaro, and I. Perlman, Phys. Rev. 130, 2000 (1963),

[502] A. Ghiorso, G. H. Higgins, A. E. Larsh, G. T. Seaborg, and S. G. Thompson. Phys. Rev. 87, 163 (1952).

[504] F. L. Reynolds, unpublished data.

[505] E. K. Hulet, S. G. Thompson, A. Ghiorso, and K. Street, Jr., Phys. Rev. 84, 366 (1951).

[506] E. K. Hulet, S. G. Thompson, and A. Ghiorso, Phys. Rev. 95, 1703 (1954).

[507] C. M. Stevens, M. H. Studier, P. R. Fields, J. F. Mech, P. A. Sellers, A. M. Friedman, H. Diamond, and J. R. Huizenga, Phys. Rev. 94, 974 (1954).

Pu^{239} irradiated at a flux of 3×10^{14} neutrons/cm^2/sec for a total irradiation of 8×10^{21} neutrons/cm^2.

Curium-245 has been found in the curium fraction isolated from the debris of thermonuclear test explosions. In one case the curium fraction was mass analyzed and found to contain 68.7 atom per cent Cm^{245}, the rest of the sample being higher mass isotopes.[508] (See Table 9.38 in the next section.) Curium isotopes made in this way arise only from β-decay processes and those below mass number 245 are blocked by β stable isotopes of plutonium or americium.

FRIEDMAN AND CO-WORKERS[509] measured the half-life of Cm^{245} by mass spectrographic techniques and determined a value of $(1.15 \pm 0.5) \times 10^4$ years. BROWNE AND CO-WORKERS[510] report a value of 14,300 years $\pm$ 20 per cent. DIAMOND[511] reports a value of $(7.5 \pm 1.9) \times 10^3$ years. CAR-NALL, FRIED, AND HARKNESS[512] obtained a value of 9320 ± 280 based on mass spectrometric assay of the isotopic composition of plutonium growing into a mixed sample of Cm^{245} and Cm^{244}. This value also depends on a choice of 17.59 years for the half-life of Cm^{244}.

The energies of the alpha particles of Cm^{245} have been measured roughly by the ionization chamber method. HULET AND CO-WORKERS[506] report a main group at 5.36 MeV and a smaller intensity group[513] at 5.45 MeV. ASARO, THOMPSON, AND PERLMAN[514] find that the prominent features of the gamma ray spectrum of Cm^{245} as determined by a scintillation spectrometer are K x-rays and 130-keV and 172-keV gamma rays. The gamma ray results indicate the existence of an alpha particle group at 5.31 MeV. They also suggest that the most intense alpha group proceeds to an excited state at 172 keV in Pu^{241} which de-excites to the ground state via a 172 keV $M1$ transition. The alpha spectrum is given as 5.45 MeV ($\sim$ 15 per cent), 5.36 MeV ($\sim$ 77 per cent) and 5.31 ($\sim$ 8 per cent). In a later measurement of the alpha spectrum with a magnetic spectrograph ASARO AND PERLMAN[515] found alpha groups at 5.356 MeV (93 per cent) and 5.301 MeV (7 per cent) measured relative to the α_{75} group of Am^{243} taken as 5.272 MeV. In these

508 P. R. Fields, M. H. Studier, H. Diamond, J. F. Mech, M. G. Inghram, G. L. Pyle, C. M. Stevens, S. Fried, W. M. Manning, A. Ghiorso, S. G. Thompson, G. H. Higgins, and G. T. Seaborg, *Phys. Rev.* **102**, 180 (1956).

509 A. M. Friedman, A. L. Harkness, P. R. Fields, M. H. Studier, and J. R. Huizenga, *Phys. Rev.* **95**, 1501 (1954).

510 C. I. Browne, *et al., J. Inorg. Nucl. Chem.* **1**, 254 (1955).

511 H. Diamond as reported in Table III, *Phys. Rev.* **107**, 1087 (1957).

512 W. T. Carnall, S. Fried, and A. L. Harkness, *J. Inorg. Nucl. Chem.* **17**, 12 (1961).

513 E. K. Hulet, unpublished information, 1956.

514 F. Asaro, S. G. Thompson, and I. Perlman, unpublished results, 1956, as cited in I. Perlman and J. O. Rasmussen, "Alpha Radioactivity," in *Handbuch der Physik* **42**, Berlin: Springer-Verlag, 1957.

515 F. Asaro and I. Perlman, unpublished results, 1960–1961.

experiments the alpha group at 5.45 MeV observed in the previous ion chamber measurements would have been obscured by a Pu^{238} alpha group from Pu^{238} activity present in the sample. The 15 per cent abundance of the 5.45 MeV group found in the ion chamber measurement might be explained as resulting from the internal coincidences of conversion electrons of the intense 172 keV transition and the 5.356 MeV alpha group.

Curium-245 is beta stable.

More experimental data are required[515a] before a reliable decay scheme can be constructed for Cm^{245}, but a few features can be interpreted in terms of Nilsson orbital assignments. This has been done in the following way by STEPHENS, ASARO, AND PERLMAN[516] and by NILSSON AND MOTTELSON.[517] The ground state spin of Pu^{241} has been measured as 5/2.

There are only two likely orbitals of spin 5/2 available for the odd neutron in a nucleus with 147 neutrons. (See Chapter 3.) One of these, 5/2 + [633], was identified as the ground state for neutron number 141. Therefore Pu^{241} with 147 neutrons is logically assigned to the other, 5/2 + [622]. The favored alpha decay of Cm^{245} leads to a state 172 keV above ground. Another state of 58 keV higher energy has been observed and interpreted as the first member of the rotational band based upon the 172 keV state.[514] This spacing suggests that the band has $K = 7/2$ or higher. The parity is fixed as *even* from the observation that the 172 keV state decays to the ground-state band by $M1$ transitions. This fact not only fixes the parity of the 172 keV state but also is consistent with the spin assignment of 7/2. The only Nilsson assignment in this region with these properties is 7/2 + [624] and the assignment is considered to be reasonably certain. On the basis that favored alpha decay occurs between parent and daughter states with the same Nilsson orbital for the odd nucleon (BOHR, FRÖMAN, AND MOTTELSON, 1955), the ground state assignment of Cm^{245} is also 7/2 + [624].

Several excited levels of Cm^{245} are seen in the α-decay of Cf^{249}, the electron capture decay of Bk^{245}, and the beta decay of Am^{245}. The interpretation of these excited levels is given in the discussion under Cf^{249}, Section 9.6.7.

9.4.10 *The Curium Isotopes Cm^{246}, Cm^{247}, Cm^{248}, Cm^{249}, and Cm^{250}*

The first evidence for Cm^{246}, Cm^{247}, and Cm^{248} came from mass spectrographic analysis of a curium fraction isolated from the debris of a thermonuclear test explosion.[518] Some U^{238} present in the test device was transmuted in the very high instantaneous flux to higher mass isotopes up through mass number 255. Beta decay which occurred subsequent to the

515a See paper by B. S. Dzhelepov et al., Sov. Phys. JETP 18, 937 (1964).

516 F. S. Stephens, Jr., F. Asaro, and I. Perlman, Phys. Rev. 113, 212 (1959).

517 S. G. Nilsson and B. R. Mottelson, Mat.-fys. Skr. Dan. Vid. Selsk. 1, No. 8 (1959).

518 P. R. Fields, et al., Phys. Rev. 102, 180 (1956).

explosion resulted in the production of isotopes of higher elements. The analysis of the curium fraction is given in Table 9.38.

TABLE **9.38.** Mass spectrographic analysis of curium samples containing isotopes of high mass number.

Isotope	Composition (in atom per cent)	
	Thermonuclear "Mike" test debris. Ref. 518	Curium from Pu^{239} irradiated with 8×10^{21} neutrons per cm^2. Ref. 519.
Cm^{242}	—	1.84
Cm^{244}	—	99.51
Cm^{245}	68.7 ± 0.4	1.27
Cm^{246}	28.4 ± 0.4	1.36
Cm^{247}	2.2 ± 0.1	0.016
Cm^{248}	0.7 ± 0.2	—

No detectable amounts of Cm^{242}, Cm^{243}, and Cm^{244} appeared in the bomb debris samples because the beta-decay chains were interrupted at Pu^{242}, Am^{243}, and Pu^{244}, respectively. For the higher-mass chains the sequences are as follows:

$$U^{245} \xrightarrow[\text{short}]{\beta^-} Np^{245} \xrightarrow[\text{short}]{\beta^-} Pu^{245} \xrightarrow[12 \pm 1 \text{ hr}]{\beta^-} Am^{245} \xrightarrow[2.08 \text{ hr}]{\beta^-} Cm^{245}$$
(Ref. 522)

$$U^{246} \xrightarrow[\text{short}]{\beta^-} Np^{246} \xrightarrow[\text{short}]{\beta^-} Pu^{246} \xrightarrow[11 \text{ day}]{\beta^-} Am^{246} \xrightarrow[25 \text{ min}]{\beta^-} Cm^{246}$$
(Ref. 525)

$$U^{247} \xrightarrow[\text{short}]{\beta^-} Np^{247} \xrightarrow[\text{short}]{\beta^-} Pu^{247} \xrightarrow[\text{short}]{\beta^-} Am^{247} \xrightarrow{\beta^-} Cm^{247}$$

$$U^{248} \xrightarrow[\text{short}]{\beta^-} Np^{248} \xrightarrow[\text{short}]{\beta^-} Pu^{248} \xrightarrow[\text{short}]{\beta^-} Am^{248} \xrightarrow{\beta^-} Cm^{248}$$

The isotopes, Cm^{246} and Cm^{247} were soon thereafter prepared by intensive neutron irradiation of Pu^{239} in high flux reactors.[519] Column 3 of the table shows a mass spectrographic analysis of a curium fraction produced in such a way.[519] The atom percentages of the higher isotopes can, of course, be increased substantially by longer irradiation of such preparations.

The isotopes Cm^{246} and Cm^{248} have also been isolated as the daughter products of Cf^{250} and Cf^{252}, respectively.[520] The production of large

---

[519] C. M. Stevens, et al., Phys. Rev. **94**, 974 (1954).

[520] J. P. Butler, T. A. Eastwood, H. G. Jackson, and R. P. Schuman, Phys. Rev. **103**, 965 (1956).

quantities of Cf^{252} in the national Program for Heavy Element Production of the U.S. Atomic Energy Commission makes this an attractive path for the production of Cm^{248}.

The alpha half-life of Cm^{246} was determined by FRIEDMAN AND CO-WORKERS[521] by a mass spectrometric technique. A curium sample with the isotopic composition given in the last column of Table 9.38 was purified thoroughly from plutonium daughter activity. Then after a two week interval the newly-formed plutonium daughter activity containing a mixture of $Pu^{238-242}$ was mass analyzed. The half-life of Cm^{246} was obtained from the following relationship:

$$t_{1/2}\,(Cm^{245}) = t_{1/2}\,(Cm^{242})\,\frac{\text{atom \% } Cm^{245}}{\text{atom \% } Cm^{242}} \times \frac{\text{atom \% } Pu^{238}}{\text{atom \% } Pu^{241}}$$

A value of 4000 ± 600 years was obtained.

BROWNE AND CO-WORKERS[522] obtained the value 2300 ± 460 years and BUTLER AND CO-AUTHORS[520] obtained 6620 ± 320 years for the same half-life by quite different methods. CARNALL, FRIED, AND HARKNESS[523] redetermined the Cm^{246} half-life by a mass spectrometric method identical with that used by FRIEDMAN AND CO-WORKERS[521] with the difference that Cm^{244} rather than Cm^{242} was used as the reference isotope. They reported a value of 5480 ± 140 years for Cm^{246} based on a Cm^{244} half-life of 17.59 years.

The energy of the principal alpha group has been reported as 5.373 ± 0.010 MeV[520] and as 5.382 ± 0.005 MeV[524] (relative to a value of 5.272 MeV for the α_{75} group of Am^{243} used as a standard). The abundance of this group is 79 per cent and that of a second group at 5.338 ± 0.005 MeV is 21 per cent. The energy of the first excited state was set at 44.9 ± 0.3 keV. HULET AND ASARO (unpublished data, 1961) measured the spectrum of an enriched source of Cm^{246} and Cm^{248} and found the energy of the first excited state to be 45.1 keV with an alpha population of 19.0 ± 0.4 per cent. The spontaneous fission half-life is $(2.0 \pm 0.8) \times 10^7$ years.[525] Curium 246 is beta stable.

DIAMOND, FRIEDMAN, GINDLER, AND FIELDS[526] have measured the half-life of Cm^{247} and have discussed the interesting possibility that it may exist in nature. The measurement of the half-life is difficult because of the lack of curium samples containing much Cm^{247}, but, on the other hand, the 4.98

[521] A. M. Friedman, A. L. Harkness, P. R. Fields, M. H. Studier, and J. R. Huizenga, *Phys. Rev.* **95**, 1501 (1954).

[522] C. I. Browne, *et al., J. Inorg. Nucl. Chem.* **1**, 254 (1955).

[523] W. T. Carnall, S. Fried, and A. L. Harkness, *J. Inorg. Nucl. Chem.* **17**, 12 (1961).

[524] F. Asaro and I. Perlman, unpublished results, 1960.

[525] S. M. Fried, G. L. Pyle, C. M. Stevens, and J. R. Huizenga, *J. Inorg. Nucl. Chem.* **2**, 415 (1956).

[526] H. Diamond, A. M. Friedman, J. E. Gindler, and P. R. Fields, *Phys. Rev.* **105**, 679 (1957).

hour Pu^{243} daughter provides a sensitive method for the detection of alpha decay. By searching for Pu^{243} daughter activity in a curium sample of known Cm^{247} content (0.024 mole per cent) and finding none, these investigators set a lower limit of 4×10^7 years for the half-life. However, in a later study by FIELDS AND CO-WORKERS[527] with a curium sample containing 30 times more Cm^{247}, a positive identification of Pu^{243} daughter activity was made and a shorter half-life of $(1.64 \pm 0.24) \times 10^7$ years was found. Other modes of decay were considered. Curium-247 should be beta stable and spontaneous fission systematics would predict a fission half-life of more than 6×10^8 years.

When it was thought that the half-life was of the order of 10^8 years it seemed possible that Cm^{247}, or daughter material attributable to the decay of Cm^{247}, might be identified in terrestrial material. If one makes a reasonable guess at the primordial abundance of Cm^{247} and sets a limit of detection for curium by mass spectrometric methods of one atom of Cm^{247} per 10^{15} atoms of rare earth, one concludes (assuming a Cm^{247} half-life of 10^8 years) that there is some hope of isolating curium in old rare earth minerals. Curium-247 is a nuclide of the $4n + 3$ type decaying into U^{235} by the following decay chain:

$$Cm^{247} \xrightarrow{\alpha} Pu^{243} \xrightarrow[4.98 \text{ hr}]{\beta^-} Am^{243} \xrightarrow[8600 \text{ yr}]{\alpha} Np^{239}$$

$$Np^{239} \xrightarrow[2.33 \text{ days}]{\beta^-} Pu^{239} \xrightarrow[24,400 \text{ yr}]{\alpha} U^{235}$$

Hence, the effects of Cm^{247} might be detected in very old rare earth minerals by finding an abnormally high ratio of U^{235} to U^{238}. Russian workers[528-530] have reported abnormally high ratios of U^{235} to U^{238} in some minerals and alpha activity attributable to Cm^{247} and its decay products in others. If the value of 1.64×10^7 years for the half-life of Cm^{247} measured by FIELDS, et al.[527] is correct these observations must be accounted for in some other way.

The isotope Cm^{248} has not been made in sufficiently high isotopic composition by the neutron irradiation technique that significant measurements of its radiations could be made. It is a product of the alpha decay of Cf^{252}, however, so that it is possible to isolate Cm^{248} alpha activity in a relatively pure state. Californium produced by neutron irradiation of plutonium

[527] P. R. Fields, A. M. Friedman, J. Lerner, D. Metta, and R. Sjoblom, *Phys. Rev.* **131**, 1249 (1963).

[528] V. V. Cherdyntsev, E. A. Isabaev, Yu. A. Surkov, D. P. Orlov, and E. S. Usatov, *Geokhimiya* **4**, 373 (1960).

[529] V. V. Cherdyntsev, D. P. Orlov, E. A. Isabaev, and V. I. Ivanov, *Geokhimiya* **10**, 840 (1961).

[530] Yu. A. Surkov, A. A. Vorob'ev, G. A. Korolev, and V. D. Vilenskii, *Atomnaya Energ.* **9**, 477 (1960).

consists of Cf^{249}, Cf^{250}, Cf^{251} and Cf^{252}, but most of the alpha activity is due to Cf^{252} since it has the shortest half-life and is prepared in high abundance.   Most of the remaining alpha activity is assignable to Cf^{250}.   Thus, the curium daughter fraction will consist mainly of Cm^{248} and Cm^{246} with very small amounts of Cm^{247} and Cm^{245}.   By this "milking" technique BUTLER AND CO-AUTHORS[520] determined an alpha half-life for Cm^{248} of $(4.7 \pm 0.4) \times 10^5$ years, based on a half-life of 2.2 ± 0.2 years for Cf^{252}. They reported an alpha particle energy of 5.054 ± 0.015 MeV.   HULET AND ASARO (unpublished data, 1961) measured the alpha spectrum of Cm^{248} in a magnetic spectrograph and observed two alpha groups.   The most intense group had an abundance of 82 per cent and an energy of 5.074 MeV with respect to a value of 5.382 MeV for the α_0 group of Cm^{246}.   The second alpha group, which populates the first excited state of Pu^{244} at 45 keV, was found to have an energy of 5.030 MeV and an abundance of 18.1 ± 1.3 per cent.

BUTLER AND CO-AUTHORS[520] measured a spontaneous fission half-life of $(4.6 \pm 0.5) \times 10^6$ years.   It is interesting that the spontaneous fission accounts for 11 per cent of the total decay events.

THOMPSON, GHIORSO, HARVEY, AND CHOPPIN[531] first found evidence for a beta-emitting Cm^{249} produced by the prolonged neutron irradiation of plutonium.   The isotope Cm^{249} was also prepared[518] by neutron irradiation of a part of the curium fraction from a thermonuclear test explosion whose composition is given in Table 9.38.   Curium-249 has a half-life of 65 minutes for the emission of 0.9 MeV beta particles.[518]   EASTWOOD AND SCHUMAN[532] report a half-life of 64 ± 3 minutes and a maximum beta energy of 0.86 ± 0.10 MeV.

The only information we have on Cm^{250} is a crude estimate of the spontaneous fission half-life which HUIZENGA AND DIAMOND[533] report to be roughly 2×10^4 years.   From the absence of Cf^{250} in the debris of the 1958 "Mike" test explosion a lower limit of 130 years has been set on the β^- decay half-life.

9.5 THE ELEMENT BERKELIUM (ELEMENT 97)

9.5.1 *The Discovery of Berkelium*

The first isotope of element 97 was identified by THOMPSON, GHIORSO, AND SEABORG[534] in 1949.   This isotope was Bk^{243} produced in the 60-inch

[531] S. G. Thompson, A. Ghiorso, B. G. Harvey, and G. R. Choppin, *Phys. Rev.* **93**, 908 (1954).

[532] T. A. Eastwood and R. P. Schuman, *J. Inorg. Nucl. Chem.* **6**, 261 (1958).

[533] J. R. Huizenga and H. Diamond, *Phys. Rev.* **107**, 1087 (1957).

[534] S. G. Thompson, A. Ghiorso, and G. T. Seaborg, *Phys. Rev.* **80**, 781 (1950).

Berkeley cyclotron by the reaction:

$$Am^{241}(\alpha, 2n)Bk^{243}$$

The energy of the alpha particles was about 35 MeV. The isotope Bk^{243} decays predominantly by orbital electron capture with a half-life of 4.6 hours although in approximately 0.1 per cent of its disintegrations it emits alpha particles.

The preparation of element 97 in this way represents a straightforward extrapolation of methods used in the initial preparation of other transuranium elements. However, a number of experimental difficulties made it necessary to modify considerably the previous experimental techniques.

The search for transcurium elements was begun in the fall of 1945. SEABORG[535] anticipated that element 97, as eka-terbium in the actinide transition series, would possess oxidation states (III) and (IV) with properties similar to curium in the (III) oxidation state and to plutonium (IV) in its quadrivalent oxidation state. It was more difficult to estimate the oxidation potential of the (III) → (IV) couple but it was expected that element 97 would be somewhat easier to oxidize than terbium (III) which is not oxidizable to higher states in aqueous solution. The salient point is that if element 97 could not be converted to an oxidation state higher than (III) in solution it would be difficult, with the techniques then available, to separate it in a short period of time from rare earth fission product elements and from the actinide elements target material from which it was produced. It appeared that it might be necessary to use tedious rare earth separation procedures in order to separate and identify the new element, whose isotopes produced by cyclotron bombardments would have short half-lives as a result of considerable instability toward alpha-particle emission and electron-capture decay.

Since irradiation with sufficiently intense beams of energetic particles of nuclear charge greater than two was not practical at the time there were only two methods of approach to the production of element 97. The first method was the bombardment of americium with helium ions or the bombardment of curium with deuterons or helium ions. The second was through intensive neutron irradiations of curium in order to produce, through successive (n, γ) reactions, an unstable curium isotope decaying by emission of a beta particle to form an isotope of element 97. Both methods were employed in attempting to observe element 97, and for each, different chemical procedures were used. Some of these procedures were designed to separate the new element in oxidation states greater than (III) and others were used on the assumption that element 97 would exist in solution only in the tripositive oxidation state.

---

[535] G. T. Seaborg, *Nucleonics* **5** (5): 16 (1949); Paper No. 21.1 "The Transuranium Elements," *Nat. Nucl. Energ. Ser.*, Division IV **14B** (New York: McGraw-Hill Book Co., Inc., 1949).

Although the broad assumptions made when the work was started were all correct, the experiments done prior to December, 1949, were unsuccessful for many reasons which may be grouped into three classes. First, the methods of predicting the decay properties of the new isotopes were relatively undeveloped and the experiments were never done with sufficient speed. The further development of the alpha-decay systematics[536] made it possible to estimate energies and half-lives for alpha-particle decay more reliably. The resulting estimated alpha-particle decay energies could be used in calculating the total energies for electron-capture decay or beta-particle decay by the method of closed decay-energy cycles. An empirical method of estimating electron-capture half-lives from disintegration energies was developed by THOMPSON.[537]

The second major difficulty was that of obtaining sufficiently large amounts of americium and curium as sources for the production of element 97. Eventually, americium became available in milligram amounts through neutron irradiation of plutonium. The curium was produced in smaller amounts by the irradiation of americium with neutrons.

The intense radioactivity of the americium and curium source materials presented the third major difficulty. The specific activities of milligram quantities of americium and curium are $\sim 10^{10}$ and $\sim 10^{13}$ disintegrations per minute, respectively. This radioactivity necessitated not only the design and development of advanced techniques and equipment for its safe handling, but also made it necessary to attain enormous separation factors in the isolation of the new element from the target material in order to be able to detect the small amounts of radioactivity due to the new element. Furthermore, this high degree of separation had to be carried out in good yield in a short time.

Three chemical steps were developed to solve these chemical problems. The conversion of the americium to a hexapositive oxidation state according to the method of ASPREY, STEPHANOU, AND PENNEMAN[538] was used in the rapid removal of the bulk of the bombarded americium. An ion exchange method involving the separation of the actinide elements as a group from the rare earth fission products by elution with concentrated HCl from a cation exchange resin column was exploited for the rapid separation of the tripositive actinide elements.[539] An ion exchange method involving elution from a cation exchange resin at elevated temperature with ammonium citrate solution was used in the rapid separation of the tripositive actinide elements from each other. These steps had been worked out adequately by December 1949 and the first successful experiment was done on December 19, 1949.

---

[536] I. Perlman, A. Ghiorso, and G. T. Seaborg, *Phys. Rev.* **77**, 26 (1950).

[537] S. G. Thompson, *Phys. Rev.* **76**, 319 (1949).

[538] Asprey, Stephanou, and Penneman, *J. Am. Chem. Soc.* **72**, 1425 (1950).

[539] K. Street, Jr. and G. T. Seaborg, *J. Am. Chem. Soc.* **72**, 2790 (1950).

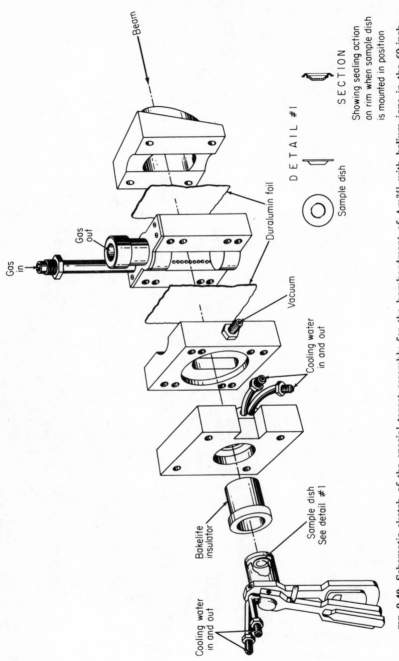

FIG. **9.40.** Schematic sketch of the special target assembly for the bombardment of Am²⁴¹ with helium ions in the 60-inch cyclotron. This assembly confines the radioactive target material during bombardment and during transportation to and from the cyclotron.

A few milligrams of americium oxide were placed in the special target assembly indicated schematically in Fig. 9.40 which was designed to prevent alpha radioactivity from entering the cyclotron and to eliminate its spread to the surroundings during transportation.   In this assembly the particle beam from the cyclotron was passed through two thin duralumin foils (each 1.5 mil in thickness) before entering the evacuated compartment containing the sample.   The compartment was isolated from the surroundings.   The beam was also passed through a thin platinum foil placed directly in contact with and over the target dish.   The back of the platinum disk containing the sample was cooled directly with a water jet.   The intensity of the beam striking the sample was about 2 microamperes per cm^2.   The energy of the alpha particles when they struck the target was about 35 MeV.   After the irradiation the element 97 fraction was separated by the chemical techniques mentioned above.

Examination of the radiations in the element 97 fraction showed alpha and x-radiation decaying with a half-life of 4.6 hours.   The alpha spectrum determined in an ionization chamber had three distinct groups: 6.20 MeV (17 per cent), 6.55 MeV (53 per cent), and 6.72 MeV (30 per cent).   Measurements of the L x-radiation in a proportional counter spectrometer showed it to be curium L x-rays which indicated that the berkelium was decaying principally by orbital-electron capture.   Chemical separation and examination of americium and curium daughter activity resulted in the identification of radiations believed to be, and subsequently proved to be, those of Am^{239} and Cm^{243}.   A complete discussion of the properties of Bk^{243} is given in the next section of this chapter.

Additional cyclotron experiments have been carried out with targets of Am^{241}, Am^{243}, Cm^{242}, and Cm^{244} which have resulted in the production and identification of Bk^{244}, Bk^{245}, Bk^{246}, and Bk^{247}.   The irradiation of Pu^{239} or of other materials such as Am^{241}, Am^{243}, or Cm^{244} in a high flux reactor results ultimately in the production of the curium isotope Cm^{249} which decays by beta emission to Bk^{249}, a 290-day beta-emitter.   The first preparation of isotopes of berkelium via the neutron-capture route was reported by THOMPSON, GHIORSO, HARVEY, AND CHOPPIN.[540]   The isotope Bk^{249} is noteworthy because of its half-life and of the fact that it can be prepared in quantity; hence, it is suitable for investigations of the chemical properties of this element. The first microgram-scale sample of berkelium was isolated by THOMPSON AND CUNNINGHAM[541] in the spring of 1958 from 8 grams of Pu^{239} which had been irradiated in the Materials Testing Reactor for several years.   With this 0.4 microgram sample, it was possible to measure several physical and

---

[540] S. G. Thompson, A. Ghiorso, B. G. Harvey, and G. R. Choppin, *Phys. Rev.* **93**, 908 (1954).

[541] S. G. Thompson and B. B. Cunningham, *Proceedings of the Second U.N. Conference on the Peaceful Uses of Atomic Energy* **28**, 346, 1958.

chemical properties of berkelium with ultramicrochemical techniques. A consideration of all the isotopes of berkelium reveals that there are probably no beta stable isotopes of this element, although the situation is borderline for Bk^{247}.

Berkelium has the predicted properties of an eka-terbium element. In solution the most stable oxidation state is (III). In addition, however, it can be oxidized to the (IV) oxidation state. This reflects the special stability of the half-filled f electron shell which terbium achieves in the (IV) state.

The name berkelium (symbol Bk) was chosen[534] after the city of Berkeley in a manner similar to that used in naming the chemical homologue terbium (atomic number 65) whose name was derived from the town of Ytterby, Sweden, where many rare earth minerals were first found.

9.5.2 Berkelium-243

The isotope Bk^{243} can be made by the following reactions:[542-545]

$$Am^{241}(\alpha, 2n)Bk^{243}$$
$$Am^{243}(\alpha, 4n)Bk^{243}$$
$$Cm^{242}(d, n)Bk^{243}$$
$$Cm^{244}(d, 3n)Bk^{243}$$

This was the first isotope of element 97 to be reported.[542] It decays chiefly by orbital-electron capture[542] with a 4.5 hour half-life forming Cm^{243} as its daughter product. The identification of the alpha activity of the Cm^{243} daughter confirms the mass assignment.[542,544] In 0.15 per cent[544] of its disintegrations Bk^{243} decays by emission[542] of alpha particles with the following energies and abundances: 6.20 MeV (17 per cent), 6.55 MeV (53 per cent), and 6.72 MeV (30 per cent).

THOMPSON, GHIORSO, AND SEABORG[542] studied the L x-rays in a xenon-filled proportional counter connected to a pulse height analyzer and identified the L_α, L_β and L_γ x-rays of curium. CHETHAM-STRODE[545] has studied the gamma radiation of Bk^{243} in a scintillation spectrometer and found K and L x-rays as well as gamma rays of energy 740 ± 40 keV, 840 ± 40 keV, and 960 ± 40 keV. The gamma rays have the relative abundances 1.0, 0.3, and 0.3, respectively. These gamma rays accompany the electron capture decay of Bk^{243}, but the decay scheme is not known in detail. The estimated total

[542] S. G. Thompson, A. Ghiorso, and G. T. Seaborg, *Phys. Rev.* **80**, 781 (1950).

[543] E. K. Hulet, S. G. Thompson, A. Ghiorso, and K. Street, Jr., *Phys. Rev.* **84**, 366 (1951).

[544] E. K. Hulet, Ph.D. Thesis, University of California, July, 1953; also published as *Univ. Calif. Rad. Lab. Report UCRL-2283*, 1953.

[545] A. Chetham-Strode, Jr., Ph.D. Thesis, University of California, June, 1956; also published as *Univ. Calif. Rad. Lab. Report UCRL-3322*, 1956.

decay energy of 1.5 MeV for the electron capture process precludes a cascade arrangement of the observed gamma rays.   Careful study of the gamma rays of Bk^{243} is made difficult if Bk^{244} is also present, because Bk^{244} decays with the same half-life.

CHETHAM-STRODE[545] used alpha-gamma coincidence techniques to study the gamma rays accompanying the small alpha branching decay of this isotope.   In addition to americium K x-rays, gamma rays of 536, 187, 146, and 42 keV were observed in coincidence with alpha particles.   The abun-dances per alpha disintegration of those five radiations was found to be 0.09, 0.10, 0.34, 0.08, and 0.04, respectively.

Information on the alpha decay of Bk^{243} is summarized in Fig. 9.41.

From a consideration of the similarities in the alpha decay patterns of Bk^{243}, Bk^{245} and Bk^{247}, STEPHENS, ASARO, AND PERLMAN[546] have made Nilsson orbital assignments to the ground states of the berkelium isotopes and to the ground state and excited levels of the americium daughter isotopes. The quantum numbers K, parity $[N, n_z, \Lambda]$ for Bk^{243} are $3/2 - [521]$ and

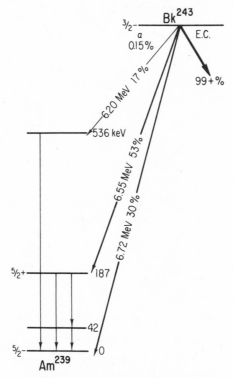

FIG. 9.41. Alpha branching decay of Bk^{243}.

546 F. S. Stephens, F. Asaro, and I. Perlman, *Phys. Rev.* 113, 212 (1959).

those for the ground state of Am^{239} are $5/2 - [523]$.   The level at 187 keV in Am^{239} is assigned as $5/2 + [642]$ and that at 540 keV is either the $3/2$ member of a rotational band based on $1/2 - [530]$ or is the Nilsson state $3/2 - [521]$.   The considerations on which these assignments are based are given in Chapter 3.   See also the publication of NILSSON AND MOTTEL-SON.[547]

9.5.3 Berkelium-244

The isotope Bk^{244} decays almost entirely by orbital-electron capture with a half-life of ~ 4.5 hours.   Since this half-life is identical with the half-life of Bk^{243}, it is difficult to make meaningful measurements of its radiations unless special care is taken during the preparative reaction to minimize the production of Bk^{243}.   HULET[544] obtained indirect evidence for the production of Bk^{244} along with Bk^{243} in the bombardment of Am^{241} with helium ions.   The pertinent reaction was:

$$Am^{241}(\alpha, n)Bk^{244}$$

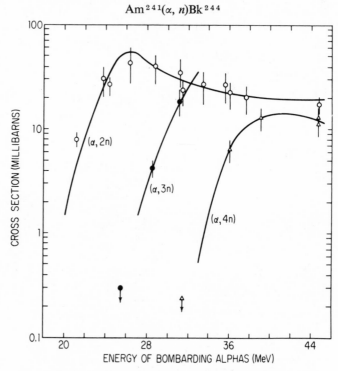

FIG. **9.42**. Excitation functions for the reactions Am^{243} (α, $2n$) Bk^{245}, Am^{243} (α, $3n$) Bk^{244} and Am^{243} (α, $4n$) Bk^{243}. CHETHAM-STRODE.[545]

[547] S. G. Nilsson and B. R. Mottelson, Mat. Fys. Skr. Dan. Vid. Selsk. 1, No. 8 (1959).

HULET showed that the curium fraction isolated after the decay of such berkelium samples differed from that found in the decay of samples of pure Bk^{243} made by the deuteron bombardment of Cm^{242}.

CHETHAM-STRODE[549] prepared Bk^{244} by the reaction:

$$Am^{243}(\alpha, 3n)Bk^{244}$$

By carrying out this reaction with helium ions in the range 28 to 32 MeV (see Fig. 9.42) the amount of Bk^{244} relative to Bk^{243} is greatly enhanced. The longer-lived isotopes, Bk^{245} and Bk^{246}, are also formed but do not interfere to the same extent as does Bk^{243}. The 5.79 MeV alpha particles of Cm^{244} were observed to grow into the purified berkelium sample which confirmed the mass assignment.

CHETHAM-STRODE[549] studied the gamma radiations of Bk^{244} in samples containing varying amounts of Bk^{243}, Bk^{245}, and Bk^{246}. The most prominent gamma rays are of energy 900 and 200 keV and these are emitted in cascade. Six other gamma rays were observed with energies in the region 0.9 MeV to 1.72 MeV but in much lower intensity; these are listed in Table 9.39. These gamma rays have not been placed in a decay scheme.

Alpha particles of 6.67 ± 0.0015 MeV energy have been observed[549] for Bk^{244} in an abundance corresponding to an alpha branching of only 6×10^{-5}. This corresponds to a partial alpha half-life of 8 ± 3 years.

TABLE 9.39. Gamma rays in decay of Bk^{244}.

Energy (MeV)	Relative intensity
0.200	—
0.900	1.0
1.06	0.07
1.16	0.11
1.23	0.05
1.37	0.007
1.50	0.02
1.72	0.002

9.5.4 *Berkelium-245*

HULET, THOMPSON, GHIORSO, AND STREET[550,551] first identified the isotope Bk^{245} produced in bombardments of a curium target with helium ions and with deuterons. The targets contained a mixture of Cm^{242},

[549] A. Chetham-Strode, Jr., Ph.D. Thesis, University of California, June, 1956; also published as *Univ. Calif. Rad. Lab. Report UCRL-3322*, June, 1956.

[550] E. K. Hulet, S. G. Thompson, A. Ghiorso, and K. Street, Jr., *Phys. Rev.* **84**, 366 (1951).

[551] E. K. Hulet, Ph.D. Thesis, University of California, July, 1953; also published as *Univ. Calif. Rad. Lab. Report UCRL-2283*, July, 1953.

Cm^{243}, and Cm^{244} and the principal reactions leading to the production of Bk^{245} were:

$$Cm^{242}(\alpha, p)Bk^{245}$$
$$Cm^{244}(d, n)Bk^{245}$$

Since milligram quantities of nearly pure Am^{243} and Cm^{244} have become available, the principal reactions used in the preparation of Bk^{245} have been the following:

$$Am^{243}(\alpha, 2n)Bk^{245}$$
$$Cm^{244}(d, n)Bk^{245}$$

A rough excitation function for the $Am^{243}(\alpha, 2n)$ reaction is given in Fig. 9.42 accompanying Section 9.5.3.

HULET AND CO-WORKERS[550,551] found that Bk^{245} decays chiefly by orbital electron capture with a half-life of 4.95 ± 0.1 days. It decays also in about 0.1 per cent of its disintegrations by the emission of alpha particles distributed among three prominent groups. MAGNUSSON AND CO-WORKERS[552] and CHETHAM-STRODE[553] have studied Bk^{245} in more detail. MAGNUSSON[552] gives the value 4.98 ± 0.02 days for the half-life.

The alpha spectrum as given by MAGNUSSON AND CO-WORKERS[552] consists of three groups: 5.89 ± 0.02 MeV (26 per cent), 6.17 ± 0.02 MeV (41 per cent), and 6.37 ± 0.02 MeV (33 per cent). These are shown in the decay scheme. The gamma rays following alpha decay were studied by CHETHAM-STRODE[553] by alpha-gamma coincidence techniques using scintillation crystal spectrometers. He reported gamma rays with energies 115 keV (K x-rays), 164 keV, 206 keV, and 480 keV. The number of photons of these radiations per total alpha disintegration was measured to be 0.11, 0.07, 0.28, and 0.18, respectively. These transitions are shown in Fig. 9.43.

The isotope Cm^{241} also decays into Am^{241}. The decay is known to proceed to the ground state and to the 480 keV level. There may be some slight branching decay to a level at 600 keV not observed in the alpha decay of Bk^{245}. There is no conflict in the information derived from these two isotopes. The beta emitter Pu^{241} also decays to Am^{241} but the decay energy is so low that only the ground state is reached.

The electromagnetic radiation accompanying electron capture has also been studied. In addition to K and L x-radiation, some photons of 250 keV and 380 keV gamma rays are observed. The conversion electrons of the 250 keV gamma rays were also measured. From the conversion coefficient the 250 keV transition is chiefly $M1$ in nature. The 250 and 380 keV transitions

[552] L. B. Magnusson, A. M. Friedman, D. Engelkemeir, P. R. Fields, and F. Wagner, Jr., *Phys. Rev.* **102**, 1097 (1956).

[553] A. Chetham-Strode, Ph.D. Thesis, University of California, June, 1956; also published as *Univ. Calif. Rad. Lab. Report UCRL-3322*, June, 1956.

[554] F. S. Stephens, Jr., F. Asaro, and I. Perlman, *Phys. Rev.* **113**, 212 (1959).

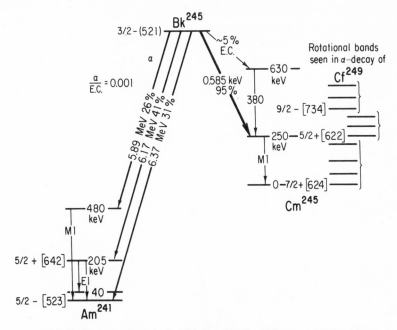

FIG. 9.43. Decay scheme of 4.98-day Bk[245]. Nilsson orbital assignments are given to most of the levels. The number given in front of and within the square brackets refer to the following quantum numbers: K, parity $[N\ n_z\ \Lambda]$. For further information on the Cm[245] level structure see Section 9.6.7.

are in cascade as shown in the figure. Approximately 94 per cent of the electron capture decay proceeds to the 250-keV level, and the rest goes to a level at 600 keV. There is no evidence for decay directly to the ground state.

The interpretation of the decay scheme of Bk[245] and in particular the assignment of Nilsson orbitals is aided by a detailed consideration of the decay schemes of Cm[241], Am[241], Am[245], Cf[249] and other nuclides. STEPHENS, ASARO, AND PERLMAN[554] as well as NILSSON AND MOTTELSON[555] give detailed arguments (many of which are reproduced in Section 3.5.5 of Chapter 3) which lead to the Nilsson assignments given in the decay scheme figure.

The level system of Cm[245] can also be studied by examining the radiations of the beta emitter Am[245] and the alpha emitter Cf[249]. The radiations of Am[245] have been studied by BROWNE AND CO-WORKERS[556] and by

555 S. G. Nilsson and B. R. Mottelson, *Mat. fys. Skr. Dan. Vid. Selsk.* 1, No. 8 (1959).

556 C. I. Browne, D. C. Hoffman, W. T. Crane, J. P. Balagna, G. H. Higgins, J. W. Barnes, R. W. Hoff, J. P. Mize, and M. E. Bunker, *J. Inorg. Nucl. Chem.* 1, 254 (1955).

FIELDS AND CO-WORKERS[557] (see Section 5.3.10) but there appears to be little correspondence with the decay scheme of Bk^{245} except for the mutual occurrence of the 250 keV gamma ray. Alpha decay of Cf^{249} proceeds to the ground state of Cm^{245} and to the levels shown at the right side of the figure. Hence, only the 250-keV level is common to the decay of Cf^{249} and Bk^{245}.

9.5.5 Berkelium-246

The 1.8 day isotope Bk^{246} is prepared by the reactions:[558-560]

$$Am^{243}(\alpha, n)Bk^{246}$$
$$Cm^{244}(\alpha, pn)Bk^{246}$$

When prepared in this manner it is contaminated with 4.98 day Bk^{245} and with lighter isotopes of berkelium in amounts depending on the energy of the bombarding particles.

Berkelium-246 decays[558,559] by orbital electron capture to Cm^{246}. CHETHAM-STRODE[560] examined the gamma ray spectrum of mixtures of Bk^{245} and Bk^{246} and found a prominent 800 keV gamma ray assignable to Bk^{246} and a composite photopeak at 1.09 MeV which could be partially resolved into components with energies of 0.980, 1.08, and 1.13 MeV. Coincidence experiments indicate that the principal electron capture decay is to levels in Cm^{246} at 840 keV and higher energies. CHETHAM-STRODE[560] has constructed the tentative decay scheme shown in Fig. 9.44. This scheme relies on the information given by the alpha decay of Cf^{250} on the low-lying levels of Cm^{246}. These levels constitute the rotational band of levels familiar in all *even-even* nuclei in this mass region. The level at 1130 keV apparently de-excites by gamma transitions to the first three members of the ground state rotational band. Further study is required before this level can be characterized as an excitation of collective vibrational motion. This is similar to the situation in the decay scheme of Bk^{250}, discussed in Section 6.5.9.

9.5.6. Berkelium-247

The isotope Bk^{247} has a half-life of 1380 $\pm$ 250 years, as determined by a mass-spectrometric isotopic dilution method,[560a] which makes it the most long-lived of all the isotopes of element 97. Hence the preparation by

---

[557] P. R. Fields, M. H. Studier, A. M. Friedman, H. Diamond, R. Sjoblom, and P. A. Sellers, *J. Inorg. Nucl. Chem.* **1**, 262 (1955).

[558] E. K. Hulet, S. G. Thompson, and A. Ghiorso, *Phys. Rev.* **95**, 1703 (1954).

[559] E. K. Hulet, Ph.D. Thesis, University of California, July, 1953; also published as *Univ. Calif. Rad. Lab. Report UCRL-2283*, July, 1953.

[560] A. Chetham-Strode, Jr., Ph.D. Thesis, University of California, June, 1956; also published as *Univ. Calif. Rad. Lab. Report UCRL-3322*, June, 1956.

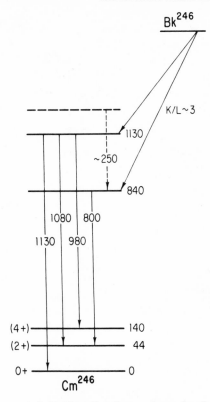

FIG. **9.44.** Tentative decay scheme for the electron capture decay of Bk²⁴⁶. Note similarities to decay scheme of Bk²⁵⁰ shown in Fig. 9.45.

cyclotron reactions of a sample large enough for convenient measurement of its radiations requires larger amounts of target material and more extensive bombardment than does the preparation of the lighter berkelium isotopes we have just discussed. Cyclotron-induced reactions which can be used include:

$$Cm^{244}(\alpha, n)Cf^{247} \xrightarrow[\text{2.4 hrs}]{EC} Bk^{247}$$

$$Cm^{244}(\alpha, p)Bk^{247}$$

$$Cm^{245}(\alpha, 2n)Cf^{247} \longrightarrow Bk^{247}$$

$$Cm^{245}(\alpha, pn) Bk^{247}$$

$$Cm^{246}(\alpha, 3n)Cf^{247} \longrightarrow Bk^{247}$$

$$Cm^{246}(\alpha, p2n)Bk^{247}$$

[560a] J. Milsted, A. M. Friedman, and C. M. Stevens, *Phys. Rev.* (1964).

In a sample containing a mixture of higher mass curium isotopes all these reactions occur simultaneously.

Berkelium-247 is *not* produced by the intensive neutron irradiation of plutonium, americium and curium because the curium isotopes of mass numbers 242 through 248 are beta stable; it is only at Cm^{249} that a beta decay path opens up leading to the production of berkelium. This is unfortunate as it would be desirable to have a means for the preparation of microgram or larger quantities of this long-lived isotope.

Berkelium-247 can be isolated in a pure state from cyclotron targets once sufficient time has elapsed for the lighter isotopes to decay, provided the curium target is principally Cm^{244}. When a chief constituent of the curium target is Cm^{246} or higher isotopes of curium, the 280-day isotope Bk^{249} is also produced.

CHETHAM-STRODE[561] first identified Bk^{247}. He prepared small samples of Bk^{247}, and purified them thoroughly by the ion-exchange elution technique. The alpha spectrum determined by ion chamber measurements has three principal groups: 5.67 MeV (37 per cent), 5.51 MeV (58 per cent), and 5.30 MeV (5 per cent). The gamma spectrum was studied by alpha-gamma coincidence techniques and the following electromagnetic radiation was found: K x-rays, 84 ± 3 keV and 265 ± 10 keV. The corrected abundances were 0.2, 0.4, and 0.3 per alpha decay.

The alpha decay scheme of Bk^{247} is given in a joint figure with the β^- decay of Pu^{243}. This figure appears in Section 9.2.13. See Fig. 9.21. The radiations de-exciting the 465-keV state have not been observed directly in the case of Bk^{247} because of the low intensity of the available samples. Some of the evidence for the Nilsson assignments given in the figure is discussed in the Pu^{243} summary (Section 9.2.13) but a more complete interpretation of the evidence is given elsewhere.[562,563] A lot of the interpretation is based on the great similarities in the α-decay schemes of Bk^{243}, Bk^{245} and Bk^{247}.

It is not known definitely whether Bk^{247} is beta unstable. From considerations of closed decay energy cycles it should be unstable by about 40 keV toward electron capture but the uncertainty in this estimate is greater than 40 keV.

9.5.7 *Berkelium-248*

The isotope Bk^{248} is best prepared[561] by the neutron irradiation of Bk^{247}:

$$Bk^{247}(n, \gamma)Bk^{248}$$

[561] A. Chetham-Strode, Jr., Ph.D. Thesis, University of California, June, 1956; also published as *Univ. Calif. Rad. Lab. Report UCRL-3322*, June, 1956.

[562] F. S. Stephens, F. Asaro, and I. Perlman, *Phys. Rev.* **113**, 212 (1959).

[563] S. G. Nilsson and B. R. Mottelson, *Mat.-fys. Skr. Dan. Vid. Selsk.* **1**, No. 8 (1959).

It can also be prepared[564] by cyclotron reactions but the simultaneous production of other berkelium isotopes of comparable half-life interferes with a study of its radiations. HULET[564] prepared the isotope for the first time through the use of these reactions:

$$Cm^{245}(\alpha, p)Bk^{248}$$
$$Cm^{246}(\alpha, p2n)Bk^{247}$$

HULET established a half-life value of 23 ± 5 hours through radiochemical measurements of the Cf^{248} daughter activity growing into his samples.

CHETHAM-STRODE[561] determined a better half-life of 16 ± 3 hours. The decay goes partially to Cf^{248} by beta emission, and the growth of the alpha particles of this daughter activity has been observed. An alternate path of decay is by orbital electron-capture to Cm^{248}. A beta-to-electron-capture ratio of 2.4 was determined from the observed beta disintegration rate and the K and L x-ray intensities. This ratio corresponds to log ft values of 6.75 and 6.7 for the electron capture and beta decay, respectively. The end point of the beta spectrum is at 650 ± 50 keV as determined from measurements with an anthracene crystal spectrometer.

No evidence has been reported for gamma transitions in either the electron capture or beta decay branches so it appears that the principal decay proceeds to the ground state in both branches.

MILSTED, FRIEDMAN, AND STEVENS[560a] found mass-spectrometric evidence for a long-lived isomer of Bk^{248} with a half-life greater than 9 years, and probably greater than 200 years.

9.5.8 Berkelium-249

This isotope was first isolated from dust samples collected after a test explosion of the "Mike" thermonuclear reaction device in November, 1952.[565] In this explosion, an extremely high momentary flux of neutrons was generated and the uranium present in the device was converted to higher-mass uranium isotopes by the capture of many neutrons. The Bk^{249} resulted from the instantaneous production of U^{249} which then decayed through a chain of short-lived beta-emitters until Bk^{249} was reached.

This isotope has also been prepared[566,567,568] by the prolonged irradiation of samples of plutonium, americium or curium in a high-flux reactor. The course of the main neutron-capture sequence starting with Am^{243}, for example, is the following:

[564] E. K. Hulet, *Phys. Rev.* **102**, 182 (1956).
[565] P. R. Fields, *et al.*, *Phys. Rev.* **102**, 180 (1956).
[566] Thompson, Ghiorso, Harvey, and Choppin, *Phys. Rev.* **93**, 908 (1954).
[567] H. Diamond, *et al.*, *Phys. Rev.* **94**, 1083 (1954).
[568] L. B. Magnusson, *et al.*, *Phys. Rev.* **96**, 1576 (1954).

$$\text{Bk}^{249}$$
$$\uparrow \beta^-$$
$$\text{Cm}^{244}(n, \gamma)\text{Cm}^{245}(n, \gamma)\text{Cm}^{246}(n, \gamma)\text{Cm}^{247}(n, \gamma)\text{Cm}^{248}(n, \gamma)\text{Cm}^{249}$$
$$\uparrow \beta^-$$
$$\text{Am}^{243}(n, \gamma)\text{Am}^{244}$$

The entire neutron-capture sequence beginning with Pu^{239} is discussed in Chapter 5. The total yield of Bk^{249} in such a long sequence of steps is low but significant.

EASTWOOD AND CO-WORKERS[569] report a yield of 3.2×10^{-9} grams from a 348 milligram sample of Pu^{239} irradiated to an integrated flux of 1.46×10^{22} neutrons per cm^2. THOMPSON, PARSONS, AND CO-WORKERS[570] isolated 0.7 micrograms of Bk^{249} from 8 grams of Pu^{239} which had been irradiated for approximately 5 years at a flux of $4-5 \times 10^{14}$ neutrons cm^{-2} sec^{-1} in the Materials Testing Reactor, Arco, Idaho. Larger samples of berkelium can be made by a sustained program of irradiation of kilogram quantities of transuranium element samples in high flux reactors. The production of Bk^{249} by this method is important since this is the only method for the preparation of decigram and larger samples of element 97 for extensive measurements of chemical and physical properties. Berkelium-249 has a half-life very close to those of polonium and Cm^{242}, for which elements extensive macroscopic chemical investigations have proved to be possible. The isotope Bk^{247} with its half-life of $\sim 10^3$ years would be more suitable for this purpose but it cannot be made in quantity by the neutron capture method, because Cm^{247} does not decay to form Bk^{247} at any appreciable rate, if at all, before it is converted to Cm^{248}.

The half-life of Bk^{249} has been reported as 290 days[568] and 314 days.[569] The end-point energy of the beta particles is reported as 80 ± 20 kilovolts,[568] 110 ± 20 kilovolts,[567] 114 ± 15 kilovolts,[569] and 125 ± 2 kilovolts.[571] The log ft value for the last-named energy is 7.1. A study of the gamma spectrum in coincidence with beta particles showed no gamma rays above a limit of about one per cent of the disintegrations.[572] MAGNUSSON AND CO-WORKERS[568] noted a slight alpha branching of $\sim 10^{-3}$ per cent for the emission of 5.40 MeV alpha particles. EASTWOOD AND CO-WORKERS[569] confirm this but report complex structure. Their figures are: total alpha-branching $= (2.2 \pm 0.3) \times 10^{-3}$ per cent, alpha particle energies 5.417 ± 0.015

[569] T. A. Eastwood, et al., Phys. Rev. 107, 1635 (1957).

[570] S. G. Thompson, T. Parsons, et al., unpublished results (1958).

[571] S. E. Vandenbosch, H. Diamond, R. K. Sjoblom, and P. R. Fields, Phys. Rev. 115, 115 (1959).

[572] A. Chetham-Strode, Jr., Ph.D. Thesis, University of California, June 1956; also published as Univ. Calif. Rad. Lab. Report UCRL-3322, June, 1956.

(96 per cent), and 5.03 ± 0.03 (4 per cent). This complex structure is borne out by the studies of gamma radiation in coincidence with alpha particles carried out by CHETHAM-STRODE[572]. These studies showed that a 320 keV gamma ray was in coincidence with about 4 per cent and that L x-rays were in coincidence with about 20 per cent of the alpha particles. MILSTED AND FRIEDMAN[573] report four α-particle groups: 5.087, 5.326, 5.376, and 5.395 MeV. These fragmentary data are insufficient for the construction of a decay scheme.

STEPHENS, ASARO AND PERLMAN[574] assign the Nilsson state 7/2 + [633] to the ground state of Bk^{249}, largely from a consideration of the alpha decay of Es^{253}. The favored alpha decay of Es^{253} goes to the ground state of Bk^{249}, and four members of the ground state rotational band have been observed to receive alpha population. This means that the ground-state configuration (Nilsson states) of Bk^{249} and Es^{253} are identical. The spacing of the band gives best agreement with a 7/2 spin.

These authors also give a ground state assignment of 9/2 − [734] to Cf^{249}. This is consistent with the log ft value of 7.1 for the beta decay of Bk^{249}.

Conclusions identical to the above are reached by NILSSON AND MOTTELSON[575]. These latter authors also point out that the favored alpha decay of Bk^{249} is to a level about 400 keV above ground in Am^{245} and that this level should be given the 7/2 + [633] assignment identical to the Bk^{249} ground state.

A lower limit of 1.5×10^9 years has been set[569] on the spontaneous fission half-life of Bk^{249}.

9.5.9 Berkelium-250

When a sample of 290-day Bk^{249} is irradiated with neutrons the isotope Bk^{250} is produced.[576]

$$Bk^{249}(n, \gamma)Bk^{250}$$

This isotope decays by beta-emission with a half-life reported originally as 3.13 hours and later as 193.3 ± 0.3 minutes.[577] Berkelium-250 can also be formed[578,579] as the alpha-decay product of 320 day Es^{254}.

[573] J. Milsted and A. Friedman, *Bull. Am. Phys. Sci.* II **7**, 353 (1962).

[574] F. S. Stephens, F. Asaro, and I. Perlman, *Phys. Rev.* **113**, 212 (1959).

[575] S. G. Nilsson and B. R. Mottelson, *Mat.-fys. Skr. Dan. Vid. Selsk.* **1**, No. 8 (1959).

[576] A. Ghiorso, S. G. Thompson, G. R. Choppin, and B. G. Harvey, *Phys. Rev.* **94**, 1081 (1954).

[577] S. E. Vandenbosch, H. Diamond, R. K. Sjoblom, and P. R. Fields, *Phys. Rev.* **115**, 115 (1959).

[578] B. G. Harvey, S. G. Thompson, G. R. Choppin, and A. Ghiorso, *Phys. Rev.* **99**, 337 (1955).

[579] Jones, Schuman, Butler, Cowper, Eastwood, and Jackson, *Phys. Rev.* **102**, 203 (1956).

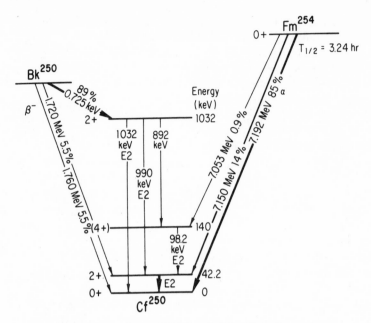

FIG. 9.45. Decay scheme of Bk[250] and of Fm[254] to the common daughter product, Cf[250].

ASARO, STEPHENS, AND THOMPSON[580] studied the gamma rays of Bk[250] in an equilibrium mixture of Es[254] plus Bk[250], and in a daughter fraction prepared by alpha recoil collection. Their measurements of the gamma spectrum and of the gamma spectrum in coincidence with beta particles and L x-rays led to the conclusion that three gamma rays with energies 1.04 MeV, 1.02 MeV, and 0.91 MeV (in low intensity) are present. Their interpretation was that these three gamma rays represented decay from a common parent level at 1.04 MeV in the daughter Cf[250] to the three lowest levels of the ground-state rotational band. The lower members of the ground-state rotational band are known from the α-decay of Fm[254] as shown in Fig. 9.45.

These results were confirmed and extended by VANDENBOSCH, DIAMOND, SJOBLOM, AND FIELDS[577] who made a more thorough study of the radiations of Bk[250] in samples prepared by neutron irradiation of Bk[249]. The beta spectrum was shown to contain two groups: 725 ± 15 keV (89 ± 1 per cent abundance) and 1760 ± 50 keV (11 ± 1 per cent abundance). Conversion lines corresponding to transitions with energies 42.2, 98.2, 890, 930, 990, and 1032 keV energy were measured with a double-lens magnetic spectrometer.

---

580 F. Asaro, F. S. Stephens, Jr., and S. G. Thompson, unpublished results, 1956.

These radiations were placed in the decay scheme as shown in the accompanying figure with the aid of quantitative $\beta\gamma$, $\gamma\gamma$ and L x-ray γ coincidence measurements. These measurements required the interpretation that the 1760 keV beta ray group observed in 11 per cent abundance be an unresolved mixture of two beta transitions in about equal abundance going to the ground state and the first excited state of Cf^{250}.

The lowest levels of Cf^{250} consist of a rotational band of levels following the $I(I + 1)$ energy-spacing rule and the $0+$, $2+$, $4+$ spin sequence. These levels are de-excited with a cascade of $E2$ gamma rays. A level at 1032 keV receives the main beta population. It is interpreted as a vibrational level of collective excitation. VANDENBOSCH, DIAMOND, SJOBLOM, AND FIELDS[577] suggest a $K = 2$, $I = 2$ and parity positive assignment for this level. This level is de-excited by a triplet of gamma rays (probably $E2$ transitions) to the first three levels of the ground state rotational band. These authors find some evidence for a level at 1074 keV which may be the first level of rotational excitation of the 1032 keV level. This level is not shown in the figure. The log ft value for the beta transitions suggest a spin and parity of $2-$ for Bk^{250}.

Mass spectrometric measurements by C. M. STEVENS[581] of the upper limit of Cm^{250} produced by the electron-capture decay of Bk^{250} present in a neutron-irradiated sample of plutonium lead to a lower limit of 50 hours for the partial half-life of Bk^{250} for decay by capture of an orbital electron.

9.6 THE ELEMENT CALIFORNIUM (ELEMENT 98)

9.6.1 *The Discovery of Californium*

In Section 9.5.1 we discussed how the discovery of berkelium hinged on the development of new experimental techniques and the refinement of methods for the prediction of radioactive characteristics of the isotopes to be investigated. These new experimental and theoretical methods were directly applicable to the problem of the preparation and identification of element 98. Hence, after the discovery of an isotope of berkelium in December, 1949, the same group of investigators, THOMPSON, GHIORSO, AND SEABORG, together with K. STREET, JR., undertook an immediate attack on the problem of element 98 and within two months were successful.[582]

The preparative method selected by these investigators was to bombard the element curium with helium ions to prepare isotopes of element 98 by (α,xn) reactions. The only curium isotope available in sufficient quantity at that time was the 162-day isotope Cm^{242}, which they prepared in microgram quantities by the neutron irradiation of Am^{241}. The highly radioactive

[581] C. M. Stevens, as reported by Vandenbosch, *et al.*, in Ref.[577].

[582] S. G. Thompson, K. Street, Jr., A. Ghiorso, and G. T. Seaborg, *Phys. Rev.* **80**, 790 (1950).

curium target material ($\sim 10^{11}$ alpha disintegrations per minute) was confined in a target of the type illustrated in the figure accompanying the description of the discovery of berkelium (Section 9.5.1).

Following the bombardment of this target with 35-MeV helium ions in the Berkeley 60-inch cyclotron, the few thousands of atoms of element 98 were separated by ion exchange techniques tailored to the assumption that element 98 should be "eka-dysprosium." Element 98 was expected to have only the tripositive oxidation state in aqueous solution. Its elution position in the elution of tracer elements with buffered citric acid from a Dowex-50 cation exchange resin was estimated from the known elution behavior of gadolinium, terbium, and dysprosium on the one hand and that of curium and berkelium on the other. The requirements for decontamination were severe since the few thousands of atoms of californium expected in the cyclotron bombardment had to be separated from the $\sim 10^{11}$ disintegrations per minute of Cm^{242} and from considerable amounts of fission product radioactivity. Consideration of nuclear systematics indicated that the longest-lived isotopes of element 98 to be expected in this experiment had half-lives of the order of 30 minutes to a few hours; hence, the chemical separations were designed for complete separation within a period of an hour.

Using these techniques, THOMPSON, STREET, GHIORSO, AND SEABORG[582] in February, 1950 produced, purified and chemically identified an isotope of element 98. This isotope had a half-life of 45 minutes. The observed mode of decay was the emission of alpha particles with energy of about 7.1 MeV. The mass assignment was tentatively made to 98^{244} but the later work of CHETHAM-STRODE, CHOPPIN, AND HARVEY[583] established that the correct mass assignment was 245.

In the selection of names for elements 95, 96, and 97 the guiding principle had been that the chosen name should emphasize the observed chemical homology to the rare earth elements 63, 64, and 65. In the case of element 98 it was difficult to suggest a suitable name stressing its relationship to the rare earth element, dysprosium (number 66). Instead, the name californium (symbol Cf) was proposed to honor the University and State of California where the work was done.

The isotopes of californium which can be produced by helium ion bombardment of Cm^{242} lie far on the neutron deficient side of beta stability and the only isotopes[582,583] to be produced with Cm^{242} as a target are 25-minute Cf^{244} and 44-minute Cf^{245}. Other heavier isotopes of californium were produced later by several types of experiments. For example, when it became possible to use cyclotron targets of curium containing appreciable percentages of Cm^{243}, Cm^{244}, and higher isotopes of curium, it was possible

583 A. Chetham-Strode, Jr., Gregory R. Choppin, and B. G. Harvey, *Phys. Rev.* 102, 747 (1956).

to prepare and identify Cf^{246}, Cf^{247}, and Cf^{248} by helium-ion bombardment of such mixtures.[584,585]

The development of methods for the acceleration of charged ions of carbon and nitrogen to energies above 100 MeV in moderate beam intensity made it possible to carry out reactions of the following type:[586,587]

$$U^{238}(C^{12}, 4n)Cf^{246}$$

A number of heavier californium isotopes have been prepared by intense irradiation of lighter elements in high-flux nuclear reactors. The irradiation of Pu^{239} or of other materials such as Am^{241}, Am^{243}, or Cm^{244} in a high neutron flux results ultimately in the production of the curium isotope Cm^{249} which decays by beta emission to Bk^{249}; this isotope in turn decays by beta emission to Cf^{249}. From this point, the capture of more neutrons produces Cf^{250}, Cf^{251}, and Cf^{252}. (See MAGNUSSON AND CO-WORKERS[588], GHIORSO AND CO-WORKERS[589], and also Chapter 5.) This is an important method of synthesis because these longer-lived isotopes can be prepared in weighable amounts and used in more detailed investigations of the chemistry of californium. The longest-lived isotopes are Cf^{249} and Cf^{251} with half-lives of about 400 years. The first isolation of californium in weighable quantities occurred in the summer of 1958 when THOMPSON AND CUNNINGHAM[590] isolated a few micrograms from 8 grams of plutonium which had been irradiated for several years in the highest flux of the Materials Testing Reactor. With this sample they were able to initiate a program of investigation of the bulk properties of californium using ultramicrochemical techniques. In later years much larger quantities were scheduled to become available under the U.S. Atomic Energy Commission's national program for heavy element production centered at the Oak Ridge HFIR reactor.

Another method of preparation of californium which is related to the buildup of higher elements by the neutron irradiation of lower elements is observed in connection with nuclear explosions as described in Section 5.4.3 of Chapter 5.

---

[584] E. K. Hulet, S. G. Thompson, A. Ghiorso, and K. Street, Jr., *Phys. Rev.* **84**, 366 (1951).

[585] E. K. Hulet, S. G. Thompson, and A. Ghiorso, *Phys. Rev.* **95**, 1702 (1954).

[586] A. Ghiorso, G. B. Rossi, B. G. Harvey, and S. G. Thompson, *Phys. Rev.* **93**, 257 (1954).

[587] A. Ghiorso, S. G. Thompson, K. Street, Jr., and G. T. Seaborg, *Phys. Rev.* **81**, 154 (1951).

[588] L. B. Magnusson, M. H. Studier, P. R. Fields, C. M. Stevens, J. F. Mech, A. M. Friedman, H. Diamond, and J. R. Huizenga, *Phys. Rev.* **96**, 1576 (1954).

[589] A. Ghiorso, S. G. Thompson, G. R. Choppin, and B. G. Harvey, *Phys. Rev.* **94**, 1081 (1954).

[590] S. G. Thompson and B. B. Cunningham, *Proceedings of the Second U.N. Conference on the Peaceful Uses of Atomic Energy* **28**, 346, Geneva 1958.

One feature of the californium isotopes which is of great interest is the high rate of decay by spontaneous fission exhibited by the heavy even-even isotopes. The Cf^{250} has an alpha-decay-to-fission ratio of only 1330, in Cf^{252} this ratio is only 31, and Cf^{254} decays almost entirely by spontaneous fission.

The radioactive decay properties of the individual isotopes are critically reviewed in the following sections.

9.6.2 Californium-244

The 25 ± 3 minute isotope Cf^{244} was produced by CHETHAM-STRODE, CHOPPIN, AND HARVEY[583] by the reactions:

$$Cm^{244}(\alpha, 4n)Cf^{244}$$
$$Cm^{242}(\alpha, 2n)Cf^{244}$$

The excitation function for the first reaction is given in Fig. 9.46. The mass

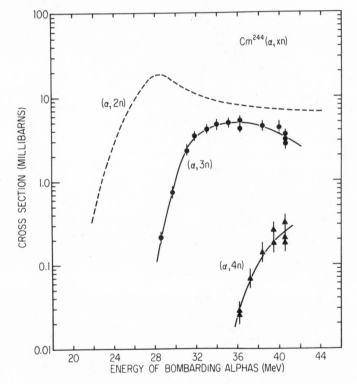

FIG. **9.46.** Excitation functions for the reactions Cm^{244} (α, xn) as given by CHETHAM-STRODE, CHOPPIN, AND HARVEY[583]. Dashed line: (α, $2n$) as determined from Cf^{246} alpha activity. Circles: (α, $3n$) as determined from Cf^{245} alpha activity. Triangles: (α, $4n$) as determined from alpha activity of Cm^{240} daughter.

assignment was confirmed by this determination of the yield as a function of the helium ion energy and by establishment of the genetic relationship of the 25-minute activity to the 26.8-day Cm^{240} daughter. Californium-244 emits alpha particles with an energy of 7.17 ± 0.01 MeV. Branching decay by electron capture is expected to be small since the decay energy available is only 0.6 MeV. Californium-244 is difficult to distinguish from Cf^{245} because of similarities in half-life and alpha particle energy; their alpha particle energies differ by only 55 keV.

It is possible to make Cf^{244} by the bombardment of uranium with carbon ions.[591]

$$U^{238}(C^{12}, 6n)Cf^{244}$$

9.6.3 Californium-245

The isotope Cf^{245} was first prepared and studied by THOMPSON, STREET, GHIORSO, AND SEABORG[592] in the experiments which constituted the discovery of element 98. The original mass number assignment was 244 but later work by CHETHAM-STRODE, CHOPPIN, AND HARVEY,[593] based largely on the excitation function for the activity when Cm^{242} and Cm^{244} targets were bombarded with helium ions, made certain that the correct assignment was 245. These preparative reactions are:

$$Cm^{242}(\alpha, n)Cf^{245}$$

$$Cm^{244}(\alpha, 3n)Cf^{245}$$

The excitation function for the second reaction is given in the figure. Californium-245 decays by emission of 7.11 ± 0.01 MeV alpha particles with a half-life of 44 minutes. Alpha-gamma coincidence experiments indicated no lower energy alpha group in greater than 2 per cent abundance. The Cf^{245} decays by orbital electron capture to Bk^{245} in 70 per cent of its disintegrations, and the berkelium daughter has been isolated and identified.[593]

This isotope can also be made by the bombardment of uranium with carbon ions or by other reactions involving heavy ions and heavy element targets:[594,595]

$$U^{238}(C^{12}, 5n)Cf^{245}$$

[591] T. Sikkeland, A. Ghiorso, and S. G. Thompson, unpublished results; see abstract in *Bull. Am. Phys. Soc. Series II*, **2**, No. 8, 385 (1957); see *Univ. Calif. Rad. Lab. Report UCRL-8142* (1958).

[592] S. G. Thompson, K. Street, Jr., A. Ghiorso, and G. T. Seaborg, *Phys. Rev.* **80**, 790 (1950).

[593] A. Chetham-Strode, Jr., G. R. Choppin, and B. G. Harvey, *Phys. Rev.* **102**, 747 (1956).

[594] A. Ghiorso, S. G. Thompson, K. Street, Jr., and G. T. Seaborg, *Phys. Rev.* **81**, 154 (1951).

[595] A. Ghiorso, G. Bernard Rossi, Bernard G. Harvey, and S. G. Thompson, *Phys. Rev.* **93**, 257 (1954).

9.6.4 *Californium-246*

GHIORSO, THOMPSON, STREET, AND SEABORG[596] produced Cf^{246} by the bombardment of natural uranium with carbon ions accelerated above 100 MeV in the Berkeley 60-inch cyclotron:

$$_{92}U^{238} + _{6}C^{12} \longrightarrow _{98}Cf^{246} + 4_0n^1$$

SIKKELAND, GHIORSO, AND THOMPSON[597] later studied the excitation function for this reaction using monoenergetic carbon ions from a linear accelerator. They found a peak yield of a few microbarns when the beam energy was about 63 MeV. HULET AND CO-WORKERS[598] prepared Cf^{246} by the more conventional reactions:

$$Cm^{243}(\alpha, n)Cf^{246}$$

$$Cm^{244}(\alpha, 2n)Cf^{246}$$

CHETHAM-STRODE, CHOPPIN, AND HARVEY[599] observed the excitation function shown in Section 9.6.3 for the latter reaction. The radioactivity of the californium fraction isolated from curium targets bombarded with helium ions is nearly entirely due to Cf^{246} once the shorter-lived Cf^{244} and Cf^{245} have decayed. The isotope Cf^{246} decays with a half-life of 35.7 hours.[596,598] The alpha spectrum as measured in a magnetic spectrograph indicates groups at 6.753 and 6.711 MeV with intensities of 78 per cent and 22 per cent, respectively.[600,601] Additional measurements[602] with silicon surface barrier detectors gave the following results: 6.753 MeV (77.9 ± 0.2 per cent), 6.714 ± 0.0007 MeV (21.9 ± 0.2 per cent), 6.621 ± 0.001 MeV (0.18 ± 0.02 per cent), and 6.465 ± 0.003 MeV (undetermined intensity). Alpha-gamma coincidence experiments[600,601,603,604] revealed gamma rays of 42, 97, and 150 keV energy. The transition intensities of the 97 and 150 keV gamma

[596] A. Ghiorso, S. G. Thompson, K. Street, Jr., and G. T. Seaborg, *Phys. Rev.* **81**, 154 (1951).

[597] T. Sikkeland, A. Ghiorso, and S. G. Thompson, *Phys. Rev.* **112**, 543 (1958). See also A. Ghiorso and T. Sikkeland, *Paper P/2440*, **15**, p. 158, *Proceedings of the Second U.N. Conference on the Peaceful Uses of Atomic Energy*, Geneva, 1958.

[598] E. K. Hulet, S. G. Thompson, A. Ghiorso, and K. Street, Jr., *Phys. Rev.* **84**, 366 (1951).

[599] A. Chetham-Strode, G. R. Choppin, and B. G. Harvey, *Phys. Rev.* **102**, 747 (1956)

[600] J. P. Hummel, F. S. Stephens, Jr., F. Asaro, A. Chetham-Strode, and I. Perlman, *Phys. Rev.* **98**, 22 (1955); also unpublished results, 1956.

[601] J. P. Hummel, Ph.D. Thesis, University of California, September 1956; also published as *Univ. Calif. Rad. Lab. Report UCRL-3456*, July, 1956.

[602] A. M. Friedman and J. Milsted, *Phys. Rev.* **131**, 772 (1963).

[603] A. Chetham-Strode, Jr., Ph.D. Thesis, University of California, September 1956; also published as *Univ. Calif. Rad. Lab. Report UCRL-3322*, June 26, 1956.

[604] F. Asaro, F. S. Stephens, Jr., S. G. Thompson, and I. Perlman, unpublished results, 1955.

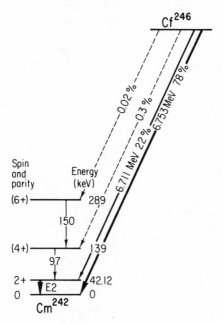

FIG. 9.47. Decay scheme of Cf[246].

rays are 0.3 per cent and 0.02 per cent of the total disintegrations. The alpha decay of the even-even nucleus Cf^{246} populates a rotational band of levels in Cm^{242}. The experimental data lead to the decay scheme shown in the figure, which closely resembles that of all other even-even alpha emitters in the transuranium region. The energy of the first excited state of Cm^{242} is known to be exactly 42.12-keV from studies of the beta decay of Am^{242}. Measurements of HULET, THOMPSON, AND GHIORSO[605] indicate a half-life for spontaneous fission of 2100 ± 300 years.

9.6.5 Californium-247

The 2.45-hour Cf^{247} was first identified by HULET, THOMPSON, AND GHIORSO[606] who prepared it by bombardment of Cm^{244}:

$$Cm^{244}(\alpha, n)Cf^{247}$$

It has also been produced, for example, by bombardment of uranium with energetic nitrogen ions:[607]

$$_{92}U^{238} + {}_{7}N^{14} \longrightarrow {}_{98}Cf^{247} + 4_0n^1 + {}_1p^1$$

[605] E. K. Hulet, S. G. Thompson, and A. Ghiorso, *Phys. Rev.* **89**, 878 (1953).

[606] E. K. Hulet, S. G. Thompson, and A. Ghiorso, *Phys. Rev.* **95**, 1703 (1954).

[607] A. Ghiorso, G. B. Rossi, B. G. Harvey, and S. G. Thompson, *Phys. Rev.* **93**, 257 (1954).

These methods of preparation result in samples containing Cf^{246} as well, which interferes somewhat with the study of the radiations of Cf^{247}.

CHETHAM-STRODE[608] has reported a half-life of 2.45 ± 0.15 hours for the decay of this isotope by orbital electron capture. Examination of the electromagnetic radiations revealed K and L x-rays plus gamma rays with energies of 295 ± 15 keV, 417 ± 8 keV and 460 ± 10 keV. Gamma-gamma coincidence experiments show that the 295-keV gamma ray decays directly to the ground state and that the 417 and 460 keV gamma rays originate at a common 460 keV level in the daughter nucleus. Approximately 90 per cent of the electron capture transitions lead directly to the ground state of Bk^{247}. Approximately 4 per cent lead to the 295 keV level and approximately 2 per cent lead to the 460 keV level.

9.6.6 Californium-248

Bombardment of curium containing appreciable amounts of Cm^{245} and/or higher mass curium isotopes gives rise to Cf^{248} via one or more of the following reactions:

$$Cm^{245}(\alpha, n)Cf^{248}$$

$$Cm^{246}(\alpha, 2n)Cf^{248}$$

$$Cm^{247}(\alpha, 3n)Cf^{248}$$

$$Cm^{248}(\alpha, 4n)Cf^{248}$$

HULET, THOMPSON, AND GHIORSO[609] first produced the isotope by the first of these reactions and proved the mass assignment by observing the growth of the 5.80 MeV alpha particle of Cm^{244}.

This isotope is not produced by the intense neutron irradiation of lighter elements either on a fast time scale (nuclear explosions) or on a slower time scale (nuclear reactors) because its formation is blocked by the beta stability of Cm^{248}. It can be produced by bombardment of lighter elements with heavy ions as in the example written below.[610]

$$_{92}U^{238} + {}_{7}N^{14} \longrightarrow {}_{98}Cf^{248} + {}_{1}p^{1} + 3{}_{0}n^{1}$$

The isotope Cf^{248} decays by the emission of alpha particles with a half-life of 350 days,[611] the main group of alpha particles having an energy of

---

[608] A. Chetham-Strode, Jr., Ph.D. Thesis, University of California, September 1956; also published as *Univ. Calif. Rad. Lab. Report UCRL-3322*, June 26, 1956.

[609] E. K. Hulet, S. G. Thompson, and A. Ghiorso, *Phys. Rev.* **95**, 1703 (1954); E. K. Hulet, Ph.D. Thesis, University of California, August 1953; also published as *Univ. Calif. Rad. Lab. Report UCRL-2283*, August 1953.

[610] A. Ghiorso, G. Bernard Rossi, B. G. Harvey, and S. G. Thompson, *Phys. Rev.* **93**, 257 (1954).

6.26 ± 0.03 MeV. HULET[611] has found that the main alpha-group abundance is approximately 82 per cent, whereas a second group in about 18 per cent abundance has an energy 45 kilovolts lower in energy. This result conforms to the pattern of decay shown by all the neighboring even-even alpha-emitters. A measurement of the spontaneous fission half-life gave a lower limit of 15,000 years.[611] Small amounts of Cf^{248} have been isolated as the daughter products of Bk^{248}, Es^{248}, and Fm^{252} decay. Cf^{248} is beta stable.

9.6.7 Californium-249

The beta-decay of 314-day Bk^{249} has been observed[612,613,614] to give rise to the long-lived alpha-emitter Cf^{249}. This isotope of californium can be produced by the intense and prolonged irradiation of uranium, plutonium, americium or curium with neutrons. The neutron-capture sequence proceeds through the isotopes of curium until mass 249 is reached; Cm^{249} then decays to Bk^{249} which decays to Cf^{249}; Cf^{249} in turn captures neutrons to give rise to several heavier isotopes of californium. The pertinent sequence is the following:

$$
\begin{array}{l}
\qquad\qquad\qquad\qquad\qquad\qquad\qquad \beta^- \uparrow \\
\boxed{Cf^{249}}(n,\gamma)Cf^{250}(n,\gamma)Cf^{251}(n,\gamma)Cf^{252}(n,\gamma)Cf^{253} \\
\beta^- \downarrow \qquad\quad \beta^- \uparrow \\
Bk^{249}(n,\gamma)Bk^{250} \\
\beta^- \uparrow \\
Cm^{244}(n,\gamma)Cm^{245}(n,\gamma) \dots Cm^{249}
\end{array}
$$

The isotopic composition of the californium samples prepared by intense neutron irradiation of Pu^{239} has been determined mass spectrometrically by MAGNUSSON AND CO-WORKERS.[614] Typical results are shown in Table 9.40.

In order to obtain pure samples of Cf^{249} it is necessary to isolate and purify the berkelium fraction from such neutron-irradiated samples and at a later date remove the daughter Cf^{249} activity.

The U.S. Atomic Energy Commission constructed an ultra high flux reactor (named HFIR for High Flux Isotope Reactor) at Oak Ridge National Laboratory for the purpose of large scale production of transplutonium nuclides. This production program provides ultimately for the isolation of Cf^{249} in gram amounts from Bk^{249}. Isotopically pure Cf^{249} prepared

[611] E. K. Hulet, unpublished results, 1956–57.

[612] A. Ghiorso, S. G. Thompson, G. R. Choppin, and B. G. Harvey, *Phys. Rev.* **94**, 1081 (1954).

[613] H. Diamond, L. B. Magnusson, J. F. Mech, C. M. Stevens, A. M. Friedman, M. H. Studier, P. R. Fields, and J. R. Huizenga, *Phys. Rev.* **94**, 1083 (1954).

[614] L. B. Magnusson, M. H. Studier, P. R. Fields, C. M. Stevens, J. F. Mech, A. M. Friedman, H. Diamond, and J. R. Huizenga, *Phys. Rev.* **96**, 1576 (1954).

in this way is desirable for many purposes because of the absence of spontaneous fission activity with its accompanying neutrons.

TABLE 9.40. Isotopic composition of californium fraction isolated from Pu^{239} sample irradiated to an integrated flux of 1.14×10^{22} neutrons/cm². (Ref. 614)

Isotope	Abundance—atom (per cent)
Cf^{249}	4.3 ± 0.5
Cf^{250}	49 ± 6
Cf^{251}	11 ± 3
Cf^{252}	36 ± 5

Californium-249 was observed for the first time in the debris of a thermonuclear test explosion.[615] Two early determinations of the half-life of Cf^{249} resulted in the values of ~400 years[612] and 470 ± 100 years.[614] A more recent result is 360 ± 40 years.[616] All three values were determined by measuring the growth of Cf^{249} daughter activity into a known amount of Bk^{249}. The half-life for spontaneous fission has been reported as 1.5×10^9 years[612] and as $\geqslant 4.5 \times 10^8$ years.[616]

TABLE 9.41. Alpha spectrum of Cf^{249}.

Energy of Cm^{245} daughter level (keV)	Alpha intensity (per cent)
0	1.9
56	1.1
124	0.4
207(?)	0.08
257	3.3
301	3.0
357	1.2
394	83.7
422(?)	0.5
450	4.4
511	0.4

The energy of the intense alpha group leading to the 394 keV level was determined to be 5.806 MeV relative to a Cm^{244} standard taken as 5.801 MeV. The energies of the other levels of Cm^{245} were determined by a joint consideration of the experimental gamma-ray and alpha-ray spectra.[619]

[615] P. R. Fields, A. Ghiorso, and co-workers, *Phys. Rev.* **102**, 180 (1956).
[616] T. A. Eastwood, *et al.*, *Phys. Rev.* **107**, 1635 (1957).

The alpha spectrum of Cf^{249} has been studied by MAGNUSSON[617] and by ASARO, STEPHENS, AND PERLMAN.[618,619]   We quote the results of the latter group[619] in Table 9.41.   This spectrum was measured in a magnetic spectrometer with special shaping of the field to accomplish double-focusing with the purpose of achieving higher transmission.   The alpha groups are also indicated in the decay scheme shown in the accompanying figure.

Three gamma rays have been reported:[619] 255 keV (3 per cent), 340 keV (15 per cent), and 394 keV (72 per cent).   The 255 keV gamma ray has been

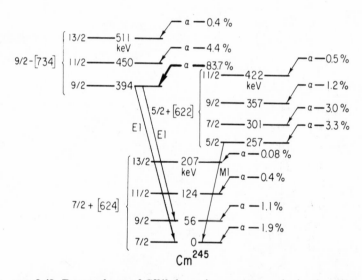

FIG. **9.48.** Decay scheme of Cf²⁴⁹ drawn in a way to emphasize the rotational band interpretation of the observed levels of Cm²⁴⁵.   The Nilsson level quantum numbers are given to the left of each set of levels: *K*, parity [*N n_z* Λ].   The energy of each level is given in keV in the center of the line representing that level.   Analysis is by ASARO, STEPHENS, AND PERLMAN.

[617] L. B. Magnusson, unpublished data (1957).

[618] F. Asaro, F. S. Stephens, and I. Perlman, unpublished data (1957).

[619] F. S. Stephens, F. Asaro, S. G. Thompson, and I. Perlman, *Bull. Am. Phys. Soc. Ser. II* **2**, 394 (1957) and private communication.

seen also from Bk^{245} electron-capture decay[620,621] (see Section 9.5.4) and from Am^{245} beta decay.[622-624] It has clearly been identified as an $M1$ transition. Conversion coefficient arguments as well as some angular correlation data indicate that the 340 and 394 keV transitions are probably $E1$. A rather satisfactory analysis of all the data in terms of three rotational bands has been given[617-619] and is reproduced in the decay scheme shown here. The principal data lacking are conversion electron spectra, which are difficult to obtain with limited amounts of Cf^{249}. In the following paragraphs we review briefly the properties of the three rotational bands, the choice of Nilsson states, and, finally, the interpretation of the alpha decay intensity pattern.

According to the Nilsson diagram of neutron states the ground state of Cm^{245} with 149 neutrons should be $7/2 + [624]$ or $9/2 - [734]$. Four members of the ground state rotational band are known at 0, 56, 124, and 207 keV. These energies fit the rotational formula

$$E_I = E_o + \frac{\hbar^2}{2\mathfrak{J}} [I(I + 1) - I_o(I_o + 1)]$$

quite well if we set $E_o = 0$, $\hbar^2/2\mathfrak{J} = 6.2$ keV and $I_o = 7/2$. Hence, the indicated ground state assignment is $7/2 + [624]$.

The levels at 257, 301, 357, and 422 are also interpreted as a rotational band. These energies agree well with the above rotational formula if $E_o = 257$ keV, $\hbar^2/2\mathfrak{J} = 6.3$ keV and $I_o = 5/2$. The Nilsson assignment is $5/2 + [622]$. This level is the ground state for Pu^{241} and Cm^{243}, both of which have 147 neutrons. A spin assignment of $5/2$ to the 257 keV level is also supported by the following evidence.

Americium-245 has spin $5/2$ and in its decay to Cm^{245} populates both the ground state and the level at 257 keV. Berkelium-245, which presumably has spin $3/2$, does not populate the ground state of Cm^{245} but only the 257 keV level. This 257 keV level decays to the ground state with an $M1$ transition and does not decay to the higher spin members of the ground state rotational band. (See discussion of Bk^{245} in Section 9.5.4.) These data, taken together with rotational band spacings, strongly support the $5/2+$ assignment to the 257 keV level. The $5/2 + [622]$ Nilsson assignment seems almost certain.

The favored alpha decay of Cf^{249} populates a rotational band whose

[620] L. B. Magnusson, A. M. Friedman, D. Engelkemeir, P. R. Fields, and F. Wagner, Jr., *Phys. Rev.* **102**, 1097 (1956).

[621] A. Chetham-Strode, Jr., Ph.D. Thesis, University of California (1956); also printed as *Univ. Calif. Rad. Lab. Report UCRL-3322*, June, 1956.

[622] C. I. Browne, *et al.*, *J. Inorg. Nucl. Chem.* **1**, 254 (1955).

[623] P. R. Fields, *et al.*, *J. Inorg. Nucl. Chem.* **1**, 262 (1955).

[624] J. P. Butler, *et al.*, *Phys. Rev.* **103**, 634 (1956).

base level is 394 keV above the ground state of Cm^{245}. According to the favored alpha decay concept introduced by BOHR, FRÖMAN, AND MOTTELSON[625], this means that the Nilsson assignment of the 394 keV level in Cm^{245} and the ground state of Cf^{249} are identical. The 394 keV level decays by $E1$ transitions to the 7/2 and 9/2 members of the ground state rotational band with no detectable branching to the 5/2 + [622] band at 255 keV. No branching to this 394 keV level was observed in the decay of either Am^{245} or Bk^{245} (spins 5/2 and 3/2). The conclusion from these facts is that the 394 keV level has spin and parity 7/2− or 9/2−, with 9/2− more likely. Alpha-gamma correlation data[619] favor the 9/2− choice. Three members of a rotational band based on the 394 keV level appear at 394, 450, and 511 keV. These energy values are consistent with a 9/2 assignment to the base state, if E_o = 394 keV and $\hbar^2/2\Im$ = 5.1 keV are substituted in the rotational formula given above. The most likely Nilsson choice for a 9/2− state in a nucleus with 149 or 151 neutrons is 9/2 − [734], and this assignment is made to the 394 keV state in Cm^{245} and the ground state of Cf^{249}.

The appreciably lower value of $\hbar^2/2\Im$ for the 9/2 − [734] band compared to the other two bands can be explained by invoking the Coriolis interaction which is larger for this band because it comes from the $j_{15/2}$ shell model orbital. RASMUSSEN[626] has pointed out that the rotational bands based on Nilsson states derived from shell-model orbitals of high j will have larger Coriolis interactions, and hence will be more compressed than other bands. The 9/2 − [734] band is a good example of this situation.

We now turn to a discussion of the alpha intensity patterns. We consider first the alpha decay to the four members of the ground state rotational band of Cm^{245}. This decay involves a change of parity or, equivalently, the emission of alpha particle waves of odd angular momentum. ASARO, STEPHENS, AND PERLMAN[619] analyzed this decay according to the method outlined by BOHR, FRÖMAN, AND MOTTELSON[625] and determined that the alpha waves going to the ground state band are a mixture of 25 per cent $l = 1$, 67 per cent $l = 3$, and 8 per cent $l = 5$. Such an analysis assumes that there is no interference between the various alpha waves. This mixture reproduces, well within the experimental error, the four alpha intensities to the band members. The hindrance factors (reciprocal of the reduced alpha transition probability) for the $l = 1, 3$, and 5 waves are 3.1×10^4, 6.9×10^3, and 2.2×10^4, respectively. The analysis into orbital angular waves is considered to be essentially correct, but the hindrance factors applicable to each partial wave must be understood independently. An approach to an

---

[625] A. Bohr, P. O. Fröman, and B. R. Mottelson, *Dan. Mat.-fys. Medd.* **29**, No. 10 (1955).

[626] J. O. Rasmussen in Hollander, Smith, and Rasmussen, *Phys. Rev.* **102**, 1372 (1956).

explanation of such intrinsic hindrance is discussed in Section 4.2 of Chapter 4, Volume I.

The alpha decay which populates the four levels of the rotational band whose base level lies 257 keV above the ground state has been analyzed similarly into angular momentum components. In this case the alpha waves are 87 per cent $l = 3$ and 13 per cent $l = 5$. The corresponding hindrance factors are 150 and 350. It is not known why the wave hindrance factors are so much lower than for the ground state band.

The favored alpha decay to the $9/2 - [734]$ band has a composition 80 per cent $l = 0$ and 20 per cent $l = 2$ with corresponding hindrance factors of 4.5 and 14. The $l = 0$ wave can, of course, only populate the $9/2-$ level itself, while the $l = 2$ can populate the $11/2$ and $13/2$ levels as well. It is perhaps worthwhile to point out again that this "favored" alpha decay is believed to be much like the ground-state-to-ground-state alpha transitions in even-even nuclei.

NAVARRO, RASMUSSEN, AND SHIRLEY[627] have studied the anisotropic angular distribution of α-particles from nuclei of Cf^{249} located in a thin surface layer on a crystal of neodymium ethyl sulfate cooled to 0.02°K. These experiments show that there is a preference for emission of α-particles from the polar regions or "tips" of the spheroidally-deformed nucleus.

9.6.8 Californium-250

In the previous section we reported how Cf^{249} is produced by the build-up of lighter isotopes by neutron capture reactions. The isotope Cf^{250} is produced in the same way when the irradiation proceeds for a sufficiently long time. In the table printed in the previous section it is shown that a californium fraction containing 49 mole per cent Cf^{250} has been prepared[628] by neutron irradiation of Pu^{239}. When the neutron buildup occurs on a very fast time scale, as in thermonuclear explosions,[629] Cf^{250} is not produced because of the beta stability or long β^- half-life of Cm^{250}. It is also possible to prepare Cf^{250} by the following reactions:

$$Bk^{249}(d, n)Cf^{250}$$

$$Bk^{249}(n, \gamma)Bk^{250} \xrightarrow[3.1 \text{ hours}]{\beta^-} Cf^{250}$$

$$Cm^{247}(\alpha, n)Cf^{250}$$

$$Cm^{248}(\alpha, 2n)Cf^{250}$$

[627] Q. A. Navarro, J. O. Rasmussen, and D. A. Shirley, *UCRL-10023, Chemistry Division Annual Report*, 1961, Lawrence Radiation Laboratory, unpublished. See also Ph.D. Thesis of Q. A. Navarro issued as *UCRL-10362*, July, 1962.

[628] L. B. Magnusson, M. H. Studier, P. R. Fields, C. M. Stevens, J. F. Mech, A. M. Friedman, H. Diamond, and J. R. Huizenga, *Phys. Rev.* **96**, 1576 (1954).

[629] P. R. Fields, et al., *Phys. Rev.* **102**, 180 (1956).

Of these methods the neutron irradiation of Bk^{249} is the best. With the amounts of berkelium now being produced it should be possible to prepare multi-milligram amounts of $Cf^{250-251}$.

Isotopically pure samples of Cf^{250} can be separated as the daughter product from aged samples of Es^{254}. The 270-day isomer of Es^{254} decays by α-emission to Bk^{250} which decays with a 3.2-hour half-life to produce Cf^{250}.

In the first work bearing on the properties of Cf^{250} GHIORSO AND CO-WORKERS[630] observed that chemically-pure samples of 3.13-hour Bk^{250} decayed to a daughter product which emitted 6.05-MeV alpha particles. The number of alpha particles corresponded to a half-life of about 12 years for Cf^{250}. In this preliminary work the ratio of the rate of alpha decay to the rate of spontaneous fission was set at 400, from which the spontaneous fission half-life of Cf^{250} was estimated as about 5000 years.

MAGNUSSON AND CO-WORKERS[628] used data from the mass spectrographic analysis and alpha spectrum analysis of a sample of californium containing 49 isotope per cent Cf^{250} to calculate a half-life of 10.0 ± 2.4 years. The alpha to spontaneous fission rate was set at 1460 ± 350 leading to a spontaneous fission half-life of $(1.5 \pm 0.5) \times 10^4$ years. These workers measured the alpha decay energy[628] of the main alpha group to be 6.031 MeV. By alpha-gamma coincidence studies they showed that an alpha group of approximately 40 keV lower energy (ca. 5.99 MeV) was in coincidence with L x-rays (from the conversion of a gamma ray of 40 keV). EASTWOOD AND CO-WORKERS[631] analyzed a somewhat similar sample of mixed californium isotopes and found for Cf^{250} a half-life of 10.9 ± 0.8 years and an alpha particle energy for the main group of 6.020 ± 0.010 MeV. PHILLIPS, GATTI, BRANDT, AND THOMPSON[632] measured a value of 1330 ± 45 for the α/SF ratio of a pure sample of Cf^{250} prepared by the α-decay of 270-day Es^{254}; in a similar experiment BARNES AND DIAMOND[633] measured a value of 1260 ± 40 for this ratio. BARNES AND DIAMOND also report a value of 13.2 ± 0.5 years for the partial alpha half-life.

ASARO, STEPHENS, HARVEY, AND PERLMAN[634] studied a mixed sample of californium in which the alpha radioactivity was 85 per cent due to Cf^{252} and 15 per cent due to Cf^{250}. Measurements in a magnetic alpha spectrograph showed a main alpha group for Cf^{250} of 6.024 MeV (83 per cent

[630] A. Ghiorso, S. G. Thompson, G. R. Choppin, and B. G. Harvey, *Phys. Rev.* **94**, 1081 (1954).

[631] T. A. Eastwood, *et al.*, *Phys. Rev.* **107**, 1635 (1957).

[632] L. Phillips, R. Gatti, R. Brandt, and S. G. Thompson, *J. Inorg. Nucl. Chem.*, **25**, 1085 (1963).

[633] R. F. Barnes and H. Diamond, unpublished information (1962); D. Metta, *et al.*, *J. Inorg. Nucl. Chem.* (1964).

[634] F. Asaro, F. S. Stephens, Jr., B. G. Harvey, and I. Perlman, *Phys. Rev.* **100**, 137 (1955).

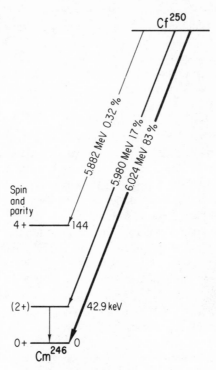

FIG. **9.49.** Decay scheme of Cf^{250}.

abundance) and a smaller group at 5.980 MeV (17 per cent abundance).
A later remeasurement[635] revealed a third group at 5.882 MeV in 0.32 per
cent abundance.   Alpha-gamma coincidence experiments showed that L
x-rays were in coincidence with alpha particles.   From their interpretation
of their quantitative measurements the 44 keV transition from the first
excited state in the Cm^{246} daughter is an $E2$ transition; the L x-rays arise
from its nearly complete conversion.   HARVEY AND HOLLANDER[636] have
measured the L_{II} and L_{III} conversion electrons of this transition and report
an energy value of 42.9 ± 0.1 keV.   The decay scheme for Cf^{250} is shown in
the figure.   A detailed study of the gamma radiations of Cf^{250} in a mixed
source of this type is somewhat hindered by the gamma radiations of other
californium isotopes present and by an appreciable amount of gamma activity
arising from the spontaneous fission of Cf^{252}.   Cf^{250} is stable toward beta
decay processes.

635 F. Asaro, S. G. Thompson, F. S. Stephens, Jr., and I. Perlman, *Univ. Calif. Rad.
Lab. Report UCRL-8369*, July 1958, p. 27, unpublished.

636 B. G. Harvey and J. M. Hollander, as reported by J. M. Hollander, *Phys. Rev.*
103, 1590 (1956).

9.6.9 *Californium-251*

The isotope Cf^{251} has been identified by mass-spectrometric analysis of californium fractions isolated from neutron irradiated plutonium;[637,638,639] see, for example, the analysis of one sample given in the table accompanying the description of Cf^{249}. Californium-251 is almost certainly beta-stable. Its long alpha half-life made it difficult to investigate its alpha spectrum in the samples first available to investigators. ASARO AND CO-WORKERS[640] identified two groups of equal intensity with energies 5.844 and 5.667 MeV. From the observed intensity of these groups and the mass spectrometric analysis of the californium sample they set a partial alpha half-life of 3200 years for each group. A net half-life of approximately 800 years was estimated by EASTWOOD AND CO-WORKERS[639] by mass spectrometric measurements of the ratio Cm^{246}/Cm^{247} in the daughter curium fraction separated from a californium fraction containing Cf^{250} and Cf^{251} in the ratio 7/2.

9.6.10 *Californium-252*

The 2.65-year isotope Cf^{252} is prepared by intense neutron irradiation of Pu^{239} or of other heavy element materials[641–643], and has been identified mass spectrometrically in californium fractions isolated from such irradiated samples.[642,643,645] It can also be prepared by multiple neutron capture on a fast time scale (i.e., lifetimes for neutron capture small compared to beta decay lifetimes) such as occurs in connection with thermonuclear reactions; it was in fact first identified in samples taken from the "Mike" thermonuclear test explosion.[644]

The production of Cf^{252} in high-flux reactors is a matter of considerable scientific importance and special reactors have been proposed for the production of Cf^{252} and other transplutonium nuclides. Refer to discussion in Chapter 5 and discussion of Cf^{249} in Sec. 9.6.7.

Cf^{252} decays by alpha emission and by spontaneous fission. It is beta

[637] H. Diamond, L. B. Magnusson, J. F. Mech, C. M. Stevens, A. M. Friedman, M. H. Studier, P. R. Fields, and J. R. Huizenga, *Phys. Rev.* **94**, 1083 (1954).

[638] L. B. Magnusson, M. H. Studier, P. R. Fields, C. M. Stevens, J. F. Mech, A. M. Friedman, H. Diamond, and J. R. Huizenga, *Phys. Rev.*, **96**, 1576 (1954).

[639] T. A. Eastwood, et al., *Phys. Rev.* **107**, 1635 (1957).

[640] F. Asaro, S. G. Thompson, F. Stephens, and I. Perlman, unpublished results 1961.

[641] A. Ghiorso, S. G. Thompson, G. R. Choppin, and B. G. Harvey, *Phys. Rev.* **94**, 1081 (1954).

[642] H. Diamond, L. B. Magnusson, J. F. Mech, C. M. Stevens, A. M. Friedman, M. H. Studier, P. R. Fields, and J. R. Huizenga, *Phys. Rev.* **94**, 1083 (1954).

[643] L. B. Magnusson, M. H. Studier, P. R. Fields, C. M. Stevens, J. F. Mech, A. M. Friedman, H. Diamond, and J. R. Huizenga, *Phys. Rev.* **96**, 1576 (1954).

[644] P. R. Fields, A. Ghiorso, and co-workers, *Phys. Rev.* **102**, 180 (1956).

stable. The ratio of alpha decay to spontaneous fission is only 31.3. The best method of measurement of the alpha decay half-life is to follow the decay of the spontaneous fission rate, since the observed rate is controlled by the rate of alpha decay. One group[643] reports an alpha half-life of 2.2 years and a spontaneous fission half-life of 66 ± 10 years. A second laboratory[645] reports 2.55 ± 0.15 years and 82 ± 6 years for these half-lives. SEVIER[646] reports an alpha-to-fission ratio of 36.4. (See also Ref. 647.)

Many features of the spontaneous fission of Cf^{252} have been studied. An account is given in the later volume on fission (Volume III, Part 1) of radiochemical studies of the fission products, of the number of neutrons emitted in fission, and other important features of the spontaneous fission of Cf^{252}. This isotope together with other even-even isotopes of very high atomic number such as Cf^{254}, Fm^{256}, etc., is highly suited for a detailed study of the spontaneous fission process. One milligram of Cf^{252} gives rise to 5×10^{10} spontaneous fission events per minute. It has been suggested that Cf^{252} might be suitable as a portable neutron source. The average number of neutrons released in this spontaneous fission is 3.7; hence, one gram of Cf^{252} releases $\sim 10^{12}$ neutrons per second. This would be a much stronger neutron source than any of the (α, n) or photo-neutron sources listed in the special tables of Chapter 5.

The energy of the main alpha particle group was given as 6.117 MeV by MAGNUSSON AND CO-WORKERS[643] who also showed by the measurement of alpha particles in coincidence with L x-rays that a second group with energy about 6.08 MeV was present. ASARO, STEPHENS, HARVEY, AND PERLMAN[648] studied a mixture of californium isotopes in which Cf^{252} accounted for 83 per cent and Cf^{250} for 17 per cent of the alpha activity. Their measurements on a magnetic spectrograph showed two alpha groups of Cf^{252}: 6.112 MeV (84.5 per cent) and 6.069 MeV (15.5 per cent). A later remeasurement[649] revealed a third group at 5.968 MeV in 0.28 per cent abundance. By alpha-gamma coincidence experiments L x-rays and gamma rays of 42 keV (0.014 per cent) and 100 keV (0.013 per cent) were assigned to Cf^{252}. The 42 keV transition is certainly $E2$ in nature and the 100 keV transition is probably $E2$. A conversion coefficient of 20 is computed for the 100 keV transition from the ratio of the photon abundance to the 5.968 MeV alpha particle. This is in excellent agreement with the theoretical $E2$ conversion coefficient. Direct

[645] T. A. Eastwood, et al., Phys. Rev. **107**, 1635 (1957).

[646] K. D. Sevier, Nucl. Instr. Meth. **14**, 318 (1962).

[647] D. Metta et al., J. Inorg. Nucl. Chem. (1964) report a total half-life of 2.646 ± 0.004 years and α/SF equal to 31.3 ± 0.2.

[648] F. Asaro, F. S. Stephens, Jr., B. G. Harvey, and I. Perlman, Phys. Rev. **100**, 137 (1955).

[649] F. Asaro, S. G. Thompson, F. S. Stephens, Jr., and I. Perlman, Univ. Calif. Rad. Lab. Report UCRL-8369, July 1958, p. 27, unpublished.

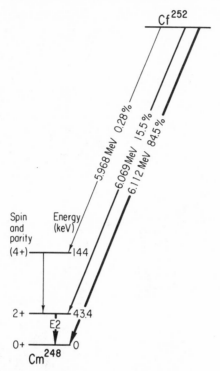

FIG. **9.50**. Decay scheme of Cf[252].

examination of the gamma rays is hindered by the presence of gamma rays accompanying spontaneous fission, but this background is eliminated by suitable coincidence techniques. The decay scheme of Cf^{252} as given in the figure is similar to that of all even-even alpha emitters in this mass region. The L_{II} and L_{III} conversion electrons of the lower energy gamma ray were measured by HOLLANDER[650] who found a transition energy of 43.4 ± 0.1 keV.

BJØRNHOLM, LEDERER, ASARO, AND PERLMAN[651] examined samples of Cf^{252} with sensitive alpha-gamma coincidence techniques to search for alpha decay to higher-lying levels of collective excitation, corresponding to the so-called beta and gamma vibrational states. They found no firm evidence and set low upper limits on the alpha population of such states in the energy region between 400 and 860 keV.

A californium sample containing a substantial percentage of Cf^{252} is a convenient source of its daughter product Cm^{248}.[652]

[650] J. M. Hollander, *Phys. Rev.* **103**, 1590 (1956).

[651] S. Bjørnholm, M. Lederer, F. Asaro, and I. Perlman, *Phys. Rev.* **130**, 2000 (1963).

[652] J. P. Butler, T. A. Eastwood, H. G. Jackson, and R. P. Schuman, *Phys. Rev.* **103**, 965 (1956).

9.6.11 *Californium-253*

Intense neutron irradiation of plutonium[653,654] or other heavy element samples results ultimately in the formation of californium fractions containing appreciable amounts of Cf^{253}. This isotope has been observed to decay by β^- emission with a half-life reported as 18 ± 3 days,[653] ~ 20 days,[655] 17 days,[656] and 17.6 ± 0.2 days.[657] These values were obtained by observing the growth of the 6.61 MeV alpha particles of the daughter product, Es^{253}, into a californium sample. The beta decay of Cf^{253} has not been studied carefully because of the interference of other radiations in the samples available for study. The isotope Cf^{253} has been found in the debris from a thermonuclear explosion,[655] and this in fact is where the isotope was discovered.

The isotope Cf^{253} is the lightest isotope of californium to decay by beta emission; hence it is the key isotope leading to the production of einsteinium and heavier elements in neutron-capture reactions.

Preliminary measurements[658] of the beta-particles indicate an end-point energy of 270 kilovolts. An upper limit of one per cent has been set on gamma radiation between 100 and 700 kilovolts.[659]

9.6.12 *Californium-254*

The isotope Cf^{254} was first found[660] during the examination of the californium fraction from the debris of the 1952 "Mike" thermonuclear test explosion. The decay curve for the rate of spontaneous fission could be resolved into two components with half-lives of 2.1 years and 55 days. The 2.1-year component could be identified with Cf^{252} spontaneous fission events and the 55-day component was assigned to Cf^{254} on the basis of yields and decay systematics. This assignment was later confirmed[661] by noting that spontaneous fission activity of this half-life grew into the californium daughter fraction of a sample of 36-hour Es^{254} prepared by neutron irradiation of Es^{253}.

---

653 L. B. Magnusson, M. H. Studier, P. R. Fields, C. M. Stevens, J. F. Mech, A. M. Friedman, H. Diamond, and J. R. Huizenga, *Phys. Rev.* **96**, 1576 (1954).

654 S. G. Thompson, A. Ghiorso, B. G. Harvey, and G. R. Choppin, *Phys. Rev.* **93**, 909 (1954); *Phys. Rev.* **94**, 1080 (1954).

655 P. R. Fields, A. Ghiorso, and co-workers, *Phys. Rev.* **102**, 180 (1956).

656 T. A. Eastwood, *et al.*, *Phys. Rev.* **107**, 1635 (1957).

657 D. N. Metta *et al.*, *J. Inorg. Nucl. Chem.* (1964).

658 C. J. Gallagher, Jr., unpublished data (1957).

659 F. Asaro, F. S. Stephens, Jr., unpublished results (1957).

660 P. R. Fields, *et al.*, *Phys. Rev.* **102**, 180 (1956); *Phys. Rev.* **119**, 2000 (1960).

661 B. G. Harvey, S. G. Thompson, G. R. Choppin, and A. Ghiorso, *Phys. Rev.* **99**, 337 (1955).

The decay of Cf^{254} is entirely by spontaneous fission. No decay by alpha particle emission has been observed and the isotope is beta stable.

The first values which were reported for the half-life for spontaneous fission were somewhat rough; the values 55 days,[660] 85 ± 15 days[661] and 60 ± 10 days[662] were reported. The importance of this half-life in astrophysics prompted HUIZENGA AND DIAMOND[663] to re-examine the data by the least-squares method. They obtained a value of 56.2 ± 0.7 days in good agreement with the astrophysical half-life of 55 ± 1 nights deduced from the light intensity curves of type I supernovae. However, a later redetermination by PHILLIPS, GATTI, BRANDT, AND THOMPSON[664] on an isotopically pure sample prepared by the neutron irradiation of Es^{253} resulted in the value 60.5 ± 0.2 days. A redetermination by H. DIAMOND[665] gave the result 60.3 ± 1.1 days based on a Cf^{252} half-life of 2.65 years.

In Chapter 5, Section 5.4.3, we have outlined the possible path of formation of heavy elements in stars by neutron capture processes and referred to the suggestion that the formation of Cf^{254} by neutron capture on a fast-time scale might possibly explain the light intensity curves seen in the supernovae explosions.

9.7 THE ELEMENT EINSTEINIUM (ELEMENT 99)

9.7.1. Discovery of Einsteinium

The first identification[666–668] of an isotope of element 99 and of element 100 came about as the result of careful analysis of heavy element samples from the "Mike" thermonuclear explosion staged by the Los Alamos Scientific Laboratory in November, 1952. The uranium in this device was subjected to a very intense, instantaneous neutron flux. Multiple neutron capture reactions gave rise to very heavy uranium isotopes which rapidly decayed by beta emission into previously uninvestigated heavy isotopes of neptunium, plutonium, americium, curium, berkelium, californium, and of the elements 99 and 100. Three teams of nuclear chemists working at the University of California Radiation Laboratory, the Argonne National Laboratory, and the Los Alamos Scientific Laboratory contributed to the chemical isolation and

[662] Bentley, et al., Paper No. P/809, Proceedings of the International Conference on the Peaceful Uses of Atomic Energy 7, p. 261, United Nations, New York, 1956.
[663] J. R. Huizenga and H. Diamond, Phys. Rev. 107, 1087 (1957).
[664] L. Phillips, R. Gatti, R. Brandt, and S. G. Thompson, J. Inorg. Nucl. Chem. 25, 1085 (1963).
[665] H. Diamond, private communication (1962).
[666] A. Ghiorso, et al., Phys. Rev. 99, 1048 (1955).
[667] P. R. Fields, et al., Phys. Rev. 102, 180 (1956).
[668] H. Diamond, et al., Phys. Rev. 119, 2000 (1960).

identification of the new elements in December, 1952 and January, 1953. The scientists involved were A. GHIORSO, S. G. THOMPSON, G. H. HIGGINS, AND G. T. SEABORG of the University of California; M. H. STUDIER, P. R. FIELDS, S. M. FRIED, H. DIAMOND, J. F. MECH, G. L. PYLE, J. R. HUIZENGA, A. HIRSCH, AND W. M. MANNING of the Argonne National Laboratory; and C. I. BROWNE, H. L. SMITH, AND R. W. SPENCE of the Los Alamos Laboratory.

The names which have been adopted for these elements are einsteinium (symbol Es), after Albert Einstein for element 99 and fermium (symbol Fm) after Enrico Fermi, for element 100.

Einsteinium and fermium are actinide elements with chemical properties very similar to americium, curium, berkelium and californium. Einsteinium and fermium apparently exist only in the tripositive state in aqueous solution. Hence, as in the identification of berkelium and californium, the ion-exchange elution technique played a prominent role in their purification and identification. Rare earth contaminants were removed by adsorbing the contaminated heavy-element fraction on Dowex-50 cation resin and eluting with 13 molar hydrochloric acid. The partially-purified, heavy-element fraction was then adsorbed on another column of Dowex-50 resin and eluted carefully with buffered ammonium citrate solution to effect separation of the individual actinide elements. These experiments showed the elution of a 6.6 MeV alpha activity ahead of the element californium and in the expected eka-holmium (element 99) position. Also a new 7.1 MeV alpha activity was found to elute in the eka-erbium (element 100) position. The conclusions from the detailed experiments were the following: An appreciable amount of U^{253} had formed in the initial nuclear explosion. This rapidly decayed by a chain of short-lived beta emissions to Cf^{253} which decayed by beta emission with a half-life of approximately 20 days to Es^{253} which decayed with the emission of 6.6 MeV alpha particles with a half-life of about 20 days. Similarly, an appreciable amount of U^{255} had formed instantaneously and had decayed via a long chain of short-lived beta-emitters to Es^{255} which decayed by beta emission with a half-life of approximately 30 days to Fm^{255} which decayed by the emission of 7.1 MeV alpha particles with a half-life of approximately 16 hours.

Since these initial experiments, other methods of synthesis of isotopes of einsteinium have been employed. Neutron irradiation of Pu^{239} in high flux reactors for extended periods of time results in the production of californium isotopes by the neutron-capture, beta-decay paths discussed in Chapter 5. The lowest mass isotope of californium capable of negative beta decay is Cf^{253}; when Cf^{253} is formed it decays with a 17-day half-life to produce 20-day Es^{253}. The Es^{253} can capture neutrons to produce higher mass isotopes such as 37-hour Es^{254m}, 270-day Es^{254}, 24-day Es^{255} and the short-lived Es^{256}. A number of lighter isotopes ranging in mass number down to 246 have been produced by helium ion or deuteron bombardment of targets containing berkelium and californium isotopes or by bombardment of heavy element targets with carbon ions, nitrogen ions or other heavy ions. All of the isotopes are discussed completely in the sections which follow.

The longest-lived of the einsteinium isotopes is 270-day Es^{254} and this isotope will eventually be the most important from the standpoint of chemical study of the element. In the early studies of the element the most suitable isotope for this purpose was 20-day Es^{253}.

9.7.2 Einsteinium-245

GHIORSO, SIKKELAND, LARSH, AND LATIMER[668a] found tentative evidence that Es^{245} is an alpha emitter with a 75-second half-life. The energy of the particles which they observed was 7.65 MeV. This activity was produced by the bombardment of targets containing Pu^{240} with accelerated ions of B^{10}. It was also synthesized by the bombardment of Np^{237} with C^{12}.

9.7.3 Einsteinium-246

The bombardment of uranium targets with nitrogen ions accelerated above 100 MeV leads to the production in low yield of the neutron deficient isotopes of einsteinium. The low yield is attributable to the high probability for fission of the compound nucleus before it can be de-excited by neutron emission. GHIORSO, ROSSI, HARVEY, AND THOMPSON[669] have identified Es^{246} among the products of such a bombardment.

$$_{92}U^{238} + {}_7N^{14} \longrightarrow {}_{99}Es^{246} + 6\ _0n^1$$

The information on this isotope is scanty. Einsteinium-246 decays by orbital electron capture: its decay was noted only through the growth of the 36-hour Cf^{246} daughter.[669] Alpha particles of 7.35 MeV were observed to decay with a half-life of 7.3 minutes.[669] These alpha particles were originally assigned tentatively to Es^{247} but they are perhaps more properly assigned to Es^{246}. GUSEVA AND CO-WORKERS[670] have also observed these alpha particles.

9.7.4 Einsteinium-247

No definite information is available on Es^{247}.

[668a] A. Ghiorso, T. Sikkeland, A. E. Larsh, and R. M. Latimer, unpublished results, 1961.

[669] A. Ghiorso, G. B. Rossi, B. G. Harvey, and S. G. Thompson, *Phys. Rev.* **93**, 257 (1954).

[670] Guseva, Filippova, Gerlit, Druin, Myasoedov, and Tarantin, *Atom. Energ.* (USSR) **2**, 50 (1956); *Sov. J. Atom. Energ.* (Consultants Bureau Trans.) **1**, 193 (1956).

9.7.5 *Einsteinium-248*

The isotope Es^{248} was first prepared by the deuteron bombardment of Cf^{249} with 18 to 22 MeV deuterons:[671]

$$Cf^{249}(d, 3n)Es^{248}$$

The targets available in the original study of this reaction contained only 10^{13} atoms of Cf^{249} so the specialized bombardment techniques discussed in the next section were employed.

Einsteinium-248 decays principally by electron capture with a half-life of 25 ± 5 minutes and also by the emission of 6.87 ± 0.02 MeV alpha particles. The ratio of electron capture to alpha decay was estimated at 400 from measurements of the alpha counting rate of Es^{248} and of the Cf^{248} which grew into the sample.

9.7.6 *Einsteinium-249*

The two-hour isotope Es^{249} is conveniently prepared by bombardment of Bk^{249} or Cf^{249} with helium ions[672] or deuterons:[671]

$$Bk^{249}(\alpha, 4n)Es^{249}$$

$$Cf^{249}(\alpha, p3n)Es^{249}$$

$$Cf^{249}(d, 2n)Es^{249}$$

In the original tests of this method the total amount of Bk^{249} available for use as a target was only 1.3×10^{-8} grams or about 3×10^{13} atoms. Special target methods were worked out to use effectively this small amount of material and to conserve it for reuse. Since these methods are of general application we shall describe them briefly.

The Bk^{249} was electrodeposited in a micro cell over a small rectangular area upon a 0.005 cm thick gold foil. This target area was exposed to a deflected collimated helium-ion beam from the 60-inch Berkeley cyclotron. The beam intensity was approximately 50 microamperes per square centimeter. The helium ions passed through the gold foil and then through the Bk^{249} target material so that nuclear reaction products were ejected from the target in the forward direction. They were caught on a 0.00025 cm thick gold "catcher" foil placed about 5.5 millimeters from the target foil. By this method it was possible to bombard the Bk^{249} target a large number of times without the necessity of dissolving it. Some 100 bombardments, amounting to a total irradiation of roughly 1000 microampere hours, were made with no loss of target material.

[671] A. Chetham-Strode and L. W. Holm, *Phys. Rev.* **104**, 1314 (1956).

[672] B. G. Harvey, A. Chetham-Strode, Jr., A. Ghiorso, G. R. Choppin, and S. G. Thompson, *Phys. Rev.* **104**, 1315 (1956).

   The energy of the helium ions was varied by inserting aluminum de-
grading foils ahead of the target.   The helium ion beam intensity was
measured with a Faraday cup placed behind the thin gold catcher foil.   The
recoil energy of the products of (α, xn) reactions is sufficiently great that
essentially complete removal of these products from the target is achieved if
the target thickness is less than about 30 micrograms per square centimeter.
   After bombardment, the thin gold "catcher" foil is dissolved and the
reaction products are chemically separated.   This technique not only con-
serves the target material for reuse but simplifies the chemical treatment of
the products since none of the target material has to be removed.

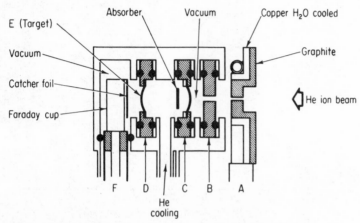

FIG. **9.51.** Schematic view of target assembly used by HARVEY AND CO-
WORKERS.[672]   The labeled parts are described in the text.

   The target arrangement can be visualized in the expanded schematic
view of the target assembly shown in Fig. 9.51.   The helium ion beam was
first collimated by means of the water cooled copper and graphite collimator
A.   The second collimator B reduced the beam to the required size.   Stain-
less steel holder C supported a 0.04 cm thick duraluminum foil which sealed
the rest of the probe assembly from the cyclotron vacuum.   Aluminum
absorber strips could be mounted behind the duraluminum foil.   Holder
D supported the target.   The foils C and D were cooled by means of rapid
circulation of helium between them.   The gold "catcher" foil E was mounted
on the end of rod F with scotch tape.   The rod F terminated in a water
cooled aluminum block which served as a Faraday cup.   The space between
the target and the catcher foil was evacuated.   The several cooling and
vacuum systems were interlocked so that the cyclotron could not be operated
until proper conditions were obtained.

The rod F could be very rapidly withdrawn after completion of a bombardment so that no time was lost in examining the products. Cooling of the foils was adequate to permit a beam as large as 200 microamperes per square centimeter to be used.

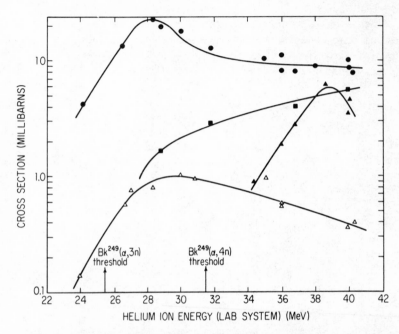

FIG. **9.52.** Excitation functions for formation of einsteinium isotopes. The target is Bk^{249} plus some Cf^{249} daughter. From HARVEY AND CO-WORKERS.[672]

KEY:

$\triangledown$ Bk$^{249}(\alpha, n)$Es^{252}

● Bk$^{249}(\alpha, 2n)$Es^{251}

■ Bk$^{249}(\alpha, 3n)$Es^{250} + Cf$^{249}(\alpha, 3n)$Fm^{250} → Es^{250} + Cf$^{249}(\alpha, p2n)$Es^{250} + Cf$^{249}(\alpha, t)$Es^{250}

▲ Bk$^{249}(\alpha, 4n)$Es^{249} + Cf$^{249}(\alpha, p3n)$Es^{249}.

When Bk^{249} is bombarded with helium ions several isotopes of einsteinium are produced. The yield of these isotopes as a function of the helium ion energy is given in Fig. 9.52. These excitation functions were important in confirming the mass assignments of the products.

Einsteinium-249 has a half-life of 2 hours, and it decays partly by emission of alpha particles with an energy of 6.76 MeV. The chief decay is by orbital electron capture to produce 360-year Cf^{249}. The ratio of orbital electron capture to alpha decay is estimated at 760. Study of the radiations of Es^{249} is hindered by the presence of the other einsteinium isotopes. The decay energy for electron capture is estimated at 1.4 MeV by the use of closed decay cycles.

9.7.7 Einsteinium-250

It is possible to prepare Es^{250} by the following reactions:

$$Bk^{249}(\alpha, 3n)Es^{250}$$

$$Cf^{249}(\alpha, 3n)Fm^{250} \xrightarrow[EC]{} Es^{250}$$

$$Cf^{249}(\alpha, p2n)Es^{250}$$

$$Cf^{249}(\alpha, t)Es^{250}$$

$$Cf^{249}(d, n)Es^{250}$$

A composite excitation function for the production of Es^{250} by a helium ion bombardment of a mixed target of Bk^{249} and Cf^{249} is given in Fig. 9.52. Suitable technique for carrying out such bombardments is discussed in the preceding section. A number of reactions of heavy ions with heavy element target materials lead to the formation of Es^{250}.

Einsteinium-250 decays by orbital electron capture with a half-life of 8 hours.[672] The branching decay by alpha emission is slight and has not been observed. The available decay energy for electron capture and alpha-particle emission have been estimated as 1.94 MeV and 6.72 MeV, respectively.

9.7.8 Einsteinium-251

The first preparation[672] of Es^{251} was carried out by the reaction:

$$Bk^{249}(\alpha, 2n)Es^{251}$$

The excitation function for this reaction is shown in Section 9.7.5. An experimental technique suitable for carrying out such a reaction is discussed in that section.

Einsteinium-251 decays by orbital electron capture and by the emission of alpha particles with 6.48 MeV energy. The observed half-life is 1.5 days and the ratio of electron capture to alpha decay is 190. The decay energy available for electron capture has been estimated as 0.41 MeV from closed decay cycles.

9.7.9 Einsteinium-252

The isotope Es^{252} was discovered as a result of the bombardment of Bk^{249} with helium ions[672]. A suitable experimental technique is discussed in Section 9.7.5. The excitation function for the preparative reaction is also given in Fig. 9.52 which appears in that section.

$$Bk^{249}(\alpha, n)Es^{252}$$

Einsteinium-252 decays by the emission of 6.64 MeV alpha particles with a half-life of ~ 140 days.[672] Einsteinium-252 is expected to be unstable toward electron capture by 1.23 MeV and toward β^- decay by ~ 0.24 MeV but no radiations corresponding to either transition have been reported.

9.7.10 *Einsteinium-253*

The first isotope of element 99 to be identified was Es^{253}. The discovery of this isotope in the debris of a thermonuclear test explosion is discussed earlier in Section 9.7.1. This nuclide can also be prepared by the intense irradiation of plutonium, americium, curium, or californium samples, with neutrons.[677-679] The pertinent neutron capture sequence starting with Cm^{244} is the following:

$$
\begin{array}{c}
Es^{253} \\
\beta^- \uparrow \quad \substack{17.6 \\ days} \\
Cf^{249}(n,\gamma)Cf^{250}(n,\gamma)Cf^{251}(n,\gamma)Cf^{252}(n,\gamma)Cf^{253} \\
\uparrow \beta^- \qquad \uparrow \beta^- \\
Bk^{249}(n,\gamma)Bk^{250} \\
\uparrow \beta^- \\
Cm^{244}(n,\gamma)Cm^{245}(n,\gamma) \ldots Cm^{249}
\end{array}
$$

Very prolonged irradiation[677-679] results in the production of higher mass isotopes of einsteinium, but it is possible to obtain pure samples of Es^{253} by isolating a californium fraction containing an appreciable amount of the 17.6 day beta-emitter Cf^{253}. After a suitable decay period pure Es^{253} can be separated chemically.

Einsteinium-253 is beta stable. The half-life for alpha emission has been measured several times;[679-682] we quote here the precise value of 20.03 $\pm$ 0.01 days determined by JONES AND CO-WORKERS.[679] A number of workers have measured the energy of the main alpha particle group by the ion chamber technique.[679,681,682] When larger samples became available, it was possible to carry out more precise measurements with magnetic spectrographs. The alpha spectrum was studied at Berkeley with a 60°-sector single focusing

---

[677] S. G. Thompson, A. Ghiorso, B. G. Harvey, and G. R. Choppin, *Phys. Rev.* **93**, 908 (1954).

[678] M. H. Studier, *et al.*, *Phys. Rev.* **93**, 1428 (1954).

[679] M. Jones, *et al.*, *Phys. Rev.* **102**, 203 (1956).

[680] A. Ghiorso, *et al.*, *Phys. Rev.* **99**, 1048 (1955); **102**, 180 (1956); **119**, 2000 (1960).

[681] G. R. Choppin, S. G. Thompson, A. Ghiorso, and B. G. Harvey, *Phys. Rev.* **94**, 1080 (1954).

[682] P. R. Fields, *et al.*, *Phys. Rev.* **94**, 209 (1954).

spectrograph and with a 180° double-focusing spectrograph.[683-686] Twelve alpha groups which seem clearly established are listed in Table 9.42, together with their relative intensities and hindrance factors. (The hindrance factors are defined as the reciprocals of the reduced alpha transition probabilities compared to those of the neighboring even-even nuclei. The term reduced transition probability refers to the corrected transition probability after the energy dependence is removed.) These alpha groups are placed in the decay scheme in Fig. 9.53; this figure also contains several tentative groups not listed in Table 9.42, which are deduced from the gamma ray measurements and other considerations.

The conversion electron spectrum of Es^{253} was first studied with 180° permanent-magnet spectrographs by ASARO, THOMPSON, STEPHENS, AND PERLMAN.[686] Intense samples were subsequently examined with a 50-cm iron-free double focusing beta-ray spectrometer by HOLLANDER, HOLTZ, NOVAKOV, AND GRAHAM,[687] and the energies and intensities of the conversion lines were measured with high precision. Twenty-three transitions were observed. The multipolarities and $E2$-$M1$ mixing ratios listed in Table 9.43 were determined by measurements of the L-subshell conversion intensities and ratios of the intra-band transitions. Because of the high precision of the measurements with the iron-free spectrometer, the assignments given in the table are unambiguous. Studies of the gamma rays accompanying Es^{253} decay have also been made with NaI scintillation counters; the results are consistent with the more accurate electron data.[679,683,686,687] The 393 keV transition is assigned as $M1$ on the basis of the large number of K x-rays relative to the 393- and 439-keV photons, whose conversion is the principal source of these x-rays.

The following discussion makes use of the results of ASARO ET AL.[686] and HOLLANDER ET AL.[687] As is indicated in Fig. 9.53, the energy levels of Bk^{249} have been divided into three rotational bands, and the base levels of each band have been assigned as a particular Nilsson state. The basis for the division into three bands is fairly clear; the energy separations, the transitions, and the alpha populations all indicate such a division. The assignment of particular Nilsson orbitals is not so obvious and will be discussed in some detail.

[683] F. S. Stephens, *Univ. Calif. Rad. Lab. Report UCRL-2970*, June 1955.

[684] J. P. Hummel, *Univ. Calif. Rad. Lab. Report UCRL-3456*, 1956.

[685] J. P. Hummel, G. R. Choppin, F. Asaro, and I. Perlman, unpublished data (1955) reported in Ref. 683.

[686] F. Asaro, S. G. Thompson, F. S. Stephens, and I. Perlman, *Univ. Calif. Rad. Lab. Report UCRL-9382* (1960); presented in somewhat different form by I. Perlman in *Proceedings of the International Conference on Nuclear Structure* at Kingston, Ontario, Aug. 29–Sept. 3, 1960, University of Toronto Press, pp. 553–557.

[687] J. M. Hollander, M. D. Holtz, T. Novakov, and R. L. Graham, unpublished data, 1963.

TABLE **9.42.** Alpha groups of Es²⁵³.

Energy (MeV)	6.633	6.624	6.594	6.592	6.552	6.540
Intensity (per cent)	90	0.8	0.7	6.6	0.75	0.85
Hindrance factor	1.93	200	165	17	100	77
Energy (MeV)	6.497	6.479	6.429	6.249	6.209	6.158
Intensity (per cent)	0.26	0.08	0.1	0.04	0.04	0.015
Hindrance factor	160	430	200	70	40	60

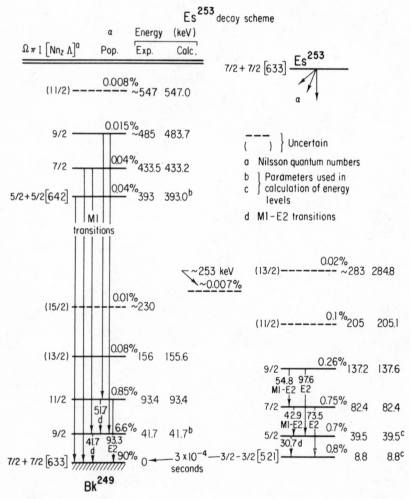

FIG. **9.53.** Decay scheme of Es²⁵³ as formulated by ASARO, THOMPSON, STEPHENS, AND PERLMAN.   Nilsson state assignments are given.

The relative energy spacings of the assigned states in the 8.8 keV band are in excellent agreement with a spin of 3/2 for the base state. In addition, the rotational constant, $\hbar^2/2\mathfrak{J}$, for spin 3/2 is 6.17 keV, in good agreement with the usual values for odd mass nuclides. Although the parity of this band cannot be determined simply from the experimental data, inspection of a

TABLE **9.43**. Gamma transitions of Es^{253} (HOLLANDER *et al.*).

Energy	Multipolarity	Energy	Multipolarity
30.84	*M*1-*E*2	114.04	*E*2
41.79	*M*1-*E*2	121.97	*E*2
42.98	*M*1-*E*2	135.50	*E*2
51.95	*M*1-*E*2	145.43	*E*2
55.11	*M*1-*E*2	368.21	*M*1
62.09		381.26	*M*1
66.84		386.2	*M*1
73.42		387.16	*M*1
73.82	*E*2	389.16	*M*1
93.74	*E*2	428.96	*M*1
98.09	*E*2	433.20	*M*1
		448.32	*M*1

Nilsson diagram (see Figure 3.25 in Chapter 3) readily shows the most probable state is 3/2 − [521]. This assignment is supported by the fact that even-parity, odd-proton levels in this region would be expected to have rotational constants smaller than 6.1. It will be shown later that the ground state spin of Bk^{249} is 7/2+. Thus an *M*2 transition might be expected between the 3/2− and 7/2+ states. Alpha-electron delayed coincidence measurements showed a half-life of 0.3 milliseconds following about 2 per cent of the Es^{253} alpha transitions, in good agreement with the total alpha population to the 3/2− band. This lifetime is retarded by about a factor of 50 over the single proton *M*2 value.[688]

The ground state and 393-keV bands are discussed together as they are closely related. From the level spacing of this ground state band, the spin of the ground state is calculated to be 3.16 ± 0.01. This value is closer to 7/2 than any other spin, but the agreement is not very good. Also, the rotational constant for this band has a value of 4.64 keV, which is unusually low. STEPHENS[683] calculated the properties of this band, however, considering the Coriolis interaction[689] as modified by the pairing correlations,[690]

[688] S. A. Moszkowski, *Beta and Gamma Ray Spectroscopy*, p. 391, edited by Kai Siegbahn (New York: Interscience Publishers Inc., Amsterdam: North Holland Publishing Company, 1955).
[689] A. Kerman, *Mat.-fys. Medd. Dan. Vid. Selsk.* **30**, No. 15 (1955).
[690] S. T. Belyaev, *Mat.-fys. Medd. Dan. Vid. Selsk.* **31**, No. 11 (1959).

and these calculations have been extended, on the basis of the precise iron-free spectrometer data, by HOLLANDER, HOLTZ, NOVAKOV, AND GRAHAM.[687] The observed properties are well explained provided the assignment 7/2+ [633] is made for this band.   The Nilsson diagram shows that this assignment is proper for element 97.   The decay characteristics and spacing of the 393-keV band are also well accounted for if the 5/2 + [642] assignment is made which, again, is an acceptable choice from the Nilsson diagram.   This case is a particularly favorable one for detailed Coriolis calculations for the following reasons: (1) within the entire 82-126 proton shell the only positive parity levels are those originating from the $i_{13/2}$ shell-model level and these can all be taken into account explicitly; the Coriolis interaction occurs only between states of the same parity.   (2) The Coriolis matrix elements are large and do not depend on details of the Nilsson wave functions, and (3) the positions and moments of inertia of two bands from the $i_{13/2}$ orbital are known.   Three adjustable parameters were used and the best least-squares fit to the data was found.   Two of the parameters adjust the amount of Coriolis interaction while the third parameter adjusts the position of the 389-keV level.   The calculated energies are given in Fig: 9.53 and agree well with the experimental values.   It is interesting to note that the mixing causes positive deviations from the $I(I + 1)$ formula in the ground $(K = 7/2)$ band and irregular deviations from the $I(I + 1)$ formula in the 393-keV $(K = 5/2)$ band.   The transition between the two bands are $M1$ as would be expected from calculations using the mixed Nilsson wave functions.

The theoretical alpha populations to various members in a rotational band are readily calculated for an alpha wave of a given angular momentum.[691] In addition, if the parent and daughter states have the same configuration, the alpha transition to the base state of the band is essentially unhindered and the relative alpha populations to the various band members can be calculated explicitly.[691]   This is the phenomenon of favored alpha decay discussed in Chapter 4.   As seen in Table 9.44, the above conditions are well met by the ground state band, resulting in the same assignment for the Es^{253} ground state, 7/2 + [633], as found for Bk^{249}.

In the hindered alpha decays to the other bands, the relative alpha populations are also in good agreement with the calculated values, consistent with the spin and parity assignments.

Independent information of $l = 2$ and $l = 0$ components in the alpha emission of Es^{253} comes from the nuclear alignment experiments of NAVARRO, RASMUSSEN, AND SHIRLEY.[692]   These workers were able to align einsteinium

[691] A. Bohr, P. O. Fröman, and B. R. Mottelson, *Dan. Mat.-fys. Medd.* **29**, No. 10 (1955).

[692] Q. A. Navarro, J. O. Rasmussen, and D. A. Shirley, Chemistry Division Annual Report 1961, Lawrence Radiation Laboratory, Berkeley, *UCRL-10023*, January 1962; Q. A. Navarro, Ph.D. thesis, *UCRL-9960*, February 1962.

nuclei deposited on the surface of a crystal of neodymium ethyl sulfate cooled nearly to absolute zero by adiabatic demagnetization techniques. Under these conditions alpha emission from the sample is strongly anisotropic with favored emission from the tips of the spheroidally-deformed nucleus.

TABLE **9.44**. Alpha decay of Es^{253} to the 7/2+ band in Bk^{249}.

Excited state energy (keV)	I	Calculated abundances* (per cent)				Experimental values (per cent)	Hindrance factors†
		$L=0$	$L=2$	$L=4$	$\sum_L$		
0	7/2	79.6	10.0	0.1	89.7	90	1.9
41.7	9/2	—	5.9	0.3	6.2	6.6	17
93.4	11/2	—	0.9	0.3	1.2	0.85	7.7
156	13/2	—	—	0.11	0.11	0.08	430
230	15/2	—	—	0.009	0.009	0.01	~1500

* The abundances are calculated from the expression

$$P_E = P_{oE} \sum_L C_L \left(C^{I_i L I_f}_{K_i K_f - K_i K_f} \right)^2;$$

$\sum_E P_E$ is the total population to the rotational band, P_{oE} is the unhindered population to a state E calculated from simple spin independent alpha decay theory, C_L is the reciprocal of the hindrance factors for the various L waves in the adjacent even-even nuclides ($C_0 : C_2 : C_4 = 1 : 0.27 : 0.023$ from Fm^{254} and Cf^{252})[693], and the last factor is a Clebsch-Gordan coefficient.

† The hindrance factors as used here are the ratio of the experimental partial half-life of a given α group to the value calculated from spin independent alpha decay theory[694] using the radii of adjacent even-even nuclides.

[693] H. V. Michel, *Univ. Calif. Rad. Lab. Report UCRL-9229*, May 1960.
[694] M. A. Preston, *Phys. Rev.* **71**, 865 (1947).

9.7.11 *The Isomers of Einsteinium-254*

Einsteinium of mass 254 exists in two isomeric forms both produced by neutron irradiation of Es^{253}. One decays chiefly by emission of a beta particle with a half-life of 38.5 ± 1.0 hours to form Fm^{254}. The second decays by alpha particle emission with a half-life of about one year to form Bk^{250}. No gamma transition connecting the two isomers is known. For convenience the 38.5-hour species is sometimes referred to as Es^{254m}. The 38.5-hour isomer was first produced and identified independently by two groups of investigators[695,696] who irradiated small samples of 20-day Es^{253}

[695] P. R. Fields, M. H. Studier, J. F. Mech, H. Diamond, A. M. Friedman, L. B. Magnusson, and J. R. Huizenga, *Phys. Rev.* **93**, 1428 (1954) and *Phys. Rev.* **94**, 209 (1954).
[696] S. G. Thompson, A. Ghiorso, B. G. Harvey, and G. R. Choppin, *Phys. Rev.* **93**, 1129 (1954) and *Phys. Rev.* **94**, 1080 (1954).

TABLE 9.45. Data summary for gamma transitions of 38-hour Es²⁵⁴ (Unik, Day, and Vandenbosch[701]).

	NaI scintillation data		Beta spectrometer data		Conversion coefficient	
Energy	Singles intensity	Intensity in coincidence with L x-rays	Energy	Conv. electron intensity	α_k (exp.)	α_k (theor.) (SL$_{IV}$ for $E2$)
L x-rays	0.90 ± 0.15	yes				
104 ± 3	0.0055 ± 0.001	yes	103.5 ± 1.0	LMN 4.0	$\alpha_{tot.} \approx 20$	$\alpha_{tot.}$ 17
123 (K x-rays)	0.06 ± 0.01	yes				
548 ± 10	0.032 ± 0.005	0.06 ± 0.01	544 ± 5	K 0.027 ± 0.008	0.03 ± 0.01	0.034
586 ± 5	0.086 ± 0.013	0.18 ± 0.02	583 ± 3	K 0.123 ± 0.013	0.04 ± 0.01	0.030
651 ± 5	1.000	1.000	648 ± 2	$\left\{\begin{array}{l} K\ 0.78 \pm 0.02 \\ L\ 0.37 \pm 0.03 \end{array}\right.$	0.023 ± 0.003	0.025
690 ± 5	0.425 ± 0.04	$\left.\begin{array}{l} 0.425 \pm 0.04 \\ - \end{array}\right\}$	692 ± 2	$\left\{\begin{array}{l} K\ 0.83 \pm 0.03 \\ L\ 0.38 \pm 0.04 \end{array}\right.$	0.021 ± 0.003	0.023
694 ± 5	0.755 ± 0.08					

with neutrons and noted the growth into the repurified einsteinium fraction of a 3.3 hour fermium alpha emitter. The half-life of the einsteinium beta emitter supporting this alpha emitter was found to be 38 hours. The long-lived form was first reported by HARVEY, THOMPSON, CHOPPIN, AND GHIORSO[697] who noted the presence of 6.44 MeV alpha particles in the einsteinium fraction many months after the neutron irradiation of a sample of Es^{253}. The mass assignment was proved by the recoil collection of the daughter product, the 3-hour beta emitter Bk^{250}. The early work on both isomers was confirmed by JONES AND CO-WORKERS.[698]

Early reports provided fragmentary information on the radiations of 38.5-hour Es^{254m}. Values of 1.1 MeV[696] and 1.04 ± 0.04 MeV[698] were reported for the main beta particle group. A gamma ray of 660 ± 15 keV was observed in an abundance of 0.6 to 0.8 decay event by JONES AND CO-WORKERS.[698] STEPHENS[699] found the 660 keV gamma peak to be in coincidence with beta particles of ~ 0.45 MeV. He also showed that the 1.04 MeV beta group was in coincidence with L x-rays.

Later studies by ASARO AND PERLMAN[700] with a scintillation spectrometer showed that the gamma spectrum was complex. Gamma rays with energy 529, 575, 636, and 680 keV were resolved. L x-rays were prominent, indicating conversion of a lower energy transition. A series of beta-gamma, K x-ray-gamma, and L x-ray-gamma coincidence experiments led to a tentative decay scheme very similar to that shown here in Fig. 9.54. This scheme was constructed on the assumption[700] that the spectrum of collective excitations universally observed in even-even nuclei throughout the transuranium element groups of nuclides would also appear in Fm^{254}.

UNIK, DAY, AND VANDENBOSCH[701] reinvestigated the radiations of 38-hour Es^{254} with scintillation and beta spectrometers. They also performed gamma-gamma and beta-gamma coincidence measurements. Electric quadrupole transitions of 103.5, 544, 583, 648, and 692 keV were identified. Details of these radiations are summarized in Table 9.45. The beta spectrum was resolved into two components: 475 ± 5 keV (75 per cent) and 1127 ± 2 keV (25 per cent). Consideration of the gamma ray data and the decay scheme results in the more complex analysis of the beta spectrum given in Table 9.46. The decay scheme as given by UNIK, DAY, AND VANDENBOSCH[701] is presented in Fig. 9.54. They assign 2+ character to 39.3-hour

---

[697] B. G. Harvey, S. G. Thompson, A. Ghiorso, and G. R. Choppin, *Phys. Rev.* **99**, 337 (1955).

[698] M. Jones, R. P. Schuman, J. P. Butler, G. Cowper, T. A. Eastwood, and H. G. Jackson, *Phys. Rev.* **102**, 203 (1956).

[699] F. S. Stephens, Jr., *Univ. Calif. Rad. Lab. Report UCRL-2970*, June 1955.

[700] F. Asaro and I. Perlman, unpublished results, 1960.

[701] J. Unik, P. Day, and S. Vandenbosch, *Nucl. Phys.* **36**, 284 (1962).

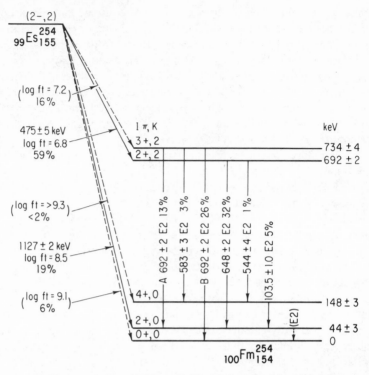

FIG. **9.54.** Decay scheme of 39-hour Es^{254}. In its essentials, this scheme was first formulated by ASARO AND PERLMAN. The energy and intensity data are those given by UNIK, DAY, AND VANDENBOSCH.[701]

Es^{254} on the basis of log ft values of the beta transitions. These workers reported a revised value of 39.3 ± 0.2 hours for the half-life.

HOLLANDER, NORDLING, AND SIEGBAHN[702] contributed to the study of

TABLE **9.46.** Resolution of beta spectrum of 38 hour Es^{254}.
(UNIK, DAY, AND VANDENBOSCH[701])

Energy of group (keV)	Energy of level populated	Intensity (per cent)	Log ft
433 ± 10	734	16	7.2
475 ± 5	692	59	6.8
1024 ± 5	148	≤ 2	≥ 9.3
1127 ± 2	44	19	8.5
1171 ± 2	0	6	9.1

702 J. M. Hollander, C. L. Nordling, and K. Siegbahn, *Arkiv Fysik* **23**, 35 (1962).

Es^{254} by precise measurement of the K-conversion electrons of the transitions from the $K = 2$ vibrational band.   These electron energies were determined in a 50-cm iron-free double focusing spectrometer set at a resolution of 0.4 per cent and transmission of 1 per cent.   Their results are summarized in the

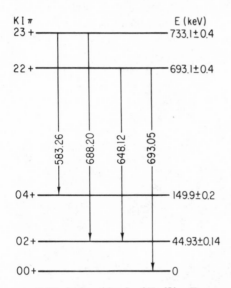

FIG. **9.55.** Assigned levels of Fm^{254}.   From HOLLANDER, NORDLING, AND SIEGBAHN.[702]

Table 9.47 and in the Fig. 9.55.   These transition energies are more precise than those of UNIK, ET AL.,[701] but are in agreement with the interpretation given by these workers.

HARVEY, THOMPSON, GHIORSO, AND CHOPPIN[697] proved the existence of a 0.1 per cent electron capture branch of 39 hour Es^{254} by detecting the growth of spontaneous fission activity of Cf^{254} into a purified einsteinium

TABLE **9.47.** Internal conversion electron data for 38-hour Es^{254}.
(HOLLANDER, NORDLING, AND SIEGBAHN)

Electron energy (keV)	Transition energy (keV)	Relative electron intensity
442.16 ± 0.13	583.26 ± 0.40	0.080 ± 0.005
507.02 ± 0.10	648.12 ± 0.40	0.45 ± 0.02
547.10 ± 0.14	688.20 ± 0.40	0.15 ± 0.01
551.95 ± 0.10	693.05 ± 0.40	0.28 ± 0.02

fraction.   A more precise value of 0.078 ± 0.006 per cent was later reported[703] for this branching.

The half-life of the long-lived form of Es^{254} has been reported as 272 days,[704] 480 ± 70 days[705] and 270 days.[706]   This is the longest half-life for any isotope of einsteinium, and, hence, this isomer is the most suitable material for the study of the chemical properties of the element.

Preliminary measurements of the alpha particle energy in an ion chamber yielded the values 6.44 ± 0.01 MeV^{697} and 6.42 ± 0.02 MeV^{698}.   McHarris, Stephens, Asaro, and Perlman[707] reinvestigated the alpha spectrum and found the complex spectrum summarized in Table 9.48.   Beta spectrometer

TABLE **9.48.** Alpha groups emitted by 270-day Es^{254}.
(McHarris, Asaro, Stephens, and Perlman)

α energy (MeV)	Intensity (per cent)	Excited state energy (keV)
6.517 ± 0.010	upper limit of 0.005	0
6.479 ± 0.005	0.31	35.6
6.430 ± 0.005	94.3	85.2
6.417 ± 0.005	1.22	99
6.385 ± 0.005	0.14	131
6.361 ± 0.005	2.43	155.6
6.349 ± 0.005	0.91	168
6.324 ± 0.005	0.055	193
6.279 ± 0.005	0.16	239.0
6.271 ± 0.005	0.23	247
6.260 ± 0.010	0.028	258
6.186 ± 0.20 (complex)	∼0.20	∼335
6.138 ± 0.010	0.008	382
6.087 ± 0.010	0.024	430
6.062 ± 0.010	0.014	460

measurements of conversion electrons emitted by Es^{254} are summarized in Table 9.49.

The construction of a decay scheme was much aided by the discovery of delayed gamma transitions.   It was found that 2.25 L x-rays are emitted per decay event and that about 90 per cent of these are delayed.   In α-x-ray delayed coincidence experiments it was observed that the delay was complex.

---

[703] L. Phillips, R. Gatti, R. Brandt, and S. G. Thompson, *J. Inorg. Nucl. Chem.* **25**, 1085 (1963).

[704] B. G. Harvey and co-workers, unpublished results, December 1955.

[705] R. P. Schuman, T. A. Eastwood, H. G. Jackson, and J. P. Butler, *J. Inorg. Nucl. Chem.* **6**, 1 (1958).

[706] J. Unik, private communication, 1962.

[707] W. McHarris, F. Stephens, Jr., F. Asaro, and I. Perlman, unpublished results, 1963.

There were prominent components of 213 and 29 microseconds half-life and a third prompt component in small abundance. From the shape of the delay curve it is clear that the 213 microsecond delay precedes the 29 microsecond delay. When the gate of a coincidence circuit was triggered by an L x-ray it was found that L x-rays in delayed coincidence had a

TABLE 9.49. γ-Transitions of 270-day Es^{254} from electron spectra.
(McHarris, Stephens, Asaro, and Perlman)

Energy of transition (keV)	Multipolarity
34.4	$M1 - E2$
35.6	$M1 - E2$
42.6	$M1 - E2$
70.4	$M1 - E2$

single component of 29 microseconds, which confirms that the 213 microsecond transition precedes the shorter one. In an α-γ coincidence experiment it was shown that a 63 keV $E1$ transition, present in 2 per cent abundance, has a half-life of 38 nanoseconds. When photons of this gamma ray were used to gate a γ-x-ray coincidence circuit, it was found that there was a 29 microsecond delay preceding the emission of the x-rays.

The details of these experiments are not discussed here nor is the detailed reasoning behind the decay scheme which summarizes the conclusions. In Fig. 9.56 the levels of Bk^{250} are grouped into rotational bands for which specific Nilsson assignments of neutron and proton states are made. Several of the higher-lying levels known from the alpha spectrum are not included in the figure.

The proton state chosen for Es^{254} is the same, $7/2 + [633]$, as that assigned to Es^{253} and to Bk^{249}. The $7/2 + [613]$ neutron state is the same as that present in the ground state of Fm^{255} which also has 155 neutrons. These states couple to $7+$. The main alpha groups represent favored alpha decay to a rotational band in Bk^{250} which has the same proton and neutron wave functions. The spacing of the rotational levels and the intensities of the alpha transitions to them agree with a $7+$, $8+$, $9+$ rotational sequence. The ground state of Bk^{250} is believed to be composed of a $3/2 - [521]$ proton (this assignment is also made to an 8 keV level in Bk^{249}) and a $1/2 + [620]$ neutron which appears as the ground state of Cf^{251}. The combination of these two orbitals according to the Gallagher-Moszkowski coupling rules lead to a resultant spin and parity $2-$, which are the values assigned to Bk^{250} from a study of its decay scheme. (See Section 9.5.9.)

We note that the ground state and the 85.2 keV state which receives the main alpha population differ in the assignment for proton and neutron. The de-excitation of the 85 keV levels involves two delayed transitions in which first the neutron and then the proton wave functions are changed. The 213 microsecond transition represents the conversion of the 7/2 + [613] neutron into a 1/2 + [620] neutron. The 29 microsecond transition involves the

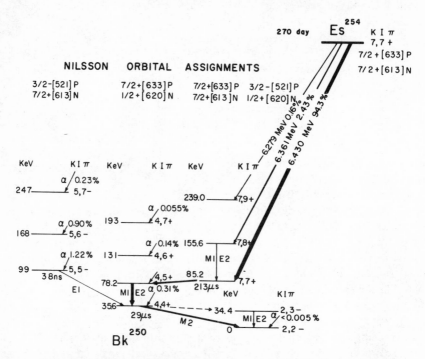

FIG. 9.56. Decay scheme of 270 day Es[254] as formulated by McHarris, Stephens, Asaro, and Perlman. Several levels of Bk[250] known from the α spectrum are not included. Each vertical set of levels is a rotational band; the Nilsson assignments of the old neutron and proton are given directly above each set of levels. The energy of each level is given in keV to the left. K I π are given to the right of each level.

change of a 7/2 + [633] proton into a 3/2 − [521] proton. Between these two delayed transitions lies a rapid 42.6 keV rotational transition. The level at 99 keV and its levels of rotational excitation are populated only to about 2 per cent in the alpha decay process. The delay in the 63 keV E1 transition between the 99 and 35.6 keV levels is only moderate notwithstanding the necessity to change neutron and proton orbitals in one step.

The spacings in the two positive parity bands do not follow exactly the $I(I + 1)$ law and the deviations are in the direction to suggest rather strong Coriolis mixing of each band with one or more bands of positive parity lying higher.

Rotational bands of Bk²⁵⁰ observed in decay of 270 day Es²⁵⁴. (HOLTZ, HOLLANDER, AND NOVAKOV)

	Energies (in keV), spins, and parities of band members					K quantum number and parity of band
Experimental values Theoretical values* fitted with $E_0 = -34.4$ keV $A = 5.73$ keV $B = 0$	0 (2−) —	34.4 (3−) —				2−
Experimental values Theoretical values* fitted with $E_0 = -45.7$ keV $A = 3.94$ keV $B = +0.0064$ keV	35.6 (4+) —	78.2 (5+) —	131 (6+) —	193 (7+) 194.8	(258) (8+) 261	4+
Experimental values Theoretical values* fitted with $E_0 = -78.8$ keV $A = 6.05$ kev $B = -0.0041$ keV	99 (5−) —	168 (6−) —	247 (7−) —	(333) (8−) 335.4		5−
Experimental values Theoretical values* fitted with $E_0 = -134.0$ kev $A = 3.53$ keV $B = +0.0069$ keV	85.2 (7+) —	155.6 (8+) —	239.0 (9+) —	(335) (10+) 337.3		7+

The first three experimental values were fitted to the equation: $E = E_0 + AI(I + 1) + BI^2(I + 1)^2$.

Deviations of the band spacings from the $I(I+1)$ law can be judged by the analysis quoted in the table from the work of HOLTZ, HOLLANDER, AND NOVAKOV[708] who restudied the conversion electron spectrum.

MCHARRIS, STEPHENS, ASARO, AND PERLMAN[707] suggest a structure for the 38-hour Es^{254} of a $3/2 - [521]$ proton and a $1/2 + [620]$ neutron coupled to $2-$. According to these assignments the two forms of Es^{254} differ in neutron and proton structure. This is a different type of isomerism from that observed in Am^{242}, Am^{244}, Np^{238} and other odd-odd nuclei in which the neutron and proton assignments are the same in both isomers. The absence of an isomeric transition between the Es^{254} isomers is accounted for by this difference in structure as well as by the difference of 5 in spin.

An upper limit of 0.0005 per cent has been set on the beta decay of Es^{254}.

9.7.12 Einsteinium-255

The isotope Es^{255} was discovered during the initial studies[709] of the heavy element fractions from the thermonuclear test which led to the discovery of elements 99 and 100. In this instance U^{238} was converted to U^{255} which decayed by a long series of beta transitions to form Es^{255}. This isotope has also been produced by the intense neutron irradiation of samples containing appreciable amounts of 20 day Es^{253} or of isotopes of lighter elements which can be converted to Es^{253}.

$$Es^{253}(n, \gamma)Es^{254}(n, \gamma)Es^{255}$$

This isotope decays by beta emission with a half-life given as 30 days,[709,710] 24 ± 2 days,[711] and 35 ± 5 days.[711a] No additional information is available on its decay scheme. The decay energy available for β^- emission is estimated as 0.38 MeV.

The decay product of Es^{255} is the 21-hour alpha-emitter Fm^{255} which can be observed to grow into a freshly purified sample.

9.7.13 Einsteinium-256

The only information available on Es^{256} is that it is a beta emitter with a short half-life (hours or less).[712] It is produced by neutron irradiation of samples containing Es^{255}.

---

[708] M. D. Holtz, J. M. Hollander, and T. Novakov, unpublished results, 1964.

[709] A. Ghiorso, M. H. Studier, C. I. Browne, and co-workers, *Phys. Rev.* **99**, 1048 (1955); *Phys. Rev.* **102**, 180 (1956); *Phys. Rev.* **119**, 2000 (1960).

[710] G. R. Choppin, S. G. Thompson, A. Ghiorso, and B. G. Harvey, *Phys. Rev.* **94**, 1080 (1954).

[711] M. Jones, R. P. Schuman, J. P. Butler, G. Cowper, T. A. Eastwood, and H. G. Jackson, *Phys. Rev.* **102**, 203 (1956).

[711a] W. McHarris and F. Asaro, private communication, 1963.

[712] G. R. Choppin, B. G. Harvey, S. G. Thompson, and A. Ghiorso, *Phys. Rev.* **98**, 1519 (1955).

9.8 THE ELEMENT FERMIUM (ELEMENT 100)

9.8.1. General Comments

The first isotope of fermium (element 100) and the first isotope of einsteinium (element 99) were identified in the same investigation. Hence the discovery of fermium is described together with the discovery of einsteinium in Section 9.7.1. The first isotope of element 100 to be discovered was 20 hour Fm^{255}. Subsequent to this work a number of other isotopes were identified in heavy element targets bombarded with neutrons, deuterons, helium ions, and heavier ions. The longest-lived of the known isotopes are 3.0 day Fm^{253} and ~ 100 day Fm^{257}. Spontaneous fission instability plays a significant role in shortening the lifetimes of some of the heavier isotopes which might otherwise be prepared in weighable amounts. Factors influencing spontaneous fission instability are not completely understood, however, and some earlier estimates of half-lives of the heavier isotopes were too pessimistic. For example, evidence was found in 1963–4 that Fm^{257} is an alpha emitter with a half-life of approximately 100 days. If this is confirmed, the possibility exists of the preparation of weighable samples of fermium and the study of its chemical properties at concentrations above the tracer level.

9.8.2. Fermium-248

GHIORSO, SIKKELAND, WALTON, AND SEABORG[713] prepared Fm^{248} by the bombardment of Pu^{240} with C^{12} ions accelerated in the Berkeley heavy ion linear accelerator (Hilac). It was shown that Fm^{248} decays by alpha particle emission to produce Cf^{244}. The measured half-life was 0.6 minutes. GUSEVA AND CO-WORKERS[714] found a little evidence for Fm^{248} in a bombardment of a uranium target with 120 MeV oxygen ions. In a chemically-separated transplutonium element fraction the 7.0 MeV alpha particles of Cf^{244} were seen and it was concluded that the Cf^{244} had been formed by the alpha decay of a short-lived Fm^{248}.

9.8.3. Fermium-249

PERELYGIN, DONETS, AND FLEROV[715] found evidence for the production of Fm^{249} in targets of U^{238} bombarded with oxygen ions of charge +5 accelerated in a cyclotron to energies in the range 84–98 MeV. The recoil

---

[713] A. Ghiorso, T. Sikkeland, J. R. Walton, and G. T. Seaborg, *Phys. Rev. Letters* 1, 18 (1958).

[714] L. I. Guseva, K. V. Filippova, Yu. B. Gerlet, V. A. Druin, B. F. Myasoedov, and N. I. Tarantin, *Sov. J. Atom. Energ.* 1, 193 (Consultants Bureau transl.) (1956).

[715] V. P. Perelygin, E. D. Donets, and G. N. Flerov, *Sov. Phys. JETP* 37 (10), 1106 (1960).

products from a thin uranium target were caught on aluminum foils which were moved from the target area and placed on a photoplate which served as an α-decay detector. The energy of the bombarding ions, the length of the bombardment, and the timing of the exposure were all varied in a systematic fashion. An alpha activity with a half-life of about 150 seconds and an alpha particle energy of 7.9 ± 0.3 MeV was assigned to Fm^{249}. Part of the evidence for the assignment was the excitation function which had a peak value at ~98 MeV, corresponding to the position expected for the Pu^{240} $(O^{16}, 5n)$ Fm^{249} reaction according to a calculation based on the Jackson statistical model, and a nuclear temperature of 1.60 MeV. Further evidence for the assignment came from the observation of the correct number of 7.1 MeV alpha particles of the Cf^{245} daughter isotope. These 7.1 MeV alpha particles originated from the same point in the emulsions.

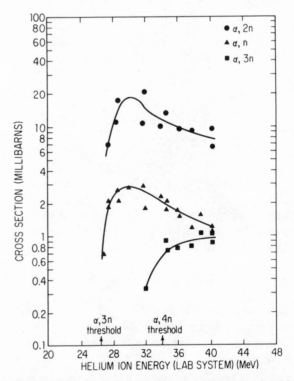

FIG. 9.57. Excitation function for fermium isotopes prepared by helium ion bombardment of Cf^{249}. The (α, n), (α, 2n), and (α, 3n) products are Fm^{252}, Fm^{251}, and Fm^{250}, respectively. From AMIEL ET AL.[717]

9.8.4 *Fermium-250*

Some tentative evidence for an isotope of element 100 with mass 250 was obtained by a Swedish research team[716] who bombarded uranium with ions of O^{16} accelerated in the 225-cm cyclotron of the Nobel Institute for Physics. After the bombardment, heavy element fractions were separated by ion exchange techniques. In the element 100 fraction a few atoms of an isotope emitting 7.7 MeV alpha particles with a half-life of about a half-hour were observed.

More evidence for Fm^{250} was found by AMIEL AND CO-WORKERS[717] in the bombardment of a small sample ($\sim 10^{13}$ atoms) of Cf^{249} with helium ions. Fermium-250 was produced by the reaction:

$$Cf^{249}(\alpha, 3n)Fm^{250}$$

The recoil collection technique described in Section 9.7.5 was used. The observed half-life was 30 minutes for the emission of 7.43-MeV alpha particles. The mass assignment is made on the basis of the excitation function shown in the figure and also on the basis of the alpha particles of Cf^{246} which were observed in the sample after decay. Fermium-250 is unstable toward electron capture by 0.94 MeV of energy, but this mode of decay was not directly observed. Fermium-250 has also been observed as the daughter of 102^{254} prepared by the bombardment of Cm^{246} with carbon ions. (See Section 9.10.)

9.8.5 *Fermium-251*

The 7-hour isotope Fm^{251} has been prepared[717] by the bombardment of Cf^{249} with helium ions using the recoil "catcher" foil technique discussed in Section 9.7.5.

$$Cf^{249}(\alpha, 2n)Fm^{251}$$

The ratio of orbital electron capture to alpha decay of Fm^{251} is about 100. The energy of the alpha particles is 6.89 MeV.

The mass assignment is based on the yield curve shown in Fig. 9.57.

9.8.6 *Fermium-252*

FRIEDMAN AND CO-WORKERS[718] first prepared Fm^{252} by bombarding a mixed target of Cf^{250}, Cf^{251}, and Cf^{252} with helium ions of 34 MeV and 42 MeV energy. AMIEL AND CO-WORKERS[717] prepared it by bombardment

---

[716] H. Atterling, W. Forsling, L. W. Holm, L. Melander, and B. Aström, *Phys. Rev.* **95**, 585 (1954).

[717] S. Amiel, A. Chetham-Strode, Jr., G. R. Choppin, A. Ghiorso, B. G. Harvey, L. W. Holm, and S. G. Thompson, *Phys. Rev.* **106**, 553 (1957).

[718] A. M. Friedman, J. E. Gindler, R. F. Barnes, R. Sjoblom, and P. R. Fields, *Phys. Rev.* **102**, 585 (1956).

of a pure sample of Cf^{249} with helium ions of several energies. The preparative reactions involved in these two studies were:

$$Cf^{250}(\alpha, 2n)Fm^{252}$$
$$Cf^{251}(\alpha, 3n)Fm^{252}$$
$$Cf^{252}(\alpha, 4n)Fm^{252}$$
$$Cf^{249}(\alpha, n)Fm^{252}$$

The half-life was reported as 22.7 hours[718] and 30 hours.[717] The energy of the alpha particles is given as 7.04[718] and as 7.05[717] MeV. The mass assignment is based on the observation of the alpha particles of the Cf^{248} daughter and on the excitation function shown in Fig. 9.57 appearing on page 966. A lower limit of 3000 days was set on the half-life for spontaneous fission.[718] Fermium-252 is beta stable.

9.8.7 Fermium-253

FRIEDMAN AND CO-WORKERS[718] made a tentative identification of Fm^{253} which was confirmed by the work of AMIEL[722]; both groups prepared the isotope by the reaction:

$$Cf^{252}(\alpha, 3n)Fm^{253}$$

AMIEL[722] isolated the product of this reaction by the recoil "catcher" foil technique discussed in Section 9.7.5. In the first few days after bombardment the major activity in the fermium fraction was 30-hour Fm^{252} produced by the $(\alpha, 4n)$ reaction. At a later period the radiations of the longer-lived Fm^{253} became more prominent.

Fermium-253 has a half-life of 3.0 ± 1.0 days.[722] In 10 per cent of its disintegrations Fm^{253} emits alpha particles with an energy of 6.94 ± 0.04 MeV.[722] In 90 per cent of its disintegrations it decays by orbital electron capture to Es^{253}. This latter decay is made evident by the growth of the 6.64 ± 0.3 MeV alpha particles of Es^{253}. This is the longest-lived of the known isotopes of fermium. There is a good likelihood that no longer-lived isotopes of fermium will be found.

9.8.8 Fermium-254

The isotope Fm^{254} is observed to grow into a sample of Es^{253} which has been irradiated with neutrons.[723,724] The sequence of reactions is:

$$\text{20-day } Es^{253}(n, \gamma)Es^{254m} \xrightarrow[\text{38.5 hours}]{\beta^-} Fm^{254}$$

[722] S. Amiel, *Phys. Rev.* **105**, 1412 (1957) and A. Ghiorso, private communication, 1963.

[723] M. H. Studier, P. R. Fields, H. Diamond, J. F. Mech, A. M. Friedman, P. A. Sellers, G. Pyle, C. M. Stevens, L. B. Magnusson, and J. R. Huizenga, *Phys. Rev.* **93**, 1428 (1954).

[724] G. R. Choppin, S. G. Thompson, A. Ghiorso, and B. G. Harvey, *Phys. Rev.* **93**, 908 (1954); **93**, 1129 (1954); **94**, 1080 (1954).

The half-life of Fm^{254} is 3.24 ± 0.01 hours for the emission of alpha particles. Fermium-254 is beta stable. The energy of the main alpha particle group has been determined by the ion chamber method. Values of 7.17 ± 0.01 MeV,[723,725] 7.22 ± 0.03 MeV,[724] and 7.20 ± 0.01 MeV[726] have been reported. In a freshly purified sample of einsteinium containing Es^{254m} these 7.2 MeV alpha particles are observed to grow rapidly to a maximum and then to decay with the 38.5 hour half-life of the einsteinium parent.

Fermium-254 is an even-even isotope, and from the great regularity of the decay scheme of even-even alpha emitters in the heavy element region it may be expected that lower energy alpha-particle groups are present leading to a 2+ excited state of about 40 keV energy and a 4+ excited state at about 140 keV. ASARO AND CO-WORKERS[727] studied the gamma radiations of Fm^{254} and found two gammas consistent with this interpretation. A gamma ray of 41 ± 2 keV energy was seen. From alpha-gamma and alpha-L x-ray measurements the intensity of the 2+ state was set at 17 ± 2 per cent. The conversion coefficient was established for the 41 keV transition and found to agree with that expected from an $E2$ transition. A second gamma ray of 96 ± 2 keV energy was seen in an intensity of 2.8×10^{-2} per cent. This is assumed to correspond to an $E2$ transition between a 4+ level at 138 keV and the 2+ level at 41 keV. This interpretation is reinforced by a study of the beta decay of Bk^{250} to the same daughter nucleus. More precise energies of 42.2 and 98.2 keV were determined from a study of that nuclide. These results were fully confirmed by a reinvestigation of the alpha spectrum of Fm^{254} in a magnetic spectrometer by ASARO, BJØRNHOLM, AND PERLMAN[728] in 1962. The energy of the main group was determined to be $7.192 \pm .005$ MeV relative to a value of 7.109 MeV for the most intense α-group of Fm^{255}. The intensity of this group was set at 85 per cent.[727] Two other groups were found: 7.150 MeV in 14 ± 1 per cent and 7.053 in 0.9 ± 0.1 per cent. The decay scheme of Fm^{254} is shown together with that of Bk^{250} in the figure presented in Section 9.5.9. See Fig. 9.45.

BJØRNHOLM, LEDERER, ASARO, AND PERLMAN[729] searched for rare alpha groups decaying to possible collective states of excitation in the 540 and 1080 keV region by alpha-gamma and alpha-electron coincidence techniques. An upper limit of 3×10^{-6} was set for such transitions.

[725] P. R. Fields, M. H. Studier, J. F. Mech, H. Diamond, A. M. Friedman, L. B. Magnusson, and J. R. Huizenga, *Phys. Rev.* **94**, 209 (1954).

[726] M. Jones, R. P. Schuman, J. P. Butler, G. Cowper, T. A. Eastwood, and H. G. Jackson, *Phys. Rev.* **102**, 203 (1956).

[727] F. Asaro, F. S. Stephens, Jr., S. G. Thompson, and I. Perlman, *Phys. Rev.* **93**, 19 (1955) and later unpublished results, 1956.

[728] F. Asaro, S. Bjørnholm, and I. Perlman, *Phys. Rev.* **133**, B291 (1964).

[729] S. Bjørnholm, M. Lederer, F. Asaro, and I. Perlman, *Phys. Rev.* **130**, 2000 (1963).

Fermium-254 undergoes spontaneous fission at a high rate. Three values of the half-life for spontaneous fission have been reported: 200 days,[724] 220 ± 40 days[725] and 246 days.[726]

9.8.9 *Fermium-255*

The discovery[730] of Fm^{255}, which constituted the discovery of element 100, is described in Section 9.7.1. Fermium-255 can be produced by the prolonged neutron irradiation of Es^{253} or of lighter isotopes such as Pu^{239}.[731,732,733] The complex chain of neutron capture and beta decay steps starting with Pu^{239} is discussed in Chapter 5. Starting with Es^{253} the synthesis of Fm^{255} occurs as follows:

$$Fm^{254}(n, \gamma)Fm^{255}$$

$$\begin{array}{cc} \beta^- \uparrow & \uparrow \beta^- \\ 38.5\,hr & 24\ days \end{array}$$

$$Es^{253}(n, \gamma)Es^{254}(n, \gamma)Es^{255}$$

One of the more precise earlier measurements of the Fm^{255} half-life was reported to be 21.5 ± 0.1 hours.[733] More recently somewhat lower values have been obtained; 19.9 ± 0.3 hours[734] and 20.07 ± 0.07 hours.[735]

Fm^{255} decays by the emission of alpha particles. Early measurements of the energy of the main group with high geometry ion chambers gave too high values of the energy, 7.1 MeV and 7.08[733] MeV, because of the abundant conversion electrons in coincidence with the main alpha groups.[735,736,737]

Later measurements of the alpha spectra by ASARO, BJØRNHOLM, AND PERLMAN[735] with a magnetic spectrograph showed 8 alpha groups. Alpha particle-gamma ray coincidence measurements with a silicon semiconductor counter showed a ninth group. The alpha particle energies, intensities, and hindrance factors and the excited state energies are shown in Table 9.50.

[730] A. Ghiorso, M. H. Studier, C. I. Browne, and co-workers, *Phys. Rev.* **99**, 1048 (1955); *Phys. Rev.* **102**, 180 (1956); *Phys. Rev.* **119**, 2000 (1960).

[731] G. R. Choppin, S. G. Thompson, A. Ghiorso, and B. G. Harvey, *Phys. Rev.* **94**, 1080 (1954).

[732] M. H. Studier, P. R. Fields, H. Diamond, J. F. Mech, A. M. Friedman, P. A. Sellers, G. Pyle, C. M. Stevens, L. B. Magnusson, and J. R. Huizenga, *Phys. Rev.* **93**, 1428 (1954).

[733] M. Jones, R. P. Schuman, J. P. Butler, G. Cowper, T. A. Eastwood, and H. G. Jackson, *Phys. Rev.* **102**, 203 (1956).

[734] L.Phillips, R. Gatti, R. Brandt and S. G. Thompson, *J. Inorg. Nucl. Chem.*, **25**, 1085 (1963).

[735] F. Asaro, S. Bjørnholm, and I. Perlman, *Phys. Rev.* **133**, B291 (1964).

[736] F. Asaro, F. S. Stephens, Jr., and I. Perlman, unpublished data (1957).

[737] F. Asaro, F. S. Stephens, Jr., S. G. Thompson, and I. Perlman, unpublished results, 1960.

TABLE 9.50. Summary of Fm^{255} alpha spectra data (ASARO, BJØRNHOLM, AND PERLMAN).

Alpha particle energy (MeV)	Intensity (per cent)	Excited state energy (keV)	Alpha decay hindrance factor
7.122	0.09 ± 0.01	0	2.8 × 10³
7.098	0.10 ± 0.01	25	2.1 × 10³
7.076	0.43 ± 0.05	48	3.9 × 10²
7.019 ± 0.004	93.4	106	1.03
6.977	0.11 ± 0.02	149	5.8 × 10²
6.960	5.3 ± 0.1	166	10.3
6.887	0.60 ± 0.03	240	44
6.803	0.12 ± 0.02	326	97
6.70	<4 × 10⁻³	426	>1000ᵃ
6.58	(4.5 ± 0.9) × 10⁻²	546	25

ᵃ This hindrance factor is valid *if* a state at ∼426 de-excites by the 320 keV gamma ray.

TABLE 9.51. Fm^{255} electron lines (keV) (ASARO, BJØRNHOLM AND PERLMAN).

Electron energy (keV)	Sub-shell	Binding energy (keV)	Gamma-ray energy (keV)	Electron relative intensities	Transition intensities (per cent)
32.31	L_I	25.98	58.29	∼0.5	
51.49	M_I	6.78	58.17	∼0.1	
		Best value	58.3 *M*1		∼19
55.46	L_{II}	25.07	80.53	∼0.2	
60.63	L_{III}	19.95	80.58	∼0.2	
74.12	M_{II}	6.37	80.49	∼0.1	
75.32	M_{III}	5.13	80.45	∼0.1	
		Best value	80.5ᵃ *E*2		∼16
56.01	L_{II}	25.07	81.08	1	
61.18	L_{III}	19.95	81.13	∼0.8	
74.69	M_{II}	6.37	81.06	∼0.3	
75.89	M_{III}	5.13	81.02	∼0.3	
		Best value	81.1ᵃ *E*2		∼65

ᵃ The best value for the energy separation between the 81.1 and 80.5 keV gamma rays is 0.56 ± 0.02 keV.

Early measurements of the gamma rays associated with Fm^{255} decay[736,737] showed, besides copious *L* x-rays, gamma rays of ∼58 and 80 keV, each in about 1.1 per cent abundance. The intensity of the *L* x-rays corresponded to 2.3 ± 0.2 conversion vacancies per Fm^{255} alpha particle. More recent measurements[735] have shown that there are two gamma rays of ~80 keV and that the principal gamma radiations deexcite a state with a half-life of $(37 \pm 2) \times 10^{-9}$ sec. Additional gamma rays of 120 keV and

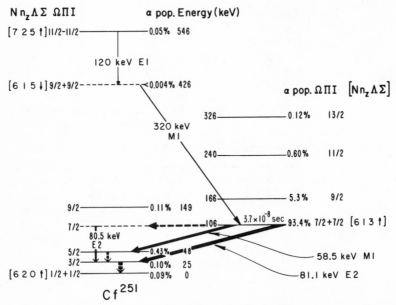

FIG. 9.58. Decay scheme of Fm²⁵⁵ as drawn by ASARO, BJØRNHOLM, AND PERLMAN.

320 keV were also observed. The gamma ray data are summarized in Tables 9.51, 9.52, and 9.53. The placement of the gamma rays is shown in Fig. 9.58.

TABLE **9.52.** Fm²⁵⁵ gamma ray transitions and multipolarity assignment.

Transition energy (keV)	Intensity of gamma rays (per cent)	Experimental conversion coefficient	Theoretical conversion coefficient			Assignment
			E1	E2	M1	
58.3	0.9 ± 0.2	~26	0.7	290	40	M1
81.1⎫ 80.5⎭	1.1 ± 0.2	~70	0.3	60	12	E2
120	$\sim 1 \times 10^{-2}$	0.6 ± 0.3	0.12	12	6.0	E1
320	$(1.9 \pm 0.5) \times 10^{-2}$	1.3 ± 0.5	0.032	0.073	1.5	M1

The following interpretation has been advanced by Asaro, Bjørnholm, and Perlman.[735]   The energy levels at 0 keV, 25 keV, 48 keV and 149 keV can reasonably be ascribed to the 1/2, 3/2, 5/2, and 9/2 states of $a \, \Omega = 1/2$ rotational band.   The decoupling parameter, a, has a value of $+0.24 \pm 0.03$ in reasonable agreement with the value $+0.29$ calculated from Nilsson wave functions for a deformation of 6η.   The rotational constant, $\hbar^2/2\mathfrak{J}$, has a value of 6.4 ± 0.3 keV in good agreement with the values found for other nuclides in this region.   The spin 7/2 state of the band would occur at ~ 105 keV and its alpha particle population would be masked by the most prominent alpha group.   The $\Omega = 1/2$ band is given the Nilsson assignment $1/2 +$ [620↑].

TABLE 9.53. Retardation of the Fm^{255} 58 and 81 keV gamma rays.

Energy of gamma ray	Multi-polarity	Partial photon half-life	Single proton half-life	Retardation
81.1 keV	E2	4.2×10^{-6} sec	3.4×10^{-7} sec	12
80.5 keV	E2	?	3.4×10^{-7} sec	?
58 keV	M1	4.1×10^{-6} sec	3.7×10^{-11} sec	1.1×10^5

The energy levels at 106, 166, 240, and 326 keV are ascribed to $a \, \Omega = 7/2$ rotational band.   From the energy spacing of the first three of these states, the calculated Ω value is 3.43 ± 0.14, i.e., 7/2.   The rotational constant, $\hbar^2/2\mathfrak{J}$, has a value 6.69 ± 0.03, somewhat higher than usually found in this region.   This band is given the Nilsson assignment $7/2 +$ [613↑].

The 58.3 and 81.1 keV gamma rays were presumed to be due to the Coriolis admixture of $\Omega = 1/2$ in the $\Omega = 7/2$ level at 106 keV.   This high order admixture occurs because of the close-lying (0.56 keV spacing) spin 7/2 levels of the $\Omega = 1/2$ and $\Omega = 7/2$ rotational band.   The admixture, 0.2 per cent $= a^2$, calculated from the 81.1 keV gamma-ray half-life is reasonably consistent with that calculated from Nilsson wave functions, 0.7 per cent.   The Nilsson assignments for the 426 and 546 keV levels shown in Fig. 9.58 are the only ones reasonably consistent with the gamma ray multipolarities.

The hindrance factor for the alpha decay to the 106 keV state is very close to unity.   An unhindered or favored transition indicates that the parent and daughter state have the same intrinsic configuration; therefore, the ground state of Fm^{255} has a spin and parity of 7/2 + and is thus also given the Nilsson assignment $7/2 +$ [613↑].

The expected alpha particle intensities to the various states of the rotational band based on the 106 keV level were calculated[735] from the observed hindrance factors for $L = 0, 2,$ and 4 angular momenta alpha waves in Fm^{254} decay. (See Table 9.54.)   The alpha decay transition probability can

TABLE 9.54. Calculated alpha populations to the $K = 7/2$ band in decay of Fm^{255}

Energy of state (keV)	I	Predicted relative intensities (per cent)				Experimental intensities (per cent)
		$I = 0$	$L = 2$	$L = 4$	Σ	
106	7/2	84.4 (norm)	9.8	0.20	93.4 (norm)	93.4
166	9/2	—	5.01	0.43	5.44	5.3 ± 0.1
240	11/2	—	0.64	0.30	0.94	0.60 ± 0.03
326	13/2	—	—	0.075	0.075	0.12 ± 0.02
427 (calc)	15/2	—	—	0.0057	0.0057	<0.05

From Asaro, Bjørnholm, and Perlman.[735]

be expressed by the equation

$$P/P_E = \frac{1}{N} \sum_{L=0,2,4} \frac{\langle I_i L K_i K_f - K_i | I_i L I_f K_f \rangle^2}{HF_{L(e-e)}}$$

where P is the alpha transition probability, P_E is the transition probability calculated from simple spin-independent alpha decay theory, $HF_{L(e-e)}$ are the

TABLE 9.55. Energy spacings and alpha populations of the $K = 1/2$ band in decay of Fm^{255}

$$P = P_E \sum_L \frac{\left\{ C^{I_i L \, I_f}_{K_i \, K_f - K_i K_f} + b_L (-1)^{I_f + K_f} C^{I_i \, L I_f}_{K_i - K_f - K_i - K_f} \right\}^2}{HF_L}.$$

I	Energy of state (keV)		P_E	Alpha abundance (per cent)	
	Calc.[a]	Observed	$P_{E=0}$	Calc.[b]	Exp.
1/2	0	0	1.00	0.11	0.09 ± 0.01
3/2	25.5 (norm)	25.5 ± 2	0.80	0.10 (norm)	0.10 ± 0.01
5/2	48.3 (norm)	48.3 ± 2	0.65	0.43[b] (norm)	0.43
7/2	105 ± 5	Masked	0.37	0.13	Masked
9/2	146 ± 5	149 ± 3	0.25	0.086	0.11 ± 0.02
11/2	236 ± 11	Masked	0.105	0.009	Masked
13/2	294 ± 11	—	0.060	0.0015[c]	—
15/2	417 ± 20	—	0.017	0.00003[c]	—

[a] The energies were calculated from equation in text with $\hbar^2/2\mathfrak{J} = 6.4$ and $a = 0.24$.

[b] The abundances were calculated from the equation with $HF_L = 160$ and $b_L = 0.2$ for the $L = 4$ alpha wave and with the relative values for the alpha-particle barrier penetrability given in column 4.

[c] These groups would have been too weak to see.

From Asaro, Bjørnholm, and Perlman.[735]

hindrance factors for the various alpha particle waves in Fm^{254} decay, and N is an adjustable parameter usually between 1 and 2. P/P_E is essentially a reduced transition probability. N can be calculated from a detailed knowledge of the nuclear wave functions.

The alpha decay to the $1/2+$ rotational band is more complex. The alpha waves allowed by parity and K selection rules would be $L = 4$, 6, etc. Since L in this case is equal or greater than $K_i + K_f$, the alpha decay can take place to states of $-K_f$ as well as $+K_f$. Thus there are two interfering components of the $L = 4$ wave. The alpha decay transition probability can be expressed by the equation

$$\frac{P}{P_E} = \sum_L \frac{\{\langle I_i L K_i K_f - K_i | I_i L I_f K_f \rangle + b_L(-1)^{(I_f + K_f)}\langle I_i L K_i - K_f - K_i | I_i L I_f - K_f \rangle\}^2}{HF_L}$$

The meaning of the terms is the same as before except b_L and HF_L are treated as arbitrary parameters, although they can be calculated from the detailed nuclear wave functions. Table 9.55 shows a comparison between the experimental and theoretical results.

Fermium-255 is beta-stable.

PHILLIPS, GATTI, BRANDT, AND THOMPSON[734] measured the spontaneous fission rate of Fm^{255} and found a SF/a ratio of $(2.4 \pm 1.0) \times 10^{-7}$ corresponding to a spontaneous fission half-life of $(1.0 \pm 0.5) \times 10^4$ years.

9.8.10 *Fermium-256*

Small samples of Fm^{256} have been prepared[738] by the neutron irradiation of einsteinium fractions containing small amounts of Es^{255}. The reaction sequence is:

$$Es^{255}(n, \gamma)Es^{256} \xrightarrow[\text{short}]{\beta^-} Fm^{256}$$

Fermium-256 has also been formed by the electron-capture decay of Md^{256} as discussed in the next section. Fermium-256 has been observed to decay by spontaneous fission with a half-life of 160 ± 10 minutes.[739] The ratio of alpha decay to spontaneous fission is estimated to be 0.04 but the alpha decay (expected energy = 6.9 MeV) was not directly observed because of the presence of large amounts of Fm^{254} and Fm^{255} in the samples. Fermium-256 should be beta stable.

---

[738] G. R. Choppin, B. G. Harvey, S. G. Thompson, and A. Ghiorso, *Phys. Rev.* **98**, 1519 (1955).

[739] L. Philipps, R. Gatti, A Chesné, L. Muga, and S. G. Thompson, unpublished information, *Phys. Rev. Letters* **1**, 215 (1958).

9.8.11 *Fermium-257 and Fermium-258*

Independent unpublished work by E. K. HULET ET AL. and A. GHIORSO ET AL. supplied evidence that Fm^{257} is an alpha emitter with a half-life of ~ 100 days. This isotope is the longest-lived form of fermium. Previously, GATTI ET AL.[740] made a tentative assignment of spontaneous fission activity of 11^{+10}_{-6} days half-life to Fm^{257} or Fm^{258}.

9.9 THE ELEMENT MENDELEVIUM (ELEMENT 101)

By intense bombardment of tiny targets of Es^{253} with 41 MeV helium ions, GHIORSO, HARVEY, CHOPPIN, THOMPSON, AND SEABORG[741] succeeded in preparing a few atoms with the chemical properties of element 101. The isotope so produced has the mass number 256:

$$_{99}Es^{253}(\alpha, n)_{101}Md^{256}$$

In this series of experiments the reaction products were collected by the recoil "catcher" foil technique discussed in Section 6.7.5 which was specially developed and used for the first time in this research. At the end of the bombardment the thin gold catcher foil was dissolved and the gold was removed by extraction into ethyl acetate and by use of an anion-exchange resin. The remainder of the solution, containing element 101 and tracer amounts of Cf^{246} and Es^{253}, was separated by adsorption of the radioactive atoms on a cation-exchange resin column and by elution of these atoms with the complexing agent, alpha-hydroxyisobutyrate. The position of the californium and einsteinium elution peaks served to define the fraction containing elements 100 and 101. Atoms decaying by spontaneous fission with a half-life of 3.5 hours were found in both fractions. These results were interpreted as follows: 101^{256} was produced in the nuclear reaction and separated chemically in the element 101 elution position; it then decayed by orbital electron capture with a half-life of the order of 30 minutes to produce Fm^{256} which decayed by spontaneous fission with a half-life of 3.5 hours. The spontaneous fission events observed in the element 100 elution position represented atoms of Fm^{256} formed by the decay of 101^{256} before the chemical separation was complete. The proof that these experiments resulted in the identification of element 101 is the following:

1. Only the very heaviest elements decay by spontaneous fission with such short half-lives.

---

[740] R. Gatti, R. Brandt, L. Phillips, and S. G. Thompson, *J. Inorg. Nucl. Chem.* **25**, 1089 (1963).

[741] A. Ghiorso, B. G. Harvey, G. R. Choppin, S. G. Thompson, and G. T. Seaborg, *Phys. Rev.* **98**, 1518 (1955).

2. The elution of the new element from the ion-exchange column immediately ahead of element 100 shows that the chemical properties are those of an element heavier than fermium and probably 101 rather than 102.

3. By the method of preparation it would not be possible to produce an element above 101.

The name mendelevium, symbol Mv, was suggested for the new element in recognition of the pioneering role of the great Russian chemist Dmitri Mendeleev, who was the first to use the periodic system of the elements to predict the chemical properties of undiscovered elements, a principle which was the key to the discovery of most of the transuranium elements. The name has been officially accepted but the adopted symbol is Md rather than Mv.

In the original experiments a total of only 17 atoms of Md^{256} were chemically isolated, an average of one atom per bombardment. This work was repeated by PHILLIPS AND CO-WORKERS[742] who produced several hundred atoms of Md^{256} and identified them by the spontaneous fission of the Fm^{256} daughter. These workers deduced a half-life of ~ 1.5 hours for Md^{256}.

PHILLIPS AND CO-WORKERS[742] also found evidence for Md^{255} produced by the reaction:

$$Es^{253}(\alpha, 2n)Md^{255}$$

The chief evidence was the isolation of a fermium daughter activity emitting 7.08 MeV alpha particles with a half-life of 21 hours. These are just the characteristics of Fm^{255}. It was deduced that Md^{255} decays by capture of an orbital electron with a half-life of about 30 minutes. There was some evidence for the emission of 7.34 MeV alpha particles by Md^{255}.

GHIORSO, SIKKELAND, AND LATIMER[743] identified the isotope Md^{257} produced by the reaction of C^{13} nuclei with a californium target (chiefly Cf^{252}). Recoil products of the reaction were collected and subjected to radiochemical analysis to isolate a mendelevium fraction. Alpha particles of about 7.1 MeV energy decaying with a half-life of about 3 hours were assigned to Md^{257}.

Mendelevium is the twelfth of the actinide series of elements and may be regarded as the homologue of thulium (element 69) of the lanthanide series. In its chemical properties it may be assumed to resemble the other tripositive actinide elements.

---

[742] L. Phillips, R. Gatti, A. Chesné, L. Muga, and S. Thompson, *Phys. Rev Letters* **1**, 215 (1958).

[743] A. Ghiorso, T. Sikkeland, and R. M. Latimer, unpublished results, 1964.

9.10 ELEMENT 102

The first report claiming the identification of an isotope of element 102 was published in 1957.[743]   An international team of investigators including members from the Argonne National Laboratory of the United States, of the Atomic Energy Research Establishment in Harwell, England, and the Nobel Institute for Physics in Sweden bombarded targets of curium in the 225 cm cyclotron at the Nobel Institute with high-energy carbon ions (C^{13}). The curium target had the composition 95 per cent Cm^{244}, 1 per cent Cm^{245}, and 4 per cent Cm^{246}.   The reaction products which recoiled out of the curium target were caught on a tygon catcher foil which was ignited on a platinum plate to make a thin source suitable for alpha-particle analysis in an ionization chamber.   In some experiments the tygon collector foil was dissolved and in one case the radioactivity was chemically separated by the same ion exchange-elution system previously used to separate and identify mendelevium.   A few atoms decaying by the emission of 8.5 ± 0.1 MeV alpha particles with a half-life of approximately 10 minutes were apparently observed.   In the one elution experiment in which such alpha particles were thought to be observed four atoms of this activity were apparently observed in an elution position close to that expected for an element 102 fraction.   It was concluded that the new activity was an isotope of element 102 produced most likely by one of these reactions:

$$Cm^{244}(C^{13}, 4n)102^{253}$$

$$Cm^{244}(C^{13}, 6n)102^{251}$$

The discovery of the new element 102 was claimed and the name nobelium, symbol No, was suggested in recognition of Alfred Nobel's support of scientific research and after the institute where the work was done.

This report was contested by a later publication of GHIORSO, SIKKELAND, WALTON, AND SEABORG[744] who found they were unable to reproduce these results after scores of attempts under experimental conditions which were much more favorable than those confronting the original investigators.   In particular, GHIORSO AND CO-WORKERS[744] were able to use the high intensity beam of monoenergetic heavy ions delivered by a linear accelerator specially designed to accelerate heavy ions.   Their report should be consulted for a statement of the reasons they were forced to conclude that the earlier claims to the discovery of element 102 were erroneous.

---

[743] P. R. Fields, A. M. Friedman, J. Milsted, H. Atterling, W. Forsling, L. W. Holm, and B. Aström, *Phys. Rev.* **107**, 1460 (1957); see also *Arkiv Fysik* **15**, 225 (1959).

[744] A. Ghiorso, T. Sikkeland, J. R. Walton, and G. T. Seaborg, *Phys. Rev. Letters*, **1**, 17, July 1958.

GHIORSO, SIKKELAND, WALTON, AND SEABORG[745] then turned to problems of the positive identification of an isotope of element 102 using the hypothesis that the half-lives of those isotopes which could be made by bombardment of the available curium targets would be very much shorter than 10 minutes. A radically new method was developed based on the apparatus shown in Fig. 9.59. The method was essentially a continuous milking experiment wherein the atoms of the daughter element 100 were separated from the parent element 102 by taking advantage of the recoil caused by the element 102 alpha particle decay. By this method the isotope 102^{254}, having a half-life of 3 seconds for alpha decay to produce 30 minute Fm^{250}, was unambiguously identified.

The target consisted of a mixture of isotopes of curium (95 per cent Cm^{244} and 4.5 per cent Cm^{246}) mounted on a very thin nickel foil. The target was approximately 0.5 mg/cm^2 thick and was covered with 75 μgm/cm^2 aluminum to prevent curium "knockover." The curium was bombarded with monoenergetic C^{12} ions at energies from 60 to 100 MeV. The transmuted atoms were knocked into helium gas to absorb the considerable recoil energy. It was found that with a sufficient electric field strength practically

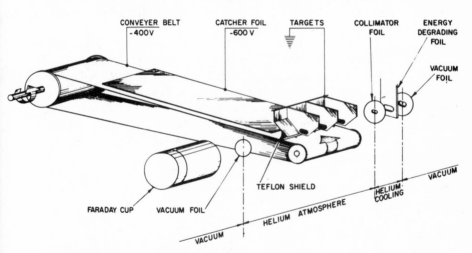

FIG. **9.59**. Schematic diagram of target assembly used by GHIORSO, SIKKELAND, WALTON, AND SEABORG in the preparation and identification of 102^{254}. Reaction products recoiling out of the curium target were collected on the electrically charged belt and transported from the region of the target. When the atoms of 102^{254} later decayed by alpha-particle emission a fraction of the Fm^{250} daughter atoms were ejected from the moving belt and collected on the charged catcher foil.

[745] A. Ghiorso, T. Sikkeland, J. R. Walton, and G. T. Seaborg, *Phys. Rev. Letters*, **1**, 18, July 1958.

all of these positively charged atoms could be attracted to a moving negatively charged metallic belt placed directly beneath the target. These atoms would then be carried on this conveyor belt under a foil which was charged negatively relative to the belt. Approximately half of the atoms undergoing alpha decay would cause their daughter atoms to recoil from the surface of the belt to the catcher foil. The catcher foil was cut transversely to the direction of the belt motion into five equal length sections after a time of bombardment suited to the half-life of the daughter atom to be examined. The five foils were then alpha-pulse-analyzed simultaneously in a multiplex assembly consisting of five Frisch-grid ion-chambers, amplifiers, a single Wilkinson-type "kick-sorter," and a printer. With this equipment it was easily possible to make all the desired measurements for identifying the atoms caught on the catcher foils and thus to measure the half-life of the parent of the recoiling atoms. The method was first successfully used in bombardments of Pu^{240} with C^{12} ions to identify a new isotope of element 100, Fm^{248}. It was shown to have a half-life of 0.6 minutes by analysis of the amounts of the 20-minute Cf^{244} caught on the catcher foils.

Experiments were then started which were aimed at finding a short-lived isotope of element 102. The most likely isotope of element 102 that could be detected with this method was deemed to be 102^{254} with a predicted half-life of seconds leading to the 30-minute, 7.43 MeV, alpha-particle-emitter Fm^{250}. In a series of experiments it was found that Fm^{250} could be collected on the catcher foils in relative amounts corresponding to a parent half-life of 3 seconds. The parent was produced in the reaction $Cm^{246}(C^{12}, 4n)102^{254}$. The excitation function for producing Fm^{250} in this manner was found to peak sharply at 70 ± 5 MeV corresponding to a $(C^{12}, 4n)$ reaction in accordance with a theoretical method for the calculation of (C, xn) reaction cross-sections.[746] Changing the belt speed was found to change the distribution of the Fm^{250} on the catcher foil in a manner conforming to a three-second parent. The number of Fm^{250} counts observed in a single experiment was as great as 40 and corresponded to a maximum cross-section of a few microbarns for the reaction with Cm^{246}.

The final identification of the activity ascribed to Fm^{250} was carried out by dissolving the activity from the catcher foil and separating it from the other actinide elements by elution with ammonium α-hydroxyisobutyrate from a column packed with Dowex-50 cation exchange resin. In one experiment 2 atoms of Fm^{250} were identified and in another 9 atoms were observed in the element 100 position.

From these results the authors concluded that there was no doubt that the existence of an alpha emitting isotope, 102^{254}, with a half-life of 3 seconds, had been demonstrated.

---

[746] T. Sikkeland, S. G. Thompson, and A. Ghiorso, *Phys. Rev.* **112**, 543 (1958).

Additional information on the alpha decay of 102^{254} was obtained in an extension of this study by GHIORSO, LARSH, SIKKELAND, AND WALTON.[747,748] In this later work ions of element 102 recoiling out of a curium target were collected as before on an aluminized mylar tape. However, the tape was stationary during the collection process. Periodically the tape was moved so that the area upon which the recoil nuclei had collected was rapidly moved into counting position in an ionization chamber equipped with a Frisch grid and pulse analyzing circuit. An alpha activity with a particle energy of 8.3 MeV and a half-life of about 3 seconds was found and assigned to 102^{254}. In addition, a second isotope with a half-life of 10 to 15 seconds and an energy of 8.8 MeV was tentatively identified as 102^{253} produced from the reactions:

$$Cm^{246} + C^{12} \rightarrow 102^{253} + 5n$$
$$Cm^{244} + C^{13} \rightarrow 102^{253} + 4n$$

GHIORSO, SIKKELAND, LARSH, AND LATIMER[749], in the course of the work leading to the identification of an isotope of element 103 (described in Section 9.11), found some evidence for an 8.2 MeV alpha emitter with a half-life of about 15 seconds, which they tentatively assigned to 102^{255}. This was produced by bombarding a target of mixed californium isotopes with C^{12}.

At the 1958 Geneva Conference, G. N. Flerov reported briefly on some experiments carried out in his laboratory in Moscow on the production of element 102.[750] A comprehensive article[751] on this work was published in 1960. Thin targets of Pu^{241} were bombarded with ions of O^{16} accelerated to 98 MeV in a cyclotron. Atoms of element 102 were formed by the interaction of the oxygen ions with the plutonium. These atoms were ejected from the thin target and caught in an aluminum catcher foil. This collector foil was mechanically moved a distance of 200 cm from the target in a time of 2 seconds and placed in front of a nuclear emulsion. Some of the alpha particles from the activity in the catcher foils entered the emulsion and were recorded. Alpha particles of 8.9 ± 0.4 MeV were detected and attributed to an isotope of element 102 having a half-life in the range of 2 to 40 seconds. No chemical identification was made. The activity was given the probable

[747] A. Ghiorso, paper delivered at Eighth Mendeleev Conference on Chemistry, Moscow, March 1959, *Univ. Calif. Rad. Lab. Report, UCRL-8714* (1959).

[748] A. Ghiorso, A. E. Larsh, T. Sikkeland, and J. R. Walton, unpublished results, 1962.

[749] A. Ghiorso, T. Sikkeland, A. E. Larsh, and R. M. Latimer, *Phys. Rev. Letters* **6**, 473 (1961).

[750] G. N. Flerov, Paper P/2299, Volume 15, *Proceedings of the Second United Nations Conference on the Peaceful Uses of Atomic Energy*, Geneva, 1958.

[751] G. N. Flerov, S. M. Polikanov, A. S. Karamyan, A. S. Pasyuk, D. M. Parfanovich, N. I. Tarantin, V. A. Karnaukhov, V. A. Druin, V. V. Volkov, A. M. Semchinova, Yu. Ts. Oganesyan, V. I. Khalizev, G. I. Khlebnikov, B. F. Myasoedov, and K. A. Gavrilov, *Zhur. Eksp. Teor. Fiz.* **38**, 82 (1960); *Sov. Phys. JETP* **11**, 61 (1960).

mass assignment of 253 or 254.   The possibility of the formation of an isotope of a lighter element emitting alpha particles with these characteristics
was considered; the authors concluded that they could rule out this possibility.

In 1963 the Dubna laboratory 'reported[752] additional work leading to
the identification of the isotope 102^{256}.   This work was modeled on the
1958 experiments at Berkeley on the isotope 102^{254} which are described
above.   The new isotope of element 102 was produced by bombarding U^{238}
with Ne^{22} ions.   The recoiling nuclei of 102 produced in the ($Ne^{22}, 4n$)
reaction were stopped in a gas and allowed to diffuse down to the surface of a
rotating drum.   The surface of the drum turned within a stationary catcher
foil so that the daughter Fm^{252} nuclei produced by the alpha decay from a
short lived 102^{256} could be attracted electrically to the surface of the foil.
These daughter atoms were dissolved from the catcher foil and identified as
Fm^{252} by chemical analysis and alpha particle energy analysis.   By the
results of runs made with different drum speeds, the half-life of the element
102 parent was determined to be 8 seconds.   Fifteen different experiments
were performed; an 8 hour bombardment produced as many as 170 Fm^{252}
counts, even though the maximum cross section was only 4×10^{-32} cm^2.

9.11 THE ELEMENT LAWRENCIUM (ELEMENT 103)

The first evidence for the identification of an isotope of element 103 was
put forth by GHIORSO, SIKKELAND, LARSH, AND LATIMER[753] in 1961.   These
workers bombarded californium targets with boron ions and produced an
8 ± 2 second alpha activity decaying with the emission of 8.6 MeV alpha
particles.   This activity could only be ascribed to decay of a new element
with atomic number 103.   Because of the small size of the available californium target and of the destruction by nuclear fission of the overwhelming
majority of intermediate nuclei involved in the nuclear reactions, only a few
atoms were made in each hour of the bombardment.   Hence, it was not
possible to obtain chemical evidence for the identity of the element and this
assignment rests entirely on nuclear evidence.   The experiments and their
interpretation will now be summarized.

The method used to produce and identify radiations from element 103
decay is shown schematically in Fig. 9.60 and is based on the one used for the
element 102 experiment.   The 3-microgram californium target had an isotopic composition of 3.3 per cent 249, 32.8 per cent 250, 12.3 per cent 251,
and 50.8 per cent 252.   It was electroplated in an area 0.10 inch in diameter

[752] E. D. Donets, V. A. Shchegolev and V. A. Ermakov, *Report P-1383*, Joint Institute
for Nuclear Research, Dubna, USSR (1963); *Atomnaya Energiya USSR*, **14**, 500 (1963); **16**,
195 (1964).

[753] A. Ghiorso, T. Sikkeland, A. E. Larsh, and R. M. Latimer, *Phys. Rev. Letters* **6**,
474 (1961).

onto nickel foil 50 micro-inches thick. The purification of the target, crucially important for the success of the experiment, was carried out on ion exchange columns with specially purified reagents. The last step in the purging of undesirable lead and bismuth impurities was accomplished by

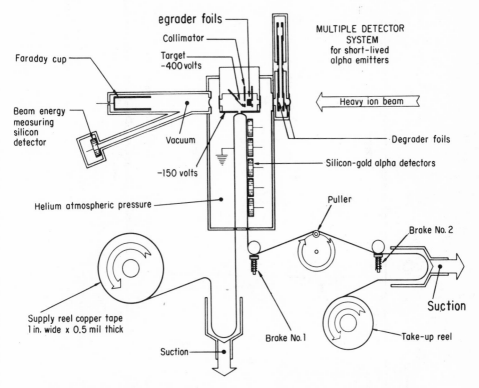

FIG. **9.60.** Schematic diagram of apparatus used in first identification of element 103.

heating the final target in vacuo by electron bombardment. Lead and bismuth impurities had to be reduced because heavy-ion bombardment of these elements produces in high yield an alpha activity with an 8.8 MeV alpha-particle energy and a 25-second half-life which can obscure the lower energy alpha activity of element 103. The heavy-ion beam of either B^{10} or B^{11} was collimated so as to pass through the tiny target and typically was limited to 0.5 microamperes to avoid melting the target foil. The transmuted atoms recoiled from the target into an atmosphere of helium. This gas flowed slowly through a nearby 0.050-inch orifice and carried the electrically charged transmutation products to a thin copper conveyor tape. This tape was periodically pulled a short distance to place the groups of collected atoms in positions successively in front of each of five solid-state Au-Si

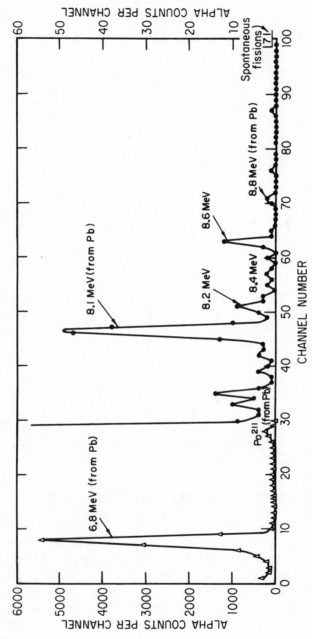

FIG. 9.61. Alpha spectrum of products recoiling from californium target bombarded with boron nuclei as observed by GHIORSO, SIKKELAND, LARSH, AND LATIMER in one set of runs.   Total bombardment time, 5.0 microampere hours.   Cycle time, 15 seconds.

surface-barrier detectors. The pulses caused by passage of alpha particles into each detector were amplified, except for a few milliseconds during the beam bursts, by separate preamplifiers in the shielded bombardment area and then sent to a main counting area to be further amplified and analyzed. In the counting area, the pulses were passed through separate window amplifiers and then analyzed by two separate electronic systems. One system consisted of five separate 100-channel pulse analyzers, and the other consisted of a multiplex unit using five punched paper tape storage units. With the multiplex unit, it was possible to determine the time when each event occurred since the conveyor tape was last advanced.

The silicon crystal detectors vitally necessary for the experiment were made of 800–1800 ohm-cm silicon, suitably etched and mounted, and covered with a layer of gold about 20 micrograms per cm^2 thick.

The energy of the boron ions was changed by degradation of the 10.3 MeV per nucleon beam in aluminum absorbers. To monitor the energy of the ions striking the target, another Si detector was calibrated against nuclear emulsions, and used at a small solid angle to measure the energy of those ions scattered forward at 20° by the Faraday cup window.

Calibration and study of the total system without beam was accomplished with either U^{230} recoil products collected onto the tape or with Po^{212} alpha particles from samples held in front of the detector assembly. Studies of the method with heavy-ion reactions were made by bombarding Sm^{147} to produce short-lived holmium alpha emitters or Pb and Bi to produce various alpha emitters with energy between 7 and 9 MeV.

In the bombardment of californium with B ions, the activity attributed to element 103 consisted of alpha particles with an energy of 8.6 MeV decaying with a half-life of 8 ± 2 seconds. Also observed were alpha particles of 8.4 and 8.2 MeV with similar half-lives of about 15 seconds, which were probably due to element 102. Figure 9.61 shows an alpha-particle spectrum from one detector obtained during one set of runs. These activities were observed repeatedly during many weeks of bombardment of the californium target with both B^{10} and B^{11} ions. Similar bombardments of Pb, Bi, Pu^{240}, and Am^{241} did not produce the new activities.

The mass number of the element 103 isotope is thought to be 257 for the following reasons. B^{11} bombardments of Cf^{250}, Cf^{251}, and Cf^{252} cause compound nucleus reactions which lead to 103^{257} by the emission of 4, 5, or 6 neutrons, while with B^{10} this same result is accomplished with 3, 4, or 5 neutrons. These are known from other experiments to be the most prominent neutron-out reactions of boron with the transuranium elements. Excitation functions with B^{11} and B^{10} ions for production of the 8.6 MeV alpha activity are consistent with the above deduction.

These excitation functions were, of necessity, very broad because the same activity could be produced by several reactions; consequently, these data could not rule out conclusively (B, pxn) reactions which would produce light isotopes of element 102. The final proof was then accomplished by accentuating the element 102 production by bombarding the californium target with C^{12} ions. It was found that the 8.6 MeV activity was decreased by more than a factor of 2, and the 8.2 MeV activity (thought to be mostly 102^{255}) was increased by a factor of about 20. This was to be expected for the element assignments given. Experiments with Pu^{240} had shown that the $(C^{12}, \alpha xn)$ cross sections would be larger, whereas the (C^{12}, pxn) cross sections would be smaller in comparison with the boron bombardments of californium. Possible light isotopes of mendelevium that could have been produced and conceivably might emit alpha particles in the 8.2–8.6 MeV region were ruled out by bombardments of Am^{243} with C^{12} ions.

In honor of the late Ernest O. Lawrence, the authors suggested that the new element be named lawrencium with the symbol Lw.

9.12   GENETIC RELATIONSHIPS OF TRANSURANIUM NUCLIDES

For some purposes it is useful to trace out the genetic relationships of the nuclides throughout the entire transuranium group of nuclides. We present here four summary diagrams (Figs. 9.62–65) which permit one to see at a glance these family relationships for the four main series of nuclides; namely the $4n$, $4n + 1$, $4n + 2$, and $4n + 3$ series. It will be recalled that the term $4n$ signifies that the mass number is evenly divisible by 4, while in the other cases the mass number is divisible by 4 with the remainders 1, 2, and 3, respectively. These figures can be regarded as an extension to higher mass numbers of the thorium series, the artificial $4n + 1$ series beginning with U^{233}, the uranium-radium series, and the actinouranium series.

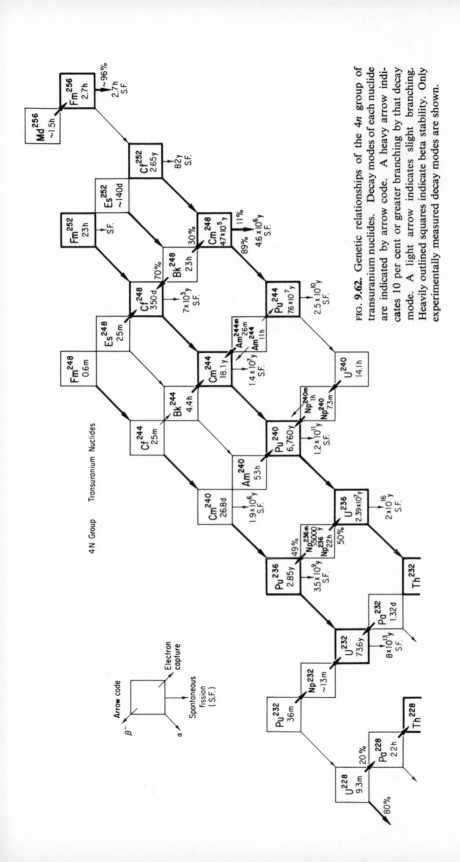

FIG. 9.62. Genetic relationships of the *4n* group of transuranium nuclides. Decay modes of each nuclide are indicated by arrow code. A heavy arrow indicates 10 per cent or greater branching by that decay mode. A light arrow indicates slight branching. Heavily outlined squares indicate beta stability. Only experimentally measured decay modes are shown.

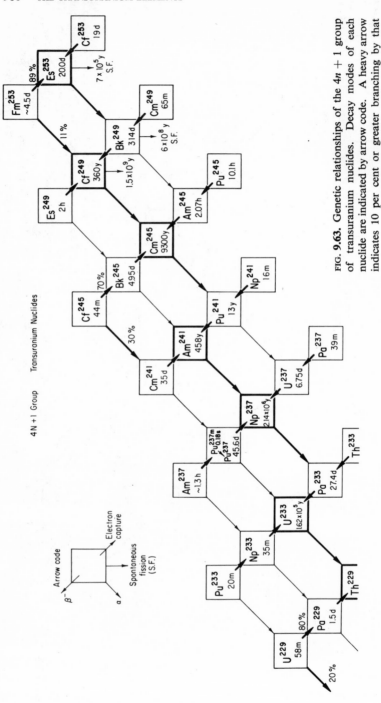

FIG. 9.63. Genetic relationships of the $4n + 1$ group of transuranium nuclides. Decay modes of each nuclide are indicated by arrow code. A heavy arrow indicates 10 per cent or greater branching by that decay mode. A light arrow indicates slight branching. Heavily outlined squares indicate beta stability. Only experimentally measured decay modes are shown.

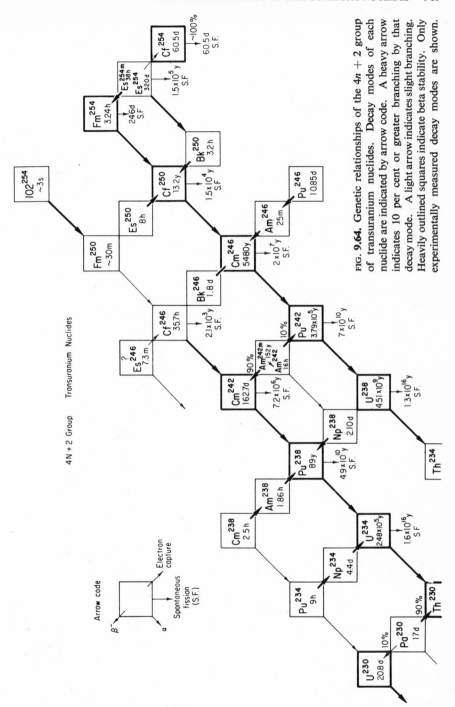

FIG. 9.64. Genetic relationships of the $4n + 2$ group of transuranium nuclides. Decay modes of each nuclide are indicated by arrow code. A heavy arrow indicates 10 per cent or greater branching by that decay mode. A light arrow indicates slight branching. Heavily outlined squares indicate beta stability. Only experimentally measured decay modes are shown.

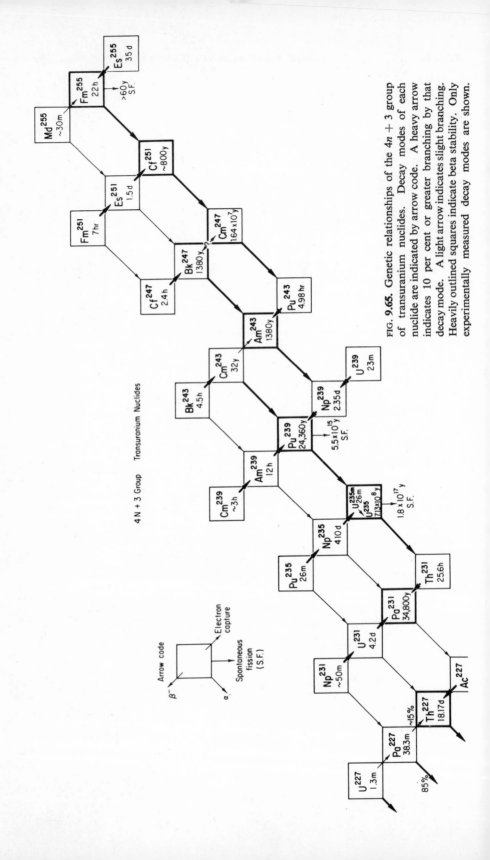

4 N + 3 Group   Transuranium Nuclides

Arrow code

Electron
capture

β⁻

α

Spontaneous
fission
(S.F.)

FIG. **9.65.** Genetic relationships of the 4*n* + 3 group of transuranium nuclides. Decay modes of each nuclide are indicated by arrow code. A heavy arrow indicates 10 per cent or greater branching by that decay mode. A light arrow indicates slight branching. Heavily outlined squares indicate beta stability. Only experimentally measured decay modes are shown.

10

NUCLEI NEAR LEAD-208

10.1 GENERAL CONSIDERATIONS

The isotopes of the transuranium elements discussed in the preceding chapter have neutron and proton numbers far removed from "magic numbers" and the typical nucleus has a spheroidal rather than a spherical shape. Nuclear states and decay schemes of such nuclides are most readily interpreted by the Bohr-Mottelson unified model of the nucleus. In this chapter we turn to a group of nuclei in the neighborhood of Pb^{208} where quite a different situation holds. The group of nuclides to be discussed, comprising all isotopes of the elements lead through radium with neutron numbers less than 127, are shown in Fig. 10.1. The interesting synthetic element astatine is included. These nuclides lie on that section of the mass-energy surface with a comparatively gentle slope just below the closed shell of 126 neutrons. The mass energy surface is shown schematically in Fig. 10.2. The closed shell of 82 protons also strongly influences the properties of nuclei in this group. Most of these nuclei are strongly stabilized in a spherical shape. Collective modes of excitation are not expected to be prominent among the low-energy excitations of the nuclei and the shell model is expected to provide a good description of single-nucleon states.

Since alpha decay is subject to a strong energy dependence it is not as prominent in this group of nuclides as in the group immediately beyond the 126 neutron shell where it is the dominant mode of decay. The nuclides in Fig. 10.1 are neutron deficient and the principal mode of decay is by electron capture. Lead and bismuth isotopes containing fewer than 126 neutrons have particularly low decay-energy for alpha-particle emission. No alpha

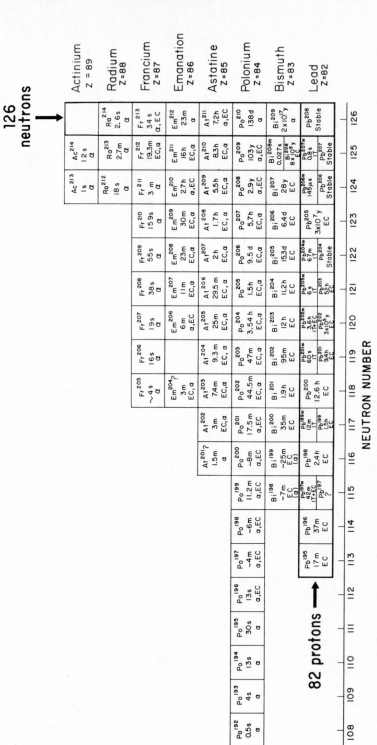

FIG. 10.1. Section of isotope chart showing group of nuclides discussed in this chapter.

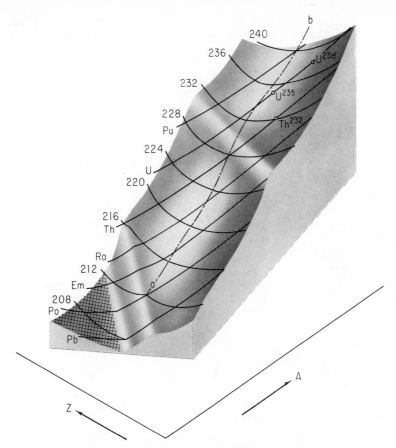

FIG. 10.2. Schematic mass energy surface. The nuclides discussed in this chapter are located on the relatively flat portion of the surface at the lower left. This part is marked with special cross-hatching. The vertical direction is proportional to the total mass of each isotope but even-odd pairing energy effects have been neglected.

activity has ever been detected in a lead isotope* below mass 210. Slight alpha activity has been found in Bi^{209} and Bi^{203}; the reported half-lives for alpha emission are 2×10^{17} and $\sim 10^4$ years, respectively. The very light isotopes of bismuth such as $Bi^{198-201}$ show slight alpha branching. Alpha decay energies for isotopes of polonium and elements of higher atomic number are greater and alpha emission has been observed in a number of isotopes.

---

* A possible exception is Pb^{204} for which Riezler and Kauw (*Z. f. Naturforsch.* **13A**, 904 (1958)) report a half-life of 1.4×10^{17} years and an alpha particle energy of 2.6 MeV on the basis of tracks seen in nuclear emulsions impregnated with enriched Pb^{204}.

The systematic trends in alpha-decay energies for the isotopes under discussion are shown in Fig. 10.3. The dramatic effect on alpha-decay energies of the 126 neutron shell is readily apparent.

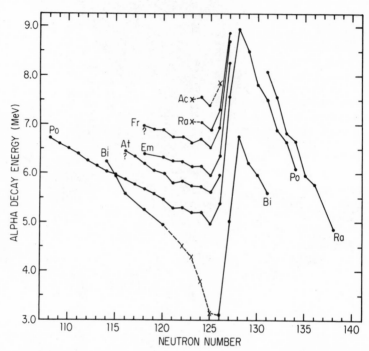

FIG. **10.3.** Alpha disintegration energy versus neutron number in the neighborhood of the 126 neutron shell.

Special attention is given in this chapter to the bismuth and lead isotopes near Pb^{208}. The radiations observed in the electron-capture decay of the bismuth isotopes provide a wealth of information on the excited levels of the lead daughter isotopes. Much additional information on the lead level schemes has come from other methods of exciting these levels. The existence of this detailed experimental information and the fact that these nuclei are only a few nucleons removed from the double-closed shell at Pb^{208} have made them attractive candidates for detailed testing of theoretical ideas regarding interparticle forces in heavy spherical nuclei. Throughout this chapter mention will be made, where appropriate, of such theoretical calculations although the available space and the general purpose of our review does not permit a detailed presentation of these calculations. Our plan is to outline the general ideas behind them and to indicate to what extent they succeed in accounting for the experimental data.

The available information on many of the nuclides listed in Fig. 10.1 is rather meager owing to the short half-lives and to the limitations on the methods of synthesis which in many cases yield complex mixtures of nuclides with very similar half-lives.

The principal methods of preparation are the following:

1. Bombardment of the stable isotopes of thallium, lead and bismuth with protons, deuterons or helium ions. It would be possible also to bombard the radioactive polonium isotopes, Po^{208}, Po^{209}, and Po^{210}.

2. Bombardment of thorium or uranium with protons, deuterons or helium ions of very high energy resulting in the production of complex mixtures of the activities under discussion by complex spallation reactions.

3. Bombardment of lead and bismuth or of lighter elements with ions of carbon, nitrogen, oxygen, neon, etc. accelerated to energies above the Coulombic barrier.

Synthesis by neutron capture reactions is of minor importance in the lead-radium region. A few cases in which neutron induced reactions are of consequence for preparative purposes are the following:

$$Pb^{204}(n, \gamma)Pb^{205}$$
$$Pb^{206}(n, \gamma)Pb^{207m}$$
$$Bi^{209}(n, 2n)Bi^{208}$$

The complexity of the mixtures of nuclides which are produced by the methods (1) and (2) above made it difficult to assign mass numbers to the activities in this region when these nuclides were first produced. In the early studies, mass assignments were based on genetic relationships established by tedious radiochemical experiments in which the yields of daughter and granddaughter products were studied as a function of time. In several cases the mass assignments were pinned to the thallium isotopes whose mass numbers had been established previously.

A typical example of the radiochemical method of mass assignment is that used by NEUMANN AND PERLMAN[1] in assigning Bi^{200} and Pb^{200}. A mixture of bismuth isotopes was isolated from a lead target bombarded with 150 MeV protons. After a one-hour decay period, lead daughter activity was removed radiochemically. From this lead fraction, thallium daughter activity was "milked" at intervals of 8 hours. In this thallium activity a 27-hour component of Tl^{200} could be identified by half-life and by its hard gamma radiation. The decrease in the amount of the Tl^{200} in successive milkings from the lead fraction corresponded to a half-life of 18 hours for a Pb^{200} precursor. This in turn was related to a Bi^{200} parent by removing lead

---

[1] H. Neumann and I. Perlman, *Phys. Rev.* **78**, 195 (1950).

daughter activity from the original bismuth fractions (containing several bismuth activities) at intervals of 50 minutes. After allowing each lead sample so obtained to decay for 25 hours, thallium fractions were removed. The decrease in the amount of 27-hour Tl^{200} activity obtained in these fractions was directly related to the half-life of the Bi^{200} parent as shown in Fig. 10.4. This established a half-life of 35 minutes for Bi^{200}.

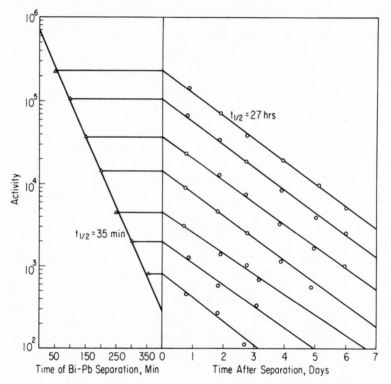

FIG. **10.4.** Data showing genetic relationship between 27-hour Tl^{200} and a 35-minute bismuth activity.

Such a complicated indirect process of mass assignment was necessary in the original identification of many of the nuclides listed in Fig. 10.1. Mass assignments made originally in this way have been cross-checked by other genetic relationships and by a much more detailed study of the decay schemes than was carried out in the initial studies.

Figures 10.5 to 10.8 have been prepared so that all possible genetic relationships for isotopes of the four mass types can be quickly visualized for the heavy nuclides with neutron number $\leqslant 126$.

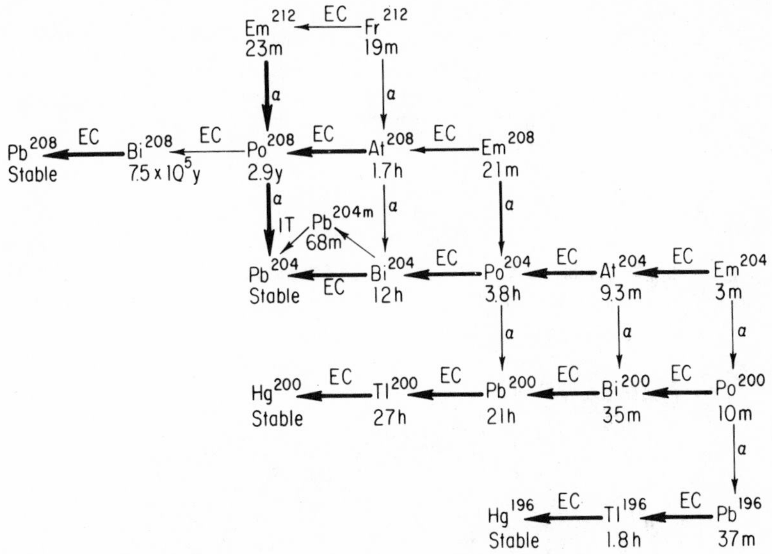

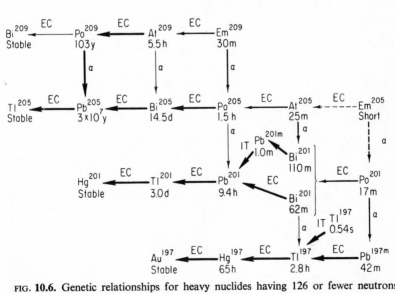

FIG. **10.5.** Genetic relationships for heavy nuclides having 126 or fewer neutrons (4*n* mass type).

FIG. **10.6.** Genetic relationships for heavy nuclides having 126 or fewer neutrons (4*n* + 1 mass type).

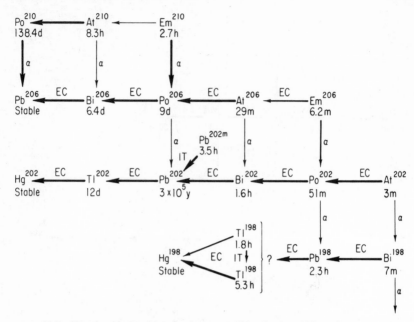

FIG. **10.7.** Genetic relationships for heavy nuclides having 126 or fewer neutrons (4*n* + 2 mass type).

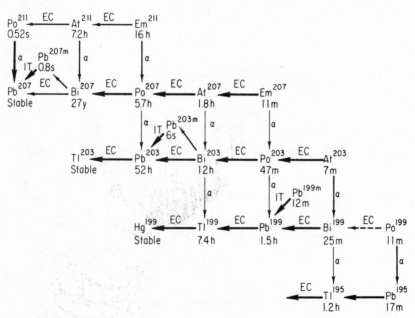

FIG. **10.8.** Genetic relationships for heavy nuclides having 126 or fewer neutrons (4*n* + 3 mass type).

10.2 THE LEVEL SYSTEMS OF THE LEAD ISOTOPES AS DEDUCED FROM THE ELECTRON CAPTURE DECAY OF BISMUTH ISOTOPES AND OTHER INFORMATION

10.2.1 *General Discussion of the Lead Isotopes*

The lighter isotopes of lead are of great interest both from the experimental and the theoretical viewpoint because (1) several of the odd-mass isotopes and several of the even-mass isotopes exist in isomeric forms, (2) the level schemes of many of them are exceedingly complex as revealed by the decay schemes of the light bismuth or thallium isotopes, and (3) the isotopes of lead provide a favorable test of the theoretical predictions of a many-particle shell model. We shall discuss several of the lead isotopes individually in some detail in the following sections, but first we make a few remarks about all the lead isotopes below Pb^{208}.

Pb^{208} has no nucleons beyond closed shells and, as would be expected, has no low-lying excited states; the first excited state falls at 2.615 MeV.[2]

The excited levels of Pb^{207} are revealed[3] by the decay of Bi^{207} and other information discussed below. The level system is simple and corresponds exactly to the levels which the shell model would predict for the low-lying levels in this nucleus which has a single neutron less than a closed shell of 126. These theoretical levels and their experimental energies are $(p_{1/2})^{-1}$ (0), $(f_{5/2})^{-1}$ (570 keV), $(p_{3/2})^{-1}$ (870 keV), $(i_{13/2})^{-1}$ (1.634 MeV), $(f_{7/2})^{-1}$ (2.35 MeV) and $(h_{9/2})^{-1}$ (3.47 MeV). Pb^{207} has an isomer with a half-life of 0.8 sec which can be isolated as a daughter of Bi^{207} or can be prepared independently. It decays by means of a 1.055 MeV $M4$ gamma ray followed by a 0.570 MeV $E2$ gamma ray. (See Fig. 10.9.) This isomer finds a very ready explanation as the de-excitation of the $i_{13/2}$ level listed above via the sequence, $i_{13/2} \xrightarrow{M4} f_{5/2} \xrightarrow{E2} p_{1/2}$.

In contrast to the simplicity of the Pb^{207} level scheme the Pb^{206} level scheme is quite complex. A detailed study of the radiation of Bi^{206} by ALBURGER AND PRYCE[4] showed 12 levels below 3 MeV in Pb^{206} and 26 transitions between these levels. Nonetheless, there appears to be fundamental simplicity to the level scheme in that all the levels in this nucleus are derivable from the few single particle states seen in Pb^{207}. Pb^{206} is two neutrons removed from the closed shell and its low-lying quantum states arise from various combinations of the single particle states. For example, one set of levels in Pb^{206} comes from the configuration $(f_{5/2}^{-1}, p_{3/2}^{-1})$. To a first approximation all levels corresponding to this configuration have the same energy, namely, the sum of the $f_{5/2}^{-1}$ and the $p_{3/2}^{-1}$ levels observed in Pb^{207}. This degeneracy is removed by taking into account the interaction between the two

---

[2] L. G. Elliott, R. L. Graham, J. Walker, and J. L. Wolfson, *Phys. Rev.* **93**, 356 (1954).

[3] D. E. Alburger and A. W. Sunyar, *Phys. Rev.* **99**, 695 (1955).

[4] D. E. Alburger and M. H. L. Pryce, *Phys. Rev.* **95**, 1482 (1954).

neutrons (more exactly between the two neutron hole states). Such a procedure is applicable only when collective modes of motion and excitation of core nucleons require such large amounts of energy that they cannot contribute to the low-lying nucleon states. This appears to be the case for Pb^{206} and for a number of other nuclei lying close to Pb^{208}. PRYCE[4] made the first attempt to calculate the interaction between the two neutrons (holes) in Pb^{206}. He did this by a simplified semi-empirical method which was adequate to show that remarkable agreement with the complex level system of Pb^{206} could be obtained. These calculations were later placed on a firmer and more elegant theoretical basis by KEARSLEY[5] and by TRUE AND FORD[6] using electronic computer assistance in the calculations. These calculations are outlined below.

A number of general comments can be made about the lead and bismuth isotopes which are independent of any specific method of application of the shell model. First, the decay-energy for electron-capture of the light isotopes of bismuth is quite high because of the sharp drop in proton binding energies just past the closed shell of 82 protons. For example, the decay energies for Bi^{204}, Bi^{205}, and Bi^{206} are estimated as 4.5, 2.7, and 3.7 MeV, respectively. This means that excited levels of the lead daughters lying several MeV above ground are energetically available during decay. Furthermore, the electron capture mode of decay has a low energy dependence compared to alpha or beta decay. The half-life for K-electron capture goes roughly as the square of the decay energy. This fact, in connection with the high decay energy means that there is a good chance that high-lying levels will be populated during decay of bismuth isotopes and that many other levels will be revealed in the resulting gamma cascade.

An additional factor is the presence of low-lying single-particle $i_{13/2}$ states. Any configuration containing an $i_{13/2}$ particle wave function in combination with other single particle wave functions can give rise to a large number of levels of different spins which add greatly to the density of levels above 2 MeV. Furthermore, the interaction between two particles operates to lower the energy of high spin states and leads to the possibility of isomerism. Every case of isomerism in the lead isotopes is attributable to states involving $i_{13/2}$ neutrons (holes). This is true of the even-mass as well as the odd-mass isotopes. The discovery of isomerism in Pb^{204} and later in Pb^{202} and Pb^{200} came as a surprise since no other cases of isomerism has been reported among even-even nuclei, but it became understandable when the role of $i_{13/2}$ single particle states was pointed out.

The parity of levels is simply related to the shell model. The single particle states available to neutrons just below the 126 neutron shell are all of

[5] M. J. Kearsley, *Nucl. Phys.* **4**, 157 (1957).
[6] W. W. True and K. Ford, *Phys. Rev.* **109**, 1675 (1958).

odd parity except the $i_{13/2}$ state. Hence, all known levels of Pb^{207} are of odd parity except the $i_{13/2}$ level. In even mass lead isotopes all levels are of even parity except those involving one $i_{13/2}$ neutron hole. The isomeric states in the even-mass lead isotopes are expected to be of odd parity and they are. The levels of the odd mass isotopes below Pb^{207} are expected to have odd parity except for those involving a single $i_{13/2}$ neutron hole. The isomeric states in these nuclei are expected to be of even parity.

Applying these general considerations to specific lead isotopes we can understand the complexity in the level schemes and the presence of isomerism.

Figures 10.9 and 10.10 show at a glance that there is a systematic pattern to the isomerism of the odd-mass and even-mass isotopes of lead. Some of the details of these schemes are discussed below.

BERGSTRÖM AND ANDERSSON[7] have written a comprehensive review article on "Nuclear Energy Levels and Multipole Transitions in the Lead Region" which covers in considerable detail the information on lead isotopes. KINSEY[8] has discussed energy levels in nuclei of lead and bismuth. ELLIOTT AND LANE[9] have discussed shell model interpretations of the level systems of these nuclei. A general treatment of the lead isotopes by the "superfluid" model of nuclear structure is cited in Section 10.2.13.

10.2.2 *The Level System of Pb^{208}; The Decay Schemes of Tl^{208} and Bi^{208}.*

The level system for Pb^{208} is unique for an even-even nucleus in that the lowest-lying excited states do not have the usual $2+$ and $4+$ character. Our principal information on the levels of Pb^{208} comes from the work of ELLIOTT, GRAHAM, WALKER, AND WOLFSON[10] on the decay scheme of Tl^{208}, the thorium C″ of the thorium decay series. This work is referred to in Section 6.3 of Chapter 6 and summarized in Fig. 6.34. Other levels are seen in reaction studies such as the $Pb^{207}(d, p)Pb^{208}$ investigations of MUKHERJEE AND COHEN.[11] The lowest levels of Pb^{208} are listed here in Table 10.1. The nucleus of doubly-magic Pb^{208} is very stiff toward collective vibrations and no states due to such vibrations are to be expected below several MeV of excitation. The most striking evidence for the unusual rigidity of Pb^{208} is the energy of its first excited state, 2.615 MeV, which is greater than the energy of any reported first excited state in any nucleus beyond mass 40.

[7] I. Bergström and G. Andersson, *Arkiv Fysik* 12, 415–479 (1957); see also I. Bergström, *et al.*, ibid 20, 93 (1961).

[8] B. B. Kinsey, "Nuclear Reactions, Levels, and Spectra of Heavy Nuclei," a contribution to *Handbuch der Physik* 40, Berlin: Springer-Verlag, 1957; see pp. 359–368.

[9] J. P. Elliott and A. M. Lane, "The Nuclear Shell Model," a contribution to *Handbuch der Physik*, 39, Springer-Verlag, Berlin 1957; pp. 301–309.

[10] L. G. Elliott, R. L. Graham, J. Walker, and J. L. Wolfson, *Phys. Rev.* 93, 356 (1954), prelim. note; *Proc. Phys. Soc.* (Canada) 48, 12A (1954).

[11] P. Mukherjee and B. L. Cohen, *Phys. Rev.* 127, 1284 (1962).

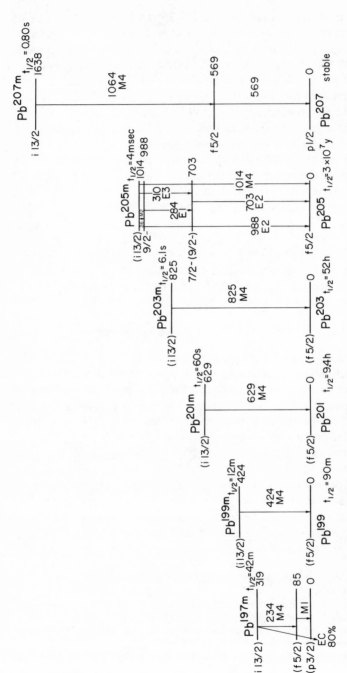

FIG. 10.9. The odd mass isomers of lead showing probable shell model assignments. The isomerism in all cases is attributed to the $i_{13/2}$ state. The isomerism in Pb[205] differs from the rest because a $7/2-$ or $9/2-$ level of complex origin slips below the $i_{13/2}$ level. This provides alternate de-excitation routes and greatly shortens the observed half-life. In Pb[197] the $f_{5/2}$ state is not the ground state; a $p_{3/2}$ has slipped below it by 85 keV. In Pb[199] it is not known for certain whether the $f_{5/2}$ or the $p_{3/2}$ state lies lower; it is believed that they lie within a few kilovolts of each other.

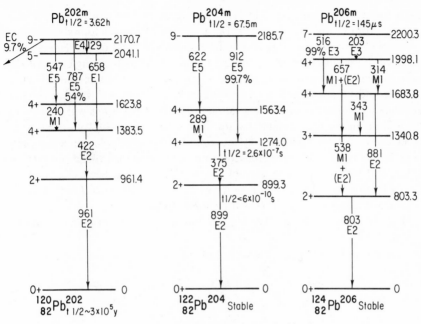

FIG. **10.10.** The even mass isomers of lead.

Particle excitation also requires a great amount of energy because of the tight binding of the particles completing the shell.   The least amount of energy for particle excitation results when a single particle is promoted from the closed shell to a single particle state in the next shell.   Hence, an explanation of most or all of the observed levels can be sought in particle-hole configurations. From an examination of shell level diagrams such as those given in Chapter 3, the following hole-particle configurations are possible contributors to the lowest-lying levels.

Proton excitation	Neutron excitation
$2d_{3/2}^{-1} 1h_{9/2}$	$3p_{1/2}^{-1} 2g_{9/2}$
$3s_{1/2}^{-1} 1h_{9/2}$	$3p_{1/2}^{-1} 1i_{11/2}$
$3s_{1/2}^{-1} 2f_{7/2}$	$2f_{5/2}^{-1} 2g_{9/2}$
	$3p_{3/2}^{-1} 1i_{11/2}$

TABLE **10.1.** Experimental levels in Pb^{208}.

Energy	Spin and parity assignment
0	0+
2.615	3−
3.198	5−
3.475	4−
3.70	5−

Each one of these hole-particle configurations can give rise to several spin states. For example, the $(2d_{3/2}^{-1} 1h_{9/2})$ configuration has four states which in order of increasing energy should be $3-, 5-$ ($4-$ and $6-$). Hence, two or more of the observed states could be accounted for by a single one of the hole-particle combinations listed above; the spins of each of the observed levels could be accounted for many times over. Detailed assignment can be made by a rigorous theoretical estimate of the energy levels which includes the energy due to the interaction with the core nucleons, the spin-orbit interaction and the central interaction between the extra particles. In a complete analysis the configuration interaction must be considered. The problem of theoretical estimates of the excited levels of Pb^{208} has been discussed by PRYCE[12] and by TAUBER[13] and by CARTER, PINKSTON, AND TRUE.[14] The results of the last-cited authors will be summarized briefly.

CARTER, PINKSTON, AND TRUE[14] calculated the spectrum of states arising

Energy levels of Pb[208] as calculated by CARTER, PINKSTON, AND TRUE[14] for a singlet-even plus triplet-even force.

	Spin					
	$2-$	$3-$	$4-$	$5-$	$6-$	$7-$
Energy	6.04	5.56	5.53	5.43	4.98	4.82
(MeV)	4.80	5.34	5.24	4.93	4.67	4.04
		4.94	4.96	4.42	4.38	
		4.27	4.55	4.34	4.08	
		3.65	4.23	4.11		
			4.21	3.77		
			3.68	3.41		

from the promotion of the $p_{1/2}$ or $f_{5/2}$ neutron into the $g_{9/2}$ or $i_{11/2}$ shell and from the promotion of an $s_{1/2}$ or $d_{3/2}$ proton into the $h_{9/2}$ or $f_{7/2}$ shell. The zero-order energies of the resulting hole states and particle states were evaluated from empirical data. The central problem of the calculation was to estimate the interaction energy in the coupling of the hole and particle states to form the several negative-parity spin states which are allowed. The only arbitrary parameters used were those needed to fix the nuclear force admixtures of Wigner, Majorana, Heisenberg and Bartlett type forces. For the finite-range nuclear force, both a singlet-even plus triplet-even force and a Rosenfeld force were used. In addition, the energy levels were calculated

[12] M. H. L. Pryce, *Proc. Phys. Soc.* (London) **A65**, 773 (1952).

[13] G. E. Tauber, *Phys. Rev.* **99**, 176 (1955).

[14] J. C. Carter, W. T. Pinkston, and W. W. True, *Phys. Rev.* **120**, 504 (1960). See also W. T. Pinkston, *Nucl. Phys.* **37**, 312 (1962).

for a zero-range nuclear force.   Each of these three forces are quite different from each other, but the calculated spectrum was not greatly different.   A sample spectrum is shown in the table.

The theoretical values of 3.68 MeV for the lowest 4− state and of 3.41 and 3.77 MeV for the lowest 5− states are only a few tenths of a MeV different from the experimental values listed in Table 10.1 and one may conclude that the character of these levels is satisfactorily identified.

One striking fact to come out of these calculations is that the experimental 3− level at 2.615 MeV *cannot* be accounted for by particle excitation. The authors conclude that their calculations support the statement of LANE AND PENDLEBURY[15] that the 3− level at 2.615 MeV in Pb^{208} represents an octupole oscillation of the core instead of a core-excited state.

These thoughts on the level systems of Pb^{208} help in the understanding of the decay scheme of Bi^{208}.   The radioactive nuclide Bi^{208} was not discovered until 1957, long after some 16 or more radioactive isotopes of bismuth had been identified among the reaction products of various heavy element targets bombarded with high energy particle beams.   NEUMANN AND PERLMAN[16] showed that the half-life of Bi^{208} is less than 30 seconds or greater than 50 years.   DE BENEDETTI AND CO-WORKERS[17] eliminated the former possibility and concluded that the half-life is long.   The decay energy available for electron capture decay has been estimated as 2.93 MeV by various authors.[18-20]   A decay energy of this magnitude coupled to a half-life of >50 years leads to a log ft value of >10 for the ground state transition. This highly forbidden transition can be explained as the consequence of a high spin change.   The ground state spin of Bi^{208} is predicted by the shell model to be 4 or 5; $g_{9/2}$ proton + $s_{1/2}^{-1}$ neutron.   If Bi^{208} does have a spin of 4 or 5 we can be fairly sure that the decay energy is greater than 2.615 MeV, the energy of the first excited state of Pb^{208}.   Otherwise Bi^{208} could decay only by a fourth forbidden transition and its lifetime would be so long that primordial Bi^{208} would still be present in natural bismuth (measured upper limit 0.002 per cent).

ROY, EASTWOOD, AND HAWKINGS[21] prepared Bi^{208} by the long bombardment of normal bismuth in the NRX reactor at Chalk River.   The Bi^{208} was prepared by the (n, 2n) reaction induced by fast neutrons:

$$Bi^{209}(n, 2n)Bi^{208}$$

[15] A. N. Lane and E. D. Pendlebury, *Nucl. Phys.* **15**, 39 (1960).
[16] H. M. Neumann and I. Perlman, *Phys. Rev.* **81**, 958 (1951).
[17] S. De Benedetti, *et al.*, *Nuovo Cim.* **6**, 682 (1957).
[18] J. R. Huizenga, *Physica* **21**, 410 (1955).
[19] N. Feather, *Phil. Mag. Supple.* **2**, 141 (1953).
[20] B. Foreman, Jr., and G. T. Seaborg, *J. Inorg. Nucl. Chem.* **7**, 305 (1958).
[21] J. C. Roy, T. A. Eastwood, and R. C. Hawkings, *Can. J. Phys.* **36**, 18 (1958).

The half-life was estimated from the yield to be 3×10^4 years with an uncertainty of a factor of about 2.   (MILLAR, EASTWOOD, AND ROY[22] corrected this to a better estimate of 7.5×10^5 years to within a factor of three.)*   The principal radiation observed in Bi^{208} was the 2.61 MeV gamma ray from the $3-$ level of Pb^{208} to the ground state.   ROY, EASTWOOD, AND HAWKINGS[21] accept WAHLBORN'S[23] assignment of $4+$ for the spin of Bi^{208} and write the decay scheme as simple electron capture to the $3-$ level of Pb^{208}.   A spin of $5+$ is also possible for Bi^{208} and the later shell model calculations of KIM AND RASMUSSEN[23a] favor it.   The $5+$ assignment is also favored by MUKHERJEE AND COHEN'S[11] study of the triton spectrum from the $Bi^{209}(d, t)$ Bi^{208} reaction.   The estimated decay energy of 200–300 keV is about right for the estimated half-life.

Bi^{208} might be expected to have some low-lying levels of very high spin arising from other configurations such as $(h_{9/2}$ proton $i_{13/2}{}^{-1}$ neutron). Isomerism of the type observed in Bi^{210} (discussed in Section 6.2 of Chapter 6) might be expected since the situation is quite similar.

There is evidence that such isomerism does exist in Bi^{208}.   LAMPOL'SKII AND CO-WORKERS[24] reported the observation in 1953 of a 2-millisecond state produced by fast-neutron irradiation of bismuth.   A later publication by LEIPUNSKII AND CO-WORKERS[25] reports the production of this activity by bombardment of bismuth and lead with 20 MeV protons and gives the half-life as 3 ± 1 milliseconds.   VEGORS, AXEL, and DUFFIELD[26] produced an isomeric state with a 2.7-msec half-life by bombardment of Bi^{209} with a bremsstrahlung beam from a 22 MeV betatron.   These investigators found gamma rays of energy 921 keV and 509 keV with this half-life and suggested the decay sequence

$$(10-) \xrightarrow{\text{E3}} (7+) \xrightarrow{\text{E2}} (5+).$$

The threshold for production was observed to be 11.4 ± 0.4 MeV which agrees with the assignment to Bi^{208}.   DE BENEDETTI[17] also gave an excitation function for the production of this isomer via the reaction,

$$Bi^{209}(\gamma, n)Bi^{208m}$$

KIM AND RASMUSSEN[23a] comment on the shell model interpretation of the states involved in this decay.

[22] C. H. Millar, T. A. Eastwood, and J. C. Roy, *Can. J. Phys.* **37**, 1126 (1959).

[23] Wahlborn, *Nucl. Phys.* **3**, 644 (1957).

[23a] Y. E. Kim and J. O. Rasmussen, "Energy levels of Tl^{208} and Bi^{208}," *Phys. Rev.* (1964).

[24] Lampol'skii, Leipunskii, Gen, and Tikhomirow, *Bull. Acad. Sci. USSR, Phys. Ser.* **19**, 338 (1955); see also P. A. Lampol'skii and V. L. Glagolev, *Zhur. Eksp. Teor. Fiz.* **40**, 743 (1961).

[25] Leipunskii, Miller, Morozov, and Lampol'skii, *Doklady Akad. Nauk, SSSR*, **109**, 935 (1956). (Translation: *Sov. Phys. Doklady* **1**, 505 (1956)).

[26] S. N. Vegors and P. Axel, *Phys. Rev.* **101**, 1067 (1956); R. B. Duffield and S. N. Vegors, *Phys. Rev.* **112**, 1958 (1958).

* Oak Ridge workers report a value of 3.68×10^5 years, accurate to 1 per cent. See report *ORNL-3488*, 1963.

10.2.3 *The Isomers of Pb^{207} and the Level System of Pb^{207}*

The isotope Pb^{207} is but one neutron removed from the doubly-magic nuclide Pb^{208}, and all the low-lying states of Pb^{207} should correspond closely to the predictions of the shell model for a single neutron vacancy in the 126-neutron shell.   One would expect a $p_{1/2}$ ground state plus low-lying states with designations $f_{5/2}$, $p_{3/2}$, $i_{13/2}$, $f_{7/2}$, and $h_{9/2}$ and this is what is found experimentally.   The level assignments in this important nucleus are on a firm basis because experimental information is available from a variety of studies; namely, from the electron capture decay of Bi^{207}, the β^- decay of Tl^{207}, the alpha decay of Po^{211} and Po^{211m}, the decay of Pb^{207m}, the inelastic scattering of neutrons by Pb^{207}, the proton spectrum from the Pb$^{206}(d, p)$Pb^{207} reactions, and the triton spectrum from the Pb$^{208}(d, t)$Pb^{208} reaction.   In Fig. 10.11 the information derived from this variety of experiments is summarized.   The level assignment and excitation energies in Pb^{207} have been used as the fundamental basis of an elaborate analysis of the Pb^{206} level system, reviewed in the next section, so that it will be worthwhile to show in

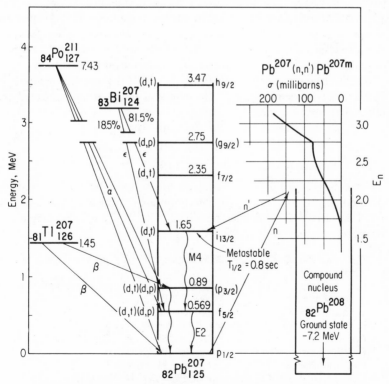

FIG. **10.11.** Summary of experimental studies giving information on the level scheme of Pb^{207}.   Adapted from STELSON AND CAMPBELL.[30]

some detail in the following paragraphs how definite the experimental data is on the levels of Pb^{207}.

Stable Lead-207. Lead-207 occurs in common lead and is the stable terminal product of the actinium decay series. Its importance in this connection is discussed in Chapter 6. The important property of Pb^{207} in connection with the present discussion is its spin which has been measured[27] as 1/2.

The 0.8 Second Isomer Pb^{207m}. CAMPBELL AND GOODRICH[28] prepared Pb^{207m} by bombarding enriched samples of Pb^{207} with neutrons.

$$Pb^{207}(n, n')Pb^{207m}$$

LASCOUX AND VENDRYES[29] prepared it in a similar way using lead targets. STELSON AND CAMPBELL[30] have carefully measured the cross section for excitation of Pb^{207m} by the (n, n') reaction. (See Fig. 10.11.) FARINELLI AND CO-WORKERS[31] measured the excitation curve for the following photoneutron reaction: $Pb^{208}(\gamma, n\gamma')Pb^{207m}$.

The mass assignment was confirmed by the chemical separation of the 0.8-second activity from a long-lived Bi^{207} parent;[32,33] a major part of the decay of Bi^{207} proceeds to the 0.8-second metastable state in Pb^{207}.

The metastable state decays by the emission of a 1.064 MeV $M4$ gamma ray followed by a 0.569 MeV $E2$ gamma ray. The multipolarity assignments are based on K-shell internal conversion coefficients and on the angular correlation of the radiations.[34-36] The decay scheme is shown in Fig. 10.9.

The Electron Capture Decay of Bi^{207}. Bi^{207} is prepared by bombarding natural lead with deuterons.[37] The deuteron energy usually selected is ~ 25 MeV. The reactions are:

$$Pb^{206}(d, n)Bi^{207}$$
$$Pb^{207}(d, 2n)Bi^{207}$$
$$Pb^{208}(d, 3n)Bi^{207}$$

If the target is allowed to cool several months before it is chemically separated the bismuth activity is nearly pure Bi^{207} because the 6-day Bi^{206} and 14-day Bi^{205} are much shorter-lived. Bi^{207} can also be prepared[37] as a daughter product from At^{211}.

[27] J. E. Mack, *Revs. Mod. Phys.* **22**, 64 (1950); P. F. A. Klinkenberg, *Revs. Mod. Phys.* **24**, 63 (1952).

[28] E. C. Campbell and M. Goodrich, *Phys. Rev.* **78**, 640 (1950) and private communication reported in *Revs. Mod. Phys.* **25**, 469 (1953).

[29] J. Lascoux and G. Vendryes, *Compt. Rend.* **233**, 858 (1951).

[30] P. H. Stelson and E. C. Campbell, *Phys. Rev.* **97**, 1222 (1955).

[31] Farinelli, Ferrero, Malvano, Menardi, and Silva, *Phys. Rev.* **112**, 1994 (1958).

[32] G. Friedlander and E. Wilson, *Phys. Rev.* **91**, 498 (1953).

[33] E. C. Campbell and F. Nelson, *Phys. Rev.* **91**, 499 (1953).

[34] F. K. McGowan and E. C. Campbell, *Phys. Rev.* **92**, 533 (1953).

[35] F. K. McGowan, *Phys. Rev.* **92**, 524 (1953).

[36] A. H. Wapstra, *Arkiv Fysik* **7**, 279 (1954).

The half-life of Bi²⁰⁷ has been reported variously as about 50 years,[37] as 8.6 ± 0.6 years,[38] as 27 ± 3 years,[39] as 28 ± 3 years,[40] and as 38 ± 3 years.[41]

A number of careful investigations[34,42–47] have been made of the radiations of Bi²⁰⁷. The following summary and the decay scheme of Fig. 10.12

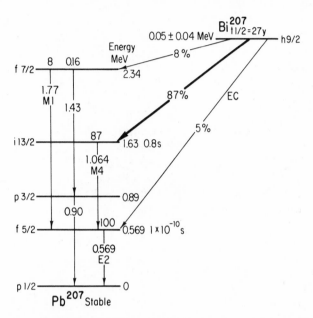

FIG. 10.12. Decay scheme of Bi²⁰⁷ (ALBURGER AND SUNYAR[46]). Total transition intensities per 100 disintegrations are shown by numbers above each gamma ray.

taken from the extensive work of ALBURGER AND SUNYAR[46] are in agreement with most of the work and conclusions of the investigators cited.

Bi²⁰⁷ decays by orbital electron capture accompanied by gamma rays of energies 0.569, 0.894, 1.0639, 1.43, and 1.77 MeV having transition intensities

[37] H. M. Neumann and I. Perlman, *Phys. Rev.* **81**, 958 (1951).
[38] L. T. Cheng, V. C. Ridolfo, M. L. Pool, and D. N. Kundu, *Phys. Rev.* **98**, 231A (1955).
[39] G. Harbottle as reported by Alburger and Sunyar, *Phys. Rev.* **99**, 702 (1955).
[40] J. Sosniak and R. E. Bell, *Can. J. Phys.* **37**, 1 (1959).
[41] E. H. Appelman, *Phys. Rev.* **121**, 253 (1961).
[42] N. H. Lazar and E. D. Klema, *Phys. Rev.* **98**, 710 1186A (1955).
[43] A. H. Wapstra, *Arkiv Fysik* **7**, 279 (1954).
[44] R. A. Ricci, *Physica* **23**, 693 (1957).
[45] J. R. Prescott, *Proc. Phys. Soc.* **67**A, 540 (1954).
[46] D. E. Alburger and A. W. Sunyar, *Phys. Rev.* **99**, 695 (1955).
[47] P. H. Stelson and F. K. McGowan, *Phys. Rev.* **99**, 112 (1955).

of 100, 0.16, 87, 0.16, and 8 per cent per disintegration, respectively. K-conversion electron intensities are 1.7, 0.0039, 8.2, 0.0009, and 0.022 electrons per 100 disintegrations, respectively.   The 0.894, 1.43 and 1.77 MeV transitions have K-conversion coefficients of $(2.4 \pm 1) \times 10^{-2}$, $(5 \pm 2) \times 10^{-3}$, and $(2.5 \pm 0.5) \times 10^{-3}$.   The first of these is in agreement with $M1$ radiation, the second with $E2$ and the third with $M1$ (if theoretical $M1$ conversion coefficients based on "finite nuclear size" are used).   Electron capture branches are 87 per cent to the $i_{13/2}$ (0.8 sec) state at 1.633 MeV, 5 ± 2 per cent to the 0.57 MeV first excited state, and 8 ± 2 per cent to a level at 2.35 MeV.   Branching to the 2.35 MeV level proceeds only by L-capture as shown from the x-ray spectrum in coincidence with (1.78 ± 0.57) MeV photopeak sum pulses.   The decay energy to the 2.35 MeV level thus lies between 15 and 90 keV and the total Bi^{207} decay energy is 2.40 ± 0.04 MeV.   Gamma-gamma and electron-gamma correlation experiments of several investigators[34, 43, 46] confirm the $1.06 - 0.57$ MeV cascade as $13/2 \rightarrow 5/2 \rightarrow 1/2$ and the 1.78-0.57 MeV gamma-gamma correlation is isotropic to within 5 per cent. A spin of $\geqslant 7/2$ for the 2.35 state is supported by the failure to observe a 2.35 keV gamma; a crossover intensity of $\leqslant 6 \times 10^{-5}$ per disintegration was determined with a photoneutron detector.   An assignment of $f_{7/2}$ to the 2.35 MeV level is compatible with all the data including the 1.78-0.57 MeV angular correlation.   This assignment was made quite definite by STELSON, SMITH, AND MCGOWAN[48] who measured the linear polarization–direction correlation in the 1.77 MeV–0.57 MeV cascade.   Their results show definitely that the spin assignment of the 2.34 MeV level is 7/2 and that the 1.77 MeV γ-ray is predominantly $M1$.   A slight amount of $E2$ contribution ($\sim$0.7 per cent) is attributed to collective motion.   Fast coincidence techniques have been used to show[49] that the 0.57 MeV level has a lifetime of $<4 \times 10^{-10}$ sec.   STELSON AND MCGOWAN[47] deduced a half-life of 1×10^{-10} sec for this state from Coulomb excitation experiments.   GERHOLM[50] measured a delay of 9×10^{-11} seconds in good agreement.

The measured half life of the 569 keV transition is of some interest because it is of the order of magnitude expected for an $E2$ transition involving proton wave functions.   However, in this case the transition presumably involves neutron wave functions and should be much slower.   The conclusion which has been drawn from this is that collective effects are of some importance even in this nucleus where one would expect the levels to be pure shell model states.   BOHR AND MOTTELSON[51] have pointed out that in the weak coupling limit of the collective model the reduced transition probability $B(E2)$ for

[48] P. H. Stelson, W. G. Smith, and F. K. McGowan, *Phys. Rev.* **116**, 167 (1959).

[49] A. W. Sunyar, *Phys. Rev.* **98**, 653 (1955).

[50] T. R. Gerholm, *Arkiv Fysik* **10**, 523 (1956).

[51] Bohr and Mottelson, *Dan. Mat.-fys. Medd.* **27**, No. 16 (1953).

transitions between neutron states may be greatly enhanced by the coupling of the states to the nuclear surface. The 569 keV transition in Pb^{207} seems to be a good example of this. TRUE AND FORD[52, 53] have made some quantitative estimates of the strength of this coupling in Pb^{207}.

The spins of the excited levels of Pb^{207} reached in the decay of Bi^{207} are those predicted by the simple shell model; hence in Fig. 10.12 the shell model orbital assignments are included.

Bi^{207} is a useful energy standard[46] in beta and gamma ray spectroscopy because of its long half-life and the prominence of the photons and electrons of the $M4$ 1.06 MeV gamma ray. For this reason YAVIN AND SCHMIDT[54] remeasured with great precision the energy of the 1.06 and 0.57 MeV transitions. They obtained 1.06343 ± 0.0050 MeV and 0.56885 ± 0.00030 MeV for these two transitions. Other precision measurements on the 0.57 MeV transition are those of BÄCKSTRÖM[55] (0.5697 ± 0.0001 MeV) and of MARMIER AND BOEHM[56] (0.5697 ± 0.0002 MeV).

The Beta Decay of Tl^{207}. In the active deposit of the actinium series there occurs the nuclide $AcC''(Tl^{207})$. (See Section 6.4 of Chapter 6.) This 4.78-minute beta emitter has a simple decay scheme since it decays chiefly by emission of 1.47 MeV beta particles to the ground state of Pb^{207}. According to SURUGUE[57] it decays in 0.5 per cent of its disintegrations to a level at 0.87 MeV in Pb^{207}. This can be identified with the $p_{3/2}$ level at 0.89 MeV reported in the decay scheme of Bi^{207}. The absence of decay to the $f_{5/2}$ level at 0.57 is understandable on spin change considerations since Tl^{207} must have a spin of 1/2. No other levels of Pb^{207} can be reached because of the low decay energy. See Fig. 10.11.

Alpha Decay of Po^{211}. The isotope Po^{211} exists in two isomeric forms[58] as discussed in Section 6.4 of Chapter 6. (See Fig. 6.46.) The well-known 0.52-second AcC' decays by alpha emission to the ground state and to levels at 0.57 and 0.87 MeV in Pb^{207}. The 25-second isomer Po^{211m} decays to the ground state and to levels at 0.87 and 1.63 MeV in Pb^{207}.

Levels of Pb^{207} from (d, p) and (d, t) Experiments. A number of workers[59-62] have bombarded lead targets with deuterons and have measured proton spectra from the $Pb^{206}(d, p)Pb^{207}$ reactions and triton spectra from

[52] W. W. True, *Phys. Rev.* **101**, 1342 (1956).

[53] W. W. True and K. W. Ford, *Phys. Rev.* **109**, 1675 (1957).

[54] A. I. Yavin and F. H. Schmidt, *Phys. Rev.* **100**, 171 (1955).

[55] G. Bäckström, *Arkiv Fysik* **10**, 393 (1956).

[56] P. Marmier and F. Boehm, quoted by Alburger and Sunyar in Ref. 46.

[57] J. Surugue, *Compt. Rend.* **212**, 337 (1941); *J. Phys. Rad.* **7**, 145 (1946).

[58] W. Jentschke, A. C. Juveland, and G. H. Kinsey, *Phys. Rev.* **96**, 231 (1954).

[59] J. A. Harvey, *Can. J. Phys.* **31**, 278 (1953) and *Phys. Rev.* **81**, 353 (1951).

[60] McEllistrem, Martin, Miller, and Sampson, *Phys. Rev.* **111**, 1636 (1958).

[61] B. L. Cohen, S. Mayo, and R. E. Price, *Nucl. Phys.* **20**, 360, 370 (1960).

[62] P. Mukherjee and B. L. Cohen, *Phys. Rev.* **127**, 1284 (1962).

the $Pb^{208}(d, t)Pb^{207}$ reaction.   Such spectra give evidence for the excited
levels listed in Table 10.2.   The higher-lying levels cannot be populated in the
electron capture decay of Bi^{207}.   Neutron hole states ($N < 126$) and neutron
states above the 126 neutron shell have been assigned to many of these levels.
For our purposes here perhaps the most important result is the identification
by MUKHERJEE AND COHEN[62] of the $h_{9/2}$ hole state at 3.47 MeV.

10.2.4 *Experimental Information on and Shell Model Analysis of the Level System
of Pb^{206}*

The nucleus Pb^{206} is but two neutrons removed from the double closed
shell nucleus Pb^{208} and is one of the most favorable cases in the heavy

TABLE **10.2.** Energy Levels of Pb^{207} as revealed in $Pb^{206}(d,p)Pb^{207}$ and
$Pb^{208}(d,t)Pb^{207}$ reaction studies.

Energy of level (MeV)	Observed in $Pb^{206}(d,p)$ reaction	Observed in $Pb^{208}(d,t)$ reaction	Probable shell model assignment
0	X	X	$(p_{1/2})^{-1}$
0.57	X	X	$(f_{5/2})^{-1}$
0.90	X	X	$(p_{3/2})^{-1}$
1.64		X	$(i_{13/2})^{-1}$
2.35		X	$(f_{7/2})^{-1}$
2.75	X		$g_{9/2}$
3.47	X	X	$(h_{9/2})^{-1}$
3.62	X		$i_{11/2}$
3.70	X		
3.81	X		
4.02	X		
4.10	X		
4.29	X		$j_{15/2}$
4.36	X		$d_{5/2}$
4.43	X		
4.51	X		
4.60	X		$s_{1/2}$
4.69	X		
4.74	X		
4.94	X		
5.03	X		
5.08	X		
5.13	X		$g_{7/2}$
5.18	X		$d_{3/2}$
5.26	X		
5.29	X		
5.36	X		
5.44	X		
5.52	X		

Data of Mukherjee and Cohen, *Phys. Rev.* **127**, 1284 (1962).

element region for testing the predictions of a two-body shell model theory. In this section we review briefly the known experimental data on the level system of Pb^{206} and then compare these data with shell model predictions. The excellent agreement found between experiment and theoretical prediction in this case represents one of the triumphs of the shell model in the region of nuclides discussed in this book.

Information on the levels of Pb^{206} has been sought in the radioactive decay of three nuclides which have it as a daughter product and in certain nuclear reaction studies. The alpha decay of RaF (Po^{210}) goes primarily to the ground state but about 10^{-3} per cent goes to the first excited state $(2+)$ at 804 keV. The beta decay of Tl^{206} proceeds entirely to the ground state and hence provides no information on the level structure of Pb^{206}. The third activity is the electron capture nuclide Bi^{206} which has 3.7 MeV of decay energy and has an exceedingly complex decay scheme involving many levels of Pb^{206}. The most detailed information on the Pb^{206} level system comes from the study of Bi^{206} carried out by ALBURGER AND PRYCE.[63] A study of the triton groups in the reaction

$$Pb^{207}(d, t)Pb^{206}$$

provides information[59] on some levels (or unresolved groups of levels) which do not appear in the decay of Bi^{206}. A study of the gamma ray spectrum[64] from the inelastic scattering of neutrons from Pb^{206} also provides information on some levels not otherwise reported.

The levels of Pb^{206} revealed by these studies are summarized in Table 10.3.

The Radiation and Decay Scheme of Bi^{206}. Bismuth-206 has a half-life of 6.4 days. It is prepared by bombardment of natural lead, of enriched lead isotopes or of natural thallium according to the following reactions:

$$Pb^{208}(d, 4n)Bi^{206}$$
$$Pb^{207}(d, 3n)Bi^{206}$$
$$Pb^{206}(d, 2n)Bi^{206}$$
$$Tl^{205}(\alpha, 3n)Bi^{206}$$
$$Tl^{203}(\alpha, n)Bi^{206}$$

Of the other bismuth isotopes which can be prepared in these cyclotron reactions, the 14-day Bi^{205} is the closest in half-life and most likely to interfere with a study of the radiation of Bi^{206}. This interference can be minimized by proper choice of target and bombardment energies. When natural

---

[63] D. E. Alburger and M. H. L. Pryce, *Phys. Rev.* **95**, 1482 (1954); see also the preliminary experimental work reported by D. E. Alburger and G. Friedlander, *Phys. Rev.* **81**, 523 (1951).

[64] Day, Johnsrud, and Lind, *Bull. Am. Phys. Soc. Ser. II*, **1**, 56 (1956), and unpublished work.

lead targets are used, a choice of 16 MeV or lower for the deuteron energy eliminates the production of Bi^{205}.

Smaller amounts of Bi^{206} can be isolated as the daughter product of 9-day Po^{206} which decays 90 per cent by electron capture. The alpha decay of At^{210} also produces Bi^{206} but the alpha branching is so slight (0.17 per cent) that only tiny samples can be prepared from this source.

TABLE **10.3.** Experimental Energies in Pb^{206}.*

Energy	Spin and parity assignment	Probable dominant configuration	Ref.
0	0+	$(p_{1/2})^2$	e
0.803	2+	$(p_{1/2}f_{5/2})$	e
1.341	3+	$(p_{1/2}f_{5/2})$	e
1.34[a]	3+(0+)	$(p_{1/2}f_{5/2})_3(f_{5/2})^2_0$	f
1.45	2+	$(p_{1/2}p_{3/2})$	f
1.37[b]		$(p_{1/2}j)$	g
1.684	4+	$(f_{5/2})^2$	e
1.71	1+	$(p_{1/2}p_{3/2})$	g
1.73	1+(2+)	$(p_{1/2}p_{3/2})_1, (f_{5/2})^2_2$	f
1.83	(2+)	$(f_{5/2})^2_2$	f
1.998	4+	$(p_{3/2}f_{5/2})$	e
2.15	1+(2+,3+,0+)	$(p_{3/2})^2_0, (p_{3/2}f_{5/2})_{1,2,3}$	f
2.200	7−	$(p_{1/2}i_{13/2})$	e
2.22[c]		$(p_{1/2}j)$	g
2.385	6−	$(p_{1/2}i_{13/2})$	e
2.526	3−	$[(d_{3/2})^{-1}(h_{9/2})]_{proton}$	e
2.783	5−	$(f_{5/2}i_{13/2})$	e
3.017	5−	$(p_{3/2}i_{13/2})$	e
3.03[d]	(3+,4+)	$(p_{1/2}f_{7/2})$	g
3.125	6+	$(f_{5/2}f_{7/2})$	e
3.280	5−	$[(d_{3/2})^{-1}(h_{9/2})]_{proton}$	e
3.404	5−	$[(s_{1/2})^{-1}(h_{9/2})]_{proton}$	e

[a] This level, excited by inelastic neutron scattering, may be the same as the 3+ level, but is also consistent with a 0+ assignment. It could be either or a superposition of both.

[b] This level, observed with poor energy resolution in the (d,t) reaction, is probably a superposition of the 3+ level at 1.34 MeV, the 2+ level at 1.45 MeV, and possibly also a 0+ level.

[c] This level, observed with poor energy resolution in the (d,t) reaction, is probably a superposition of the 7− level at 2.200 MeV and the 6− level at 2.385 MeV.

[d] This level was reported as probably a doublet. It is probably a superposition of the 3+ and 4+ levels arising from the configuration $(p_{1/2}f_{7/2})$ and distinct from the other levels indicated in the neighborhood of 3 MeV.

[e] D. E. Alburger and M. H. Pryce, *Phys. Rev.* **95**, 1482 (1954). Decay of Bi^{206}.

[f] Day, Johnsrud, and Lind, *Bull. Am. Phys. Soc. Ser. II*, **1**, 56 (1956). $Pb^{206}(n, n'\gamma)$.

[g] J. A. Harvey, *Can. J. Phys.* **31**, 278 (1953). $Pb^{207}(d, t)Pb^{206}$.

* This table is reproduced from the paper of True and Ford, *Phys. Rev.* **109**, 1675 (1958).

An outstanding experimental investigation of the exceedingly complex radiations of Bi[206] was carried out by ALBURGER AND PRYCE.[63] The conversion electrons of the gamma rays were measured in beta ray spectrometers of high resolution; for the more intense conversion lines the resolution employed was 0.22 per cent. The energies of the electrons were precisely measured against known standards. The coincidence or non-coincidence of electron-electron pairs was studied in a double beta spectrometer of moderate resolution. The gamma rays were measured in scintillation spectrometers and some electron-gamma coincidence experiments were performed. In all, some 28 gamma rays were found in the energy region 100–2000 keV, nearly all of which were placed with reasonable certainty in a decay scheme. A number of weak conversion electrons in the region below 96 keV were not characterized sufficiently for placement in a decay scheme. The gamma rays are listed in Table 10.4. The K-line energies of 19 of these gamma rays is accurate to 5 parts in 10,000. For the rest, the K-line accuracy is 1.5 in 1000. Table 10.4 is taken from the later publication of TRUE AND FORD[65] who used ALBURGER AND PRYCE's[63] data but reinterpreted the K-conversion coefficients, and hence the gamma ray intensities, using later tables of conversion coefficients. Hence, Table 10.4 is slightly different from a similar table given in the original paper of ALBURGER AND PRYCE. A few additional assignments of multipolarity were made by NOVAKOV, HULTBERG, AND ANDERSSON[66] who measured the conversion lines emitted by an external converter placed in front of a Bi[209] sample.

Of particular interest are two $E3$ transitions with energies 202.5 keV and 516.1 keV. These both originate at a 7− level at 2200.2 keV which has a half-life of 145 ± 15 microseconds.[67, 68] This delayed transition is analogous to the 68 minute isomeric transition in Pb[204]. Refer to Fig. 10.10 showing the occurrence of isomerism in several even-even lead isotopes.

The gamma rays of Table 10.4 have been arranged in the decay scheme of Fig. 10.13. The arguments upon which this scheme is based are too detailed to review here but most of the levels, with the exception of one labelled with question marks, are uniquely established. This rather complex decay scheme and the pattern of gamma ray de-excitation can be clarified somewhat by redrawing the levels of Pb[206] as a Grotrian diagram as shown in Fig. 10.14.

Bismuth-206 has a spin of 6 as determined by the atomic beam magnetic resonance technique.[69, 70] The electron capture decay goes nearly

[65] W. W. True and K. W. Ford, *Phys. Rev.* 109, 1675 (1958).

[66] T. Novakov, S. Hultberg and B. Andersson, *Arkiv Fysik* 13, 117 (1958); see also R. Stockendal and S. Hultberg, *Arkiv Fysik* 15, 33 (1959).

[67] D. E. Alburger and M. H. L. Pryce, *Phys. Rev.* 92, 514 (1953).

[68] P. Tove, *Nucl. Inst.* 1, 95 (1957). This author gives the half-life as 123 ± 4 microseconds.

[69] L. L. Marino, et al., *Bull. Am. Phys. Soc. II*, 2, 383 (1957).

[70] C. M. Johansson and I. P. K. Lindgren, *Nucl. Phys.* 9, 44 (1958–9).

TABLE 10.4. Transitions and intensities in Pb^{206}.

No.	Transition energy (keV)	Parent[e]	Assumed[e] daughter	Type	Relative K-electron intensity[b] I_K	Conversion coeff.[c] α_K	Relative gamma intensity[b] I_γ	Assumed[d] $(L+M+\cdots)/K$	Relative total transition rate
1	184.1	6-,1	7-,1	$M1$	28	1.35	20.7	0.20	54.3
2	234.3	5-,2	5-,1	$M1$	0.24	0.68	0.35	0.20	0.64
3	262.8	5-,3	5-,2	$M1$	2.1	0.50	4.2	0.20	6.7
4	343.4	4+,1	3+,1	$M1$	$6.6-X_1$	0.240	$27.5-4.17X_1$	0.20	$35.4-5.37X_1$
	(341.8)	6+,1	5-,1	$E1$	X_1	0.0178	$56.2X_1$	0.20	$57.4X_1$
5	386.0	5-,4	5-,2	$M1$	0.13	0.176	0.74	0.20	0.90
6	398.1	5-,1	6-,1	$M1$	1.76	0.160	11.0	0.20	13.1
7	497.1	5-,3	5-,1	$M1$	1.37	0.091	15.1	0.20	16.7
8	516.1	7-,1	4+,1	$E3$	1.95	0.0487	40.0	0.73	43.4
9	537.5	3+,1	2+,1	$M1$	2.08	0.074	28.1	0.20	30.6
10	620.6	5-,4	5-,1	$M1$	0.27	0.0505	5.35	0.20	5.7
11	632.2	5-,2	6-,1	$M1$	0.21	0.0485	4.33	0.20	4.6
12	657.3	4+,2	3+,1	$M1$	0.084	0.0435	1.93	0.20	2.0
13	803.3	2+,1	0+,1	$E2$	0.85	0.0080	106	0.27	107
14	880.5	4+,1	2+,1	$E2$	$0.48-X_2$	0.0067	$71.6-149X_2$	0.26	$72.2-150X_2$
	(878.0)	5-,4	3-,1	$E2$	X_2	0.0067	$149X_2$	0.26	$150X_2$
15	895.1	5-,3	6-,1	$M1$	0.32	0.0193	16.6	0.20	17.0
16	1018.8	5-,4	6-,1	$M1$	0.11	0.0140	7.86	0.20	8.0
17	1098.6	5-,1	4+,1	$E1$	0.029	0.00177	16.4	0.18	16.4
18	1596.3	5-,3	4+,1	$E1$	0.0054	0.00094	5.74	0.18	5.8
19	1719.7	5-,4	4+,1	$E1$	0.029	0.00083	34.9	0.18	34.9
20	123.6	5-,4	5-,3	$M1$	0.069	4.10	0.0168	0.20	0.10
21	202.5	7-,1	4+,2	$E3$	0.020	0.410	0.049	5.8^{a}	0.185
22	313.6	4+,2	4+,1	$M1$	0.14	0.305	0.46	0.20	0.63

23	739.9	6+,1	6−,1	E1	0.011	0.00363	3.03	0.18	3.0
24	753.9	5+,3	3−,1	E2	0.0074	0.0091	0.81	0.28	0.82
25	816.3	5−,2	7−,1	E2	$0.0025-X_3$	0.0077	$0.325-130X_3$	0.27	$0.33-131X_3$
	(~816)	6−,2	7−,1	M1	X_3	0.0245	$40.8X_3$	0.20	$42X_3$
26	841.7	3−,1	4+,1	E1	0.0050	0.00287	1.74	0.18	1.75
27	1405.2	5−,4	4+,2	E1	0.0020	0.00114	1.75	0.18	1.75
28	107.2	6+,1	5−,2	E1	$0.23-X_4$	0.300	$0.77-3.33X_4$	0.23	$1.05-4.56X_4$
	(~107)	6+,1	6−,2	E1	X_4	0.300	$3.33X_4$	0.23	$4.56X_4$
...	...	...	...	...	...	...	...	...	...
29	662	2+,2	2+,1	M1			4		4
30	1460	2+,2	0+,1	E2			1		1
31	1730	1+,1	0+,1	M1					
32	1830	2+,3	0+,1	E2					
33	1350	1+,2(2+,4)	2+,1	M1					

* This table is reproduced from the paper of True and Ford, *Phys. Rev.* **109**, 1675 (1958).

[a] The first 28 transitions are numbered as by Alburger and Pryce. Transitions 29–33 are additional transitions observed by Day, Johnsrud, and Lind (reference f in Table III).

[b] The K-electron intensities are taken from reference 4. The normalization of intensities for transition 29 and 30 is unrelated to the normalization of transitions 1–28.

[c] The K-conversion coefficients are taken from L. Sliv and I. Band, University of Illinois Report 57 ICC K1, April, 1957 (unpublished).

[d] The L/K ratios are evaluated by interpolation among values distributed by M. E. Rose (Oak Ridge National Laboratory) based on point nucleus calculations. We arbitrarily set $(L+M+\cdots)/K=1.20(L/K)$.

[e] The notation 6−, 2 means the second state of spin 6 and odd parity, in order of increasing energy.

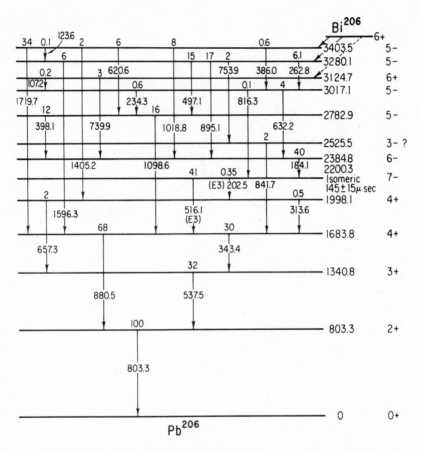

FIG. **10.13.** Decay scheme of Bi²⁰⁶ as given by ALBURGER AND PRYCE. The number at the head of each transition is the intensity per 100 disintegrations. These numbers are slightly different from those given in Table 10.4. The assignments of the levels at 3124.7 keV and 3017.1 keV have been changed to agree with the analysis of TRUE AND FORD.[65]

exclusively to two 5— states of Pb²⁰⁶ lying at 3280 and 3403 keV. The theoretical significance of the selection of final states in the Bi²⁰⁶ decay has been discussed by ALBURGER AND PRYCE.[63] These states then deactivate by complex cascades of gamma rays through the many nuclear levels lying between them and the ground state. During these cascades some Pb²⁰⁶ atoms are converted to the 7— level at 2200 keV which is metastable because the state of next lower spin lying beneath it has a spin value of only 4.

The decay of Bi²⁰⁶ has proved to be well suited for the detection of an interesting effect predicted in 1953 by SLIV.[71] SLIV predicted that a

[71] L. A. Sliv, *Zhur. Eksp. Teor. Fiz.* **25**, 7 (1953); *J. Phys. Radium* **16**, 589 (1955).

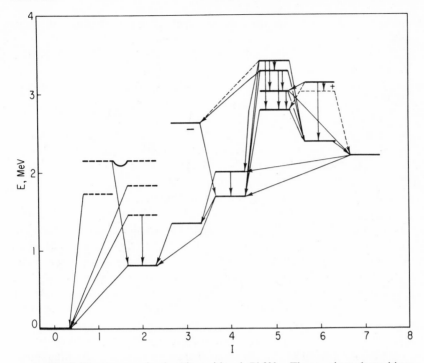

FIG. **10.14.** Known energy levels and transitions in Pb^{206}. The energies and transitions follow almost uniquely from experiment. Some of the spin and parity assignments may be incorrect, however. Dashed energy levels are those seen in inelastic neutron scattering. Solid energy levels are those seen in the decay of Bi^{206}. Dashed transitions are those which may exist in the decay of Bi^{206} but may be masked by other more intense transitions with nearly identical energies. All levels with $I \leq 4$ are of even parity unless otherwise marked. All levels with $I \geq 5$ are of odd parity unless otherwise marked. Prepared by W. W. TRUE.

monoenergetic positron would be emitted from a nucleus which was excited by more than 2 mc^2, where m is the mass of the electron, and which at the same time had a vacancy in one of the inner electronic shells of the atom.   If an electron-positron pair is created, there is a certain probability that the electron will be captured in the empty electronic orbit and the positron emitted.

This effect was first observed experimentally in Bi^{206}. BRUNNER, LEISI, PERDRISAT, AND SCHERRER[72] showed that monoenergetic positrons were emitted in association with the 1.72 MeV $E1$ transition to the extent of 7×10^{-8} per gamma transition. The effect was confirmed by WIENER, CHASMAN, HARIHAR, AND WU[73] who report an intensity of 3.2×10^{-8} per

[72] J. H. Brunner, H. J. Leisi, C. F. Perdrisat, and P. Scherrer, *Phys. Rev. Letters* **2**, 207 (1959); *Helv. Phys. Acta* **34**, 161 (1961); and *Helv. Phys. Acta* **35**, 175 (1962).

[73] R. Wiener, C. Chasman, P. Harihar, and C. S. Wu, *Phys. Rev.* **130**, 1069 (1963).

gamma ray. Both teams of investigators report the presence of three high
energy gamma rays not observed earlier in the study of Bi^{206} decay; these are
a 1.845 MeV El transition, a 1.880 MeV El transition and a 1.903 MeV
transition of uncertain multipolarity.

Shell Model Calculations of Pb^{206} Level System.   PRYCE[74] suggested that
the shell model should be able to predict the levels of Pb^{206} up to a few MeV
of excitation. It is known from the level system in Pb^{208} that neither
collective effects nor the excitation of protons from a closed shell contributes
to excited levels below 3.4 MeV.   Lead-206 is two neutrons removed from a
closed shell and the levels up to about 3 MeV should be those which arise
from a combination of two neutron (hole) states.*   PRYCE[74] suggested that
the energies and spectroscopic identifications of the single neutron states in
Pb^{207} were on a sufficiently firm basis that one should be able to use them in a
calculation of the levels in Pb^{206}.   Consider the possible combinations listed
in Table 10.5.   The single particle states combine in first approximation to
give a series of degenerate states with energy equal to the sums of the single
particle (neutron hole) energies.   As an example, the configuration $f_{5/2}p_{3/2}$
can couple according to the ordinary vector coupling rules to give states of
spin 1, 2, 3, 4, all of even parity.   If there were no interaction between the hole
states, the energy of these levels would be just the sum of the energies of the
two Pb^{207} levels in the configuration and all four Pb^{206} levels derived from
this configuration would have the same energy.   Because of the interaction
between the two hole states, the degeneracy is removed and some states are
shifted upwards while others are shifted down.   The heart of the shell model
calculation is the estimation of these interaction effects between the hole
states.

In the original form of the theory pioneered by PRYCE[63,74] the interaction
was not calculated rigorously by an explicit integration over the radial wave
functions of the single neutron levels and including nuclear exchange forces of
all possible types.   Instead of this, zero-range nuclear forces of pure singlet
exchange character were used and the interaction parameters were estimated
by a rough empirical method.   Configuration interaction for levels of the
same spin and parity which were predicted by this crude treatment to lie
together could not be allowed for in the few instances where it was important,
particularly the 0+ levels, and this effect had to be estimated by an additional
empirical adjustment.   Despite the approximations of this method the results
were highly satisfying.   Not all of the predicted levels were seen (or should
have been seen) in the decay of Bi^{206}, but all but two of the experimental
levels could be identified with predicted levels in a natural manner.

---

[74] M. H. L. Pryce, *Proc. Phys. Soc.* (London) **A65**, 773 (1952).

* For the purpose of calculating energy states two holes in a closed shell behave in
exactly the same way as two nucleons outside a closed shell.

The two exceptions are the 3− level at 2.525 MeV and the 5− level at 3.403 MeV. It is noteworthy that levels of this spin and parity appear at about the same excitation in Pb^{208} (see Table 10.1 above). In the Pb^{208} case these levels are attributed to proton core excitation or, possibly, in the case of the 3− level, to collective octupole vibration. It seems natural to assign the corresponding levels in Pb^{206} to similar causes. In the ALBURGER AND PRYCE[63] analysis a particularly impressive prediction was that the lowest level of spin 7 should lie lower in energy than any levels of spin 5, 6, and ⩾8. This prediction neatly explained the isomeric level at 2.200 MeV which is de-excited by a pair of $E3$ gamma rays.

TABLE **10.5.** Possible Pb^{206} states arising from the combination of single particle neutron states identified in Pb^{207}.

Configuration	Energy of levels without interaction energy contribution (MeV)	Spins	Parity
$p_{1/2}^2$	0	0	+
$p_{1/2}f_{5/2}$	0.570	2, 3	+
$p_{1/2}p_{3/2}$	0.900	1, 2	+
$f_{5/2}^2$	1.140	0, 2, 4	+
$f_{5/2}p_{3/2}$	1.470	1, 2, 3, 4	+
$p_{1/2}i_{13/2}$	1.634	6, 7	−
$p_{3/2}^2$	1.800	0, 2	+
$f_{5/2}i_{13/2}$	2.204	4, 5, 6, 7, 8, 9	−
$p_{1/2}f_{7/2}$	2.35	3, 4	+
$p_{3/2}i_{13/2}$	2.534	5, 6, 7, 8	−
$f_{5/2}f_{7/2}$	2.920	1, 2, 3, 4, 5, 6	+
$p_{3/2}f_{7/2}$	3.250	2, 3, 4, 5	+
$i_{13/2}^2$	3.268	0, 2, 4, 6, 8, 10, 12	+

The success of this analysis encouraged others to undertake the very considerable labor of a more exact calculation of the two particle interaction. This was done by KEARSLEY[75] and by TRUE AND FORD.[65] The basic assumptions of these calculations are summarized in Table 10.6. Both used harmonic oscillator wave functions to express the radial form of the neutron (hole) states. TRUE AND FORD[65] assumed pure singlet exchange forces and used a Gaussian form for the shape of the potential. KEARSLEY[75] used singlet-even and triplet-odd exchange forces in the ratio −1 to +0.559 and a two-body potential shape of the Yukawa type. Both studies result in prediction of the spins, parities, and energies of numerous levels. Furthermore, since configuration interaction was calculated exact eigenfunctions of

---

[75] M. J. Kearsley, *Nucl. Phys.* **4**, 157 (1957).

all levels are predicted.   The two studies give remarkably concordant values for these quantities, showing that the calculations are not greatly sensitive to the shape of the interaction potential or (within limits) to the amount of triplet force.   The highly satisfactory fit of the predicted levels to the experimental levels is shown in Fig. 10.15.   All experimental levels can be matched to the theoretical levels in a consistent fashion.   The theory (Fig. 10.15) makes it clear that many more levels of Pb^{206} occur in the energy region between 800 keV and 4 MeV than are experimentally observed in the decay of Bi^{206}, which involves only those levels selected by the gamma ray cascades. The gamma ray cascades in turn are determined by the particular levels (chiefly the 5− levels at 3.280 and 3.403 MeV) selected by the decay of Bi^{206}.

More searching tests of the theoretical wave functions were made by

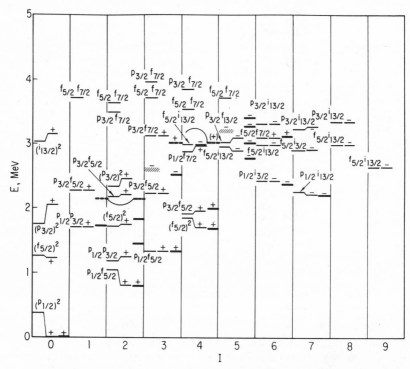

FIG. **10.15.** Energy levels of Pb^{206}.   For each spin, the first column gives the energy levels as calculated by TRUE AND FORD in lowest order with singlet forces, together with the configuration assignment.   The second column gives the theoretical energy levels calculated by exact diagonalization of the energy matrix for the lowest few states of each spin and parity.   The third column gives the empirical levels.   The positions of all of the energy levels are reasonably certain, but the spin and parity assignment of a few levels are uncertain.   Cross-hatched bands indicate probable location of 3− and 5− levels arising from excitation of core protons.   The experimental levels of Pb^{208} were used as a guide to the location of these levels.   From TRUE AND FORD.[65]

estimating gamma-ray transition rates with the aid of the theoretical eigen-functions and comparing these with experimental values.   This is discussed in some detail in the paper of TRUE AND FORD[65] which should be consulted for details.   The probabilities of electric transitions are definitely higher than predicted as is shown by the isomeric $E3$ transition which has a much shorter half-life than would be expected if the electric moment of the transition resulted only from the displacement of a neutron.   Also, the strength of the 880 keV $E2$ crossover gamma ray de-exciting the 4+ level at 1.684 MeV is higher than expected.   STELSON AND McGOWAN[76] have used the Coulombic

TABLE 10.6. Comparison of parameters used in shell model calculations of Pb^{206} levels.

Quantity	PRYCE	KEARSLEY	TRUE AND FORD
Energies of single neutron (hole) states	Experimental Pb^{207} levels	Experimental Pb^{207} levels	Experimental Pb^{207} levels
Two-body potential shape	Delta function zero range forces	Yukawa	Gaussian $V = V_0 \exp(-r^2/\beta^2)$
Range parameter of potential (10^{-13} cm)	0	1.37	$\beta = 1.85$
Depth parameter of potential		$V_0 = -42$ MeV	$V_0 = -32.5$ MeV
Singlet-triplet exchange force ratio	$-1/00$	$-1/+0.559$	$-1/00$
Wave functions		Harmonic oscillator	Harmonic oscillator

excitation process to excite the 2+ level of Pb^{206} at 810 keV.   From the cross section for the process they calculate a reduced transition probability, B($E2$), which is about twice that expected for a pure single particle transition.

These results suggest that the theoretical analyses given above are in-complete and that some allowance has to be made for collective effects. TRUE AND FORD[65] performed such a reanalysis.   They used the observed rate of the 810 keV $E2$ transition to estimate the strength of the coupling of the motion of the single particle (neutron hole) with the nuclear core.   Their model for this coupling was the weak-coupling model of particle-core coupling introduced by BOHR AND MOTTELSON[77] and developed by a number of authors.   As in their previous analysis the unperturbed energy of the neutron states was taken from the experimental levels of Pb^{207}.   Also, as before, these states were allowed to interact with each other through a Gaussian short range

---

[76] P. H. Stelson and F. K. McGowan, *Phys. Rev.* **99**, 112 (1955).

[77] A. Bohr and B. M. Mottelson, *Dan. Mat.-fys. Medd.* **27**, No. 16 (1953).

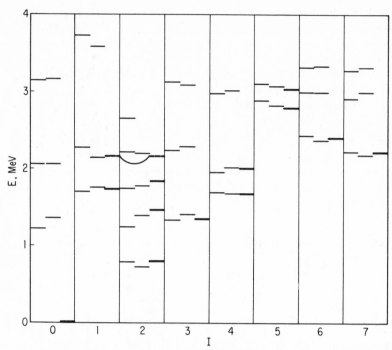

FIG. **10.16.** Comparison of Pb^{206} levels predicted with pure singlet forces (first column for each spin value), energies predicted with 75 per cent singlet forces plus collective coupling (second column for each spin value), and empirical energies (third column for each spin value). Both sets of theoretical energies are normalized to the ground state. From TRUE AND FORD.

force, purely singlet in character. In addition these states interacted with the collective vibrational motion of the core. (Only one phonon of vibrational excitation was considered.) This computation led to a new set of predictions of spins, parities, energy and configurational composition for the energy levels of Pb^{206}. Best agreement with experiment was obtained by adjusting the strength of the singlet forces to 75 per cent of that used in their original analysis. The results are summarized in Fig. 10.16. It is seen that the second set of theoretical levels has nearly the same energies as the first but the new set is in somewhat better agreement with experiment. The configurational mixing in the predicted states is somewhat different in the two cases, and this leads to revised predictions of gamma ray transition rates, branching ratios, etc. More experimental data on gamma ray lifetimes is needed to test these predictions.

KISSLINGER AND SORENSEN[78] have carried through a calculation of the

---

[78] L. S. Kisslinger and R. A. Sorensen, *Dan. Mat.-fys. Medd.* **32**, No. 9, 1960; see also R. W. Richardson and N. Sherman, *Nucl. Phys.* **52**, 253 (1964).

levels of Pb^{206} using a nuclear model which idealizes the residual interaction between the two neutron (hole) states as a "pairing force" plus a long-range quadrupole force. This model is sometimes referred to as the "super-conductivity" or "superfluid" model because it is patterned after the BARDEEN, COOPER, SCHRIEFFER[79] theory of conductivity. Brief mention of the general nature of this nuclear model is made in Chapter 3. The calculations of KISSLINGER AND SORENSEN result in the prediction of a large number of levels below 3 MeV of excitation which are in reasonably good agreement with those of TRUE AND FORD.[65] In those cases where comparison with experimental levels can be made there is agreement within a few tenths of one MeV. This agreement is, as expected, not as good as it is for TRUE AND FORD's technique, but the calculations of KISSLINGER AND SORENSEN are much simpler to carry out than those of TRUE AND FORD. The fact that the results of the two theoretical studies are reasonably close is important as it suggests that the calculations of the energy levels of lighter mass lead isotopes carried out by KISSLINGER AND SORENSEN are valid. See the further discussion of these calculations in Section 10.2.13.

10.2.5 The Ground State of Lead-205

The properties of Pb^{205} were completely unknown for many years. It seemed evident for some time from a consideration of energy cycles that Pb^{205} must be unstable toward electron capture decay to Tl^{205}, but the extent of this instability was in doubt. Unsuccessful attempts[80,81] to identify Pb^{205} positively among the products of bombardment of thallium targets in cyclotrons made it evident that Pb^{205} was quite long-lived and possibly long-lived enough to be of some geophysical significance.

HUIZENGA AND STEVENS[82] used a mass spectrograph to identify Pb^{205} in the lead fraction produced by an intensive bombardment of thallium with 21 MeV deuterons.

$$Tl^{205}(d, 2n)Pb^{205}$$

The authors estimated a lower limit of 6×10^7 years for decay by K-electron capture. If K-capture were the main mode of decay one might expect Pb^{205} in natural lead; since it does not occur there (upper limit 0.001 per cent) it must decay more prominently by L- or M-capture.

It is difficult to interpret these results if one estimates the decay energy of Pb^{205} by the upper cycle of Fig. 10.17. The beta disintegrations of Tl^{204} and Tl^{206} both go to the ground state, and the absence of gamma-radiation makes the decay energy determination straightforward. The neutron

[79] J. Bardeen, L. N. Cooper, and J. R. Schrieffer, *Phys. Rev.* **108**, 1178 (1957).

[80] D. H. Templeton, J. J. Howland and I. Perlman, *Phys. Rev.* **72**, 766 (1947).

[81] P. F. D. Shaw and J. R. Prescott, *Proc. Phys. Soc.* (London) **A67**, 283 (1954).

[82] J. R. Huizenga and C. M. Stevens, *Phys. Rev.* **96**, 548 (1954).

binding energies for $Tl^{204 \to 205}$ and $Tl^{205 \to 206}$ are taken from the work of
KINSEY, BARTHOLOMEW, AND WALKER.[83] The $Pb^{205 \to 206}$ neutron binding
energy is that reported by HARVEY.[84] This cycle leads to a decay energy of

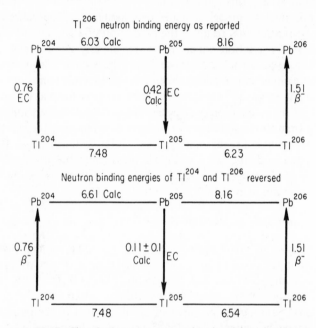

FIG. 10.17. Closed decay-energy cycles involving lead and
thallium isotopes and Tl^{204} and Tl^{206} binding energies as
reported (*upper*) and decay cycles with the reported binding
energies of Tl^{204} and Tl^{206} reversed (*lower*). The two versions
lead to different predictions for the decay energy and the neutron
binding energy of Pb^{205}. For both predictions, the lower version
is to be preferred. From FRITSCH.[86]

420 ± 100 keV for Pb^{205}. If K-capture is to be delayed by as long as
5×10^7 years for a decay energy of this magnitude, the log ft value must be
~ 15. On the basis of the shell model and of our knowledge of level assignments for the lead and thallium isotopes this large log ft value is unreason-
able; the spin of Pb^{205} is probably 5/2.

HUIZENGA[85] calculated the decay energy of Pb^{205} by closing the cycle
involving the following nuclides: $Pb^{205} \xrightarrow{n} Pb^{206} \xrightarrow{n} Pb^{207} \xrightarrow{n} Pb^{208} \xrightarrow{n} Pb^{209} \xrightarrow{\beta^-} Bi^{209} \xrightarrow{\alpha} Tl^{205} \xleftarrow{EC} Pb^{205}$. The neutron binding energies and

[83] B. B. Kinsey, G. A. Bartholomew, and W. H. Walker, *Phys. Rev.* **82**, 380 (1951).

[84] J. A. Harvey, *Phys. Rev.* **81**, 353 (1951).

[85] J. R. Huizenga, *Physica* **21**, 410 (1955).

the alpha decay energy of Bi^{209} were taken from the literature. This calculation leads to a value of 0.055 ± 0.130 MeV for the decay energy of Pb^{205}. The binding energy of Pb^{206} used by HUIZENGA was 60 kilovolts lower than that used in the binding energy systematics reviewed in Chapter 2. The higher value results in an estimated decay energy for Pb^{205} of 115 kilovolts; within the limits of error this difference does not change the conclusions to be drawn from the magnitude of the decay energy. This low decay energy explains the absence of observable K-capture and accounts satisfactorily for the long half-life. It has the further consequence that the neutron binding energy of Tl^{206} as given in the upper cycle of Fig. 10.17 must be incorrect.

FRITSCH[86] arrived at the same conclusion regarding the thallium binding energies in a slightly different way. The neutron binding energies of Tl^{204} and Tl^{206} are measured simultaneously in the (d, p) reaction method[84] or the (n, γ) reaction method[83] since the thallium target is a mixture of Tl^{203} and Tl^{205}. The assignment of binding energies was done on an arbitrary basis[84] and FRITSCH postulates that an incorrect assignment was made. If the two binding energies are reversed the lower closed cycle of Fig. 10.17 can be used to calculate the decay energy of Pb^{205} resulting in the value of ~ 100 kilovolts. The upper and lower cycles lead to different values also for the neutron binding energy of Pb^{205}. A consideration of the trends of neutron binding energies for the lead and thallium isotopes indicates clearly that the values given in the lower version of Fig. 10.17 are to be preferred.

If the decay energy of Pb^{205} is of the order of 50 keV, K-capture cannot occur, and the long half-life receives a natural explanation. The probable absence of K-capture in Pb^{205} was confirmed by HERBER AND CO-WORKERS[87] who set a lower limit of 10^{10} years to the half-life for this mode of decay.

HUIZENGA AND WING[88] isolated a Pb^{205} sample from an intense pure sample of 14-day Bi^{205} and found a small number of L x-rays from which they estimated an approximate L-capture half-life of 5×10^7 years. WING, STEVENS, AND HUIZENGA[89] prepared a larger sample by irradiating samples of Pb^{204} with an intense flux of neutrons to a total integrated flux of 1.7×10^{21} and 7.5×10^{21} neutrons per square centimeter. The Pb^{205} content after irradiation was determined in a mass spectrometer. The disintegration rate was computed from the observed rate of emission of L x-rays corrected for fluorescence yield and counting factors. The half-life was computed to be $(3.0 \pm 0.5) \times 10^7$ years.

The half-life of Pb^{205} is of some geologic significance in view of the possibility that extremely old lead ores may contain detectable quantities of

[86] A. R. Fritsch, Ph.D. Thesis, University of California, June, 1956, also published as *Univ. Calif. Rad. Lab. Report UCRL–3452*, June, 1956.

[87] Herber, Sugihara, Coryell, Bennett, and Huizenga, *Phys. Rev.* **103**, 955 (1956).

[88] J. R. Huizenga and J. Wing, *Phys. Rev.* **102**, 926 (1956).

[89] J. Wing, C. M. Stevens, and J. R. Huizenga, *Phys. Rev.* **111**, 590 (1958).

radiogenic Tl^{205} and that measurements of such Tl^{205} content might give information on the time interval between the formation of the elements and the deposition of ores.[90]

10.2.6 *The Level System of Pb^{205} Observed from the Decay of Bi^{205}*

KARRAKER AND TEMPLETON[91] identified 14.5 day Bi^{205} among the products of high-energy bombardments of lead and bismuth. ALBURGER AND PRYCE[63] observed the conversion electrons of 11 gamma rays. FRITSCH AND HOLLANDER[92] report a half-life of 15.3 ± 0.7 days for decay by orbital electron capture. These authors measured the conversion electron spectrum in permanent magnet spectrographs and reported evidence for numerous gamma rays. SCHMORAK, STOCKENDAL, McDONELL, BERGSTRÖM, AND GERHOLM[93] independently measured the conversion electrons in permanent magnet spectrographs and in a double focusing spectrometer. In addition, the latter group measured coincidences between pairs of conversion electrons in a double long-lens spectrometer and coincidences between the photons of high-energy gamma rays and the conversion electrons of low-energy gamma rays. Positrons were discovered with a maximum energy of 925 keV; taken together with coincidence information this established the total decay energy of Bi^{205} as 2.65 MeV. The Bi^{205} samples used in these studies were prepared by bombarding natural lead with deuterons and were necessarily contaminated with Bi^{206} and Bi^{207}. The conversion lines from the contaminating isotopes aided in the calibration of the energy scale but otherwise were troublesome.

The interference from Bi^{206} and Bi^{207} can be reduced by use of radiogenic lead (85 per cent Pb^{206}) as a target for bombardment. STOCKENDAL AND HULTBERG[94] did this and used the Bi^{205} samples so prepared to study the photolines excited in an external uranium converter by the gamma ray photons emitted by Bi^{205}. A comparison of the intensity of the external conversion lines with the internal conversion lines (with no external converter present) made it possible to determine absolute K-conversion coefficients. A comparison of these coefficients with the theoretical coefficients published by SLIV AND BAND[95] made it possible to give firm multipolarity assignments to the gamma transitions. In most cases these were in agreement with those given previously by SCHMORAK AND CO-WORKERS.[93]

[90] See, for example, a review by T. P. Kohman, *Ann. N.Y. Acad. Sci.* (1954).

[91] D. G. Karraker and D. H. Templeton, *Phys. Rev.* **81**, 510 (1951).

[92] A. R. Fritsch and J. M. Hollander, *J. Inorg. Nucl. Chem.* **6**, 165 (1958).

[93] M. Schmorak, R. Stockendal, J. A. McDonell, I. Bergström, and T. R. Gerholm, *Nucl. Phys.* **2**, 193 (1956); see also T. R. Gerholm, *Arkiv Fysik* **11**, 55 (1956).

[94] R. Stockendal and S. Hultberg, *Arkiv Fysik* **15**, 33 (1959).

[95] L. Sliv and J. Band, "Tables of Internal Conversion Coefficients of Gamma Rays." Published by Academy of Sciences of the USSR. Moscow-Leningrad, 1956.

STOCKENDAL[96] contributed additional information on some radiations of key importance to the construction of a decay scheme. Some of his measurements were made on Bi^{205} sources which had been electromagnetically separated from contaminating Bi^{206} activity. Using electron-electron and electron-gamma coincidence techniques HERRLANDER[97] checked the positions of many transitions in the decay scheme.

Table 10.7 lists the gamma rays reported in these studies. Some of the weaker gamma rays, concerning which there are some uncertainties, have not been entered in the table. The gamma ray energy measurements were made with high precision (1 part in 10,000 or better). This precision is helpful in the construction of a decay scheme when the sum of the energies of two or more transitions equals precisely the measured energy of another single gamma ray.

SCHMORAK AND CO-WORKERS[93] combined information from gamma-ray sums, from total disintegration energy determinations, from gamma ray multipolarity determinations, from a limited number of electron-electron and electron-photon coincidence measurements, and from transition intensities to construct a detailed decay scheme. This scheme has 18 levels below 2.6 MeV and accounts for the majority of the gamma rays in Table 10.7.

More recent experimental results forced a revision of this tentative decay scheme in two important respects. The first of these concerns the location of the first excited state, which SCHMORAK ET AL.[93] had placed at 282 keV. FRITSCH AND HOLLANDER[92] pointed out that ASARO AND PERLMAN[98] had studied the alpha decay of Po^{209} to its daughter Pb^{205} and had shown that the first excited state of Pb^{205} lies at 260 ± 2 keV rather than 282 keV. This is also supported by the work of DAGGETT AND GROVE[99] on the alpha decay of Po^{209} and the work of HARVEY[100] on the triton groups emitted in the (d, t) reaction on lead. STOCKENDAL[96] restudied this problem and found a prominent 262.8 keV gamma ray in the decay of Bi^{205}. This gamma ray had previously been overlooked in sources which had not been subjected to electromagnetic separation from Bi^{206}, because an identical transition occurs in the decay of Bi^{206}.

The presence of the 262.8 keV level was confirmed by the electron-electron and electron-gamma coincidence studies of HERRLANDER,[97] but his studies revealed an additional complexity in the decay of this level. He found that in addition to the 262.8 keV transition to ground there exists a 260.5 keV $M1$ transition to a 2.3 keV level. This 2.3 keV level is believed to be a $p_{1/2}$ state

[96] R. Stockendal, *Arkiv Fysik* **17**, 553 (1960) and *Phys. Rev.* **118**, 1074 (1960).

[97] C. J. Herrlander, *Arkiv Fysik* **20**, 71 (1961).

[98] F. Asaro and I. Perlman as quoted in Ref. 78.

[99] E. H. Daggett and G. R. Grove, *Phys. Rev.* **99**, 1 (1955).

[100] J. A. Harvey, *Can. J. Phys.* **31**, 278 (1953).

TABLE 10.7. Transitions observed in Bi²⁰⁵ decay.

E_γ (keV)		I (K-line)			Multipolarity assignment	
FRITSCH AND HOLLANDER[92]	SCHMORAK et al.[93]	FRITSCH AND HOLLANDER[92]	SCHMORAK et al.[93]	STOCKENDAL AND HULTBERG[94]	SCHMORAK et al.[93]	STOCKENDAL AND HULTBERG[94]
	26.22*		3600* (LM)		E1*	
	90.04*		28(L)*			
112.2	115.2	11.5 (L)	81*		M1*	—
131.2	—					
149.0	—					
192.6	185*		40*		M1, E2*	—
	235.9		8			
260.5	260.5	83	110	170	M2	M1
	262.8*		46*		M1*	
282.4	282.3	33	41	50	M1	(M1)
284.0	284.2	116	160	190	M1	M1
	313.1*		5*		M1, E1*	E1 and E2 excluded
349.3	349.4	29	28	30	M1	
	310.5*		4.3*		E3	
383.3	383.2		6			
493.5	493.6	11	11			E1 and E2 excluded
511.7	511.7	16	22		M1	M1
526.0	—					
531.1	—					
550.3	550.0		6.3	6.3		E1
570.7	571.0	77	74	89	M1	M1

573.7	—	—	—	24	M1	E2
579.7	580.0	26	24	—		E2
626.2	626.5	—	6.7	—		
—	688.9	—	1	—		
703.3	703.3	100.0	100.0	100.0	E2	E2
744.6	745.0	—	2.1	—		
758.6	758.3	—	3.1	—		
—	761.0	—	2.0	—		
910.7	910.8	—	9.8	8.4	E2	E2
987.5	987.8	21	27.5	27	E2 (E1)	E2
—	1002.7	—	2.1	—	—	
1014.0	1014.2	—	4.9	—	M4*	E1 excluded
1043.5	1043.7	22	32.5	28	M1	M1
1073.3	—	—	—	—		
1190.1	1190.3	—	7.6	—	M4, M3 or E2	—
~1346	1337	—	0.3	—		
—	1351.5	—	1.1	—		
—	1502.5	—	0.4	—		
—	1552.0	—	0.8	—		
~1617	1614.6	—	3.1	—	E2 (+M1)	M1
—	1766.4	—	43.6	34	(E1)	(M1)
—	1777.4	—	5.2	4.0	E1	E1
—	1863.3	—	2.0	1.3	(E1)	E1
—	1906.5	—	0.6	0.40		
—	~2600	—	<0.5	—		

* This result reported by R. Stockendal.[96]

predicted by theory. HERRLANDER[97] confirmed his proposal by examining the electron spectrum of a Po^{209} source and identifying the K-electrons of the 260.5 and 262.8 keV transitions in the same relative abundance as in the Bi^{205} samples.

The second important way in which earlier conceptions of the decay scheme of Bi^{205} have had to be revised concerns the $M4$ "isomer problem" in Pb^{205}. It was known for some years that an $M4$ isomer occurs in all the odd-mass isotopes of lead from Pb^{197} through Pb^{207} with the single exception of Pb^{205} (see, for example, Fig. 10.9 introduced earlier in this chapter). From the systematic behavior of these isomers one might expect an energy of ~980 keV and a half-life of 1.5 seconds for an $i_{13/2} \rightarrow f_{5/2}$ odd-neutron transition in Pb^{205}. However, STOCKENDAL, ET AL.[101] and FRITSCH AND HOLLANDER[92] were unable to find this expected activity, nor could BENDEL, TOMS, AND TOBIN[102] produce it by (γ, n) reactions on lead. These failures led to the conclusion that a state with spin intermediate between 13/2 and 5/2 slips in below the $i_{13/2}$ level and destroys the possibility of a prominent $M4$ de-excitation of this level.

However, the possibility of an isomeric transition of a lower multi-polarity might still exist. The first evidence for this was supplied by VEGORS AND HEATH[103] who performed experiments on the 987 keV gamma ray by the delayed coincidence technique and found an apparent half-life of 4.7 ± 1.5 milliseconds for its decay. It was not possible to explain this long half-life by assigning a high multipolarity to the 987 keV transition because the K-conversion coefficient[94,103] clearly indicates it is $E2$ in character. The alternate possibility was that some highly converted transition of low energy was feeding the 988 keV level and that the previously unobserved parent level was long-lived. This alternative was explored and fully confirmed by STOCKENDAL[96] whose results are summarized in Fig. 10.18(a). The key finding was the highly converted 26.22 keV transition with $M2$ character. This finding was also made independently by ALBURGER[104]. This fixes the location of the $13/2+$ level at 1013.8 keV. STOCKENDAL[96] also found evidence for a 310.5 keV $E3$ transition and a 1014.0 keV transition originating at this $13/2+$ level. Thus the $M4$ isomer problem of Pb^{205} is solved. The expected 1.5 second half-life is not observed because of the competition of the possible decay by $M2$ and $E3$ transitions. The half-life of the $13/2+$ state has been remeasured by BERGSTRÖM ET AL.[105] and found to be 4.0 ± 0.2

[101] R. Stockendal, J. A. McDonell, M. Schmorak, and I. Bergström, *Arkiv Fysik* **11**, 165 (1956).

[102] W. L. Bendel, M. E. Toms, and R. A. Tobin, *Phys. Rev.* **99**, 672A (1955).

[103] S. H. Vegors and R. L. Heath, *Phys. Rev.* **118**, 547 (1960).

[104] D. Alburger, *Phys. Rev. Letters* **4**, 331 (1960) and *Phys. Rev.* **118**, 1076 (1960).

[105] Bergström, Bonacalya, Jech, Perey, and Thieberger, *Nucl. Inst. and Meth.* **8**, 151 (1960).

milliseconds. GLAGOLEV, MOROZOV, AND YAMPOLSKII[106] contributed to the study of the isomer by producing and identifying it in the reactions $Tl^{205}(p, n)Pb^{205m}$ and $Pb^{206}(n, 2n)Pb^{205m}$.

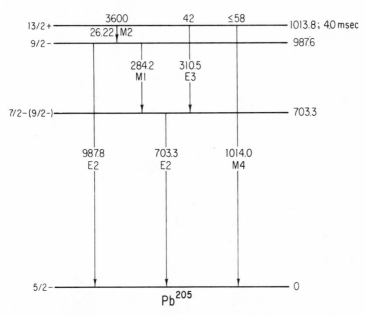

FIG. **10.18(a)**. Decay of the 4-millisecond $i_{13/2}$ state in Pb^{205} as drawn by STOCKENDAL.[96] For clarity the separation between the 1013.8 and 987.6 keV levels is exaggerated. Relative transition intensities are given at the head of the isomeric transitions.

We present in Fig. 10.18(b) the decay scheme of Bi^{205} as drawn in 1961 by HERRLANDER.[97] It is very similar to that published in 1960 by STOCKENDAL.[96] Not all of the known transitions are placed in this scheme and it is certain that a reinvestigation* of the conversion electron spectrum of a very pure source of Bi^{205} with a high resolution spectrometer will reveal additional complexity in the level scheme of Pb^{205}.

The reasonable assignments 5/2− and 9/2− are given to the ground states of Pb^{205} and Bi^{205}, respectively. The most likely shell model configuration for Pb^{205} is $[(p_{1/2}^{-2} f_{5/2}^{-1})J = 5/2]$ and for Bi^{205} is $[(p_{1/2}^{-2} f_{5/2}^{-2})J = 0$ coupled to $g_{9/2}^{-1}$ proton]. Direct confirmation of the 9/2

---

[106] V. L. Glagolev, A. M. Morozov, and P. A. Yampolskii, *Sov. Phys. JETP* **12**, 1131 (1961).

* Such a reinvestigation was made by Vegors, Heath, and Proctor in a very comprehensive study published after this review was completed. See *Nucl. Phys.* **48**, 230 (1963).

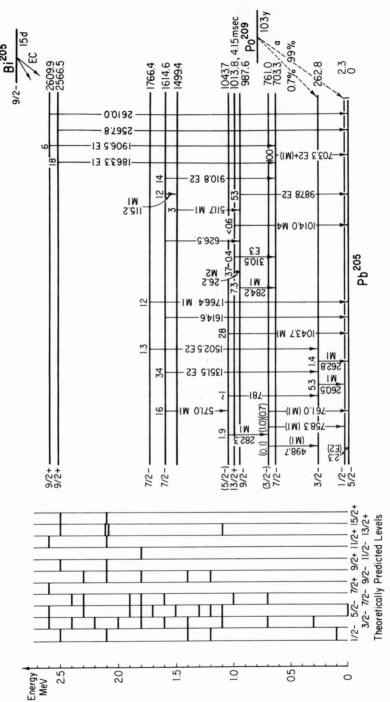

FIG. 10.18(b). Decay scheme of Bi[205] as drawn by HERRLANDER.[97] Transition intensities given above the origin of the transition arrows are calculated from conversion line intensities and theoretical conversion coefficients. Multipolarities, intensities, and level assignments given in parentheses are considered to be uncertain. Levels theoretically predicted by PRYCE are shown to the left. Not all the known gamma transitions are placed in this scheme.

spin of Bi^{205} comes from the atomic beam experiments of JOHANSSON AND LINDGREN.[70]

We turn now to a consideration of the calculation of the level system of Pb^{205} from theory. The Pb^{205} nucleus is an interesting test case for the application of a multiparticle shell model. Lead-205 is three neutrons removed from a closed shell. The energies of the low-lying levels should consist of two parts: (1) the sum of the energies of the neutron hole states in the effective field of the nucleus as a whole; to a first approximation the identity of these states and the unperturbed energy of these states can be evaluated empirically from the levels of the nucleus Pb^{207}. And (2) the sum of the pairwise interactions of the hole states; precisely these same pairwise interactions occur in the calculations of the level scheme of Pb^{206} and these can be taken over in a calculation of the Pb^{205} level system.

Such a calculation has been made by PRYCE[107] and a similar but more sophisticated calculation has been carried through by TRUE[108] and by BUKAT.[109] We shall outline only the calculations of TRUE.[108] These represent an extension of the work of TRUE AND FORD[65] on Pb^{206} and a similar choice of parameters was made in the two studies. The same choice of a singlet-even potential with a Gaussian shape for the radial dependence was made. Harmonic oscillator wave functions were used to represent the neutron hole states. This calculation led to a set of many levels lying below 3 MeV with half-integer spins ranging from 1/2 through 13/2. TRUE[108] compared his predictions with some 10 experimental levels of Pb^{205} selected for their definite energy, spin and parity assignments. He concluded that the agreement between theory and experiment was not good.

TRUE[108] then repeated his calculations with a singlet-even potential three quarters as strong and with, in addition, a weak coupling of the particle motion to the quadrupole collective motion of the core. This prescription was taken over from the earlier work of TRUE AND FORD[65] who had found that not only did this give a better prediction of the energy levels of Pb^{206} but also explained the strong $E2$ transition rates in Pb^{206} and Pb^{207} (see mention of this point in Section 10.2.4). The results of this revised calculation are presented numerically in Table 10.8 and graphically in Fig. 10.19. This figure also shows several experimental levels and the observed gamma transitions between them. The agreement of theory and experiment is rather good. It is particularly striking that the "isomer problem" in Pb^{205} is completely explained by the calculations and that this explanation is in agreement with the experimental results of STOCKENDAL[96] and of ALBURGER.[104] It is now clear that a 3-particle state of spin 7/2 and one of spin 9/2 have slipped

[107] M. H. L. Pryce, *Nucl. Phys.* **2**, 226 (1956).

[108] W. W. True, *Nucl. Phys.* **25**, 155 (1961).

[109] G. M. Bukat, *Bull. Acad. Sci. USSR, Phys. Ser.* **26**, 225 (1962), Columbia Technical Translations.

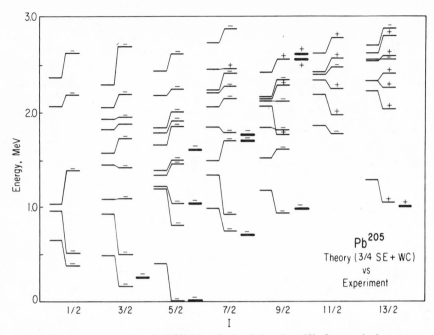

FIG. **10.19** Energy levels of Pb^{205} as calculated by TRUE[108] for a singlet-even plus weak coupling force.   For each spin the first column gives the energy levels in lowest order.   The second column gives the energy levels and parities obtained from diagonalization of the energy matrix.   The third column gives selected experimental levels.

below the $i_{13/2}$ state and destroyed the possibility of an isomeric form of Pb^{205} with a half-life of ~ 1.5 seconds.   PRYCE'S[107] calculations also led to this explanation of the "missing" isomer.   TRUE'S calculation shows the first spin 1/2 level lying above the first spin 3/2 state which does not agree well with HERRLANDER'S[97] finding that $p_{1/2}$ state lies at 2.3 keV.   In BUKAT'S[109] calculation the $p_{1/2}$ state lies below but close to the 3/2− state and hence also disagrees with the tentative placement of an experimental 1/2− level at 2.3 keV.

Figure 10.19 shows that the low-energy spectrum of Pb^{205} is much more complex than would be deduced from a study of the decay of radioactive isotopes.   The levels seen in such decay include only those reached by the primary decay events and those involved in the resulting gamma-ray cascades. Other types of experiments are needed to reveal the other states.   One alternate way to obtain information on these states is a study of triton spectra in the reaction.

$$Pb^{206}(d, t)Pb^{205}$$

This has been done by HARVEY[100] and by MUKHERJEE AND COHEN.[110]   The

110 P. Mukherjee and B. L. Cohen, *Phys. Rev.* **127**, 1284 (1962).

latter authors find levels at 0.26, 0.41, 0.58, 0.79, 1.00, 1.06, 1.60, 1.76, and 2.72 MeV. These Pb^{205} levels are those in which only one neutron is changed from the ground state configuration. Four of these levels, namely, those at 0.41, 0.58, 0.79, and 2.72 MeV do not appear in the decay scheme of Bi^{205}, but the first three can reasonably be associated with TRUE's predicted levels.

We can predict that further levels of excitation will appear in Pb^{205} above 2.5 MeV resulting from (1) particle (hole) states not considered in the calculations of lower levels, from (2) "core-excited states" in which a neutron or proton is promoted from the even-even core into a particle state beyond the closed-shell configuration, and from (3) collective excitation.

TABLE **10.8.** Energy eigenvalues in MeV for a singlet-even force with weak coupling to the collective motion. The parity of the level is given directly after the eigenvalue. From W. W. True, *Nuclear Physics* **25**, 155 (1961).

			Spin of the level			
1/2	3/2	5/2	7/2	9/2	11/2	13/2
2.615−	2.693−	2.616−	2.882−	2.557+	2.775+	2.880+
2.177−	2.193−	2.251−	2.458+	2.340−	2.574+	2.800+
1.390−	1.952−	2.011−	2.417−	2.292+	2.476−	2.583+
0.508−	1.876−	1.916−	2.284−	2.121−	2.249+	2.556−
0.379−	1.726−	1.860−	2.147−	1.808+	1.972+	2.413+
	1.419−	1.497−	1.789+	1.769+	1.778−	2.262+
	1.089−	1.458−	1.706−	1.612−		2.040+
	0.503−	1.043−	0.928 −	0.938−		1.051+
	0.158−	0.812−	0.746 −			
		0 −				

In spite of the excellent data on the decay of Bi^{205} now available, it is clear that additional experimental data are necessary to fix the level scheme of Pb^{205} with more certainty.* The interaction of theory and experiment will undoubtedly prove very helpful in these later investigations.

Another calculation of the level scheme of Pb^{205} was carried through by KISSLINGER AND SORENSEN[111] by a method of estimation developed by BELYAEV[112] which was derived from the theory of superconductivity introduced by BARDEEN, COOPER AND SCHRIEFFER.[113] For the case of $Pb,^{205}$ KISSLINGER AND SORENSEN estimated the residual interparticle interactions

[111] L. S. Kisslinger and R. A. Sorensen, *Det. Kongel. Danske. Videnskab. Selskab. Matt.-fys. Medd.* **32**, No. 9, 1960; see also R. W. Richardson and N. Sherman, *Nucl. Phys.* **52**, 253 (1964).

[112] S. T. Belyaev, *Kgl. Danske. Videnskab. Selskab. Matt.-fys. Medd.* **31**, No. 11 (1950).

[113] J. Bardeen, L. N. Cooper, and J. R. Schrieffer, *Phys. Rev.* **108**, 1175 (1957).

* See work of S. H. Vegors, R. L. Heath, and D. G. Proctor, *Nucl. Phys.* **48**, 230 (1963).

with a "pairing force" and a long-range force idealized as a P_2 (cos θ) force. The results of KISSLINGER AND SORENSEN agree with the results of TRUE[108] for a singlet-even plus weak coupling potential.   This indicates that a pairing force is a good approximation to the effective force between particles.   Since this is true, and since calculations by the pairing force approach are easier to do for a many-particle system this approach should come into wide use for calculating various nuclear properties for many-particle systems.   The KISSLINGER AND SORENSEN calculations are discussed more fully in Section 10.2.13.

10.2.7 *The Isomers of Pb^{204} and the Level Scheme of Pb^{204}*

The ground state of Pb^{204} is a beta stable isotope occurring in natural lead.   It is not the end-product of any of the natural radioactive families nor is it the end-product of any extinct natural radioactivity.   Hence, the Pb^{204} in any natural lead sample is primeval in origin and the 204 content can be used as a guide to the primeval lead content of any natural lead sample, as discussed in Section 6.6 of Chapter 6.   A recent study of RIEZLER AND KAUW[114] indicates that Pb^{204} may have a measurable half-life for alpha decay.   These workers impregnated nuclear emulsions with enriched Pb^{204} and observed alpha tracks whose range corresponded to an energy of 2.6 MeV and whose intensity corresponded to a half-life of 1.4×10^{17} years.

Information on the excited levels of Pb^{204} comes from the decay of the isomer Pb^{204m} and from the complex decay of Bi^{204}.   It is logical to discuss first the decay scheme of Pb^{204m} since it is much simpler and much more firmly established and provides a solid framework upon which any decay scheme of Bi^{204} must be based.

The Isomer Pb^{204m}.   The 67.5 minute lead isomer Pb^{204m} has been made by the following reactions:

$$Tl^{203}(d, n)Pb^{204m}$$
$$Tl^{205}(d, 3n)Pb^{204m}$$
$$Pb^{204}(n, n')Pb^{204m}$$
$$Pb^{204}(d, 2n)Bi^{204} \xrightarrow{EC} Pb^{204m}$$

References to early work on this activity are given in a previous compilation.[115]   The early work limited the mass assignment to Pb^{204} or Pb^{205} and favored Pb^{204}.   The mass assignment has been made certain by the mass-separator experiments of THULIN.[116]

---

[114] W. Riezler and G. Kauw, *Z. f. Naturforsch* **13a**, 904 (1958).

[115] Several references to early work given by J. M. Hollander, I. Perlman, and G. T. Seaborg, *Revs. Mod. Phys.* **25**, 469 (1953).

[116] S. Thulin as reported in *Physica* **20**, 521 (1954).

This mass assignment was of considerable interest because Pb^{204m} was the first even-even nucleus found to have a long-lived metastable state. The study of its radiations was a matter of considerable interest for the same reason. Several investigators reported the presence of two gamma rays. SUNYAR AND CO-WORKERS[117] measured conversion electrons of a 905 keV and a 374 keV gamma ray. Gamma-gamma and electron-electron delayed coincidence experiments indicated that the 374 keV transition had a half-life of 3×10^{-7} seconds. GOLDHABER AND SUNYAR[118] interpreted these data to mean that a 905 keV $E5$ transition was followed by a 375 keV $E2$ transition to the ground state. MAEDER AND CO-WORKERS[119] reinvestigated the conversion spectrum and confirmed the multipolarity assignments.

A number of objections which were raised to this decay sequence were resolved when the further gamma-gamma coincidence experiments of KROHN AND RABOY[120,121] resulted in the discovery of an additional gamma ray 15 keV lower in energy than the 905 keV gamma ray. This third gamma ray, which is an electric quadrupole transition, had previously been overlooked because of its low conversion coefficient and the closeness in energy of the 905 and 890 keV radiations. The three gamma rays of Pb^{204m} are in cascade. BERGKVIST AND CO-WORKERS[122] measured the conversion electrons of the third gamma ray and reported an energy of 899.3 keV.

The detailed angular correlation experiments of KROHN AND RABOY[121,123] have confirmed the 9–4–2–0 spin sequence presented in Fig. 10.20 although it was necessary to assume some multipole mixing in the gamma transitions to account precisely for the results. The 912 keV $E5$ gamma was estimated to have 1 per cent $M6$ admixture and the 375 keV gamma was estimated to have 1/2 per cent admixture of $M3$. HERRLANDER, STOCKENDAL, MCDONELL, AND BERGSTRÖM[124] revised this figure downward. KROHN AND RABOY[121] also report that the gyromagnetic ratio of the 4+ level is $+0.054 \pm .005$ nuclear units and the magnetic moment $\mu = 0.22 \pm 0.02$ nuclear magnetons.

FRITSCH[125] found evidence that the decay scheme of Pb^{204m} is somewhat

[117] A. W. Sunyar, D. Alburger, G. Friedlander, M. Goldhaber, and G. Scharff-Goldhaber, *Phys. Rev.* **79**, 181 (1950).

[118] M. Goldhaber and A. W. Sunyar, *Phys. Rev.* **83**, 906 (1951).

[119] D. Maeder, A. H. Wapstra, G. J. Nijgh, and L. Th. M. Ornstein, *Physica* **20**, 521 (1954).

[120] V. E. Krohn and S. Raboy, *Phys. Rev.* **95**, 1354, 608A (1954).

[121] V. E. Krohn and S. Raboy, *Phys. Rev.* **97**, 1017 (1955).

[122] Bergkvist, Bergström, Herrlander, Hultberg, Slätis, Sokolowski, Wapstra, and Wiedling, *Phil. Mag.* **46**, 65 (1955).

[123] J. R. Huizenga, V. E. Krohn, and S. Raboy, *Phys. Rev.* **102**, 1063 (1956).

[124] C. J. Herrlander, R. Stockendal, J. A. McDonell, and I. Bergström, *Nucl. Phys.* **1**, 643 (1956).

[125] A. R. Fritsch, *Univ. Calif. Rad. Lab. Report, UCRL-3452*, June 1956.

more complex.   He separated Pb^{204m} from Bi^{204} and examined the electron spectrum in a high resolution permanent magnet spectrograph.   In addition to the prominent conversion electrons from the 912, 374, and 899 keV transitions discussed above, he observed a weak but definite line corresponding to a 289.5 keV gamma ray.   In a further examination of the electron

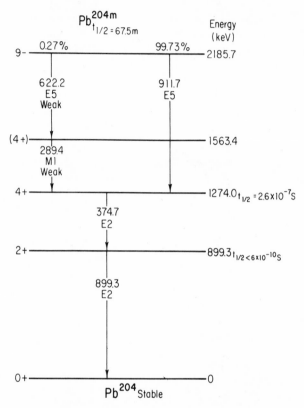

FIG. **10.20.** Decay scheme of Pb^{204m} as drawn by HERRLANDER AND CO-WORKERS[124] and by FRITSCH.[125]

spectrum of Bi^{204}, FRITSCH[125] observed electrons in weak intensity from a 621.7 keV transition with the K/L and $L_1/L_2/L_3$ ratios expected for an $E5$ transition.   He concluded that an additional $4+$ level must be located below the long-lived $9-$ level of Pb^{204}, as shown in Fig. 10.20, and that the de-excitation of the $9-$ levels proceeds through two competing $E5$ transitions of which the well known 912 keV transition is much the stronger.   The weakness of this postulated $621.7 - 289.5$ keV cascade (which sums to 911.2 keV) makes it difficult to prove this with certainty.   FRITSCH states that the $9-$ level may de-excite by still other gamma ray cascades in even lower intensity. HERRLANDER, STOCKENDAL, McDONELL, AND BERGSTRÖM[124] independently observed this competing 622 keV $E5 - 289.4$ keV $M1$ cascade and confirmed all the above mentioned features of the decay scheme. The decay scheme of Pb^{204m} is given in Fig. 10.20.

The Electron Capture Decay of Bi^{204}. It is possible to prepare intense samples of Bi^{204} by cyclotron bombardments of lead or thallium targets. In either case it is advantageous to use targets which have been enriched in the suitable isotope by electromagnetic separation.

$$Pb^{204}(p, n)Bi^{204}$$
$$Pb^{204}(d, 2n)Bi^{204}$$
$$Tl^{203}(\alpha, 3n)Bi^{204}$$

Since neither Pb^{204} nor Tl^{203} is ordinarily available in high isotopic purity, some simultaneous production of other bismuth activities is inevitable. The 6-day Bi^{206} is a prominent contaminant. Traces of 15-day Bi^{205} and 27-year Bi^{207} are also made. The isotope Bi^{203} is particularly troublesome because it has a half-life very close to that of Bi^{204}, but it is possible to eliminate it almost entirely by choosing a cyclotron beam energy just below the threshold for its production. Electromagnetic separation of Bi^{204} after its preparation may also be used for its purification.[128]

Bismuth-204 decays entirely by orbital electron capture with a half-life of 11.6 ± 0.2 hours.[126] (STOCKENDAL reports the value 11.22 ± 0.10 hours.) Positron emission is less than 0.6 per cent.[125] Several authors have contributed to the study of Bi^{204}, but the most detailed study appears to be an unpublished study by FRITSCH[125] summarized by FRITSCH AND HOLLANDER.[127] Because of the extraordinary complexity of the radiations of Bi^{204} only instruments of high resolution give any significant data. FRITSCH AND HOLLANDER depended almost entirely on permanent magnet spectrographs with a resolution of 0.1 per cent. They reported over 150 conversion electrons from which they made assignments of the 67 gamma transitions listed in Table 10.9. Very similar data has been published by STOCKENDAL AND CO-WORKERS.[128, 129] FRITSCH attempted to construct a decay scheme using these data and additional data obtained from the gamma ray spectrum studied in scintillation spectrometers, from gamma-gamma and electron-electron coincidence measurements, and from a consideration of a numerical analysis of sums and differences of the gamma transition energies. We shall not review these data since he concluded it was impossible to construct a reasonably complete decay scheme. In spite of the high precision of

[126] G. K. Wertheim and R. V. Pound, *Phys. Rev.* **102**, 185 (1956).

[127] A. R. Fritsch and J. M. Hollander, *J. Inorg. Nucl. Chem.* **6**, 165 (1958).

[128] R. Stockendal, T. Novakov, B. Johansson, and M. Schmorak, *Arkiv Fysik* **14**, 65 (1958).

[129] R. Stockendal, *Arkiv Fysik* **17**, 579 (1960).

the energy determinations there are several thousand sums obtained from the 67 transitions and many accidental coincidences of the sums of two transitions with other sums of two transitions must inevitably occur.   A few conclusions may be reached.   (1) The first and second excited states lie high and correspond to the 2+ and 4+ levels at 899.2 keV and 1274.5 keV, respectively, seen prominently in the decay of Pb^{204m}.   (2) All gamma cascades appear to

TABLE **10.9.** Gamma transitions of Bi^{204} (FRITSCH AND HOLLANDER).

E_γ	Conversion lines observed	K-line intensity*	E_γ	Conversion lines observed	K-line intensity*
78.62	$L_{II}L_{III}M_IM_{II}M_{III}N_{III}$	3080 (L_{II})	2nd confidence group		
80.21	$L_IL_{II}M_IN_I$	2090 (L_I)	109.1	$L_IL_{II}M_{II}$	VW (L_I)
100.4	$L_IL_{II}M_I$	270 (L_I)	164.9	$K\,L_I$	W
119.8	$K\,L_I$	W	184.9	L_IL_{II}	90 (L_I)
140.9	$K\,L_IM_I$	1230	213.5	$K\,L_{II}$	170
144.5	$K\,L_IM_IN_I$	M	252.4	$K\,L_I$	80
170.0	$K\,L_IM_I$	1820	440.2	$K\,L_I$	50
212.7	$K\,L_I$	90	3rd confidence group		
216.2	$K\,L_IM_I$	1630	105.5	L_I	VVW
219.5	$K\,L_{II}L_{III}M_{II}M_{III}N_{II}$	500	168.8	K	340
222.5	$K\,L_IM_IN_I$	940	209.1	K	W
227.1	$K\,L_I$	80	332.1	K	110
240.7	$K\,L_IM_I$	290	340.6	K	70
249.1	$K\,L_IM_IN_I$	1820	376.8	K	210
289.5	$K\,L_I$	1440	468.3	K	120
291.0	$K\,L_I$	570	542.2	K	40
330.9	$K\,L_I$	170	545.7	K	30
375.0	$K\,L_IL_{II}L_{III}M_IN_I$	3970	548.8	K	W
405.5	$K\,L_I$	130	585.4	K	W
412.4	$K\,L_I$	120	615.2	K	W
421.8	$K\,L_I$	120	621.7	K	VW
438.8	$K\,L_I$	230	646.4	K	VVW
501.8	$K\,L_I$	150	684.3	K	VVW
522.2	$K\,L_{II}L_{III}M_{II}$	120	718.5	K	50
532.6	$K\,L_I$	260	745.2	K	VW
661.5	$K\,L_I$	210	748.5	K	110
663.4	$K\,L_IL_{II}$	80	765.4	K	VW
671.0	$K\,L_IL_{III}M_IN_I$	810	832.3	K	40
710.4	$K\,L_I$	120	834.3	K	50
725.3	$K\,L_I$	50	844.1	K	100
791.9	$K\,L_I$	90	933.6	K	VW
899.2	$K\,L_IL_{III}N_I$	1000	1056.7	K	30
911.5	$K\,L_{II}L_{III}M_{II}N_{II}$	1330	1139.8	K	VVW
918.4	$K\,L_IM_I$	110	1203.9	K	VW
			1211.5	K	VW

* The letter code has the following meaning: W—weak; VW—very weak; VVW—very, very weak.

funnel through the 2+ level with little or no decay occurring directly to ground from other levels.   (3) Roughly 10 per cent of the decay of Bi^{204} proceeds through the 9− isomeric state.   (4) A large number of levels lie above 2 MeV.

STOCKENDAL AND CO-WORKERS[128] supplemented their measurements of conversion line energies and intensities with electron-gamma and gamma-gamma coincidence data which provided some but not substantial assistance in the construction of a decay scheme.   This decay scheme is shown in Fig. 10.22.   However, these authors also agree that only those levels of Pb^{204} observed in the decay of the 67.5 minute 9− isomeric state are known with certainty.

Shell Model Calculations.   TRUE[130] made shell model calculations of the expected levels of Pb^{204} using the theory of PRYCE[131, 132] which we outlined above in the discussion of Pb^{206}.   (Section 10.2.4.)   In the case of Pb^{204} the problem is to calculate levels for a nucleus with four neutron holes with configurations based on the various possible combinations of single neutron orbitals.   It is also assumed that the individual neutron holes in Pb^{204} will to a first approximation have the same energy as the single neutron (hole) orbitals have in Pb^{207}, as discussed previously in Section 10.2.3.   The levels which are expected in Pb^{204} by various combinations of 4 of these Pb^{207} levels are shown in Table 10.10.   The zero-order energy of each level is shifted by the short range interaction of particles (holes) on each other, and the degeneracy of each level is also removed by this interaction.   TRUE[130] estimated these shifts using the semi-empirical two particle interaction parameters given previously by ALBURGER AND PRYCE.[132]   When levels of

TABLE **10.10.** Zero-order energy levels of Pb^{204}.

Configuration	Zero-order energy (MeV)	Possible I's	Parity
$p_{1/2}^2 f_{5/2}^2$	1.14	0,2,4	+
$p_{1/2}^2 p_{3/2} f_{5/2}$	1.44	1,2,3,4	+
$f_{5/2}^3 p_{1/2}$	1.71	1,2,3,4,5	+
$p_{1/2}^2 p_{3/2}^2$	1.74	0,2	+
$f_{5/2}^2 p_{1/2} p_{3/2}$	2.01	0,1,2,3,4,5,6	+
$p_{1/2}^2 f_{5/2} i_{13/2}$	2.20	4,5,6,7,8,9	−
$f_{5/2}^4$	2.28	0,2,4	+
$(p_{3/2}^2, J_1 = 2)(p_{1/2}f_{5/2}J_2 = 3)$	2.31	5[a]	+
$p_{1/2}^2 p_{3/2} i_{13/2}$	2.50	5,6,7,8	−
$(f_{5/2}^3, J_1 = 9/2) p_{3/2}$	2.58	5[a],6[a]	+

[a] Only the indicated spin values were investigated by TRUE.

[130] W. W. True, *Phys. Rev.* **101**, 1342 (1956).
[131] M. H. L. Pryce, *Proc. Phys. Soc.* (London) **A65**, 773 (1952).
[132] D. E. Alburger and M. H. L. Pryce, *Phys. Rev.* **95**, 1482 (1954).

the same spin lie close together it is necessary to consider configuration interaction effects but this was not considered in this preliminary calculation. The result of TRUE's work was a table showing 49 distinct levels below 2.5 MeV of excitation.   These levels are shown in Fig. 10.21 together with an

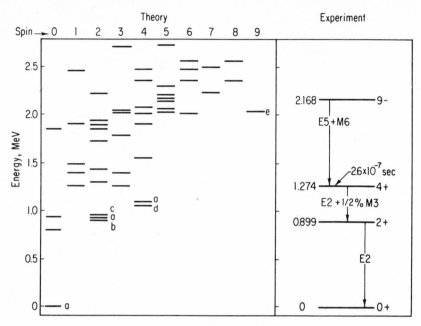

FIG. **10.21.** Energy levels of Pb^{204} calculated by TRUE[130] according to the model of PRYCE.[131]

(incomplete) decay scheme of Pb^{204m}.   The principal success of the calculation is the prediction of a 9— isomeric state of 2.05 MeV energy compared with the observed 9— isomeric state at 2.19 MeV.   From this state the predicted dominant gamma ray cascade 9— to 4+ to 2+ to 0+ agrees with experiment.   The complexity of the level scheme below 2.5 MeV also accounts qualitatively for the complexity (67 known gamma transitions) observed in the decay of Bi^{204}.   A quantitative assignment of experimental and theoretical levels and transitions cannot be made without more refined treatment of the theory and more extensive experimental work on the decay scheme.

BLOMQVIST[133] has recalculated TRUE's energy values using later interaction parameters published by PRYCE;[134] the revised level scheme is shown in Fig. 10.22(a) and compared with the experimental results of STOCKENDAL

[133] J. Blomqvist, unpublished results cited by STOCKENDAL in Ref. 128.

[134] M. H. L. Pryce, *Nucl. Phys.* **2**, 226 (1956/7).

AND CO-WORKERS.[128]   TRUE AND FORD[135] report that they have carried out
a more exact calculation of the energy shifts due to the interaction of the hole
states.

KISSLINGER AND SORENSEN[111] have carried through a calculation of the
levels of Pb^{204} using a nuclear model patterned after the BARDEEN,
SCHRIEFFER, AND COOPER[113] theory of superconductivity.   In the nuclear
model used by KISSLINGER AND SORENSEN the residual interaction between the
neutrons is idealized as a "pairing force" plus a long range force represented
by a quadrupole force.   Experimental data on the levels in lead isotopes

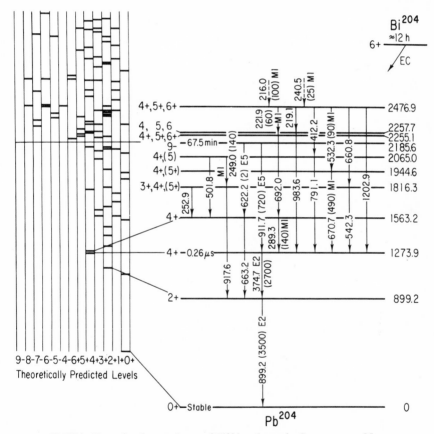

FIG. **10.22(a)**. Tentative decay scheme of Bi^{204} as drawn by STOCKENDAL, NOVAKOV,
JOHANSSON, AND SCHMORAK.[128]   In cases where multipolarity information is available
the total relative transition intensity is given below the energy value. BLOMQVIST's
theoretical values based on a recalculation of TRUE's energy values are shown to
the left of the figure.

[135] W. W. True and K. W. Ford, *Phys. Rev.* **109**, 1675 (1957).

close to the Pb²⁰⁸ are used to set parameter choices in the calculation.   The
results of this calculation are presented graphically in Fig. 10.22(b).   The few

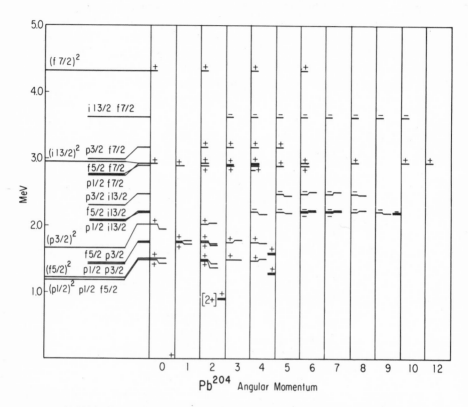

FIG. **10.22(b)**. Energy levels of Pb²⁰⁴ as calculated by KISSLINGER AND SORENSEN.[111]
Residual interactions of the four neutron (hole) states idealized as a pairing force
plus long-range quadrupole force.   Labeled unperturbed states are given to the left
of the diagram.   States of different spin which appear when the residual interactions
are turned on are shown in the main part of the diagram.   For each spin the horizontal line to the left gives the energy of the state.   The second horizontal line shows
the effect of the inclusion of a $P_{22}^{(2)}$ force.   A few experimental levels are given to
the right in a few of the spin columns.   The lowest 2+ level, marked [2+] is a
collective level.

levels of Pb²⁰⁴ which are known unambiguously from experiment are also
shown in the figure and in all cases but one these can be reasonably well
associated with theoretical levels.   The exception is the experimental 2+
level at 899 keV which KISSLINGER AND SORENSEN conclude must be a state of
collective rather than particle excitation.

10.2.8 *The Isomers of Pb^{203} and the Level System of Pb^{203}*

Decay of 52 *hour* Pb^{203}. The isotope Pb^{203} exists in two isomeric forms. The ground state decays by orbital electron capture to Tl^{203} with a half-life of 52 hours. It is prepared by the bombardment of thallium with protons or neutrons or by the bombardment of lead with neutrons or gamma rays:[136]

$$Tl^{203}(d, 2n)Pb^{203}$$

$$Tl^{203}(p, n)\ Pb^{203}$$

$$Pb^{204}(n, 2n)Pb^{203}$$

$$Pb^{204}(\gamma, n)Pb^{203}$$

The decay scheme of Pb^{203} is quite simple as shown in Fig. 10.23 and is well

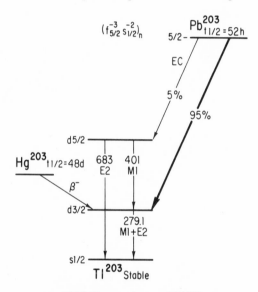

FIG. **10.23** Decay scheme of Pb^{203}.

established by the work of several groups of experimenters. (See Refs. 129, 136–142.) Gamma-gamma angular correlation measurements with the

[136] Early reference to Pb^{203} given in *Revs. Mod. Phys.* **25**, 589 (1953).

[137] A. H. Wapstra, D. Maeder, G. J. Nijgh, and L. Th. M. Ornstein, *Physica* **20**, 169 (1954).

[138] Nijgh, Wapstra, Ornstein, Salomons-Grobben, Huizenga and Almen, *Nucl. Phys.* **9**, 528 (1958).

[139] J. R. Prescott, *Proc. Phys. Soc.* **67A**, 254 (1954).

[140] J. Varma, *Phys. Rev.* **94**, 1688, 795A (1954); *J. Franklin Inst.* **257**, 247 (1954).

[141] Z. Sujkowski, *Arkiv Fysik* **20**, 243 (1961).

[142] L. Persson and Z. Sujkowski, *Arkiv Fysik* **19**, 309 (1960).

279 keV–404 keV pair are consistent with the $5/2 \to 3/2 \to 1/2$ spin sequence. Strong confirmation of the Tl^{203} level system comes from the work of STELSON AND McGOWAN[143] who produced the 279 keV and 683 keV levels in Tl^{203} by Coulombic excitation.

Since Tl^{203} has one proton less than a closed shell of 82 it is likely that the low-lying levels of Tl^{203} correspond to those expected for a single proton hole in this shell.   On this basis the 1/2, 3/2, 5/2 spin sequence leads to the assignment of $s_{1/2}$, $d_{3/2}$, and $d_{5/2}$ single proton orbitals.

The total electron capture decay energy of 52.1 hour Pb^{203} was found by PERSSON AND SUJKOWSKI,[142] to be 817 ± 12 keV from a measurement of the L_1/K capture ratio.

The Isomer, Pb^{203m}.   A 5.6 second isomer of Pb^{203} was first found by HOPKINS,[144] although he assigned it to Pb^{202}.   FISCHER[145] reassigned it to Pb^{203} on the basis of excitation function curves for the reaction:

$$Tl^{203}(p, n)Pb^{203m}$$

$$Tl^{205}(p, 3n)Pb^{203m}$$

She obtained a value of 6.6 seconds for the half-life and a value of 800–900 keV for the single gamma ray.   BERGSTRÖM AND WAPSTRA,[146] STOCKENDAL AND CO-WORKERS,[147] and FRITSCH[149] found that this isomer was populated in the decay of Bi^{203}.   FRITSCH noted that bismuth-203 activity can be placed on an anion exchange column as the strongly-adsorbed chloride complex of bismuth.   The Pb^{203m} daughter activity can then be rapidly eluted from the column with dilute HCl and studied in a scintillation spectrometer.   A single gamma ray with energy 826 ± 5 keV decaying with a half-life of 7.00 ± 0.5 second is observed.   An $M4$ assignment can be given this transition on the basis of half-life, K-conversion coefficient, K/L conversion ratio and L-subshell ratios.[147–148]   ÅSTRÖM[150] reports a half-life value of 6.09 ± 0.10 seconds.

Since the ground state spin of Pb^{203} is probably 5/2 from its decay scheme, it is likely that Pb^{203m} has the spin 13/2.   From a study of the conversion electrons in Bi^{203} decay FRITSCH[149] measured a precise energy of 824.9 keV

[143] P. H. Stelson and F. K. McGowan, *Phys. Rev.* **99**, 112 (1955).

[144] N. J. Hopkins, *Phys. Rev.* **88**, 680 (1952).

[145] V. K. Fischer, *Phys. Rev.* **99**, 764, 672A (1955).

[146] I. Bergström and A. H. Wapstra, *Phil. Mag.* **46**, 61 (1955).

[147] R. Stockendal, J. A. McDonell, M. Schmorak, and I. Bergström, *Arkiv Fysik* **11**, 165 (1956).

[148] L. Persson and R. Stockendal, *Arkiv Fysik* **19**, 303 (1960).

[149] A. R. Fritsch, Ph. D. Thesis, University of California, June 1956; also published as *Univ. Calif. Rad. Lab. Report, UCRL-3452,* June 1956.   See also A. R. Fritsch and J. M. Hollander, *J. Inorg. Nucl. Chem.* **6**, 165 (1958).

[150] B. Åström, *Arkiv Fysik* **12**, 237 (1957).

for the transition energy. STOCKENDAL AND CO-WORKERS[147, 152] report the value 825.2 keV. Figure 10.9, given previously, compares the decay scheme of Pb^{203m} with those of other odd-mass lead isotopes. STOCKENDAL[152] discusses the likely possibility that the 13/2 state is partially de-excited by an unobserved 5 keV $M2$ transition to a 9/2− level at 820.1 keV.

Decay of Bi^{203}. Bismuth-203 is prepared by the bombardment of lead or thallium targets, but, at the beam energies which must be used to produce Bi^{203}, considerable amounts of other bismuth isotopes are produced. The most troublesome impurity is Bi^{204}, which has a half-life identical with Bi^{203}, unless an isotope separation is made. The gamma rays of both Bi^{203} and Bi^{204} are numerous, and those of Bi^{203} can be studied only in the presence of the known radiations of Bi^{204}.

Recent values of the half-life of Bi^{203} are 11.5 ± 1.0 hours,[149] 12.3 ± 0.7 hours[147], and 11.76 ± 0.05 hours.[152] NOVAKOV AND CO-WORKERS[151] measured the conversion electrons of the gamma rays listed in Table 10.11. The radiations were also studied by scintillation spectrometer and by γ,γ and e^-,γ coincidence techniques. FRITSCH[149] reported nearly the same list of gamma transitions deduced from his conversion electron measurements. STOCKENDAL[152] measured the absolute values of the internal conversion coefficients of several transitions by the comparison of conversion lines with photolines excited in an external uranium converter. BERGSTRÖM AND CO-WORKERS[153] report a half-life of 75 ± 3 nanoseconds for the half-life of the 126 keV transition.

Bismuth-203 decays partially by positron emission; two β^+ groups with end-point energies of 1.35 and 0.74 MeV have been reported.[120] The intensity of these positrons is low; there are only 0.014 positrons for every 825.2 keV $M4$ gamma transition.

NOVAKOV, STOCKENDAL, SCHMORAK, AND JOHANSSON[151] constructed the tentative decay scheme shown in Fig. 10.24. The spin of Bi^{203} has been measured[154] by the atomic beam resonance technique and found to be 9/2. This is in agreement with the 9/2 spin found for Bi^{205} and Bi^{207}; presumably in all three cases the 83rd proton is in the $h_{9/2}$ orbital and the neutrons are paired to spin zero. The ground state spin of Pb^{203} is believed to be 5/2. Lead-203 has 5 neutrons less than a closed configuration. Preliminary calculations[155] of the level system to be expected from this 5-hole system have been made. The level systems of Pb^{205} and Pb^{203} appear to be rather similar both in theory and in experiment.

[151] T. Novakov, R. Stockendal, M. Schmorak, and B. Johansson, *Arkiv Fysik* **14**, 85 (1958).

[152] R. Stockendal, *Arkiv Fysik* **17**, 579 (1960).

[153] I. Bergström, C. J. Herrlander, P. Thieberger, and J. Uhler, *Arkiv Fysik* **20**, 93 (1961).

[154] Lindgren and Johansson, *Arkiv Fysik* **15**, 445 (1959).

[155] M. H. L. Pryce, *Nucl. Phys.* **2**, 226 (1956/7); see also results cited by Bergström and Andersson in *Arkiv Fysik* **12**, 415 (1957).

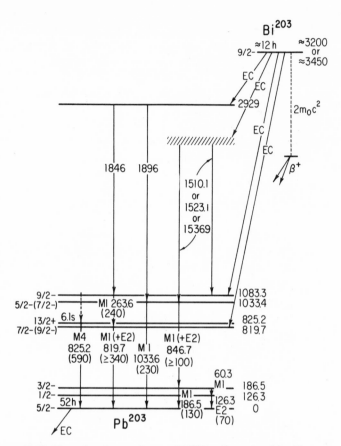

FIG. **10.24.** Tentative decay scheme of Bi^{203} as formulated by NOVAKOV, STOCKENDAL, SCHMORAK, AND JOHANSSON[151]. STOCKENDAL[152] gives slightly different energy and intensity values in a few cases.

Bismuth-203 also has a measurable alpha branching because of its great neutron deficiency. DUNLAVEY AND SEABORG[156] have found tracks of 4.85 MeV alpha particles in nuclear emulsions impregnated with Bi^{203} solution. The alpha branching is roughly 1 part in 10^7.

10.2.9 *The Isomers of Pb^{202}*

MAEDER, WAPSTRA, NIJGH, AND ORNSTEIN[157] bombarded thallium with 25 MeV deuterons. In the lead fraction, they found some 68-minute Pb^{204m},

[156] D. C. Dunlavey and G. T. Seaborg, *Phys. Rev.* **85**, 757A (1952).

[157] D. Maeder, A. H. Wapstra, G. J. Nijgh, and L. Th. M. Ornstein, *Physica* **20**, 521 (1954); *Phys. Rev.* **93**, 1433 (1954).

some 2.3-day Pb^{203}, and considerable 3.5-hour activity which they assigned to Pb^{202m} produced by the reaction:

$$Tl^{203}(d, 3n)Pb^{202m}$$

The studies of these authors plus the later work of BERGKVIST AND CO-WORKERS,[158] of MCDONELL AND CO-WORKERS,[159] and JOHANSSON[160]

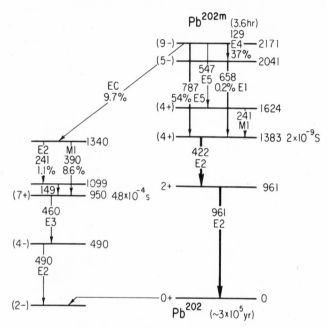

FIG. **10.25.** Decay scheme of Pb^{202m} and Pb^{202}. Spins and parity assignment are given to the left of the levels. Energy assignments are given in keV to the right.

have provided us with detailed information on the radiations of Pb^{202m} leading to the decay scheme of Fig. 10.25. We shall not review the detailed evidence upon which this scheme is based. The reader may find an excellent summary in the paper of MCDONELL.[159]

The decay scheme of Pb^{202m} is very similar to that of Pb^{204m}; in both cases the isomerism is due to a 9— level. Lead-202 is 6 neutrons short of the closed shell of 126 while Pb^{204} is 4 neutrons short. The 9— level must arise from a configuration of neutron orbitals involving the $i_{13/2}$ orbital which

[158] K. E. Bergkvist, I. Bergström, C. J. Herrlander, S. Hultberg, H. Slätis, E. Sokolowski, A. H. Wapstra, and T. Wiedling, *Phil. Mag.* **46**, 65 (1955).

[159] J. A. McDonell, R. Stockendal, C. J. Herrlander, and I. Bergström, *Nucl. Phys.* **3**, 513 (1957).

[160] Johansson, *Arkiv Fysik* **14**, 439 (1959).

is low-lying in this region; the isomerism is believed to result from transitions of the $i_{13/2} \rightarrow f_{5/2}$ type. Lead-202m differs from Pb^{204m} in that some de-excitation by electron capture to Tl^{202} is observed.

The ground state of Pb^{202} is long-lived. It is too short-lived to appear in natural lead sources but it is so long-lived that many attempts to identify it among the products of cyclotron bombardments were unsuccessful until HUIZENGA AND STEVENS[161] carried out an intense bombardment of thallium with a beam of 21 MeV deuterons, examined the lead fraction in a mass spectrograph and identified Pb^{202}. The identification was made certain by observing the growth of 12-day Tl^{202} activity. From the equilibrium amount of Tl^{202} and an assumed cross section for production of Pb^{202}, the half-life of Pb^{202} was estimated as 3×10^5 years. This isotope decays by L- and M-electron capture because the disintegration energy is too low for K-capture to occur.

Bismuth 202 was reported by KARRAKER AND TEMPLETON[162] as the daughter of Po^{202} produced in the bombardment of lead targets with high energy

TABLE **10.11.** Gamma transitions in the decay of Bi^{203}.*

Energy (keV)	Multipolarity assignment	Intensity
59.99	$M1$	(95)
126.3	$E2$	70 (120)
186.5	$M1$	130 (280)
263.9	$M1$	240 (250)
381.4	$E2$	
626.3		
722.4	$E2$	120
758.3		
820.1	$E2$	≥ 340 (1080)
825.2	$M4$	590 (590)
846.7	$E2$	≥ 100 (260)
932		
1033.6	$M1$	230 (260)
1184.2		
1256.8		
1510.1		
1523.1		
1536.9		
1846		
1896		

* From NOVAKOV, et al.[151] and STOCKENDAL.[152] The intensity figures in parentheses are from STOCKENDAL.

161 J. R. Huizenga and C. M. Stevens, *Phys. Rev.* **96**, 548 (1954).
162 D. G. Karraker and D. H. Templeton, *Phys. Rev.* **81**, 510 (1951).

deuterons. It decays by orbital capture to Pb^{202} with a half-life of 95 minutes. McDonell and co-workers[159] studied the conversion electrons emitted in the decay of Bi^{202} and found electrons corresponding to 422 and 961 keV gamma transitions. These are undoubtedly identical with the transitions shown in Fig. 10.25. Nothing further is known about the radiations of Bi^{202}. A nuclear spin value of 5 was determined for Bi^{202} by the atomic beam magnetic resonance method.[163]

10.2.10 *The Isomers of Pb²⁰¹*

Fischer[164] produced a 60-second isomer of Pb^{201} by bombarding thallium with protons. The variation of production cross section with the energy of the protons corresponded to that expected of the reaction:

$$Tl^{203}(p, 3n)Pb^{201m}$$

Hopkins[165] made similar observations. Fischer[164] reports an energy of 650 keV and a conversion coefficient $\alpha_K = 0.75$ for the single gamma ray emitted. The half-life and conversion coefficient correspond to an $M4$ transition. Stockendal and co-workers[147] confirmed this assignment and characterized the $M4$ transition more precisely. It has an energy of 629 keV, a K-conversion coefficient of 0.6, a K/L ratio of 2.3, and an $(L_I + L_{II})/L_{III}$ ratio of 4. It may be assumed that this isomerism in Pb^{201} is related to that observed in Pb^{203} and Pb^{207} and is to be ascribed to an $i_{13/2} \rightarrow f_{5/2}$ transition of the odd neutron. Refer to Fig. 10.9. The isotope Bi^{201} decays by electron capture[147] with a half-life of 1.9 hours to form Pb^{201m}. The nuclear spin of Bi^{201} has been measured by the atomic beam nuclear paramagnetic resonance technique.[163] The value of 9/2 so found is in agreement with the simple shell model ($h_{9/2}$ orbital for the 83rd proton) and consistent with electron capture decay to an $i_{13/2}$ state in Pb^{201}.

Gamma rays of 9.4-hour Pb²⁰¹.

129.1	692
284.4	708?
310.0	766
330.3	825?
361.2	907
394.3	946
405.6	1099
585	

163 S. Axensten, C. M. Johansson, and I. Lindgren, *Arkiv Fysik* **15**, 463 (1959).
164 V. K. Fischer, *Phys. Rev.* **99**, 764, 672A (1955).
165 N. J. Hopkins, *Phys. Rev.* **88**, 680 (1952).

The ground state of Pb^{201} is radioactive and decays by electron capture[166] to Tl^{201} with a half-life of 9.4 hours.[167]   This decay is accompanied by the gamma rays listed on the previous page.[167,168]

10.2.11 Lead-200

No isomerism has been reported in lead of mass number 200 although it has been looked for.   The ground state of Pb^{200} decays by electron capture with a half-life of 21.5 hours to Tl^{200}.   BERGKVIST AND CO-WORKERS[167] have identified several gamma rays and have proposed a decay scheme. ÅSTRÖM, JOHANSSON, AND BERGSTRÖM[169] investigated the 148 keV transition from the first excited state of Tl^{200} and measured a half-life of 8 millimicroseconds for it.   GERHOLM[170] investigated the decay scheme by an electron-electron coincidence measurement in a coincidence spectrometer.   The gamma radiations of Pb^{200} are listed in Table 10.12.

A bismuth activity with a half-life of 35 minutes was identified by NEUMANN AND PERLMAN[166] and assigned to Bi^{200}.   It decays by electron capture to produce Pb^{200}, but no details of the radiations accompanying this decay are known.   A spin value of 7 has been measured for Bi^{200} by the atomic beam nuclear paramagnetic resonance technique.[163]

10.2.12 Lead and Bismuth Isotopes with Mass Number Less than 200

ANDERSSON AND CO-WORKERS[171-175] have prepared several very light isotopes of lead by the bombardment of thallium with high energy protons. Although no reports on the preparation of these light isotopes by heavy ion reactions have been published, it is clear that bombardment of lighter target materials with heavy ions offer an alternate approach to the preparation of these isotopes uncontaminated with higher-mass lead activities.   In the work of ANDERSSON AND CO-WORKERS, the conversion electrons of the gamma

[166] H. Neumann and I. Perlman, Phys. Rev. 78, 191 (1950).

[167] K. E. Bergkvist, I. Bergström, C. J. Herrlander, S. Hultberg, H. Slätis, E. Sokolowski, A. H. Wapstra, and T. Wiedling, Phil. Mag. 46, 65 (1955).

[168] A. H. Wapstra, D. Maeder, G. J. Nijgh, and L. Th. M. Ornstein, Physic 20, 169 (1954).

[169] B. Åström, B. Johansson and I. Bergström, Arkiv Fysik 12, 205 (1957).

[170] T. R. Gerholm, Arkiv Fysik 11, 55 (1956).

[171] G. Andersson, E. Arbman, I. Bergström, and A. H. Wapstra, Phil. Mag. 46, 70 (1955).

[172] G. Andersson, E. Arbman, and B. Jung, Arkiv Fysik 11, 297 (1957).

[173] B. Jung, G. Andersson, and T. Stenström, Nucl. Phys. 36, 31 (1962).

[174] B. Jung, Nucl. Phys. 10, 440 (1959).

[175] A general discussion of nuclear energy levels and multipole assignments of gamma transitions in the light isotopes of lead, thallium, mercury, gold, and platinum is given by I. Bergström and G. Andersson, Arkiv Fysik 12, 415–479 (1957); see also I. Bergström, C. J. Herrlander, P. Thieberger, and J. Uhler, Arkiv Fysik 20, 93 (1961).

TABLE 10.12. Radiations of lead isotopes of mass < 201.

Isotope	Half-life	Mode of decay	Gamma radiations (keV)	Ref.
Pb[200]	21.5 hrs	EC	32.8, 109.5, 142.2 (K/L 4.5), 148.0 (K/L 0.52) $L_I/L_{II}/L_{III}$ = 0.12/1/0.7, 158.9, 235.3(K/L 5.5), 257.3 (K/L 4.5), 268 (K/L 4.5), 290, 450	166, 167, 169, 170
Pb[199]	90 min	EC, β^+ (weak)	353 (K/L 5.3, $L_I + L_{II}/L_{III}$ 40) 367 (K/L 4.4; $L_I + L_{II}/L_{III}$ 7.4), 721	166, 171, 172
Pb[199m]	12.2 min	Isomeric transition	424 $M4$ (K/L 1.9 $L_I + L_{II}/L_{III}$ 3.2)	147, 171, 172
Pb[198]	2.40 hrs	EC	30.8 116.9 (K/L 7.1), 122.6 (K/L = 5), 173.4 (K/L = 0.73) 259.5 (K/L = 5.3), 290.3 (K/L = 5.3), 365.4 (K/L = 6.0), 382.0 (K/L = 5.1), 389.5, 397.7, 467.8, 575.0 (K/L = 6 ± 2), 605.9, 649.0, 865.3, others. All are $M1$ except 173.4 and 649 which are $E2$.	171, 172, 174
Pb[197m]	42 min	Isomeric transition and EC	With IT, 234.0 $M4$ (K/L 0.3, $L_I + L_{II}/L_{III}$ 1.5) 85 $M1$, With EC 221.9 $E3$ (K/L 0.28, $L_I + L_{II}/L_{III}$ 2.5) 384.8 (K/L 5.7), 387 (K/L 3.5)	171, 172
Pb[196]	37 min	EC	166.8, 252.9 (K/L 4.7)	172
Pb[195]	17 min	EC	99 ($L_I + L_{II}/L_{III}$ 1.8) 383, 393	172

transitions of these isotopes were carefully measured, gamma-gamma coin-cidence studies were made, and decay schemes were established. The results are summarized in Table 10.12. All of these isotopes decay by orbital elec-tron capture to thallium daughters and the gamma radiations provide inter-esting information on the low-lying levels of the light thallium isotopes. These level assignments lie beyond the scope of interest of this chapter and the principal feature of the radiations of this group of lead isotopes to which we wish to call attention is the occurrence of isomers in the odd-mass isotopes Pb^{199} and Pb^{197}. $M4$ radiation is seen in these instances in complete analogy to the isomeric transitions in Pb^{201}, Pb^{203}, and Pb^{207}. See Fig. 10.9. The odd neutron in all cases is presumed to undergo an $i_{13/2} \rightarrow f_{5/2}$ shift.

Lead-199 and Pb^{198} are produced by the electron capture decay of Bi^{199} and Bi^{198} which decay with half-lives of ~ 25 minutes and ~ 7 minutes, respectively.[166] Nothing has been published concerning the gamma rays emitted in the electron capture branching of these isotopes. A slight alpha branching of ~ 0.01 per cent for the emission of alpha particles of 5.47 MeV energy has been noted[166] in the case of Bi^{199}. Similarly Bi^{198} emits 5.83 MeV alpha particles in ~ 0.05 per cent of its disintegrations. The nuclear spin[163] of Bi^{199} is 9/2.

10.2.13 The Superfluid Model Description of the Lead Isotopes

We have seen in the above discussion that a wealth of experimental information is available on the properties of the lead isotopes. We have also seen that a number of theoreticians have attacked the problem of calculating the excitation spectra of these isotopes, particularly those of Pb^{206}, Pb^{205}, and Pb^{204}. The difficult part of these calculations is the evaluation of the residual interactions of the 2 or more neutrons missing from the closed shell of 126. These difficulties increase greatly as the number of interacting neutrons increases.

The calculations can be greatly simplified by use of a very simple approxi-mation to the short range interaction known as the "pairing" interaction. The pairing interaction is one of the essential elements of a nuclear model known as the "superconductivity" or "superfluid" model which has been developed in many publications since its applicability was first discussed by BOHR, MOTTELSON, AND PINES[176] in 1958, and BELYAEV[177] in 1959. KISS-LINGER AND SORENSEN[111] illustrated the power of this calculation method in a paper which presented predictions of the level systems of all lead isotopes from 207 through 196. It is appropriate to mention this work briefly here and to present some of the results which they obtained.

---

[176] A. Bohr, B. R. Mottelson, and D. Pines, *Phys. Rev.* **110**, 936 (1958).
[177] S. T. Belyaev, *Dan. Mat.-fys. Medd. Vid. Selsk.* **31**, No. 11 (1959).

The basic assumption of the pairing force representation is that a pair of particles of the same angular momentum j with angular momentum vectors oriented opposite to each other (and hence coupled to angular momentum zero) can interact with another pair of particles similarly coupled to zero angular momentum. Unless the particles are so coupled there is no interaction. All interacting pairs of particles are assumed to interact with a force of the same strength.

In the absence of the pairing force the ground state of the lead isotopes is simply the sum of the wave functions of all the shell model states up to the Fermi level; all states below the Fermi level are completely filled and all states above are completely vacant. When the pairing force is operative there is a scattering of pairs of neutrons out of the top levels just below the Fermi level into a few states above it; the last few neutron pairs of particles are diffused over several levels below and above the Fermi level. In the case of excited states the main contribution to the excitation energy is the energy involved in raising one or more particles to some excited level or levels. But this change in configuration is accompanied by a readjustment of the pairing forces which may give rise to a sizeable shift in the excitation energy.

The pairing force is an idealization of the short range part of the residual force. The long range part of the force is not so important and in many applied calculations can be neglected. KISSLINGER AND SORENSEN[111] approximated the long-range part of the force by a P_2 force where $P_2(\cos \theta)$ is the Legendre polynomial of order two. One justification of this choice of force is that it is known that the long range force has a weak angular dependence such as that of $P_2(\cos \theta)$. Also ELLIOT[178] has shown that the collective quadrupole deformation and the associated rotational spectra can be obtained for particles in a harmonic-oscillator or potential interacting with a specific two-body force with angular dependence given by $P_2(\cos \theta)$ where θ represents the angle between the particles.

In the calculations of KISSLINGER AND SORENSEN[111] the neutron hole states in lead nuclei just below the 126-neutron closed configuration were considered to interact not only with a pairing force, but with a $P_2(\cos \theta)$ long range force. This approximation to the long range force gave small, but significant corrections to the wave functions and the positions of the predicted levels.

There is evidence from experimental data on transition rates and excitation energies that one must also consider the collective oscillations of the core in the lead isotopes below Pb^{208}. The chief evidence relates to the first excited $2+$ state which occurs systematically in the even-A nuclei of lead. The large transition probabilities for the $E2$ radiation which de-excites this state cannot be explained without assigning to this state a collective origin. We have

[178] J. P. Elliott, *Proc. Roy. Soc.* **245A**, 128, 562 (1958).

mentioned this point in connection with our discussion of Pb^{206} in Section 10.2.4 above, in particular the discussion of TRUE AND FORD'S[135] analysis. Also, this lowest 2+ state lies well below the predicted state, if the predicted state is based on a pairing force of such a magnitude as to be consistent with other data. Hence, KISSLINGER AND SORENSEN introduced a collective harmonic oscillation and considered the effects of a coupling of particle motions to it. This part of their calculation affects mainly the total binding energy and the properties of the 2+ first excited state.

KISSLINGER AND SORENSEN used shell model oscillator wave functions,

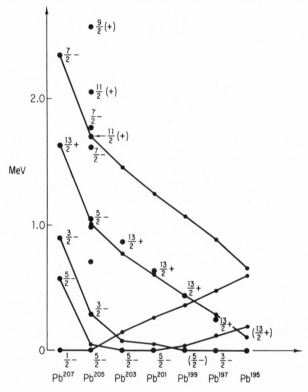

FIG. **10.26.** Energy levels of the odd A-isotopes of lead as drawn by KISSLINGER AND SORENSEN[111] in 1960. Experimental points are large dots with spin and parity assignments placed on the right when known. Theoretical results for the pairing force calculation are the small dots joined by solid lines given the positions of the one quasi-particle states for optimum choices of parameters. The effect of the coupling of the quasi-particle to the collective oscillation is included for the lowest few states. The labels on the experimental curves are the angular momenta of the one quasi-particle states.

but took the energies of these states from experimental data on Pb^{207}.   In the computation of the pairing interaction they followed the usual practice of a shift to a "quasi-particle" representation because of the calculational simplification which this shift introduces.   They used selected experimental data to determine the most appropriate value of the parameters in the basic

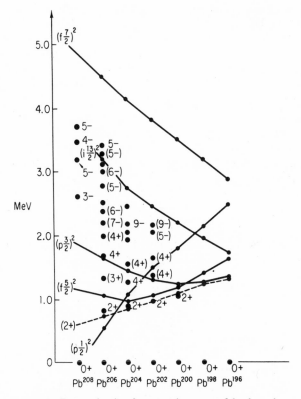

FIG. 10.27. Energy levels of even-A isotopes of lead as drawn by KISSLINGER AND SORENSEN[111] in 1960.   The experimental points are large dots with spin and parity assignments placed on the right when known.   Theoretical points from the pairing force calculation are indicated by small dots.   Those theoretical points which are joined by solid lines are the two identical quasi-particle states and are labeled to the left by the angular momenta of the quasi-particles.   The effect of the P_2 (cos θ) force is not included for these states.   The other two quasi-particle energies are found by taking the average energy between the appropriate two levels.   See, for example, the theoretical spectrum of Pb^{204} given in Fig. 10.22(b).   The collective 2+ theoretical level is shown by small dots joined by a dashed line.

pairing force plus P_2 force equations and computed the properties of the ground and excited states of the lead nuclei. Figures 10.26 and 10.27 summarize some of the principal results.

We can make the following comments on them. There are strong shifts in the positions of levels, but these shifts occur smoothly over the group of nuclei considered. We note in the odd-A spectra that the correct ground state spin is predicted in nearly every case. In the case of Pb^{205} the calculation predicts 1/2 with a 5/2 state lying very close to ground whereas, in fact, the ground state is 5/2 with the 1/2 state 2.3 keV above. The trend in the $i_{13/2} \rightarrow f_{5/2}$ spacing is well reproduced. Experimentally, the transition between these levels is easy to identify because the high spin change involved in these $M4$ transitions gives rise to the isomerism reported in the odd-A nuclei. (See Fig. 10.9 in Section 10.2.1.)   KISSLINGER AND SORENSEN found that the reduced transition probabilities of these $M4$ transitions computed by use of their wave functions showed little change with mass number, in agreement with experiment; this feature depends essentially on the strongly-mixed configurations resulting from the pairing force. A more drastic change in transition probability is predicted by the independent particle model without residual interactions.

In the even-A nuclei the most systematic experimental feature is the position of the first excited $2+$ state. This state is collective in nature and lies in the gap between the ground state and the first state of particle excitation. It has a rather constant energy compared to the shifts in the 2-quasi-particle states. In the calculations this state is identified as the first excited quadrupole vibration.

In the case of Pb^{206} and Pb^{204} KISSLINGER AND SORENSEN made a particularly detailed calculation and comparison with experimental spectra. The Pb^{204} results are summarized in Fig. 10.22b introduced earlier in Section 10.2.7. The agreement in the case of Pb^{206} is not as good as the more exact treatment of TRUE AND FORD[135] discussed above in Section 10.2.4. However, all the experimental levels with assigned spins can be matched with predicted levels to within a few tenths of one MeV. Also the differences in the isomerism in Pb^{206}, Pb^{204} and Pb^{202} (see Fig. 10.3) are accounted for by the relative positions of the levels of spin 6, 7, and 9.

BERGSTRÖM AND CO-WORKERS[179] made a detailed comparison of experimental data on the odd-A isotopes of lead with the predictions of KISSLINGER AND SORENSEN.

10.3 LIGHT ISOTOPES OF POLONIUM

We are not concerned here with Po^{210}(RaF) and higher-mass isotopes of polonium since these are members of the four principal decay chains and are

---

[179] I. Bergström, C. J. Herrlander, P. Thieberger, and J. Uhler, *Arkiv Fysik* **20**, 93 (1961).

discussed in Chapters 6 and 7. In this chapter we shall discuss some of the important features of the decay of Po^{209}, Po^{208}, Po^{207}, and Po^{206} and shall make a few general comments about the occurrence of alpha decay in the light polonium isotopes. The chief radioactive characteristics of all polonium isotopes below Po^{210} are listed in Table 10.13.

10.3.1 Polonium-209

KELLY AND SEGRÈ[180] produced Po^{209} by bombardment of bismuth with deuterons:

$$Bi^{209}(d, 2n)Po^{209}$$

Other reactions which have been employed are:

$$Bi^{209}(p, n)Po^{209}$$
$$Pb^{208}(\alpha, 3n)Po^{209}$$
$$Pb^{207}(\alpha, 2n)Po^{209}$$
$$Pb^{206}(\alpha, n)Po^{209}$$

The cross section for the production of Po^{209} by some of the above reactions is discussed in articles by JOHN,[181] by ANDRE, ET AL.[182] and by RAMLER, ET AL.[183]   Some of these data are summarized in Section 5.2 of Chapter 5.

Polonium-209 decays more than 99 per cent by alpha emission with a half-life of 103 years.[182a] For 99.4 per cent of the alpha particles the alpha particle energy is 4.877 MeV.[184]   By alpha-gamma coincidence experiments it is known that 0.6 per cent of the alpha transitions proceed by emission of 4.62 MeV alpha particles to reach a level at 260 keV in the daughter.[185,187] The 260 keV photon intensity is only 4×10^{-3} per total alpha transition. DAGGETT AND GROVE[186] report some evidence for additional gamma rays of 570 keV and 865 keV energy in about the same low intensity. HERRLANDER[188] found evidence in the electron spectrum emitted by Bi^{205} in its decay to Pb^{205} (see Section 10.2.6 above) that the 262.8 keV level decays to the ground state by emission of a 262.8 keV gamma ray and by emission of a 260.5 keV and 2.3 keV cascade. He also studied the electron spectrum of

[180] E. L. Kelly and E. Segrè, Phys. Rev. 75, 999 (1949).

[181] W. John, Phys. Rev. 103, 704 (1956)

[182] C. G. Andre, et al., Phys. Rev. 101, 465 (1956).

[182a] Eichelberger, Groves, and Jones report a revised value of 40.2 ± 0.26 years for the Po^{209} half-life. Unpublished work, Mound Laboratory, 1963.

[183] W. J. Ramler, J. Wing, D. J. Henderson, and J. R. Huizenga, Phys. Rev. 114, 154 (1959).

[184] F. Asaro and W. Heimann, unpublished information (1951).

[185] F. Asaro, F. S. Stephens, and I. Perlman, unpublished results, (1957).

[186] E. H. Daggett and G. R. Grove, Phys. Rev. 99, 1 (1955).

[187] G. R. Hagee and R. C. Lange, Bull. Am. Phys. Soc. II, 9, 19 (1964).

[188] C. J. Herrlander, Arkiv Fysik 20, 71 (1961).

TABLE 10.13. Light isotopes of Polonium*

Isotope	Type of decay	Half-life	Energy of radiations Particles	Gamma rays	Method of production
Po^{192}	α	0.5 sec	6.58	no data	Bi-p-18n
Po^{193}	α	4 sec	6.47	,,	Bi-p-17n
Po^{194}	α	13 sec	6.38	,,	Bi-p-16n
Po^{195}	α	30 sec	6.26	,,	Bi-p-15n
Po^{196}	α, EC	1.9 min	6.14	,,	Bi-p-14n Pt + C[12,13]
Po^{197}	α, EC	~4 min	6.040	,,	Bi^{209}-p-13n ,,
Po^{108}	α, EC	~6 min	5.935	,,	Bi^{209}-p-12n ,,
Po^{199}	α, EC	~11 min	5.846	,,	Bi^{209}-p-11n ,,
Po^{200}	α, EC	~8 min	5.770	,,	Bi^{209}-p-10n ,,
Po^{201}	α, EC	18 min	5.671		Bi^{209}-p-9n ,,
Po^{202}	98% EC 2% α	52 min or 43 min	5.575		Bi^{209}-p-8n ,, Pb-α-spall daughter Em^{206}
Po^{203}	EC 93.9% α (7%)	47 min	5.48		Bi^{209}-p-7n Pb-α-spall ,,

Isotope	Type of decay	Half-life	α energy	Remarks	Methods of production
Po^{204}	EC 99%+ α 0.63%	3.8 hr	5.370		Bi^{209}-p-$6n$ Pb-α-spall Pb^{204}-α-$3n$
Po^{205}	EC (99+%) α (0.074%)	1.5 hr	5.2		
Po^{206}	EC (95%) α (5%)	9 day	5.218	See Section 10.3.4	Bi^{209}-p-$4n$ Pb^{204}-α-$2n$ daughter Em^{210}
Po^{207}	EC (99+%) α (0.014%) β^+ ($\sim$0.2%)	5.7 hr	5.10	See Section 10.3.3	Pb^{206}-α-$3n$ daughter Em^{211}
Po^{208}	α EC (weak)	2.89 yr	5.108	0.285, 0.60 MeV See Section 10.3.2	Pb^{206}-α-$2n$ Bi^{209}-d-$3n$ Bi^{209}-p-$2n$
Po^{209}	α > 99% $EC \approx$ 0.5%	103 $\pm$ 4 yr	4.877 (99.4%) 4.62 (0.6%)	See Section 10.3.1	Bi^{209}-d-$2n$ Bi^{209}-p-n Pb^{208}-α-$3n$ Pb^{217}-α-$2n$ Pb^{206}-α-n

* For references to original literature see Strominger, Hollander, and Seaborg, *Revs. Mod. Phys.* (1958) and Table 10.18 below.

Po^{209} and found the same result.   Hence, a $p_{1/2}$ level is located just 2.3 keV above the 5/2− ground state.

Polonium-209 decays by orbital electron capture to Bi^{209} in about 0.5 per cent of its total disintegrations.   Decay to the ground state is highly forbidden because the ground state spin of Bi^{209} is 9/2 (a single $h_{9/2}$ proton beyond a closed shell) and the ground state spin[188a] of Po^{188a} is 1/2 ($p_{1/2}$ odd neutron).   All electron capture apparently proceeds to a level at 910 keV in Bi^{209}.[185]

10.3.2 Polonium-208

The isotope Po^{208} is prepared by bombardment of lead or bismuth targets.[189]

$$Pb^{206}(\alpha, 2n)Po^{208}$$

$$Pb^{207}(\alpha, 3n)Po^{208}$$

$$Pb^{208}(\alpha, 4n)Po^{208}$$

$$Bi^{209}(d, 3n)Po^{208}$$

$$Bi^{209}(p, 2n)Po^{208}$$

The yield of Po^{208} in such reactions is discussed in several research reports.[181-183, 190]   (See Section 5.2 of Chapter 5.)

LIVINGSTON AND MARTIN[191] studied the production of large quantities of Po^{208} by the $Bi^{209}(p, 2n)Po^{208}$ reaction and discussed the economics of ultimate production costs in a multicyclotron installation.   This isotope has a half-life of 2.89 ± 0.01 years.[192]   Polonium-208 is a very pure alpha emitter in the sense that it emits alpha particles of only a single energy (reported as 5.108 MeV[184] and 5.109 MeV[193]); furthermore it has only a tiny amount of gamma radiation from an alternate mode of decay.   The single observed alpha group in Po^{208} is a consequence of the great energy (899 keV) of the first excited (2+) state of Pb^{204}.

Polonium-208 is unstable toward electron capture by an energy of the order of 1.3 MeV.   PERLMAN AND CO-WORKERS[194] have detected K x-rays and gamma rays with energies of 285 and 600 keV. The 600 keV radiation may be a doublet with ∼570 and ∼620 keV components. The intensity of

[188a] K. L. Van der Sluis and P. M. Griffin, *J. Opt. Soc. Amer.* **45**, 1087 (1955).

[189] D. H. Templeton, J. J. Howland, Jr., and I. Perlman, *Phys. Rev.* **72**, 758 (1947).

[190] R. E. Bell and H. M. Skarsgard, *Can. J. Phys.* **34**, 745 (1956).

[191] R. S. Livingston and J. A. Martin, "Production of Po208," *Oak Ridge National Laboratory Report ORNL-1392*, 1952, unpublished.

[192] D. H. Templeton, *Phys. Rev.* **78**, 312 (1950); G. L. Fox et al., unpublished, 1963.

[193] S. Rosenblum and H. Tyren, *Compt. Rend.* **239**, 1205 (1954).

[194] I. Perlman, F. Asaro, F. S. Stephens, J. P. Hummel, and R. C. Pilger, unpublished results, 1955.

the 285 keV photons is only 3 per 10^5 alpha disintegrations, whereas that of the $\sim$600 keV peak is twice this. Gamma-gamma coincidence experiments[185] indicate that the 285 keV gamma ray is in coincidence with K x-rays and with both components of the 600 keV doublet. KIM AND RASMUSSEN[194a] discuss a possible interpretation of these results.

10.3.3 *Polonium-207*

The level system of Bi^{207} revealed by a study of the complex radiations of Po^{207} has some theoretical interest because Bi^{207} differs from the double-closed shell nucleus Pb^{208} by only three nucleons and is a favorable case for the testing of a multi-particle shell model theory.

TEMPLETON, HOWLAND, AND PERLMAN[189] identified the 5.7 hour Po^{207} among the products of the bombardment of lead isotopes with helium ions. Some cross section measurements of the $Pb^{206}(\alpha, 3n)Po^{207}$ and the $Bi^{209}(p, 3n)Po^{207}$ reactions are reported by JOHN[181] and by BELL AND SKARSGARD.[190] STONER[195] has prepared isotopically-pure Po^{207} as the alpha decay product of Em^{211} which in turn had been prepared by high-energy spallation of thorium. Polonium-207 decays chiefly by capture of an orbital electron, but a branching decay of 1.4×10^{-2} per cent by the emission of 5.10 MeV alpha particles has been reported.[189] Low intensity positrons are also emitted.[195, 196] STONER[195] studied the complex gamma and conversion electron spectrum of this nuclide with a scintillation spectrometer, a double-focusing beta spectrometer and permanent magnet spectrograph. A thorough study was carried out by ARBMAN, BURDE, AND GERHOLM[196] whose results we quote here. These workers measured the energies and relative intensities of the numerous conversion electrons in a double-focusing spectrometer with a resolution of 0.2 per cent. This work was supplemented with photon intensities measured in a NaI scintillation spectrometer and with electron-electron coincidence measurements carried out in a double lens coincidence spectrometer. The low intensity positron spectrum was measured and resolved into two components. In addition, the spectra of gamma ray photons and conversion electrons in coincidence with positrons were investigated. The gamma rays and the pertinent data concerning them are listed in Table 10.14. The decay scheme of Fig. 10.28 was constructed based on a detailed analysis of the gamma ray sum relations, the transition intensities and the extensive coincidence information. All gamma rays except the weak 1586.1 keV transition were placed in the decay scheme. The decay scheme shows 16 levels in the Bi^{207} nucleus, of which 11 are considered by the authors to be well established, while the remaining 5 levels (shown as dotted

194a Y. E. Kim and J. O. Rasmussen, "Energy Levels of Tl208 and Bi208," *Phys. Rev.* (1964).

195 A. Stoner, *Univ. Calif. Rad. Lab. Report UCRL-3471*, June 1956, unpublished.

196 E. Arbman, J. Burde, and T. R. Gerholm, *Arkiv Fysik* 13, 501 (1958).

TABLE **10.14.** Gamma transitions in the decay of Po^{207} (ARBMAN, BURDE, and GERHOLM[196]).

Energy (keV)	Conversion lines observed	$K/\Sigma L$	$\dfrac{L_I + L_{II}}{L_{III}}$	Multipolarity	Relative total transition intensity
100.0 ± 0.1	$L_{I,II,III}$ $M_I N_I O_I$	—	8.2	$M1 + E2$	80
149.6 ± 0.1	$K\,L_I M_I N_I$	(5.2)	≥ 16	$M1$	20
156.1 ± 0.1	$K\,L_I M_I$	5.8	—	$M1$	12
158.0 ± 0.1	$K\,L_{I,II,III}$ $M_{II,III},N_{II}$	0.75	1.9	$M1 + E2$	61
205.2	$K\,L_I M_I$	5.1	—	$M1(?)$	2.6
222.0	$K\,L_{I,III}$	3.5		$E1$	73
222.7	$K\,L_I M_I N_I$	(5.6)	≥ 15	$M1$	34
224.0	$K\,L_I M_I N_I$	5.5	≥ 15	$M1$	12.5
249.6	$K\,L_I M_I N_I$	5.6	≥ 160	$M1$	150
288.0	$K\,L_I$	5.6		$M1(?)$	3.3
307.5	$K\,M_I N_I$	5.6	≥ 18	$M1$	56
330.2	$K\,M_I$	4.2		$M1(?)$	20
345.2	$K\,L_{I,II} M_I N_I$	5.6	≥ 90	$M1$	173
369.3	$K\,L_I$	6.0		$M1(?)$	10
402.4	$K\,L_I$	5		$M1(?)$	6.5
405.7	$K\,L_I M_I N_I$	5.7	≥ 160	$M1$	723
531.7	$K\,L_I$	6.4		$M1(?)$	22
629.9	$K\,L_I M_I N_I$	6.2	≥ 30	$M1$	91
669.5	$K\,M_I$	(6.2)		$M1(?)$	42
687.5	$K\,L_I$	6		$E1(?)$	109
742.7	$K\,L_I M_I N_I$	6.1	≥ 100	$M1$	1800
770.7	$K\,L_I$	5.3		$M1(?)$	26
892.4	$K\,L_I$	~ 5		$(M1 + E2)?$	26
911.8	$K\,L_I M_I$	5.4		$E1$	1000
947.8	$K\,L_I$	3.2		$M1(?)$	75
992.6	$K\,L_I M_I N_I$	6.0	≥ 80	$M1$	3470
1148.8	$K\,L_I M_I$	5.3		$E2$	347
1211.6	$K\,L_I M_I$	3			
1317.9	K			$M2(?)$	1
1360.7	$K\,L_I$	5.3		$E2(?)$	75
1373.1	$K\,L_I M_I$	5.5		$E2$	80
1586.1	K				
1662.7	$K\,L_I$	~ 5			
1762.7	$K\,L_I$	~ 5		$E2(?)$	13
1847.0					
2060.8	$K\,L_I M_I$	5.5		$E3$	72

lines) are less certain since they could not be checked by coincidence measurements. The main decay of Po^{207} proceeds via the four strongly excited levels of energies 2060.4, 1148.6, 992.5 and 742.9 keV. The observation of transitions from these levels directly to the ground state helped to fix the spin assignments of these levels. Other levels are only weakly excited.

Some of the main features of this decay scheme can be understood by a consideration of the shell model. Bismuth-207 has one proton more and two neutrons less than Pb^{208}, and the low-lying levels should be ascribable to the

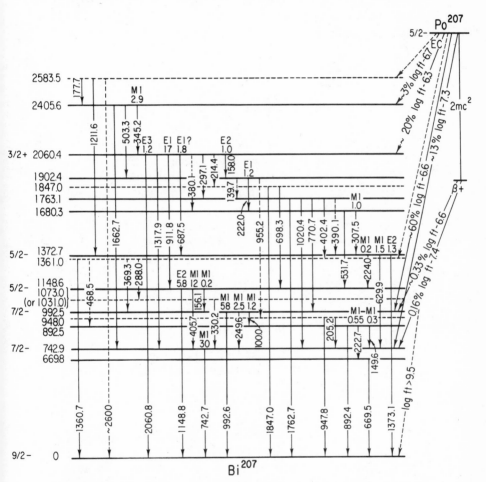

FIG. **10.28.** Decay scheme of Po^{207} as proposed by ARBMAN, BURDE, AND GER-HOLM.[196] Multipolarities and intensities in per cent per disintegration are given at the head of some transitions. Less certain levels and transitions are indicated by dotted lines. The 992.5 and 742.9 keV levels are fed by positrons of endpoint energies 893 and 1140 keV, respectively.

coupling of the extra proton to the neutron holes in various ways. The complexity of the experimentally observed level scheme makes it clear that the excitation of the extra proton cannot by itself account for the levels and that the excitation of the two neutron hole states must be important. The possible modes of excitation of two neutron holes in the 126 neutron shell is known in detail from the experimental and theoretical studies of the level system of $_{82}\text{Pb}^{206}_{124}$ which is discussed in some detail in Section 10.2.4. WAHLBORN[197] has used parameters obtained in the study of Pb^{206} in a calculation based on the principles introduced by PRYCE[198] to determine the first order energy levels of Bi^{207}. Configuration mixing was not taken into account. The ground state configuration can be written with some confidence as $[(p_{1/2})^{-2}_{\text{neutrons}}\, h_{9/2\,\text{proton}}]J = 9/2$. The ground state spin of Bi^{207} has not been measured directly but it seems very likely that it should have the same spin as Bi^{209} of which a direct measurement has been made. Not much is known of the excited proton states for the first proton beyond 82, but the inelastic neutron scattering work of KIEHN AND GOODMAN[199] on Bi^{209} suggests an $f_{7/2}$ state at 900 keV and a 13/2 state at 1.56 MeV. If this information is combined with Pb^{206} configurations given previously in Section 10.2.4, one might expect the low-lying levels of Bi^{207} to be derived from the combinations listed in Table 10.15. WAHLBORN'S estimates of the

TABLE **10.15.** Configurations of Bi²⁰⁷.

Three particle configuration	Possible spins	Parity
$p_{1/2}^{-2}\, h_{9/2}$	9/2	—
$(p_{1/2}^{-1} f_{5/2}^{-1})_{J=2}\, h_{9/2}$	5/2, 7/2, 9/2, 11/2, 13/2	—
$(p_{1/2}^{-1} p_{3/2}^{-1})_{J=2}\, h_{9/2}$	5/2, 7/2, 9/2, 11/2, 13/2	—
$(f_{5/2}^{-2})_{J=0}\, h_{9/2}$	9/2	—
$(p_{1/2}^{-1} f_{5/2}^{-1})_{J=3}\, h_{9/2}$	3/2, 5/2, 7/2, 9/2, 11/2, 13/2, 15/2	—
$(f_{5/2}^{-2})_{J=4}\, h_{9/2}$	1/2, 3/2, 5/2, 7/2, 9/2, 11/2, 13/2, 15/2, 17/2	—
$p_{1/2}^{-2}\, f_{7/2}$	7/2	—
$(f_{5\,2}^{-2})_{J=2}\, h_{9/2}$	5/2, 7/2, 9/2, 11/2, 13/2	—

position of the resultant levels are given in Fig. 10.29. ARBMAN, BURDE, AND GERHOLM[196] discuss the possible identification of some of their experimental levels with these theoretical levels. Here only two general features will be pointed out. In agreement with experiment (1) all theoretical levels below about 1.7 MeV have odd parity and (2) no level of spin 5/2 is predicted below about 1.5 MeV.

Polonium-207 has two protons outside the closed shell of 82 protons and

[197] S. Wahlborn, *Nucl. Phys.* **3**, 644 (1957) and results quoted by Arbman, Burde, and Gerholm.[196]

[198] M. H. L. Pryce, *Proc. Phys. Soc.* **A65**, 773 (1952); *Nucl. Phys.* **2**, 226 (1956/57) and D. E. Alburger and M. H. L. Pryce, *Phys. Rev.* **95**, 1482 (1954).

[199] R. M. Kiehn and C. Goodman, *Phys. Rev.* **95**, 989 (1954).

three holes in the 126 neutron shell. The ground state configuration is
probably

$$[(h_{9/2}^2)_{\text{proton}}(p_{1/2}^{-2}f_{5/2}^{-1})_{\text{neutron}}]$$

coupling to give the experimentally indicated spin of 5/2. The transition

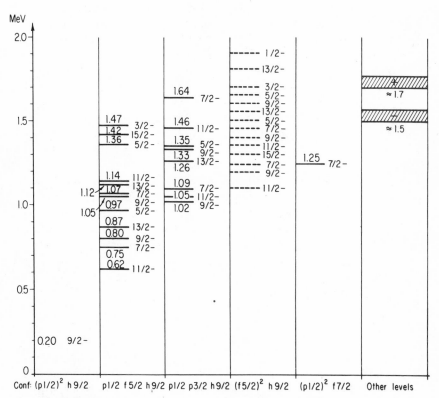

FIG. 10.29. First order energy levels of Bi²⁰⁷ as given by WAHLBORN[197]. The calculation was performed with δ-forces and with the aid of PRYCE's interaction
parameters. The dotted levels in the fourth column are only roughly estimated.
In the last column the estimated lower limits for the distribution of all other levels
of positive and negative parities have been indicated. The configuration mixing
has not been taken into account. From ARBMAN ET AL.[196]

from the ground state of Po²⁰⁷ to the ground state of Bi²⁰⁷ involves the
conversion of an $h_{9/2}$ proton into an $f_{5/2}$ neutron. The direct transition
would be second forbidden ($\Delta I = \Delta l = 2$, no) and does not occur to an
observable extent.

10.3.4 *Polonium-206*

The 9-day isotope Po^{206} is prepared[189] by bombardment of bismuth with protons or of lead isotopes with helium ions. The yield of Po^{206} in such reactions is discussed by BELL AND SKARSGARD[190] and by JOHN.[181] See Section 5.2 of Chapter 5.

An alternate method[195] is to prepare Em^{210} by bombardment of thorium with high energy (350 MeV) protons, and then to isolate its Po^{206} daughter product. The emanation fraction collected from such thorium targets and purified a few hours after bombardment consists of a mixture of 2.7 hour Em^{210} and 16 hour Em^{211}. The polonium daughter fraction consists of Po^{206} and Po^{207}. The alpha activity of this polonium is entirely caused by Po^{206} because of the small alpha branching of Po^{207}. To study the gamma activity of Po^{206} in a sample so prepared it is necessary to wait until the 5.7 hour Po^{207} has decayed before the Po^{206} is given its final purification.

Polonium-206 could also be prepared by bombardment of lighter target elements such as gold or platinum with complex nuclear projectiles such as C^{12} or N^{14}.

Alpha Decay of Po^{206}. Polonium-206 decays 5 per cent by alpha emission and 95 per cent by orbital electron capture.[200] The observed alpha spectrum consists of a single group with energy 5.218 MeV.[195, 201] No other groups are present in intensity greater than one per cent of the main group in the energy region 0–480 keV below the main group. Alpha-gamma coincidence experiments set an upper limit of 1.7×10^{-4} photons per alpha in the energy region 100–300 keV.[202]

Electron Capture Decay of Po^{206}. STONER[195] studied the conversion electrons of Po^{206} in permanent magnet spectrographs and a double focusing spectrometer. He also studied the gamma rays in a scintillator spectrometer and carried out some coincidence experiments. This work revealed eleven gamma rays, the reported results on which were for the most part confirmed and considerably extended by the independent investigation of ARBMAN[203] whose results are quoted here. ARBMAN first measured the complex Auger electron and conversion electron spectrum in a double focusing electron spectrometer with high resolution. The energy determinations were aided by the presence in the samples of the conversion electrons of the Bi^{206} daughter whose energies had been precisely measured previously by ALBURGER AND PRYCE.[204] The absolute intensities of the conversion electrons of Po^{206} could also be determined by comparison to the K-electrons of the 803.3 keV

200 F. F. Momyer, Jr. and E. K. Hyde, *J. Inorg. Nucl. Chem.* **1**, 274 (1955).
201 J. P. Hummel, *Univ. Calif. Rad. Lab. Report UCRL-3456* (1956).
202 F. S. Stephens, unpublished information (1956).
203 E. Arbman, *Nucl. Phys.* **3**, 625 (1957).
204 D. E. Alburger and M. H. L. Pryce, *Phys. Rev.* **95**, 1482 (1954).

$E2$ transition occurring in 100 per cent abundance in the decay of Bi^{206}. The gamma ray studies were also aided by scintillation spectrometer measurements of the photon spectrum.   The observed gamma rays are listed in Table 10.16 together with multipolarity assignments and transition intensities.   To aid in the construction of a decay scheme, ARBMAN[203] considered sum relations; i.e., he determined those pairs of gamma rays whose energy sum differed by less than 2 parts in 1000 from the energy of a third gamma ray.   The high accuracy of the experimental energy measurements made this a useful aid in the formulation of the decay scheme.   In addition, he measured electron-electron coincidences for about 30 combinations of the gamma rays whose conversion electron intensities are most intense.   A combined consideration of the sum relations, the coincidence data, and transition intensities led to the decay scheme of Fig. 10.30.   This scheme agrees with nearly all the

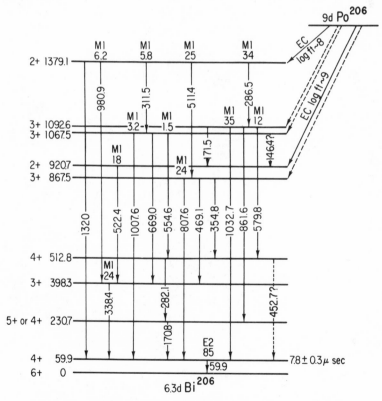

FIG. 10.30. Decay scheme of Po[206] as proposed by ARBMAN. Established coincidences are indicated by large dots. At the head of some transitions the multipolarities and intensities in per cent per disintegration are given. From ARBMAN AND TOVE.[205]

experimental information, and only 6 transitions of those listed in Table 10.16 have not been placed.   A chief feature of this decay scheme is that the principal electron capture decay of Po^{206} leads to a 1379 keV level in Bi^{206} which de-excites by 5 alternate cascades of gamma transitions.   Another striking feature is that all disintegrations pass through the first excited state of Bi^{206} lying at 59.9 keV.   The $E2$ gamma ray which de-excites this level has been specially studied by ARBMAN AND TOVE[205] who measured a half-life of

TABLE 10.16. Gamma rays emitted by Po^{206} (Arbman).

γ-ray energy (keV)	Lines observed	K-line intensity (per cent)	K/L	Assumed multipolarity	Total transition intensity (per cent)
59.9 (3)	$L_I, L_{II}, L_{III}, M_{II},$ $M_{III}, N_{III}, O_{III}$	31.3[a]	—	$E2$	85
82.9	L_I, M_I, N_I	0.31[b]	—		
117.6	K, L_I, M_I	0.55	4.5 ± 1.0		
140.6	K, L_I, M_I	0.32	4.7 ± 1.0		
170.8	K, L_I	0.41	5.3 ± 1.0	$M1$ or $E1$	0.7 or 4.7
171.5	K, L_I	0.10	3.5 ± 1.0		
282.1	K, L_I	0.32	5.8 ± 1.0	$M1$	0.8
286.5*	K, L_I, M_I, N	9.75	5.6 ± 0.6	$M1$	34
311.5*	K, L_I, M_I, N	1.54	6.0 ± 0.6	$M1$	5.8
338.4*	K, L_I, M_I, N	5.20	5.6 ± 0.6	$M1$	24
354.8	K, L_I	0.090	5 ± 2		
463.5	K, L_I, M	0.21	6.5 ± 0.7	$M1$	2.0
469.1	K, L_{II}	0.032	4 ± 2		
511.4*	K, L_I, M_I, N	2.09	5.6 ± 0.6	$M1$	25
522.4*	K, L_I, M_I, N	1.32	5.5 ± 1.0	$M1$	18
554.6	K, L_I, M_I	0.11	6.2 ± 1.0	$M1$	1.5
579.8	K, L_I	0.076	5.6 ± 1.0	$M1$	1.2
645.6	K, L_{II}	0.017	4.3 ± 1.0		
669.0	K, L_I	0.038	5.6 ± 1.0		
677.8	K, L_{II}	0.014	3 ± 2		
807.6*	K, L_I, M_I, N	0.64	5.6 ± 0.6	$M1$	24
861.6	K, L_I	0.026	5.4 ± 0.9		
980.9*	K, L_I, M_I	0.10	5.7 ± 0.9	$M1$	6.2
1007.6	K, L_I	0.045	4.5 ± 1.0	$M1$	3.2
1032.7*	K, L_I, M_I, N	0.50	6.0 ± 0.6	$M1$	35
1320.0	K	0.002			

[a] Intensity of L_{II} line.
[b] Intensity of L_I line.
* Energy accuracy 5 parts in 10,000.

$7.8 \pm 0.3 \times 10^{-6}$ seconds for it by a delayed-coincidence technique and also verified the position of the transition in the decay scheme.

[205] E. Arbman and P. A. Tove, *Arkiv Fysik* **13**, 61 (1958).

One puzzling feature of the decay scheme is that the low-lying Bi^{206} levels at 83 and 167 keV, respectively, revealed in the complex alpha decay of At^{210} to this nucleus[206], are not involved in the electron capture decay of Po^{206} in spite of the complexity of the radiations in this latter case.

Polonium-206, being an even-even nucleus, is assumed to have spin and parity $0+$. The Bi^{206} daughter has 83 protons, one past a closed shell and hence most likely an $h_{9/2}$ proton, and three neutrons less than a closed shell. By analogy to Pb^{205} it is probable that the ground state neutron configuration is $f_{5/2}^{-1}$, $p_{1/2}^{-2}$ coupling to a resultant spin and parity of $5/2-$. Hence, the ground state spin of Bi^{206} may have a high value; at any rate the ground state spin is too high to permit an appreciable direct decay by electron capture to the ground state. According to the decay scheme, nearly all the decay proceeds to the high-lying 1379 keV level to which ARBMAN assigns the value $2+$.

WAHLBORN[207] has carried out a tentative theoretical investigation of the energy levels in Bi^{206} using the general method introduced by PRYCE.[198] Bismuth-206 is 4 particles removed from the doubly-closed nucleus Pb^{208} and

TABLE **10.17.** Configurations of Bi^{206}.

Configuration (three neutron holes plus one proton)	No.	Zero-order energy (MeV)	Parity	Spin-values (exponents = multiplicities)
$(p_{1/2})^2 f_{5/2} h_{9/2}$	Ih	0	$+$	2, 3, 4, 5, 6, 7
$(p_{1/2})^2 p_{3/2} h_{9/2}$	IIh	0.32	$+$	3, 4, 5, 6
$p_{1/2} (f_{5/2})^2 h_{9/2}$	IIIh	0.57	$\cdot +$	0, 1^2, 2^3, 3^4, 4^5, 5^5, 6^4, 7^3, 8^2, 9
$p_{1/2} f_{5/2} p_{3/2} h_{9/2}$	IVh	0.89	$+$	0, 1^3, 2^5, 3^7, 4^8, 5^8, 6^7, 7^5, 8^3, 9
$(p_{1/2})^2 i_{13/2} h_{9/2}$	Vh	1.06	$-$	2, 3, 4, 5, 6, 7, 8, 9, 10, 11
$(f_{5/2})^3 h_{9/2}$	VIh	1.14	$+$	0, 1, 2^2, 3^3, 4^3, 5^3, 6^3, 7^2, 8, 9
$p_{1/2} (p_{3/2})^2 h_{9/2}$	VIIh	1.21	$+$	2, 3^2, 4^3, 5^3, 6^2, 7
$(f_{5/2})^2 p_{3/2} h_{9/2}$	VIIIh	1.46	$+$	0, 1^4, 2^6, 3^8, 4^9, 5^9, 6^8, 7^6, 8^4, 9^2, 10
$p_{1/2} f_{5/2} i_{13/2} h_{9/2}$	IXh	1.63	$-$	0^2, 1^5, 2^7, 3^9, 4^{11}, 5^{12}, 6^{12}, 7^{12}, 8^{12} 9^{11}, 10^9, 11^7, 12^5, 13^3, 14
$(p_{1/2})^2 f_{5/2} f_{7/2}$	If	$\begin{cases} e_1 \approx \\ 0.90 \end{cases}$	$+$	1, 2, 3, 4, 5, 6
$(p_{1/2})^2 p_{3/2} f_{7/2}$	IIf	1.22	$+$	2, 3, 4, 5
$p_{1/2} (f_{5/2})^2 f_{7/2}$	IIIf	1.47	$+$	0, 1^3, 2^4, 3^5, 4^5, 5^4, 6^3, 7^2, 8
$(p_{1/2})^2 f_{5/2} i_{13/2}$	Ii	$\begin{cases} e_2 \approx \\ 1.56 \end{cases}$	$-$	4, 5, 6, 7, 8, 9

Reproduced from Arbman, *Nucl. Phys.* **3**, 644 (1957).

[206] R. W. Hoff, Ph.D. Thesis, *Univ. Calif. Rad. Lab. Report UCRL-2325*, Sept. 1953, unpublished.

[207] S. Wahlborn, *Nucl. Phys.* **3**, 644 (1957).

the low-lying levels up to a few MeV of excitation may result primarily from the superposition of the wave functions of the 4 particle or hole states with suitable correction for the two-body interactions of the extra nucleons.   The principal configurations which need to be considered are listed in Table 10.17. The energies of the individual neutron and proton states are taken from the experimental data on the levels of Pb^{207} (see Section 10.2.3) and of Bi^{209}, respectively.   The symbols e_1 and e_2 in the table refer to the first two excited levels observed in the inelastic scattering of neutrons[199] from Bi^{209} and assigned, without proof, to the orbitals $f_{7/2}$ and $i_{13/2}$.   It is seen that each configuration leads to a complex group of degenerate levels.   WAHLBORN[207] has roughly estimated the first-order interaction effects which cause shifting of the zero-order energy and removal of the degeneracies.   He has published a list of spins, parities and energies for numerous levels below 1.5 MeV and has made some tentative identifications of a few of his theoretical levels with the experimental levels observed by ARBMAN.[203]

10.3.5 *Polonium Isotopes with Mass Number Less than 206*

A few properties are known for the polonium isotopes of mass 205 down to 196, but owing to the difficulties of preparing pure samples of these isotopes and to their short half-lives no detailed study of them has been made.   All of them decay partly by alpha particle emission and partly by orbital electron capture.   The genetic relationship of these polonium isotopes to their electron capture decay descendants has been established in some cases, but essentially no information has been obtained on the details of the decay schemes for this mode of decay.   The principal information which has been sought for each isotope in addition to its half-life and mass number is the alpha particle energy.   The meager data available on the light polonium isotopes is summarized in Table 10.18.

KARRAKER, TEMPLETON, AND GHIORSO[208, 209] prepared polonium iso-topes in the mass range 200 to 205 by the bombardment of lead isotopes with high energy helium ions or of bismuth with high energy protons.   Each polonium isotope was laboriously identified by chemical separation of polonium, bismuth, lead and thallium fractions and by establishing the genetic relationship of the products of a long chain of activities produced from each other by electron capture processes.   The work was made difficult by the complex mixture of activities of rather similar half-life.   The alpha particle energies were measured in a gridded ionization chamber coupled to a pulse height analyzer.

More precise measurements of the alpha particle energies of the polonium isotopes Po^{197} through Po^{204} were made by a magnetic field method by

[208] D. G. Karraker and D. H. Templeton, *Phys. Rev.* **81**, 510 (1951).

[209] D. G. Karraker, A. Ghiorso, and D. H. Templeton, *Phys. Rev.* **83**, 390 (1953).

TABLE **10.18.** Alpha particle energies and half-lives of neutron deficient polonium isotopes

Research team and method of preparation

Mass number of polonium isotope	KARRAKER, GHIORSO AND TEMPLETON (1951) Bi + p		ROSENBLUM AND TYREN (1954) Bi + p		ATTERLING, FORSLING AND ÅSTRÖM (1958–9) W + Ne Pt + C12,13		TOVE (1958) Bi + p		FORSLING AND ALVÄGER (1961) Pt + C12 W + Ne (magnetic separation)		HOFF, ASARO AND PERLMAN (1963)	
	E_α (MeV)	$T_{1/2}$	E_α (MeV)	$T_{1/2}$	E_α (MeV)	$T_{1/2}$	E_α (MeV)	$T_{1/2}$	E_α (MeV)	$T_{1/2}$	E_α (MeV)	$T_{1/2}$
192							6.58	0.5 ± 0.1 sec				
193							6.47	4 sec				
194							6.38	13 sec				
195							6.26	30 sec				
196					6.13	1.8 min						
197			6.040	4 min	6.03	4 min						
198			5.935	6 min	5.93	7 min						
199			5.846	11 min	5.86	12 min			5.87	13 min		
200	5.84	11 min	5.770	8 min	5.77	10 min			5.86 + 5.75	12 min	5.860	9.4 min
201	5.70	18 min	5.671	17 min	5.68	18 min			5.57 + 5.67 + 5.77	16 min	5.674	19.5 min
202	5.59	52 min	5.575	55 min	5.58	43 min			5.57	50 min	5.580	44 min
203		47 min			5.48	45 ± 10 min			5.48			
204	5.37	3.8 hr	5.370	3.8 hr	5.38	3–4 hr			5.39	3.6 hr		
205	5.2	1.5 hr							5.24			

ROSENBLUM AND TYREN.[210] These investigators prepared samples by bombarding bismuth targets with 170 MeV protons in the Uppsala cyclotron. They then prepared polonium samples by electrodeposition on silver discs and used a portion of the cyclotron magnet as an alpha spectrometer. The focused alpha particles were detected in a suitably positioned nuclear emulsion. The magnetic field was held constant to one part in 10,000 during these measurements.

TOVE,[211] also working at Uppsala, has extended the measurement of the alpha particle energies to lighter isotopes by an ingenious experimental technique. In his experiment, a thin bismuth target was bombarded with a pulsed beam of high energy protons to prepare polonium activities. Then, without removal of the target from the cyclotron, the alpha particles emitted from the freshly formed polonium atoms in the target were focused in the magnetic field of the cyclotron, passed through a collimating slit, and allowed to strike a ZnS phosphor detector. The target, the slit and the detector formed the elements of a simple 180°-type magnetic spectrometer. With suitable timing of the beam pulse and of the sensitive time of the detector the half-life of particular alpha particle groups could be measured. The results of TOVE's study are summarized in Table 10.18. Mass assignments were made strictly by consideration of systematic trends in alpha-decay properties.

BELYAEV, KALYAMIN, AND MURIN[212] measured the ratio of alpha to the total decay rate for three of the light polonium isotopes; their results were: Po^{200} 0.80 ± 0.23 per cent, Po^{201} 0.79 ± 0.31 per cent, and Po^{203} ~ 0.02 per cent.

It is interesting to consider the variation in alpha disintegration energy versus mass number for the polonium isotopes which is shown in Fig. 10.31. There is a regular trend on both sides of the 126-neutron shell and a very abrupt change at the shell edge. This curve and others like it for other heavy elements are discussed in a general way in Chapter 1 and in considerable detail in Chapter 4.

Further study of the lightest isotopes of polonium should be greatly aided by new methods for their preparation, particularly by the bombardment of much lighter elements with heavy ions. A start in this direction has been made by ATTERLING, FORSLING, AND ÅSTRÖM[213] and by FORSLING AND ALVÄGER[213a] who bombarded tungsten with neon ions and platinum with

[210] S. Rosenblum and H. Tyren, *Compt. Rend.* **239**, 1205 (1954).

[211] P. A. Tove, *Arkiv Fysik* **13**, 549 (1958).

[212] B. N. Belyaev, A. V. Kalyamin, and A. N. Murin, *Bull. Acad. Sci. USSR, Phys. Ser.* (Columbia Transl. Series) **25**, 886 (1961).

[213] H. Atterling, W. Forsling, and B. Åström, *Physica* **22**, 1193A (1956); see also *Proceedings of the Conference on Reactions Between Complex Nuclei* held at Gatlinburg, Tennessee, May 1958; *Oak Ridge National Laboratory Report ORNL-2606* (1958). See also *Arkiv Fysik* **15**, 81, 279 (1959).

[213a] W. Forsling and T. Alväger. *Arkiv Fysik* **19**, 353 (1961).

carbon ions to produce polonium isotopes in the mass range 196 to 202. HOFF, ASARO, AND PERLMAN[213b] contributed data on Po^{200}, Po^{201}, and Po^{202}. The results of these three studies are summarized in Table 10.18.

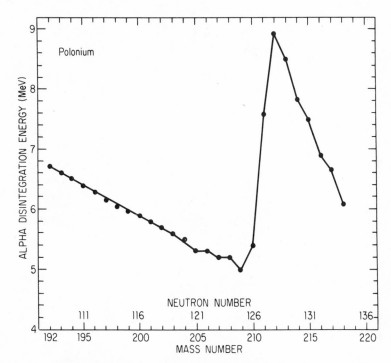

FIG. **10.31.** Alpha disintegration energies of polonium isotopes plotted against mass number.

10.4 THE ISOTOPES OF ASTATINE

10.4.1 *General Discussion of Astatine—The Discovery of Astatine*

From our present knowledge of astatine and the nuclear energy surface in the region of this element we know that all isotopes are radioactive with quite short half-lives.   In fact, of the first 100 elements in the periodic system only francium (element 87) is more unstable.   Astatine occurs in nature only as a short-lived trace element continuously replenished by the decay of longer-lived antecedents.   Before this fact was known, several investigators endeavored to isolate material from natural sources with the chemical and physical properties of the missing halogen element of atomic number 85.

213b R. W. Hoff, F. Asaro, and I. Perlman, *J. Inorg. Nucl. Chem.* **25**, 1303 (1963).

These earlier unsuccessful searches, or erroneous reports of successful searches, are summarized briefly in the first edition of a textbook by EMELEUS AND ANDERSON[214] and are discussed critically in review articles by KARLIK[215] and by HULUBEI.[216]

The first reliable description of the properties of element 85 came from the famous 1940 work of CORSON, MACKENZIE, AND SEGRÈ[217] who synthesized At[211] by the bombardment of bismuth with helium ions in the 60-inch cyclotron of the University of California by the reaction,

$$Bi^{209}(\alpha, 2n)At^{211}$$

This isotope has a half-life of 7.5 hours and decays 40 per cent by alpha particle emission and 60 per cent by K-electron capture. The radiochemical properties were studied in some detail and shown to be distinct in some significant way from every heavy element which could possibly be produced in such a cyclotron bombardment, and indeed, from any element in the periodic system. CORSON, MACKENZIE, AND SEGRÈ[217] are credited with the discovery of element 85 and have chosen the name astatine from a Greek word meaning unstable. Astatine has some of the expected properties of an eka-iodine but is much more metallic and in many ways resembles its neighbor element polonium. The chemical properties of astatine are discussed elsewhere.[218-223] Although some 20 or more isotopes of astatine are now known, At[211] remains the most suitable for use in the study of the chemistry of this element. From this it can be seen that a study of the chemistry of astatine in other than trace concentrations is out of the question.

The isotopes of astatine at or below the 126 neutron shell, to be discussed in this chapter, are prepared in three general ways:

1. Bombardment of bismuth with helium ions of moderate to high energy.

2. Bombardment of thorium or uranium with protons (or deuterons or helium ions) of very high energy (hundreds of MeV).

[214] H. J. Emeleus and J. S. Anderson, *Modern Aspects of Inorganic Chemistry*, 1st Ed. (New York: Van Nostrand, 1938).

[215] B. Karlik, *Monatsh* **77**, 348 (1947).

[216] H. Hulubei, *J. Chem. Phys.* **44**, 225 (1947).

[217] D. R. Corson, K. R. MacKenzie, and E. Segrè, *Phys. Rev.* **57**, 457, 1089 (1944); *Nature* **159**, 24 (1947).

[218] D. R. Corson, K. R. MacKenzie, and E. Segrè, *Phys. Rev.* **58**, 672 (1940).

[219] G. L. Johnson, R. F. Leininger, and E. Segrè, *J. Chem. Phys.* **17**, 1 (1949).

[220] E. Anders, *Ann. Rev. Nucl. Sci.* **9**, 203 (1959).

[221] E. H. Appelman, Ph.D. Thesis, University of California, 1959; see *Univ. Calif. Rad. Lab. Report UCRL-9025*, 1959.

[222] E. H. Appelman, "The Radiochemistry of Astatine," Report issued by Subcommittee on Radiochemistry of National Academy of Sciences, National Research Council, 1960. *NAS-NS-3012*.

[223] E. L. Kelly and E. Segrè, *Phys. Rev.* **75**, 999 (1949).

3. Bombardment of lighter elements with complex nuclear projectiles. An example is the bombardment of gold with nitrogen ions.

Several years after the historic work of CORSON, MACKENZIE, AND SEGRÈ,[218] KELLY AND SEGRÈ[223] looked again at the products of bombardment of bismuth using helium ions of 38 MeV and found 8.3 hour At^{210} produced by the $(\alpha, 3n)$ reaction. The decay of this species is more than 99 per cent by electron capture. Later measurements by HOFF AND ASARO[224] indicated an alpha-branching of 0.17 per cent; the partial alpha half-life is about 0.55 years. Further discussion of At^{211} and At^{210} is reserved for Sections 10.4.3 and 10.4.4 below.

The list of astatine isotopes has been extended well below mass number 209 by two types of preparative reactions. The first is represented by the work of BARTON, GHIORSO, AND PERLMAN[225] who bombarded bismuth with helium ions of 350 MeV energy and measured some properties of isotopes with mass numbers ranging down to 203. Nuclear reactions involving heavy ions as projectiles are another general method of preparation of the lighter isotopes. Astatine isotopes have been identified[226] in the bombardment of gold targets with energetic ions of C^{12}, C^{13}, N^{14}, and O^{16} and of platinum targets with N^{14} ions. The published results of all these studies are summarized in Table 10.19.

Although orbital electron capture is a prominent mode of decay for all of these isotopes, no careful study of the radiations emitted in this process has been made. The chief information we have on each species is the half-life and the energy of the main alpha particle group. Isomerism has been reported in At^{208}, At^{206}, and At^{204}, but the 1963 work of THORESEN, ASARO, AND PERLMAN[227] indicates that earlier reports are incorrect and that only one form exists of each of these isotopes.

Table 10.20 lists the isotopes of astatine containing more than 126 neutrons in their nuclei. All of these are very short-lived alpha-emitters. Three of them occur as members of the decay chains of uranium and actinium. The natural occurrence of astatine is covered in the following subsection of this chapter. The other isotopes listed in Table 10.20 are members of the families of artificial radioactivities collateral to the four main decay chains and are discussed in Chapter 7. The only information available on them is a half-life and an alpha particle energy.

The alpha disintegration energy of the astatine isotopes is plotted versus

[224] R. W. Hoff and F. Asaro, unpublished results (1953).

[225] G. W. Barton, A. Ghiorso, and I. Perlman, *Phys. Rev.* **82**, 13 (1951).

[226] The first report in the literature was that of Miller, Hamilton, Putnam, Haymond, and Rossi, *Phys. Rev.* **80**, 486 (1950); later reports are cited in Table 10.19.

[227] P. E. Thoresen, F. Asaro, and I. Perlman, unpublished results, 1963; in publication, *J. Inorg. Nucl. Chem*, 1964.

mass number in Fig. 10.32.   This curve shows the characteristic break at the
126-neutron shell.   The most stable isotope is At^{210} with 125 neutrons.
Astatine isotopes lighter than those now known would be expected, from an
extension of this curve in the light mass direction, to have high alpha energy

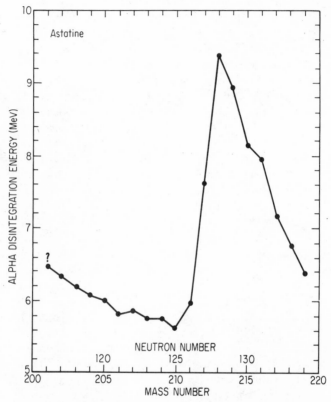

FIG. **10.32.** Alpha disintegration energy versus mass number
of astatine isotopes.

and short alpha-decay half-lives. Also, such isotopes will certainly have
short half-lives for decay by capture of an orbital electron. This figure
would also predict that heavy isotopes with mass number greater than 219 will
be more stable toward alpha decay.   However, an examination of the trends
in beta-decay energy suggests that such nuclei will be so unstable toward
negative beta decay that their half-lives will be quite short. From these
observations we can conclude that the prospects for the discovery of a long-
lived form of astatine are slight and that 8.3 hour At^{210} is likely to remain the
longest-lived form of the element.

TABLE **10.19.** Isotopes of astatine with 126 or fewer neutrons.

Isotope	Half-life	Observed mode of decay	Alpha energy (MeV)	Method of preparation
At^{212}	0.22 sec	α	—	$Bi(\alpha, n)$[1]
	0.20 ± 0.04 sec[21]	α	7.87 ± 0.07	$Bi(\alpha, n)$[21]
	0.305 sec[22]	α	$\begin{cases} 7.60\ (20\%) \\ 7.66\ (80\%) \end{cases}$	$Bi(\alpha, n)$[22]
At^{212m}	0.120 sec[22]	α	$\begin{cases} 7.82\ (80\%) \\ 7.88\ (20\%) \end{cases}$	$Bi(\alpha, n)$[22]
At^{211}	7.5 hr[3]	$\alpha\ (40.9\%)$	5.862[5]	$Bi(\alpha, 2n)$ Ref. 3
	7.21 hr[19]			
	7.2 hr[7]	$EC\ (59.1\%)$[4]		daughter Em^{211} Ref. 6
At^{210}	8.3 hr[8]	$\alpha\ (0.17\%)$	$\begin{cases} 5.519\ (32\%) \\ 5.437\ (31\%) \\ 5.355\ (37\%) \end{cases}$[5]	$Bi(\alpha, 3n)$ Ref. 8
		$EC\ (99+\%)$[5]		daughter Em^{210} Ref. 6
At^{209}	5.5 hr[9]	$\alpha\ (\sim 5\%)$	5.642[10]	$Bi(\alpha, 4n)$ Ref. 9
		$EC\ (\sim 95\%)$[9]		daughter Em^{209} Ref. 6
At^{208}	1.7 hr[11]	$\alpha\ (0.5\%)$	5.65[11]	$Bi(\alpha, 5n)$ Ref. 9, 12
		$EC\ (99.5\%)$[11]		daughter Fr^{212} Ref. 11
At^{207}	1.8 hr[14,13,18]	$EC\ (\sim 90\%)$	5.75[9,18]	$Bi(\alpha, 6n)$ Ref. 9
	2.0 hr[9]	$\alpha\ (\sim 10\%)$[9]	5.750[15]	$Au + N^{14}$ Ref. 13, 14, 15, 18
				daughter Em^{207} Ref. 13
				$Pt + N^{14}$ Ref. 16
At^{206}	$\begin{cases} 22\ \text{min.}[15] \\ \\ 29.5\ \text{min}[17] \end{cases}$	$\alpha\ (0.9\%)$[17] $\\ \\$ $EC\ (99+\%)$	5.699[15] $\\ \\$ $5.70, 5.80, 5.90(?)$[18]	$Au + C^{12}, N^{14}, O^{16}$ Ref. 15, 17, 18 $\\ \\$ $Bi(\alpha, 7n)$ Ref. 20
At^{205}	$\begin{cases} 26.2\ \text{min}[15,17] \\ 25\ \text{min}[9,14] \\ \\ 22.7\ \text{min}[16] \end{cases}$	$\alpha\ (18\%)$[17] $\\ \\$ $EC\ (82\%)$	5.90[18] $\\ 5.899$[15]	$\begin{cases} Bi(\alpha, 8n)\ \text{Ref. 9} \\ Au + C^{12}, N^{14}, O^{16} \\ \text{Ref. 14–18} \\ Pt + N^{14}\ \text{Ref. 16} \end{cases}$
At^{204}	9.3 min[15,17]	$\alpha\ (4.5\%)$[17]	5.950[15]	$Au + C^{12}, N^{14}, O^{16}$ Ref. 15, 17, 18
At^{203}	9 min[18]	$EC\ (95.5\%)$	5.95[18]	$Bi(\alpha, 9n)$ Ref. 20
	7 min[9,18]	$\alpha\ (14\%)$[17]	6.10[9]	$Bi(\alpha, 10n)$ Ref. 9
	7.4 min[15,17]	$EC\ (86\%)$	6.086[15]	$Pt + N^{14}$ Ref. 16
	7.1 min[16]		6.09[18]	$Au + C^{12}, N^{14}, O^{16}$ Ref. 15, 17, 18
At^{202}	3 min[15,17,18]	$\alpha\ (12\%)$[17]	$6.133\ (64\%)$	$Au + C^{12}, N^{14}, O^{16}$ Ref. 15, 17, 18
		$EC\ (88\%)$	$6.231\ (36\%)$[15]	
At^{201}	1.5 min[15]	α	6.348[15]	$Au + C^{12}, N^{14}, O^{16}$ Ref. 15, 17
At^{200}(?)	0.8 min[15]	α	$6.42\ (\sim 60\%)$ $\\ 6.47\ (\sim 40\%)$	$Au + C^{12}$, Ref. 15

[1] M. Weisbluth, T. M. Putnam, and E. Segrè, unpublished results (1948).

[2] M. M. Winn, *Proc. Phys. Soc.* (London) **67A**, 949 (1954).

[3] D. R. Corson, K. R. MacKenzie, and E. Segrè, *Phys. Rev.* **58**, 672 (1940).

[4] H. M. Neumann and I. Perlman, *Phys. Rev.* **81**, 958 (1951).

[5] R. W. Hoff, *Univ. Calif. Rad. Lab. Report, UCRL-2325* (1953).

[6] F. F. Momyer, Jr. and E. K. Hyde, *J. Inorg. Nucl. Chem.* **1**, 274 (1955).

[7] P. R. Gray, *Phys. Rev.* **101**, 1306 (1956).

[8] E. L. Kelly and E. Segrè, *Phys. Rev.* **74**, 999 (1949).

[9] G. W. Barton, Jr., A. Ghiorso, and I. Perlman, *Phys. Rev.* **82**, 13 (1951).

[10] J. P. Hummel, *Univ. Calif. Rad. Lab. Report UCRL-3456* (1956).

[11] E. K. Hyde, A. Ghiorso, and G. T. Seaborg, *Phys. Rev.* **77**, 765 (1950).

[12] A. Stoner, *Univ. Calif. Rad. Lab. Report UCRL-3471* (1956).

[13] A. Stoner and E. K. Hyde, *J. Inorg. Nucl. Chem.* **4**, 77 (1957).

[14] W. E. Burcham, *Proc. Phys. Soc.* (London) **67A**, 555, 733 (1954).

[15] R. W. Hoff, F. Asaro, and I Perlman, *J. Inorg. Nucl. Chem.* **25**, 1303 (1963).

[16] W. E. Burcham and B. C. Haywood, *Proc. Phys. Soc.* (London) **69A**, 862 (1956).

[17] R. Latimer, G. E. Gordon, and T. D. Thomas, *J. Inorg. Nucl. Chem.* **17**, 1 (1960).

[18] Forsling, Alväger, Holm, Melin, Uhler, and Åström, *Arkiv Fysik* **19**, 83 (1961); isotope separation used to identify mass numbers.

[19] E. H. Appelman, *Phys. Rev.* **121**, 253 (1961).

[20] P. E. Thoresen, F. Asaro, and I. Perlman, unpublished results cited in *Report UCRL-10624*, (1963).

[21] J. C. Ritter and W. G. Smith, *Phys. Rev.* **128**, 1778 (1962).

[22] W. B. Jones, *Phys. Rev.* **130**, 2042 (1963).

[23] P. E. Thoresen, F. Asaro, and I. Perlman, unpublished results, 1963. These authors have evidence disproving the existence of 6.3 hr At^{208}, 2.9 hr At^{206}, and 25 min At^{204}. In publication, *J. Inorg. Nucl. Chem.* (1964).

TABLE **10.20**. The isotopes of astatine with more than 126 neutrons.

Isotope	Half-life	Observed mode of decay	Measured energy of alpha radiation (MeV)	Source
At^{219}	0.9 min	α (97%) β (3%)	6.27	Natural source— daughter AcK
At^{218}	1.5–2.0 sec	α	6.6975 (94%) 6.653 (6%)	Natural source— daughter RaA
At^{217}	0.018 sec	α	7.05	Daughter Fr^{221} in U^{233} decay chain
At^{216}	$\sim 3 \times 10^{-4}$ sec	α	7.79	Daughter Fr^{220} in Pa^{228} decay chain
At^{215}	$\sim 10^{-4}$ sec	α	8.00	Daughter Fr^{219} in Pa^{227} decay chain
At^{215}	short	α	8.04	Natural source— daughter AcA
At^{214}	2×10^{-6} sec est.	α	8.78	Daughter Fr^{218} in Pa^{226} decay chain
At^{213}	$\ll 1$ sec	α	~ 9.2	Descendant Pa^{225} (preliminary study)

PERLMAN, GHIORSO, AND SEABORG[228] discussed the question whether any isotopes of astatine are beta stable and reached the conclusion that it is borderline whether At^{213} and At^{215} are or are not. FOREMAN AND SEABORG,[229] from a consideration of data published later, concluded that At^{213} is unstable by 0.24 MeV but still found that the stability of At^{215} with respect to Em^{215} was unsettled. It is quite possible that astatine, like elements 43 and 61, has no β^- stable form. Whatever the final decision on this, we note from Fig. 10.32 that At^{213} and At^{215} fall at the maximum of alpha instability and have no possibility of long existence.

10.4.2 Astatine in Nature

Because of the high nuclear instability of all astatine isotopes, the search for element 85 in natural sources is reduced to an investigation of possible short-lived isotopes present in heavy element mineral sources as the result of the radioactive decay of long-lived parent isotopes.

In Section 6.6 of Chapter 6 is discussed the research of PEPPARD AND CO-WORKERS[230] proving the presence of minute amounts of the $4n + 1$ series in uranium ores. These investigators found about 2×10^{-12} parts by mass of Np^{237} to one part of U^{238}. Since the 0.02-second At^{217} is a member of the $(4n + 1)$ series, this report implies the existence of this astatine isotope in uranium ores, and, indeed, the α-particles of At^{217} were observed by them in the α-spectrum analyses of Ac^{225} samples isolated from uranium ores.

In the uranium-radium series it is known from the work of KARLIK AND BERNERT[231] and the confirmatory work of WALEN[232] that RaA (Po^{218}) undergoes a very slight β^- branching to produce At^{218} (see also Section 6.2). In these experiments, alpha particles of 6.63 MeV energy were observed to grow into a freshly deposited sample of the 3.05 minute RaA and these were ascribed to At^{218}.

$$3 \text{ min RaA} \xrightarrow[2 \times 10^{-2}\%]{\beta^-} \begin{array}{c} At^{218} \\ \sim 2 \text{ sec} \end{array}$$

$$99 + \% \Bigg\downarrow \alpha \qquad\qquad \Bigg\downarrow \alpha$$

It has also been reported that ThA in the thorium decay series undergoes

[228] I. Perlman, A. Ghiorso, and G. T. Seaborg, *Phys. Rev.* **77**, 26 (1950).

[229] B. M. Foreman, Jr. and G. T. Seaborg, *J. Inorg. Nucl. Chem.* **7**, 305 (1958).

[230] D. F. Peppard, G. W. Mason, P. R. Gray, and J. F. Mech, *J. Am. Chem. Soc.* **74**, 6081 (1952).

[231] B. Karlik and T. Bernert, *Naturwiss* **31**, 298 (1943); *Zeit Phys.* **123**, 51 (1944); see also the later work of F. Hessberger and B. Karlik, *Sitzungsber, Ost. Akad. der Wissenschaften* **161**, 51 (1952).

[232] R. J. Walen, *J. Phys. Rad.* VII, 95 (1949); *Compt. Rend.* **227**, 1090 (1948).

rare β^- branching to produce At^{216}.   This report is discussed in section 6.3 where reasons are given why this claim must be rejected.

In the case of the actinium decay series, the main line of decay does not include an isotope of astatine.   The isotope AcA (Po^{215}) decays overwhelmingly by alpha emission, but from closed decay energy cycles it is known that AcA is unstable toward beta emission by about 0.7 MeV and hence might have a detectable branching to form At^{215}.   From studies of the Pa^{227} collateral series, this isotope is known to have a half-life of $\sim 10^{-4}$ seconds for the emission of 8.00 MeV alpha particles.   The work of KARLIK AND BERNERT[233] as extended by AVIGNON[234] indicates that AcA undergoes β^- branching to the extent of 5×10^{-4} per cent to form At^{215}.   (See also Section 6.4.)

There is an additional place in the actinium series where an isotope of astatine appears as a result of rare branching decay events.   This is discussed fully in Section 6.4 of Chapter 6 and is exhibited graphically in Fig. 6.35 in that section.   Actinium-227 decays by alpha branching in 1.2 per cent of its decay events to produce Fr^{223} (AcK); this isotope in turn decays by alpha emission in 4×10^{-3} per cent of its disintegrations to produce At^{219}. HYDE AND GHIORSO[235] were able to isolate At^{219} chemically from a francium fraction which in turn had been separated from a 20 millicurie source of Ac^{227}.   It was shown that At^{219} has a half-life of 0.9 minutes, and that it decays 97 per cent by alpha emission and 3 per cent by beta emission.   This is the longest-lived astatine isotope in nature and the only one long-lived enough to permit chemical isolation.

10.4.3 *Astatine-211*

The yield of At^{211} as a function of helium ion energy in the reaction $Bi^{209}(\alpha, 2n)At^{211}$ was measured by KELLY AND SEGRÈ[236] and by RAMLER, WING, HENDERSON, AND HUIZENGA.[237]   (See Section 5.2 of Chapter 5.) It is important to note that if pure At^{211} is desired a beam energy below the 29 MeV threshold for the $(\alpha, 3n)$ reaction should be used.   Pure At^{211} uncontaminated with At^{210} is desirable for tracer studies of the chemistry of astatine, because At^{210} decays into the 138-day alpha emitter Po^{210}; if one is counting the alpha particles of At^{211} to determine its chemical behavior, the presence of Po^{210} alpha activity is objectionable.

Several studies of the decay scheme of At^{211} carried out to extend the original work of CORSON, MACKENZIE, AND SEGRÈ[238] have shown the decay

[233] B. Karlik and T. Bernert, *Z. Physik* **123**, 51 (1944); *Naturwiss* **32**, 44 (1943).

[234] P. Avignon, *J. Phys. Rad.* **11**, 521 (1950).

[235] E. K. Hyde and A. Ghiorso, *Phys. Rev.* **90**, 267 (1953).

[236] Kelly and Segrè, *Phys. Rev.* **75**, 999 (1949).

[237] Ramler, Wing, Henderson, and Huizenga, *Phys. Rev.* **114**, 154 (1959).

scheme to be quite simple. The half-life has been revised slightly to 7.2 hours.[239] The division of the At[211] disintegrations between orbital electron capture and alpha particle emission has been measured by NEUMANN AND PERLMAN[240] to be 59.1 per cent electron capture and 40.9 per cent alpha emission. The alpha spectrum consists of a single group[241] at 5.862 MeV

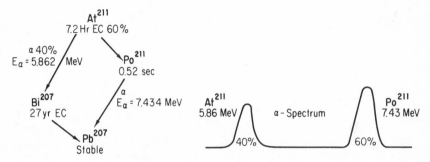

FIG. 10.33. Decay scheme of At[211]. The characteristic alpha spectrum of At[211] and its short-lived Po[211] daughter is shown. The 40/60 ratio of the 5.862 MeV and 7.430 MeV serves as the "signature" of any *bona fide* sample of At[211].

leading to the ground state of Bi[207]. Since Bi[207] has a 27-year half-life its radiations make a negligible contribution to the radiations of a sample of At[211]. The electron capture decay proceeds only to the 0.52-second isomer of Po[211] since the decay energy is too low to permit the formation of the 25-second isomer. MIHELICH, SCHARDT, AND SEGRÈ[242] examined the radiation of intense sources of At[211]. In addition to K and L x-rays and Auger electrons, some small-intensity photo peaks of 880, 562 and 671 keV gamma rays appeared. The first two are the expected transitions in Pb[207] following the decay of Po[211]. The gamma ray of 671 keV which appears in 0.4 per cent abundance may follow a small electron capture branching to an excited state, but this is uncertain. GRAY[239] also found preliminary evidence for the conversion electrons and photons of a 62.3 keV transition present in low intensity in the decay of At[211].

GRAY[239] has studied the Auger electron spectrum of At[211] in order to measure the Auger coefficient of polonium for which he obtained the value 0.058. HOFF[243] has made careful measurements on the Auger electron energies as given in Table 10.21.

The nuclear spin of At[211] has been measured by the method of atomic

[238] D. R. Corson, K. R. MacKenzie, and E. Segrè, *Phys. Rev.* **57**, 459, 1087 (1944).

[239] P. R. Gray, *Phys. Rev.* **101**, 1306 (1956).

[240] H. M. Neumann and I. Perlman, *Phys. Rev.* **81**, 958 (1951).

[241] R. W. Hoff and F. Asaro, unpublished information, 1953.

[242] J. W. Mihelich, A. W. Schardt, and E. Segrè, *Phys. Rev.* **95**, 1508 (1954).

beams by GARVIN, GREEN, LIPWORTH, AND NIERENBERG.[244] This was an achievement of some magnitude because of the difficulty of forming a monatomic beam of astatine.   A nuclear spin value of 9/2 was found; this is the value expected from the nuclear shell model.

10.4.4 *Astatine-210*

The isotope At^{210}, discovered by KELLY AND SEGRÈ,[236] and shown by them to have a half-life of 8.3 hours is prepared by the reaction

$$Bi^{209}(\alpha, 3n)At^{210}$$

The threshold for this reaction is at 29 MeV and the peak yield falls at about 40 MeV.   At this most favorable energy the yield of the $(\alpha, 2n)$ product, At^{211}, is low by comparison.   However, if the helium ion energy is raised beyond 40 MeV, some 5.5 hour At^{209} is produced by the $(\alpha, 4n)$ reaction, which is undesirable if the purpose of the sample preparation is to study the radiations of At^{210}.   On the other hand, considerable At^{211} contamination

TABLE 10.21. Energies of *K*-Auger electrons from At^{211} decay.*

K-Auger electron	Energy experimental (keV)
$K - L_{I}L_{I}$	58.85
$K - L_{II}L_{I}$	59.56
$K - L_{III}L_{I}$	62.00
$K - L_{II}L_{III}$	62.63
$K - L_{II}L_{III}$	65.12
$K - L_{II}L_{II}$	60.18
$K - L_{I}M_{I}$	72.04
$K - L_{I}M_{II}$	—
$K - L_{I}M_{III}$	72.61
$K - L_{II}M_{II}$	72.90
$K - L_{I}M_{V}$	73.37
$K - L_{II}M_{III}$	—
$K - L_{III}M_{II}$	75.14
$K - L_{III}M_{III}$	—

* For information on *K*-Auger electrons for the entire heavy element region see Appendix III, Volume I.

These data collected by HOFF.[243] Similar data have been published by GRAY.[239]

[243] R. W. Hoff, unpublished information.

[244] H. L. Garvin, T. M. Green, E. Lipworth, and W. A. Nierenberg, *Phys. Rev. Letters* **1**, 74 (1958).

can be tolerated because the radiations of At^{211} are so simple. HOFF AND HOLLANDER[245] recommend an alpha-particle energy of 38 MeV. Astatine-210 may also be prepared by an indirect method[207] involving the bombardment of thorium with 350 MeV protons to produce Em^{210} which is isolated from the other reaction products and later used as a source of its At^{210} daughter.

Astatine-210 decays by alpha emission to a slight extent (0.17 per cent) to form Bi^{206}. The alpha spectrum is complex and consists of the following three groups[247]: 5.519 MeV (32 per cent), 5.437 MeV (31 per cent), and 5.355 MeV (37 per cent).

The principal mode of decay of At^{210} is by orbital electron capture to the nucleus Po^{210}. The decay energy available for this process is about

TABLE 10.22. Principal gamma transitions in the decay of At^{210}.

Energy (keV)	Multipole order	Basis of multipole assignment	Transition intensity	
			HOFF-HOLLANDER[245]	MIHELICH et al.[248]
46.5	E2	L-subshell conversion ratios	44	34
83.4	E2	L-subshell conversion ratios		
116.1	M1	L-subshell conversion ratio and K/L ratio	12	5
125.2	E2	L-subshell ratios		
245.1	E2	L-subshell ratio K/L ratio K conversion coeff.	97	99
402.1	not E1	K conversion coeff.	≤4	
1181	E2	K conversion coeff. K/L conversion ratio	100	100
1436 1482	E1	K conversion coeff.	}61	1436–35 1482–48
1598	(E1)		18	19
2226				weak

[245] R. W. Hoff and J. M. Hollander, *Phys. Rev.* **109**, 447 (1958).

[246] F. F. Momyer, Jr. and E. K. Hyde, *J. Inorg. Nucl. Chem.* **1**, 274 (1955).

[247] R. W. Hoff and F. Asaro as reported by R. W. Hoff in *Univ. Calif. Rad. Lab. Report UCRL-2325*, September 1953, unpublished.

4 MeV so that high-lying levels in Po^{210} may be reached and the resulting gamma ray cascades can lead to a very complex decay scheme.

The radiations accompanying the electron capture decay of At^{210} have been carefully investigated by two research groups.[245, 248] The most precise information was obtained from careful studies of conversion electrons in a series of permanent-magnet electron spectrographs, but valuable supplementary information was obtained from scintillation spectrometers, from electromagnetic beta spectrometers, gamma-gamma coincidence spectrometers, and electron-photon coincidence spectrometers. The principal gamma ray transitions are listed in Table 10.22. In addition to these transitions the conversion electrons of a number of other transitions were seen in such low intensity that they could not be completely characterized or placed with any certainty in a decay scheme. Auger electrons were also observed. FUNK, ET AL.[249] measured half-lives of 1.8 ± 0.2 nsec and 38 ± 5 nsec for the 1431- and 1478-keV levels, respectively. The decay scheme of At^{210} as given by HOFF AND HOLLANDER[245] and including all the more prominent radiations is reproduced in Fig. 10.34. This decay scheme is nearly identical with one given by MIHELICH, SCHARDT, AND SEGRÈ[248] and these two papers should be consulted for the detailed arguments upon which this scheme is based.* A number of the weaker transitions are not placed in this scheme.

The level scheme of Po^{210} is of some theoretical interest since Po^{210} has just two more protons than Pb^{208}. In this respect it is similar to the Pb^{206} nucleus which has two neutrons less than Pb^{208}. In the case of Pb^{206} some highly successful shell model calculations of the level scheme have been carried through as is discussed in some detail earlier in this chapter. Similar calculations can be made for Po^{210} with the one important difference that the necessary empirical data on the proton states beyond the 82 proton shell are not well established.

A preliminary estimation of the theoretical level system of Po^{210} has been carried out by HOFF AND HOLLANDER[245] according to the general procedure laid down in an earlier paper by PRYCE.[250] These authors examined the experimental data on the inelastic scattering of neutrons[251] by Bi^{209} and concluded that the lowest states of protonic excitation were $h_{9/2}$ (ground),

[248] J. W. Mihelich, A. W. Schardt, and E. Segrè, *Phys. Rev.* **95**, 1508 (1954).

[249] E. G. Funk, Jr., *et al.*, *Phys. Rev.* **129**, 757 (1963).

[250] M. H. L. Pryce, *Proc. Roy. Soc.* (London) **A65**, 773 (1952).

[251] M. A. Rothman and C. E. Mandeville, *Phys. Rev.* **93**, 793 (1954); Eliot, Hicks, Beghian, and Halban, *Phys. Rev.* **94**, 144 (1954); R. M. Kiehn and C. Goodman, *Phys. Rev.* **95**, 989 (1954); Scherrer, Allison, and Faust, *Phys. Rev.* **96**, 386 (1954).

[252] N. Newby and E. J. Konopinski, *Phys. Rev.* **115**, 434 (1959).

* A later paper by F. Schima, E. G. Funk, Jr., and J. W. Mihelich, *Phys. Rev.* **132**, 2650 (1963), may also be consulted.

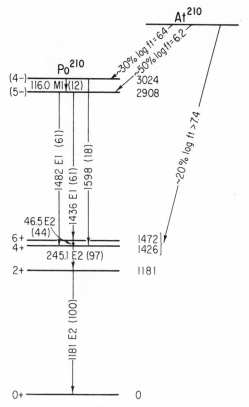

FIG. **10.34.** Decay scheme for the electron
capture decay of At[210] as drawn by HOFF
AND HOLLANDER.[245]

$f_{7/2}$ (900 keV), and $i_{13/2}$ (1.60 MeV). It was assumed that the low-lying levels
in Po[210] would arise from all possible double combinations of these proton
states. With the proton-proton interactions energy neglected these combinations would lead to the states listed in Table 10.23. The high degeneracy

TABLE **10.23.** Po[210] proton configuration.

Configuration	Unshifted energy (MeV)	Spins	Parity
$h_{9/2}{}^2$	0	0, 2, 4, 6, 8	+
$h_{9/2}\,f_{7/2}$	0.90	1, 2, 3 ⋯ 8	+
$h_{9/2}\,i_{13/2}$	1.60	2, 3, 4 ⋯ 11	−
$f_{7/2}{}^2$	1.80	0, 2, 4, 6	+
$f_{7/2}\,i_{13/2}$	2.50	3, 4, 5 ⋯ 10	−
$i_{13/2}{}^2$	3.20	0, 2, 4 ⋯ 12	+

of the states listed in this table is lifted when the interparticle forces are considered. HOFF AND HOLLANDER estimated the effects of these forces by a very crude semi-empirical method and arrived at a theoretical spectrum which accounted satisfactorily for all the experimental levels below 3 MeV.

NEWBY AND KONOPINSKI[252] carried through a more exact calculation based on the same zero-order states listed in Table 10.23. They computed the

TABLE **10.24.** Calculated levels in $Po^{210}*$.

Configuration	J	Energy (keV)
$h_{9/2}{}^2$	0	0^{b}
	2	1085^{c}
	4	1430^{c}
	6	1545^{c}
	8	1636
$h_{9/2} f_{7/2}$	1	2702
	2	2634^{c}
	3	2633
	4	2557^{c}
	5	2597
	6	2450^{c}
	7	2573
	8	2030
$h_{9/2} i_{13.2}$	2	3367
	3	3308
	4	3337
	5	3229
	6	3326
	7	3145
	8	3329
	9	2988
	10	3329
	11	Not calculated
$f_{7/2}{}^2$	0	1806^{b}
	2	2983^{c}
	4	3305^{c}
	6	3390^{c}
$f_{7/2} i_{13/2}$	3–10	Not calculated
$i_{13/2}{}^2$	0	4478^{b}
	2	4481^{c}
	4	4646^{c}
	6	4731^{c}
	8, 10, 12	Not calculated

* From Newby and Konopinski, *Phys. Rev.* **115**, 442 (1959).

b Mixing of $h_{9/2}{}^2$, $f_{7/2}{}^2$, and $i_{13/2}{}^2$.

c Mixing of $h_{9/2}{}^2$, $h_{9/2} f_{7/2}$, $f_{7/2}{}^2$, and $i_{13/2}{}^2$.

two proton interactions for a central interaction potential of the form

$$V(1, 2) = U(r)[\pi_t + p\pi_s] \times (1/2)(1 + P_M)$$

where the radial function $U(r)$ is of Gaussian form with parameters (not shown) evaluated from free nucleon-nucleon forces; π_t and π_s are triplet and singlet projection operators, and P_M stands for the Majorana exchange operator. Configuration mixing was computed for all levels arising from the $h_{9/2}{}^2$ configuration. The levels having $J = 2, 4, 6$ were computed by diagonalizing the matrices involving the $h_{9/2}{}^2$, $(h_{9/2}, f_{7/2})$, $f_{7/2}{}^2$ and $i_{13/2}{}^2$ configurations. The effect of Coulomb interaction was also calculated.

TABLE 10.25. Calculated eigenfunctions in Po^{210}.

Energy (keV)	Eigenfunctions			
	$h_{9/2}{}^2$	$f_{7/2}{}^2$	$i_{13/2}{}^2$	$h_{9/2} f_{7/2}$
$J = 0$				
0	0.9432	0.1008	0.3167	
1806	0.0390	0.9127	0.4068	
4478	0.3301	−0.3960	0.8569	
$J = 2$				
1085	0.9821	0.0417	0.0542	0.1755
2634	−0.0478	0.9958	0.0773	0.0067
2983	−0.0068	−0.0737	0.9672	0.2431
4481	0.1820	0.0334	0.2360	0.9540
$J = 4$				
1430	0.9927	0.0690	0.0373	0.0919
2557	−0.0738	0.9960	0.0391	0.0330
3305	−0.0233	−0.0366	0.9914	0.1231
4646	0.0928	0.0422	0.1188	0.9876
$J = 6$				
1545	0.9935	0.0945	0.0250	0.0590
2450	−0.0979	0.9936	0.0390	0.0410
3390	−0.0174	−0.0380	0.9968	0.0676
4731	0.0560	0.0491	0.0646	0.9951

From Newby and Konopinski, *Phys. Rev.* **115**, 442 (1959).

Results are summarized in Tables 10.24 and 10.25 and in Fig. 10.35. Table 10.24 shows the calculated levels and Table 10.25 gives the composition of those states for which configuration mixing was taken into account. Perhaps the most interesting presentation of the results is that given in Fig. 10.35, which shows the experimental levels of HOFF AND HOLLANDER and the theoretical levels which are believed to correspond to them.

The similarity between the two schemes is rather striking. The calculations predict a band of even-parity levels arising from the $h_{9/2}{}^2$ configuration. These have the spin sequence 0, 2, 4, 6, 8. Only the 8+ level is missing in the experimental spectrum and its absence is not surprising. The theoretical level scheme also predicts some odd parity levels at around 3 MeV of excitation arising from the $h_{9/2} i_{13/2}$ configuration. The observed 5– level at 2.908 MeV and the 4– level at 3.024 MeV may be associated in a natural way with those predicted levels. In the work of NEWBY AND KONOPINSKI[252]

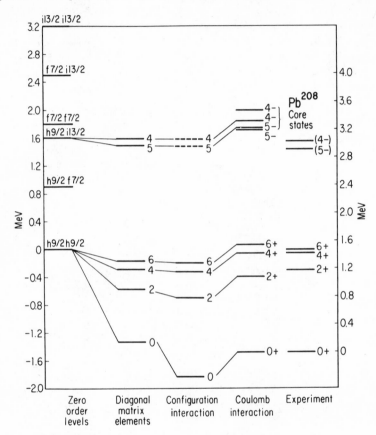

FIG. **10.35.** Comparison of theory and experiment in Po^{210}. Theoretical results are those of NEWBY AND KONOPINSKI.[252] Experimental spectrum is that of HOFF and HOLLANDER.[245]

no account was taken of the 4– and 5– states of "core excitation" which must occur around 3 to 3.5 MeV in analogy to the states seen in Pb^{208}. Mixing of these states with states of like spin and parity arising from the $h_{9/2} i_{13/2}$ configurations will tend to lower the predicted 4– and 5– states into closer agreement with the experimentally observed 4– and 5– states.

A consideration of the single-particle states available for the odd proton and neutron in At^{210} leads to the conclusion that the parity of the ground state is almost surely even and that the spin is 4 or 5. The nucleus of At^{210} has three protons beyond a closed shell and it seems likely that the ground state proton configuration is $(h_{9/2})^3{}_{J=9/2}$. The odd neutron should have the same configuration as the odd neutron in Pb^{207} which is in a $p_{1/2}$ state. The proton and neutron configurations should couple to yield a 4+ or 5+ ground state for At^{210}. HOFF AND HOLLANDER have discussed the log ft values for the beta transitions (electron capture decay) of At^{210}.

10.4.5 Astatine-209

The 5.5 isotope At^{209} was first prepared[253] by the reaction:

$$Bi^{209}(\alpha, 4n)At^{209}$$

This is still the best method of preparation of large amounts of At^{209} activity. Such samples are necessarily contaminated with other astatine isotopes, but by proper choice of bombardment energy the relative amount of At^{209} can be maximized. Astatine-209 may also be isolated as the electron capture daughter product of Em^{209} isolated from thorium targets bombarded with 350 MeV protons.[254, 255] However, this method also does not produce pure samples since other emanation isotopes are present which decay to astatine daughter products.

A more indirect method, leading to the production of small samples of quite pure At^{209}, is based on the isolation of Ra^{213} from thorium targets bombarded with 350 MeV protons and the subsequent isolation of At^{209} produced by the decay sequence:[254, 255]

$$Ra^{213} \xrightarrow[2.7 \text{ min}]{\alpha} Em^{209} \xrightarrow[30 \text{ min}]{EC} At^{209}$$

Because of the low yield and short half-life of Ra^{213} this method is of very limited application.

Astatine-209 decays by capture of an orbital electron and by alpha emission. BARTON, GHIORSO, AND PERLMAN[253] reported that the alpha branching was 5 per cent. STONER AND HUMMEL[256] measured the alpha-particle energy and found a single group at 5.642 ± 0.005 MeV with no evidence for complex structure.

The gamma radiation of At^{209} accompanying electron capture decay is rather simple and consists of the four transitions listed in Table 10.26. Precise measurements have been made of the conversion electron spectrum

[253] G. W. Barton, A. Ghiorso, and I. Perlman, *Phys. Rev.* **82**, 13 (1951).

[254] F. F. Momyer, Jr. and E. K. Hyde, *J. Inorg. Nucl. Chem.* **1**, 274 (1955).

[255] A. W. Stoner, Ph.D. Thesis, University of California, June 1956; also published as *Univ. of Calif. Rad. Lab. Report UCRL-3471*, June 1956.

[256] A. W. Stoner and J. P. Hummel, unpublished results, 1956.

of mixtures of At^{209} and At^{210} with beta ray spectrometers and, particularly, permanent magnet spectrographs of high resolution.[255, 257] STONER[255] has made measurements with a sodium iodide scintillation spectrometer and gamma-gamma coincidence spectrometer on pure samples of At^{209} isolated from Ra^{213} as outlined above. These studies prove that the 195, 545 and 780 keV gamma rays are in triple cascade. The total intensity of these three gamma rays are equal, within experimental error, while the intensity of the 90.8 keV transition is a factor of ~ 4 less.

TABLE 10.26. Gamma rays in the electron capture decay of At^{209} (Refs. 255, 257)

Gamma ray energy (keV)	Photon intensity (relative)	Conversion electrons observed	K/L ratio	Multipolarity-based on
90.8		$L_{II}L_{III}M_{II}M_{III}$ $N_{II}N_{III}O_{II}O_{III}$		$E2$ (subshell conv. ratios)
195	24	$K\ L_{I}M_{I}$	4.9	$M1$ $(+E2)$ (K/L ratio, photon intensity subshell conv. ratios)
545	66	$K\ L_{I}M_{I}$	3.8	$M1$ Derived conversion coeff. based on 195 keV being $M1$
780	100	K		$M1$ Derived conversion coeff. based on 195 keV being $M1$

Note: An additional gamma ray of 83.8 keV assigned to At^{209} in the published literature[257] actually belongs to At^{210}, according to STONER.[255]

STONER[255] has discussed a possible decay scheme for At^{209}. The daughter isotope Po^{209} has just two protons beyond the closed shell of 82 and is one neutron short of the closed shell of 126. The expected ground state configuration is:

$$\left[\begin{array}{cc} h_{9/2}^2\ J = 0, & p_{1/2}^{-1} \\ \text{protons} & \text{neutron} \end{array} \right] J = 1/2$$

The measured ground state spin of 1/2 is in agreement with this.[258] One might expect that the energy required to uncouple the $h_{9/2}$ protons would be large and that the low-lying states would simply correspond to excitation of the single neutron (hole). In particular, one might expect a close resemblance between the low-lying levels of Pb^{207} and Po^{209}. However, aside from the simplicity of the level scheme of Po^{209}, there does not appear to be much similarity of the levels of Po^{209} and Pb^{207}. It would be of considerable interest to

[257] J. W. Mihelich, A. W. Schardt, and E. Segrè, *Phys. Rev.* **95**, 1508 (1954).
[258] K. L. Van der Sluis and P. M. Griffin, *J. Opt. Soc. Am.* **45**, 1087 (1955).

have a further elucidation of the decay scheme of At^{209}. LAWSON AND URETSKY[259] have discussed a possible shell model interpretation of STONER'S experimental results on At^{209}.

10.4.6 *Astatine-208*

It was well established by HYDE, GHIORSO, AND SEABORG[260] that the alpha branching of Fr^{212} gives rise to an At^{208} daughter isotope with a half-life of 1.7 hours. Astatine-208 emits alpha particles with an energy of 5.65 MeV but the α-branching is only 0.55 per cent and the principal decay is by electron capture to 2.93 year Po^{208}. Using alpha-gamma coincidence counting STONER[255] showed that photons of a gamma ray of 120 ± 10 keV are present in 0.03 per cent of the alpha decays. The gamma radiation accompanying electron capture decay is quite simple and consists only of x-rays, a prominent 660 keV gamma ray, a 175 keV gamma ray about one-fourth as intense as the 660 keV gamma ray, plus a very weak 250 keV gamma ray revealed only in 660=250 keV coincidence measurements. The 662 keV gamma ray is believed to be an $E2$ transition dropping from the first excited (2+) state in Po^{208} to the 0+ ground state.

Evidence for a second form of At^{208} came from the work of BARTON, GHIORSO, AND PERLMAN[253] who found indirect evidence that this isotope had a half-life of 6.3 hours. These authors prepared astatine isotopes by bombarding bismuth with high energy protons. The astatine fraction from such bombardments contained a complex mixture of astatine isotopes with similar half-lives, and it was impossible to learn anything about At^{208} by a direct examination of the astatine fraction. However, by removing polonium daughter activities at timed intervals, and measuring the Po^{208} alpha activity, it was possible to deduce a half-life of 6.3 hours for At^{208}. These experiments were completed before the work of HYDE, GHIORSO, AND SEABORG[260] had established a 1.7-hour half-life for At^{208}. Later, STONER[255] repeated the indirect method of BARTON, GHIORSO, AND PERLMAN[253] using particular care to see whether the yield of Po^{208} daughter changed in a way to indicate two values of the parent half-life. He did in fact obtain a two component curve indicating parent half-lives of 1.6 ± 0.2 hours and 6.2 ± 0.3 hours. However, THORESEN, ASARO AND PERLMAN[261] in 1963 did not succeed in reproducing this result, and, in experiments designed to determine why they did not, they were able to show that the 2-component half-life curve was a spurious effect caused by slow achievement of equilibrium between chemical states of polonium involved in the polonium extraction procedure.

[259] R. D. Lawson and J. L. Uretsky, *Phys. Rev.* **108**, 1300 (1957).
[260] E. K. Hyde, A. Ghiorso, and G. T. Seaborg, *Phys. Rev.* **77**, 765 (1950).
[261] P. E. Thoresen, F. Asaro, and I. Perlman, *J. Inorg. Nucl. Chem.* (1964).

10.5 THE NEUTRON-DEFICIENT ISOTOPES OF EMANATION (ELEMENT 86)

In Chapter 6 the gaseous activity radon and the other emanation isotopes which occur in the decay chains of the natural radioactive series are discussed in considerable detail. In Chapter 7 several other heavy isotopes of this element which occur in the collateral series produced artificially by cyclotron reactions are discussed. We now wish to discuss the interesting group of synthetic isotopes of emanation with mass number 212 or less. As has

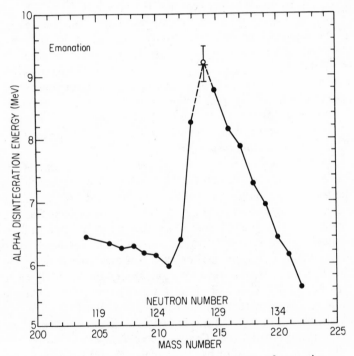

FIG. **10.36.** Disintegration energies of the isotopes of emanation as a function of mass number. The point for Em^{214} is an estimate.

been mentioned repeatedly in this book the alpha disintegration energies are strikingly lower for isotopes with 126 or fewer neutrons and the alpha half-lives strikingly longer than are those of the isotopes with a few neutrons more than 126. This conclusion is summarized graphically for the emanation isotopes by Fig. 10.36.

These isotopes cannot be made by any simple cyclotron reaction carried out with the conventional light-mass charged particles of low energy since element 86 is several elements removed from any suitable target material, but

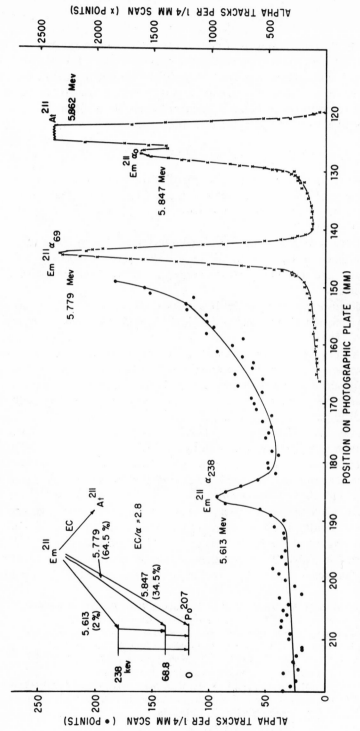

FIG. 10.37. Alpha spectrum and decay scheme of Em^{211}. The recording of the alpha particles started 8.4 hours after bombardment of thorium target with 350-MeV protons. The exposure lasted 20 hours. The 2 per cent group at 5.163 MeV is shown on an expanded scale.

bombardment of thorium with protons accelerated to an energy greater than 200 MeV produces a mixture of these isotopes.[262, 263] The yields are in the range of tens of millibarns but have not been accurately measured. The neutron-deficient isotopes of emanation with mass number 208 or less are conveniently prepared by bombardment of gold with nitrogen ions as was shown by BURCHAM[264] and by STONER AND HYDE.[265]

$$_{79}Au^{197} + {}_7N^{14} \longrightarrow Em^{208-7-6, \text{etc.}} + xn^1$$

Other combinations of target and bombarding ion could be used.

In the case of Em^{212} it is possible to prepare a pure sample by isolating it as the daughter of Fr^{212} which is prepared by high energy proton bombardment of thorium.[266]

GRIFFIOEN AND MACFARLANE[267] identified Em^{213} among the products of bombardment of Hg^{204} with C^{12} ions. They measured its half-life as 19 milliseconds and its alpha particle energy as 8.13 MeV with a gold-doped silicon detector.

All these isotopes decay partially by orbital electron capture and partially by alpha emission except Em^{212} and Em^{213} which decay entirely by alpha emission. The most definite data available on the radiations of these isotopes are the alpha particle energies which in several cases were measured with great accuracy in a magnetic spectrometer.[268] The study of these isotopes was greatly aided by the development of a glow-discharge deposition method for affixing the gaseous samples to a metallic surface so they could be examined by methods applicable only to non-gaseous samples.[263] Figure 10.37 shows the alpha spectrum of Em^{211} as determined in a magnetic spectrograph using samples prepared in this fashion.

The conversion electrons and gamma radiations emitted by Em^{211} were determined carefully by STONER[269] who used gamma-ray scintillation spectrometers and electron spectrometers. Emanation-211 has a half-life of 16 hours, much longer than any of its neighbors, so that pure samples may be prepared by waiting a suitable length of time until these neighboring isotopes have decayed below the level of detection. The radiations of Em^{211} are summarized in Table 10.27, but their placement in a decay scheme is not settled. The spin of $_{86}Em^{211}_{125}$ is very probably 1/2− since the 125th neutron

[262] A. Ghiorso, W. W. Meinke, and G. T. Seaborg, *Phys. Rev.* **76**, 1414 (1949).

[263] F. F. Momyer and E. K. Hyde, *J. Inorg. Nucl. Chem.* **1**, 274 (1955).

[264] W. E. Burcham, *Proc. Phys. Soc.* **A67**, 555 (1954).

[265] A. W. Stoner and E. K. Hyde, *J. Inorg. Nucl. Chem.* **4**, 77–83 (1957).

[266] E. K. Hyde, A. Ghiorso, and G. T. Seaborg, *Phys. Rev.* **77**, 765 (1950).

[267] R. D. Griffioen and R. N. MacFarlane, unpublished results 1961.

[268] F. F. Momyer, F. Asaro, and E. K. Hyde, *J. Inorg. Nucl. Chem.* **1**, 267 (1955).

[269] A. W. Stoner, Ph.D. Thesis, University of California, June 1956; also published as *Univ. Calif. Rad. Lab. Report UCRL-3471*, June 1956.

TABLE **10.27.** Gamma transitions observed in the decay of Em^{211}.
(Energies in keV)

In alpha decay branch		
68.7	$E2$	
169	—	(See Fig. 10.35)
234	—	

In electron capture decay branch	
32	680
114	865
168.6	946
232	1131
264	1374
296	1820
333	
345	
445	

TABLE **10.28.** The neutron-deficient isotopes of emanation.*

Isotope	Half-life	Modes of decay	Alpha particle energy (MeV)	Methods of production
Em^{213}	19 m sec	α (100%)	8.13	
Em^{212}	23 min	α (100%)	6.264 ± 0.005	Daughter of Fr^{212}
				Th (p, spallation)
Em^{211}	16 hr	α (26%)	5.847 ± 0.002 (33.5%)	
		EC (74%)	5.779 ± 0.003 (64.5%)	Th (p, spallation)
			5.613 ± 0.007 (2%)	
Em^{210}	2.7 hr	α (96%)	6.037 ± 0.003	Th (p, spallation)
		EC (4%)		
Em^{209}	30 min	α (17%)	6.037 ± 0.010	Th (p, spallation)
		EC (83%)		
Em^{208}	23 min	α (20%)	6.141 ± 0.004	Th (p, spallation)
		EC (80%)		Au (N^{14}, $3n$)
Em^{207}	11 min	α (4%)	6.14	Th (p, spallation)
		EC (96%)		Au (N^{14}, $4n$)
Em^{206}	6–7 min	α (65%)	6.25	Au(N^{14}, $5n$)
		EC (35%)		
Em^{204}(?)	3 min	α (?%)	6.28	Au (N^{14}, $7n$)
		EC (?%)		

* No data are listed on gamma radiations since only in the case of Em^{211} (see Table 10.25) have these been studied.

would be expected to be in a $p_{1/2}$ neutron orbital.   The ground state spin of At^{211} has been measured[244] and found to be 9/2.   The shell model assignment would be $h_{9/2}$ making it a negative parity state.   Therefore, one would not expect electron capture decay to lead directly to the ground state or to the lowest lying levels of At^{211}.   The decay energy is ~ 2.6 MeV.   Electron capture apparently proceeds largely to a level at 2488 keV energy which de-excites to ground through a number of competing gamma-ray cascades.

The most complete general account of these emanation isotopes is given by MOMYER AND HYDE.[263, 268]   In these references the methods of preparation and purification and the studies by which the genetic relationships to astatine and polonium daughter products were established are described in detail.   The properties of the light isotopes of emanation are summarized in Table 10.28.   The genetic relationships involving the light isotopes of emanation are apparent from an inspection of Figs. 10.5 through 10.8 appearing in the introduction to this chapter, Section 10.1.

10.6 THE ELEMENT FRANCIUM

In this section we shall discuss the properties of all francium isotopes including those lying above the 126 neutron shell.

One is impressed at once with the fact that francium is the prime example of a trace element.   All the elements through atomic number 99, with the exception of astatine and francium, have at least one isotope with half-life sufficiently long to permit, at least in principle, the chemical isolation of the element in weighable quantities.   In the case of francium the longest-lived isotope has a half-life of only 21 minutes; francium has the distinction of being the most unstable of the first 100 elements.

Long before the great nuclear instability of francium was known, element 87 was sought in minerals and some reports claiming discovery of the element were published.   Since it is now quite certain that these reports were erroneous, we shall not review this earlier history.   A short account of it is given in the first edition of the text of EMELEUS AND ANDERSON[270] or in BAGNALL'S book on the rare radioelements.[271]

The presently known isotopes of francium are listed in Table 10.29.   The best known of these is AcK discovered by MLLE. M. PEREY[272] in 1939.   She proved that the alpha decay of actinium which occurs in 1.2 per cent of the actinium disintegrations gives rise to a 21 minute, beta-emitting istope of element 87.   Because she was the first to identify conclusively an

---

[270] H. J. Emeleus and J. S. Anderson, *Modern Aspects of Inorganic Chemistry*, 1st Ed. (New York: Van Nostrand, 1938).

[271] K. W. Bagnall, *Chemistry of the Rare Radioelements*, (New York: Academic Press, 1957).

[272] M. Perey, *J. Phys. Rad.* **10**, (7) 435 (1939); *Compt. Rend.* **208**, 97 (1939).

TABLE **10.29**. Isotopes of Francium.

Isotope	Half-life	Mode of decay	Energy of radiations (MeV)	Method of production
Fr^{224}	~2 min (est)	$\beta^-(100\%)$	—	Daughter of Em^{224} indirect evidence only
Fr^{223}	21 min	$\beta^-(100\%)$ $\alpha\,(4-6\times10^{-3}\%)$	1.2 5.34	Natural source— daughter Ac^{227}
Fr^{222}	15 min	β	—	Th (p, spallation)
Fr^{221}	4.8 min	α	6.332 (84%) 6.116 (16%)	member U^{233} decay chain
Fr^{220}	27.5 sec	α	6.69	member Pa^{228} decay chain
Fr^{219}	0.02 sec	α β stable	7.30	member Pa^{227} decay chain
Fr^{218}	5×10^{-3} sec (est)	α	7.85	member Pa^{226} decay chain
Fr^{217}	unknown	α	8.3	member Pa^{225} decay chain (insufficient evidence)
Fr^{215}	<1 msec	α	9.4	$Pb^{208}+B^{11}$
Fr^{214}	3.9 msec	α	8.55	$Pb^{208}+B^{11}$
Fr^{213}	34 sec	α (99.5%) EC (0.5%)	6.77	$Pb^{208}+B^{11}$ $Tl^{203,5}+C^{12}$
Fr^{212}	19.3 min	α (44%) EC (56%)	6.411 (37%) 6.387 (39%) 6.342 (24%)	Th (p, spallation) $Pb^{208}+B^{11}$ $Tl^{203,5}+C^{12}$
Fr^{211}	3 min	α	6.55	$Pb^{208}+B^{11}$ $Tl^{203,5}+C^{12}$
Fr^{210}	159 sec	α	6.55	$Pb^{208}+B^{11}$ $Tl^{203,5}+C^{12}$
Fr^{209}	55 sec	α	6.65	$Pb^{208}+B^{11}$ $Tl^{203,5}+C^{12}$ $Au^{197}+O^{16}$
Fr^{208}	38 sec	α	6.65	,,
Fr^{207}	19 sec	α	6.77	,,
Fr^{206}(?)	16 sec	α	6.79	,,
Fr^{205}(?)	~4 sec	α	6.91	,,
Fr^{204}(?)	~2 sec	α	7.02	,,

isotope of element 87, she earned the right to name the element. All the detailed publications on the radiations of AcK are summarized in Section 6.4 of the chapter on the natural radioactivities.

Francium-221 is a member of the synthetic $4n+1$ series and as such is discussed in Section 7.1 of Chapter 7. Francium-222 is considered to be a collateral member of the U^{230} decay series. (See Fig. 7.8 in Section 7.2.1.) The very short-lived isotopes $Fr^{217-220}$ are members of collateral decay

chains with protactinium isotope antecedents and as such are discussed in
Chapter 7, Sections 7.2.2 to 7.2.5, but Table 10.37 here lists all the known
information on these isotopes.   Indirect evidence on the properties of Fr^{224}
was obtained by BELLIDO.[273]   He bombarded thorium with 230 MeV
protons, immediately afterward dissolved the target and trapped the emanation activities, and later chemically identified Ra^{224} in the traps in which the
emanation activity had decayed.   He thus found evidence for the decay
chain,

$$Em^{224} \xrightarrow{\beta^-} Fr^{224} \xrightarrow{\beta^-} Ra^{224}$$

He estimated a half-life of 2 minutes for Fr^{224}.

Additional work was done by the same general technique by BUTEMENT
AND ROBINSON[273a]. They established a half-life of 114 ± 6 minutes for Em^{224}
and set an upper of two minutes for the Fr^{224} half-life. They also established
a value of 43 ± 5 minutes for the half-life of Em^{223}.

When it became apparent that no long-lived isotopes of francium were
to be expected among the heavier isotopes of this element, additional research
was done on the neutron deficient isotopes.   This search was motivated by
the knowledge that the 126 neutron shell had a profound influence on the
alpha decay properties of bismuth, polonium and astatine.   It seemed likely
that isotopes of francium at and immediately below the 126-neutron shell
might be stabilized sufficiently that they could be chemically isolated for
study, and possibly that they would be longer lived than AcK, and hence more
suitable for tracer studies.

The first result of this research was the discovery of Fr^{212} by HYDE,
GHIORSO, AND SEABORG.[274]   When thorium is bombarded with protons
of hundreds of MeV energy many isotopes of francium are made by complex
spallation reactions.   HYDE, GHIORSO, AND SEABORG isolated Fr^{212} from
such targets and showed that it decayed partially by alpha decay to 1.7-hour
At^{208} and partially by electron capture to Em^{212}.   The resultant half-life
is 19.3 minutes, just slightly shorter than that of AcK.   Sufficiently large
samples have been isolated to permit measurements of the alpha spectrum
in a magnetic spectrograph.[275]   Efforts of MOMYER AND HYDE[276] to discover
the other francium isotopes in this region yielded negative results.   Since
these other isotopes were certainly made during the cyclotron bombardments
in approximately the same yield as Fr^{212} it was concluded that the maximum
half-life for any isotope of francium with mass number less than 212 is 5
minutes.   This observation is in agreement with the fact that the most stable

273 A. V. Bellido, *J. Inorg. Nucl. Chem.* **19**, 197 (1961).

273a F. D. S. Butement and V. J. Robinson, *J. Inorg. Nucl. Chem.* **26**, 1 (1964),

274 E. K. Hyde, A. Ghiorso, and G. T. Seaborg, *Phys. Rev.* **77**, 765 (1950).

275 F. F. Momyer, F. Asaro, and E. K. Hyde, *J. Inorg. Nucl. Chem.* **1**, 276 (1955).

276 F. F. Momyer and E. K. Hyde. *J. Inorg. Nucl. Chem.* **1**. 274 (1955).

light isotope of polonium, astatine and emanation is that isotope with 125 neutrons.

A better path to the formation of the lighter isotopes of francium is the bombardment of elements in the neighborhood of lead with accelerated ions of such complex elements as boron, carbon or oxygen. This path was very successfully exploited by GRIFFIOEN AND MACFARLANE[277] who worked out

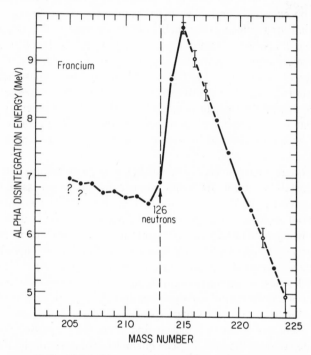

FIG. **10.38.** Alpha disintegration energy versus mass number for isotopes of francium (element 87). Experimental data shown by solid dots. Predictions shown by crosses and dotted lines.

experimental techniques for the study of alpha emitters with half-lives as short as a few seconds or even a few milliseconds. A whole series of isotopes from Fr^{205} to Fr^{215} was identified by bombardment of Pb^{208} with B^{11}, Tl^{205} with C^{12}, Tl^{203} with C^{12}, and Au^{197} with O^{16}. The measured properties are summarized in the table.

Figure 10.38 shows the variation in alpha decay energy with mass number. Since the minimum in this curve occurs at Fr^{212}, and since, even at this minimum, the partial alpha half-life is only 44 minutes, it is apparent that

[277] R. D. Griffioen and R. D. Macfarlane, unpublished results, 1961; *Phys. Rev.* **133**, B1373 (1964).

alpha instability precludes the existence of any long-lived species of francium in the region below 126 neutrons.   Electron capture instability is also high throughout this region.   In the mass region $Fr^{213}-Fr^{220}$ alpha decay energy is quite large, and alpha decay with short half-life is the only decay process observed.   Toward the high mass number end of Fig. 10.36 the alpha decay energy decreases rapidly.   The measured partial alpha half-life of AcK, for example, is of the order of one year and much longer partial alpha half-lives may be expected for higher mass numbers.   However, one may not expect to find long half-lives for such isotopes because in this range of mass numbers it is β-instability that controls the lifetime.   A direct measurement of beta decay energy is available only for AcK but estimates from closed decay energy cycles make it clear that Fr^{224} and all higher mass isotopes will be quite short-lived.   Since our knowledge of the nuclear spectroscopic states of the heavy elements in this region is still rather rudimentary, it is still possible that some isomer with a somewhat longer half-life than AcK may eventually be discovered but at present the prospects for such a discovery are small.

Closed decay-energy cycles indicate that Fr^{219} is β-stable; if it were not for alpha instability, francium would appear on earth in massive quantities with the atomic weight 219.   In actual fact, element 87 appears on earth only in the form of AcK, which as a branch member of the U^{235} decay chain, is constantly being replenished and is maintained in a steady concentration of about 2 parts by weight in 10^{17} parts of natural uranium.   There is an even smaller steady-state concentration of francium in the form of Fr^{221}, a member of the $4n + 1$ series, which series occurs in nature in vanishingly small amounts as the result of the interactions of neutrons and alpha particles within uranium minerals.   See Section 6.6 of Chapter 6.

An excellent review of the nuclear and chemical properties of francium has been prepared by PEREY.[278]   The chemical properties of the element are reviewed in a monograph by HYDE.[279]

10.7 RADIUM AND ACTINIUM ISOTOPES NEAR THE 126 NEUTRON SHELL

By analogy to polonium, astatine, emanation, and francium (see Fig. 10.3) one might expect that the longest-lived isotopes of radium and actinium in the region of the 126 neutron shell would be those with 125 neutrons; i.e. Ra^{213} and Ac^{214}.   One might also predict from the steady decrease in the magnitude of this half-life minimum with increase in atomic number that these "long-lived" isotopes of radium and actinium would have decay periods of a

---

[278] M. Perey, "Francium", Tome *III*, *Nouveau Traité de Chimie Minérale*, Masson et Cie, Éditeurs, Paris (1957).

[279] E. K. Hyde, "The Radiochemistry of Francium," report NAS-NRC 3003 issued 1960 by National Academy of Sciences. National Research Council.

few minutes or a few seconds at most.   These predictions have been borne
out by experiment.

The first attempt to identify radium isotopes with mass number close to
213 was made by MOMYER AND HYDE[276] who bombarded thorium with
protons with energy of hundreds of MeV.   In this type of experiment the
higher-mass isotopes of radium are also prepared and the radiations from

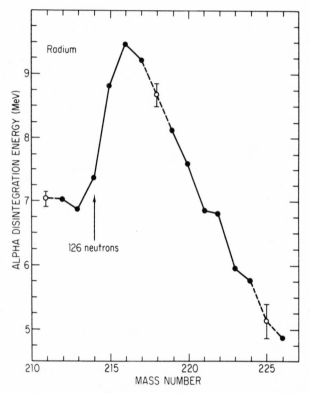

FIG. **10.39.** Alpha disintegration energy versus mass number
for isotopes of radium.   Predictions for unmeasured isotopes
are given with crosses and error bars.

these completely obscure those of the neutron-deficient isotopes.   However,
indirect evidence for Ra^{213} was found by preliminary radiochemical isolation
of a radium fraction, a subsequent isolation of emanation daughter activity,
and, finally, an identification of 5.5 hour At^{209} in the emanation fraction after
its decay.   This provides evidence for the decay sequence

$$Ra^{213} \xrightarrow[\text{minutes}]{\alpha} Em^{209} \xrightarrow[\text{30 min}]{EC\ (83\%)} At^{209}$$

Further evidence for Ra²¹³ was obtained by these authors²⁷⁶ by bombardment of lead targets with carbon ions:

$$Pb^{208}(C^{12}, 7n)Ra^{213}$$

In the radiochemically separated radium fraction alpha particles of approximately 6.9 MeV energy were observed to decay with a 2.7 ± 0.3 minute half-life, and a small amount of Em²⁰⁹ daughter activity (6.04 MeV alpha particles) was observed to decay with a 30-minute half-life. Better data on Ra²¹³ were later obtained by GRIFFIOEN AND MACFARLANE²⁷⁷ who also prepared it by C¹²-ion bombardment of lead as well as by B¹¹-ion bombardment of bismuth. They confirmed the 2.7 minute half-life but revised downward the alpha-particle energy. They reported complex structure with peaks at 6.74 and 6.61 MeV. These workers also found evidence for several other

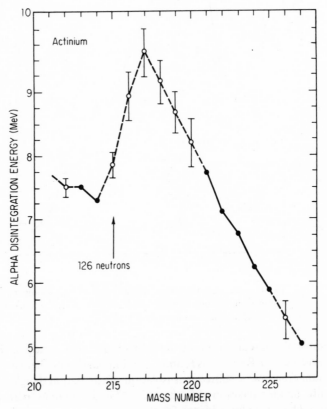

FIG. **10.40.** Alpha disintegration energy versus mass number for isotopes of actinium. Predictions for several unmeasured isotopes are given with crosses and error bars.

TABLE 10.30. Isotopes of radium and actinium isotopes near the 126-neutron shell.

Isotope	Number of neutrons	Half-life	Alpha particle energy (MeV)
Ra^{212}	124	18 sec	6.90
Ra^{213}	125	162 sec	6.74 ($\sim 50\%$)
			6.61 ($\sim 50\%$)
Ra^{214}	126	2.6 sec	7.17
Ra^{215}	127	1.6 msec	8.7
Ra^{216}(?)	128	<1 msec	9.3
Ra^{217}(?)	129	---	9.0
Ac^{213}	124	1 sec (est)	7.42
Ac^{214}	125	12 sec	7.12 ($\sim 33\%$)
			7.18 ($\sim 33\%$)
			7.24 ($\sim 33\%$)

From unpublished data of R. D. Griffioen and R. D. Macfarlane.

radium isotopes of shorter lifetime. (See Table 10.30 for properties.) The decay energies of these isotopes are displayed with those of the higher-mass isotopes of radium in Fig. 10.39. It can be seen that the shift in decay energy at the 126 neutron shell is very similar to that observed in lower Z elements.

GRIFFIOEN AND MACFARLANE[277] prepared light nuclei of actinium by carbon ion bombardment of lead and obtained some evidence for properties of Ac^{213} and Ac^{214} which are listed in the table. Figure 10.40 shows the decay energies of all the actinium isotopes. The estimated decay energies of several unknown isotopes are also shown in the figure.

AUTHOR INDEX

VOLUMES I AND II*

A

Abelson, P. H., 747, 778, 792, 793, 813
Abraham, M., 784
Adamchuk, Y. B., 373
Adams, J. S., 173
Adams, N. I., 437, 489
Adamson, A. M., 407, 654, 662
Adloff, J. P., 535
Agapkin, I. I., 485
Ahlf, J., 700–705
Ahrens, L. H., 568
Aitken, K. L., 371
Alaga, G., 130–34, 186, 197, 198, 740, 784
Albridge, R. G., 404, 700–707, 771–73, 776, 819, 820, 883
Albuoy, G., 438, 491, 651, 689, 701, 702, 704, 817
Alburger, D. E., 80, 999, 1009, 1013–18, 1028, 1032, 1035, 1039, 1043, 1068, 1070
Alder, K., 85, 91, 99, 115, 116, 157, 192, 197, 740
Aldrich, L. T., 566, 567, 569
Alichanian, A. I., 515, 522

Alley, N. P., 372
Allison, B. A., 1088
Almén, O., 1047
Alpher, R. A., 561, 562
Alväger, T., 341, 1076, 1082
Alvarez, L. W., 342
Amaldi, E., 583
Ambrosino, G., 244
Ames, D. P., 448, 451
Amiel, S., 170, 336, 804, 821, 880–82, 966–68
Amos, D. P., 451
Anders, E., 569, 1078
Andersen, T., 721
Anderson, H. L., 383, 571
Anderson, J. S., 1078, 1100
Anderson, O. E., Jr., 794
Andersson, B., 1015
Andersson, G., 1001, 1049, 1054
Andre, C. G., 59, 61, 323, 325, 1063
Andreev, Y. N., 481, 482
Anikina, M. P., 373, 718, 721
Antonoff, G. N., 423, 428
Appleman, E. H., 1009, 1078, 1082
Araújo, J. M., 103, 199

* Pages 1–407 refer to Volume I; pages 409–1107 refer to Volume II.

Hill, R. D., 389, 390, 399, 404, 773
Hillary, J. J., 527
Hincks, E. P., 51, 61, 585, 595
Hindman, J. C., 814, 822
Hirsch, A., 813, 944
Hirsch, J., 734
Hoff, R. W., 176, 373, 397, 547, 743, 754, 758, 759, 787, 799, 823, 836, 859, 860, 863, 876, 915, 1073, 1075, 1077, 1079, 1082, 1085–93
Hoffman, D. C., 170, 695, 754, 757, 801–5, 809, 836, 837, 876, 877, 881, 884, 915
Hoffman, K. A., 413, 423, 467
Hogg, B. G., 492
Hollander, J. M., 64, 132, 133, 152, 168–70, 176, 177, 183, 188, 191, 340, 342, 390, 447, 459, 476, 509, 530, 531, 602, 628, 645–53, 667, 675, 682, 689, 697, 700–705, 713, 715, 737, 741, 743, 762, 768, 771–73, 776, 779, 780, 783, 784, 787, 804, 805, 810, 819, 820, 826, 843–45, 852, 857–59, 869, 870, 887, 897, 935, 938, 941, 951, 953, 954, 958, 959, 963, 964, 1028–32, 1038, 1041, 1064, 1087, 1088–93
Holloway, M. G., 547
Holm, G. B., 484
Holm, L. W., 336, 348, 946, 967, 978, 1082
Holmes, A., 559, 569
Holtz, M., 390, 951, 954, 963, 964
Hönigschmid, O., 412, 455, 492
Hopkins, H. H., Jr., 675, 750, 752, 757, 761–63, 769, 800, 801, 803, 806, 824
Hopkins, N. J., 1048, 1053
Hörnfeldt, O., 398, 400
Hornshøj, P., 701
Horrocks, D. L., 829
Horton, J. W., 511, 514
Houtermans, F. G., 241, 558, 559, 561, 562, 569
Howard, F. T., 349
Howland, J. J., Jr., 479, 480, 778, 779, 1025, 1062, 1065
Hoyle, F., 381, 564
Hoyt, H. C., 503
Hubbard, E. L., 349
Hubbs, J. C., 784, 822, 870
Hughes, D. J., 371, 372, 373, 480

Huizenga, J. R., 39, 53, 59, 61, 63, 173, 188, 312–19, 322–27, 336, 372, 594, 737, 754, 758, 763, 764, 779, 804, 820, 831, 834, 875, 896–900, 903, 905, 925, 931, 936, 939, 942, 943, 944, 955, 968–70, 1005, 1025–27, 1039, 1047, 1052, 1061
Hulet, E. K., 170, 373, 743, 787, 823, 859, 860, 891, 895, 896, 899, 900, 903, 910, 912–16, 919, 925, 928–30
Hull, D. E., 528
Hultberg, S., 1015, 1028, 1030, 1039, 1051, 1054
Hulubei, H., 1078
Hummel, J. P., 590, 591, 629, 640, 685, 689, 690, 802, 830, 868, 887, 897, 898, 928, 951, 1062, 1070, 1082, 1093
Huster, E., 530
Hutchinson, W. P., 884
Hutchison, C. A., Jr., 722, 731
Huus, T., 85, 91, 99, 116, 192, 197
Hyde, E. K., 192, 348, 373, 441, 526, 533, 534, 538, 584, 588, 592, 596, 597, 604–6, 627, 640, 675, 677, 693, 712, 719, 742, 750, 752, 753, 757, 761, 785, 796, 799, 801, 803, 823, 839, 1070, 1082, 1084, 1087, 1093, 1095, 1098, 1100, 1102, 1104, 1105

I

Iashin, N. M., 722, 822
Iddings, G. M., 355, 708
Igo, G., 263, 284, 316, 319
Ikawa, M., 526, 581, 748
Ingelstam, E., 397
Inghram, M. G., 372, 437, 552, 561–63, 568, 823, 833, 836, 869, 900
Isaac, N., 558
Isabaev, E. A., 904
Israel, H. I., 817
Itoh, J., 470, 515
Ivanov, R. B., 590, 718, 723, 817, 885, 897, 904

J

Jackson, H. G., 372, 438, 491, 651, 724, 902, 921, 941, 957, 960, 964, 969, 970

Jackson, J. D., 319, 320, 321
Jaffe, H., 397, 762, 770–73, 777, 849, 859
Jaffy, A. H., 526, 645, 646, 647, 693, 734,
   806, 809, 813
James, R. A., 750, 752, 757, 758, 761,
   762, 769, 800, 801, 803, 806, 824,
   826, 828, 838, 842, 844, 846, 859,
   860, 877, 878, 880, 881, 883
Jancey, G. E. M., 432
Jastram, P. S., 522
Jean, M., 100, 101, 103, 472
Jech, A., 1032
Jedrzejowski, H., 450
Jeffery, P. M., 564
Jeffries, C. D., 784
Jelley, J. V., 585, 593
Jenkins, E. N., 653
Jenkner, K., 595
Jensen, E. N., 511, 515–17, 523
Jensen, J. H. D., 37, 69, 71, 72, 73, 197
Jentschke, W., 550, 587, 1011
Jesse, W. P., 815
Johansson, A., 515
Johansson, B., 1041, 1045, 1049–51, 1054
Johansson, C. M., 1015, 1035, 1049, 1053
Johansson, S. A. E., 7, 8, 35, 116, 151,
   465, 654, 655, 730
John, E. R., 372
John, W., 324, 327, 1061, 1065
Johnson, G. L., 1078
Johnson, J. E., 515
Johnson, V., 462, 463
Johnson, W. H., Jr., 38, 39, 53
Johnsrud A. E., 1013, 1014, 1017
Johnston, F. T., 373
Joliot, F., 303
Joliot-Curie, I., 303, 432, 529
Jones, L. V., 1061
Jones, M. E., 372, 742, 823, 829, 830,
   835, 836, 876, 921, 950, 957, 964,
   969, 970
Jones, W. B., 342, 1082
Jones, W. M., 815
Jopson, R. C., 405, 407
Jordan, K. C., 484
Juliano, J. O., 645, 647, 649
Jung, B., 1054
Juric, M. K., 448
Juveland, A. C., 550, 1011

K

Kageyama, S., 461, 470
Kalashnikova, V. I., 652
Kalckar, F., 84
Kaliteevskii, N. I., 722, 822
Kalyamin, A. V., 1076
Kane, W. R., 511, 514–18, 522
Kaplan, I., 248–51
Kaplan, N., 572
Karamyan, A. S., 981
Karlik, B., 65, 460, 505, 506, 541, 546,
   588, 1078, 1083, 1084
Karnaukhov, V. A., 981
Karraker, D. G., 1028, 1052, 1074, 1075
Katz, J. J., 449, 526, 569, 686, 719, 794,
   796, 839
Katzin, L. I., 526, 585, 686
Kauranen, P., 478
Kauw, G., 993, 1038
Kearsley, M. J., 81, 82, 1000, 1021, 1023
Kedzie, R. W., 784
Keenan, T., 839, 859
Keetman, B., 424
Keller, H. B., 700, 701
Kelly, E. L., 313, 322–26, 335, 1061,
   1078, 1079, 1082, 1084, 1086
Kelvin, W. T., 419
Kemble, E. C., 242
Kennedy, J. W., 584, 748, 769, 793, 794,
   805, 813
Kerler, W., 511, 516, 517
Kerman, A. K., 111, 139–41, 174, 198,
   732, 953
Keys, J. D., 613, 663
Khalizev, V. I., 981
Kharitonov, Y. I., 484, 518
Khlebnikov, G. I., 810, 826, 981
Kiehn, R. M., 1068, 1088
Kienberger, C. A., 437
Kim, Y. E., 479, 484, 515, 1006, 1065
Kimura, K., 526, 581, 748
Kinderman, E. M., 372, 780, 781, 791
King, R. W., 64
Kinsey, B. B., 61, 63, 198, 407, 475, 1001,
   1026
Kinsey, G. H., 550, 1011
Kirby, H. W., 372, 501, 503, 633, 686
Kislov, M. I., 481, 482
Kisslinger, L. S., 83, 102, 1024, 1025,
   1037, 1038, 1045, 1046, 1056–60

SUBJECT INDEX

VOLUMES I AND II *

IMPORTANT NOTE: *In addition to this Subject Index, there is an Isotopic Index which may be used to locate information on specific nuclides.*

A

Accelerators as neutron sources, 386–88

Actinium:
  discovery of, 413
  as target material, 306

Actinium isotopes (*see* Isotopic Index for complete indexing of individual isotopes)
  alpha disintegration energy versus mass number, 1106
  anomalous $E1$ transitions in, 188
  complete table of alpha spectra, 220, 221
  hindrance factors in alpha decay, 273, 276
  negative parity states in even nuclei, 155, 156
  neutron capture cross sections and reactions, 362, 369
  neutron deficient isotopes, 1104–7
  Nilsson level assignments in, 166, 173, 174, 664, 665, 678, 690–93

Actinium isotopes (*cont.*)
  rotation levels in, 161
  yields in targets bombarded with d, p, or α, 331

Actinon, early history, 413, 414

Actinouranium series, 523-52

Active deposits:
  early history, 420–24
  from actinon, 548–51
  from radon, 456–86
  from thoron, 506–23

Age of the earth, 559–63

Age of minerals, 552–69

Alpha decay (*see* Alpha radioactivity)

Alpha decay energies:
  decay energy cycles, 28–34
  systematic trends, 34
  variation with mass number for individual elements:
    actinium, 1106
    astatine, 1080
    emanation, 1096

* Pages 1–407 refer to Volume I; pages 409–1107 refer to Volume II.

xxiii

C

D

Dating of minerals, 552–69 (*see also* Geochronology, Geologic importance of heavy nuclei)

Decay energy cycles, 28–34

Discovery of:
actinium, 413
americium, 838, 839
berkelium, 905–9
californium, 923, 924
curium, 877–79
einsteinium, 943–45
element 102, 978–82
fermium, 943–45
francium, 530, 531
ionium, 424
lawrencium, 982–85
mendelevium, 975–77
neptunium, 745–50
plutonium, 792–96
polonium, 411
radioactivity, 409–11
radium, 411–12

Displacement rules in radioactive decay, 428–30

E

Ejection of orbital electron during alpha decay, 301, 302

Einsteinium, discovery of, 943–45

Einsteinium isotopes (*see* Isotopic Index for complete indexing of individual isotopes)
all isotopes discussed in detail, 943–65
complete table of alpha spectra, 235, 236
hindrance factors in alpha decay, 275, 276
neutron capture cross sections and reactions, 368, 371
Nilsson-level assignments in, 166, 179, 952, 958, 961–62, 964
production in *n*-capture reactions, 364, 366, 368
production in thermonuclear explosions, 379–81
reaction Q-values, 339, 346, 347
as target materials, 309

Einsteinium isotopes (*cont.*)
yields of in targets bombarded with *d*, *p*, or *α*, 332, 334

Electric quadrupole effects on alpha emission, 294–300

Electron binding energies, heavy elements, App. I, 389–93

Element 102:
complete table of alpha spectra, 237
discovery of, and general discussion, 978–82

Emanation isotopes (*see* Isotopic Index for complete indexing of individual isotopes)
alpha disintegration energy versus mass number, 1096
complete table of alpha spectra, 216, 217
correlation of alpha decay rate data, 254, 255
hindrance factors in alpha decay, 262, 264, 269
level schemes in even nuclei, 99
negative parity levels in, 154, 155
neutron capture cross sections and reactions, 362
neutron-deficient isotopes, 1096–1100
properties of 2+ states in even nuclei, 184
radii from alpha decay data, 251, 252
yields in targets bombarded with complex nuclear projectiles, 350

Extinct natural radioactivity, 576

F

Favored alpha decay concept, 277–79, 284, 285

Fermium, discovery and general comments, 943–45, 965

Fermium isotopes (*see* Isotopic Index for complete indexing of individual isotopes)
all isotopes discussed in detail, 965–75
calculation of alpha decay rate by nuclear overlap model, 293, 294
complete table of alpha spectra, 237
correlation of alpha decay rate data, 254, 255
hindrance factors in alpha decay, 263, 265, 272

ISOTOPIC INDEX

VOLUMES I AND II

Isotope	Half-life	Mode of radioactive disintegration†	Page ref.* to radiations, decay scheme, history, and method of synthesis
Thallium‡			
Tl^{207}(AcC'')	4.76 min	β^-	424, 547–50
Tl^{208}(ThC'')	3.1 min	β^-	421, 506–11, 521–23
Tl^{210}(RaC'')	1.32 min	β^-	423, 433, 434, 456–59, 472–75
Lead			
Pb^{195}	17 min	E.C.	1002, 1055
Pb^{196}	37 min	E.C.	1055
Pb^{197m}	42 min	I.T. and E.C.	1002, 1055
Pb^{198}	2.40 hr	E.C.	1055
Pb^{199m}	12.2 min	I.T.	1002, 1055
Pb^{199}	90 min	E.C., β^+(weak)	1055
Pb^{200}	21.5 hr	E.C.	1054, 1055
Pb^{201m}	60 sec	I.T.	1002, 1053
Pb^{201}	9.4 hr	E.C.	1053
Pb^{202m}	3.5 hr	I.T., E.C.(9.7%)	1003, 1050–52
Pb^{202}	3×10^5 yr (est.)	E.C.	1050–52
Pb^{203m}	7.0 sec	I.T.	1002, 1048
Pb^{203}	52 hr	E.C.	1047, 1048
Pb^{204m}	67.5 min	I.T.	1003, 1038–41
Pb^{204}	1.4×10^{17} yr	α	1038
Pb^{205}	3×10^7 yr	E.C.	1025–28
Pb^{206}	stable	stable	433, 434, 486
Pb^{207m}	0.8 sec	I.T.	1002, 1008
Pb^{207}	stable	stable	424, 427, 429, 552
Pb^{208}	stable	stable	421
Pb^{209}	3.22 hr	β^-	582, 593, 614
Pb^{210}(RaD)	19.4 yr	β^-	422, 423, 433, 434, 475–77
Pb^{211}(AcB)	36.1 min	β^-	423–27, 547–50
Pb^{212}(ThB)	10.6 hr	β^-	421, 506–13

Pb²¹³	10.2 min	β⁻	588
Pb²¹⁴(RaB)	26.8 min	β⁻	422, 433, 434, 456–62
Bismuth			
Bi¹⁹⁸	~7 min	E.C., α(~0.05%)	
Bi¹⁹⁹	~25 min	E.C., α(~0.01%)	
Bi²⁰⁰	35 min	E.C., α(slight)	1054
Bi²⁰¹	1.9 hr	E.C., α(slight)	
Bi²⁰²	95 min	E.C.	1052–53
Bi²⁰³	12 hr	E.C., α(~10⁻⁵%), β⁺(slight)	1049, 1050
Bi²⁰⁴	11.2 hr	E.C.	1041–43
Bi²⁰⁵	15.3 d	E.C.	1028–37
Bi²⁰⁶	6.4 d	E.C.	1013–19
Bi²⁰⁷	28 yr	E.C.	1008–11
Bi²⁰⁸ᵐ	0.027 sec	I.T.	1006
Bi²⁰⁸	7.5 × 10⁵ yr	E.C.	1005–6
Bi²⁰⁹	2 × 10¹⁷ yr	α	582, 594, 595
Bi²¹⁰(RaE)	5.01 d	β⁻, α(1.3 × 10⁻⁴%)	422, 423, 433, 434, 478–84
Bi²¹¹(AcC)	2.16 min	α(99.7%), β⁻(0.32%)	424, 427, 547–50, 610
Bi²¹²(ThC)	60.5 min	β⁻(66.3%), α(33.7%)	421, 506–11, 513–18
Bi²¹³	47 min	β⁻(98%), α(2%)	582, 592
Bi²¹⁴(RaC)	19.7 min	β⁻, α(0.021%)	422, 423, 433, 434, 456–59, 462–72
Bi²¹⁵	8 min	β⁻	532–34
Polonium			
Po¹⁹²	0.5 sec	α	1061, 1074–77
Po¹⁹³	4 sec	α	1061, 1074–77
Po¹⁹⁴	13 sec	α	1061, 1074–77

* Pages 1–407 refer to Volume I; pages 409–1107 refer to Volume II.

† Symbols in this column have the following meaning: α, alpha decay; β⁻, beta decay; E.C., decay by nuclear capture of orbital electron; I.T., decay by isomeric gamma transition; S.F., decay by spontaneous fission.

‡ The only thallium isotopes included are those which occur in decay of the natural radioelements.

Isotope	Half-life	Mode of radioactive disintegration†	Page ref.* to radiations, decay scheme, history, and method of synthesis
Polonium (*cont.*)			
Po^{195}	30 sec	α	1061, 1074–77
Po^{196}	1.9 min	α, E.C.	1061, 1074–77
Po^{197}	~4 min	α, E.C.	1061, 1074–77
Po^{198}	~6 min	α, E.C.	1061, 1074–77
Po^{199}	11.2 min	α, E.C.	1061, 1074–77
Po^{200}	~8 min	α, E.C.	1061, 1074–77
Po^{201}	17.5 min	α, E.C.	1061, 1074–77
Po^{202}	44.5 min	E.C.(98%), α(2%)	1061, 1074–77
Po^{203}	47 min	E.C.(93%), α(7%)	1061, 1074–77
Po^{204}	3.54 hr	E.C.(99+%), α(0.63%)	1062, 1074–77
Po^{205}	1.5 hr	E.C.(99+%), α(0.074%)	1062, 1074–77
Po^{206}	9 d	E.C.(95%), α(5%)	1062, 1070–74
Po^{207}	5.7 hr	E.C.(99+%), α(0.014%), β^+(~0.2%)	1062, 1065–69
Po^{208}	2.89 yr	α, E.C.(weak)	1062, 1064, 1065
Po^{209}	40.2 yr	α(>99%), E.C.(~0.5%)	1062–64
Po^{210}(RaF)	138.4 d	α	423, 433, 434, 456, 484–86
Po^{211m}	25 sec	α	550, 551
Po^{211}(AcC')	0.52 sec	α	290–91, 547–51, 617
Po^{212}(ThC')	3.04 × 10^{-7} sec	α	421, 506–11, 518, 519
Po^{212m}	45 sec	α	519–21
Po^{213}	4.2 × 10^{-6} sec	α	582, 593, 614
Po^{214}(RaC')	1.58 × 10^{-4} sec	α	422, 433, 434, 456–59, 462, 463
Po^{215}(AcA)	1.83 × 10^{-3} sec	α	423–27, 546–48
Po^{216}(ThA)	0.158 sec	α	421, 505, 506
Po^{217}	<10 sec	α	588, 589
Po^{218}(RaA)	3.05 min	α(99.98%), β^-(0.02%)	422, 433, 434, 456–61

Astatine

At$^{200(?)}$	0.8 min	α	1081
At^{201}	1.5 min	α	1081
At^{202}	3 min	E.C.(88%), α(12%)	1081
At^{203}	7.4 min	E.C.(86%), α(14%)	1081
At^{204}	9.3 min	E.C.(95.5%), α(4.5%)	1081
At^{205}	25 min	E.C.(82%), α(18%)	1081
At^{206}	29.5 min	E.C.(99+%), α(0.9%)	1081
At^{207}	2 hr	E.C.($\sim$90%), α($\sim$10%)	1081
At^{208}	1.7 hr	E.C.(99.5%), α(0.5%)	1081, 1095
At^{209}	5.5 hr	E.C.($\sim$95%), α($\sim$5%)	1081, 1093–95
At^{210}	8.3 hr	E.C.(99+%), α(0.17%)	1079, 1081, 1086–93
At^{211}	7.2 hr	E.C.(59.1%), α(40.9%)	1078, 1081, 1084–86
At^{212m}	0.120 sec	α	1081
At^{212}	0.20 sec	α	1081
At^{213}	<1 sec	α	613, 1082, 1083
At^{214}	2 $\times$ 10^{-6} sec (est.)	α	611, 612, 1082
At^{215}	short	α	546–48, 610, 611, 1082–84
At^{216}	$\sim$3 $\times$ 10^{-4} sec	α	607, 609, 1082
At^{217}	0.018 sec	α	582, 592, 1082
At^{218}	1.5–2.0 sec	α	459–61, 1082, 1083
At^{219}	0.9 min	α(97%), β(3%)	532–34, 1082, 1084

Emanation

Em$^{204(?)}$	3 min	α, E.C.	1099
Em^{206}	6–7 min	α(65%), E.C.(35%)	1099
Em^{207}	11 min	E.C.(96%), α(4%)	1099
Em^{208}	23 min	E.C.(80%), α(20%)	1099
Em^{209}	30 min	E.C.(83%), α(17%)	1093, 1099
Em^{210}	2.7 hr	α(96%), E.C.(4%)	1099
Em^{211}	16 hr	E.C.(74%), α(26%)	1097–1100
Em^{212}	23 min	α	1098, 1099
Em^{213}	19 msec	α	1098, 1099

Isotope	Half-life	Radiation	References	
Fr^{220}	27.5 sec	α	607, 609, 1101	
Fr^{221}	4.8 min	α	582, 592, 1101	
Fr^{222}	15 min	β	599, 605, 606, 1101	
Fr^{223}(AcK)	21 min	β^-($\sim$100%), α(4–6 $\times$ 10^{-3}%)	530–35, 1100, 1101	
Fr^{224}	$\sim$2 min (est.)	β^-	1101, 1102	
Radium				
Ra^{212}	18 sec	α	1107	
Ra^{213}	162 sec	α	1105–7	
Ra^{214}	2.6 sec	α	1107	
Ra^{215}	1.6 msec	α	1107	
Ra^{216}(?)	<1 msec	α	1107	
Ra^{217}(?)	?	α	1107	
Ra^{219}	est. $\sim 10^{-3}$ sec	α	617	
Ra^{220}	0.023 sec	α	616, 617	
Ra^{221}	30 sec	α	614, 615	
Ra^{222}	38 sec	α	99, 155, 599, 601–4	144, 628
Ra^{223}(AcX)	11.22 d	α	427, 540–45	144, 635, 636
Ra^{224}	3.64 d	α	99, 155, 419, 420, 426, 503–5	
Ra^{225}	14.8 d	β^-	582, 586–88	638, 639
Ra^{226}	1622 yr	β^-	99, 155, 433, 434, 444–55	144, 642–44
Ra^{227}	41 min	β^-	362	
Ra^{228}	6.7 yr	β^-	426, 492, 493	144
Ra^{229}	<5 min	β^-	362, 584	
Ra^{230}(?)	1 hr	β^-	none	
Actinium				
Ac^{213}	1 sec (est.)	α	1107	
Ac^{214}	12 sec	α	1107	
Ac^{221}	<<1 sec	α	613	
Ac^{222}	5.5 sec	α	611, 612	
Ac^{223}	2.2 min	α	610, 611	664, 665

Isotope	Half-life	Mode of radioactive disintegration†	Page ref.* to radiations, decay scheme, history, and method of synthesis	Spectroscopic information on levels of this nucleus; chiefly rotational and vibrational bands and Nilsson assignments
Actinium (cont.)				
Ac^{224}	2.9 hr	E.C.(90%), α(10%)	155, 607, 609	161, 174, 678
Ac^{225}	10.0 d	α	582, 588–92, 614, 615	
Ac^{226}	29 hr	β−(80%), E.C.(20%)	155, 599, 604, 605	166, 173, 174, 690–93
Ac^{227}	21.6 yr	β−, α(1.2%)	427–29, 527–38	
Ac^{228}(MsTh₂)	6.13 hr	β−	427, 492–500	
Ac^{229}	66 min	β−	362, 584	
Ac^{230}(?)	<1 min	β−	none	
Ac^{231}	15 min	β−	none	
Thorium				
Th^{223}	0.9 sec	α	617, 625	711
Th^{224}	1.05 sec	α	616, 617, 626	712
Th^{225}	8.0 min	α(~95%), E.C.(~5%)	614, 615, 626	
Th^{226}	30.9 min	α	599, 601, 627, 628	144, 154, 155, 713, 714
Th^{227}(RdAc)	18.17 d	α	427, 534, 539, 628–33	144, 148, 154, 155, 495, 499, 500, 671–74, 716
Th^{228}(RdTh)	1.910 yr	α	425–26, 500–503, 582, 633–36	161, 167, 720, 722, 723
Th^{229}	7,340 yr	α	585–86, 636–40	144, 148, 154, 155, 682–84, 724, 725
Th^{230}(Io)	(7.52 ± 0.16) × 10⁴ yr	α	424, 425, 430, 433, 434, 440–44, 640–44	161, 167, 649, 730–33
Th^{231}(UY)	25.6 hr	β−	427, 428, 525, 526, 644–51	144, 145, 148, 195, 735, 736
Th^{232}	1.39 × 10¹⁰ yr	α	487–92	163
Th^{233}	22.1 min	β−	652, 653	
Th^{234}(UX₁)	24.10 d	β−	419, 420, 425, 430, 435, 436, 439, 440, 653–56, 662	144
Th^{235}	<5 min	β−	662	

Protactinium

Isotope	Half-life	Decay mode		
Pa²²⁵	2 sec	α	613, 663	
Pa²²⁶	1.8 min	α	611, 663	
Pa²²⁷	38.3 min	α(85%), E.C.(15%)	609, 610, 663	664
Pa²²⁸	22 hr	E.C.(98%), α(2%)	606–8, 665–75	674
Pa²²⁹	1.4 d	E.C.(99+%), α(0.25%)	614, 615, 675–78	175, 672–76
Pa²³⁰	17 d	E.C.(~90%), β⁻(10%), α(~0.003%)	598, 599, 678–86	684
Pa²³¹	34,800 yr	α	428, 429, 526, 527, 686–93	161, 175, 648, 649, 691, 692, 760
Pa²³²	1.32 d	β⁻	693–99	
Pa²³³	27.4 d	β⁻	582, 699–707	161, 175, 706, 766–69
Pa²³⁴(UX₂)	1.18 min	β⁻	425, 431, 439, 440, 656–62	656
(UZ)	6.7 hr	β⁻		
Pa²³⁵	23 min	β⁻	707	
Pa²³⁶	12.5 min	β	708	
Pa²³⁷	39 min	β	708–10	

Uranium

Isotope	Half-life	Decay mode		
U²²⁷	1.3 min	α	617, 618, 710	
U²²⁸	9.3 min	α	616, 617, 710	
U²²⁹	58 min	E.C.(80%), α(20%)	613–15, 711	712
U²³⁰	20.8 d	α	599–601, 712	144, 685
U²³¹	4.2 d	E.C., α(5.5 × 10⁻³%)	644–51, 714	168
U²³²	73.6 yr	α	715–19	144, 148, 697–99, 802
U²³³	1.62 × 10⁵ yr	α	582–84, 719–23	161, 168, 706, 722
U²³⁴(U_II)	2.48 × 10⁵ yr	α	425, 429, 430, 433–35, 438, 723–27	144, 148, 154, 155, 660–62, 754–57, 812
U²³⁵ᵐ	26.5 min	I.T.	820–22	161, 163, 818–22
U²³⁵(AcU)	7.13 × 10⁸ yr	α	429, 435, 436, 523–25, 727–33	161, 163, 168, 731, 758, 759, 818–22
U²³⁶	2.39 × 10⁷ yr	α	734–36	144, 148, 154, 155, 824–26
U²³⁷	6.75 d	β⁻	581, 582, 736–41, 748, 749	169, 710, 828

Isotope	Half-life	Mode of radioactive disintegration†	Page ref.* to radiations, decay scheme, history, and method of synthesis	Spectroscopic information on levels of this nucleus; chiefly rotational and vibrational bands and Nilsson assignments
Uranium (*cont.*)				
$U^{238}(U_I)$	4.51×10^9 yr	α	430, 435, 436, 438, 741	144, 145, 148, 154, 155, 193, 830
U^{239}	23 min	β^-	742	169
U^{240}	14 hr	β^-	742–44	
Neptunium				
Np^{231}	~50 min	E.C., $\alpha(\sim 1\%)$	751	
Np^{232}	13 min	E.C.	751	
Np^{233}	35 min	E.C.($> 99\%$), $\alpha(10^{-5}\%)$	752	
Np^{234}	4.40 d	E.C., $\beta^+(0.046\%)$	752	
Np^{235}	410 d	E.C., $\alpha(1.6 \times 10^{-3}\%)$	757–61	176, 177, 760, 761, 843
Np^{236m}	22 hr	E.C.(50%), $\beta^-(50\%)$	761–63	763
Np^{236}	$t_\beta \geqslant 5{,}000$ yr		763	181, 763
Np^{237}	2.14×10^6 yr	α	582, 583, 748–50, 764–69	161, 162, 176, 177, 193, 280, 737–40, 768, 769, 804, 805, 849, 852, 855–58
Np^{238}	2.10 d	β^-	748, 769–77	181, 776, 777, 866, 867
Np^{239}	2.35 d	β^-	745–50, 777–85	161, 176, 177, 784, 843, 869, 870
Np^{240}	60 min	β^-	790, 791	743, 744, 791
Np^{240m}	7.3 min	β^-	785–90	743, 744, 790
Np^{241}	16 min	β^-	792	792
Plutonium				
Pu^{232}	36 min	E.C.($\approx 90\%$), $\alpha(\approx 10\%)$	617, 796, 797	
Pu^{233}	20 min	E.C., $\alpha(0.1\%)$	797–99	

Isotope	Half-life	Decay mode		
Pu^{234}	9 hr	E.C.(94%), α(6%)	799	
Pu^{235}	26 min	E.C., α(3 × 10^{-3}%)	800	
Pu^{236}	2.85 yr	α	800–802	144, 763
Pu^{237m}	0.18 sec	I.T.	881	
Pu^{237}	45.63 d	E.C., α(0.0026%)	803, 804	169, 804, 881, 882
Pu^{238}	86.41 yr	α	792, 793, 804–13	144, 145, 148, 154, 155, 771, 774–76, 841, 886–91
Pu^{239}	24,360 yr	α	792–94, 813–22	161, 162, 170, 780–85, 821, 892–95
Pu^{240}	6,240 yr	α	822–26	144, 148, 154, 155, 788–90, 845, 898, 899
Pu^{241}	13.3 yr	β⁻, α(0.005%)	826–29	161, 170, 828, 901
Pu^{242}	3.8 × 10^5 yr	α	829–31	144
Pu^{243}	4.98 hr	β⁻	831–33	171, 832, 833
Pu^{244}	7.6 × 10^7 yr	α	833–35	
Pu^{245}	10.6 hr	β⁻	836	
Pu^{246}	10.85 d	β⁻	836, 837	

Americium

Isotope	Half-life	Decay mode		
Am^{237}	1.3 hr	E.C., α(0.005%)	840	842
Am^{238}	1.86 hr	E.C.	840–42	177–79, 843, 911, 912
Am^{239}	12 hr	E.C., α(0.005%)	842–44	845
Am^{240}	53 hr	E.C.	844	177–79, 849, 882, 883, 915
Am^{241}	457.7 yr	α	280, 838, 839, 846–58	860, 862–67
Am^{242m}	152 yr	I.T.	859–67	181, 860, 862–67
Am^{242}	16.01 hr	β⁻(84%), E.C.(16%), α(0.48%)	859–67	
Am^{242m2}	0.014 sec	S.F., I.T.(?), α(?)	85	177–79, 832, 833, 869, 870
Am^{243}	7,951 yr	α	867–70	181, 873, 874
Am^{244}	10.1 hr	β⁻(~100%), E.C.(0.039%)	871–75	
Am^{244m}	26 min	β⁻(~100%)	871–75	
Am^{245}	2.08 hr	β⁻	876	921
Am^{246}	25 min	β⁻	876, 877	

Isotope	Half-life	Mode of radioactive disintegration†	Page ref.* to radiations, decay scheme, history, and method of synthesis	Spectroscopic information on levels of this nucleus; chiefly rotational and vibrational bands and Nilsson assignments
Curium				
Cm^{238}	2.5 hr	E.C., α(2.5%)	879	
Cm^{239}	3 hr	E.C.	880	
Cm^{240}	26.8 d	α	880	
Cm^{241}	35 d	E.C., α(0.96%)	881	171, 881
Cm^{242}	162.5 d	α	878, 883–91	144, 929
Cm^{243}	32 yr	α, E.C.(slight)	207–8, 891–95	171
Cm^{244}	18.11 yr	α	895–99	144, 182, 871–73, 875
Cm^{245}	9,320 yr	α	899–901	161, 163, 171, 172, 901, 915, 933–35
Cm^{246}	5,480 yr	α	901–3	917, 938
Cm^{247}	1.64×10^7 yr	α	901, 903, 904	
Cm^{248}	4.7×10^5 yr	α, S.F.(11%)	901, 904, 905	941
Cm^{249}	64 min	β⁻	905	
Cm^{250}	2×10^4 yr	S.F.	905	
	>130 yr	β⁻		
Berkelium				
Bk^{243}	4.5 hr	E.C., α(0.15%)	905–12	179, 911
Bk^{244}	~4.5 hr	E.C., α(6×10^{-3}%)	912, 913	
Bk^{245}	4.98 d	E.C., α(~0.1%)	913–16	179, 882, 883
Bk^{246}	1.8 d	E.C.	916	
Bk^{247}	1,380 yr	α	916–18	179, 833
Bk^{248}	16 hr	β⁻(70%), E.C.(30%)	918, 919	
Bk^{248m}	>9 yr	α(?), I.T.(?)	919	
Bk^{249}	314 d	β⁻, α(2.2×10^{-3}%)	919–21	161, 921, 952–55
Bk^{250}	193.3 min	β⁻	921	961–64